ENCYCLOPEDIA OF INFANT AND EARLY CHILDHOOD DEVELOPMENT

ENCYCLOPEDIA OF INFANT AND EARLY CHILDHOOD DEVELOPMENT

EDITORS-IN-CHIEF

MARSHALL M. HAITH
and
JANETTE B. BENSON
Department of Psychology, University of Denver,
Denver, Colorado, USA

AMSTERDAM • BOSTON • HEIDELBERG • LONDON • NEW YORK • OXFORD
PARIS • SAN DIEGO • SAN FRANCISCO • SINGAPORE • SYDNEY • TOKYO
Academic Press is an imprint of Elsevier

ACADEMIC
PRESS

Academic Press is an imprint of Elsevier
The Boulevard, Langford Lane, Kidlington, Oxford OX5 1GB, UK
525 B Street, Suite 1900, San Diego, CA 92101-4495, USA

First edition 2008

British Library Cataloguing in Publication Data
A catalogue record for this book is available from the British Library

Library of Congress Catalog Number: 2007930619

ISBN: 978-0-12-370460-3

For information on all Elsevier publications
visit our website at books.elsevier.com

PRINTED AND BOUND IN CANADA
07 08 09 10 11 10 9 8 7 6 5 4 3 2 1

EDITORS-IN-CHIEF

Marshall M. Haith received his M.A. and Ph.D. degrees from U.C.L.A. and then carried out postdoctoral work at Yale University from 1964–1966. He served as Assistant Professor and Lecturer at Harvard University from 1966–1972 and then moved to the University of Denver as Professor of Psychology, where he has conducted research on infant and children's perception and cognition, funded by NIH, NIMH, NSF, The MacArthur Foundation, The March of Dimes, and The Grant Foundation. He has been Head of the Developmental Area, Chair of Psychology, and Director of University Research at the University of Denver and is currently John Evans Professor Emeritus of Psychology and Clinical Professor of Psychiatry at the University of Colorado Health Sciences Center.

Dr. Haith has served as consultant for Children's Television Workshop (Sesame Street), Bilingual Children's Television, Time-Life, and several other organizations. He has received several personal awards, including University Lecturer and the John Evans Professor Award from the University of Denver, a Guggenheim Fellowship for serving as Visiting Professor at the University of Paris and University of Geneva, a NSF fellowship at the Center for Advanced Study in the Behavioral Sciences (Stanford), the G. Stanley Hall Award from the American Psychological Association, a Research Scientist Award from NIH (17 years), and the Distinguished Scientific Contribution Award from the Society for Research in Child Development.

Janette B. Benson earned graduate degrees at Clark University in Worcester, MA in 1980 and 1983. She came to the University of Denver in 1983 as an institutional postdoctoral fellow and then was awarded an individual NRSA postdoctoral fellowship. She has received research funding form federal (NICHD; NSF) and private (March of Dimes, MacArthur Foundation) grants, leading initially to a research Assistant Professor position and then an Assistant Professorship in Psychology at the University of Denver in 1987, where she remains today as Associate Professor of Psychology and as Director of the undergraduate Psychology program and Area Head of the Developmental Ph.D. program and Director of University Assessment. Dr. Benson has received various awards for her scholarship and teaching, including the 1993 United Methodist Church University Teacher Scholar of the Year and in 2000 the CASE Colorado Professor of the Year. Dr. Benson was selected by the American Psychological Association as the 1995–1996 Esther Katz Rosen endowed Child Policy Fellow and AAAS Congressional Science Fellow, spending a year in the United States Senate working on Child and Education Policy. In 1999, Dr. Benson was selected as a Carnegie Scholar and attended two summer institutes sponsored by the Carnegie Foundation program for the Advancement for the Scholarship of Teaching and Learning in Palo Alto, CA. In 2001, Dr. Benson was awarded a Susan and Donald Sturm Professorship for Excellence in Teaching. Dr. Benson has authored and co-authored numerous chapters and research articles on infant and early childhood development in addition to co-editing two books.

EDITORIAL BOARD

Richard Aslin is the William R. Kenan Professor of Brain and Cognitive Sciences at the University of Rochester and is also the director of the Rochester Center for Brain Imaging. His research has been directed to basic aspects of sensory and perceptual development in the visual and speech domains, but more recently has focused on mechanisms of statistical learning in vision and language and the underlying brain mechanisms that support it. He has published over 100 journal articles and book chapters and his research has been supported by NIH, NSF, ONR, and the Packard and McDonnell Foundations. In addition to service on grant review panels at NIH and NSF, he is currently the editor of the journal *Infancy.* In 1981 he received the Boyd R. McCandless award from APA (Division 7), in 1982 the Early Career award from APA (developmental), in 1988 a fellowship from the John Simon Guggenheim foundation, and in 2006 was elected to the American Academy of Arts and Sciences.

Warren O. Eaton is Professor of Psychology at the University of Manitoba in Winnipeg, Canada, where he has spent his entire academic career. He is a fellow of the Canadian Psychological Association, and has served as the editor of one of its journals, the *Canadian Journal of Behavioural Science.* His current research interests center on child-to-child variation in developmental timing and how such variation may contribute to later outcomes.

Robert Newcomb Emde is Professor of Psychiatry, Emeritus, at the University of Colorado School of Medicine. His research over the years has focused on early socio-emotional development, infant mental health and preventive interventions in early childhood. He is currently Honorary President of the World Association of Infant Mental Health and serves on the Board of Directors of Zero To Three.

Hill Goldsmith is Fluno Bascom Professor and Leona Tyler Professor of Psychology at the University of Wisconsin–Madison. He works closely with Wisconsin faculty in the Center for Affective Science, and he is the coordinator of the Social and Affective Processes Group at the Waisman Center on Mental Retardation and Human Development. Among other honors, Goldsmith has received an National Institute of Mental Health MERIT award, a Research Career Development Award from the National Institute of Child Health and Human Development, the James Shields Memorial Award for Twin Research from the Behavior Genetics Association, and various awards from his university. He is a Fellow of AAAS and a Charter Fellow of the Association for Psychological Science. Goldsmith has also served the National Institutes of Health in several capacities. His editorial duties have included a term as Associate Editor of one journal and membership on the editorial boards of the five most important journals in his field. His administrative duties have included service as department chair at the University of Wisconsin.

Richard B. Johnston Jr. is Professor of Pediatrics and Associate Dean for Research Development at the University of Colorado School of Medicine and Associate Executive Vice President of Academic Affairs at the National Jewish Medical & Research Center. He is the former President of the American Pediatric Society and former Chairman of the International Pediatric Research Foundation. He is board certified in pediatrics and infectious disease. He has previously acted as the Chief of Immunology in the Department of Pediatrics at Yale University School of Medicine, been the Medical Director of the March of Dimes Birth Defects Foundation, Physician-in-Chief at the Children's Hospital of Philadelphia and Chair of the Department of Pediatrics at the University Pennsylvania School of Medicine. He is editor of "Current Opinion in Pediatrics" and has formerly served on the editorial board for a host of journals in pediatrics and infectious disease. He has published over 80 scientific articles and reviews and has been cited over 200 times for his articles on tissue injury in inflammation, granulomatous disease, and his New England Journal of Medicine article on immunology, monocytes, and macrophages.

Jerome Kagan is a Daniel and Amy Starch Professor of Psychology at Harvard University. Dr. Kagan has won numerous awards, including the Hofheimer Prize of the American Psychiatric Association and the G. Stanley Hall Award of the American Psychological Association. He has served on numerous committees of the National Academy of Sciences, The National Institute of Mental Health, the President's Science Advisory Committee and the Social Science Research Council. Dr. Kagan is on the editorial board of the journals *Child Development* and *Developmental Psychology*, and is active in numerous professional organizations. Dr. Kagan's many writings include *Understanding Children: Behavior, Motives, and Thought, Growth of the Child, The Second Year: The Emergence of Self-Awareness*, and a number of cross-cultural studies of child development. He has also coauthored a widely used introductory psychology text. Professor Kagan's research, on the cognitive and emotional development of a child during the first decade of life, focuses on the origins of temperament. He has tracked the development of inhibited and uninhibited children from infancy to adolescence. Kagan's research indicates that shyness and other temperamental differences in adults and children have both environmental and genetic influences.

Rachel Keen (formerly Rachel Keen Clifton) is a professor at the University of Virginia. Her research expertise is in perceptual-motor and cognitive development in infants. She held a Research Scientist Award from the National Institute of Mental Health from 1981 to 2001, and currently has a MERIT award from the National Institute of Child Health and Human Development. She has served as Associate Editor of Child Development (1977–1979), Psychophysiology (1972–1975), and as Editor of SRCD Monographs (1993–1999). She was President of the International Society on Infant Studies from 1998–2000. She received the Distinguished Scientific Contribution Award from the Society for Research in Child Development in 2005 and was elected to the American Academy of Arts and Science in 2006.

Ellen M. Markman is the Lewis M. Terman Professor of Psychology at Stanford University. Professor Markman was chair of the Department of Psychology from 1994–1997 and served as Cognizant Dean for the Social Sciences from 1998–2000. In 2003 she was elected to the American Academy of Arts and Sciences and in 2004 she was awarded the American Psychological Association's Mentoring Award. Professor Markman's research has covered a range of issues in cognitive development including work on comprehension monitoring, logical reasoning and early theory of mind development. Much of her work has addressed questions of the relationship between language and thought in children focusing on categorization, inductive reasoning, and word learning.

Yuko Munakata is Professor of Psychology at the University of Colorado, Boulder. Her research investigates the origins of knowledge and mechanisms of change, through a combination of behavioral, computational, and neuroscientific methods. She has advanced these issues and the use of converging methods through her scholarly articles and chapters, as well as through her books, special journal issues, and conferences. She is a recipient of the Boyd McCandless Award from the American Psychological Association, and was an Associate Editor of *Psychological Review*, the field's premier theoretical journal.

Arnold J. Sameroff, is Professor of Psychology at the University of Michigan where he is also Director of the Development and Mental Health Research Program. His primary research interests are in understanding how family and community factors impact the development of children, especially those at risk for mental illness or educational failure. He has published 10 books and over 150 research articles including the *Handbook of Developmental Psychopathology, The Five to Seven Year Shift: The Age of Reason and Responsibility*, and the forthcoming *Transactional Processes in Development*. Among his honors are the Distinguished Scientific Contributions Award from the Society for Research in Child Development and the G. Stanley Hall Award from the American Psychological Association. Currently he is President of the Society for Research in Child Development and serves on the executive Committee of the International Society for the Study of Behavioral Development.

FOREWORD

This is an impressive collection of what we have learned about infant and child behavior by the researchers who have contributed to this knowledge. Research on infant development has dramatically changed our perceptions of the infant and young child. This wonderful resource brings together like a mosaic all that we have learned about the infant and child's behavior. In the 1950s, it was believed that newborn babies couldn't see or hear. Infants were seen as lumps of clay that were molded by their experience with parents, and as a result, parents took all the credit or blame for how their offspring turned out. Now we know differently.

The infant contributes to the process of attaching to his/her parents, toward shaping their image of him, toward shaping the family as a system, and toward shaping the culture around him. Even before birth, the fetus is influenced by the intrauterine environment as well as genetics. His behavior at birth shapes the parent's nurturing to him, from which nature and nurture interact in complex ways to shape the child.

Geneticists are now challenged to couch their findings in ways that acknowledge the complexity of the interrelation between nature and nurture. The cognitivists, inheritors of Piaget, must now recognize that cognitive development is encased in emotional development, and fueled by passionately attached parents. As we move into the era of brain research, the map of infant and child behavior laid out in these volumes will challenge researchers to better understand the brain, as the basis for the complex behaviors documented here. No more a lump of clay, we now recognize the child as a major contributor to his own brain's development.

This wonderful reference will be a valuable resource for all of those interested in child development, be they students, researchers, clinicians, or passionate parents.

T. Berry Brazelton, M.D.
Professor of Pediatrics, Emeritus Harvard Medical School
Creator, Neonatal Behavioral Assessment Scale (NBAS)
Founder, Brazelton Touchpoints Center

PREFACE

Encyclopedias are wonderful resources. Where else can you find, in one place, coverage of such a broad range of topics, each pursued in depth, for a particular field such as human development in the first three years of life? Textbooks have their place but only whet one's appetite for particular topics for the serious reader. Journal articles are the lifeblood of science, but are aimed only to researchers in specialized fields and often only address one aspect of an issue. Encyclopedias fill the gap.

In this encyclopedia readers will find overviews and summaries of current knowledge about early human development from almost every perspective imaginable. For much of human history, interest in early development was the province of pedagogy, medicine, and philosophy. Times have changed. Our culling of potential topics for inclusion in this work from textbooks, journals, specialty books, and other sources brought home the realization that early human development is now of central interest for a broad array of the social and biological sciences, medicine, and even the humanities. Although the 'center of gravity' of these volumes is psychology and its disciplines (sensation, perception, action, cognition, language, personality, social, clinical), the fields of embryology, immunology, genetics, psychiatry, anthropology, kinesiology, pediatrics, nutrition, education, neuroscience, toxicology and health science also have their say as well as the disciplines of parenting, art, music, philosophy, public policy, and more.

Quality was a key focus for us and the publisher in our attempts to bring forth the authoritative work in the field. We started with an Editorial Advisory Board consisting of major contributors to the field of human development – editors of major journals, presidents of our professional societies, authors of highly visible books and journal articles. The Board nominated experts in topic areas, many of them pioneers and leaders in their fields, whom we were successful in recruiting partly as a consequence of Board members' reputations for leadership and excellence. The result is articles of exceptional quality, written to be accessible to a broad readership, that are current, imaginative and highly readable.

Interest in and opinion about early human development is woven through human history. One can find pronouncements about the import of breast feeding (usually made by men), for example, at least as far back as the Greek and Roman eras, repeated through the ages to the current day. Even earlier, the Bible provided advice about nutrition during pregnancy and rearing practices. But the science of human development can be traced back little more than 100 years, and one can not help but be impressed by the methodologies and technology that are documented in these volumes for learning about infants and toddlers – including methods for studying the role of genetics, the growth of the brain, what infants know about their world, and much more. Scientific advances lean heavily on methods and technology, and few areas have matched the growth of knowledge about human development over the last few decades. The reader will be introduced not only to current knowledge in this field but also to how that knowledge is acquired and the promise of these methods and technology for future discoveries.

CONTENTS

Several strands run through this work. Of course, the nature-nurture debate is one, but no one seriously stands at one or the other end of this controversy any more. Although advances in genetics and behavior genetics have been breathtaking, even the genetics work has documented the role of environment in development and, as Brazelton notes in his foreword, researchers acknowledge that experience can change the wiring of the brain as well as how actively the genes are expressed. There is increasing appreciation that the child develops in a transactional context, with the child's effect on the parents and others playing no small role in his or her own development.

There has been increasing interest in brain development, partly fostered by the decade of the Brain in the 1990s, as we have learned more about the role of early experience in shaping the brain and consequently, personality, emotion, and intelligence. The 'brainy baby' movement has rightly aroused interest in infants' surprising capabilities, but the full picture of how abilities develop is being fleshed out as researchers learn as much about what infants can not do, as they learn about what infants can do. Parents wait for verifiable information about how advances may promote effective parenting.

An increasing appreciation that development begins in the womb rather than at birth has taken place both in the fields of psychology and medicine. Prenatal and newborn screening tools are now available that identify infants at genetic or developmental risk. In some cases remedial steps can be taken to foster optimal development; in others ethical issues may be involved when it is discovered that a fetus will face life challenges if brought to term. These advances raise issues that currently divide much of public opinion. Technological progress in the field of human development, as in other domains, sometimes makes options available that create as much dilemma as opportunity.

As globalization increases and with more access to electronic communication, we become ever more aware of circumstances around the world that affect early human development and the fate of parents. We encouraged authors to include international information wherever possible. Discussion of international trends in such areas as infant mortality, disease, nutrition, obesity, and health care are no less than riveting and often heartbreaking. There is so much more to do.

The central focus of the articles is on typical development. However, considerable attention is also paid to psychological and medical pathology in our attempt to provide readers with a complete picture of the state of knowledge about the field. We also asked authors to tell a complete story in their articles, assuming that readers will come to this work with a particular topic in mind, rather than reading the Encyclopedia whole or many articles at one time. As a result, there is some overlap between articles at the edges; one can think of partly overlapping circles of content, which was a design principle inasmuch as nature does not neatly carve topics in human development into discrete slices for our convenience. At the end of each article, readers will find suggestions for further readings that will permit them to take off in one neighboring direction or another, as well as web sites where they can garner additional information of interest.

AUDIENCE

Articles have been prepared for a broad readership, including advanced undergraduates, graduate students, professionals in allied fields, parents, and even researchers for their own disciplines. We plan to use several of these articles as readings for our own seminars.

A project of this scale involves many actors. We are very appreciative for the advice and review efforts of members of the Editorial Advisory Board as well as the efforts of our authors to abide by the guidelines that we set out for them. Nikki Levy, the publisher at Elsevier for this work, has been a constant source of wise advice, consolation and balance. Her vision and encouragement made this project possible. Barbara Makinster, also from Elsevier, provided many valuable suggestions for us. Finally, the Production team in England played a central role in communicating with authors and helping to keep the records straight. It is difficult to communicate all the complexities of a project this vast; let us just say that we are thankful for the resource base that Elsevier provided. Finally, we thank our families and colleagues for their patience over the past few years, and we promise to ban the words "encyclopedia project" from our vocabulary, for at least a while.

Marshall M. Haith
and
Janette B. Benson
Department of Psychology, University of Denver
Denver, Colorado, USA

HOW TO USE THE ENCYCLOPEDIA

The Encyclopedia of Infant and Early Childhood Development is intended for use by students, research professionals, and interested others. Articles have been chosen to reflect major disciplines in the study of infant and early child development, common topics of research by academics in this domain, and areas of public interest and concern. Each article serves as a comprehensive overview of a given area, providing both breadth of coverage for students, and depth of coverage for research professionals. We have designed the encyclopedia with the following features for maximum accessibility for all readers.

Articles in the encyclopedia are arranged alphabetically by subject in the Contents list. The index is located in volume 3. Some topics are covered in a multitude of articles from differing perspectives, while other topics may have only one entry. We encourage use of the index for access to a subject area, rather than use of the Contents list alone, so that a reader has a full notion of the coverage of that topic. The influence of the family on an infant, for example, may be covered under separate articles on Family Dynamics, Birth Order, Siblings and Sibling Rivalry, Family Influences, and Parenting Styles and Their Effects. A reader searching under F for family in the Contents list would easily find one of these articles but would miss the others.

Each article contains a glossary, cross-references to other related encyclopedia articles, and suggested readings where applicable, and relevant websites for additional information. The glossary contains terms that may be unfamiliar to the reader, with each term defined *in the context of its use in that article.* Thus, a term may appear in the glossary for another article defined in a slightly different manner or with a subtle nuance specific to that article. For clarity, we have allowed these differences in definition to remain so that each article is fully understandable on its own.

Each article has been cross-referenced to other related articles in the encyclopedia at the close of each article. We encourage readers to use the cross-references to locate other encyclopedia articles that will provide more detailed information about a subject.

The suggested readings include recent secondary sources to aid the reader in locating more detailed or technical information. Review articles and research articles that are considered of primary importance to the understanding of a given subject area are also listed. These suggested readings are not intended to provide a full reference listing of all material covered in the context of a given article, but are provided as next steps for a reader looking for additional information.

CONTRIBUTORS

B Ackerson
University of Illinois at Urbana–Champaign, Urbana, IL, USA

D Adams
National Institutes of Health, Bethesda, MD, USA

K E Adolph
New York University, New York City, NY, USA

A Ahuja
National Jewish Hospital, Denver, CO, USA

N Akhtar
University of California, Santa Cruz, Santa Cruz, CA, USA

A Almas
University of Toronto, Toronto, ON, Canada

S Al'Otaiba
Florida State University, Tallahassee, FL, USA

H Als
Harvard Medical School, Boston, MA, USA

K M Andrews
McGill University, Montreal, QC, Canada

M E Arterberry
Colby College, Waterville, ME, USA

J B Asendorpf
Humboldt-Universität zu Berlin, Berlin, Germany

D H Ashmead
Vanderbilt University Medical Center, Nashville, TN, USA

R N Aslin
University of Rochester, Rochester, NY, USA

J W Astington
University of Toronto, Toronto, ON, Canada

J Atkinson
University College London, London, UK

L E Bahrick
Florida International University, Miami, FL, USA

D B Bailey
RTI International, Research Triangle Park, NC, USA

L A Baker
University of Southern California, Los Angeles, CA, USA

A Balasubramanian
University of California, Riverside, Riverside, CA, USA

R Barr
University of British Columbia, Vancouver, BC, Canada

P J Bauer
Emory University, Atlanta, GA, USA

A Baxter
University of South Alabama, Mobile, AL, USA

A Belden
Washington University School of Medicine, St. Louis, MO, USA

D Benoit
University of Toronto, Toronto, ON, Canada;
The Hospital for Sick Children, Toronto, ON, Canada

D Bergen
Miami University, Oxford, OH, USA

K Bernard
University of Delaware, Newark, DE, USA

B I Bertenthal
Indiana University, Bloomington, IN, USA

J Bhagwat
Cornell University, Ithaca, NY, USA

N Bhullar
Widener University, Chester, PA, USA

A E Bigelow
St. Francis Xavier University, Antigonish, NS, Canada

M M Black
University of Maryland, Baltimore, MD, USA

E Blass
University of Massachusetts, Amberst, MA, USA

N J Blum
University of Pennsylvania School of Medicine, Philadelphia, PA, USA

C A Boeving
Yale University School of Medicine, New Haven, CT, USA

C F Bolling
Cincinnati Children's Hospital Medical Center, Cincinnati, OH, USA

M H Bornstein
National Institutes of Health, Bethesda, MD, USA

L Bosch
Universitat de Barcelona, Barcelona, Spain

O Braddick
University of Oxford, Oxford, UK

J Brooks-Gunn
Columbia University, New York, NY, USA

R T Brouillette
McGill University, Montreal, QC, Canada

A W Burks
Duke University Medical Center, Durham, NC, USA

S C Butler
Harvard Medical School, Boston, MA, USA

J P Byrnes
Temple University, Philadelphia, PA, USA

M L Campbell
Kennedy Krieger Institute, Baltimore, MD, USA

R L Canfield
Cornell University, Ithaca, NY, USA

S M Carlson
Institute of Child Development, Minneapolis, MN, USA

A S Carter
University of Massachusetts Boston, Boston, MA, USA

M Casasola
Cornell University, Ithaca, NY, USA

L M Casper
University of Southern California, Los Angeles, CA, USA

I Chatoor
Children's National Medical Center, Washington, DC, USA

A I Chin
University of California, Los Angeles, Los Angeles, CA, USA

R Clark
University of Wisconsin, Madison, WI, USA

A Clarke-Stewart
University of California, Irvine, Irvine, CA, USA

C M Connor
Florida State University, Tallahassee, FL, USA

J Coolbear
University of Toronto, Toronto, ON, Canada;
The Hospital for Sick Children, Toronto, ON, Canada

M L Courage
Memorial University, St. John's, NL, Canada

M J Cox
University of North Carolina, Chapel, NC, USA

A Crawford
University of Toronto, Toronto, ON, Canada;
Mount Sinai Hospital, Toronto, ON, Canada

E M Cummings
University of Notre Dame, Notre Dame, IN, USA

L A Dack
University of Toronto, Toronto, ON, Canada

M W Daehler
University of Massachusetts, Amherst, MA, USA

S R Daniels
University of Colorado Health Sciences Center, Denver, CO, USA

R B David
St. Mary's Hospital, Richmond, VA, USA

G Dawson
University of Washington, Seattle, WA, USA

L F DiLalla
Southern Illinois University School of Medicine, Carbondale, IL, USA

J A DiPietro
Johns Hopkins University, Baltimore, MD, USA

B M D'Onofrio
Indiana University, Bloomington, IN, USA

R L Doty
University of Pennsylvania School of Medicine, Philadelphia, PA, USA

M Dozier
University of Delaware, Newark, DE, USA

W O Eaton
University of Manitoba, Winnipeg, MB, Canada

C Edwards
University of Nebraska–Lincoln, Lincoln, NE, USA

K K Elam
Southern Illinois University School of Medicine, Carbondale, IL, USA

R R Espinal
University of Chicago, Chicago, IL, USA

R S Everhart
Syracuse University, Syracuse, NY, USA

D Fair
Washington University School of Medicine, St. Louis, MO, USA

F Farzin
University of California, Davis, Davis, CA, USA

D J Fidler
Colorado State University, Fort Collins, CO, USA

T Field
University of Miami School of Medicine, Miami, FL, USA

B H Fiese
Syracuse University, Syracuse, NY, USA

K W Fischer
Harvard Graduate School of Education, Cambridge, MA, USA

H E Fitzgerald
Michigan State University, East Lansing, MI, USA

D R Fleisher
University of Missouri School of Medicine, Columbia, MO, USA

M J Flory
New York State Institute for Basic Research, Staten Island, NY, USA

B Forsyth
Yale University School of Medicine, New Haven, CT, USA

S Fowler
University of Kansas, Lawrence, KS, USA

R C Fretts
Harvard Vanguard Medical Associates, Wellesley, MA, USA

J J Gallagher
University of North Carolina at Chapel Hill, Chapel Hill, NC, USA

J M Gardner
New York State Institute for Basic Research, Staten Island, NY, USA

J-L Gariépy
The University of North Carolina at Chapel Hill, Chapel Hill, NC, USA

M A Gartstein
Washington State University, Pullman, WA, USA

M Gauvain
University of California at Riverside, Riverside, CA, USA

D R Gemmill
California Sudden Infant Death Syndrome Advisory Council, Escondido, CA, USA

I R Gizer
Emory University, Atlanta, GA, USA

M M Gleason
Tulane University Health Sciences Center, New Orleans, LA, USA

M M Gleason
Brown University School of Medicine, Providence, RI, USA

R L Gómez
The University of Arizona, Tucson, AZ, USA

L Godoy
University of Massachusetts Boston, Boston, MA, USA

W A Goldberg
University of California, Irvine, CA, USA

E C Goldfield
Harvard University, Boston, MA, USA

S Goldin-Meadow
University of Chicago, Chicago, IL, USA

H H Goldsmith
University of Wisconsin–Madison, Madison, WI, USA

C Golomb
University of Massachusetts Boston, Boston, MA, USA

E L Grigorenko
Yale University, New Haven, CT, USA

J E Grusec
University of Toronto, Toronto, ON, Canada

L M Gutman
University of London, London, UK

M de Haan
University College London Institute of Child Health, London, UK

J W Hagen
University of Michigan, Ann Arbor, MI, USA

R J Hagerman
University of California, Davis, Medical Center, Sacramento, CA, USA

N Halfon
University of California, Los Angeles, Los Angeles, CA, USA

G S Halford
Griffith University, Brisbane, QLD, Australia

J Harel
University of Haifa, Haifa, Israel

K M Harrington
Emory University, Atlanta, GA, USA

H Hayne
University of Otago, Dunedin, New Zealand

L J Heffner
Boston Medical Center, Boston, MA, USA

N Heilbron
University of North Carolina, Chapel, NC, USA

R W Hendershot
University of Colorado at Denver Health Sciences Center, Denver, CO, USA

M Hernandez-Reif
University of Miami School of Medicine, Miami, FL, USA

K Herold
University of California, Santa Cruz, Santa Cruz, CA, USA

A H Hindman
University of Michigan, Ann Arbor, MI, USA

J A Hofheimer
University of North Carolina at Chapel Hill, Chapel Hill, NC, USA

C von Hofsten
Uppsala University, Uppsala, Sweden

G Hollich
Purdue University, West Lafayette, IN, USA

J R Hollister
University of Colorado at Denver and Health Sciences Center, Denver, CO, USA

A H Hoon
Kennedy Krieger Institute, Baltimore, MD, USA

N Howe
Concordia University, Montréal, QC, Canada

C Howes
University of California, Los Angeles, Los Angeles, CA, USA

A Hupbach
University of Arizona, Tucson, AZ, USA

J S Hyde
University of Wisconsin, Madison, WI, USA

J Isen
University of Southern California, Los Angeles, CA, USA

J S Jameson
Coloradoes State University, Fort Collins, CO, USA

T Jirikowic
University of Washington, Seattle, WA, USA

R Jochem
University of California, Davis, Davis, CA, USA

M H Johnson
University of London, London, UK

S P Johnson
New York University, New York, NY, USA

T R B Johnson
The University of Michigan, Ann Arbor, MI, USA

M V Johnston
Kennedy Krieger Institute, Baltimore, MD, USA

J Jones-Branch
University of Nebraska–Lincoln, Lincoln, NE, USA

T A Jusko
University of Washington, Seattle, WA, USA

J Kagan
Harvard University, Cambridge, MA, USA

J Kapala
McGill University Health Centre, Montréal, QC, Canada

B Z Karmel
New York State Institute for Basic Research, Staten Island, NY, USA

T G Keens
Keck School of Medicine of the University of Southern California, Los Angeles, CA, USA

D J Kelly
The University of Sheffield, Sheffield, UK

S King
University of Washington, Seattle, WA, USA

P Kitchen
University of Southern California, Los Angeles, CA, USA

J Koontz
University of California, Riverside, Riverside, CA, USA

C B Kopp
Los Angeles, CA, USA

C D Kouros
University of Notre Dame, Notre Dame, IN, USA

L L LaGasse
Warren Alpert Medical School of Brown University, Providence, RI, USA

F G Lamb-Parker
Columbia University, New York, NY, USA

M Lampl
Emory University, Atlanta, GA, USA

A L Lathrop
University of Rochester, Rochester, NY, USA

R A Lawrence
University of Rochester School of Medicine and Dentistry, Rochester, NY, USA

M S Leidy
University of California, Riverside, CA, USA

E M Lennon
New York State Institute for Basic Research, Staten Island, NY, USA

T A Lenzi
Vanderbilt University Medical Center, Nashville, TN, USA

S E Lerman
University of California, Los Angeles, Los Angeles, CA, USA

B M Lester
Warren Alpert Medical School of Brown University, Providence, RI, USA

H Liang
King's College London, London, UK

K Libertus
Duke University, Durham, NC, USA

E Lieven
Max Planck Institute for Evolutionary Anthropology, Leipzig, Germany

B Lozoff
University of Michigan, Ann Arbor, MI, USA

J S Lu
David Geffen School of Medicine at UCLA, Los Angeles, CA, USA

M C Lu
David Geffen School of Medicine at UCLA, Los Angeles, CA, USA

J Luby
Washington University School of Medicine, St. Louis, MO, USA

R Lucas-Thompson
University of California, Irvine, Irvine, CA, USA

L E Lurye
New York University, New York, NY, USA

M Macaoay
Children's National Medical Center, Washington, DC, USA

S C Mangelsdorf
University of Illinois at Urbana–Champaign, Champaign, IL, USA

M Martinos
University College London Institute of Child Health, London, UK

D Matthews
University of Manchester, Manchester, UK

K McCrink
Yale University, New Haven, CT, USA

M McIlreavy
University of Georgia, Athens, GA, USA

L M McKelvey
University of Arkansas for Medical Sciences, Little Rock, AR, USA

G W McRoberts
Haskins Laboratories, New Haven, CT, USA

A N Meltzoff
University of Washington, Seattle, WA, USA

D Messinger
University of Miami, Coral Gables, FL, USA

S Meyer
University of California Davis, Davis, CA, USA

L J Miller
Sensory Processing Disorder Foundation, Greenwood Village, CO, USA

M A Miller
University of California, Riverside, CA, USA

W R Mills-Koonce
University of North Carolina, Chapel, NC, USA

K Minde
Montreal Children's Hospital, Montreal, QC, Canada

J L Miner
University of California, Irvine, Irvine, CA, USA

K L Morris
University of California, Riverside, Riverside, CA, USA

F J Morrison
University of Michigan, Ann Arbor, MI, USA

M C Moulson
Massachusetts Institute of Technology, Cambridge, MA, USA

M E Msall
University of Chicago, Chicago, IL, USA

M Muenke
National Institutes of Health, Bethesda, MD, USA

P Y Mullineaux
Southern Illinois University School of Medicine, Carbondale, IL, USA

J P Murray
Kansas State University, Manhattan, KS, USA

A D Murray
Kansas State University, Manhattan, KS, USA

L Nadel
University of Arizona, Tucson, AZ, USA

A Needham
Duke University, Durham, NC, USA

C A Nelson
Harvard Medical School, Boston, MA, USA

L M Oakes
University of California, Davis, Davis, CA, USA

H Carmichael Olson
University of Washington, Seattle, WA, USA

M Y Ono
University of California, Davis Medical Center, Sacramento, CA, USA

C W Oppenheimer
University of North Carolina at Chapel Hill, Chapel Hill, NC, USA

T Ostler
University of Illinois at Urbana–Champaign, Urbana, IL, USA

K P Palmer
University of Arkansas for Medical Sciences, Little Rock, AR, USA

R Panneton
Virginia Tech, Blacksburg, VA, USA

R D Parke
University of California, Riverside, Riverside, CA, USA

O Pascalis
The University of Sheffield, Sheffield, UK

D L Paulhus
University of British Columbia, Vancouver, BC, Canada

F S Pedroso
Universidade Federal de Santa Maria, Santa Maria, Brazil

J L Petersen
University of Wisconsin, Madison, WI, USA

S L Pillsbury
Richmond, VA, USA

J Pinkston
University of Kansas, Lawrence, KS, USA

F Pons
Universitat de Barcelona, Barcelona, Spain

G Posada
Purdue University, West Lafayette, IN, USA

A Pressel
University of North Carolina, Chapel, NC, USA

H H Raikes
University of Nebraska–Lincoln, Lincoln, NE, USA

J T Rapp
St. Cloud State University, St. Cloud, MN, USA

H E Recchia
Concordia University, Montréal, QC, Canada

M Regalado
University of California, Los Angeles, Los Angeles, CA, USA

J M Retrouvey
McGill University Health Centre, Montréal, QC, Canada

C A Reynolds
University of California, Riverside, Riverside, CA, USA

J E Richards
University of South Carolina, Columbia, SC, USA

J Richmond
Harvard University, Boston, MA, USA

J Robinson
University of Connecticut–Storrs, Storrs, CT, USA

M K Rothbart
University of Oregon, Eugene, OR, USA

D N Ruble
New York University, New York, NY, USA

J A Rudolph
Children's Hospital Medical Center, Cincinnati, OH, USA

P A Rufo
Children's Hospital Boston, Boston, MA, USA

S Russ
University of California, Los Angeles, Los Angeles, CA, USA

A Sadeh
Tel Aviv University, Tel Aviv, Israel

R C Schaaf
Thomas Jefferson University, Philadelphia, PA, USA

A Scher
University of Haifa, Haifa, Israel

B L Schlaggar
Washington University School of Medicine, St. Louis, MO, USA

T J Schofield
University of California, Riverside, Riverside, CA, USA

E K Scholnick
University of Maryland, College Park, MD, USA

S Schwartz
McGill University Health Centre, Montréal, QC, Canada

D C Schwebel
University of Alabama at Birmingham, Birmingham, AL, USA

N Sebastián-Gallés
Universitat de Barcelona, Barcelona, Spain

R Seifer
Brown University, Providence, RI, USA

M Shah
University of Pennsylvania School of Medicine, Philadelphia, PA, USA

E Simonoff
King's College London, London, UK

D P Sladen
Vanderbilt University Medical Center, Nashville, TN, USA

D L Smith
The Children's Hospital, Denver, CO, USA

K A Snyder
University of Denver, Denver, CO, USA

J B Soep
University of Colorado at Denver and Health Sciences Center, Denver, CO, USA

K C Soska
New York University, New York, NY, USA

M M Stalets
Washington University School of Medicine, St. Louis, MO, USA

L Sterling
University of Washington, Seattle, WA, USA

M Sumaroka
National Institutes of Health, Bethesda, MD, USA

H N Switzky
Northern Illinois University, DeKalb, IL, USA

D E Szwedo
University of Virginia, Charlottesville, VA, USA

A Taddio
The Hospital for Sick Children, Toronto, ON, Canada and University of Toronto, ON, Canada

B Taubman
University of Pennsylvania School of Medicine, Philadelphia, PA, USA

D M Teti
The Pennsylvania State University, University Park, PA, USA

A M Tharpe
Vanderbilt University Medical Center, Nashville, TN, USA

C R Thomann
University of Massachusetts, Boston, MA, USA

R A Thompson
University of California Davis, Davis, CA, USA

N Tolani
Columbia University, New York, NY, USA

M Tomasello
Max Planck Institute for Evolutionary Anthropology, Leipzig, Germany

C M Torrence
University of Denver, Denver, CO, USA

N Towe-Goodman
The Pennsylvania State University, University Park, PA, USA

S E Trehub
University of Toronto at Mississauga, Mississauga, ON, Canada

R E Tremblay
University of Montréal, Montreal, QC, Canada

E Tronick
University of Massachusetts, Boston, Boston, MA, USA

A Tullos
The University of Texas, Austin, TX, USA

C D Vallotton
Harvard Graduate School of Education, Cambridge, MA, USA

I D Waldman
Emory University, Atlanta, GA, USA

J S Wallerstein
The Judith Wallerstein Center for the Family in Transition, Corte Madera, CA, USA

S E Watamura
University of Denver, Denver, CO, USA

N Wentworth
Lake Forest College, Lake Forest, IL, USA

R A Williamson
University of Washington, Seattle, WA, USA

K Willoughby
University of Toronto, Toronto, ON, Canada

M A Winter
Syracuse University, Syracuse, NY, USA

M S Wong
University of Illinois at Urbana–Champaign, Champaign, IL, USA

J D Woolley
The University of Texas, Austin, TX, USA

K Wynn
Yale University, New Haven, CT, USA

P D Zeanah
Tulane University Health Sciences Center, New Orleans, LA, USA

C H Zeanah
Tulane University Health Sciences Center, New Orleans, LA, USA

P D Zelazo
Institute of Child Development, Minneapolis, MN, USA

P Zelkowitz
McGill University, Montreal, QC, Canada

C Zera
Brigham and Women's Hospital, Boston, MA, USA

D Zlotnik
National Institutes of Health, Bethesda, MD, USA

K M Zosuls
New York University, New York, NY, USA

CONTENTS

VOLUME 1

A

B

VOLUME 2

G

H

I

L

M

N

O

P

VOLUME 3

R

S

T

V

Reasoning in Early Development

E K Scholnick, University of Maryland, College Park, MD, USA

Glossary

Analogical reasoning – Based on the discovery that two systems have some similar internal relations, inferences are made that there additional ways the systems correspond to one another.

Basic level – The most accessible level of categorization in a hierarchy because the instances in the class are fairly similar but also are fairly distinct from members of other categories. In the hierarchy of poodles, dogs, and canines, 'dogs' is the basic category.

Deduction – Drawing the implications of a sentence according to a set of laws.

Essentialism – The belief that for each category of things found in nature, whether they are animals, vegetables, or minerals, there is an underlying invisible essence that causes things to be the way they are.

Induction – Reasoning from knowledge of one particular to another particular or from a particular fact to a general law.

Modus ponens – A form of conditional reasoning which permits a deduction from an if-statement 'If p, then q'. When p is true, then q must also be true.

Modus tollens – A form of conditional reasoning which permits a deduction from an if-statement 'If p, then q'. If q is false, then p must be false, too.

Natural kinds – Classes of entities occurring in nature such as animals, plants, and minerals. Instances of a class seem to share a common essence (see essentialism).

Pragmatic schema – A set of rules for social interactions, such as permissions and obligations.

Introduction

Why does the topic of reasoning belong in a volume devoted to infants and preschoolers? Should we expect toddlers to exercise the rules of thought that enable the derivation of new information from earlier material? Suppose the child is promised, "If it is sunny, we will go to the zoo tomorrow." When the child wakes up the next day and learns the zoo trip is canceled, can we expect her to rush to the window to see the rain? If the toddler is told that he needs exercise to make him strong, will he infer that his dog does, too? Clearly having strong reasoning skills would be advantageous to young children in their quest to grasp the intricate patterns that shape our universe and our daily lives. The child would not have to repeat the same lesson every time a new event or object appeared. The early emergence of reasoning would explain how easily children learn to name objects, embark upon a vocabulary spurt, figure out how to combine words, and construct a grammar. But the realm of deduction has been the exclusive purview of philosophers and geometers, and induction and analogy are the tools of scientists and inventors. Are there really practicing Aristotles in the nursery? If so, what enables them to do it? Maybe they are simply practicing 'toy' versions of reasoning with miniature tools that will grow in size, power, and complexity just as their body grows throughout childhood.

The study of early reasoning is fascinating because it tracks the origins of processes that uniquely characterize our species. These origins have been controversial because the cognitive revolution in psychology was accompanied by a second revolution in developmental psychology which eradicated the barriers between mature and infant thought. Additionally computational models have redefined the nature of the processes by which inductions, deductions, and analogies are accomplished and the methods by which they are studied. The debates about whether, when, and how youngsters reason are intimately linked to the process of taking reasoning from the nursery into the laboratory and using laboratory data to model thought.

A Framework for Understanding Issues in the Development of Reasoning

The deduction about the zoo trip was triggered by a sentence with a subordinate if-clause followed by a main clause, or in formal logic, an initial premise with antecedent (if p) and consequent (then q) clauses. A second premise provided new information that denied the consequent (not q, no trip). Conditional logic dictates the conclusion about the status of the antecedent precondition (not p, no sun). 'If' often signals that the original premise is hypothetical. Who knows tomorrow's weather? The sentence describes a familiar event. The toddler has visited the zoo under diverse weather conditions and knows that thunderstorms ruin excursions. Pragmatically, the parent has promised an excursion under certain preconditions. In daily life, interpretations of conditional premises draw upon knowledge of logic, syntax, social interactions, and events, and the child who is developing competence in reasoning is simultaneously gaining social and linguistic competencies which may support reasoning. There are multiple redundant cues and multiple redundant processes by which the information can be extended. But the scientific study of psychological processes is analytic and focuses on single processes at their simplest level. This reductionist approach presents barriers to the study of children's reasoning. Each facet of reasoning, its syntax, semantics, pragmatics, and logical form, facilitates reasoning. As each is removed, reasoning becomes harder and more inaccurate and young children seem less competent. Moreover, our models of reasoning and its origins become impoverished because they do not encompass the multiple inroads available to children depending on the circumstances and skills of the child.

The definition of reasoning is also elusive. Four new pieces of information could follow the premise, "If it is sunny, we will go to the zoo." Two focus on the antecedent if-clause and either affirm the precondition of a sunny day (modus ponens) or deny it, citing rain, and then leave the reasoner to decide whether there will be a zoo trip. Two others focus on the consequent, either affirming that the zoo trip occurred, or as in the modus tollens example that canceled the trip, denying the consequent clause, leaving the reasoner to infer the weather conditions. Modus ponens reasoning is accessible to toddlers but college sophomores studying logic err in the inferences they draw from affirming the consequent or denying the antecedent because the inference is indeterminate. The if-premise states what happens when its precondition is satisfied, but says nothing about what happens when it is not satisfied. The abysmal performance of adults on problems with indeterminate answers led to claims that some or all of conditional logic falls outside the province of mature reasoners, much less children. The more encompassing the definition of reason, the more likely complex processing will be required to exhibit the skill, and competence will appear late in development.

There are also levels of understanding of reasoning, and where the bar is set may determine the age of emergence and the level of competence attributed to the reasoner. Children may know the agenda for a zoo trip on a sunny day. Do children also know that canceling the excursion on a sunny day would make their mother a liar? Forms of inference and their ramifications, like falsification strategies, may not emerge simultaneously. Just as President Clinton once tried to evade his questioners by noting that it depends on what the meaning of 'is' is, analyses of reasoning depend on what the meaning of reasoning is.

Debates about the emergence of reasoning fall into three camps. The first camp inspired the question, "What's the topic of reasoning doing in this volume?" Reasoning is a higher order skill best studied with abstract materials, and embedded in two interlocking systems, of mutually entailing rules and conscious awareness of their conditions of operation. The rules are idealizations that most individuals rarely attain. Only logicians and scientists reason with any facility. The rules exemplify what children can aspire to master. The study of logic in childhood is either an oxymoron or a search for the roots. The second, opposing view posits scientists in the crib, born with either powerful reasoning devices that undergird learning or powerful belief systems about domains like biology or social behavior that support reasoning. The early emergence of reasoning demonstrates the power of our evolutionary endowment to prepare children to adapt to the world. The third view is developmental. There are pronounced changes in children's reasoning skills. This perspective encompasses lively debates about starting points, developmental mechanisms, benchmarks of change, and final destinations. Some researchers ground early reasoning in dumb mechanisms like attention, perception, and association that become smarter and more abstract. Alternatively the initial theory of the world that undergirds reasoning may undergo radical changes. The choice of theory and its characterization of young children reflect prior choices of the definition of reasoning and the contexts in which it is studied. This article provides a survey of 2–5-year-old's inductive, analogical, and deductive inference performance that bears on these debates.

Induction

Induction extends information known about one particular to another or from a particular to the general. Scientists use induction when they take a pattern in a sample of data as the basis for a general law. It is also a tool for everyday learning. My collie Spot likes to chew on bones. Other collies like Rover should like to chew on bones, too. There is no certainty that Rover likes to chew on bones, but knowledge of dogs might enable toddlers to guess what might please a new dog. The inference is based on the assumption that the unfamiliar target instance (Rover) is like the familiar Spot in some respect. Therefore, Rover might resemble Spot in other ways. Debates about induction revolve around three issues: (1) the meaning of 'like', the original linkage that supports induction; (2) the properties of the familiar or source stimulus, Spot, that children are willing to project onto inductive targets like Rover; and (3) the mechanisms enabling linkage of the base and target and projection of properties.

If Spot and Rover were identical twins, the task of inferring similar food preferences would be simple. Animals that look alike in one way might be alike in others. Perceptual similarity enables the inference. But if Rover is a poodle, a wolf, or a tiger, would the child assume these animals share Spot's food preferences? They would have to search for the category to which both the dog and the target animal belong. Children would then need to draw upon their knowledge of dogs, canines, or animals as the basis for induction. The base and target are both dogs, canines, or animals so they must have similar body structures. Because the child might not recognize that dogs and tigers are both animals, they might not recognize they share some common properties. Thus induction might depend on knowledge of categories. The likelihood of inferences also depends on properties. If the property projected is visible like diet, validating an inference is easy. But if the property is invisible, like having an omentum, then ordinary observation cannot validate inductions. The child must have a theory or causal narrative that explains why all dogs or all canines or animals probably have an omentum. Because induction tasks can differ in the relations between the base and target entities and the properties that are projected, there are different stories of the origin and course of induction in early childhood.

Every theory acknowledges that even infants recognize common categories such as females and males and can make simple inductions from one member of a narrow category to another. Twelve- to 14-month-olds who learn that a novel object is squeezable will attempt to squeeze highly similar objects. They will even make inductions about objects that are not close replicas if the objects share the same name. Word learning indicates inductive capacities, too. When my son began to label dogs 'woof-woof', he called every dog by that name as well as neighborhood cats.

Susan Gelman claims that this early appearing inductive capacity is deployed to make inferences about members of certain kinds of categories. The infant starts with a cognitive bias to carve the world into pieces, each associated with a story justifying the way the world is sliced. Those stories enable the child to make inductions among events, entities, and phenomena in each realm because they obey the same laws or they have the same infrastructure. A key line of demarcation is between natural entities, such as animals and minerals, and artifacts like automobiles and buildings. Susan Gelman's research on induction focuses primarily on living creatures and a naive biological theory, essentialism, that explains their appearances and behaviors. Upon hearing that one creature is called a 'bird' and another, a 'bat', the child has an all-purpose theory to explain why different creatures receive different names. All creatures within each named category have a common invisible essence that accounts for why they are the way they are and do what they do. We often hear people say things like "Boys will be boys." This belief bias is a placeholder for later, more scientific explanations invoking genetic causation for traits, behavior, and appearances.

The structure of categories provides a tool for testing theory-based induction as opposed to perceptually based induction. Although members of a category usually resemble each other, not all members of a category look alike. Angelfish do not resemble sharks but both are fish because their internal anatomy supports the capacity to live under water and they have similar reproductive systems. Appearances can also be deceiving. Dolphins look like sharks but they breathe air and bear live young. If children made inductions simply on the basis of perceptual appearances they would infer that a novel property of sharks also characterizes dolphins. But if they had a theory of fish 'essences' they would instead assume that sharks and angelfish share the same properties. Susan Gelman demonstrated that young children 's inductions were governed by an essentialist theory. She showed children two line drawings, for example, an angelfish and a dolphin. Each animal was named and children were told a property. "This fish stays underwater to breathe. This dolphin pops above water to breathe." They then saw a picture of a shark, and were asked whether it breathes like the fish (angelfish) or the dolphin. Four-year-olds' choices were based primarily on category membership. The same pattern of induction is shown by 32-month-olds. For example, when they saw a picture of a bluebird which they were told lives in a nest, they acknowledged that other bluebirds lived in a nest and so do dodos who do not look much like bluebirds. They did not think that pterodactyls, the flying winged dinosaurs, lived in nests. The children usually made the correct inference that birds and dinosaurs have different living places. For young children the trigger for an essentialist induction is naming. If they heard the name of the creature or knew its name, they decided that the weird dodo bird lived in a nest while the pterodactyl, despite its bird like appearance, lived elsewhere. Without those labels most answers were based on appearances.

Young children do not make inductions indiscriminately. When categories are labeled by proper nouns like 'Tabby' which denote individuals, they do not make category-based inferences. Adjectives won't suffice either, perhaps because they do not tap into the categories that index causal essences. If the property is transient or accidental, such as 'fell on the floor this morning' inductions are less because it is also unlikely to play a causal role in defining identity. Category labels appear to play an important role in triggering children's inductions, and Susan Gelman theorizes that they may help children construct essentialist categories. When she observed parents reading picture books to young children, she found that they used generic common nouns like 'dolphin' more frequently to describe animals, which are the subject of essentialist theories, than artifacts. Their children show the same labeling bias, using generics especially for animate terms. These labels also draw attention to the stability and coherence of categories and thus indirectly support the child's inferences. Thus growth in inferential skill in the biological domain might reflect changes in the understanding of categories or revisions in the theory of natural kinds.

The mechanism for inference is referral of the base instance, for example, angelfish, to a higher order category, fish, and projection of essential properties of one fish to other category members. But angelfish are fish, vertebrates, and animals, too. Given a familiar animal with a novel property like having an omentum, how far up the category hierarchy do children go in making inductions? Research on the scope of induction in young children echoes research on categorization. The toddler's categories are very broad, animate or inanimate, plant or animal, but they quickly form categories at the basic level where there are sufficient commonalities among category members to form a coherent set, and also enough distinctiveness to easily differentiate one category from another. Sharks are finned, scaly, and gilled, but dogs are not. But it is difficult to discriminate nurse sharks from tiger sharks. Basic level categories are also usually assigned a single noun name, for example, shark rather than tiger shark. Induction follows the same route. With age, the scope of induction narrows. Two-year-old wills will generalize a property like "needing biotin to live" from animals to plants. But 3–4-year-olds prefer to make property inductions within basic categories like fish or birds. Experts in fields narrow their inferences further because they know that species of fish and birds may behave very differently. For example, penguins do not fly. The privileged level for experts' reasoning is very narrow because their category hierarchy includes more differentiated subspecies. When preschoolers in families who lived in rural areas or who worked in biological fields were tested, they, too, were more discerning in their inductions. They would project what they knew about one subspecies to another but not to broader categories. Category-based induction may reflect changes in children's theories of categories in different domains.

Although preschoolers make categorical inductions, unlike adults, they do not fully understand what constitutes good evidence for inductions. Some inductions are more convincing than others. For adults, inductive inferences are stronger if they are based on a great variety of examples. This is termed categorical coverage. You are told both cats and buffalos have cervicas inside them. Additionally cows and buffalos have ulnaries inside them. Based on this information what do you think kangaroos have inside them, cervicas or ulnaries? Because cats and buffalos are two very different species, cervicas may be a very general property of animals and could apply to kangaroos, which also fit under the animal umbrella. But buffalos and cows are both hoofed mammals, and a kangaroo is a marsupial. So it would be safer to claim the kangaroo has cervicas than ulnaries. Adults also believe that the more similar the source and target animals, the stronger the inference. If both a zebra and a horse possess ulnaries, it is safer to conclude a donkey possesses ulnaries than a kangaroo does. Kindergartners acknowledge that information about animals similar to the target of the inference provides a more reliable base for induction than information about source items dissimilar to the target. But they do not believe that the strength of an inference is related to the span of category coverage. Seven-year-olds recognize that categorical coverage matters, too, but only if they are reminded they are making inferences to all the animals.

Why should children do so well on making inferences but not on judging the strength of the evidence? Why should they be more sensitive to similarity evidence than category coverage? These judgment tasks present more information to process. Each argument set includes several instances. The overburdened 5-year-old may reduce the information by choosing a single similar animal in the base set to compare with the target. Additionally, children had to take the extra step of generating the relationship between the target and the inclusive class, animal, which forms the basis for inference. When the target of inference was labeled an animal, it made the task easier for 7-year-olds. The rules are also subtle. Diversity and similarity are opposite sides of the coin, yet both strengthen arguments. Success on these tasks requires metacognitive understanding of the rules of inference and their domain of application. Although kindergartners can easily make simple inferences, they may be stymied when the tasks require conscious awareness of the ground rules for induction.

There is another possibility. Even kindergartners know arguments are stronger if the base and target animals are similar but they do not appreciate the role of category coverage. Vladimir Sloutsky has claimed that early inductive inference is mediated by similarity and shifts toward categorization later. Sloutsky refined Gelman's research in two important ways. He obtained information about children's judgments of similarity and then he assessed children's performance on category, similarity, and naming tasks to tease apart their relative contributions to induction. Susan Gelman usually asked children to choose between a source of inference that looked like the target or that belonged to the same category as the target. But the mere appearance and categorical matches varied in their resemblance to the target items. Since some categorical inductions were harder than others, perhaps similarity accounted for these variations. So Sloutsky asked 4- and 5-year-olds to judge whether the mere appearance or the shared category picture was more like the target and also elicited inductions. He found that children were more likely to make essentialist categorical inductions if the category match closely resembled the target item and the mere appearance match was not very similar to the target. In short similarity supported the categorical induction. Conversely if the mere appearance match was indeed rated as very similar and the category match was dissimilar, the child was more likely to make inductions based on appearance. Therefore, Sloutsky asserted that categorical induction is not a higher order reasoning skill but is governed by simpler perceptual and attentional mechanisms that are the foundation for later developing categorical knowledge.

Susan Gelman argued that labels influence essentialist inductions by enabling children to detect essentialist categories and apply essentialist knowledge. Vladimir Sloutsky provided evidence that 4-year-olds use names for another purpose, enhancing the similarity between category members. He created a set of imaginary animals and then asked children to make similarity judgments. For example, there were two animals, equally similar to the target animal. When the animals were unnamed, the children chose at random. If the target and one animal were both called 'lolos' but the other animal was a 'tipi', the child chose the animal with the same name as the target as more similar to the target. Maybe labels influence induction in the same way, by enhancing the resemblance between the source and target of induction. He then demonstrated that when children were presented with tasks requiring similarity judgments, categorization, naming, and induction, their performance was highly correlated. In Sloutsky's view, initially, induction, naming, and categorization are based on similarity, which is grounded in deployment of simple attentional and perceptual mechanisms. Naming enhances the similarity between instances, and similarity-based category structure supports induction. Early induction is a bottom-up process, not a theory-driven one. During the elementary school years, induction becomes more knowledge-driven as a result of exposure to schooling. His view falls within a rich tradition describing a developmental shift from similarity to knowledge-based approaches.

The debate between Susan Gelman and Vladimir Sloutsky returns us to the issues raised in the introduction. The basis for induction may depend on the pull of the task. When the stimuli are line drawings that are lean on perceptual detail and that depict familiar natural kinds, these inputs tap a rich linguistic and conceptual knowledge base that primes theory-based induction. Increase the stimulus detail and decrease stimulus familiarity by using artificial creatures and the child relies more heavily on similarity. When the child is ignorant of the category, similarity may be the default strategy.

Attempts to partial out similarity from categorical understanding reflect the attempt to isolate single mechanisms even though the components of induction are intertwined. The search for a single mechanism leads to varying just one aspect of induction or finding cases at the edge where the several sources of input may conflict. Category members usually resemble one another and resemblance is the basis for initial category formation. However, there is also considerable variation among members in a category and some instances overlap with other categories. The categorizer and inductive reasoner always indulge in a guessing game about whether a feature possessed by one member applies to another and where the category boundaries end. Essentialism helps the reasoner to make inductions in the boundary cases where similarity is insufficient or misleading. These are the cases Gelman probes, and these are also the challenges reasoners are more likely to encounter as they gain deeper acquaintance with categories. Essentialist theory enables children to sharpen the categorical divide by creating a mythical entity shared by all the diverse members that accounts for their membership in the category. Essentialist theory also helps the child decide which properties are good candidates for defining class membership and making property projections.

Analogical Reasoning

At first blush, the process by which the knowledge of elephant anatomy is extended to rhinos seems dissimilar to the process by which one infers that dark is to light as night is to day. Because the Miller analogy test, which contains these 'proportional'analogies in the form, A : B :: C : D, is often required for entrance to graduate school, analogical reasoning seems to be another skill that prompted the query, "Why do discussions of higher order reasoning appear in an encyclopedia on early childhood?" However, the processes and origins of induction and analogical reasoning have much in common. Like inductions, analogies extend current knowledge to new instances. In induction, the reasoner encounters a new instance, relates it to an old one, and projects the properties of the familiar instance onto the new instance, based on the guess that the two instances are the same in some way. Analogies involve the same processes on a broader scale. Again, there is a familiar base or source and an unfamiliar target the individual wishes to understand. Reasoners use their representations of the relational structure of the well-known source to find correspondences in the unfamiliar target on the assumption that target and source work the same way. For example, preschoolers often use humans as an analogical base to make inferences about animals, rather than an abstract essentialist theory. They assume that the anatomical functions of humans are also possessed by creatures resembling them.

Like the study of categorical induction, descriptions of the timetable of emergence for analogical reasoning reflect assumptions about the nature and origin of the reasoning process and the choice of tasks. Some theories postulate a single analogical skill. Usha Goswami assumes there is an inbuilt powerful capacity ready to go in infancy providing the baby has sufficient experience to extract the likenesses on which analogies build. The engine is ready to go, but the child needs knowledge to fuel it. Growth of analogical reasoning reflects gains in knowledge. Three-year-olds can solve pictorial analogies depicting familiar causal relations, such as bread : sliced bread :: lemon : ?. They do not complete the analogy by choosing the same object, a lemon, with the wrong causal transformation, or the wrong object with the right transformation, or an object resembling a lemon. Instead they choose a lemon slice. Both adults and preschoolers are competent reasoners but adults, who are more knowledgeable about causal and categorical relations, can construct more analogies.

Graeme Halford counters that the engine needs to increase its horsepower and a maturational timetable governs the expansion of engine power. Performance depends on the number of variables that need to be related in a representation of a problem regardless of problem content. Lemon: sliced lemon is a binary relation linking two terms and the analogy between slicing bread and slicing lemons is another binary relation. Halford claims that 2-year-olds can process these binary relations, but three-term relations, such as the transitive inference, $a>b$, $b>c$, and therefore $a>c$, cannot be solved until 5 years of age. However, Trabasso has provided evidence that with appropriate training, 3-year-olds can solve transitive inference problems.

These views, which posit a generic prowess, are problematical because analogical reasoning performance varies. Two-year-olds, given the appropriate linguistic and perceptual prompts, can grasp analogies, so more than processing capacity is at issue. Accounts based on knowledge fail to explain why adults often fail to apply what they know to structure a new domain. Dedre Gentner's theory of analogical development addresses these issues and also provides a framework for resolving controversies on induction and deductive reasoning. She exemplifies the approach that introduced this article. Her theory is as follows. Because our environment contains multiple overlapping sets of cues, it provides multiple bases for detecting correspondences and drawing analogies. Often appearances and relational structure are correlated and these correlations provide support for analogies. In animals, appearance, anatomy, and function are often related. The growth of analogical skill reflects changes in the child's representation of the diverse facets of source and target phenomena with a shift from solely representing perceptual similarities to greater emphasis on structural relations. Early global similarity detection becomes more analytic. This lays the groundwork for detection of isolated superficial relations that gradually become deeper and more integrated.

Babies form analogies. Neonates imitate an adult sticking out her tongue at them by forming an analogy between the adult's behavior and their own. Upon witnessing an adult using a rake to reel in a desirable toy, in the absence of a rake, toddlers select a similar tool to attain the same end. But their ability to form analogies and apply the right means-end behavior is fragile and context-dependent. Babies can match objects that are very similar if not identical. Slightly change the object or its setting and the perceived correspondence between objects vanishes. Early mapping is global and context dependent.

However, with increasing familiarity with objects, children start to differentiate each object's properties and to form categories of similar but not identical objects. The advent of the ability to name objects both capitalizes on this ability and strengthens it. Upon hearing a new name, for example, 'dog' the child applies it to poodles and dachshunds and the acquisition of nominal terms prompts the child to look for other instances belonging to the same categories. Knowledge becomes more abstract, analytic, and portable. In addition to perceptual features, members of categories share functional and causal resemblances, too. Dogs communicate, breathe, grow, and reproduce in the same way. Increased familiarity with objects in a category exposes the child to relations among properties of objects and these relations become accessible for use in analogical reasoning. At this point children can detect relational analogies like dog : puppy :: horse : foal. Understanding of these relations will, in turn, become more abstract and the concept of birth will be applied to planets, not just the origin of babies.

These changes are influenced by linguistic experience and the opportunities to make comparisons between objects. Languages employ a set of relational terms, such as 'middle', prepositions, such as 'on', and inflections, such as '-er', to draw attention to dimensions and their interrelations. Different grammars vary in the extent to which they require encoding various relations and the ease of encoding. Homes also differ in the extent to which they prompt children to make the perceptual comparisons that underlie extraction of dimensions of similarity and to coordinate dimensional information into deep, coherent networks.

Dedre Gentner's research on the origins of analogy focuses most intensively on preschoolers although she has also tested the role of similarity and relational components of analogy in college students and through computer modeling. In her research children are asked to find correspondences between two series of objects, such as two sets of objects arranged in descending size order. In one experiment, 3- and 4-year-olds were shown a sticker on the bottom of an object in one set and asked to locate the corresponding sticker in the other set (by going to the same location). In the baseline conditions, the items in the series differed only in size, three clay pots arranged in descending order from large (pot 3) to medium sized (pot 2) to small (pot 1). When the experimenter showed a sticker under the middle pot in one series, the child had to pick the middle pot in the other series. Size and position jointly determine the correspondence. In a contrasting condition, the objects differed in identity as well as size and position. Each series contained a plant, a dollhouse, and a coffee mug. Three-year-olds performed poorly on the sparsely detailed stimulus set, but were usually correct when the object's size, identity, and position jointly contributed to correspondence. The 4-year-olds produced few errors with either stimulus set. The younger child needed more cues to map ordinal relations.

In order to ascertain the comparative strength of perceptual vs. relational similarity in determining correspondences, the two sources of similarity were placed in opposition. As before, both the child and adult had a series of three objects differing in size (see **Table 1**). The adult revealed a sticker that was pasted on the object that was the middle size in her series. The child was to infer that the middle object in the child's series would have a sticker, too. The child's choice was to be guided by relational size information. However, the child's series presented a conflict because the child could instead use other absolute perceptual cues. In the 'sparse' condition, there was only one perceptual conflict, absolute size. The stimuli in both the child's and adult's set were pots. But the sizes of pots differed. Let us designate the relative sizes as 1 through 4. The adult's pots were arranged in descending size order 3, 2, 1 with the sticker under pot 2. The child's pots remained arranged in descending size order, but the sizes in the second series were 4, 3, and 2. Pot 2 was the middle pot in one series but the smallest in the other. To find the corresponding pot, the child must ignore the absolute size of each middle pot to focus on its relational position. In the rich detail condition, a second source of perceptual conflict was added, the identity of the objects. Thus in the adult series, there was a big house, smaller cup, and an even smaller car. The sticker was under the cup which occupied the middle position in size and location. The contrasting series contained a very large vase, followed by the large house and the smaller cup. Now the large house was in the middle position. To find the sticker, the child must ignore the identity and absolute size of each middle object to focus on its middle relational position. When object identity was not a competing cue, the performance of 5-year-olds in the task was superlative. They ignored absolute size to focus on ordinal position. But when the stimuli differed in identity, 5-year-olds' performance deteriorated although it was still above chance. Four-year-olds could not handle either task.

In order to understand the contributors to age changes, Dedre Gentner and colleagues tried to bolster 3-year-olds' attention to ordinal relations. The child was taught to apply names for a familiar series, 'Daddy, Mommy,

Table 1 Where is the child's sticker?

Series	*Biggest*	*Middle*	*Smallest*
Sparse			
Adult's	Large pot(3)	Medium pot(2) with sticker	Small pot(1)
Child's	Very large pot(4)	Large pot(3)	Medium pot(2)
Relation of child's sticker to adult's pot with sticker			
Size	Wrong	Wrong	Same
Relative position	Wrong	Same	Wrong
Rich			
Adult's	Large house(3)	Medium cup(2) with sticker	Small car(1)
Child's	Very large vase(4)	Large house(3)	Medium cup(2)
Relation to child's sticker to adult's toy with sticker			
Size	Wrong	Wrong	Same
Relative position	Wrong	Same	Wrong
Identity	Wrong	Wrong	Same

Baby', to families of stuffed bears and stuffed penguins and to select the animals in both series that played the same familial role. Armed with this knowledge, they were able to solve even the difficult task of detecting relational correspondences with competing cues (cross-mapping) with rich stimuli because relational language made position in an ordinal series more salient than object similarity. The family series helped the child attend to the relational structure of the analogy.

Finding corresponding ordinal positions in two size series is a comparatively simple task. Dedre Gentner has also assessed analogical performance on higher-order relational reasoning and the contribution of language and perceptual comparison to its development. In these tasks the child saw one series and must find a series that matches it. One series consisted of three circles increasing in size and the child had to choose between two triads of squares, which were either arranged in ascending size order or in random order. Higher-order relations were introduced in two ways. One involved a cross-dimensional match. The standard showed circles increasing in size but the correct match depicted squares increasing in brightness from black to white. The match is based on representing both the source and choice stimuli as increases. Alternatively, the circles differed in direction. Instead of increasing in size, the squares decreased in size. Both stimuli incorporated linear size changes. The most challenging task changed both direction and dimension. The series of circles increasing in size was to be mapped to three squares decreasing in brightness. The basis for matching is very abstract, linear change. Performance should increase in difficulty as the number of differences between the source and target increased. The same direction-same dimension match ought to be easier than either the same direction-opposite dimension or the opposite direction-same dimension matches and these in turn should be easier than the opposite direction-opposite dimension match. Four-year-olds performed above chance only in the same direction-same dimension condition which requires minimal relational abstraction. Six-year-olds performed above chance in all four conditions but were hampered somewhat by changes in either dimensionality or direction. Eight-year-olds had difficulty only when both aspects of the match were changed. These older children seemed to be shifting toward a higher-level relational analysis.

Again Dedre Gentner used training to diagnose determinants of the shift in reasoning. Even analogical reasoning in same dimension, cross-dimensional matches seemed beyond 4-year-olds' reach. When they learned relational terms, such as 'more and more' their analogical reasoning improved. Perceptual training also boosted performance. When 4-year-olds were given practice on the same direction-same dimension tasks, one dimension at a time, they were then able to find correspondences across dimensions. Gentner attributed the change to more abstract encoding. After repeated experience with size series the child begins to code them economically and abstractly as 'increases' and repeated exposure to brightness series produces the same economical code. Once the two series are both represented abstractly as increases, the child is prepared to do cross-mapping.

Rather than treating analogy as a readymade tool for the infant, Gentner asserts that analogies exist at different levels of abstraction from object correspondence to higher order relational correspondence. The more the task relies on global similarities, the easier the process and the earlier its emergence. Everyone finds analogies based on perceptual similarities easier than analogies requiring cross-relational or higher-order relational mapping. With age access to more conceptual analogies increases. Expertise brings with it the detection of a network of dimensional relations that becomes deeper and more coherent and more accessible for use as a source of analogies. That expertise is fostered by verbal interchanges and perceptual comparisons. The initial steps in analogical reasoning belong in a article like this, but the ability to draw analogies continues to change across the lifespan as the individual learns to abstract the deep causal structure of knowledge. These developmental shifts in analogical reasoning are similar to the course of deductive reasoning.

Deduction

There is agreement that induction appears very early despite debates on the mechanisms enabling its emergence and use. There is less agreement about the emergence of deduction, due to Jean Piaget's claims that logical competence emerges in adolescence and subsequent research demonstrating that even adult logic is flawed. These data appear to support the belief that discussion of logical reasoning does not belong in volumes devoted to infants and preschoolers.

The problems college students encounter can be illustrated with a selection task devised by Peter Wason. Imagine a pack of cards with letters on one face and numbers on the other. A rule explains the design of the cards. "If a card has a vowel on one face, the other side has an even number." You view the faces of four cards, showing A or B or 4 or 7. What cards must be turned over in order to verify the rule (if A is on one face, then 4 is on the back)? The problem can be solved by applying a truth table for conditional logic, such as **Table 2**. In conditional statements, the occurrence of the event in the antecedent if-clause necessitates the co-occurrence of the event in the consequent, main clause. If the antecedent is false, predictions of the consequent are unwarranted. Two cases falsify the rule, a vowel card but the wrong digit, an odd number, on the back, or conversely, an

Table 2 A conditional truth-table for "If it has a vowel, it has an even number"

Card content	*Vowel*	*Consonant*
Even number	True	True
Odd number	False	True

odd number with a vowel on the back. College students usually do not choose the converse case. The task requires grasping the pattern within the entire truth table, generating a strategy to falsify the pattern, and applying the strategy to abstract and arbitrary content. Why would anyone expect preschoolers to succeed on this task? Can they succeed when the material is meaningful and the task is simplified?

The selection task entails verifying two types of inferences. Modus ponens calls for the joint presence of the antecedent(p) and consequent(q). "If there is a vowel, there is an even number." Modus tollens is the contrapositive, the denial of the consequent implies denial of the antecedent (not p, not q). Odd number cards do not have vowels. By their third birthday, children make these inferences during conversations.

Mark (44 months): If you want no raisins in it, then you call it bran. (p.q).
And I want no raisins in it. (p).
So I call it bran (q) (Modus ponens).

Father: If you don't eat food, you're going to die. (p.q).

Ross (49 months): If he wants to be alive (not q).
He 'll have to eat his food (not-q) (Modus tollens).

Father: If you're not hungry (and eat the rest of your dinner), then you can't eat cracker jacks. (p.q).

Abe (43 months): If I'm not hungry, I can…I'll just sneak in the car and get some. (p not q). (Refutation):

These interchanges, drawn from the CHILDES database, differ from the Wason task in crucial respects. The children make deductions when they wish, not on demand, as in the laboratory. In the Wason task, the reasoner must simultaneously make modus ponens and modus tollens inferences and realize what would falsify each. Conversational inferences rarely combine all three elements of the Wason task. Additionally, children's inferences are often joint. The parent produces the initial if-premise and the child supplies the second premise and deduction. Consequently, even before producing 'if', 2-year-olds refute and make inferences from their conversational partner's premises. Adults scaffold and prompt deductions. Adult use of if-statements and particularly, "What if?" questions is correlated with the frequency of children's inferences. Older children are more likely to produce inferences from their own initial premises.

Unlike the Wason task, conversation is meaningful. Two of the examples reflect a popular conversational topic, social control. Rule statements produce resistance (refutations) or concessions (modus ponens). Note that two of the examples also refer to the child. Children are more likely to make inferences when the premise mentions them than when it does not. When the content is meaningful, children's inferences are often quite sophisticated. In the following example from the CHILDES database of conversations, Mark makes an essentialist deduction by using predicate logic to apply information about a general class to a specific instance.

Father: If you have blood you'll die.

Mark (51 months): Do dinosaurs have blood?

Father: Some blood.

Mark: Some blood, then they'll die.

Children also exploit the hypothetical nature of if-sentences to refute parental premises. Abe's father states, "If you're ice, you better get outside (in the cold) or you'll melt." Abe's refusal is justified by explaining that warmth melts ice, but Abe is not ice, only as cold as ice.

When investigators have simplified the traditional laboratory tasks of deduction, they also have unearthed early conditional inferences. Martin Braine's theory of mental logic posits that deduction evolved along with language to handle the comprehension of discourse and to integrate diverse pieces of data. Even before children speak, they grasp contingent, causal, and probabilistic information and they represent these relations in a format that provides a template for comprehending 'if'. Once children have mapped the template onto 'if', they automatically make the inferences. Upon hearing the precondition expressed in an if-clause, even young children expect the main clause to predict the consequences of satisfying that precondition (if it snows, schools will close), and a subsequent discussion of the status of the precondition (it is snowing). They then automatically use modus ponens logic to infer a school holiday. Braine's research focuses on testing the deductions which should appear when young children begin to comprehend and produce the connectives, 'if', 'and', and 'or' and negation ('not').

Braine claims these deductions are produced by a packet of reasoning schemes. Each form of premise cues a simple reasoning program that functions like a computer routine that takes in premises and spits out inferences. The routines are universally available, and can be applied almost effortlessly and flawlessly, even by young children. Many of these schemes are definitional, determined by the meaning of the conjunction. When I say, "I have a cat. I have a dog," it is true that I have both a cat 'and' a dog, and it would be contradictory to deny that I have a cat. Reasoning with 'and' is based on making lists including every item. Understanding of 'or' is derived from experiences selecting some items for the list. Modus ponens reasoning with 'if' reflects understanding the meaning of contingencies. However, some logical routines, like modus tollens, require more steps than others and are generated from combinations of other routines. These produce slower and more inaccurate inferences because they make more demands on memory. Unlike the universal schemas which constitute a natural logic, the latter routines are acquired through education in analytic thinking. This is the same kind of thinking that allows people to reason from counterfactual content.

Although Martin Braine acknowledges that reasoners can use various resources, including their pragmatic knowledge of threats and promises, to bolster employment of reasoning schemes, his research eliminates the influence of these cues by using arbitrary content, such as, "If there is a fox in the box, there is an apple. There is a fox. Is there an apple?" Second graders handle modus ponens problems easily.

Preschoolers can make modus ponens deductions on laboratory tasks with meaningful content and even solve problems akin to the Wason task. They have little difficulty with evaluating the implications of permission rules and detecting violations. A permission rule requires some precondition to be satisfied before an action is taken. If children want to go outside (action), they must don their coat (precondition). Four-year-olds know the kind of naughty behavior that would violate the rule, a little girl outdoors but coatless, an action taken without satisfying its precondition, and they can justify why she is naughty. Sally needs her coat! Three-year-olds know what violates the rule but cannot explain why. It might be argued that the children were simply remembering what happened to them when they tried to go out without a coat but the children do as well with arbitrary, unfamiliar permission rules.

Children's understanding of the logic of permission rules is not surprising. In daily life protective authority figures impose limits on child behavior, and children push these limits. Children know what happens when they violate the permission rules. They also understand obligations, such as "If I give you candy, you must share it with your brother." When they encounter problems that fit these familiar pragmatic schemes, they easily make deductions. There is debate about whether these schemas are inherent or derived from experience. Perhaps children are born with the ability to comprehend the social contracts that make it possible to live harmoniously in a group. Alternatively children may slowly accumulate different social scripts for permissions, promises, and obligations.

There is evidence that children understand the logic of other kinds of rules. Four-year-olds know when a stated contingency is false. Suppose your nephew states, "If I play soccer, I always wear red sneakers." You know that seeing your nephew on the soccer field shod in blue sneakers would prove him a liar. Four-year-olds would agree. However 4-year-olds knowledge is very specific. When it is a permission rule, they can tell who disobeys it but they cannot tell what evidence would falsify the rule. When the statement describes a descriptive sequence like the soccer playing example, they know what evidence falsifies it, but they cannot describe when someone violates the rule. It appears as if they possess certain very specific reasoning scripts enabling them to detect when meaningful pragmatic rules are followed and violated and other scripts detailing meaningful sequential rules and the conditions for their falsification. They possess pieces of deductive competence but not an abstract, coherent set of rules.

Although children's early deductions seem to be content-specific, sometimes young children seem to be able to set aside their own belief system to make deductions. For Jean Piaget, the hallmark of formal reasoning is the ability to represent any conditional problem as an instantiation of an abstract formula. Under some circumstances 4-year-olds who hear a patently false sentence like "All snow is black" followed by the query, "Tom sees some snow. Is it black?" can use modus ponens logic to answer in the affirmative. They disregard their own knowledge if the counterfactual nature of the situation is made salient by explaining that Tom lives in an alternative universe, or by requesting the child to construct an imaginary picture of the dark precipitation. These instructions alert the child that the sentence is to be taken at its face value for the moment so that the child no longer is as concerned with ascertaining whether the sentence is true but ascertaining what conclusion can be drawn if the speaker believes it to be true. Similar instructions enable 4-year-olds to make modus ponens inferences from the abstract proposition, "All mib is black."

Early representations have been described as knowledge in pieces. Two-year-olds know when rules are broken and lies are told. Three- and 4-year-olds dispute and draw conclusions from their conversational partners' if-statements. In laboratory tasks, 4-year-olds show fragments of deductive competence with if-statements stating contingencies and pragmatic rules. The more information available for use, the more expert the child appears. It is difficult to ascertain which piece is privileged, because each piece, syntactic, semantic, or pragmatic can trigger a procedure for generating a new deduction or a reminder of a past deduction. Deduction, like induction and analogy, is the product of multiple abilities and is achieved by multiple routes. Whether anyone but logicians or computer programmers ever operates on a purely abstract basis is debatable. Nature is not abstract. Natural logic may not be either.

Four-year-olds' mastery of logic is incomplete. Modus tollens reasoning often eludes them. Like many adults, they do not appear to operate with a complete logical truth table that includes indeterminate problems. Unless the conditional rule expresses a familiar pragmatic scheme, preschoolers, like adults, are challenged by the Wason selection task which requires integration of the complete truth table Although 4- and 5-year-olds can determine whether a rule statement is empirically correct, they are not particularly sensitive to logically incompatible arguments and logical necessity. Supposing that seeing is believing, 4-year-olds may not recognize that deductions are a source of a reliable belief. However, the presence of older siblings, who are undoubtedly eager to point out the child's flaws in reasoning, prompts growing sensitivity to self-contradictions. Exposure to schooling and tasks like reading that require inferences to integrate information reinforces the realization that deductions may provide a valid source of knowledge. During the school years, children add metalogic to their own logic.

As in the realm of analogies, the basis for deduction shifts. Initial concrete and experientially based deductions give rise to inferences based on specific abstract schemas such as permission. Eventually children may generate deductions derived from deep relations among schemes and general logical rules. This passage through the levels may be very experience- and task-dependent, but it begins in early childhood, making reasoning an appropriate topic for a article like this.

See also: Categorization Skills and Concepts; Cognitive Development; Cognitive Developmental Theories; Piaget's Cognitive-Developmental Theory.

Suggested Readings

Braine MDS (1990) The 'natural logic' approach to reasoning. In: Overton WF (ed.) *Reasoning, Necessity and Logic: Developmental Perspectives*, pp. 133–157. Hillsdale, NJ: Erlbaum.
Gelman SA (2003) *The Essential Child: Origins of Essentialism in Everyday Thought.* New York: Oxford University Press.
Gentner D (2003) Why we're so smart. In: Gentner D and Goldin-Meadow S (eds.) *Language in Mind: Advances in the Study of Language and Thought*, pp. 195–235. Cambridge, MA: MIT Press.
Goswami U (2001) Analogical reasoning in children. In: Gentner D, Holyoak KJ, and Kokinov BN (eds.) *The Analogical Mind: Perspectives from Cognitive Science*, pp. 437–469. Cambridge, MA: MIT Press.
Moshman D (2004) From inference to reasoning: The construction of rationality. *Thinking and Reasoning* 10: 221–239.
Scholnick EK (1990) The three faces of if. In: Overton WF (ed.) *Reasoning, Necessity and Logic: Developmental Perspectives*, pp. 159–182. Hillsdale, NJ: Erlbaum.
Sloutsky VM and Fisher AV (2004) Induction and categorization in young children: A similarity-based model. *Journal of Experimental Psychology: General* 133: 166–188.

Reflexes

F S Pedroso, Universidade Federal de Santa Maria, Santa Maria, Brazil

Glossary

Agonist muscle – A muscle that on contracting is automatically checked and controlled by the opposing simultaneous contraction of another muscle – 'prime mover'.
Athetosis – A derangement marked by ceaseless occurrence of slow, sinuous, writhing movements, especially severe in the hands, and performed involuntarily; it may occur after hemiplegia, and is then known as 'posthemiplegic chorea'. Called also 'mobile spasm'.
Automatism (self-action) – Aimless and apparently undirected behavior that is not under conscious control and is performed without conscious knowledge; seen in psychomotor epilepsy, psychogenic fugue, and other conditions. Called also 'automatic behavior'.
Cephalocaudal – Proceeding or occurring in the long axis of the body especially in the direction from head to tail.
Clonus – A series of alternating contractions and partial relaxations of a muscle that in some nervous diseases occurs and is believed to result from alteration of the normal pattern of motor neuron discharge.
Distal to proximal – Maturation process that follows the direction from the trunk to the limbs.
Extrasegmental – Involvement of other segments of the spinal cord beyond primary stimulated.
Lower neuron – Motor neurons that belong to the anterior horn in the spinal cord or brainstem, when compromised, these cause atrophies, weakness, and muscular hypotonia.

Myelination – The process of acquiring a myelin sheath around the axons of neurons by oligodendrocytes or Schwann cells.
Ontogenesis – The development or course of development of an individual organism.
Pyramidal injury – Injury of cortex cerebral or the central motor way responsible for the body voluntary movements.
Tone – The normal degree of vigor and tension; in muscle, the resistance to passive elongation or stretch.

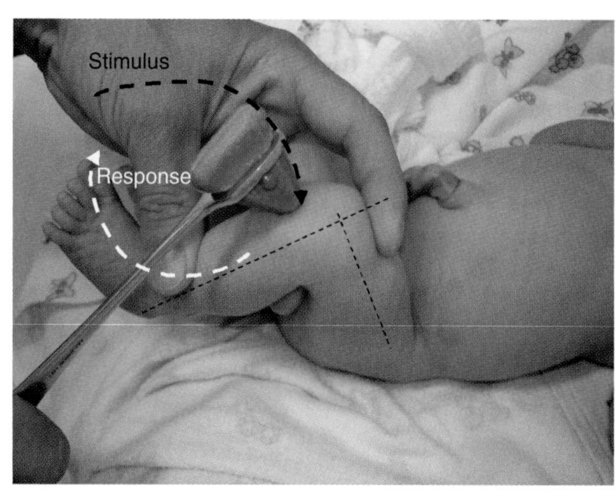

Figure 1 Knee jerk reflex.

Introduction

Reflex is defined as an involuntary motor response, secretory or vascular, elicited shortly after a stimulus, which may be conscious or not. The response to the stimulus is unalterable, it cannot be changed or adapted according to needs or circumstances. It can be concluded, thus, that the response is stereotyped and has a fixed reflex arc, whose response is also fixed. The reflex arc – stimulus reception and motor response to the same stimulus – is a physiological unit of the nervous system (NS).

In its most simple form, the reflex arc comprises: (1) a receptor which corresponds to a special sensory organ, or nerve terminations in the skin or neuromuscular spindle, of which stimulation initiates an impulse; (2) the sensory or afferent neuron, which carries the impulse through a peripheral nerve to the central nervous system (CNS), where it synapses with an internuncial neuron; (3) an internuncial neuron relays the impulse to the efferent neuron; (4) the motor or efferent neuron conducts the impulse through a nerve to the effector organ; and (5) the effector can be a muscle, gland, or blood vessel that manifests the response.

Despite this narrow definition of segmental integration, the polysynaptic involvement of other NS segments is common, constituting intra-, extrasegmental, and contralateral reflexes to the stimulus origin. For the reflex motion to occur, it is necessary to contract the agonist muscles and relax the muscles that perform the opposite motion (antagonist), regarding the latter, instead of causing the muscle to contract, inhibitory synapses will prevent muscle contraction. An example is the knee jerk reflex or patellar reflex: contraction of the quadriceps and extension of the leg when the patellar ligament is tapped (**Figures 1** and **2**).

However, reflex manifestations are typically diverse after a specific stimulation, as occurs with most primitive reflexes (PRs). **Figures 3** and **4** show the complexity of responses to hand-compression stimulus.

The newborn is endowed with a set of reflex and automatic movements, which makes his NS apt to react to the environment where he lives in; the responses necessary to his adaptation and subsistence, such as suction, crying, deglutition, defense, and escape reactions, cannot be simply defined as reflexes in the strict sense of the definition, since these can be subject to alteration or adapted to needs and circumstances, and are therefore alterable, as the responses elicited by a given excitation do not manifest themselves in a clearly predeterminate way, nor are exactly identical over time. These responses express the neurophysiological state upon stimulation, constituting reflex reactions or automatisms; hence, these motor manifestations have been named differently by different authors, such as: PRs, primary reflexes, archaic reflexes, reflex responses, special reflexes, automatic reflexes, neonatal reflexes, primary responses, and developmental reflexes. Without a denomination of their own, some authors have included them among reflexes in general; in this article we call them PRs.

In order to define a reflex, we also need to specifically know its stimulation area, its integration center, and its response. Regarding PRs, it is still necessary to associate a functional concept that accounts for their ontogenetic and phylogenetic purpose. Although it is didactical to study each reflex isolately, we should bear in mind that this is a theoretical abstraction, convenient for the analysis of nervous phenomena, which does not exist in real life, since the PRs constitute a harmonic ensemble and are closely intertwined with one another, depending on the child's physiological needs and environmental conditions at the moment they are elicited.

Origin

Reflex activities are inherited, ranging from one species to another and oscillating according to life conditions peculiar to each one. During human development, reflex,

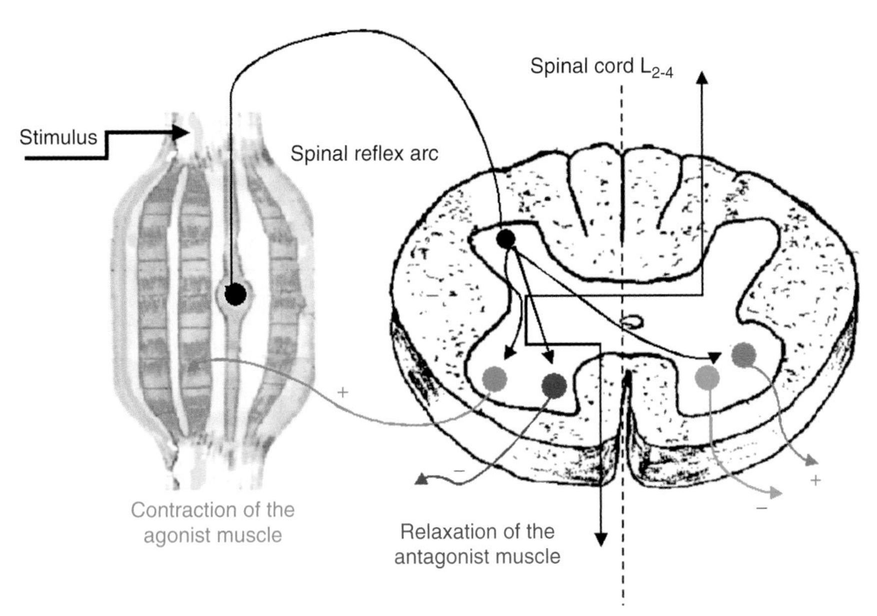

Figure 2 Spinal reflex arc.

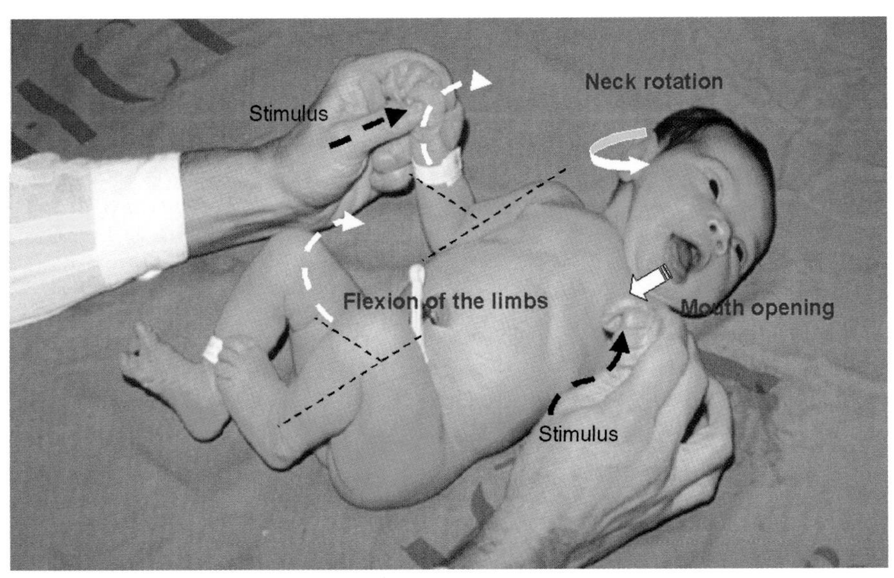

Figure 3 Babkin reflex and other responses to hand compression stimulus.

automatic, and voluntary motor control appear consecutively, which are anatomically processed respectively in the spinal cord/brainstem, basal ganglia, and cerebral cortex. The maturation process (cell organization and myelination) of these structures occurs at first in the caudocephalic direction, starting with reflex motor activity, which is exclusive until the 24th week of pregnancy. Thereafter, neural activities of reticular formation begin in the brainstem, enabling tonic movements of the head and neck and, subsequently, of the root of limbs. Later, with the maturation of the extrapyramidal prosencephalic nuclei, more complex motions appear, such as those of feet and hands. From the 37th to 40th week of gestation on, it is already possible to observe the early manifestation of cortical functioning, often evident via visual attention, sensory habituation, and first voluntary movements.

Classification

In function of the possibility of a diversity of names for the same reflex activity, one becomes useful to present here the classification of the consequences under different aspects as: place of origin of the stimulus, time of permanence during the development, by purpose evolution landmarks, and clinical significance.

By Stimulus Location

Superficial or exteroceptive reflexes

Those that originate in external parts of the organism, elicited by noxious or tactile stimulation of the skin, cornea, or mucous membrane, exemplified by the following reflexes: corneal, palatal, abdominal, cremasteric, and anal (**Table 1**).

- *Corneal.* Closure of the eyelid when the cornea is touched.
- *Palatal.* Contraction of the pharyngeal constrictor muscle (causes swallowing) elicited by stimulation of the palate or touching the back of the pharynx.
- *Abdominal.* Contractions of the abdominal muscles on stimulation of the abdominal skin (**Figure 5**).
- *Cremasteric.* Stimulation of the skin on the front and inner thigh retracts the testis on the same side.
- *Anal.* Contraction of the anal sphincter on irritation of the anal skin.

Proprioceptive or deep reflexes

Proprioceptive or deep reflexes originated in receptors within the body, in skeletal muscles, tendons, bones, joints, vestibular apparatus, etc. They comprise all deep tendon reflexes, postural reactions, and some PRs. The deep reflexes are elicited by a sharp tap on the appropriate tendon or muscle to induce brief stretch of the muscle, followed by contraction. They are examples of the deep reflex (**Table 2**):

- *Glabella or orbicularis oculi.* Normal contraction of the orbicularis oculi muscle, with resultant closing of the eye, on percussion at the outer aspect of the supraorbital ridge, over the glabella, or around the margin of the orbit (**Figure 6**).
- *Oris-orbicularis.* Pouting or pursing of the lips induced by light tapping of the closed lips in the midline.

Table 1 Superficial (exteroceptive) reflexes innervation

Reflex	*Innervation*
Corneal	Cranial nerves, pons, and VII
Palatal	Cranial nerves IX, medulla, and X
Abdominal	Spinal nerve, spinal cord $T_{7–12}$
Cremasteric	Ilioinguinal, genitofemoral nerves, spinal cord $L_{1–2}$
Anal	Inferior hemorrhoidal nerve, spinal cord $S_{3–5}$

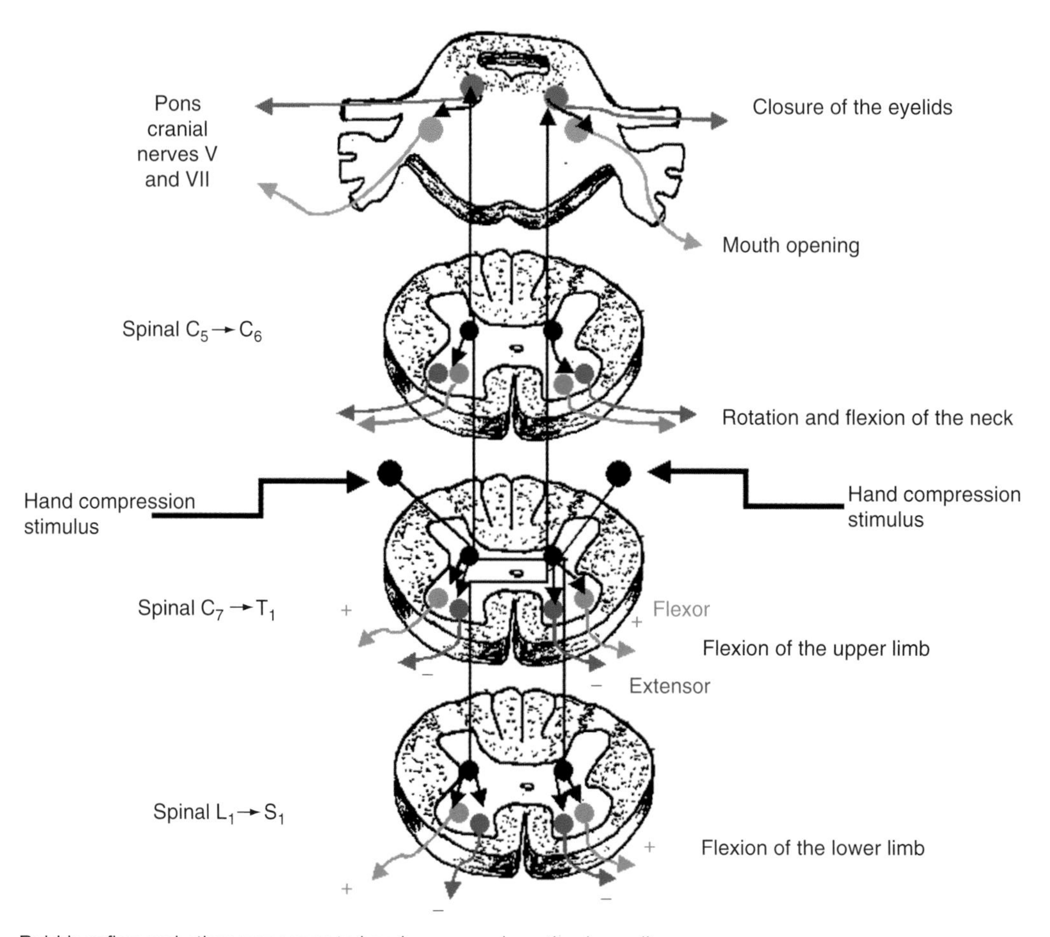

Figure 4 Babkin reflex and other responses to hand compression stimulus – diagram.

- *Jaw jerk.* Closure of the mouth caused by tapping at a downward angle between the lower lip and chen.
- *Biceps.* Contraction of the biceps muscle when its tendon is tapped.
- *Triceps.* Contraction of the belly of the triceps muscle and slight extension of the arm when the tendon of the muscle is tapped directly, with the arm flexed and fully supported and relaxed.
- *Brachioradialis.* With the arm supinated to 45°, a tap near the lower end of the radius causes contraction of the brachioradial (supinator longus) muscle.
- *Knee jerk (patellar).* Contraction of the quadriceps and extension of the leg when the patellar ligament is tapped (**Figure 1**).
- *Thigh adductors.* Contraction of the adductors of the thigh caused by tapping the tendon of the adductor magnus muscle while the thigh is abducted.
- *Ankle jerk (Achilles).* Plantar flexion caused by a twitch-like contraction of the triceps surae muscle, elicited by a tap on the Achilles tendon, preferably while the patient kneels on a bed or chair, the feet hanging free over the edge.

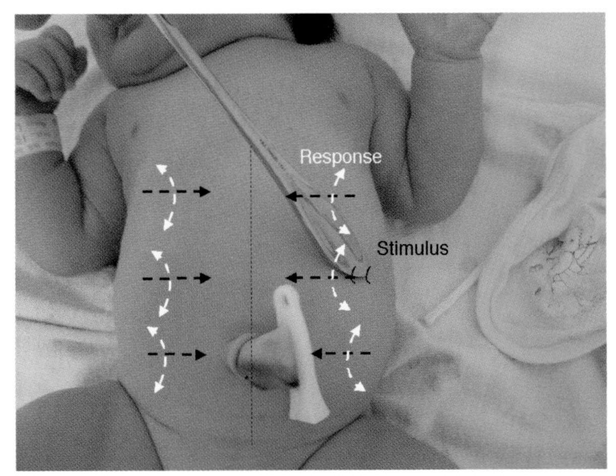

Figure 5 Abdominal reflex.

Table 2 Deep tendon (muscle stretch) reflexes innervation

Reflex	*Innervation*
Glabella	Cranial nerves V, pons, and VIII
Oro-orbicularis	Cranial nerves V, pons, and VIII
Jaw jerk	Cranial nerves V, pons, and V
Biceps	Muscolocutaneous nerve, spinal cord C_{5-6}
Brachioradialis	Radial nerve, spinal cord C_{6-8}
Triceps	Radial nerve, spinal cord C_{6-7}
Knee jerk (Patellar)	Femoral nerve, spinal cord L_{2-4}
Thigh adductors	Obturator nerve, spinal cord L_{2-4}
Ankle jerk (Achilles)	Tibial nerve, spinal cord L_5–S_2

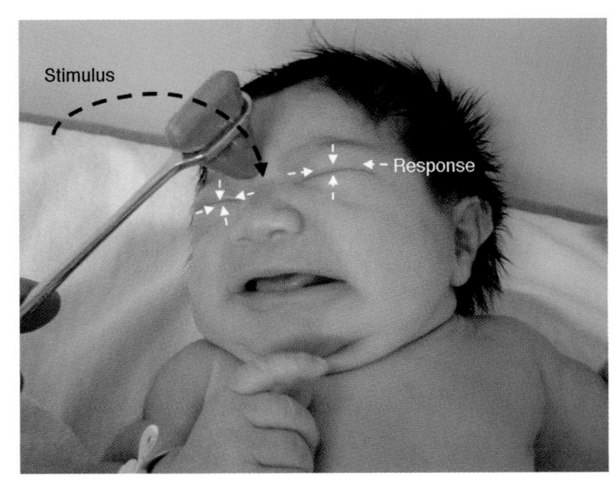

Figure 6 Glabella reflex.

Viceroceptive or autonomic reflexes

Those that originate in the viscera and have, as responses, actions on smooth muscles, glands, and vessels, as, for instance, the emptying of the rectum and the bladder by rectal and vesical reflexes, and the increase in gastric juice secretion and contractibility of the stomach during food ingestion. They are examples of the viceroceptive reflex (**Table 3**):

- *Oculocardiac.* Slowing of the rhythm of the heart following compression of the eyes.
- *Carotid sinus.* Slowing of the heartbeat on pressure on the carotid artery at the level of the cricoid cartilage.
- *Vesical.* Contraction of the walls of the bladder and relaxation of the trigone and urethral sphincter in response to a rise in pressure within the bladder; the reflex can be voluntarily inhibited and the inhibition readily abolished to control micturition.
- *Rectal reflex.* Normal response to the presence of feces in the rectum.

Sensory special reflex

These are generated by a distant stimulus in specialized organs of the senses as eyes and ears (pupillary, optical blink, and acoustic blink). They are examples of the sensory special reflex (**Table 4**):

- *Pupillary.* Contraction of the pupil on exposure of the retina to light.
- *Optical blink.* Contraction of the orbicularis oculi muscles (closure of both eyes) after stimuli of the retina to light.

Table 3 Autonomic (viceroceptive) reflexes innervation

Reflex	*Innervation*
Oculocardiac	Cranial nerves V, medulla, and X
Carotid sinus	Cranial nerves IX, medulla, and X
Vesical and rectal	Sacral autonomic fiber, spinal cord S_{2-4}

- *Acoustic blink.* Contraction of the orbicularis oculi muscles (closure of both eyes) to an intense sound.

By Development

There are three forms of motor manifestations in this category (**Figure 7**), which coexist and overlap over time, yet they represent distinct stages of the CNS maturation.

Static reflexes

Those that remain stable all life long and represent the most primitive and caudal manifestations of the CNS, predominantly processed at the level of the spinal cord and some in the brainstem, represented by the deep tendon, pupillary and acoustic blink reflexes.

Table 4 Sensory especial reflexes innervation

Reflex	*Innervation*
Pupillary	Cranial nerve II, mesencephalon, and III
Optical blink	Cranial nerve II, mesencephalon, pons, and, VII
Acoustic blink	Cranial nerve VIII, pons, and VII

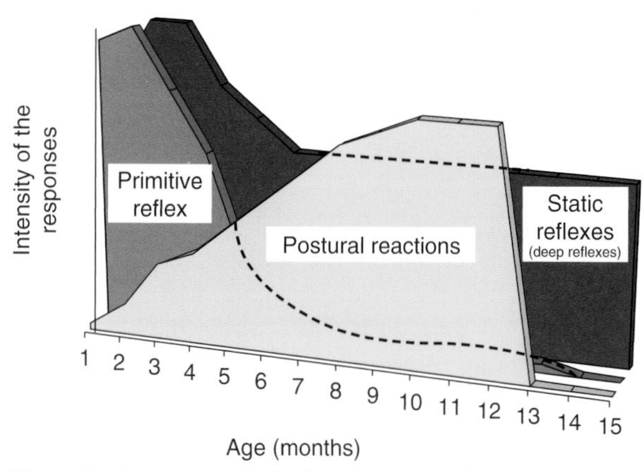

Figure 7 Development of reflex and postural reactions.

Primitive or developmental reflexes

These develop during pregnancy and are processed from the spinal cord to the basal ganglia; hence, they show a greater complexity in their manifestations (automatisms). They are present at birth, and thereafter begin to be integrated with the CNS, most disappearing within the first 6 months of life. There are several tens of these reflexes, the author describes some and illustrates the exam technique of other reflexes of this group.

- *Plantar grasp.* It consists of a flexion response in the toes when the sole of the feet is stimulated (**Figure 8**).
- *Palmar grasp.* Flexion or clenching of the fingers on stimulation of the palm.
- *Asymmetrical tonic neck or Magnus-De Kleijn.* It must be tested with the child at a supine position, eliciting a rotation of the head to one side produces extension of extremities on that side and contralateral flexion – the 'fencer' posture (**Figure 9**).
- *Babkin.* When the palms of the two hands are strongly pressed, the mouth opens in response, often associated with neck rotation, flexion of limbs, and closing of the eyes (**Figure 3**).
- *Moro.* It is tested by many ways, for example, by displacing the child's gravity center, or by visual or auditory stimulus. As a response, an abduction and extension of the limbs will occur, with extension and opening of the fingers, except for the distal phalanges of the index fingers and thumbs, which remain flexed. Then occurs the aduction and flexion of limbs.
- *Diving.* Stimulation of the face or nasal cavity with water or local irritants produces apnea in neonates. Breathing stops in expiration, with laryngeal closure,

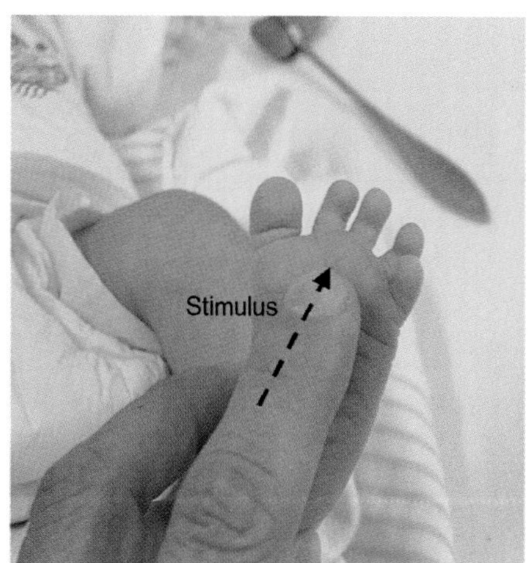

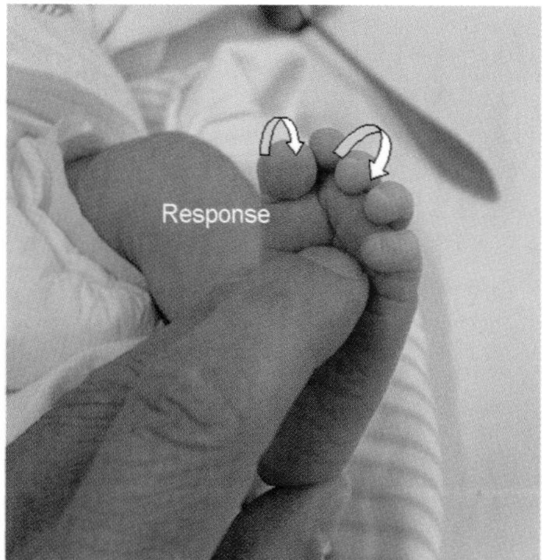

Figure 8 The plantar grasp.

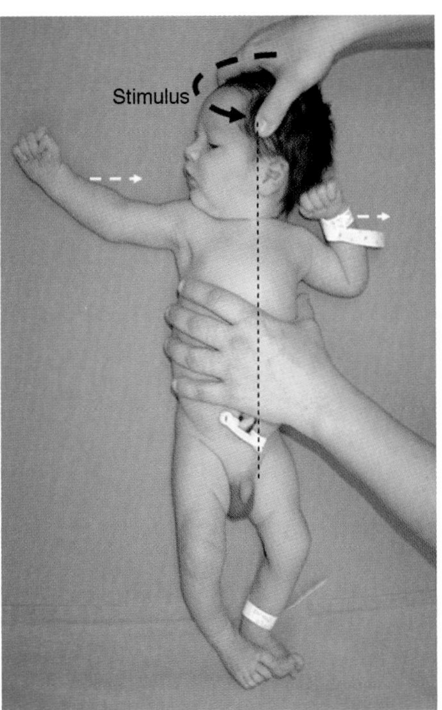

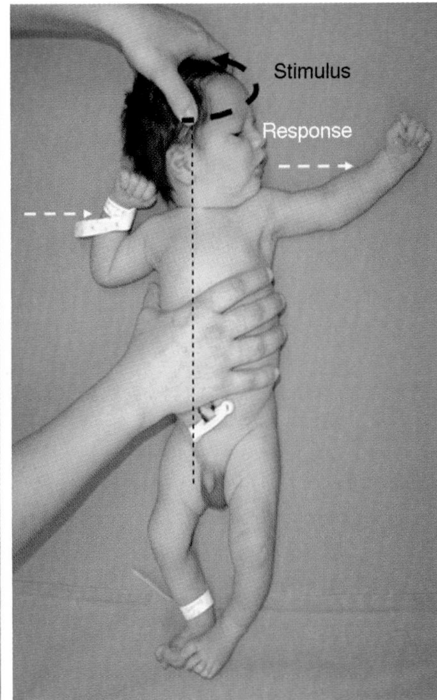

Figure 9 The asymmetrical tonic neck reflex.

and infants exhibit bradycardia and a lowering of cardiac output. Blood flow to the skin, splanchnic areas, muscles, and kidneys decreases, whereas flow to the heart and brain is protected.

- *Sucking.* Sucking movements of the lips of an infant elicited by touching the lips or the skin near the mouth.
- *Rooting.* Reflex consisting of head-turning and sucking movements elicited in a normal infant by gently stroking the side of the mouth of cheek.
- *Magnet.* It is tested by light pressure made upon a toe-pad with the finger causes reflex contraction of the limb extensors; the limb is thus pressed gently against the finger, and when the finger is withdrawn slightly, the experimenter has the sensation that the finger is raising the limb or drawing it out as by a magnet.
- *Galant.* It is elicited by holding the newborn in ventral suspension (face down) and stroking along the one side of the spine. The normal reaction is for the newborn to laterally flex toward the stimulated side.
- *Palmo-mental.* Unilateral (sometimes bilateral) contraction of the mentalis and orbicularis oris muscles caused by a brisk scratch made on the palm of the ipsilateral hand.
- *Withdrawal.* A nociceptive reflex in which a body part is quickly moved away from a painful stimulus.
- *Crossed extensor.* When the reflex occurs the flexors in the withdrawing limb contract and the extensors relax, while in the other limb the opposite occurs. An example of this is when a person steps on a nail, the leg that is stepping on the nail pulls away, while the other leg takes the weight of the whole body.
- *Placing.* Flexion followed by extension of the leg when the infant is held erect and the dorsum of the foot is drawn along the under edge of a tabletop; it is obtainable in the normal infant up to the age of 6 weeks.
- *Positive support or plantar support.* In vertical suspension, the stimulation of the ball of foot produces leg extension to support the weight.
- *Walking.* When the child is held at a vertical position and keeps the feet in contact with a surface, alternate movements of the lower limbs may appear, with a general morphology similar to stepping.
- *Extensor plantar.* Stroking the lateral part of the foot – a sequence of stimuli applied more laterally – (the Chaddock technique) produces extension (dorsiflexion) of the big toe, often with extension and abduction of the other toes. It is not Babinski reflex.

Postural reaction

It is defined as a fixed response or posture from the initiation of the stimulus until its removal, lasting for as long as the stimulus persists. A postural response represents complex motor responses to a plurality of afferences such as the joints, the tendons, the muscles, the skin, receptors (eye and ear), and, of course, the labyrinth. They are characterized by a certain stereotyped posture of the trunk, head, and extremities, when the examiner attempts a strictly defined sudden change of position. The postural reactions are all absent in infancy and appear gradually later, simultaneously with the diminution of PRs. They involve the highest level of motor control that is voluntary, represented by the Landau, parachute, and lateral propping reactions. The Landau' reaction develops at 3 months. When held in ventral suspension, the infant's head, legs, and spine extend. When the head is depressed, the hips, knees, and elbows flex. This reflex continues to be present in most infants during the second 6 months of life, but then it becomes increasingly difficult to demonstrate. The parachute reaction occurs when the baby is suspended ventrally and dropped suddenly with the head directed toward a table. This prompts a defensive reaction in which the upper limbs are extended and the hands are opened in order to prevent the fall. This reflex appears starting at 6 months of age. Lateral propping usually appears between 6 and 8 months of age, when the child is able to sit without assistance. If the infant is pushed sideways with an abrupt shove on one shoulder while sitting, s/he extends the appropriate arm and puts his/her open hands over the support plane near the legs or in the angle formed by them.

By Purpose Evolution Landmarks

Alimentary

These landmarks are involved in oral motor activity, with the purpose of search, capture, and ingestion of food, among them are the rooting, sucking, palmar grasp, and Babkin reflexes.

Defense and escape

These account for the maintenance of the organism's integrity (e.g., withdrawal, diving, and Galant reflexes).

Support and locomotion

These account for a better body positioning in relation to gravity, to objects in the environment, and for grasping these. In this group we find the palmar grasp, plantar grasp, extensor plantar, Moro, plantar support, withdrawal, crossed extensor, walking, placing, and magnet reflexes.

By Clinical Significance

Normal reflexes

Normal reflexes are those for which intensity, location, symmetry, diffusion, onset time, and integration time follow normal physiological patterns.

Pathological reflexes

These are normal reflexes that stop complying with the physiological conditions or are physiopathological manifestations of the CNS, as the Babinski reflex and the reflex of spinal automatism.

Normal Development of Reflexes in Childhood

The ontogenesis of reflexes in the human being contributes to the identification of evolutionary stages in our species. In intrauterine life, the reflexes follow a cephalic to caudal onset pattern, while in the limbs their pattern is from distal to proximal, differing from the muscle tone, which is the opposite – it increases with gestational age from caudal to cephalic. The spinal reflex arc is fully developed by the 8th week of gestation and the deep tendon reflex at the knees and ankles may be elicited in premature infants at 19–23 weeks of gestation, but they all become evident only after the 33rd week of gestation. In examining a 28-week-old preterm infant, we also find the deep tendon, the withdrawal, the cutaneous extensor plantar, and the palmoplantar grasp reflexes, the extensor phase of the Moro reflex, and the Galant, rooting, acoustic blink, and optical blink reflexes. The pupillary reflex is absent before 28 weeks of gestation and present after 30 weeks of gestation, Glabella around 32 weeks, the neck-righting reflex appears between 34 and 37 weeks; head turning in response to light appears between 32 and 36 weeks. Full-blown walking and crossed extensor reflexes appear only between 35 and 37 weeks.

After birth, the direction of maturation is now only cephalo–caudal, as occurs with the myelination of the pyramidal tract, which enables the voluntary control of more cephalic than caudal segments. It is already possible to observe at the first 3 months of life manifestations of voluntary control of the facial muscles that are used to smile and eat, and subsequently the control of neck muscles, the voluntary use of the hand, the ability of sitting down, the control of the standing position, and finally the control of the sphincter (**Figure 10**). This sequence in maturation allows the muscle tone to decrease and many PRs to be integrated in the CNS.

In preterm infants, the reflexes, as well as the tone and the voluntary movements, show a lagged evolution in comparison with full-term infants. The same does not occur with the sensory function which in the premature child maturates before the motor one. From the 37th week of gestation on, the infant is already capable of performing conditioned reflexes and learning.

This ability of learning is supported by the reflex motor activity, which enables a contact with the external environment in ample and diversified ways, thereby resulting in new sensory inputs that, integrated with cortical levels, will create a feedback able to gradually turn movements that are initially reflex or automatic into voluntary. The predominatly inhibitory synaptic connections of the cerebral cortex to the brainstem (cortico-subcortical integration process) are known to be able to change the reflexes, leading the infant to learn how to use these basic patterns of reaction in his automatic activities, and later in the voluntary activities as well. The reflexes are thus partially discarded and partially incorporated into new patterns of motor expressions (**Figure 11**). The reflex multiplicity, especially the primitive, is, therefore, of paramount importance to neuropsychological evolution.

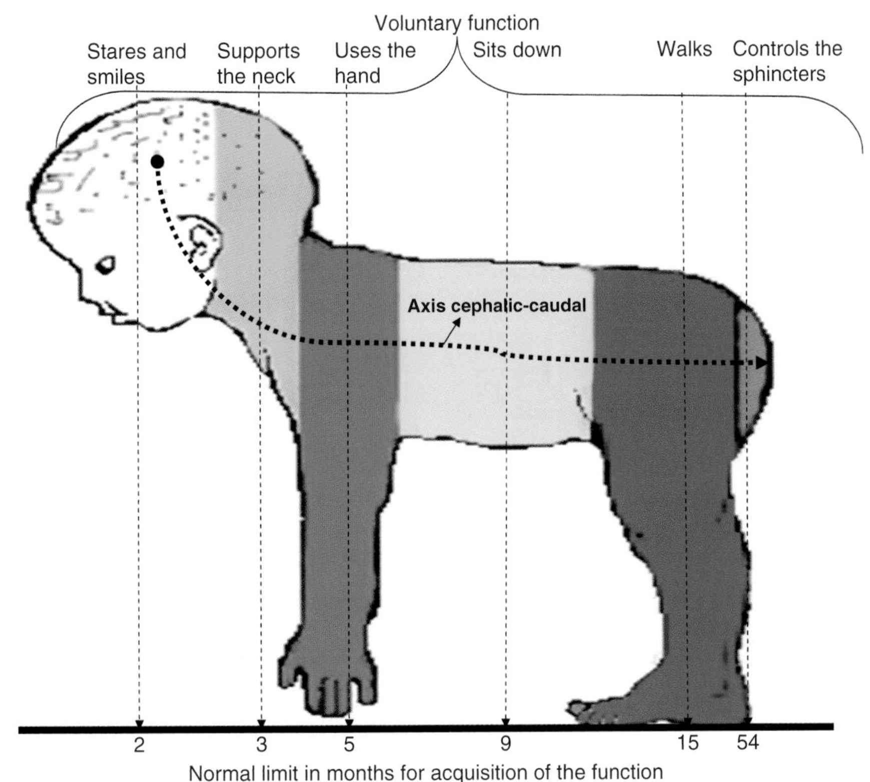

Figure 10 Sequence of voluntary motor control.

Despite a few conjectures that some PRs are the precursors to voluntary activities, as the walking and palmar grasp reflexes, for instance, these have not been supported, since the results of studies, including those carried out by us, do not show any relationship between the age of extinguishing of these reflexes and the age at which the first voluntary activities are observed, both being able to coexist.

We should also consider the period of transition from reflex activities to voluntary ones, an intermediate behavior in which many reflexes become more or less conditioned and full of patterns of repetitious movements, which precede the voluntary control (called the rhythmic stereotypes, e.g., the movements of the toes of the feet). Another example are the rhythmic vocalizations, which provoke one feedback auditory which is basic for the development of the hearing and the language. The decline of rhythmic stereotypes is related with the progressive prevalence of voluntary behavior.

Assessment of Reflex Activity in the Child – General Considerations

The reflexes constitute one of the earliest, and most frequently used tools among developmental neurologists and pediatricians all over the world to assess the CNS integrity of infants and young children. The examination of reflexes is far more difficult in children than in adults, since they do not understand, do not collaborate, feel afraid, and, hence, are too agitated, often crying, and do not relax their muscles suitably. In order to increase the chances for a successful examination, we must consider:

- examination location (adverse conditions, as within an incubator);
- gestational age at birth (if premature, make corrections for age);
- general clinical conditions (temperature, pO_2, etc.);
- support therapies (drug use; immobilization, catheter, etc.);
- neurological pathology (coma, convulsions, hemorrhage, etc.);
- time of life ('birth shock' within the first 48–72 h);
- time after last breastfeeding (satisfied or hungry);
- behavioral states of the newborn and breastfed infant (**Figure 12**); and
- physiological properties of reflexes (stimulation site, excitation threshold, latency, fatigue, central inhibition, volitional inhibition, refractory period).

We still have to proceed patiently, applying the exam protocols in an 'accidental' sequence, seizing the opportunities, consoling the child to bring her to more suitable behavioral states and saving for the end of the procedure

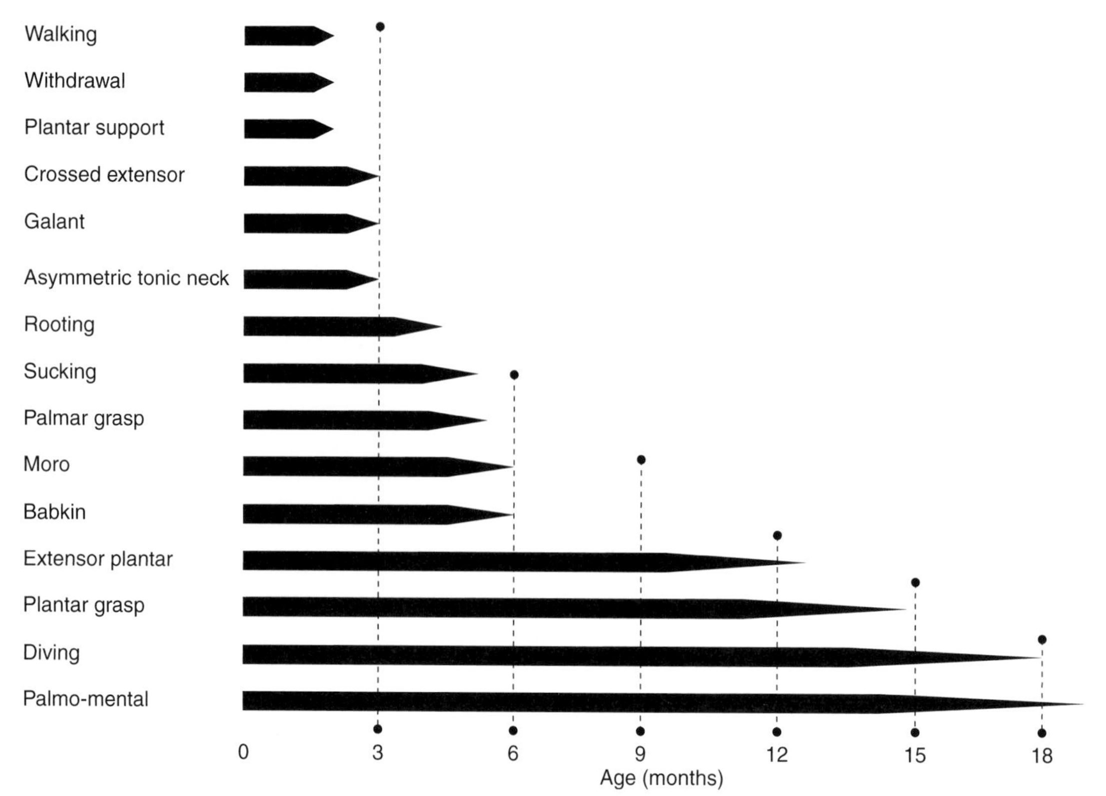

Figure 11 The development of primative reflexes.

State 1: eyes closed, regular respiration, no movements
State 2: eyes closed, irregular respiration, no gross movements
State 3: eyes opened, no gross movements
State 4: eyes opened, gross movements, no crying
State 5: eyes opened, gross movements, crying
State 6: other states (coma, etc.)

Figure 12 Behavioral states.

those maneuvers that may cause the infant to cry, also extracting from the latter the necessary information for a more thorough examination.

The five behavioral states that must be observed in the examination of the newborn and small infant are based on sleeping patterns, respiratory rhythm, changes in ocular opening, alert-state activity, and crying. The assessment of these states via polygraphic tests (brain electric activity, heart rate, and muscle contraction) demonstrates that these are different ways of cerebral activity, each state being a qualitatively different condition, a particular mode of CNS functioning. Therefore, it is of paramount importance to learn about these, especially in the neonatal period, since many reflex and behavioral responses depend on them to be modified. Overall, the best state is the 3rd, next coming the 4th, the 2nd, the 1st, and finally the 5th (crying); however, it is possible that in sound sleep the deep tendon reflexes are enhanced. It is necessary to comment on the time period elapsed from birth to the first 48–72 h of life, when the delivery stress causes a rebound effect of lower neurologic energy in which the reflexes, as well as the muscle tone, are found to be diminished, a period known as 'birth shock'.

Assessment of Deep Tendon Reflexes

The deep tendon reflexes are the elementary unit of the neurological processes based on the reflex arc; they are part of the motor activity exam, along with the muscle tone and muscle strength test, which is useful for the location of NS lesions. Usually, the reflex hammer is used, which must be suitable for the child's age, with a long, flexible handle and a sufficiently elastic and soft percussion area. The stimulus to be used should not be more intense than necessary to elicit a reflex, which may necessitate two or three stimuli of increasing intensity. The assessment of a reflex is mandatorily followed by the assessment of the same reflex on the opposite side for symmetry. The examiner must adapt his technique to the conditions of each case. Maneuvers such as that of Jendrassik (closing the eyes and performing an isometric contraction of untested limbs) in older children can be useful, especially for those with difficulty relaxing and when the reflexes are hypoactive.

The knee jerk reflex is the best known one and is always present in normal children, another reflex of greater clinical significance is the ankle jerk (Achilles) reflex, which is useful in the diagnosis and follow-up of lesions in the lower neuron, such as poliomyelitis, Guillain–Barre syndrome, metabolic disorders as hypocalcemia, etc.

To illustrate just the technique indicated for the knee jerk reflex – with the child sitting up, with legs hanging loosely and relaxed, or lying on her belly, with the knee slightly folded, and supporting the palm of the examiner's hand – the quadriceps tendon (below the patella) is tapped, and the leg is expected to kick out (**Figure 1**).

Deep tendon reflexes can be normal, absent, diminished, brisker, or asymmetrical, largely ranging in intensity from one person to another; in some rare cases they cannot be elicited even by using the best technique under normal conditions. Any asymmetry should be considered pathological, but it may be difficult to say if the abnormal reflex corresponds either to the side that seems brisker or to the side on which it seems diminished.

As a rule, the reflex that most differs from the individual's pattern of reflexes and/or the one that coexists with other anomalies in the motor exam is abnormal. A second element to value is hyperreflexia (range, quickness of response, and increase in the reflexogenic zone), which can be an important pathological sign of a central injury. If the reflexes are hyperactive, we need to test the clonus (there are many responses to a single stimulus) and when it is inexhaustible, it is always a sign of abnormality, and even if it is the only alteration in the reflexes, it is a safe pyramidal sign of CNS injury. The clonus of the patella and foot (Achilles tendon) is the most frequent one. For example, the Achilles reflex is tested by performing sudden flexion movements in the foot and maintaining this position, with the leg partially flexed.

The clinical significance of a pathological hyperreflexia is the loss of the normal inhibition to which the reflex arc is subject; it appears when there is injury in an inhibitory structure, most often in the pyramidal tract. However, in the initial stage of a pyramidal injury by trauma of the spinal cord or stroke, a transitory hyporeflexia or areflexia occurs. The diminution or extinguishing of deep tendon reflexes implies the existence of an injury in any one of the reflex arc components, most often indicating a peripheral injury. The deep tendon reflexes must be rated according to the following scale: 4+ hyperactive with clonus; 3+ hyperactive without clonus, with increase in the reflexogenic zone; 2+ normal; 1+ hypoactive; and 0+ no response.

Assessment of Superficial Reflexes

In this group of reflexes, we are going to illustrate the abdominal reflex, which is elicited with a blunt object stimulating the lateral regions of the abdomen (upper, middle, and lower) toward the middle line, and, when present, a contraction of the stimulated musculature is observed (**Figure 5**). Just like the deep reflexes, the superficial ones must be compared with the opposite side at each of the three levels. The response is normal when a unilateral contraction occurs and abnormal when the reflex is absent or asymmetric. The superficial reflex (abdominal, cremasteric), in the initial stage of a pyramidal injury of acute onset as occurs with a stroke, may disappear contralaterally to the injury, even before a change in strength, and remain absent or hypoactive, as occurs in children with cerebral palsy (CP). In obese individuals or after abdominal surgery, muscle contraction may be absent.

Assessment of Primitive Reflexes

The presence of all PRs during the first weeks of life is indicative of the CNS integrity. They can outlast the usual time, be absent, diminished, or increased in relation to the normal state or disappear when some compromising of the cortical integration occur by pre- or perinatal events. A normal motor development is unlikely with the PR outlasting the usual time, as their disappearance is necessary for the improvement of early voluntary motor activity in childhood.

Studies in an animal model, as those by Sherrington, in 1898, who surgically disconnected the CNS inhibition in order to observe more primitive reflex responses, are in agreement with concepts still used today to explain the outlasting of the PRs or their reappearance in humans with compromised cerebral functions. In these cases, the upper injury liberates the lower centers, more specifically the brainstem, which is the underlying structure of these connections.

Understanding the normal development of motor functions is possible only when the patterns of PRs are known, which are the precursors to those functions, since they are the best tools to early detect motor disorders in childhood, being one of the early markers for CP. This fact underscores the importance of the assessment of PRs in the newborn and infant, not only for understanding the neuropsychological development of the human being, but also for the neurologic assessment of the child, with the intent to identify possible damage to the CNS in the pre- and perinatal periods. This important semiological tool helps every professional involved in the rehabilitation of children with neurological pathology not only with respect to the prognosis, but also to the planning of more suitable treatment methods. Among these are the therapies based on the Bobath method, which inhibit the PR and stimulate more advanced stages of development.

Primitive reflex activities are closely dependent on the infant's physiological needs upon stimulation and interact with one another, at times facilitating and at other times inhibiting, as can be observed at the moment of hunger when oral reflexes have already been exacerbated, and an increase in the palmar grasp reflex and movements of general flexion of the body concomitantly occur, associated with a diminution of extensor reflexes such as the Moro, plantar support, and crossed extensor. The elicitation of the palmar grasp reflex normally inhibits the Moro reflex, which can make the infant calm down, while conversely labyrinthine stimuli and/or sudden stimuli in general elicit crying and an unstable attitude which is well characterized in the extensor phase of the Moro reflex; even in this situation the lower limbs tend to a flexor predominance and exacerbation of the plantar grasp reflex.

The techniques of examination of some PRs already had been indicated together with the description of the same ones, and in the diagrams of figures in the item of the classification of reflex.

Reflexes and Clinical Significance

Different methods have been used to evaluate the NS of infants: neurological examination, neurophysiological examination, imaging studies, laboratory investigation, and observation of spontaneous and/or provoked behavior. The integrity and maturation of the NS can be evaluated by a structured neurological examination that provides information for diagnosis, follow-up, and prognosis.

The changes found in the reflexes during the development are of paramount importance to the definition of normality.

Several screening tests to assess child development have been recommended, such as the Bayley test, the early language milestones, which is another instrument suitable for office screening that was designed for identifying delays in language in children less than 3 years old, and the Denver II, the latter being the best known among pediatricians. It has a good sensitivity for detection of developmental delays, but only evidences these when the neurologic function expected for the respective age is not present. In these cases, an earlier thorough examination may indicate the existence of dysfunction or neurologic injury, for example, the persistence of PRs and a deep hyperreflexia predominantly involving the lower limbs in an infant less than 1-year-old can indicate a CP of diplegic form and that the walking reflex will not appear at the expected age, although other aspects of the child's development may be normal. Another shortcoming of screening tests is the wide qualitative–quantitative spectrum in the presentation of developmental disorders, which demands detailing in the exam of each child, rendering the aforementioned tests inviable.

The emphasis placed on a reflex or any motor response in a neurological evaluation depends on what is known about this item, and on the possibility of associating it with specific pathologies, as is the case with the plantar support reflex, asymmetric tonic neck reflex, and tonic labyrinth reflex in the early diagnosis, rehabilitation, and prognosis of CP.

The failure in extinguishing PRs such as the Moro, Galant, and plantar grasp reflexes, regardless of postural reactions, indicates a possible CP of the athetoid (extrapyramidal) type, while in the CP of spastic type, when the brain injury is predominantly cortical, the persistent PRs are others, such as the crossed extensor, cutaneous extensor plantar, and Rossolimo reflexes. Evidently, the mixed forms of CP must be considered, when this association loses, then, its specificity.

The situation in which the PRs evolve normally, but not their postural reactions, is more likely to indicate a developmental delay than a CP. The reappearance or nonextinguishing of some PR both in children and in adults may imply a cortical impairment, especially in the frontal lobus, as seen in Down syndrome, degenerative encephalopathies in general (e.g., HIV), Alzheimer's disease, schizophrenia, multiple sclerosis, Parkinson, and hydrocephalus. An exception is made for the palmomental reflex, which may remain in normal individuals all life long; in this case its intensity and the extension of the reflexogenic zone are discreet.

In our study, the cutaneous plantar response was extensor for all infants; however, there are authors that find a prevalence of the cutaneous flexor plantar response in 3% of term newborns. It is known that the cutaneous extensor plantar response will become flexor after a few months as maturation takes place, and that the flexor response does not occur in the newborn, nor in the infant in the first 4 months of life, it is the plantar grasp reflex that occurs, triggered spontaneously or by the Chaddock technique – a sequence of stimuli applied more laterally – as there is a predominance of the grasp reflex over the extensor plantar. Plantar reflexes usually become flexor between 6 and 15 months, and this inversion is not correlated with the ability to walk. The discrepancies observed in the prevalence of plantar reflexes certainly result from the lack of theoretical–conceptual uniformity and the methodology adopted.

An extensor plantar response may coexist with the normal development up to 15 months of life postnatally in the full-term newborn, and that is not the Babinski's sign. However, it is possible that an injury or any compromising of the CNS during this early period of life can cause the Babinski's sign, which is an exacerbation and/or qualitative change in the normal extensor plantar response.

The result of our exam can show that the reflexes may be: absent, diminished, brisker than normal, asymmetrical, and primitive, outlasting the usual time, or returning after their disappearance. The knowledge of a wide range of PRs also provides the clinician with a sometimes unique, broad spectrum of opportunities for the diagnosis of a pathology, since the range of PRs can vary according to different ages (maturation), the anatomical location of injuries, specific neurologic pathologies, and individual variations for still unknown physiopathological motives. The set of PRs found in a child, associated with deep tendon reflexes, muscle tone, strength, and postural reactions set a motor pattern that makes up, along with the exam of sensitivity, the upper cerebral functions and the clinical history, the 'jigsaw puzzle' of most neurological diagnoses.

To establish that a reflex is absent, one has to know how to look for it, an absent response may have no clinical significance, and a single exam may not suffice to make a decision. An experienced examiner is the best judge of what laboratory investigations should be performed, since the sophisticated neurodiagnostic technology now available for complementary examinations does not preclude the use of neurological examination. A serial clinical follow-up of the development is the safest and most economic way to make long-term predictions, constituting the gold standard for prognosis.

The assessment of neurological functions through a thorough neurologic exam that includes reflexes provides a complement for developmental screening tests, since these are not useful as a diagnosis or for therapeutic planning, being only the first step that will conduct an interdisciplinary evaluation. Despite the recognition of the great usefulness of modern and sophisticated exams in the management of acute neurologic pathology, these are not available in most hospitals in several countries around the world.

See also: Bayley Scales of Infant Development; Birth Complications and Outcomes; Birth Defects; Brain Development; Brain Function; Cerebral Palsy; Neuropsychological Assessment; Newborn Behavior; Premature Babies.

Suggested Readings

Allen MC and Capute AJ (1990) Tone and reflexo development before term. *Pediatrics* 85: 343–399.

Ashwal S, Russman BS, Blasco PA, *et al.* (2004) Practice parameter: Diagnostic assessment of the child with cerebral palsy. *Neurology* 62: 851–863.

Bayley N (1993) *Bayley Scales of Infant Development,* 2nd edn. San Antonio, TX: The Psychological Corporation.

Cans C, Dolk H, Platt MJ, Colver A, Prasauskiene A, and Kkrägeloh-mann I (2007) Recommendations from the SCPE collaborative group for defining and classifying cerebral palsy. *Developmental Medicine and Child Neurology* 49(s109): 35–38.

Capute AJ, Shapiro BK, Accardo PJ, *et al.* (1982) Motor functions: Associated primitive reflex profiles. *Developmental Medicine Child Neurology* 24: 662–669.

Jacobs SE, Sokol J, and Ohlsson A (2002) The newborn individualized developmental care and assessment program is not supported by meta-analyses of the data. *Journal Pediatrics* 140: 699–706.

Paine RS (1960) Neurological examination of infants and children. *Pediatric Clinics North America* 17: 471–510.

Paine RS, Brazelton TB, Donovan DE, *et al.* (1964) Evolution of postural reflexes in normal infants and in the presence of chronic brain syndromes. *Neurology* 4: 1036–1048.

Pedroso FS and Rotta NT (2003) Neurological examination in the healthy term newborn. *Arquivos Neuropsiquiatria* 61: 165–169.

Prechtl HFR (1977) The neurological examination of the full-term newborn infant. *Clinics in Developmental Medicine 63,* 2nd edn. London: William Heinemann.

Sandra Rees S and Inder T (2005) Fetal and neonatal origins of altered brain development. *Early Human Development* 81: 753–761.

Spreen O, Risser AH, and Edgell D (1995) *Developmental Neuropsychology.* New York: Oxford University Press.

Volpe JJ (2001) *Neurology of the Newborn,* 4th edn. Philadelphia, PA: Saunders.

Zafarian DI (2004) Primitive reflexes and postural reactions in the neurodevelopmental examination. *Pediatric Neurologic* 31: 1–8.

Risk and Resilience

L M Gutman, University of London, London, UK

Glossary

Competence – Successful achievement of critical developmental tasks that vary according to the particular age of the child.

Intervention – Effort designed to change the course of children's lives toward a more positive direction. Within the framework of resilience, programs focus on both fostering competence and preventing future problems.

Protective factors – Attributes of persons, environments, situations, and events that relate to positive adaptation for children under conditions of adversity.

Resilience – Developmental process wherein children demonstrate positive adaptation despite experiencing significant adversity.

Risk factors – Stressors that have proven or presumed effects in increasing the likelihood of maladjustment in children.

Vulnerability factors – Attributes of persons, environments, situations, and events that relate to maladjustment for children under conditions of adversity, that is, the opposite of protective factors.

Introduction

For more than three decades, researchers have been interested in the study of resilience in which children demonstrate positive adaptation despite experiencing significant risk in their lives. Risk factors – such as war, maltreatment, and poverty – increase the likelihood of maladjustment in children. Protective factors – such as children's psychological and personality characteristics, their families, and the availability of external support systems – buffer the effects of risk factors leading to positive development. Resilience is not indefinite, instead it is a developmental process that can be modified as new risks and/or protective factors emerge with changing life circumstances.

Why do some children develop well despite facing severe life adversities such as war, natural disasters, maltreatment, and poverty? For more than three decades, researchers have been interested in the study of resilience in which children demonstrate positive adaptation despite experiencing significant risk in their lives. To infer resilience, a child must have two coexisting conditions: (1) exposure to threat or severe adversity and (2) achievement of positive adaptation. Resilience is not necessarily an attribute or personality trait that some children possess and others do not, but rather a developmental process. Resilience is not indefinite: children who meet the criteria for resilience may not necessarily be doing well continually, in every possible circumstance, and in totality. Children may experience resilience yet still suffer from the residual effects of trauma. Resilience does not mean unharmed or invulnerable. Rather, resilience is demonstrated by adaptive behaviors and life patterns. In this sense, resilience is a process that can be modified as new risks and/or strengths emerge with changing life circumstances.

The historical roots of resilience can be traced to research on individuals with psychopathology. The work of Norman Garmezy and his colleagues was particularly important in this regard. During the 1940s and 1950s, Garmezy examined the history and prognosis of patients with serious mental disorders including schizophrenia. In the 1960s, Garmezy was interested in understanding the antecedents of mental illness and thus began to focus on the children of mentally ill parents due to their elevated risk of developing disorders. He was surprised to discover that many of these children were doing well. By the early 1970s, Garmezy and his research team shifted their focus to the study of competence in children who were at risk due to parental mental illness, poverty, and stressful life experiences. In 1976, Ann Masten joined the research team which was renamed Project Competence. Their research represents one of the earliest efforts to define the positive factors that compensate for the presence of risk in children's lives.

Another landmark study was conducted by Emmy Werner and Ruth Smith. This longitudinal study spanning more than four decades followed the development of nearly 700 children born on the Hawaiian island of Kauai in 1955. The children were followed from birth to adulthood. Although most of the children experienced some level of risk such as poverty and low parental education, one-third experienced multiple risks. Despite these risks, one-third of the children with more than four risks developed well in terms of getting along with their parents and peers, doing well in school, and having good mental health. This resilient group had more resources such as good temperaments and positive parenting in their lives. Most of these children have grown up to be successful adults – in stable marriages and jobs and satisfied with their relationships and life circumstances. These findings indicate that positive factors can make more of a profound impact on the life course of children who grow up in adverse conditions than specific events or risk factors.

These early efforts have played a crucial role in the recognition of childhood resilience as a major theoretical and empirical field of study. These endeavors have enhanced our understanding of the pathways to psychopathology and the processes that lead to normal development. More importantly, this body of work has challenged deficit models that characterized the developmental course of disadvantaged children as deterministic, with an inevitable trajectory leading to maladjustment and pathology. This early work has inspired others to focus on how resilience research may inform social policy and shape prevention and intervention programs to improve the lives of vulnerable children and families.

Following this earlier research, scholarly interest in the study of resilience burgeoned. More contemporary researchers, however, have criticized some of the conceptualizations and methods used by resilience researchers. One of the main criticisms concerns the absence of a unifying conceptual framework across disciplines and specialized areas. A scientific basis for intervention research necessitates precise terminology to build upon earlier classifications and to ensure its continued vitality. A consistent and systematic framework is essential to facilitate the work of researchers and practitioners who pursue work in this area, to integrate findings across diverse fields, as well as to provide guidance for the identification and implementation of age-appropriate, optimal targets for preventive interventions. For these reasons, it is essential to delineate the main concepts involving the study of resilience including risk factors and protective/vulnerability factors as well as to describe its models of risk and resilience and definitions of successful developmental outcomes.

Risk Factors

Defining Risk Factors

Risk factors have been defined as stressors that have proved or presumed effects in increasing the likelihood of maladjustment in children. Risk factors include catastrophic events such as war and natural disasters, family adversities such as bereavement and divorce, economic conditions such as poverty, and exposure to negative environments such as community violence. Risk factors pose a pervasive threat through the deprivation of children's basic needs such as physical sustenance and protection, emotional security and attachment, and social interaction. As a result, exposure to risk factors predicts a variety of difficulties in adjustment and adaptation across the lifespan.

Children's exposure to risk varies according to age. Children in the first few years of life have not established any independent functioning and therefore are highly dependent on their families. As a result, young children are particularly vulnerable to adversities involving their parents and caregivers. However, infants are less likely to suffer from the atrocities of war or the significance of major disasters by their lack of understanding of what is happening. Adolescents, in contrast, have larger and more varied social communities and therefore may have access to supportive environments other than their family. Yet, adolescents are more influenced by the loss and devastation involved in war and natural disasters. They have a greater understanding of what these events signify for their future, a realization that extends beyond the mental capabilities of young children (**Table 1**).

Table 1 Examples of risk factors for children

Domain	*Factor*
Family processes	Bereavement Family dissolution Maltreatment Harsh parenting
Parent characteristics	Poor mental health Substance abuse Low education
Family structure	Single parenthood Numerous stressful life events Household crowding Poverty
Peers	Peer rejection Delinquent peers
Schools	Lower qualified teachers Lack of school resources
Community	Violence Poverty Crime Victimization
Societal	Discrimination Racism Prejudice
Environment	War Catastrophic natural events

One of the most immediately traumatizing events for children and adolescents is the death of a parent. Parental bereavement represents a permanent loss and separation from the primary caregiver. The process of bereavement can be aggravated by additional stressors such as family restructuring, new expectations of children's behavior, parental grief and distress, and death reminders. Family dissolution from parental divorce also increases children's risk for psychological, behavioral, social, and academic problems in comparison to two-parent nondivorced families. Risk is greatest for children of divorced parents who experience high interparental conflict, loss of contact with one parent, problems with the mental health of parents, less economic stability, and multiple marital transitions. Although the intensity diminishes across time, offspring of divorced and remarried families experience difficulties that extend into adolescence and young adulthood. Nevertheless, resilience is the normative outcome for children who are faced with their parents' marital transitions and, in the absence of additional adversities, the vast majority of children of divorced parents develop into reasonably competent well-adjusted adults.

Child abuse and maltreatment also pose a severe threat to children's development. Child abuse involves a significant deviation from the normative environment required for children's successful development and, as a result, few maltreated children experience resilience. Despite this, there are maltreated children who achieve higher levels of adaptation than others. This is likely due to the heterogeneity of maltreatment experiences. Children who are older at the age of onset of maltreatment and who are exposed to shorter, less severe, and pervasive experiences of abuse are more likely to experience resilience.

Parental psychological disturbances such as mental health problems and drug/alcohol use have also been linked to a variety of behavioral, socioemotional, and cognitive problems in children. Many of these disorders coexist and therefore it is often difficult to disentangle their effects on children. For instance, drug-abusing parents also tend to report a higher degree of psychological disturbances. Parental psychological disturbances interfere with interpersonal relationships within the family as well as compromise family functioning in which daily tasks are not accomplished. These aspects of impaired functioning may be the pathways through which problems persist into adulthood.

Childhood poverty – defined by living in a family whose income falls below a specified level necessary for minimum coverage of basic expenses – has been shown to increase the risk of negative child outcomes. Poverty has more detrimental effects for those children who are under the age of 5 and who live in extreme or enduring impoverished conditions. Such negative effects include poor physical health; lower academic and school performance and attainment; and increased likelihood of social, emotional, and behavioral difficulties. Other factors associated with economic circumstances exact their toll on children. Low parental education is also a risk factor for children's cognitive and social development. Parental education influences the educational advantages of the family and their access to key educational resources and opportunities. A larger family size, or greater number of children living in the home, also increases the risk of negative outcomes for children. This is most likely due to the fact that a greater number of family members decreases the amount of resources that is available per person.

Another risk factor concerns the number of stressful life events encountered by the child and/or family. These life events can range from the trivial to severe and from the desirable to undesirable. For example, moving home may be stressful even if it is to a more desirable location. Daily hassles – or the irritating, frustrating experiences that happen nearly every single day – can also exacerbate stress. Although stressful life events may have more of an impact on parents, evidence suggests that both major and minor events contribute to variation in children's development.

In children's larger environment, peers, schools, and neighborhoods can also pose a risk to children's development. Children living in impoverished urban areas are particularly at risk for experiencing a variety of difficult circumstances. Children living in inner-city environments more likely to live in inadequate housing, have less access to good-quality schools and other social resources, and more likely to be exposed to negative peers and multiple violent events. Recent attention has particularly been focused on community violence. Community violence includes many forms such as victimization, witnessing violence, and listening to violence experienced by friends and family members. A growing body of research links this exposure to both psychological and behavioral problems and school underachievement.

In a larger context, societal mechanisms of discrimination, racism, and prejudice have been shown to negatively influence the lives of ethnic minority children. Racial and ethnic discrimination has been linked to a number of psychological symptoms such as low perceived control, anxiety, and frustration. Many children experience discrimination in everyday exchanges and these greatly undermine their mental health. Racism and discrimination also influence other resources in children's lives. For example, research indicates that teachers have lower expectations for, and respond less positively to, ethnic-minority students. Ethnic-minority students are also more likely to be placed in lower academic tracks than their counterparts. These experiences undoubtedly play a role in the underachievement of many ethnic minority children.

On a broader scale, catastrophic events such as war, extreme privation, and natural disasters clearly disrupt children's development. In such severe trauma, children experience devastation on an extreme and massive scale. Children are often less capable of coping with the consequences of such catastrophes – including the lack of basic necessities for existence. These children experience loss of their loved ones and witness unimaginable atrocities. The experience of resilience is defined by their very survival. Yet, studies of children who have experienced such catastrophes suggest that most, when placed in new environments, lead normal, competent lives.

Assessing Risk Factors

Early studies of risk often focused attention on a single risk factor such as child poverty or maltreatment. Many investigators soon realized that the examination of a single risk factor does not address the reality of most children's lives. Children rarely experience risk in isolation, rather risk tends to cluster, usually encompassing a sequence of stressful experiences instead of a single event. For example, children living in poverty are often exposed to other chronic stressors such as family disruption, inadequate housing, and community violence. Child maltreatment tends to co-occur with other environmental threats to children's development such as parental mental illness, parental substance abuse, poverty, parental conflict, and community violence. Evidence also suggests that the effects of an isolated risk factor tend to be rather modest. The exposure to a specific risk factor does not necessarily cause difficulties, but rather it is a life history characterized by the accumulation of family disadvantages, social and economic life events, and adverse conditions that predict maladjustment. For these reasons, many investigators have taken broader perspective when examining the risk factors that impact children's development.

Given the importance of studying multiple influences simultaneously, the next question would be to identify the best analytic strategy. Although regression analyses with a large set of variables might be considered optimal, the relatively small sample sizes of most developmental studies militate against the use of an approach. In situations where many risk indices are considered, it is often impractical to have a large number of predictor variables included in a single regression analysis particularly when sample sizes are limited. Therefore, a number of researchers have employed a cumulative risk model that incorporates a large set of risk factors created by aggregating information about stressful life experiences or risk indices.

In both instances, the cumulative risk score is calculated by dichotomizing each condition into two groups, representing the presence (1) or absence (0) of an event or risk, and then adding all of the resultant scores.

In general, cumulative risk models indicate that the more the risks children experience, the worse their developmental outcomes. In his sample of 10-year-old children of mothers with a psychiatric disorder, Michael Rutter computed a cumulative risk score based on six factors including severe marital distress, low socioeconomic status, large family size or overcrowding, paternal criminality, maternal psychiatric disorder, and placement of the child in foster care. Rutter found that it was not any particular risk factor but the number of risk factors in a child's background that led to the diagnosis of a disorder. Psychiatric risk rose from 2% for children in families with zero or one risk factors to 20% for children in families with four or more risk factors.

Similar findings were evident in research conducted by Arnold Sameroff and his colleagues in the Rochester Longitudinal Study (RLS). The RLS followed a sample of children from birth to young adulthood from families with a high level of maternal psychopathology. Ten environmental risk factors were examined: (1) a history of maternal mental illness; (2) high maternal anxiety; (3) parental perspectives that reflected rigidity in the attitudes, beliefs, and values that mothers had in regard to their child's development; (4) few positive maternal interactions with the child observed during infancy; (5) head of the household in an unskilled occupation; (6) minimal maternal education; (7) disadvantaged minority status; (8) single parenthood; (9) stressful life events; and (10) large family size. When there was no clear definition of risk, 25% of the sample with the worst scores was labeled as high risk. Each of these risk factors was associated with lower preschool competence. Once the risk score was computed, the researchers found that the greater number of risks, the worse cognitive and mental health outcomes for children. Moreover, most children with only a single risk factor did not have a major developmental problem.

Another question regarding the cumulative risk model is whether quality or quantity matters in terms of the negative effects of risk on developmental outcomes. Using the 4-year data in the RLS, Arnold Sameroff and colleagues examined families that experienced a moderate number of risks (3–5 out of 10) to determine whether specific combinations of risk factors had worse effects than others. The families fell into five groups with different combinations of high-risk conditions. Despite these differences, the children had similar developmental outcomes across the five groups. Therefore, it was the number of risk factors, not the combination, which was most important in predicting children's outcomes. This suggests that is it unlikely that the same intervention will be successful for all families. For each family, a unique combination of risk factors will require a specific set of intervention strategies to address the specific risks facing that family.

Recent studies also indicate that there is a universality of risk factors. The same risk factors have been found to influence multiple outcomes such as depression, delinquency, and substance abuse, and each disorder has multiple risk factors. Studies of single risk factors and single outcomes neglect the contribution and congruence of multiple risk and multiple outcomes. The comprehensiveness and the unity of the developmental process require a broader perspective in order to avoid a distorted view of the importance of any single factor.

Protective and Vulnerability Factors

The examination of children who experience developmental success despite adversity has led to an investigation of the mechanisms that either support or undermine resilience. For children who succeed despite less than optimal conditions, the presence of protective factors may compensate for the risks that exist in their lives and environments. Protective factors are those attributes of persons, environments, situations, and events that relate to positive adaptation for children under conditions of adversity. Vulnerability factors, on the other hand, are those attributes that relate to maladjustment for children experiencing adversity. Protective or vulnerability factors are considered the opposite dimension of the same concept, not a different one. In this sense, vulnerability factors are considered the negative pole, whereas protective factors are considered the positive pole of the same variable, for example, parental warmth defined as positive and parental abuse defined as negative.

On the basis of his review of research in the area, Garmezy identified three broad sets of variables that have been found to operate as protective factors including: (1) personal characteristics of the child such as gender, intelligence, and personality characteristics; (2) family characteristics such as warmth, cohesion, and structure; and (3) the availability of external support systems such as peers and schools (**Table 2**).

Personal Characteristics

Personal attributes found to operate as protective factors include both genetic and constitutional factors such as gender, intelligence, temperament, and personality characteristics. Although personal characteristics are always active in a child's life, they influence the way children react when negative situations do occur. A similar situation event will elicit different reactions and responses from children depending on these characteristics. Some children may be more upset than others even when

Table 2 Examples of protective factors for children

Domain	*Factor*
Personal	Gender
	Intelligence
	Temperament
	Sociability
	Perceived control
	Self-esteem
	Coping style
Family	Attachment style
	Parent–child interactions
	Parenting style
	Family cohesion
	Family routines
	Family support
	Family resources
External	Friendships
	Teacher support
	School resources
	Organized activities
	Neighborhood cohesion

experiencing exactly the same event and these responses will influence the way they can handle such stress.

There have been a number of suggestions in the literature that gender may also modify or influence children's responses to adversity. Specifically, evidence indicates that females are less susceptible to emotional and behavioral disturbances than boys when exposed to family stress. This finding is interactive indicating that boys do not simply have a higher rate of disturbances in general but rather their risk is much greater when exposed to family discord compared to girls. Michael Rutter has noted that there are several reasons why boys may be more vulnerable than girls. First, males may have more direct experiences of family discord, for example, parents may argue in front of boys more than girls. Second, when families break up, sons are more likely to be placed in institutional care than daughters. Third, boys are more likely to react with disruptive oppositional behavior rather than emotional distress. Fourth, parents may react more negatively to aggression in boys compared to girls. For these reasons, the protection afforded to girls may be the result of a reduced exposure to risk factors rather than a biological component due to gender itself. However, the protective effects may lessen with age. In their study of Hawaiian youth, for example, Werner and Smith found that males in their sample showed greater vulnerability than females during the first decade of life, but this lessened during the second and third decades.

One of the most widely investigated variables in resilience research is children's intellectual ability. Although there is less support that intelligence is a protective factor for children's social success and mental health, there has been some evidence indicating its protective effects on academic achievement. Studies of younger children have found that high-risk children with higher intelligence perform better in school than their high-risk peers with lower intelligence. However, several studies have found counterintuitive results indicating that intelligence may sometimes operate as a vulnerability factor. These studies indicate that higher intelligence may be positively related to school achievement at low levels of risk, whereas children with higher intelligence lose their advantage at high levels of risk. It has been suggested that age may be the contributing factor for this difference. Intelligence may serve a protective function for younger children, yet as children mature into adolescents, they may be more likely to use their talents in areas other than educational achievement.

Several studies have suggested that temperament and personality characteristics operate as protective factors for children. Children who have a positive constellation of characteristics such as easy temperament, social responsiveness, and humor are more likely to elicit positive responses and support from other people. Child temperament – measured by characteristics such as mood, activity level, attention span or distractibility, adaptability or malleability, and emotion reactivity – has received much attention as a protective factor. Evidence suggests that children with an easier temperament are less likely to be the target of negative parenting during stressful situations. Children's negative temperaments may also influence the amount of family discord and increase the likelihood that children will experience its adverse effects. In this sense, parents who are experiencing more distress may be more likely to release their negativity on children with difficult temperaments.

Several researchers have also suggested that psychological characteristics such as perceived locus of control, self-esteem, and coping style are key protective factors. Perceived locus of control refers to beliefs about the sources of one's successes and failures. Children with high levels of perceived internal locus of control believe that their successes and failures are due to their own attributes or actions, whereas children who have high levels of external locus of control believe that other people or unknown causes account for such outcomes. High-risk children who perceive more internal locus of control over their lives tend to have better mental health and higher functioning than their high-risk peers with a more external locus of control. Self-esteem has also been shown to operate as a protective factor for children exposed to risk. A positive sense of self has been shown to have a positive impact on children experiencing stress and may facilitate the development of other characteristics such as perceived internal control which mitigate the effects of risk. Coping strategies also influence children's response to negative life situations. Children who have more active coping skills such as problem-solving and social support seeking are better apt at handling difficult situations. Children who do not learn to cope with stress and use ineffective skills such as distraction and avoidance are more likely to be overwhelmed by adverse circumstances.

Family Characteristics

A number of studies have examined the protective effects of family characteristics including more proximal factors such as parent–child interactions and more distal factors such as parents' financial and educational status. For proximal factors, one of the most important protective factors is a secure parent–child attachment particularly during infancy and early childhood. Research consistently demonstrates that a secure attachment defined by a responsive, supportive, structured, and affectively stimulating relationship between parent and child contributes to children's positive development. A secure attachment has also been shown to be particularly important for children exposed to adversity. For example, the security of attachment between child and mother has been shown to differentiate positive versus negative outcomes in those children experiencing risk. A sensitive, securely attached caregiver relationship also fosters the development of children's sense of self worth and their capabilities to adapt to changing circumstances with positive coping strategies, problem-solving skills, and social competence. In this way, a secure parent–child attachment not only operates as a protective factor for recent exposure to risk, but also enables children to develop the capacity for resilience in the future.

The quality of parenting plays an essential role in children's response to stressful situations. Parenting may either protect children from life circumstances or make them more vulnerable to adversities. Research suggests that authoritative parenting provides the most beneficial environment for children's development. Authoritative parents create a warm and supportive environment for their children with the appropriate amount of structure and consistent discipline. Although authoritative parenting is optimal for most children, it may serve a protective function particularly for children who are experiencing stressful events and situations. Children who are exposed to adversities such as family dissolution are more likely to need additional emotional support and structure that authoritative parents provide. However, there is some evidence to suggest that optimal parenting strategies may vary depending on the specific risks to which children are exposed. Although research has found that poor families tend to engage in more controlling, harsh parenting, some have suggested that these types of strategies may be more adaptive for children living in impoverished environments. For children living in inner-city neighborhoods, more controlling parenting behaviors may protect them from exposure to danger and violence leading to more positive outcomes.

Family-level resources such as cohesion, positive interactions, and support may also operate as protective factors. Adversity makes it difficult for families to maintain their normal family-level interactions and routines. For example, parental divorce disrupts family events such as outings and decreases interaction with the noncustodial parent. However, children exposed to stressful events such as family disruption may have a greater need for these family-level resources in order to maintain a sense of normality and structure. These family-level resources may also exert their protective effects by influencing children's psychological adjustment and parent–child interactions. For instance, family cohesion may enhance children's perceived internal control and their coping strategies. Alternatively, family routines such as eating meals together create a context where warm, supportive parenting can occur.

More distal characteristics of families may also operate as protective factors. For example, some researchers have demonstrated the protective effects of household income for specific adverse conditions. For example, children of divorced parents benefit when their fathers provide more financial support. Research indicates that children in mother-custody families who receive child-support payments from their fathers tend to have better relationships with their fathers and experience more positive outcomes. Parents' level of education may also serve as a protective factor for children through the increased access to resources and advantages that higher education affords.

External Support Systems

As children mature, external support systems play an increasingly significant role in children's development. Children's friendships are particularly important for children experiencing adverse life circumstances. Reciprocal, positive friendships may provide additional avenues of self-esteem and emotional support for children whose families offer less positive engagement and interaction. For example, studies suggest that friendships may be particularly important for maltreated children as they often have fewer opportunities to learn and practice social skills in their family setting. On the other hand, peer rejection has been shown to exacerbate the deleterious consequences of many life stresses such as divorce. Another vulnerability factor regarding peer relationships is the association with negative friends. When children disengage from their family relationships and spend more time with negative friends, they are at greater risk for the development of antisocial behavior and academic problems. However, a supportive relationship even with a single friend may act as a protective factor from the negative effects of both peer rejection and other adverse circumstances.

Teachers and school environments have also been shown to be beneficial for children experiencing risk. In early childhood, child-care attendance and quality are protective factors particularly for those children living in low-income environments. Evidence suggests that children living in impoverished conditions including shelters or poverty-level housing may benefit more from higher quality child-care than children from more optimal home environments. Supportive teachers and school environments are also consequential for children's development. Teachers can play a crucial role as caring adults or mentors for those students who need additional support. School environments characterized by defined schedules and rules, high expectations, and the use of warm yet consistent discipline have been associated with social and academic achievement for children exposed to risk. These protective effects may be especially salient for those children with no supportive and authoritative parent or caregiver at home. School attendance and achievement also appear to be protective factors for children exposed to adverse circumstances. Evidence indicates that school attendance and academic achievement are associated with fewer behavioral problems and antisocial outcomes among children in high-risk families.

There is also increasing evidence that communities play a protective role for high-risk children. Social processes within a neighborhood are particularly important. Social processes within a neighborhood refer to the perceived social support and cohesion among neighbors, supervision of children and adolescents by other adults in the community, participation in voluntary organizations, and a general sense of belonging to the community by its members. These neighborhood social processes have been shown to help protect against structural disadvantages (e.g., poverty and violence) even in more impoverished communities. Youth-serving community organizations and participation in organized after-school activities may also provide some protection from the structural disadvantages of a neighborhood. Unfortunately, youth-serving programs are less likely to exist in those neighborhoods with the greatest need for such organizations. Participation in organized after-school activities is also lower for low-income families compared to their more advantaged peers due to the overall unavailability of such activities in poorer areas.

Theoretical Models of Risk and Resilience

Considering models of resilience, it is essential to distinguish between risk factors and those factors which either support or undermine children facing multiple risks. Researchers have employed a number of models to describe the relations among risk and protective/vulnerability factors. These include interactive effects, main effects, and mediating effects models (**Table 3**).

Interactive Effects Models

The earliest models of resilience used the term 'protective factor' only for those effects involving adversity. The concept was first systematically defined by Rutter who argued that to be meaningful, protective/vulnerability factors must be evident only in combination with a risk factor. In this framework, the essential question of resilience research is: what factors explain positive development in the face of adversity but have little or no positive impact on development in the absence of adversity? To address this question, protective/vulnerability effects are required to have an interactive relationship with the risk factor(s) thereby either having no effect in low-risk populations or its effect being magnified in the presence of risk. Whether the variable itself is considered a protective or vulnerability factor lies in its connection with the risk variable, not in terms of whether it has positive or negative qualities. Protective factors decrease the effect of risk, whereas vulnerability factors increase the effect of risk. A protective factor may not necessarily be a socially desirable characteristic of the individual or a positive event. Therefore, protection for a high-risk child may even come from a factor that itself is a risk to the mental health or social functioning of a low-risk child. On the other hand, a vulnerability factor for high-risk children may be related to positive development for low-risk children.

In a hypothetical example of an interactive effects model, a researcher may compare the effects of high versus low child-care quality on the cognitive development of young children with varying degrees of risk: (1) high risk, low quality; (2) low risk, low quality; (3) high risk, high quality; and (4) low risk, high quality. Quality of child-care would be a protective factor only if high-risk children in a high quality child-care environment had

Table 3 Models of risk and resilience

Model	*Terms*	*Relation with risk*
Interactive effects	Protective/vulnerability	Interactive relationship with risk thereby either having no effect in low-risk populations or its effect being magnified in the presence of risk
Main effects	Compensatory/promotive	Direct relationship with risk thereby having an equally beneficial effect on high-risk and low-risk children
Mediating effects	Deterioration/mobilization	Mediational relationship linking risk to developmental outcomes

significantly higher cognitive development than high-risk children in a low quality child-care environment and there were no differences in the cognitive development of low-risk students regardless of the quality of child-care. According to Rutter, this interactive process must be determined empirically, in order to differentiate risk from vulnerability factors.

Main Effects Models

Although interactive effects models provide a distinction between vulnerability and risk factors, not all factors may conform to the interactive requirement. Consider, for example, physical attractiveness. Children who are physically attractive may generally receive more positive responses from others, but there is no specific reason why attractiveness may be beneficial for high-risk children but not low-risk children. The absence of interactive effects may also simply be an artifact of the research design. In a high-risk sample, for example, differences between those who are well adjusted and those who are not may represent interactions in other samples with a wider distribution of risk. Considering this, many researchers use main effects models that examine the direct effects of positive factors on children's outcomes. In these models, the positive factor has an equally beneficial effect on those children exposed and those not exposed to adversity. Main effects models may be differentiated in terms of whether homogeneous or heterogeneous risk samples are examined.

Researchers focusing on a homogeneous risk sample, such as children living in poverty, may examine main effect differences between high and low competence children experiencing adversity. In these studies, protective factors are defined as those positive variables that differentiate high-risk children who are experiencing positive adaptation from those high-risk children who are not. These studies may be better at detecting processes that are protective for a specific risk condition. The meaning or definition of resilience may also differ for children exposed to a specific risk. Maltreated children, for instance, rarely approach the functioning of nonmaltreated children. Yet, variation in adaptation does exist suggesting that some children achieve better than expected. Studies focusing on a within-group sample, such as maltreated children, can examine more closely profiles of resilient adaptation rather than specific, isolated attributes to understand the meaning of such variability.

Rather than examining individuals experiencing high levels of risk, other studies identify factors that are associated with positive outcomes for a heterogeneous sample of individuals. These researchers use the term protective factors to describe main effect models that identify factors associated with desirable outcomes independent of the occurrence of social disadvantage or adverse circumstances. For example, athletic talent does not necessarily insulate the children from adverse circumstances, but instead may provide opportunities for additional successes. For such effects, more appropriate terms have been proposed including promotive or compensatory, none of which suggest that the attribute provides a buffer which protects the child from risk factors.

Mediating Effects Models

Mediating effects models define protective factors as those variables linking risk variables to developmental outcomes. These studies test variables hypothesized to serve as mediating factors between risk factors and developmental outcomes. There are two forms of mediation: deterioration and mobilization. In the deterioration model of mediation, the occurrence of risk decreases the ability of children and families to function effectively. For example, impoverished parents may experience greater depression which, in turn, decreases their ability to use effective parenting strategies. In the mobilization model of mediation, the occurrence of risk increases the ability of children and families to function effectively. For example, bereaved children with more active coping strategies may be better at eliciting support from others.

Developmental Outcomes: Competence and Maladjustment

The definition of resilience depends on the outcome being assessed. Past researchers have defined resilience according to the absence of social deviance or psychopathology. Although the importance of competence was recognized in developmental research, the medical model which emphasizes symptoms, diseases, and treatments dominated the field. More recently, there has been a return toward positive psychology. This has encouraged a shift in focus from maladjustment to more positive developmental outcomes. As there has been so little attention to positive aspects of adaptation in the past, more recent researchers of resilience have developed a variety of methods to assess competence.

Several researchers have examined social competence as a measure of resilience. Social competence is defined according to the success of a person meeting societal expectations. Other criteria include personal development and self-actualization. Studies have measured social competence on the basis of observable, behavioral criteria often assessed by multiple sources including the children themselves and their parents, teachers, and peers. These broader assessments may have greater validity due to its multiple informants. The definition of social competence also depends on the developmental stage being assessed. For example, social competence in infancy may be operationalized as having a secure mother–child attachment and positive affect. In early childhood, social competence may include measures of autonomous functioning and behavioral and emotional functioning. In middle childhood and adolescence, social competence can be defined according to positive friendships and academic achievement.

Research in resilience has traditionally focused on defining competence in a single domain such as academic achievement. However, studies focusing on multiple dimensions of competence have realized that children who may be doing well in one area of development may suffer in another. For example, in distinguishing between externalizing (i.e., acting out) behaviors from internalizing (i.e, thought-centered) behaviors, so-called resilient children may react to their stressful experiences in a more covert, internal manner. In resilience research, there is the tendency to assume that if children are doing well in more external behaviors, they have managed to overcome adversity. However, evidence indicates that many so-called resilient children who have outstanding behavioral profiles experience considerable emotional distress. Since resilient children tend to be at higher developmental levels, as reflected in their intellectual maturity, their pathology is more likely to be expressed with internal symptoms rather than behavioral disturbances. For these reasons, some researchers have suggested that in order for high-risk children to be labeled as resilient, they must excel in multiple domains of competence.

There has also been some disagreement whether competence should be defined according to a representative, heterogeneous sample or within a high-risk, homogeneous group. Some researchers consider high-risk children to be resilient when they demonstrate behavior within the expected average range of a normative cohort. Other researchers examine competence within a high-risk sample and define resilience in terms of doing better than other equally disadvantaged counterparts. The latter method considers the specific adversity and takes into account that the expression and definition of competence may differ according to the risk condition. However, the level of positive adaptation in a high-risk sample often does not equate with the competence of a more normative cohort.

The definition of resilience is also dynamic and developmental in nature. Competence at one stage in development can serve as a protective effect at a later point in time. For example, high-risk children who are socially competent may have a greater capacity to elicit positive and support responses from others which, in turn, strengthens their positive development. Children are better able to benefit from protective factors in the future when they possess the capacity to engage in their environments in the present. On the other hand, there may be a cascade effect where maladjustment at one stage may contribute to the development of later problems. For example, antisocial behavior in childhood may undermine academic achievement which, in turn, contributes to later problems. Developmental research explores the dynamic, ongoing processes involved in children's capacity for resilience. A key aim of developmental research is to understand the integration and organization of experiences that enable children to become successful, competent individuals.

A Resilience Framework for Interventions

Resilience research has provided new avenues of policy and practice for vulnerable children and families. Rather focusing on maladapative functioning and psychopathology, a resilience framework emphasizes the promotion of competent functioning and fosters the development of policies and interventions that reflect the belief in resilient adaptation. Intervention programs are also more developmental in nature in that they focus on redirecting children's trajectories and strengthening cumulative protective processes in children's lives. A resilience framework has been proposed by Ann Masten which conceptualizes mission statements, models, measures, methods for policy and practice.

Mission Statements

Mission statements are key objectives for the development and implementation of policies and interventions. Within a resilience framework, mission statements are framed in terms of promoting competence rather than merely focusing on the reduction of problematic behaviors. The promotion of competence is one of the most effective methods of prevention. Comprehensive programs for high-risk children work better when goals include promoting positive achievements, in addition to preventing negative behaviors. The promotion of competence is also more appealing to policy makers and stakeholders. Parents and teachers, for example, who are usually involved as key players respond more positively when programs are focused on fostering success. Certainly, the focus of intervention – children – also respond better when their positive assets and potentials are reinforced rather than their challenges and problems.

Models

Resilience and prevention scholars have elucidated theoretical and empirical models that focus on how children experience positive outcomes in the face of adversity. These models represent important steps in the development of programs that focus on promoting children's assets and strengths. These models provide a springboard for policies and interventions that redirect children toward positive development, focus on improving the chances of good outcomes, encourage the development of protecting characteristics, and reduce the exposure to risk and vulnerabilities. Effective models must be development and be fully informed by current developmental theories and research. Developmental models consider the risks, protective processes, and competencies that are relevant to a specific age group and conceptualize interventions in terms of dynamic, ongoing processes that evolve and adapt to new developmental tasks and challenges.

Measures

Resilience research has highlighted the importance of developing appropriate measures assessing children's capacity for resilience and the processes that support its development. Measures designed for children need to consider the major developmental tasks as well as the characteristics of the contexts of development such as families, schools, and communities that are relevant for a specific age group. Although resilience research has encouraged the development of measures for assessing competence, there is still work to be done that encourages the use of such tools in more field-friendly ways.

Methods

Within the resilience framework, there are several strategies to consider when developing interventions for policy and practice. Masten has outlined three types of designs for policy and practice. Risk-focused designs attempt to reduce the level of risk exposure in children's development. For example, risk-focused designs would include programs that provide sexual education to prevent teenage pregnancy and give low-income mothers more prenatal care to prevent low-birth weight infants. Asset-focused designs attempt to directly provide higher quality and/or more quantity of assets in children's lives. They may also attempt to increase the presence and ability of individuals who are assets in the lives of children such as parents and teachers. For example, asset-focused designs would include teaching job skills to parents, training teachers to enhance the learning and achievement of their students, and increasing the after-school activities available in the neighborhood. Process-orientated programs attempt to improve the most important adaptational systems for children such as key relationships, intellectual functioning, and self-regulation systems. Process-orientated programs can focus on different system levels such as children, families, schools, and neighborhoods as well as their interactions such as parent–school involvement, children's self-monitoring of school tasks, and student–teacher mentoring relationships. Interventions programs may also involve more than one design, for example, such as drug treatment along with programs to increase parent–infant attachment that may help reduce the risks facing infants of drug-abusing mothers.

Conclusions

According to Masten, resilience arises from ordinary magic in the sense that children are capable of astonishing resistance, adaptation, recovery, and success in the face of adversity using only the normal capacities and resources that individuals rely on to function everyday. Despite these strengths and capacities, however, children cannot simply make themselves enduringly resilient in the face of continuous adversities in their environments. As Emmy Werner has noted, when risk factors outweigh protective processes even the most resilient child will experience difficulties. With this in mind, research in resilience is shifting away from describing individual characteristics of resilient children and instead focusing more sharply on how children's environments – families, peers, schools, and neighborhoods – can be adapted to meet the needs of children facing adversity. Evidence indicates that effective and effortful family-based and community-level interventions play an essential role in promoting resilience in the lives of vulnerable children.

Yet, as Masten has noted, there is no magic bullet for resilience. That is, there is no one solution that can be adapted to promote children's resilience in any and all circumstances. Risks are multifaceted and thus interventions must also be multifaceted to reflect the diverse experiences and environments of a child's life. At the same time, a number of risks in children's lives – for example, premature birth, malnutrition, and homelessness – are preventable. Policies that provide families and children their basic needs such as healthcare, food, and shelter remain critical in order to maximize the potential of the future generations.

See also: Abuse, Neglect, and Maltreatment of Infants; Attachment; Child and Day Care, Effects of; Depression; Divorce; Family Influences; Mental Health, Infant; Mental Health, Intervention and Prevention; Parental Chronic Mental Illnesses; Parenting Styles and their Effects; Self-Regulatory Processes; Temperament.

Suggested Readings

Glanz M and Johnson JL (eds.) (1999) *Resilience and Development: Positive Life Adaptations.* New York: Plenum.

Luthar SS (ed.) (2003) *Resilience and Vulnerability: Adaptation in the Context of Childhood Adversities.* Cambridge: Cambridge University Press.
Masten A (2001) Ordinary magic: Resilience processes in development. *American Psychologist* 56: 227–238.
Rutter M (1987) Psychosocial resilience and protective mechanisms. *American Journal of Orthopsychiatry* 57: 316–331.
Werner EE and Smith RS (2001) *Journeys from Childhood to Midlife: Risk, Resilience, and Recovery.* Ithaca, NY: Cornell University Press.

Routines

B H Fiese and R S Everhart, Syracuse University, Syracuse, NY, USA

Glossary

Behavior management techniques – Methods used to help children change or modify their existing behaviors, such as positively reinforcing good behavior or using time-outs to alter negative behaviors.
Collectivism – Belief in the primary importance of the group and in the virtue of collective values.
Conversational turn taking – How two or more people alternate and shift in response to questions and statements made while talking with each other.
Family rhythms – Tempo and pace with which family sets its daily activities such as waking, eating, and going to work.
Habits – Repetitive behaviors that individuals perform without conscious thought.
Individualism – Belief in the primary importance of the individual and in the virtues of self-reliance and personal independence.
Joint book reading – Typically involves adult and child reading together with adult and child commenting on different aspects of the story line and illustrations.
Ritual routines – A sequence of highly ordered steps that occur in common settings such as mealtimes, bedtimes, and leisure activities.

Introduction

The early childhood years are replete with routines. Establishing routines around eating, sleeping, and toilet training are not only a topic of conversation for parents of toddlers but consume much of the daily life of families with young children. Children of preschool age learn to make the transition from "being a baby" to "I'm a big girl now!" through becoming more engaged in routines such as family mealtimes, nighttime stories, and household chores. Successful transition to school is often marked by negotiating such routines as learning to stand in line, respecting naptime as a set aside quiet time, and knowing that Friday's are for show and tell. In this article, we discuss the importance of child routines from several different vantage points. First, we define what we mean by routines and how they are distinguished from such concepts as habits. Second, we identify the developmental course of childhood routines that encourage the child to take on a more active role as he becomes more competent. Third, we present some of the findings that suggest that predictable and regular routines in a child's life are associated with positive outcomes such as enriched language development, empathy and caring for others, and well-regulated behavior. Finally, we discuss how children's engagement in routines differs across cultures suggesting that cultural practices are conveyed, in part, by children's engagement in daily routines.

What Are Children's Routines?

How might we best define and identify the routines that are important for child development? Families organize their busy daily lives through structuring routines around waking, eating, working (including homework), and leisure activities. At its most basic level, children's routines include those that must sustain physical growth and development. These include activities that revolve around sleeping, eating, and toilet training. Thus, activities such as establishing regular naptimes, making the decision to introduce solid foods, and when to begin toilet training are geared toward fostering the child's growth as a more mature individual. Routines are also organized to promote the child's cognitive and social development and these include such activities as play, book reading routines, household chores, and parental discipline routines. Many of these routines are folded into daily family gatherings

Table 1 Description of common routines in early childhood

Class of routine	*Examples*
Basic biological rhythms	Naptime
	Feeding
	Toilet training
Social development	Mealtime conversations
	Household chores
Cognitive development	Joint book reading
	Homework

such as mealtimes and planned leisure activities. We can group these routines along lines of those that support biological rhythms, social development, and cognitive development. We present examples of these routines in **Table 1**. Although we outline these as classes of routines that evolve across developmental periods, we want to emphasize that these distinctions are somewhat artificial. For example, bedtime routines can reassert their importance when a child moves from a crib to a 'big boy' bed, assignment of chores evolve as the child can take on more responsibilities, and homework routines are negotiated throughout the child's school career. Thus, we provide these classes of routines for illustrative purposes and are not meant to be sharp taxonomies.

Routines are different than habits and rituals. Habits are repetitive behaviors that individuals perform without conscious thought. Behavioral habits are done automatically and typically involve a restricted range of behaviors. For example, a child may have a habit of sucking on the end of her blanket when going to sleep. A routine, in contrast, involves a sequence of highly ordered steps. A child's bedtime routine might include taking a bath, brushing teeth, reading a book, saying prayers, and then sucking on the end of a blanket before going to sleep. Rituals, on the other hand, tend to be more symbolic and linked to emotional bonds within the family. They often provide continuity across generations and are unique and meaningful to the family. A routine has the ability to become a ritual when it is repeated over time and takes on symbolic meaning.

As we focus on children's routines, we must also consider how the environment around them supports, or derails, these structured steps that constitute a full fledged routine. Certainly, parents play an important role. Children are also active contributors in the process, however. Let us examine the early years of establishing sleep, feeding, and social routines and how parents and children figure in this dynamic process.

Early Feeding and Sleep Routines

The birth of an infant brings new challenges to young parents. It takes a while for new parents to adjust their daily routines to accommodate to the needs of an infant. For most families, daily routines such as dinnertime and weekend activities do not 'get back on track' until the child is of preschool age. Parents who have had previous experience in childcare routines before the birth of their first child often feel more confident in caring for their newborn. Feeding routines are one of the first caregiving routines established in infancy. The extent to which these practices run smoothly depends, in part, on the match between parent and child rhythms and parent understanding of child social signals. There are at least three dimensions to establishing feeding routines in infancy: timing, social interactions, and biological rhythms. First, feeding routines evolve based on how often the infant is hungry and needs sustenance. This will depend on whether the child is breastfed or bottle-fed. Breastfed infants typically empty their stomachs every 2–3 h and bottle-fed babies are hungry every 3–4 h. Thus, the frequency and timing of the routine will depend on whether the mother is breastfeeding or not.

An important part of early feeding routines is the opportunity for social interaction. At its most basic level, the child's cry for food sets the stage for a developing awareness that his or her actions can influence others. Once in the arms of the caregiver, there are added opportunities for social interaction. Interestingly, the distance between a caregiver's and an infant's face during feeding is the optimal distance for social engagement. It is not an accident that during feeding infants will look intensely at their caregiver (often before falling asleep) and that responsive caregivers will use this as a time to talk in a soothing voice or even sing to the child. The third aspect of feeding routines is biological rhythms. Feeding routines are embedded in 24 blocks and become aligned with the child's circadian rhythms. There is even some evidence that children who establish regular feeding schedules are also easier to calm to sleep and establish regular sleep schedules.

The establishment of feeding and sleep routines during infancy is not a one-way street with parents imposing their wishes on the child – just ask any parent! It is the match between parent and child rhythms that allows for a relatively smooth or rocky launch of family routines. Establishing sleep routines illustrates this intersection between infant and family rhythms. Close to 25% of parents with children under the age of 5 report that getting their child to bed or having their child wake in the middle of the night is a problem. Although many sleep problems occur during the first 6 months of life, they are often seen as variations in normal development and may also be related to environmental factors such as disruptions in family routines or illness. As such, sleep behavior disorders are not diagnosable until after 12 months of age when sleep patterns are more stable. Children who wake less at night are perceived by their mothers as easier to care for and are more likely to be raised in homes with higher levels of routines. Further, when routines are in place parents feel more competent overall and their children experience fewer night-time waking problems. If this seems like a circular pattern with little assuredness of what comes first – child sleeping through the night or regular family routines – that is because the research literature is correlational and cross-sectional in nature. To date, we do not have strong longitudinal evidence that can answer whether regular family routines create easier sleep patterns in children or whether children who are easier to get to sleep by virtue of their biological rhythms make it easier to create family routines. We suspect that both cases may be true. The research evidence does suggest however, that when regular routines are in place in the home then children experience fewer sleep disturbances overall and that systematic alterations in bedtime routines can lead to a reduction in night-time tantrums, waking in the middle of the night, and poor sleep habits.

Social Routines

We have commented on the importance of feeding routines in terms of eliciting social interactions between the infant and mother. However, there are also social routines that play an important role in the communicative and cognitive development of an infant. These social routines are often exhibited as sustained play routines (e.g., 'peek-aboo', patty-cake', 'where's your nose?') with the infant becoming a more active play partner. Such routines might follow a feeding routine during which the infant is already intensely focused on the caregiver. These simple social routines are instrumental in enabling the infant to learn the skills of taking turns in conversations and how to be a partner in a conversation. Further, these social routines are important for the infant's cognitive development. For instance, the infant is introduced to the temporal order of interactions and begins to learn to identify different objects and even parts of the face. Moreover, by participating in these social routines, infants learn to associate a sequence of actions with a routine and ultimately anticipate a future or final state of the routine.

As we have seen, during infancy many of the caregiving routines are directed toward stabilizing the child's day and night so that the child can fit in with the rhythms of the larger social world. Once the child is on a schedule that fits with the rest of the household, then the child becomes a more active participant in shaping daily routines. Let us now examine some of the daily living routines evident during the preschool years.

Child Routines During the Preschool Years

There are a variety of routines that absorb much of a preschool child's day. These include mealtimes, household chores, 'getting ready', joint book reading, and response to discipline routines. Let us examine each one in turn for how they get established and altered during the preschool years. In the following sections we will consider how these routine activities contribute to such important outcomes as cognitive and social development.

In many ways, mealtimes can be seen as a microcosm of family life. Such mundane aspects of mealtimes as seat assignment, rules for conversational turn taking, and how the meal ends and begins reflect important features of family life that support child development. For preschool age children, mealtimes are settings where families decide when a child is old enough to sit at the table with everyone else and thus join in important conversations. They are also settings where opinions can be solicited (or not) and thus reinforces the child's sense of belonging to the family as a whole. Household chores are another way that preschool children are brought into the fold of family life. Initially assigned relatively simple tasks such as cleaning up one's toys, these roles and responsibilities are expanded to include other members of the family such as feeding a pet or looking after younger siblings.

Every child perhaps has his or her own set of 'getting ready' routines. These can range from laying out clothes the night before school to elaborate bedtime routines that must be followed before getting settled in. Recall how we defined routines as a series of behavioral steps that are followed in sequence? For the preschool child, 'getting ready' for school, a visit to grandmother's house, or going to bed involves ordering a sequence of steps that evolve into a routine. The young toddler needs considerable assistance in ordering these steps and is somewhat at a loss as to whether socks go on before shoes. However, the competent preschooler cannot only tell you what steps need to be taken in carrying out a routine they can do so on their own. It is this sense of individual accomplishment in carrying out routines that adds to the child's growing sense of competence and independence that is fostered before the transition to school. The expression of 'getting ready' routines is one arena where preschool children experience growing self-reliance and competence.

Independence and autonomy do not come without restrictions, however. Parents must shape their child's behavior in such a way that they are protected from harm and limits are set in a consistent way. Discipline routines are typically developed during the preschool years. For some families this may mean instituting 'time out' policies whenever the child breaks a rule or misbehaves. Embedded within the practice of discipline routines are children's understandings that families have a set of rules that are to be followed. These rules are relatively simple during the toddler and early preschool years and revolve around safety issues to protect the child. As the child grows older into the later preschool and early elementary years, the rules expand to include transgressions against others and understanding of others' feelings.

One of the ways in which children begin to understand others' feelings and the impact that individual actions have on the family group as a whole is through the assignment of household chores. The participation of young children in household chores or everyday routines, such as feeding the pets or making their bed, provides a major pathway for children to develop socially. Children are able to develop a sense of partnership, of helping others, and even the belief that they are competent and good enough to help others. Participating in such routines also encourages children to take responsibility for their actions and to acknowledge how such routines benefit the family as a whole. Neglecting everyday chores may lead to conflict within the family or even a sense that the child has let the family down. Encouraging children to participate in routines also allows children to develop a sense of concern for others, including people other than family members.

To summarize, the daily life of young children is organized around routines that promote their growth and development. For infants many of these routines are centered around establishing regular feeding and waking routines so that the child can grow into a healthy participant in family life. Once the child's rhythms are aligned with the larger social world, then expectations about participation in other activities such as mealtime, bedtime, and household chores evolve with expanding roles and responsibilities for the child. Newfound competence can be established as the child takes on a sense of accomplishment in carrying out their own routines such as 'getting ready' for the day or helping out around the house. Discipline routines are set into place to ensure that the child is kept safe and impart family rules. The regularity with which these activities are practiced and support social interactions is associated with important cognitive and behavioral outcomes in the early childhood years. Let us examine some of these links.

Routines and Child Developmental Outcomes

We have mentioned that family mealtimes are one setting where regular routines are practiced and reinforced. It is estimated that about 73% of US families eat dinner together at least four times a week. Although 2006 surveys suggest this rate declines by about 15% for families with an adolescent, mealtimes continue to be an important routine for families with children of all ages. For young children, the flow of a brief mealtime allows for multiple opportunities for the child to engage in conversation with older members of the family. These mealtime conversations have been found to be related to a variety of child developmental outcomes. For example, adult's use of rare or unusual words at the dinner table such as 'oxygen' and 'stegosaurus' is associated with children's language development and reading achievement scores during the early school years. Researchers who examine these mealtimes in depth have found a variety of characteristics that promote literacy and prepare the child for successful academic performance. Routine conversations during mealtime that are explanatory and engage the child in extended discourse are more likely to be associated with enriched language development than conversations that are primarily directive and focus on getting the child to behave. Further, routine conversations that incorporate rare words such as 'twirl', 'colander', and 'iguana' expand the child's vocabulary in predictable ways. Researchers in this area argue that because children are exposed to these rare words during the course of an everyday event that includes rich social cues, children are more likely to retain and use these words than if they were drilled on them via flashcards or word lists.

Politeness routines are another aspect of mealtime conversations that have been studied during the preschool years. Prompts such as "What do you say?", "What's the magic word?" are typically responded to with "please", "thank you", or "you're welcome". In an observational study of families with preschool age children it was found that these types of politeness routines were used, on average, 14 times per mealtime. Careful examination of these utterances have led researchers to consider that these politeness routines support the development of complex sentence structures as the child learns to pair words in a sequence – "May I have some more ...please?" Thus, a simple please and thank you extends beyond good table manners.

Further, there is evidence to suggest that conversational routines between parent and preschool age children, which occur during mealtimes, are important in helping a child to understand temporal sequencing in conversations. We noted the importance of these routines (e.g., 'peekaboo', 'patty-cake') for infant cognitive and communicative development. Conversational routines continue to be important as the child matures. For preschool age children, research studies have found that conversations between parent and child about past events as well as conversations about future events aid in developing child memory. Moreover, conversations focused on past and future events serve to increase children's awareness of sequencing and the order of events.

Joint book reading routines can also support literacy and language development during the early childhood years. Just as there are multiple aspects to mealtime conversations and their effects on child development, joint book reading routines are composed of several layers. First is the frequency with which parents set aside routine times to read with their children. The evidence is fairly clear that frequency of joint book reading routines is related to later literacy skills and school success. The question then becomes, what is it about reading together that promotes literacy? While reading with their preschool age children, parents are able to limit distractions and direct the child's attention to key points of the story or picture. Parents use this opportunity to highlight interesting points in the storyline or even humorous aspects of the illustrations. Researchers refer to this strategy as 'specific commenting', a style of social interaction that has been found to be related to print awareness and academic success. Oftentimes the types of comments that parents make during joint book reading link back to experiences familiar to the child during routine activities such as "Remember when we went to the zoo?" or "Remember your last birthday party?". Overtime, this type of reminiscing may aid children in understanding how they fit into a larger social world.

Parents' beliefs about joint book reading routines are also associated with how regularly they practice such activities. Parents who believe that book reading is important are more likely to read to their children on a regular basis and their children, in turn, are more likely to ask to be read to than in families where less value is placed on reading. Again, we are faced with the dilemma of which set of behaviors causes the establishment of regular routines. Do families who value book reading cause their children to read more or do children who like to read cause their parents to create more book reading routines? The answer to this question is not a simple one – as we have pointed out both parents and children contribute to the creation of routines over time. Let us now consider stability of routines over time and how they are associated to child developmental outcomes.

There is some longitudinal evidence to suggest that stability, or predictability, in routines over time is associated with more optimal outcomes for children during the preschool and early school years. Families that practice regular and meaningful routines such as dinnertime and weekend activities when their children are of preschool age have children who perform better academically in the early school years. Further, when routines are disrupted and decline in importance during these formative years, children are at greater risk for developing behavioral problems associated with poorer school performance. Some researchers have found that even under highly stressful conditions, such as low-income single parent households, boys benefit academically and emotionally from regular and predictable routines. Authors have speculated that more routinized homes provide children with a sense of control and reduce the likelihood of developing behavioral problems that thwart school success. Recall, the early establishment of daily routines is often associated with the child's sense of competence and self-reliance.

While stability of routines during the preschool and early school years is associated with academic success and a sense of self-assurance, the converse is also true. Environments characterized by persistent chaos and lack of order over time bode poorly for child development. Children exposed to high degrees of environmental stress frequently experience a lack of order and unpredictability on a daily basis. Limited economic resources, environmental crowding, parental work stress, inaccessible transportation, and poor-quality childcare have all been found to contribute to parents' feelings of hassle and burden that compromises their ability to carry out daily routines. This is not to say that predictable routines require lavish environmental support. This is certainly not the case. There is convincing research evidence that supports the notion that families who are able to create more predictable routines under challenging environmental conditions are able to protect their children from some of the harmful effects of limited economic resources. However, it should also be noted that when environmental stressors pile up it is more difficult for families to organize their daily routines and their children are placed at greater risk for developing academic and social-behavioral problems. Let us now consider some of the ways in which routines have been found to be associated with social and behavioral development.

We have already mentioned that the predictability of routines may be associated with children's emerging sense of competence of self assurance. There is also some evidence to suggest that regularity of routines is associated with controlling and regulating behavior. A major developmental task for preschool and early elementary school age children is learning how to control their behavior. Whether it is 'getting the jitters' out of their legs as they squirm in their seats waiting for the end of a school day or controlling an impulse to hit their baby sister, children learn to control their behavior, in part, by attending to routines that have order and consequences. The most obvious of these would be discipline routines that parents create to dissuade children from 'acting out', throwing temper tantrums, and learning the basic rules of the household. Families vary considerably in terms of the types of discipline routines that they create. Just as we noted that predictability and regularity of mealtime and book reading routines was associated with more positive outcomes, the same holds true for discipline routines. Consistency is the key element in most discipline routines – although they should never be carried out with harsh control.

Much of the research literature on routines and discipline has evolved out of concern for behavior monitoring for children with developmental disabilities. For families with a child with a developmental disability, common household routines such as washing the dishes and preparing dinner are often interrupted by the child's demand for attention. In some cases, the family's routines are disrupted to the extent that daily life is put on hold to attend to the needs of one child. In these circumstances, the routines need to be put back in order by measured discipline of the child who is upsetting family life. Oftentimes this can be affected in relative short order with the use of behavior management techniques.

When we consider discipline routines and behavior management the focus is primarily on setting consequences for unacceptable behavior. There are other aspects of children's routines that may also be associated with regulating behavior. The emotional investment in carrying out routines over time may foster stronger connections within the family unit. The creation of these emotional bonds in routine settings such as dinnertime, weekends, and special celebrations (i.e., birthdays, Thanksgiving) have been found to be associated with aspects of mental health and well-being of children. The empirical literature has focused primarily on children in the later school years and adolescence. In these studies, the importance of family routines and emotional investment made during these gatherings have been found to be related to lower rates of problematic drinking, sexual risk taking, anxiety problems, and somatic complaints. Pertinent to our focus on early childhood is how the meaning conveyed during these routines is related to parents' satisfaction with their marital relationship. Some research has indicated that couples with preschool age children who ascribe more emotional connections during their family routines are more satisfied with their marriages. Why is this important for child development? Considerable research has documented the adverse effects of unhappy marriages on children. Parents who experience marital distress tend to be less effective as parents thus placing their children at risk for problems. In this regard, stable and meaningful routines may bode for better marriages which in turn allow parents to attend more fully to all the caretaking tasks we previously outlined.

There is some evidence that for children of kindergarten age, regular routines and the emotional investment made in continuing them over time is associated with lower frequency of behavior problems as assessed by teachers and school nurses. The reason for this pattern of results is likely multifold. First, as we have noted, regularity of routines may provide behavioral guides for children such that they are able to follow a sequence, or steps, of events. These are crucial skills that come into play when entering a kindergarten classroom. Learning how to get in and stay in line is a monumental task for many children and often one of the settings where teachers note misbehavior. Children who understand how to follow a sequence of steps embedded in routines may be better equipped to follow directions and comprehend structure of a school day. Success in accomplishing 'good line behavior' may, in turn, lead to feelings of self-confidence and assurance that the next challenge – learning the alphabet – is also one that can be conquered. This may be a somewhat simplistic description of a relatively complex set of developmental achievements. However, the point to be made here is that the order and predictability experienced in the home translates to school settings as well.

Cultural Variations in Children's Routines

Culture refers to the shared meaning of a group of people and the shared values, beliefs, and attitudes that are expressed through practices. One of the reasons that developmental psychologists are interested in the study of routines is because of the variations in daily activities across cultures. For example, while all children are likely to engage in some sort of play activity during the early preschool years the types of objects that they play with will vary by culture. Children in European American homes will often play with toys associated with children's movies (such as stuffed animals from *The Lion King*) and with objects such as toy miniatures of dolls, cars, dishes, or telephones. In Chinese homes, children tend to have a modest number of play objects in relation to American homes, typically having a few toy cars or dolls. There are other ways, however, in which cultural variations in routines also express how development is tightly regulated to conform to values held by societies. These values and mores can be detected in the practices of some of the routines we have already examined such as feeding, sleeping, and mealtime.

The time at which infants are weaned from the breast differs across cultures. For example, in Japanese and Philippine communities, infants are typically weaned before their first birthday. In rural Mexican families, infants are weaned around 4 months of age and in West African families, infants are often weaned at about 20 months of age. On the other hand, Caucasian infants are typically weaned between the ages of 1 and 2 years. The timing at which solid foods are introduced into an infant's diet and the child is weaned from the breast depends, in part, on judgments made by society as to when children are 'old enough' to begin to eat on their own. Thus, the timings associated with age related routines are very much embedded in cultural contexts. One area that has received considerable empirical attention is how mealtime routine practices vary across cultures, particularly in the care and feeding of young infants and preschool age children. Intuitively, it is easy to think of variations among rural and urban communities, economically thriving cultures vs. those with strained resources, and between violent and safe neighborhoods. However, as most of the empirical literature has been directed toward individualistic vs. collectivistic cultures, our discussion will focus on these cultures. Differences between these cultures typically revolve around themes of whether the culture holds values for independence and autonomy (e.g., individualism) or places relative value on group cohesiveness and contributing to the betterment of the group (e.g., collectivism). Such differences can be seen in terms of each culture's use of highchairs and infant seats in feeding routines. With respect to feeding routines, comparisons made among primarily Caucasian American, Filipino American, Pacific Islanders native to Hawaii, and Japanese American families have found differences in mealtime practices. For example, Filipino American mothers are more likely to hold their infants in their laps and spoon-feed them in comparison to American mothers. Researchers consider this a reflection of Filipino American mothers' concern for good behavior and conduct and that it is only once the child can be fully competent should they be allowed to feed themselves. In contrast, American mothers are said to foster independence in their young infants and allow them to eat finger foods (i.e., breakfast cereals, crackers) at a younger age than their Filipino age mates. Tolerance for movement away from the dining table also varies by culture. Native-born Hawaiians are more likely to allow their toddler to roam around the kitchen with food in his hand than their neighbors of Japanese descent. These differences are thought to arise from cultural variations in values held for conduct of the individual and the group.

We previously discussed how mealtime conversations may be associated with such child outcomes as literacy skills and academic performance. The topics of conversation vary systematically by culture. American families are more likely to engage in conversations about events that happened to individuals during the day. These are frequently referred to as 'today' stories – "What happened at school today?" "How was work today?" "Did you score a goal in the game today?" Researchers suggest that the focus of 'today' conversations is to highlight individual accomplishments. In contrast, Japanese and Taiwanese families have been observed to engage in daily conversations with their young children that revolve more around group activities and planning for the future. These types of conversations are proposed to reinforce the predominance of group needs over individual accomplishments.

Behaviors during book reading routines in young children are also found to vary by culture. For example, research has found that when compared to Caucasian mothers, African-American mothers ask significantly fewer questions when reading with a young child. Caucasian children are more likely to respond to the mother's questions, while African-American children elicit more spontaneous questions. Young Japanese children are also more likely to mimic their mother's labeling during stories than American children, while American children are more likely to produce labeling after information-seeking questions from the mother.

Discipline routines also vary by culture. Young children get into trouble for different reasons depending on which culture they live in. While parents in American culture may punish their 4-year-old for backing the car out of the garage (an event actually noted in the research literature) they will also speak of it with some pride as evidence of their child's ingenuity and independence. Parents in Taiwan, however, will more likely discipline their preschool age children for causing shame to the family such as whining in public over an Aunt's refusal to allow the child to ride a mechanical pony in a shopping mall (another example drawn from the literature). We provide these examples to illustrate that discipline routines created in the early years will be measured in accordance to cultural values and what counts as a transgression.

Our discussion of routines in the context of families is by no means exhaustive. Different patterns in co-sleeping, childcare routines, and children in the workplace are also observed across cultures. In fact, the American routine of putting children in a crib to sleep by themselves through the night is an anomaly when compared to other cultures. For instance, research has found that Mayan mothers believe co-sleeping is important to the psychological development of infants. Co-sleeping in Mayan families is not only seen as a protective behavior against early mortality, but also as a way to socialize infants into a group as early as possible. On the other hand, Americans do not typically support co-sleeping as it opposes their cultural values of independence and autonomy.

Solitary Routines

Thus far, we have discussed children's routines in the context of interacting with others – primarily family members and teachers in the preschool and early school years. Young children can also develop routines that are more solitary in nature. Following our definition of routine as a sequence of behaviors (rather than an isolated habit), we can consider some individual activities as part of the child's routine daily life. Recent surveys suggest that young children under the age of 6 spend 2 h a day watching television. Further, a 2003 survey conducted by the Kaiser Family Foundation of more than 1000 parents of children between birth and 6 years of age in the US found that 36% of those surveyed reported their children had television sets in their bedrooms. For families with children between the ages of 4 and 6, the rate was 43%. Not surprisingly, for those families where there was heavy television viewing in the children's room there was less book reading in the home. Although there is not good research documenting whether children's television viewing would meet our criteria for a full fledged routine, we do know that higher rates of television viewing is associated with consuming more snack foods and lower rates of family mealtimes. Thus, at the very least heavy television viewing may be said to disrupt other routines that have been shown to have a positive effect on children's development.

Another type of solitary routine in the early childhood years is the development of repetitive behavior routines. The incidence of these behaviors is very low in young childhood, although 2–4-year-olds exhibit the highest rates of such repetitive behaviors among young children. Research indicates that repetitive behavior routines begin to disappear around the age of 6. These repetitive behavior routines in children are often observed in children's games, such as tag, hopscotch, or even in reciting rhymes about stepping on a crack. In these examples, behaviors are followed to ward off harm, and they fulfill our criteria of routines in that they must follow an ordered sequence of steps. Other repetitive behaviors exhibited by young children might include requests to hear the same story over and over again, or to watch a video several times in a row. This insistence on repetition is used by children to prolong a situation in which they are comfortable and to reduce any anxious feelings they might have.

Summary

In this article we have outlined several of the routines that children engage in during the early childhood years. What may appear as relatively mundane events such as getting fed, going to sleep, and being asked to clean up after yourself are integral parts of social and cognitive development. These are the everyday aspects of development that foster, in part, the child's growing sense of competence and allow him or her to become more fully engaged with the social world. Because routines include an ordered sequence of steps, they provide behavioral guides for children that translate into more complex cognitive achievements during the elementary school years. The repetition of routines over time and the social interactions that accompany many of these routines provide the child with a sense of belonging and connection to the family and to peers that promote well-being. Many of these practices vary by culture to reinforce the values held by society. Thus, something as simple as saying please and thank you at the dinner table can serve to aid the young child in becoming a competent and self-assured member of society.

See also: Discipline and Compliance; Future Orientation; Family Influences; Language Development: Overview; Literacy.

Suggested Readings

Fiese BH (2006) *Family Routines and Rituals.* New Haven, CT: Yale University Press.

Fiese BH, Tomcho T, Douglas M, Josephs K, Poltrock S, and Baker T (2002) Fifty years of research on naturally occurring rituals: Cause for celebration? *Journal of Family Psychology* 16: 381–390.

Fivush R, Reese E, and Haden CA (2006) Elaborating on elaborations: Role of maternal reminiscing style in cognitive and socioemotional development. *Child Development* 77: 1568–1588.

Hofferth SL and Sandberg JF (2001) How American children spend their time. *Journal of Marriage and the Family* 63: 295–308.

Huston AC, Wright JC, Marquis J, and Green SB (1999) How young children spend their time: Television and other activities. *Developmental Psychology* 35: 912–925.

Kubicek LF (2002) Fresh perspectives on young children and family routines. *Zero to Three* 22: 4–9.

Larson RW, Wiley AR, and Branscomb KR (2006) Family mealtime as a context for development and socialization. *New Directions for Child and Adolescent Development. No. 111.* San Francisco: Jossey Bass.

Martini M (2002) How mothers in four American cultural groups shape infant learning during mealtimes. *Zero to Three* 22: 14–20.

Parmar P, Harkness S, and Super CM (2004) Asian and Euro-American parents' ethnotheories of play and learning: Effects on preschool children's home routines and school behaviour. *Journal of Behavioral Development* 28: 97–104.

Rideout VJ, Vandewater EA, and Wartella EA (2003) *Zero to Six: Electronic Media in the Lives of Infants, Toddlers, and Preschoolers.* Menlo Park, CA: Henry J. Kaiser Foundation.

Sprunger LW, Boyce WT, and Gaines JA (1985) Family-infant congruence: Routines and rhythmicity in a family adaptations to a young infant. *Child Development* 56: 564–572.

Weisner T (2002) Ecocultural understanding of children's developmental pathways. *Human Development* 45: 275–281.

Safety and Childproofing

D C Schwebel, University of Alabama at Birmingham, Birmingham, AL, USA

Glossary

Active intervention – An intervention that requires the individual or someone else (e.g., his/her adult supervisor) to complete some sort of action or behavior in order to maintain safety; usually the action is completed on repeated occasions.

Electrocution – An injury caused by coming in contact with electrical power; occurs most frequently to young children when they insert fingers or objects into electrical outlets.

Intentional injury – Scientific term for injuries resulting from self-inflicted wounds or abuse by others.

Motor vehicle crashes – Scientific term for automobile accidents or car crashes.

Passive intervention – An intervention that prevents injuries passively; once it is completed, neither the potential victim nor others (e.g., adult supervisors) needs to do anything further to be safe in the future.

Pedestrian injuries – Accidental injuries that occur while a person is walking, running, or playing on streets, sidewalks, driveways, or parking lots. Most often, the injury is caused when a person is struck by a motor vehicle.

Suffocation – An injury that occurs when someone is unable to breathe.

Temperament – Manifested by how a person reacts and behaves. Temperament is driven by both internal and external stimuli, is based in biological processes but influenced by the environment, and appears early in life and remains relatively stable across time, situations, and environments.

Unintentional injury – Scientific term for accidents, or accidental injuries.

Introduction

Between their first and fourth birthdays, more American children die from injuries than from all other causes of death combined. According to the latest data available from the US Centers for Disease Control and Prevention, over 3000 American children ages 3 years and younger die from injuries annually; a very large majority of these injuries are unintentional, and a smaller percentage the result of purposeful homicide. Of course, a much larger number of children experience nonfatal injuries each year. Roughly 2 million injury-related emergency room visits are reported annually in the US for children ages 0–3 years, and nearly every American child incurs several injuries each year that are treated with band-aids, ice, or other minor first aid techniques.

As a result of these and similar statistics, parenting websites, magazines, and classes routinely teach parents how important it is that they take steps to protect their young children's safety. This article addresses child safety and the ways parents might protect children from injury from the perspective of behavioral science. The entry is divided into three sections. First, epidemiological data on the frequency and types of injuries young children incur are reviewed. Second, the broad risk factors that are attributed to risk for injury among infants and toddlers are discussed, with an emphasis on the psychological risk factors. Third, the major types of injuries these children experience are reviewed. This section includes discussion concerning the ways parents and others can prevent those injuries, with an emphasis on the two most effective techniques: safeguarding the environment and careful supervision of young children.

Epidemiological Background through Early Development

Before their fourth birthday, children experience remarkable cognitive, social, perceptual, and motor development

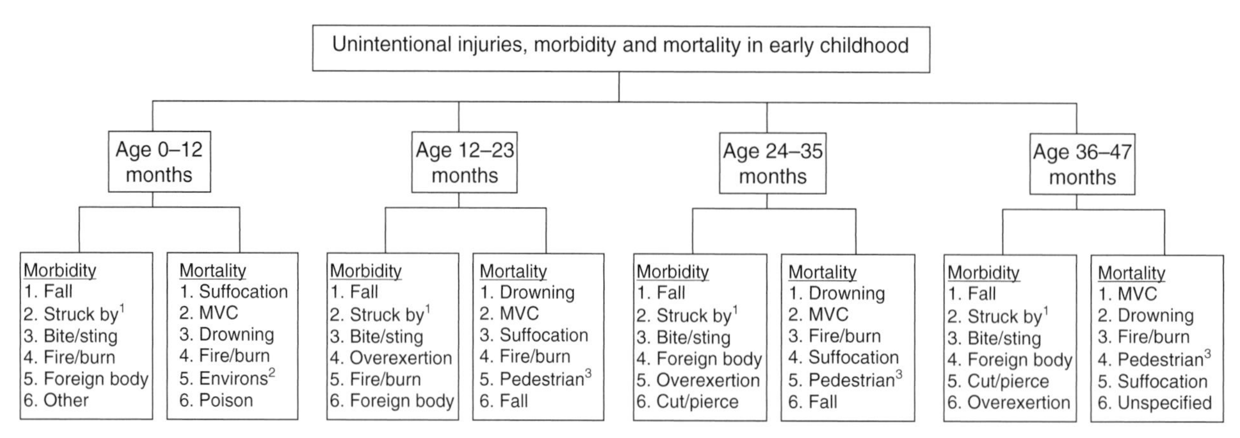

Notes. Data downloaded from National Center for Injury Prevention and Control, Centers for Disease Control website, on 21August, 2006. Morbidity data is from 2004 and mortality data from 2003. Data represent full population of the US. MVC, motor vehicle crash.
[1] Struck by refers to being struck by or against moving objects or other people.
[2] Environs refers to the natural physical environment.
[3] Pedestrian refers to injuries suffered while a pedestrian in driveways, roads, or parking lots.

Figure 1 The leading causes of morbidity (emergency room visits) and mortality, children ages 0–3 years.

growth. These maturational changes influence children in a multitude of ways; among those influences are the child's risks for different types of injuries. As shown in **Figure 1**, some types of injury remain concerning throughout early childhood – included among these are nonfatal injuries from falls, being struck by objects, and being bit or stung by animals as well as fatal injuries from drowning, motor vehicle crashes, and fires/burns.

Other types of injuries are particularly concerning only at certain ages. In fact, there is evidence that particular developmental windows – as measured by how many months old the child is – may greatly elevate risk for particular injuries during early childhood. Falls down stairways peak, for example, between the ages of 6 and 12 months, as children develop the ability to crawl. Burns from hot liquids and vapors are particularly concerning from the ages of 12–17 months, when toddlers begin walking and reaching for objects of interest. Pedestrian injuries peak later – during the fourth year of life – when children are playing outdoors more frequently, but have poor awareness of the dangers of motor vehicles.

All in all, researchers conclude that a child's development plays a major role in injury risk – but that there are significant risks at all ages. Fortunately, there is also a range of effective prevention techniques at each age, as discussed below.

Psychological Risk Factors for Child Injury

Risk for pediatric injury is multifaceted. Part of the risk is clearly environmental – the safety of the home, school, and community is closely related to a child's chances of getting hurt or remaining unharmed. Such environmental risks are touched upon in the present review, but remain more the domain of engineers, geographers, city planners, and other specialists. Other aspects of risk are behavioral – and these psychologically influenced factors form the foci of the present review. Behavioral risks particularly relevant to a child's injury risk include his or her own behaviors and thoughts, as well as the influences from parents, child care providers, and the community.

Child-Oriented Risk Factors

As parents who have two or more children will readily admit you, even very young children have distinct personalities, ways of behaving, and ways of reacting to the world. These differences are transparent among siblings starting soon after birth, even when the siblings are born of the same biological parents and raised in the same household, and those individual differences influence most all aspects of the child's development, including risk for unintentional injury. Individual differences of interest can be divided into three broad domains: motor skills, cognitive skills, and temperament. All three appear to play a role in children's safety.

Differences in motor skills – including balance, strength, and coordination – seem relatively simple on the surface, and are driven largely by children's age and capabilities. One would not expect, for example, that a 3-month-old infant might accidentally fall into an ungated swimming pool simply because children at that age do not yet have the mobility to reach a swimming pool. An unsupervised child approaching her third birthday, however, is at great risk for drowning in an ungated swimming pool but is much less likely to drown in a small bucket of water left by a parent in the bathroom.

Although part of motor development is as simple as having the mobility to propel oneself to a location where it is possible to 'accidentally' encounter an ungated swimming pool, other aspects of motor development are more complicated. Reaching and grasping ability, for example, develop rapidly during the first 2 years of life, and influence the child's capacity and likelihood of grasping dangerous objects such as scissors, matches, or screwdrivers. As infants develop visual and perceptual skills, brightly colored objects – including poisonous houseplants and flowers, paint chips with lead in them, and cigarette lighters – become appealing and hazardous objects to put in one's hands and mouth.

The tremendous growth in strength, balance, and agility during the early years of human life is accompanied by similarly rapid growth in thinking skills. This cognitive growth, and the rate at which it occurs, affects children's safety just as development of motor skills does. As an example, normally developing children gain the ability to recognize causality during the toddler and preschool years. If a child has the ability to recognize that walking on a wall well above the ground might result in injury if she were to fall, she will typically become more cautious about walking on that wall. Without development of the thinking skills to recognize that falling from a height might result in injury, children have no reason to exhibit caution in such environments. Similarly, if a toddler develops the ability to listen to, remember, and follow directions, then he might be protected from injury following warnings from parents or other adults. A growing body of research suggests that parents spend a tremendous amount of time teaching toddlers what they should and should not do, and encouraging toddlers to learn and follow directions; prominent among these warnings are concerns about child safety.

The development of cognitive skills also aids children to judge the safety of environments themselves, without adult input. Young children are quite poor at recognizing whether particular environments possess danger or not. Recognizing one's own abilities and limitations, the dangers in particular environments, and the potential harm that can come from engaging in particular behaviors are important lessons that children learn and hone as they grow, and much of this growth begins during the toddler years.

Finally, individual differences in temperament play a significant role in children's safety. Temperament, which is defined as the way people react to both internal and external stimuli, and which is influenced by both biological drives and external influences, appears to play a significant role in how children behave when faced with hazards. Children who are highly impulsive, and who have poor ability to inhibit impulses when exposed to desirable or novel stimuli, are more likely to injure themselves. Children who are more controlled, and who think before acting, remain safer.

Temperamental activity level also plays a role in young children's safety. Active children – who run, jump, climb, and explore more frequently and more quickly – are prone to injuries at a higher rate than children who do not behave in those ways. This is likely due to exposure: if children are exposed to more dangerous situations, simple laws of probability suggest they may experience injury more often.

One final individual difference that impacts a toddler's safety is his or her ability to learn from previous actions. Consider a child who manages to climb on top of a table, and then topples off it, injuring herself. Some children will learn from this experience, and avoid climbing on tables or to other elevated locations. Other children fail to learn from these experiences – and in some cases are even motivated to try them repeatedly. Such differences are likely to impact a child's risk for injury.

Parent-Oriented Risk Factors

Since young children are cognitively immature, motorically undeveloped, and socially dependent, parents play an immense role in protecting their safety. In fact, injury scientists argue that adult supervision is probably the most important behavioral mechanism available to prevent unintentional injury in very young children. Conversely, poor supervision is described as the leading behavioral cause of injury in young children. Why, then, is supervision so lacking in many households?

One problem is cultural. American parents tend to be overcommitted – they are busy people with many responsibilities. They are chronically fatigued; easily distracted by work and home responsibilities, social engagements, and entertainment outlets such as the television and Internet; and they spend less time playing with and engaging their children than parents in many other cultures or eras. Beyond cultural contributions, parents also fail to recognize the importance of supervision to protecting child safety. Parents frequently assume children know what they can or cannot do safely, but this assumption is false. Many parents also erroneously believe they have safeguarded their home extensively, and therefore do not see a need to supervise. Finally, some parents view injuries as accidental, or the result of fate or bad luck, and therefore unavoidable. Each of these misconceptions causes parents to inadequately supervise their children, and places young children at risk.

Along with misconceptions about the seriousness and risks of unintentional injury, parenting deficits play a significant role in children's safety. Parents who have deficits due to disabilities or illness – for example, parents who abuse substances, who are depressed, or who are chronically ill – have children with higher rates of injury, presumably because adult supervision is inadequate in those households. Single parents, who have less time and resources, also have children with slightly higher risk of injury compared to children with two parents in the home.

Finally, parent personality and parenting style play a role in child safety. Parents who score high in conscientiousness seem to have safer children – perhaps because those parents conscientiously safeguard the home and supervise their children. Parents who spend more time with the children, and who are more skilled in their parenting techniques, protect children; those who are less skilled and spend less time have children with greater risk.

In summary, parents play an absolutely critical role in protecting their children from injury. Much of this role is active – parent must actively supervise their children, anticipating dangerous behaviors and preventing them before they occur. They must also actively teach safety – training their youngsters to grow into safe decision makers and safe actors. Other aspects of parenting are more passive. Parents must take the initiative to safeguard their homes by removing environmental hazards, but following that process children are protected from injury in the home as a result of their parents' efforts.

Risks Associated with Child Care Centers

Especially in the US, a growing number of young children attend child care centers outside the home during weekdays. Most research suggests the risk of injury in child care centers is roughly equivalent to that in homes, or perhaps slightly less. Because government agencies monitor the safety of licensed child care centers (which comprise many but not all of the centers where children spend their days), the physical environments of child care centers tend to be comparatively safe. Supervisors of children – those individuals working in the child care centers – are often charged with supervising the safety of large numbers of children, but have some level of dedication to children, professional training, and recognition of hazards in children's environments.

From a supervision perspective, many of the individual difference risks associated with parents are also true of child care workers. It is unclear if professional child care workers fully recognize the limitations of children, understand the fact that most injuries can be prevented (i.e., they are not truly accidental), or comprehend all the tasks needed to safeguard a child's environment. Compounding risk are the facts that child care jobs are repetitive and therefore somewhat boring at times, that management of large numbers of children for long periods can be emotionally exhausting, and that salaries of child care workers are usually quite low, resulting in a workforce with comparatively poor education and training.

Family, Community, and Cultural Risk Factors

Beyond children, their parents, and their child care providers, children's safety is influenced by broader contextual factors such as extended family, culture, and the community.

Depending on frequency of contact with the extended family, children's safety may or may not be greatly influenced by grandparents, aunts, uncles, older siblings, and other adult family members. The influence of extended family on children's safety comes from two directions. First, the mere presence of more adults in the home tends to increase adult supervision of children, and therefore protect children from injury more effectively. Second, in many families there is assistance from extended family to the parents in supervision and babysitting, and in that way the personality, behavior, and style of other adults directly influences the safety of the children in a way that parallels the influence of parents.

The topic of culture greatly overlaps, of course, with a number of other injury risk factors, including the role of the extended family in a child's life. But more broadly, culture influences the ways children, parents, families, and even communities behave. As an example, some cultures promote independence and risk-taking – although positive in many ways for children's development, such encouragement can lead to higher injury rates. In some cultures around the world, parents even guide children to use sharp knives and fire independently at very young ages – before they can even walk! Other cultures promote caution and a heavy reliance on parents through early childhood – also positive in many ways, this sort of behavior protects children somewhat from injury. The influences of culture on children's safety remain complex and poorly understood, but researchers agree that culture plays a critical role in children's safety. Researchers also agree that cultures differ in the ways they promote parental supervision, child risk-taking and exploration, and how to best respond to children's injury incidents. Such cultural differences inevitably affect future injury risk.

The influence of the community, more broadly, is enwrapped in individual differences, culture, and societal expectations. It also overlaps greatly with poverty or wealth, with government systems, and with the culture of the people living in the community. Despite these complications, it is indisputable that the community a child lives in effects his or her safety and risk for injury. Some examples are straightforward: in communities with older homes, lead-based paint chips are present, and create a risk for poisoning. In urban communities, pedestrian injuries are more common; in rural communities, there is risk of injury from agricultural equipment. Other examples are a bit more complicated. In some places, community playgrounds are constructed in safe ways; in other communities, they possess many dangers; and in still other communities, there are no playgrounds whatsoever so children are at risk while they play elsewhere. Stray dogs create risk for dog bites in some communities; stray gunshots create risk for bullet wounds in others.

Bottom line: where a child lives makes a difference in the extent and types of dangers to which a child is exposed, but no child is immune from the risk of injury.

The Types of Injuries Children Incur, and Practices that Help Prevent Those Injuries

As reviewed at the start of this article, young children are at risk for a wide range of injury types. In this final section, each major type of injury is discussed, describing the dangers involved and the recommended prevention mechanisms. In doing so, it is important to differentiate two types of injury prevention techniques, active prevention and passive prevention. Active prevention requires active behavior by the potential victim or his/her supervisor. This active behavior might include a toddler who follows his parent's rule to not play with bottles of medication, a parent who decides to supervise carefully her 2-year-old on the playground instead of reading the newspaper, or a parent who prevents his infant from grabbing a cigarette lighter on the floor.

Unlike active prevention, passive prevention involves changing the environment permanently (or semi-permanently) so that injuries will not occur. Examples include legislation that toys designed for infants do not have any small pieces that could present choking hazards; installation of gates at the top of a stairwell to prevent young toddlers from falling downstairs; and changing the temperature on one's hot water heater to avoid scalding injuries to young children. In general, passive prevention does not require any decisions or actions by potential victims (or their supervisors) once they are instituted; active prevention requires decisions and/or actions to be maintained or continuously instituted.

Both active and passive prevention can be highly effective in preventing injury to infants and toddlers. In some circles, passive prevention techniques are viewed to be more effective. This is largely because they remain effective indefinitely: once they are done, they are done. Active interventions can be equally effective, but do require maintenance; they must be completed each time the hazard presents itself.

Below, a series of major injury types that young children are exposed to are considered. In discussing them, both active and passive prevention techniques that have proved to be successful are reviewed. The injury types are presented in alphabetical order and prevention strategies briefly summarized in **Table 1**.

Burns

Burns are extremely painful injuries that are almost always preventable with appropriate changes to the

Table 1 Primary injury risks to young children, and examples of active and passive prevention strategies

Injury risk	*Active intervention example*	*Passive intervention example*
Burns	Turn handles of pots toward the inside when cooking	Turn water heater temperature to a level that will not scald young children
Choking	Cut grapes into quarters before feeding toddler	Move crib to location of the room out of reach from window blind cords
Cuts, scrapes, bumps, and bruises	Carefully supervise young children so that they run on grass at a park instead of concrete	Store scissors and knives in a drawer beyond the reach of young children
Dog and other animal bites	Teach children to avoid petting dogs while the dogs are eating	Place sleeping dogs in cages away from children
Drowning	Teach children to swim	Install fencing around backyard swimming pools
Electrocution	Supervise children carefully when they play in locations that are not 'childproofed'	Distribute and install outlet covers to at-risk families and homes
Falls	Supervise children carefully while climbing ladders on playground equipment	Install railings that extend to floor of balconies
Firearm injuries	Use firearms only when toddlers are not present	Store guns in locked cabinets, and separate from ammunition
Injuries from agricultural and other machinery	Teach young children how to safely operate basic farm equipment	Keep barn doors locked, and keys inaccessible to young children
Motor vehicle crashes	Be sure children are properly restrained, even for short trips	Improve automobile engineering to reduce impact of motor vehicle crashes on small passengers
Pedestrian and bicycling injuries	Hold hands with young children while walking in parking lots	Place speed bumps on heavily trafficked residential streets where children live
Poisoning	Supervise children carefully when they are in unfamiliar homes where poisons may be accessible	Manufacture all medication containers with 'childproof' caps
Suffocation	Prevent young children from playing with plastic bags	Avoid use of plastic bags in trash cans in the home

Note. See text for more detailed discussion of injury types and prevention strategies.

household environment. Burns occur in a number of locations, and for a number of reasons.

To state the obvious, what makes fire can cause burn injuries, and what makes fire is often of interest to curious toddlers. Matches, cigarette lighters, candles, and actual fires (in fireplaces or campfire settings) are among the biggest culprits of unintentional pediatric flame-burn injuries. Prevention is remarkably simple but surprisingly underutilized. Matches and lighters should never be left within reach of unsupervised children; even child-proof lighters can be lit by moderately persistent young children. The same goes for lit objects. Candles are highly entertaining to developing children, who enjoy the flickers, the novelty, and the beauty (as well as the odors, in the case of scented candles). But, of course, most young children do not recognize the danger in touching lit objects such as candles and will invariably attempt to touch flames if they are not prohibited from doing so by some combination of adult intervention and safe placement of the candle.

Open fires – whether in fireplaces, campfire pits, or cooking areas – are also highly dangerous to curious toddlers. Infants and toddlers learn and develop by exploring the world around them, and much of this exploration comes from touching objects with the mouth and hands. Because young children typically have no concept of the danger present in touching fire, intense supervision near open flames is absolutely essential.

Another dangerous area for burns is in the kitchen. Cooking while holding an infant is not advised – there is too much risk for the infant to reach to touch hot pots, pans, or dishes. Pots left on the stove should have no handles dangling outward, where curious toddlers might reach for them and tip boiling water onto themselves. Oven doors should be latched tight or supervised carefully. Hot dishes and drinks should never be carried over or near young children, where they may be bumped or pushed onto vulnerable youngsters.

When the cooking is done and it is time to feed an infant or toddler, burn risks continue. Hungry youngsters can be demanding and fussy, and neglectful parents might begin feeding the child without considering the heat of the food. Food that is too hot can burn children's mouths; the best strategy is for parents to touch or taste hot food before feeding. A second option is use of commercially available utensils and dishes that signify when food is hot by changing colors.

Another significant risk for burns in the household is scalds from tap water – either to the hand in a sink or to the body in a bathtub. In fact, scald burns are much, much more frequent in young children than are burns from flames. Prevention of scalds is again simple but often neglected. Parents should reduce the temperature of hot water heaters to lower levels, and should always test water before allowing infants or toddlers to touch it.

Two other types of burns are worth mentioning, house fires and sunburns. Although seemingly disparate, both are unique in that the risk for these burns is as great for older children and adults as it is for young children.

House fires are started by a wide range of mechanisms, including lightning strikes, human error (e.g., unwatched candles that tip over), faulty electrical wiring, dangerous play by children, and intentional setting. In all cases, house fires can be highly dangerous to young children, who sleep more often and more deeply than adults and who have less mobility to escape a burning home. Infants and toddlers in cribs usually cannot escape without adult assistance.

Two aspects of prevention are recommended. First, families must work to prevent fires from starting – this can be done through taking care with open flames, inspecting and repairing suspicious electrical wiring, updating outdated electrical connections and outlets, and keeping children away from dangerous fire sources like cigarette lighters and matches. Second, families must be prepared in the event that a house fire begins. Perhaps the most critical preparation is installation and maintenance of smoke detectors throughout the home. An astounding number of homes are without these inexpensive, easy-to-install, and highly effective devices. Efforts to distribute and install smoke detectors are moderately successful, although long-term maintenance of functioning batteries in those detectors is modest. Beyond installation and maintenance of smoke detectors, families must develop escape plans from their home, determine how infants and toddlers will be rescued from their rooms if asleep, and teach children emergency telephone numbers that should be called in the event of a fire.

Risk of sunburn has been prominent in popular news outlets, with many scientists arguing environmental pollution has resulted in increased risk of sunburn – and subsequent skin cancer as a result of those burns. Sunscreen with high levels of sun protection factor (SPF) are recommended; to protect the eyes, sunglasses that block dangerous sun radiation are recommended, even for young children.

Although risk of skin cancer in childhood is low, scientific evidence suggests exposure to sun and sunburn during childhood correlates strongly with incidence of skin cancer in adulthood. Parents are advised to keep children out of the sun during midday hours; to use sun lotion generously; to apply sun-blocking lip balm to children's lips; and to use sun-blocking clothing, hats, and sunglasses. Sunscreen should be re-applied frequently, especially when children are swimming or perspiring. Parents should also model safe behavior by protecting themselves in the same way they protect their children.

Choking

The propensity of infants and toddlers to put things into their mouths places them at great risk of choking injuries, both from foreign objects and from food. Foreign objects of greatest concern are small parts that might break off toys, small toys designed for older children, natural materials such as rocks and twigs, and small household objects like coins and buttons. When swallowed – usually unintentionally – by young children, these objects can cause very serious internal injuries or death. Similar outcomes can result from chunks of food; of greatest concern in this domain are small round foods such as grapes, candies, and chunks of hot dog.

The best preventive measure is to keep small objects away from curious infants and toddlers – in other words, remove potential accidents from the environment. Supervision can help, as well. If dangerous foods are consumed, they should be divided into smaller pieces – quarters or halves of grapes, for example, are much safer than full ones.

Cuts, Scrapes, Bumps, and Bruises

Although rarely fatal, cuts, scrapes, bumps and bruises comprise the majority of daily minor injuries that children incur, and for this reason represent a significant stressor and concern for many parents. Cuts and scrapes result from contact of the skin with rough or sharp surfaces; bumps and bruises usually result from direct severe contact with hard objects. Among toddlers, these injuries can occur from falls (e.g., on driveways or into furniture), from playing with dangerous objects (e.g, scissors, baseball bats), and from play with others (e.g., a kick from a sibling, scratch from a dog, or bump into a playmate).

Prevention is best accomplished actively through supervision and passively through removal of dangerous objects from the environment. Parents should also work to anticipate problems by examining their home (or other environments their children encounter) from the perspective of the child: what objects are potentially appealing, within reach, and dangerous?

Dog and Other Animal Bites

Roughly half of American infants and toddlers live in homes with pets. For the most part, pet–toddler interactions are positive, healthy, and fun for children, parents, and animals. On occasion, however, the interaction can become injurious. The greatest risk occurs when young children disrupt pets – and especially dogs – when the animals do not want to be disrupted. A secondary risk occurs with stray dogs and wild animals.

With pet dogs, trouble occurs primarily because young children do not recognize that there are times when animals prefer not to be pet or bothered – for example, when they are eating, sleeping, or toileting. Young children also fail to recognize that most animals prefer not to be pet on the face or legs. Parents can supervise children to prevent many of these injuries, and can educate children to be careful about when they play with pets. This is true both for children who have pets in their home – and therefore interact regularly with dogs or other animals – as well as for children who do not have pets in their home, but who encounter them periodically when visiting other people's homes.

A related problem with animals is the fact that young children often find pets' toys and balls attractive, and animal–child conflict over ownership of attractive toys can quickly develop. When young children engage in activities like playing with a dog's toy, the animal will become angered and might retaliate by biting. Again, supervision and education are the primary means of prevention.

Along with educating children about the dangers of animal bites, it is necessary also to educate animals. When young, dogs should be exposed to young children so that they understand the excited, rapid movements of toddlers. Many dogs can be successfully trained to permit more aggressive petting typically engaged in by youngsters, and in some cases dogs can even be successfully trained to permit petting while eating or resting.

Of related concern is the risk present from stray dogs and wild animals. Risks vary widely – from bee and wasp stings to attacks by hungry stray dogs to snakebites experienced by children playing in wilderness areas. Prevention is rather similar across situations, however. Parents should be educated about the proper reaction to risks they may encounter – in most cases, remaining still and quiet is recommended (along with avoiding disruption of animals' habitat), but in other cases, running away quickly or even climbing trees are the preferred escapes from wild or stray animals. Educated parents must then supervise and protect young children, who may not be able to remember or obey safety precautions independently. Of course, young children should be educated on safe behavior around animals, and will begin to learn those behaviors as they grow older.

Drowning

Drowning is the second-leading cause of death in American children ages 1–3 years (following congenital anomalies). Much to the surprise of many parents, young children can drown not only in swimming pools, lakes, and oceans, but also in bathtubs, toilet bowls, and buckets. In fact, the combination of curiosity to explore the world, developing mobility, and immature motor skills creates a very dangerous situation when infants and toddlers are near water. Prevention both outdoors and in the home is surprisingly straightforward, but also alarmingly unpracticed.

Prevention of outdoor drowning in larger bodies of water (e.g., lakes, rivers, swimming pools, and oceans) is best achieved through three means: (1) careful supervision of children who are swimming or playing near water, (2) use of lifejackets and flotation devices, and (3) installation of fencing around neighborhood swimming pools and, where practical, other waterfronts. Supervision is critical when young children are unprotected near open bodies of water, because children have a tendency to explore their surroundings without recognizing the danger that might be present. Supervisors must be vigilant and constantly alert; fatal drowning in swimming pools can happen, for example, in a matter of minutes. Falls from boats can occur even quicker. Also important is that supervisors remain sober; there is evidence that children are at greater risk of all types of injury when supervised by intoxicated adults.

Use of lifejackets is straightforward – when children fall from boats, for example, proper lifejackets will keep their heads elevated and usually save their lives. Without them, children are much more likely to drown. Installation of fencing is particularly important around private swimming pools. Toddlers who wander unsupervised near backyard pools – either at their own home or at neighbors' – are at great risk.

In the home, risks are present wherever there is water – bathtubs, pails, buckets, and toilet bowls. One of the greatest drowning tragedies that occurs is in the child's own bathtub – a supervising parent might step out briefly to answer the telephone, retrieve a towel, or respond to a sibling's cries – and a bathing infant or toddler drowns while unsupervised. This scenario is most common in infants between the ages of 6 and 12 months. Less common but equally devastating are drowning in uncovered toilet bowls or cleaning pails that have not been emptied. Supervision is the foremost prevention strategy. Also important are environmental changes – closing toilet seat covers and bathroom doors, emptying pails of water, and so on.

Electrocution

Electrical outlets are amazingly appealing to most toddlers. Children seem to enjoy the challenge and novelty of putting fingers, toys, screwdrivers, and any number of other objects in electrical sockets, creating great risk of electrocution injury. There are some bits of good news here, however. The risk of electrocution injury from electrical outlets is one injury risk that parents tend to be aware of. Further, the most effective prevention tool is inexpensive and widely available in the US: small plastic covers that are placed into the socket. Despite the availability, low cost, and reasonably high recognition of the risk of electrical sockets, however, many parents do not install them in their homes, perhaps because they feel their children are at less risk than other children or because they feel they supervise their own children adequately to prevent electrocution injuries. Parental education and wide distribution of the outlet covers are recommended prevention strategies.

Falls

Falls can be particularly devastating injuries to families because they are rarely anticipated, surprisingly common, and have widely varying consequences. Many infants withstand falls from diaper tables, cribs, and other furniture without any consequence whatsoever but others suffer debilitating injuries to the brain, limbs, or joints. Falls in the home (rather than outside the home) are most common among children ages 0–3 years, and frequently occur when a parent is momentarily distracted or neglectful. As an example, a mother may place an infant on the diaper table and realize that no new diapers are available. Instead of carrying the infant with her to retrieve a new diaper, the mother will leave the infant on the table unsupervised for a brief moment, but long enough for the infant to roll off the table and fall to the floor. Another common error is for parents to leave toddlers in a crib with the crib side lowered or unsecured. For example, a fatigued father might place a toddler in bed for a nap, forget to lift the side door, and then, a few minutes later, hear piercing screams from the toddler who attempted to crawl out of the crib, elevated herself over the lowered side, and fell to the floor.

Prevention of falls from diaper tables, cribs, and other furniture requires diligent supervision, anticipation of problems, and maintenance of safe equipment. Parents should never leave infants or toddlers in elevated locations without careful supervision. Crib mattresses must be lowered as young children develop. Infants in 'bouncy chairs' should be placed on the floor rather than on tables, since they might manipulate themselves off the edge of the table. Youngsters should never be left to sleep on beds, sofas, or tables where they might roll off.

Another fall-risk in many American homes is stairways. Falls down stairs can be particularly injurious since the vertical decline is often several feet. Prevention is straightforward: installation of stair gates prevents children from climbing down or up stairs. The gates must be installed both at the top and the bottom of stairways since many children manage to climb partway up a stairwell from the bottom, and then fall down. Finally, researchers have urged the banning of infant walkers, wheeled devices designed to help children learn to walk, partly because many children fall down stairways while using them.

Also in the home, children are at risk of injury when they fall into sharp corners of coffee tables, fireplace hearths, or other household furniture. As one-year-olds develop balancing and walking skills, they topple over almost incessantly. These falls are a normal part of development and are not particularly dangerous in most environments. When the house includes objects with sharp corners, however, toppling toddlers are at risk of cuts and punctures. The recommended solution is installation of padding in potentially dangerous areas.

A final significant fall risk for older toddlers occurs outside the home, at playgrounds. Engineers have made remarkable progress in developing safer playgrounds over the past few decades, but even the safest modern playgrounds contain areas where young children are at risk of falling and injuring themselves. Confounding this fact, there are still thousands of outdated playgrounds across the US and around the world, and the older equipment poses much greater risk than more recent playground constructions. Supervision again ranks as the primary mechanism to prevent playground falls. Other prevention techniques include identification of age-appropriate play areas – toddlers should not climb on equipment designed for 8-year-olds; instruction on safe and unsafe playground behavior; and exploration of which nearby playgrounds might be the safest ones for young children to play on.

Firearm Injuries

Thankfully, firearm injuries to children under the age of 3 years are extremely rare. Unfortunately, however, when they do occur they are very serious and often fatal. Firearm injuries can occur in two ways. First, unsupervised young children can discover loaded guns in their home or elsewhere, begin playing with them, and then accidentally fire the weapon, shooting themselves, a sibling, or a playmate. Second, an adult may be cleaning, storing, or using a firearm with a young child nearby, and it will accidentally or purposefully discharge, striking the young child.

In both cases, prevention relies almost entirely on the adults in the home. Young children should be taught never to touch firearms – but more importantly, adults must be highly conscientious about safe storage and usage of firearms. Guns should be stored unloaded and locked in secure cabinets. Ammunition should be stored elsewhere, and should also be locked. Firearms should rarely be used when children are nearby; if they are used, extreme caution must be taken to prevent accidents.

Injuries from Machinery in Agricultural and Other Settings

Both large and small machinery can be very dangerous to young children. The risk is particularly concerning in agricultural settings, where large machinery with blades, belts, and other dangerous moving parts are widely used. Risks are multiple, but include: (1) falls from elevated equipment; (2) serious cuts and scrapes from sharp parts; and (3) crushing injuries from being run over or crushed inside machinery. Prevention strategies include supervision of young children, placement of fencing and locked doors/garages in carefully selected locations, and early instruction in safe and unsafe behaviors near machinery.

Although children in rural areas have perhaps the greatest risk of injury from machinery due to the agricultural equipment present in that environment, suburban and urban children are not immune. Lawnmowers, paper shredders, and two-, three-, and four-wheel motorized vehicles (e.g., all-terrain vehicles (ATVs), motorcycles) are of particular concern; prevention strategies parallel those used in rural settings.

Motor Vehicle Crashes

The leading cause of death in American children, motor vehicle crashes (or car accidents, in lay terms), are blamed for over 500 mortalities and over 50 000 emergency room visits by children under the age of 4 years in the US annually. A comprehensive review of the large literature on prevention of motor vehicle crashes is beyond the scope of this piece, but major recommendations are reviewed below.

Some preventative measures are relevant specifically to young children. When traveling in a car, van, truck, or similar motor vehicle, young children should be placed in specially designed car seats. These seats are constructed to protect children from serious injury by supporting anatomically underdeveloped parts of the body that might be susceptible to injury during a crash. Infants typically face backward in their seats; as toddlers develop neck and back muscles, they are switched to forward-facing seats.

Child safety seats should be installed, when possible, in the center of the vehicle, away from possible impact points, and not in a location where air bags might inflate during a crash. Seats should be fastened tightly using a range of available fasteners; the choice of fastener used depends on the age and features available in the automobile. Proper installation remains highly problematic; some studies suggest that well over half – and perhaps closer to three-quarters – of child safety seats are installed incorrectly. Although improperly installed seats generally protect children to some degree, properly installed seats are the safest traveling option.

Beyond child-specific safety measures such as car seats, other measures to prevent motor vehicle crashes are widely discussed in scientific outlets and the popular media. These include legislative means such as reduced speed limits and enforcement of traffic laws; environmental manipulations such as guardrails and speed bumps; behavioral recommendations such as reduction of driving while intoxicated or fatigued; and engineering mechanisms such as safer automobile and road design.

Pedestrian and Bicycling Injuries

Pedestrian and bicycling injuries are somewhat more threatening to older children, but toddlers also suffer from such injuries at alarmingly high rates. The most common scenario is highly tragic: a toddler will be playing in his or her driveway. A parent, often rushed, distracted, and unaware, will back out of the driveway and strike the toddler, thinking he or she was safely out of the path of the car. These sorts of injuries can be very severe and, of course, are psychologically devastating to both child and parent. Less common but still concerning are incidents when toddlers run or bicycle into a street and are struck by passing vehicles. Also of note are injuries – usually comparatively minor – when toddlers fall while riding bicycles or tricycles.

Prevention of pedestrian and cycling injuries lies primarily with adults, who must be aware of children's locations and be sure to inspect roadways before traversing them (and in particular, be sure driveways are clear before backing). Instruction on pedestrian safety skills can begin during the toddler years, but will not be mastered by children until middle childhood – thus necessitating careful supervision by parents of all young children. Safe bicycling habits – including use of helmets at all times – should also be established early.

Poisoning

Poisoning is the sixth leading cause of death in children under the age of 1 year, and remains a very significant concern throughout early childhood. Poisoning can occur in a number of different ways; the two most common occurrences are discussed below.

One source of poisoning is when children discover and ingest dangerous substances; this typically results in acute poisoning from a single ingestion of a toxic substance. Among the more common culprits are cleaning supplies, medications and vitamins, and toiletry articles (e.g., perfume, liquid soap). Another dangerous household item – and one that parents sometimes overlook – is houseplants; some varieties of houseplants are highly toxic when eaten. Manufacturing laws in the US and much of the developed world have decreased risk of poisoning from some products (e.g., medications, cleaning supplies) through 'childproof packaging', but active prevention efforts must continue.

Paralleling many other types of injuries, supervision and environmental modifications fall at the top of the prevention list. Supervision of children is critical, particularly when children are exposed to new environments and environments that have not been 'childproofed'. Environmental modifications involve a careful inspection of the home, and removal of potentially dangerous substances from the reach of children. Cleaning, toiletry, and household repair supplies should be moved to upper shelves or placed in locked or latched cabinets or closets. Medications should similarly be stored in inaccessible locations. Dangerous houseplants should be removed or placed in out-of-reach locations.

A second source of poisoning is from ingestion of toxic substances in small quantities over time. The most dangerous substance, lead, is found in most paint and paint chips present in American homes built before the 1950s, and in some homes dating to the late 1970s. Of particular concern are chips of paint containing lead that might be present on balconies, porches, or in areas near the home where toddlers play. Purposeful or accidental ingestion of such paint chips can cause permanent brain damage or death; effective prevention mechanisms include inspection and repair of chipping paint and supervision of children in dangerous areas.

Suffocation

Three scenarios are particularly concerning as risks for suffocation in young children: plastic bags, articles left in cribs, and window blind cords. Plastic bags are ubiquitous in today's culture, and for good reason: they are inexpensive to produce, lightweight, and convenient to carry a wide range of goods. Unfortunately, they also create a highly dangerous object for young children. Parents are unlikely to successfully avoid using plastic bags in today's world, but they should be careful to store them out of reach from unsupervised youngsters, and to teach their children that plastic bags and similar plastic materials are inappropriate play objects.

Equally concerning as a suffocation risk are items left in young children's cribs. Before infants develop the motor skills to free themselves from suffocating objects while asleep, it is dangerous to leave sheets, stuffed animals, or blankets without holes in them, in infants' cribs. Many parents are unaware or unconcerned with this risk, however, and suffocations result. Education of parents is the primary prevention strategy.

Window blind cords are particularly dangerous when they hang low enough for children to grasp them (from the floor or from a crib). Like many other dangerous household items, toddlers find the cords of window blind fascinating toys, and somehow manage to become tangled in them during play to the point of accidental strangulation. Prevention is best achieved by tying window cords above children's reach and moving cribs to locations in the home away from windows.

Intentional Injury: Child Abuse and Neglect

Although this article focuses primarily on unintentional injury to young children, it would be remiss to neglect mention of intentional injury to that age group. Intentional injury, which is known in lay terms as abuse and neglect, encompasses physical abuse, sexual abuse, and child neglect, and comes most frequently at the hands of children's parents and adult caregivers.

Many of the risks described for unintentional injury apply also for intentional injury. From the perspective of the child, temperamentally difficult children seem to suffer from abuse and neglect more frequently than laid back, easily managed children. The direction of this relationship is unknown – but one hypothesis is that difficult children elicit angry reactions from parents and other adults, and therefore place themselves at greater risk of abuse and neglect.

From the perspective of the parent, again there is overlap between risk for intentional and unintentional injury. Not surprisingly, parents who have psychopathology – most prominently, those who abuse substances or who are seriously depressed – are more likely to abuse and neglect their children. Some of the most dramatic and unfortunate abuse and neglect cases occur to children raised by parents chronically addicted to drugs, and who are intoxicated to the point that they forget or ignore the responsibility to feed, bathe, and shelter their young children. Parents who are highly impoverished also are at risk for harming their children, most frequently through neglect. In many cases, this neglect is not intentional but rather is due to extreme poverty, and the parents' inability to shelter or provide adequate nutrition to their young children.

Unlike the situation with unintentional injury – which is frequently seen as accidental, unavoidable, and unpreventable by the lay public – there is considerable public concern of the risks and tragedy involved in intentional injury. Every state in the US has organized staff that are responsible for protecting the welfare of children who are suspected of suffering from neglect or abuse at the hands of adults.

Beyond government oversight, prevention of abuse and neglect requires changing the behavior of parents and other adults who are abusive. Mental health treatment; resources to help overworked, overstressed, and fatigued parents; and social services for homeless or impoverished families are promising intervention strategies. Also important is education of the population. Children can be educated to recognize inappropriate sexual advances from adults and inform trusted people about such activity. Similar education of children can be helpful to prevent physical abuse. Teachers, physicians, mental health workers, religious leaders, and other trustworthy adults must be trained to recognize signs of abuse and report those signs to government authorities. Government agencies must receive adequate funding to investigate and act upon founded abuse and neglect cases.

Finally, support for new parents is essential. The highest rate of battering abuse injuries occurs to infants from 0 to 5 months. During this time period, parents are often fatigued, confused, and anxious. Social support, community support, and opportunities for 'breaks' from parenting may be highly effective in preventing abuse injuries to young infants.

Conclusion

As the leading cause of mortality in children ages 0–3 years, unintentional injuries are of great concern to parents, researchers, and government officials. Tremendous progress has been made in the past few decades: a combination of environmental changes, legislation on manufacturing of child-oriented toys and goods, and behavioral change among children, parents, and daycare workers has yielded a slow but steady decrease in incidence of fatal injuries to young American children.

Despite this progress, there is much work to be done. From a behavioral perspective, there are five keys to success in safeguarding children's environments (see also **Table 2**):

1. Educate parents and other adults to recognize children's vulnerability to injury. Injuries are not accidental, and should not be viewed that way. Preventive action can and should be taken.
2. Educate parents on the injury risks present in the home environment. Some parents read parenting books, magazines, and websites, and are educated; many are not. Reaching the uneducated is an important step in preventing injuries.
3. Educate parents and other adults to anticipate injurious situations. Inspect locations where children spend time, and especially the home, to identify and modify potentially dangerous items and areas.
4. Make changes to the environment to protect children. Safeguard the home by installing outlet covers and stair gates. Purchase and correctly install car seats. Close bathroom doors and move poisonous cleaning supplies to safe locations. Install fences around swimming pools and place adequate mulch under playgrounds.

Table 2 A summary of the keys to preventing injury in young children

Five keys to success in preventing injury in young children
1. Educate parents and other adults to recognize children's vulnerability to injury. Injuries are usually not accidental.
2. Educate parents on the injury risks present in the home environment.
3. Educate parents and other adults to anticipate injurious situations. Identify and modify potential dangers.
4. Change the environment to protect children.
5. Convince parents and other adults to supervise children carefully.

5. Convince parents and other adults of the need to supervise children carefully. This is perhaps the most important preventive mechanism, and also one of the hardest to achieve. Psychological research on ways to improve adult supervision of infants and toddlers is likely to continue for some time.

See also: Abuse, Neglect, and Maltreatment of Infants; Demographic Factors; Exploration and Curiosity; Lead Poisoning; Mortality, Infant; Parenting Styles and their Effects; Temperament.

Suggested Readings

Agran PF, Anderson C, Winn D, Trent R, Walton-Haynes L, and Thayer S (2003) Rates of pediatric injuries by 3-month intervals for children 0 to 3 years of age. *Pediatrics* 111: e683–e692.
Damashek A and Peterson L (2002) Unintentional injury prevention efforts for young children: Levels, methods, types and targets. *Journal of Developmental and Behavioral Pediatrics* 23: 443–455.
Morrongiello BA (2005) Caregiver supervision and child-injury risk: I. Issues in defining and measuring supervision. II. Findings and directions for future research. *Journal of Pediatric Psychology* 30: 536–552.
Morrongiello BA, Ondejko L, and Littlejohn A (2004) Understanding toddlers' in-home injuries: II. Examining parental strategies, and their efficacy, for managing child injury risk. *Journal of Pediatric Psychology* 29: 433–446.
Pickett W, Streight S, Simpson K, and Brison RJ (2002) Injuries experienced by infant children: A population-based epidemiological analysis. *Pediatrics* 111: e365–e370.
Powell EC and Tanz RR (2002) Adjusting our view of injury risk: The burden of nonfatal injuries in infancy. *Pediatrics* 110: 792–796.
Schwebel DC and Barton BK (2006) Temperament and children's unintentional injuries. In: Vollrath M (ed.) *Handbook of Personality and Health*, pp. 51–71. New York: Wiley.
Schwebel DC and Gaines J (2007) Pediatric unintentional injury: Behavioral risk factors and implications for prevention. *Journal of Developmental and Behavioral Pediatrics* 28: 245–254.

Relevant Websites

http://www.aap.org – American Academy of Pediatrics.
http://www.cdc.gov – Centers for Disease Control and Prevention.
http://www.safekid.org – Children's Safety Association of Canada.
http://www.childrenssafetynetwork.org – Children's Safety Network.
http://www.nsc.org – National Safety Council.
http://www.phac-aspc.gc.ca – Public Health Agency of Canada.
http://www.safekids.org – Safe Kids Worldwide.
http://www.who.int/violence_injury_prevention – World Health Organization.

School Readiness

F J Morrison and A H Hindman, University of Michigan, Ann Arbor, MI, USA

Glossary

Child-by-instruction interactions – Not all literacy instruction yields the same gains for all children. Rather, children's learning from instruction depends in part on the skills and levels of understanding that they bring to the learning situation. These child-by-instruction interactions have been found in preschool through third grade. This principle yields two important implications related to the multidimensional nature of school readiness. First, even children who are 'ready' will not have identical skills and interests; in other words, there are multiple patterns and degrees of readiness. Second, upon school entry, the amount and type of instruction that will optimize children's learning is very likely to vary across children.

Dimensions of instruction – Recent research points to four salient dimensions of instruction. These include the (1) explicit focus of instruction (explicit vs. implicit), (2) manager of the students' attention (teacher-vs. child-managed), (3) content of the instruction (code-based or word-level vs. meaning-based or higher order), and (4) change in amount of instruction over the school year. As instruction is multidimensional, it is important to consider how each of these aspects of a child's classroom environment supports or even hinders readiness.

Dimensions of parenting – While sometimes considered as a multidimensional construct, data suggest that three proximal dimensions of parenting most directly contribute to children's literacy skills. These are (1) the family learning environment, (2) parental warmth/responsivity, and (3) parental control/discipline. A separate distal dimension has been posited, parental knowledge and beliefs, which operates primarily through the other three proximal sources. These dimensions exert independent influences on different aspects of a child's behavior

and can be either independent of or correlated with one another.
Ecological perspective – Set forth by Uri Bronfenbrenner, the ecological perspective on child development suggests that children grow and learn in the midst of a complex system of forces. Some forces are very proximal, or close, such as parents and teachers. Others are more distal, or distant, such as employment trends. These proximal and distal forces shape the ways in which children develop; for example, a child learns the language that his or her family speaks at home. These forces can also shape one another; parents and teachers might share information and learn from one another, changing the ways that they interact with children to better support their learning. Finally, children shape these forces. For example, a child who is very talkative and asks many questions will likely demand more verbal interaction from their parents and/or teachers than would a child who rarely initiates conversation, which might well affect the number of words the child learns. This perspective, then, posits that development is a complex process influenced by many interacting forces in a child's environment, including the child him- or herself.
School readiness – School readiness includes both cognitive and social–emotional skills. Many assessments of school readiness measure general cognitive skills, including language and problem solving, as well as concrete academic concepts such as identifying letters, numbers, colors, and parts of the body. Social–emotional skills necessary for participation in a classroom community include self-regulation of one's own attention, behavior, and emotion; as well as knowledge of interpersonal relations, including cooperation and conflict resolution.

Introduction

The effort to understand and improve children's literacy skills and school achievement in America has begun to focus increasingly on their readiness for school, for a number of reasons. First, it is becoming evident that meaningful individual differences in important language, cognitive, literacy, and social skills emerge before children begin formal schooling in kindergarten or first grade. Second, this early variability is influenced by a number of factors in the child, family, preschool, and larger sociocultural context. Third, these contributing influences do not operate in isolation, but interact with each other in complex ways to shape children's variable trajectories. Finally, the early schooling experiences of American children are highly variable, in some cases exacerbating the degree of difference found among children prior to school entry. Children who enter the primary grades without core competencies in early language, literacy, self-regulation, and interpersonal relations are at far greater risk than their more knowledgeable peers of encountering difficulty in reading and in academics more generally. Cumulatively, these trends have sharpened scientific and societal focus on the process of school transition as a unique and important milestone in the academic development of children and as a foundational experience for early school success. In this context, understanding the nature and sources of variability in children's school readiness has received heightened attention.

In this article, a working conceptualization (or model) of the nature and sources of children's literacy development across the school transition period, from roughly 3 years of age to third grade will be presented. The empirical literature on the major factors contributing to school readiness and early literacy skill growth will ther be reviewed. Finally, the implications for research and for improving literacy in the US will be considered.

Conceptualizing School Readiness and Transition

Working from the ecological perspective first asserted by Uri Bronfenbrenner, scientists have attempted to develop a coherent conceptualization of the process of school transition. **Figure 1** depicts a working model of the major factors shaping children's literacy development and their independent and combined influences over the school transition period. Four features should be noted. First, the model includes and distinguishes those processes that occur prior to school entry from those operative once school begins. At the same time, the model depicts the continuity of influences (e.g., from parenting) across the two periods.

Second, the model attempts to capture the interplay of distal and proximal factors in shaping children's literacy trajectories. In particular, the mediational role of proximal factors linking distal factors to literacy outcomes is depicted. Hence, in the preschool period, the contribution of sociocultural factors, like parental education or income, is shown as operating through their effect on more proximal parenting or preschool influences. Likewise, during early schooling the impact of teacher education or experience is seen in the model as manifesting itself primarily through the ongoing instructional activities of the teacher in the classroom.

Third, the model includes some of the important components within each of the larger factors. For parenting, research has highlighted the unique influence of the

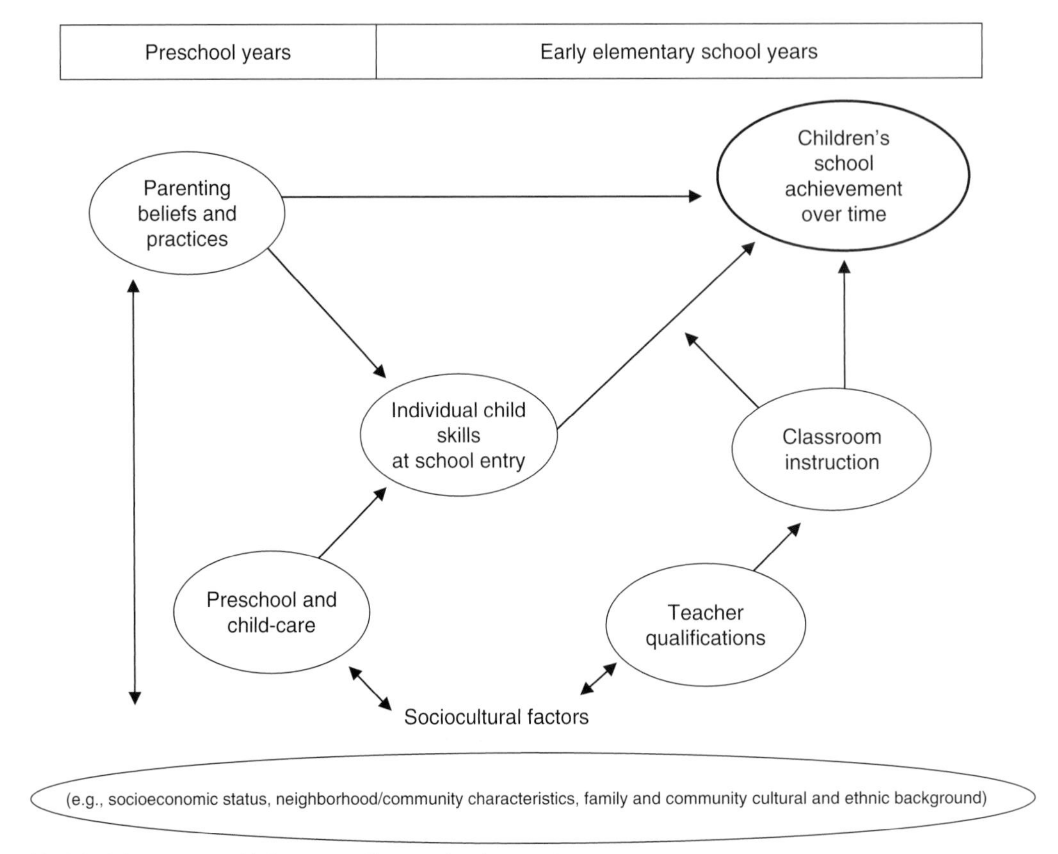

Figure 1 Model of the sources of influence on literacy development.

learning environment, parental warmth/responsivity, and control/discipline. Finally, the model depicts some of the important interactions among these factors, recognizing the emerging consensus that these factors do not operate in isolation. For example, while the home learning environment contributes directly to children's literacy growth and self-regulation skills, parental control/discipline contributes to literacy growth primarily through its impact on self-regulation. On a broader plane, accumulating evidence increasingly highlights the need to capture the complex interplay of forces shaping children's literacy trajectories across the school transition period. For these reasons, understanding children's school readiness must necessarily include consideration of the environmental context of early development as well as the role of early formal instruction in enhancing or impeding children's early skill growth.

Before Children Get to School

Child Factors

Whether through inherited genetic or acquired differences, child characteristics by themselves and in interaction with environmental factors shape the course of children's early development. In reality, these child qualities are what we mean when we typically refer to 'school readiness'. While most scientists now view readiness as a two-way street (with schools needing to be ready to deal with children's individual differences), there is still intense interest in factors within the child that are most crucial for school readiness and successful school transition.

One of the most important policy goals to emerge in the last decade is that all children will arrive at school 'ready to learn'. But what exactly does 'ready to learn' mean? What knowledge and skills are important prerequisites for children's success in school, how many children are not 'ready to learn', and what are the consequences?

As researchers investigate the construct of school readiness, they include both cognitive and social–emotional skills. For example, standardized assessments of school readiness usually assess general social interaction, cognitive skills, and concrete academic concepts such as identifying letters, numbers, colors, and parts of the body. Social–emotional skills necessary for participation in a classroom community include self-regulation of one's own attention, behavior, and emotion, all of which aid children in learning from instruction, following directions, and persisting through challenges. Further, the focus on large- and small-group activities and play in many early classrooms requires that children build knowledge of interpersonal relations, including cooperation and conflict resolution.

Unfortunately, too many of children in the US are not ready for the transition into a formal schooling environment, either socially or academically. Among a national sample of almost 3600 teachers studied by Sara Rimm-Kauffman, Robert Pianta, and colleagues, over one-third maintained that about half of their class or more began kindergarten socially and emotionally unprepared for the demands of the classroom. Considering that these teachers managed classrooms with an average of 22 students, this estimate translates into a staggering number of children. Teachers reported that at least half or more of the students in their class had difficulty following directions (46%), difficulty working independently (34%), and difficulty working as part of a group (30%) when they began school. Other pressing problems included students' lack of academic skills (36%), disorganized home environment (35%), or lack of any formal preschool experience (31%). Note that these teachers identified as many social–emotional skills as they did academic and cognitive skills.

These skills matter a great deal. Accumulating research reveals that a child's profile of literacy and social competence in early elementary school is highly predictive of academic achievement in junior high and high school, as well as whether students will drop out of high school. Consequently, children's ease with the transition to school and their cognitive and social/behavioral skills at kindergarten entry have meaningful implications for their later educational and vocational success.

The bulk of our discussion of readiness will focus on the role of oral language, literacy, and self-regulation skills. Nevertheless, there are a number of issues of particular concern to parents and teachers that are important to consider initially.

Entrance Age

A child's age at kindergarten entry is often a source of concern for parents and teachers. Older kindergartners have experienced almost 1 year more of language and literacy exposure than their younger classmates, and may be more socially mature. National surveys indicate that 9% or 10% of parents delay their child's entrance to kindergarten, especially if they are among the youngest in their classroom (i.e., their birthday falls close to the school cutoff date). Earlier research may have unduly influenced parents' fears by suggesting that younger children were at greater risk for poor academic performance, grade retention, and special education referrals.

More recent investigations have utilized a variety of methods to evaluate how young children perform in school compared to their older peers. Researchers have compared: (1) children who entered school when eligible with children who delayed entrance for 1 year; (2) the oldest and youngest children in the same grade; and (3) same age children in different grades. This last technique has provided the most rigorous strategy for distinguishing effects of experiencing a year of schooling from maturational (age) effects. However, across all of these methods, any early discrepancies that favored older children in kindergarten significantly diminished by second or third grade. Overall, younger children benefit from formal instruction as much as do their older peers and are able to match the performance of older classmates within a relatively short amount of time.

While these studies persuasively demonstrate that entrance age, in and of itself, is not a useful predictor of early academic achievement, two issues remain unresolved. First, although the early effects of entrance age appeared short-lived, the long-term effects have not been adequately examined. It is possible that despite substantial reductions in entrance age gaps during early elementary school, the influence of age on cognitive and social domains may reemerge as schooling requirements become more complex and student-managed. A recent analysis of approximately 14 000 children from the National Education Longitudinal Study (NELS) offered encouraging evidence that the early narrowing of the entrance age gap is maintained throughout formal schooling. For example, no significant differences emerged between younger and older kindergartners across a range of long-term educational and social outcomes, such as high-school dropout, college attendance, behavior problems, and arrests. Second, it is also still not clear whether entrance age is an independent risk factor, or whether the risk is produced when being young at school entry is combined with other child factors, such as weaker cognitive skills or social immaturity. For example, the largest discrepancies in school success are between older and younger students who were in the lowest 25th percentile of cognitive ability. Nevertheless, while some questions remain to be addressed, chronological age at school entry does not appear to be an important source of school readiness.

Gender

Gender differences in verbal and mathematics abilities have been tracked for decades. Early reviews in the 1970s indicated that discrepancies detected at young ages were generally small, whereas consistently significant sex differences that favored boys in verbal, mathematics, and spatial abilities did not often emerge until 10 or 11 years of age. In contrast, later evidence revealed girls' advanced verbal abilities and comparable mathematics and memory performance to boys'. By the end of the 1980s, the size of the gender differences in math and verbal skills had substantially declined. The gender gaps in academic achievement not only narrowed, but disparities in math performance actually began to favor females.

So, now that the women who entered the workforce and pursued professional degrees in the 1970s and 1980s are sending their own sons and daughters to school, what has happened to the gender gap? According to 2003 NAEP data, female students in fourth and eighth grade outscored male students in reading by an average of 7–11 points. In contrast, the mathematics gap is much smaller, with boys scoring higher than girls by only 2 or 3 points. Furthermore, the magnitude of these gender gaps has remained fairly consistent since the early 1990s.

It is important to keep in mind that these national data reflect academic achievement, but not necessarily school performance. Girls' achievement, especially in math and science, was once a major educational concern, but researchers and educators are now arguing that a 'new gender gap' has emerged in American schools: as recently noted in the *New York Times* "Every time I turn around, if something good is happening, there's a female in charge,' says Terrill O. Stammler, principal of Rising Sun High School in Rising Sun, Md. "Boys are missing from nearly every leadership position, academic honors slot, and student-activity post at the school. Even Rising Sun's girls' sports teams do better than the boys'." On a larger scale, data suggest that, by high school, girls now show higher grades and higher scores on achievement tests. This new achievement disparity continues after high school as well. For more than 10 years, women have surpassed men in earning postsecondary degrees (e.g., bachelors or masters degrees), and current projections anticipate a widening of the gap in men's and women's educational attainment over the next decade.

So how early do these gender differences appear? Female toddlers exhibit greater rates of vocabulary production and language complexity, expression, and comprehension. However, these differences are usually small in size and diminish by 20–24 months of age. In preschool measures of emergent literacy, significant gender discrepancies are generally not found or weakly favor girls.

Some researchers are currently arguing that, rather than gender *per se*, disparities in social maturity or the socialization practices that girls and boys experience may also place girls at an advantage both in the classroom and the workplace. James Garbarino, professor and author of *Lost Boys: Why Our Sons Turn Violent and How We Can Save Them*, contends that "Girls are better able to deliver in terms of what modern society requires of people – paying attention, abiding by rules, being verbally competent, and dealing with interpersonal relationships in offices." Along these lines, higher levels of self-discipline, or self-regulation, may undergird girls' greater achievement. It is important to recognize that, in and of itself, focusing on gender may not be terribly illuminating in helping us understand the growing divergence among boys and girls in school success. In a sense, gender, like socioeconomic status (SES), is a distal factor that operates through more proximal sources of influence/characteristics, like parenting, social maturity, or self-regulation.

Cognitive Skills and IQ

Another commonly recognized characteristic of children that greatly contributes to literacy acquisition is their intelligence. Although this attribute goes by many names (e.g., IQ or cognitive competence), in a classroom, it is readily evident that some children are able to learn and apply new information with greater ease and accuracy than their peers. Efforts to somehow measure or quantify these abilities are generally constrained by children's language development. In other words, if we want to examine the influence of children's intelligence on the variability in children's literacy skills at kindergarten entry, the earliest we could administer a standardized IQ test would be around age 2 years, when children are better able to produce answers to questions. In response, psychologists have also utilized more global mental and psychomotor scales, such as the Bayley Scales of Infant Development (BSID), to assess major areas of infants' and toddlers' cognitive development, such as sensation, perception, memory, and language. Scores on the BSID at 2 years of age have been useful for detecting language delays and are strongly associated with later academic and language skills during the preschool and elementary school years. In recent decades, cognitive researchers have devised several techniques to obtain indicators of infants' cognitive development at very young ages, presumably when performance would better represent biological traits rather than environmental experiences. For example, infants' abilities to distinguish new from familiar sounds or pictures during the first year of life predict cognitive scores 2–8 years later.

Not only are there age issues to consider when assessing children's intelligence, but researchers continue to disagree about the aspects of intelligence to include in standardized tests. Most IQ tests contain verbal (e.g., vocabulary, comprehension, general information) and quantitative (e.g., arithmetic, problem-solving, spatial reasoning) components that can be aggregated to form a global score. However, Howard Gardner has argued that each individual possesses multiple intelligences that include naturalist, musical, bodily-kinesthetic, interpersonal, and intrapersonal domains, in addition to the more traditional intelligence domains of linguistic, logical–mathematical, and spatial skills. Despite the controversy surrounding the content of IQ tests, children's verbal and quantitative abilities in preschool and early elementary school do predict a variety of later academic outcomes, such as grades and standardized test scores of reading and mathematics, and even high school dropout. Further, IQ scores are often among the most predictive of factors for academic competence, over and above measures of SES, parenting practices, and children's social and behavioral skills.

Nevertheless, it is important to reiterate that while western culture reifies intelligence as a heritable trait, IQ scores are not good indicators of genetic characteristics. For instance, since verbal ability assessments are related to children's language comprehension skills, environmental effects on children's vocabulary development cannot be underappreciated. Adopted children's IQ scores increased substantially more if they were adopted into families of higher SES than of lower SES households. More specific still, IQ scores of preschool children in high-poverty communities showed significant growth after exposure to high-quality curriculum in school for just 1 year, and even greater gains with continued enrollment in the program. Therefore, these indicators or proxies of cognitive competence that researchers rely upon are clearly responsive to environmental enrichment.

Language/literacy skills

One of the most important discoveries of the past two decades has been the critical role that language plays in early literacy development. Several language skills independently contribute to reading acquisition, and there may be interactions among these components over the course of learning to read. Of particular focus has been the role of phonological skills (particularly phonemic awareness) in learning to read. Increasing competence at consciously manipulating the component sounds in the speech stream facilitates the child's task of 'cracking the code', that is, learning the symbol-sound correspondence rules and utilizing them in ever more sophisticated ways to derive accurate word pronunciations. Locating the smallest units, phonemes, within a word seems to be the most critical level of segmentation for early word decoding. Children who have difficulty at this level, for whatever reason, experience significant problems progressing in word decoding. Vocabulary, both receptive and expressive, has also been shown to predict early reading skill. The number of different words a child understands, as well as the number s/he speaks, helps word decoding efforts and may facilitate growth of phonological awareness. Finally, children's knowledge of the alphabet when they enter kindergarten is one of the best predictors of learning to read. Letter knowledge predicts more advanced phonological awareness and better word decoding skills throughout elementary school.

There is some uncertainty at present about how and when each of these component skills exerts its influence. Some studies have demonstrated that vocabulary uniquely predicts early reading skills only through kindergarten, after which it contributes indirectly via its association with phonological processes, which continue to predict reading well into early elementary school. Other recent studies appear to find an independent contribution for vocabulary and other oral language skills through third grade. There is agreement, though, that development of early oral language facility, including vocabulary, is essential to later comprehension skills.

Self-regulation

As noted above, increasing attention in recent years has been paid to a class of skills that has been variously called executive functioning, learning-related social skills, social competence, and self-regulation. They refer to the coordination of processes involved in response inhibition, sustaining attention over time, and planning and organization in working memory. They contribute, among other things, to a child's ability to work independently, control impulses, and complete tasks on time. There is a growing sense that difficulties with self-regulation among American children are contributing in major ways to the literacy problems in the nation.

Children with poor learning-related social skills at the beginning of kindergarten have been shown to perform more poorly academically at school entry and at the end of second grade. Likewise, a child's skill at sustaining attention and restraining restlessness predicts academic functioning in first grade. The close connection between social and academic skills persists throughout school. Adolescents rated more highly by teachers and peers on complying with rules and expectations outperformed their lower scoring peers on measures of academic achievement. Clearly, development of self-regulation is an important task for preschool children over the school transition period and one that has sustained influence throughout a child's life.

Motivation

Motivational skills refer to students' values and beliefs when approaching school tasks, including their engagement with the material, interest in the topic, beliefs about self-efficacy as well as their attributions of success or failure and their goal orientations. The study of motivational processes in education has a long history, yet surprisingly little research has been conducted on young children. This is unfortunate since, in practically every other area of academic functioning, it has become clear that the seeds of later success are sown during the preschool years. Hence laying a foundation of academic engagement, coupled with a strong sense of mastery and self-efficacy prior to school entry, could be expected to reap long-term benefits throughout a child's academic career. Clearly, more systematic empirical inquiry is needed on the early roots of motivational processes in children and their influence on academic functioning.

As with language and literacy skills, it is clear that multiple sources of influence, including parenting and schooling, shape growth of social and motivational processes, though research is just beginning to delve into the nature and impact of these relations.

In summary, research since the mid 1980s has clearly revealed that a number of potent forces, independently and in combination, shape the literacy development of preschool children. Factors in the child, family, preschool, and broader sociocultural context all contribute to create the significant variability American children present when they walk in the school door.

Sociocultural Factors

Several decades of research have documented strong connections between SES and academic achievement. Likewise, accumulating evidence has established links between race/ethnicity and school success, particularly the persistently poorer performance of African-American students compared to their European-American peers. These factors are obviously linked, since the poverty rate among black families in the US continues to be higher than it is for White families. Recently, scientists have attempted to disentangle the independent and combined influences of social, economic and racial/ethnic influences on academic development.

Socioeconomic disadvantage and academic achievement

Whether measured by income, education, or occupational status, socioeconomic factors are substantially linked to a child's school success. The National Assessment of Educational Progress reports that 9-, 13-, and 17-year-old students from families with less than high school education scored lower on tests of reading, math and science than did children whose parents completed some education after high school. More significant for our discussion is the recent realization that children from low-SES families start school behind their more affluent peers and progress more slowly through the early years of elementary school. More recent work has unearthed that children from lower-SES families demonstrate delays in language and emergent literacy skills. In a pioneering study, Betty Hart and Todd Risley found that preschool children from welfare families had smaller vocabularies compared to children from working-class and professional families as early as 3 years of age. Moreover, their rates of vocabulary acquisition were much slower.

How does SES affect academic achievement? Despite the strong association between socioeconomic disadvantage and poor school performance, it is not obvious how SES factors operate to shape children's academic trajectories, especially in the preschool years. In their efforts to probe more deeply into the mechanisms underlying the SES–performance connection, scientists have distinguished between direct and mediated pathways of influence.

Direct pathways reflect influences that operate directly on the child to affect academic performance. For example, poor children are more likely to have experienced negative perinatal events, like prematurity or low birth weight, in addition to poorer nutrition and healthcare in early childhood, all of which can directly limit a child's cognitive growth and potential. Yet, increasingly, scientists are describing the impact of SES as operating through more immediate influences in the child's environment. For instance, mothers living in poverty are less likely to receive adequate prenatal care, which could contribute, in part, to the connection between SES and prematurity. Researchers describe these as mediated pathways, where SES is viewed as a distal variable that exerts its influence through a more immediate or proximal variable. The whole process is described as a mediated relation. Scientists are increasingly seeing the effects of SES as mediated through more proximal factors, one of which is parenting. Parents living in poverty are less likely to talk to their preschool children; they communicate with a more limited vocabulary, offer fewer questions or descriptive statements to them, and are more repetitive. In general, parents with fewer economic and/or educational resources are less likely to provide the stimulating home environments children seem to require if they are to be maximally ready for school. The important insight gained from seeing SES in this mediated fashion is that improving a family's economic circumstances alone may not translate into improved parenting, the more immediate causal agent shaping the child's development.

Race, ethnicity, and academic achievement

Similar issues have surfaced in trying to explain the disparities across racial and ethnic groups in academic attainment. Clearly, race and ethnicity, in and of themselves, are distal variables that won't directly affect academic performance. Their influence must be mediated by more proximal sources. Since most progress in understanding these complex relations comes from the study of differences between African-American and European-American students, we will focus on this issue here.

Of particular import is the Black–White test score gap. In general, African-American children do not perform as well academically as their European-American counterparts on the NAEP. While some variation has been noted over the last three decades, sizable differences have persisted throughout the period in which scientists have been tracking children's performance.

The most common explanations for 'the gap' have leaned on socioeconomic and sociocultural factors. In particular, the higher rate of poverty among African-American families has been offered as an obvious cause for poorer performance in black children. Likewise, the legacy of racial discrimination, which limits opportunities for Black children, has been put forth as a contributor to lower academic attainment.

While these factors are reasonable and, no doubt, play some role in the gap, two recent findings have caused scientists to reassess the nature and sources of the black–white discrepancies. First, it has become clear that the test-score gap is not limited to lower-SES groups. Black middle-SES children are performing more poorly than their white peers. Second, the gap in academic performance emerges before children begin school. These two findings have caused researchers to look more deeply into the proximal environments of black families for a more comprehensive understanding of the roots of academic problems. For example, studies from the Center for Disease Control and Prevention have found that infant mortality rates are higher in black families, and more significantly, this difference occurs independently of SES.

Perhaps the most salient and controversial proximal factor implicated in the Black–White test score gap is parenting. Mounting evidence has pointed to differences across racial groups in the types of learning experiences provided to children and other aspects of the literacy environment. These differences also seem to extend to middle-class parenting practices. While the reasons for these differences in parenting are not clearly understood, and many distal factors are implicated, the focus on parenting and related proximal causes is yielding a clearer, more comprehensive picture of the complex forces contributing to the continued underperformance of black children.

Early Childcare and Preschool

Over 60% of the almost 20 million preschoolers in this country will spend some amount of time in alternate care. Hence, researchers have become increasingly interested in the psychological consequences of childcare for children under 5 years of age as well as its impact on school transition and later school functioning. In addition, for children most at risk for school failure, intensive interventions during the preschool years have attempted to help children at risk for academic failure (e.g., children living in poverty) catch up to their peers and be equally ready for school. In this section we will first review the evidence on the impact of childcare on children's cognitive and social development. Next we will summarize the evidence on the outcome of early interventions for children at-risk of academic underachievement.

Is day care good or bad for children?

While stated rather simplistically, the above question accurately captures the essence of the debate on the impact of early childcare for preschool children. The importance of this question can be appreciated by realizing that the Federal government undertook to fund a major national study of the nature and consequences of early childcare in the late 1980s. That study, the National Institute of Child Health and Human Development (NICHD) Study of Early Childcare, as well as others, have yielded valuable insights on the role of childcare experiences in children's development and school performance.

As we stated above, the question of whether childcare is good or bad oversimplifies the issue. Closer examination reveals that two variables – quality and quantity of care – are crucial to understanding the role of childcare in children's lives. In broad terms, higher-quality childcare produces positive effects on children's cognitive, language, and literacy skills, while high quantities of care (defined as more that 30 h per week) have been associated with poorer social outcomes. Even these conclusions do not capture the complexity of the role of childcare. Parents are active agents in choosing alternate care for their child, and more educated mothers have been shown to be more sensitive and responsive to their children than mothers with less education. The more educated and responsive mothers likely chose higher-quality childcare, monitored it more closely, and could afford to pay for it. In fact, when direct comparisons have been made between parenting and childcare environments, the impact of the quality of parenting was 3–4 times greater than that of childcare on children's language and social skills. Nevertheless there is early evidence that, independent of quality, children who spend more than 30 h per week in center-based care may be less socially competent and somewhat more disruptive to other children and teachers.

Thus, in answer to our original question, research over the last two decades permits us to conclude that, in and of itself, daycare is neither good nor bad for preschool children. High-quality childcare enhances children's cognitive growth, while high amounts of childcare per week may put children at risk for slightly poorer social outcomes.

Are early intervention programs for at-risk students effective?

Here, too, the question of program quality is central to answering this question. High-quality interventions can significantly enhance development. But poor-quality programs can impede children's progress. High-quality preschool interventions have been shown to significantly improve children's prospects for academic success, to promote stronger language and literacy development, and to demonstrate significant return on investment over children's lifetimes.

A number of interventions have been implemented for at-risk children. The most visible (and controversial) is Head Start, the mixed outcomes of which illustrate the crucial importance of ensuring high-quality programs for producing consistently positive effects. Some of the more prominent and successful model programs include the Perry Preschool Project, the Abecedarian Project, the School Development Program, and the Chicago

Title 1 Child–Parent Centers. In virtually every instance, children receiving these interventions showed significantly stronger academic and social skill development compared to equally at-risk children not enrolled in such programs.

On balance then, the mounting weight of evidence demonstrates that high-quality childcare and interventions for at-risk children can and do improve the psychological well-being of preschool children, enhance their school readiness, and improve their chances for successful school transition.

But what defines high-quality care? Examining the characteristics of programs that work, like those listed above and others, there are at least five crucial elements of high-quality early care programs:

1. Strong support for parents. Successful programs coupled intensive intervention with home visits, parent education, and parent involvement.
2. Intensity. Programs that were more available to children all day, 5 days a week, such as the Abecedarian project, tended to produce stronger, more durable outcomes for children.
3. Starting earlier. Programs that yielded greater cost-benefit ratios (e.g., Abecedarian and Chicago Title 1) began their interventions when participants were infants.
4. Well-qualified teachers. Programs with more teachers who were certified produced more consistently positive effects than those with fewer certified teachers.
5. Rich linguistic and literacy environment. Perhaps most fundamental to success was an explicit focus on improving the language and literacy skills needed for early school success. Included were emphases on vocabulary, syntax, world knowledge, phonology, alphabet knowledge, and elementary word decoding.

In summary, the nature of a child's experience in alternate forms of care outside the home can have a measurable effect on subsequent psychological development and preparation for school. While perhaps not as crucial as parenting (to which we will turn next), high-quality experiences in a childcare environment can improve cognitive functioning in children at risk. Alternatively, for some children, more than 30 h per week in childcare, particularly prior to 1 year of age, may pose some short-term risks for their social behavior. On this latter point, it would, therefore, seem prudent to examine current parental leave policies to see if giving parents more leave time with young infants might reduce the number of hours infants spend in childcare and forestall some of the problems that may arise.

Parenting

Throughout the previous sections we have referred to parenting as a critical mediator of the effects of SES, as well as being inextricably linked to the influences of childcare. While it would seem obvious that parenting is an important, and perhaps the most important, factor shaping a child's development, again, the picture is not so simple. Recent work on the genetic bases of development has challenged the once-dominant position of parental socialization as the primary instrument through which human nature is molded. Further, efforts to improve parenting in at-risk families have proved to be surprisingly unsuccessful. In this section we will review these issues and, while we will conclude that parenting is a critical source of children's development, we will need to broaden our conceptualization of parenting in order to appreciate its full sweep and power.

Does parenting matter?

Until the mid-1980s, parenting was tacitly assumed to be the preeminent force shaping children's development. Most developmental theories accorded parents primacy over genetics, peers, and other contextual influences. Nevertheless, in the past two decades, behavior-geneticists and others have challenged this simple view. Utilizing twin and related research methods designed to separate genetic from environmental influences, researchers have found that: (1) children's development can withstand substantial variability in parenting practices and emerge intact; and (2) other socializing forces, particularly peers, can exert long-term influence on selected personality traits.

This work has had the salutary effect of yielding a more balanced view of the complex forces shaping human development. More recent work has attempted to gauge the intricate interplay of parenting and genetic and other factors and its effects on child development. As an example, in a French study of late-adopted children (3–5 years old) with below-average IQs, those children who were adopted into higher SES families exhibited substantially greater IQ gains (19 points) by 11–18 years of age than did children adopted into lower SES households (8 points). This finding neatly demonstrates that children with similar genetic characteristics make differential progress depending on the SES of the family in which they are reared; this difference is, presumably, mediated in part by differing parenting practices.

Can parenting be modified?

One way to examine the power of parenting is to conduct intervention studies to examine whether programs actually improve parenting skills and, subsequently, whether there are corresponding increases in children's literacy skills. Two strategies have been adopted: (1) family-focused early childhood education (ECE) coupled with home-based services; and (2) exclusively parent-focused home visiting programs. Recent reviews have concluded that home-based interventions alone, without a center-based child-intervention component were surprisingly ineffective in improving children's cognitive skills. Many of these adult-based efforts did not substantially increase parental outcomes (e.g., educational attainment), which, in part, may explain why their children's cognitive performance did not improve.

If parenting is so important to a child's development, then why haven't the interventions been more powerful? Actually, there are several reasons these efforts may have fallen short. First, as the authors themselves noted, case managers in these studies quickly found that they needed to deal with a number of family crises and chronic adversities, like inadequate housing, lack of food and heat and legal problems, and that it was difficult to move beyond crisis intervention to work on parenting-for-literacy. In addition, there were sizable differences across families in the uptake of services or the 'dosage' effect. Specifically, since participation in these interventions was, ultimately, voluntary, parental participation varied widely, with about half the scheduled visits actually taking place. Significantly, when eligible families were split by their participation level, children in families with greater involvement made greater gains than did their peers whose families participated less. Finally, it should be noted that smaller, more focused interventions (e.g., around book reading) have yielded measurable gains in children's oral language skills.

What is parenting anyway?

Most of the intervention efforts to improve parenting have been relatively limited in time and scope. For example, in the Comprehensive Child Development Program, parents received training from a home visitor for a maximum of 13 h (30 min, biweekly), which may be insufficient to promote and maintain lasting change over time in parental habits. Further, interventions that focus primarily on one aspect of parenting may necessarily be limiting their impact. Research over the past 20 years has clearly demonstrated that parenting for literacy involves more than reading to children and even more than providing a rich literacy environment.

It has become useful to think of parenting not as a single construct, but as varying along a number of dimensions, with three proximal dimensions being most salient for shaping literacy skills. These are: (1) the family learning environment, (2) parental warmth/responsivity, and (3) parental control/discipline. A separate distal dimension has been posited, parental knowledge and beliefs, which operates primarily through the other three proximal sources. These dimensions are conceived to exert independent influences on different aspects of a child's behavior and to be potentially independent of one another (although correlated in most instances). For example, parents who provide a rich learning environment for their child might not necessarily also give the child the high degree of emotional warmth needed for emotional security nor the rules, standards and limits needed to develop cognitive or moral self-regulation.

Family learning environment

In large national datasets, measures of 'cognitive stimulation' or 'home learning' have predicted preschoolers' IQ and receptive vocabulary, as well as reading, math and vocabulary skills in elementary school. Analyses with a sample of preschool children and their families recently revealed that the home learning environment positively predicts code- and meaning-related skills, as well as self-regulation skills. Recent efforts have focused on identifying more precisely the connections between specific parental behaviors and child outcomes. This work has revealed a high degree of specificity in the impact of the learning environment; namely, parental behaviors such as book reading, promote language development but do little for specific literacy skills like letter knowledge and word decoding. In contrast, deliberate efforts by parents to teach these emergent literacy skills to their children help to promote their alphabet and word decoding skills but do little to enrich vocabulary.

Language-promoting behaviors include frequent labeling and describing of objects in the environment. The overall amount and complexity of parental speech to children predicts their vocabulary and complex grammar acquisition. Beyond size and content, the manner of speaking and interacting with children contributes to oral language growth. Children with relatively limited vocabularies in the Betty Hart and Todd Risley study received a greater proportion of commands and prohibitions from their parents. In other work, parents who maintained longer periods of joint attention on an object had children with larger vocabularies.

Shared book-reading has generally been demonstrated to be a powerful tool, for some children, to enhance vocabulary development. In randomized experiments, book reading styles that involve actively labeling and describing illustrations or encouraging and assisting children's storytelling significantly enhance vocabulary development.

In general, literacy-promoting activities by parents may require more explicit instruction than do those that nurture oral language growth. When parents explicitly teach their children how to name and print letters and words, children's print knowledge improves as does later word decoding and comprehension skills in school.

In summary, parents' efforts to promote language and literacy in their children can substantially improve their development and school readiness. An important insight has been gained in recognizing the high degree of specificity in what parents do and what children learn.

Parental warmth/responsivity

The degree to which parents display open affection to their children, offer physical or verbal reinforcement and show sensitivity to their feelings and wishes is predictive of preschoolers' literacy and language skills as well as their later school achievement. Mothers' sensitivity to children's developmental progress during the first 2 years of life has been shown to predict cognitive and language skills later in preschool, kindergarten and first grade. More responsive mothers are more likely to reduce the length of their utterances to their infants so that children can better comprehend them. Other research has shown that at-risk groups of children can make substantial progress when mothers interact with them in a highly responsive manner. A classic situation combining elements of the learning environment along with warmth/responsivity is shared book-reading, especially during bed-time. In addition to the benefits to cognitive and language skills, shared book reading promotes emotional closeness, affection, and provides the child with the undivided attention of a loving parent. Such interchanges may nurture self-regulation and emotional well-being.

However, recent work on parenting of preschoolers in one middle-class sample revealed that parents rated their warmth/sensitivity, as gauged by 13 items on a questionnaire, as very high (on average, 4 out of a scale from 1 to 5, with no respondent reporting a 1 or 2). Analyses relating this factor, along with the two other dimensions of parenting, to children's code, meaning, and self-regulation outcomes suggested that high levels of warmth were negatively associated with children's code-focused learning, but not linked to any other outcomes. One interpretation of these findings is that parents with very high levels of warmth might engage in permissive behaviors that actually impede children's learning of the challenging but constrained skills related to decoding words. This raises questions for future study regarding the distinction between responsiveness and permissiveness, both as grounded in research and in the minds of parents, as well as optimal levels of these parenting practices for children's early learning.

Parental control/discipline

Though less well researched, the degree to which parents establish rules, standards and limits for a child's behavior creates a structured and supportive context for literacy development. Book reading, for example, affords parents the opportunity to resist children's fidgeting and squirming, and to sustain their attention until the story is finished. In one study, parents' use of disciplinary practices did not directly predict literacy outcomes, but did reliably predict self-regulation measures (e.g., cooperation, independence and responsibility), which in turn contributed positively to literacy skill levels at kindergarten entry; similar results have been found among preschool children and families.

In summary, the weight of evidence at this point supports a strong role for parenting in shaping children's literacy development, albeit in complex ways. Future research will evaluate whether and to what extent more intensive and comprehensive interventions (encompassing more dimensions of parenting) will yield measurable improvements in the literacy attainment of at-risk children.

Once Children Begin School

Stability of Language and Literacy Skills

Children who begin school with strong language skills tend to be more successful academically throughout their school career than are those with weaker language skills. Students who start first grade knowing the letters of the alphabet and with a firm grasp of other emergent literacy skills achieve stronger reading skills by the end of first grade than do students with weaker skills. Indeed, some have proposed a critical period for reading development encompassing the first three elementary school grades. Research reveals that students who fail to reach grade expectations by third grade are unlikely to experience success in school later on. The stability of students' language and literacy development may be one reason that the achievement gap between children from low-SES and high-SES families is both pervasive and persistent. As we discussed in the beginning of this article, children from low-SES families begin school with language and early reading skills that fall well behind those of their more affluent peers, with multiple sources of influence on this development – home, parenting, preschool, and child characteristics.

The Effect of Schooling and the Specificity of Learning

In the face of this stability, some have questioned whether schooling has any appreciable direct effect on children's cognitive development. However, there are studies that demonstrate causal effects of schooling on children's literacy skill growth. Some of these studies utilize a natural experiment employing the rather arbitrary birth date that school districts mandate for school entry. Children who just make or just miss this cut-off birth date are essentially the same age chronologically, but those whose birthdays fall before the cutoff date start first grade while those whose birthdays fall just before go to kindergarten. In this way, the schooling and maturational effects on children's development can be examined separately. If both groups demonstrate similar rates of growth in a particular skill, then that skill is most likely a product of maturation – there is not a 'schooling effect'. On the other hand, if children who are the same age but a grade ahead demonstrate rates of skill growth that are greater than their age-peers who are a grade behind them, then there is a 'schooling effect'.

First-grade schooling effects are evident for alphabet recognition, word decoding, phonemic (individual sounds within words) awareness, general knowledge, addition, short-term memory, sentence memory, and visuo-spatial memory. Yet there are no schooling effects for receptive vocabulary, rhyming, conservation of number and quantity, addition strategies, and narrative coherence. Children demonstrate similar rates of growth in these skills regardless of whether they are in kindergarten or first grade. For example, for 89 children who attended the same school district, and taking into account cognitive abilities and parents' education, there were kindergarten but not first-grade effects for letter naming. There were kindergarten and first-grade effects for basic reading skills, including word decoding. There were only first-grade effects for general information, mathematics, and phonemic segmentation (identifying the individual sounds in words).

These results are particularly revealing if we consider the three phonological awareness tasks. These tasks differed only in the level of segmentation the child was asked to complete – syllabic, subsyllabic, and phonemic. For the syllabic segmentation task, children were asked to identify the number of syllables in a word. For example, 'cucumber' has three syllables, 'cu-cum-ber'. In the sub-syllabic task, children were asked to say the first sound in each word. For example, /t/ is the first sound in the word 'toy'. For the phonemic task, children were asked to count the number of sounds in a word. For example, rest has four sounds, /r-e-s-t/. The study revealed that there were schooling effects but only for specific skills. For syllabic segmentation, neither first grade nor kindergarten had an effect on growth in these skills. For sub-syllabic segmentation, both first grade and kindergarten affected growth. In contrast, first grade but not kindergarten had an effect on phonemic segmentation. Additionally, emerging research reveals that once the amount and type of instruction students receive is taken into account, the schooling effect disappears. Thus, the schooling effect is most likely the result of instructional differences in kindergarten and first grade. In other words, learning is highly specific and related to the explicit focus of the instruction students receive. In first grade, children are provided with more time in activities that support their decoding skill growth, which results in first graders' stronger decoding skills when compared to their same-age peers who are in kindergarten.

Parents' and Teachers' Beliefs about Readiness

Apart from the research presented above, evidence indicates that parents and teachers have their own perceptions and beliefs about what skills comprise readiness, and these views in many ways outline the arena in which the translation of research into practice must occur. Recent research has illuminated several fundamental trends in parent and teacher attitudes and beliefs about readiness. First, evidence indicates that, overall, both parents and teachers are aware that children must be 'ready' for school and feel pressure to achieve this readiness, reporting a sense that demands for early learning are high. At the same time, many express a lack of clarity concerning what skills are needed or how they can be nurtured and assessed.

Second, despite possible confusion, parents and teachers do report conceptualizations of what readiness entails, and they share many of the same perceptions. For example, both parents and teachers of preschoolers were more likely to identify a child as ready to move from preschool to kindergarten if the child was well within the chronological age window for attendance, appeared to be adaptable (e.g., did not have outbursts and could manage in different social environments), demonstrated interpersonal skills, and displayed task persistence. These results are consistent with prior work indicating that both parents and teachers perceive social skills, particularly those related to self-control and interpersonal cooperation and compliance, as important for readiness.

Yet some evidence of fairly systematic differences between parents' and teachers' beliefs about readiness is apparent. Several studies suggest that parents more frequently assert academic components to readiness, including competence in English and in basic concepts. In contrast, teachers differed from parents in that their ideas about readiness also included gender, indicating that girls tended to be more ready than boys, and inhibited behavior, suggesting that children with more independent, outgoing behaviors were more ready than those who were shy. Across kindergarten teachers involved in the Early Childhood Longitudinal Study – Kindergarten Cohort, some disparities were apparent along sociodemographic background variables; female teachers were more likely to emphasize social development, while younger teachers were more likely to emphasize academics.

The findings above indicate not only that parents' and teachers' views of readiness are not identical, but that, on average, neither the average parent nor the average teacher conceptualizes readiness in the complexity set forth by prior research. Thus the final trend we will discuss, related to the relative malleability of parents' and teachers' views on readiness, is of particular import. A primary influence on teachers' beliefs about readiness are their administrators and colleagues, and emerging data suggest that parents glean much of their information from booklets and other materials provided by the school, which are often few in number. One future task, then, will likely involve disseminating information in ways that can be easily understood and applied to foster early learning.

Conclusions

As the foregoing discussion illustrates, the conceptualization of school readiness has undergone significant revision in the last two decades, from a simple child-centered notion to a deeper appreciation of the broad range of influences shaping a child's trajectory across the crucial school transition process. We have learned a great deal about how parents, preschools, early elementary schools and the larger sociocultural milieu contribute independently and interact to influence a child's growth. Fuller understanding of the complex pathways children follow will ultimately pave the way for successful efforts to ensure that all children are maximally ready to benefit from their early schooling experiences.

See also: Bayley Scales of Infant Development; Child and Day Care, Effects of; Cognitive Development; Demographic Factors; Emotion Regulation; Family Influences; Gender: Awareness, Identity, and Stereotyping; Head Start; Language Development: Overview; Literacy; Mortality, Infant; Parenting Styles and their Effects; Premature Babies; Preschool and Nursery School; Self-Regulatory Processes; Social-Emotional Development Assessment.

Suggested Readings

Bornstein MH (2002) *Handbook of Parenting*, 2nd edn. Mahwah, NJ: Lawrence Erlbaum Associates.

Bowman BT, Donovan S, and Burns MS (2000) *Eager to Learn: Educating Our Preschoolers*. Washington, DC: National Academy Press.

Chall J (1967) *Learning to Read: The Great Debate* New York: McGraw-Hill Book Co.

Dickinson DK and Newman SB (2006) *Handbook of Early Literacy Research,* vol. 2. New York: Guilford Press.

Dickinson DK and Tabors PO (2001) *Beginning Literacy with Language.* Baltimore: Paul H. Brookes Publishing.

Morrison FJ, Bachman HJ, and Connor CM (2005) *Improving Literacy in America: Guidelines from Research.* New Haven: Yale University Press.

National Reading Panel (2000) *Teaching Children to Read: An Evidence-Based Assessment of the Scientific Literature on Reading and Its Implications for Reading Instruction* (Summary). Washington, DC: National Reading Panel.

Neuman SB and Dickinson DK (2006) *Handbook of Early Literacy Research*, vol. 1. New York: Guilford Press.

Relevant Websites

http://www.childtrends.org – Children's home and school experiences in the United States, as well as their health and well-being.

http://nces.ed.gov – Children's home lives, their preschool and early elementary educations.

http://www.ed.gov – Major recent research findings pertaining to reading and education more generally, as well as descriptions of initiatives to help children learn to read.

http://nces.ed.gov – Students' performance reports, including on measures of reading skills, over the last decade, as well as break-downs of achievement by race, gender, and socioeconomic status.

Screening, Newborn, and Maternal Well-Being

H Als and S C Butler, Harvard Medical School, Boston, MA, USA

Glossary

Newborn neurobehavioral assessment – Refers to the infant's examination in terms of functional neurological status, behavioral repertoire, and behavior regulation. These aspects may be indicative of specific underlying brain lesions and/or diagnoses of diffuse brain compromise.

Newborn physical and neurological examination – Refers to a series of physical examinations which evaluate the infant's gestational age, growth parameters, vital signs, central nervous system intactness, and overall physical competency.

Newborn screening – Refers to the biochemical testing for inherited disorders, generally metabolic and chromosomal or specific gene-based in origin. Some may be at least partially correctable by either dietary or drug interventions.

Postnatal screening – Includes a review of both newborn and maternal risk factors, such as, assessment of parental readiness for discharge, confidence to provide care for the infant, assessment of family, environmental, and social risk factors, maternal and infant physical, behavioral–functional, and emotional health, and mother and infant blood screening for toxins and infectious agents.

Introduction

Recent advances in newborn medicine, obstetrics, and pediatrics have brought about changes in the care of newborn infants and their mothers. Continual re-evaluation of old routines and stronger commitment to mothers and infants has led to improvements in medical care and safety. Increased appreciation for the complexity and competencies of newborns has resulted in the expansion of newborn screening measures from simple blood tests to evaluation of brain function, social interactive ability, and availability for parental attachment. The societal importance of physically, emotionally, and socially healthy mothers and families is slowly gaining recognition in the evaluation of newborn overall functioning. The mission of newborn screening and assessment has evolved from the diagnosis and prevention of abnormalities to the assurance of physical health and well-being of the child and mother, along with provision of appropriate supports and education in assurance of emotional and life-adaptive well-being during the critical prenatal and neonatal periods.

Postnatal Parent Assessment

Screening for Maternal Medical, Social, and Emotional Health

The impact of labor and delivery, as well as of the metabolic and physiologic adaptations involved in transition to extra-uterine life, must be assessed in terms of the effect on the infant and postpartum mother. Maternal risk factors should be evaluated in the immediate postpartum period. The US Federal Newborn and Mothers Health Protection Act, 1996, mandates health insurance payment for at least 48 h postpartum hospitalization for a vaginal birth, and 96 h for Cesarean births. This timeframe largely precludes thorough assessment of mothers' emotional, social, and economical readiness for discharge. The specific criteria established by the American Academy of Pediatrics (AAP) and American College of Obstetricians and Gynecologists (ACOG) for parental readiness for discharge assessment, to be performed by the caregiving clinician, include physiological stability, functional ability, preparedness for self-care at home, caregiver competence, availability of social support, access to healthcare, psychosocial adequacy and coping skills, and knowledge about what to expect at discharge. The AAP recommends additional explicit screening criteria for both mother and infant before discharge, that include evaluation of mothers' knowledge, ability, and confidence to provide adequate care for the infant; assessment of family, environmental, and social risk factors including evaluation for substance abuse, history of child abuse, and mental illness; review of maternal blood screening results; completion of infant-screening tests and vaccinations; completion of infant physical assessment; and clearing of barriers to follow-up care such as transportation and economic challenges.

Placental examination

Maternal medical and social–emotional screening consists of thorough placental examination, maternal interview, and medical record review. The placenta, part of fetus and mother, is critical for all aspects of pregnancy from implantation to delivery. The placenta is dedicated to the survival of the fetus and attempts to buffer fetal effects of maternal malnutrition, disease, and teratogens. However, there are limits to the placental barrier's effectiveness. Many stressors lead to significant placental damage, fetal compromise, and ultimately pregnancy loss. Placental microscopic examination may reveal stressors experienced by the fetus and indication for further screening. The current trend toward intensified placental examination may lead to better understanding of poor pregnancy-outcome etiologies and ultimately to preventive measures.

Parental medical, social, and emotional screening

The perinatal visit presents an important opportunity for healthcare providers to begin a positive relationship with mother and infant. A full maternal history intake, including high-risk medical and social information should be performed, with review of the mother's obstetric and mother/infant's perinatal charts. Prenatally, most women are screened with routine blood tests, urine tests, and specialized tests for major congenital parasitic and viral infections, congenital bacterial infections, teratogens, and chromosomal and genetic abnormalities and malformations. Mothers' current use of medication, history of lactation, breast irregularities, surgeries, and family and social histories should also be reviewed. In the absence of a standardized initial maternal/child screening assessment tool, the initial assessment's depth and quality are dependent upon individual physicians and hospitals.

Childbearing is a complex human experience, which incorporates physical and psychological aspects. It is commonplace to assess mothers' physical well-being, yet often neglected is assessment of emotional well-being. This neglect carries significant risks for mother, infant, and family. Following delivery, screening for mental health, readiness for discharge, and psychosocial stressors is critical for appropriate treatment and increased positive long-term outcome.

The perceived readiness for discharge after birth scale (PRDS) is a useful self-report instrument for the assessment of a new mother's pain, strength, energy, mood, functional ability, self-care knowledge, and knowledge about infant care. It is predictive of later psychological and psychosocial problems, and of spontaneous utilization of health services in the first postpartum weeks.

Maternal postpartum depression

Postpartum depression continues to be under-recognized and prepartum depression is even less well-understood. Many depressed mothers remain untreated, and many postpartum women ignore, minimize, or deny their condition. Postpartum depression seriously diminishes mothers' life-enjoyment and affects the mother–infant relationship, the child's development, and overall family relations. Postpartum depression is a unique type of depression which characteristically occurs within 4 weeks of delivery. Risk factors include complications during labor and/or birth, infant health problems, and low parent confidence. Unclear diagnostic criteria and definitional merging of postpartum blues, depression, and psychosis make diagnosis and treatment difficult. The diagnosis of postpartum blues is reserved for a transient syndrome that resolves spontaneously. It is experienced by 80% of postpartum women, usually begins in the second to fourth day after birth, and may include mild and short-term fatigue, crying, mood instability, anxiety, and mild confusion. Postpartum depression, experienced by 10–30% of women, is characterized by significant bouts of tearfulness, mood swings, despondency, inability to cope with the infant's care, and increasing guilt about the birth and performance as mother. Fatigue, irritability, impaired concentration, and anxiety may also be present. Postpartum psychosis occurs much less frequently (1/1000). Onset is typically within 3 weeks of delivery. Symptoms include psychotic events, disturbance with major affect, and schizophrenic ideation. For postpartum depression and postpartum psychosis, treatment involves psychotherapy and possibly psychopharmacology.

The Edinburgh postnatal depression scale (EPDS), the postpartum depression checklist, and the schedule of affective disorders – pregnancy and postpartum guidelines are all self-report scales, developed to assist health professionals in screening mothers specifically for postnatal depression. They are more effective than generally used depression instruments, which are insensitive to the changes experienced by women after giving birth. The EPDS, completed within 5 min, is the most widely used (23 countries) standardized screening method for postnatal depression. Diagnosis of depression should always include careful direct clinical assessment aside from self-report measures.

Postnatal Newborn Assessment

Newborn screening is a term used to describe various types of assessment employed during the first few hours after an infant's birth. Newborn screening is a critical public health component of early detection and treatment, in order to prevent negative health outcomes. Newborn screening includes physical and sensory evaluation, metabolic and genetic screening, screening for rare disorders, and neurological and behavioral assessment.

Physical Evaluation of the Newborn

Physical evaluation is critical in determining whether the newborn infant will profit from special support and attention. The Apgar score assesses the infant's transition into extra-uterine life. In 1953, Virginia Apgar proposed an infant rating scale for immediate post-parturition status, ranging from 0 to 2 for five parameters (heart rate, respiratory effort, reflex irritability, muscle tone, and color). A total score of 0 reflects absent or poor functioning and a score of 10 reflects excellent performance. The Apgar score is rated separately at 1, 5, and 10 min after delivery, often by the attending anesthesiologist or obstetrician. Extreme scores have very high predictive validity with the probability of neonatal deaths essentially nil with ratings of 8 or better, and very high with ratings of 0–3.

Infants typically receive a physical examination at three distinct time periods: immediately after birth, in the newborn nursery or mother's room within 12 h of birth, and before discharge. A labor and delivery nurse or the physician may carry out a brief initial examination in order to ensure absence of significant cardiopulmonary instability and/or congenital anomalies. A complete physical examination, carried out in the presence of the family, provides an opportunity to assess the infant's postnatal adaptation and possible abnormalities, and to highlight the infant's strengths. The infant's growth parameters, vital signs, and overall physical competency are reviewed just before discharge. Many hospitals employ checklists for infant physical assessment; a federal- or state-mandated list of physical screening measures is not in effect.

During the infant's physical examination, their postmenstrual age (calculated post mother's last menstrual period, PMA) is also assessed. The most widely used system for postnatal PMA assessment is the New Ballard score (NBS). It includes assessment of physical and neuromuscular maturity, by scoring muscle tone, posture, muscle resistance, and physical characteristics, such as thickness of skin and skin creases. Performance time is 10–15 min.

The infant's weight, head circumference, and height are also measured and plotted daily on growth charts such as the Gairdner–Pearson Growth Charts. Another measure of intrauterine growth is the Ponderal Index (PI), a weight-to-height proportion measure. Infants, who weigh less than 2500 g, are considered low birth weight. Infants whose birth weights and/or PI are below the 10th percentile for PMA are considered small for gestational age (SGA) or fetal growth restricted (FGR), which indicates inadequate prenatal growth and may require added support and attention. SGA/FGR infants are at higher risk for poor energy reserve and increased metabolic requirements, which may lead to problematic birth-transition, feeding difficulty, hypothermia, hypovolemia (decrease in volume of blood plasma), and hypoglycemia. Infants whose birth weight and/or PI is greater than 90th percentile are considered large for gestational age (LGA) and may be at risk for hypoglycemia and birth trauma such as clavicle fracture, scalp hematoma, and brachial plexus injuries.

Each infant body system is carefully examined for signs of health and normal function, including stability of body temperature of 98.6 °F or 37 °C in a normal room environment, pulse rate of 120–160 beats per minute, and breathing rate of 30–60 breaths per minute. The infant's general well-being is examined for physical activity, tone, posture, and level of consciousness. The skin is examined for color, texture, nails, and intactness. Assessed for appearance and shape are head and neck; fontanels (soft spots between the infant's skull bones); clavicles (bones across the upper chest); face with eyes, ears, nose, and cheeks; and mouth with palate, tongue, and throat. The lungs are listened to for clarity and pattern of breath sounds, and the heart for absence of murmurs and extra beats. The femoral groin and the abdomen are examined for the absence of masses and hernias. The genitals and anus are evaluated for appearance and open passage for urine and stool. The hips, back, spine, arms, and legs are assessed for muscle tone, movement, and appropriate development.

Sensory evaluation of the newborn

Sensory evaluation of the newborn includes primarily hearing and vision screening (see **Table 1**). Hearing screening determines presence of hearing loss and usually is performed before hospital discharge. Infants born outside the hospital should have a hearing screening at their first pediatric visit within seven days of birth. Approximately one in three infants per 1000 has bilateral hearing loss. Profound impairment of receptive and expressive language development results from bilateral hearing loss, if undetected in the first year. This, in turn, leads to poorer acquisition of other milestones. When intervention begins within 3 months of birth, improved progression in language, cognitive, and social skills result. Interventions may include the use of various hearing aids, coupled with speech and language therapy. Infant-hearing is screened with one of two tests, acoustic emission (AE), or auditory brainstem response (ABR). AE screening uses a small cushion placed in the ear to present a signal. When the sound reaches the inner ear, the inner ear produces an echo that is computer-analyzed. ABR testing uses small sensors placed on the head (scalp electrodes) and a small cushion placed in the ear to present a signal. The brainwaves in response to sound are computer-analyzed to determine whether the brain received and processed the sound. These noninvasive tests are usually performed in the newborn hospital nursery. If either test shows abnormal results, the infant is referred for more extensive evaluation.

Early detection and treatment of eye and vision disorders in newborns is important to avoid lifelong visual impairment. The AAP recommends that visual examinations be performed in the newborn period and at all well-child visits. Newborns should be screened for ocular structural abnormalities, such as cataract (cloudy lens), corneal opacity (scar tissue), and ptosis (drooping eyelids). Newborn structural eye examination consists of ocular history-taking, vision assessment, external inspection of eyes and lids, ocular motility assessment, such as examination for strabismus and other eye movement disorders, pupil and red reflex examination (detection of opacities in the visual axis due to cataracts or corneal abnormalities). Newborn functional vision assessment consists of an evaluation of the infant's fixation and visual pursuit of a moving object. Object fixation, maintenance of fixation, and visual pursuit into various positions are examined. Specific failures might indicate structural and/or visual-processing impairments. The assessments are performed binocularly and monocularly. Infant-screening typically requires specially trained personnel. Early detection and treatment of visual disorders are essential to maximize adequate long-term visual function. Intervention may consist of corrective lenses, and/or surgery, and/or educative therapy.

Low birth weight preterm infants are at increased risk for retinopathy of prematurity (ROP), a disorder of the immature retina. The extent of retinal immaturity depends mainly on the degree of prematurity at birth. Given the proven benefits of timely treatment in reducing visual loss, the AAP recommends that all infants born at less than 1500 g or 32 weeks PMA receive carefully timed retinal examinations by an ophthalmologist experienced in the examination of preterm infants. The most effective proven treatments for ROP involve alteration of the retinal periphery in order to slow or reverse abnormal growth of blood vessels. Laser therapy burns the peripheral area and cryotherapy freezes areas on the eye's surface that overlie the periphery of the retina. Both treatments may impair peripheral vision.

Newborn conjunctivitis may be caused by irritation, a blocked tear duct, or infection. Conjunctivitis in the infected newborn eye appears as drainage from the eyes, causing the eyelids to become puffy, red, and tender. If left untreated, infection may cause perforation of the cornea and destruction of deeper eye structures. Treatment consists of antibiotic eye drops and ointments.

Screening for Inherited Metabolic Disorders

In 2002, the US General Accounting Office on Newborn Screening determined that newborn screening led to the identification of approximately 3300 infants with inherited metabolic disorders (IMDs). It is widely accepted that only with early detection of such disorders may early treatment and amelioration of detrimental effects occur. Newborn metabolic screening began in the early 1960s when Robert Guthrie, PhD, developed a blood test that detected phenylketonuria (PKU). In addition to PKU, there are a number of other metabolic diseases caused by genetically determined, inherited defects in protein and fatty acid metabolism. Children with these conditions typically appear well at birth; symptoms develop acutely during the

Table 1 Newborn screening and evaluation

Newborn screening	*Incidence rate*	*Symptoms/impairments*	*Treatment approaches*
Inherited metabolic disorders			
Phenylketonuria (PKU)	1/14 000	Brain damage, seizures, and mental retardation	Low phenylalanine diet
Congenital hypothyroidism (CH)	1/3000	Low metabolic rate, respiratory distress, constipation, umbilical hernias, jaundice, slowed mental and physical development, oversized heads, tongues, and bellies	Oral thyroid hormone assures normal development
Congenital adrenal hyperplasia (CAH)	1/19 000	Hyperfunction and hyperplasia of the adrenals, low blood sugar, salt-wasting, elevated blood potassium, acidosis, psychomotor disabilities, and death	Hormone replacement, stress reduction, and endocrinologist consultation
Galactosemia (GALT)	1/53 000	Death in infancy, blindness, and mental retardation	Dietary supplements and galactose free diet
Cystic fibrosis (CF)	1/9066	Greasy and bulky stools, breathing problems, digestive problems, slow growth, lung damage and often death	Mucus-thinners, bronchodilators, lung transplantation, antibiotics, high-calorie supplemented diet, anti-inflammatories, pancreatic enzymes
Maple syrup urine disease	1/230 000	Urine smells sweet, mental retardation, physical disability, coma, death	Elimination of branched chain amino acids
Biotinase deficiency	1/40 000–60 000	Seizures, hypotonia, immune system impairment, skin infections, hair loss, hearing loss, and mental retardation	Oral biotin supplementation
Homocystinuria	1/340 000	Seizures, eye lens abnormalities, mental retardation, skeletal abnormalities, and abnormal blood clotting	Special diet and vitamin supplements
Muscular dystrophies (MD)	1/650 000	Scoliosis, congestive heart failure, arrhythmia, respiratory failure, cognitive disability, and heart problems	No known cures. Treatment controls symptoms
Sickle cell disease (SCD)	1/3777	Weakness, slow growth, late onset puberty, complications with blood circulation and immune response, infections, stroke, acute chest syndrome, pain, death	Folic acid, pain medications, antibiotics, and in rare cases bone marrow transplants
Vitamin K deficiency	1/10 000	Abnormal bleeding, severe bruising, and many infants will die or sustain significant brain damage	Vitamin K administration immediately after birth
Viral infections			
Human immuno-deficiency virus (HIV)	2.3 million children	Failure to thrive, swollen abdomen and lymph nodes, diarrhea, pneumonia, oral thrush	Antiretroviral drugs
Prophylactic treatment			
Glucose levels	2%	Hypoglycemia, hypothermia, sepsis	Extra breastfeeding, supplemental glucose, intravenous treatments
Congenital heart defects	1/115–150	Feeding difficulties, tachypnea, sweating, and severe growth impairment.	Administration of influenza and pneumococcal vaccines
Developmental hip dysplasia	11.5/1000	Dislocated or malformed hip	Referral to orthopedics and repeat examinations
Hyperbilirubinemia	1/50	Jaundice, brain damage, cerebral palsy, hearing loss, visual and dental problems, mental retardation	Phototherapy and exchange transfusions
Teratogen exposure drug		Placental abruption, prematurity, microcephaly, congenital anomalies, necrotizing enterocolitis, mental retardation, stroke, hemorrhage, and withdrawal symptoms, hypertonia, jitteriness, diarrhea, and seizures	Maternal treatment prior to delivery, infant resuscitation, supplemental oxygen fluids, small feedings of hyper-caloric formula and drug therapy
Teratogen exposure lead	6–22% for children 1–5 years	Poor attention, auditory problems, abnormal balance, poor eye–hand coordination, slowed reaction times, sleep disturbances, mental retardation, aggression, delinquent behaviors, seizures, coma, and death	Lead-free environments, nutritional interventions (iron and calcium supplementation), reduced-fat diet, and frequent meals; chelating agents

Continued

Table 1 Continued

Newborn screening	*Incidence rate*	*Symptoms/impairments*	*Treatment approaches*
Hepatitis B	1–10%	Cirrhosis of liver, liver cancer	Vaccinations
Hearing loss	1/1000 bilateral	Speech and language disability, poor acquisition of other milestones	Hearing aids, speech and language therapy
Vision loss			Corrective lenses, surgery, educative therapy
Conjunctivitis		Eye irritation, blocked tear duct, eye infection, perforation of cornea, destruction of eye structures	Antibiotic eye drops, and ointments

first year, by which time damage is already irreversible. Identification before onset of symptoms may dramatically improve prognosis. Screening and the cost of detection in the newborn period is generally lower than the socioeconomic burden of the disease and its complications. Newborn screening is now widespread in developed nations such as the US, Australia, Europe, and many Southeast Asian countries. Depending on the prevalence of IMDs, country-specific programs and screening guidelines have been established. In the US and Europe, newborn screening is routine for PKU, congenital hypothyroidism, congenital adrenal hyperplasia, galactosemia, cystic fibrosis, maple syrup urine disease, biotinase deficiency, homocystinuria, the muscular dystrophies, and the hemoglobinopathies (see **Table 1**).

Phenylketonuria

Infants with PKU do not process phenylalanine, an amino acid found in most foods; phenylalanine builds in the bloodstream and causes brain damage and mental retardation. PKU affects 1 in 14 000 infants. Most are diagnosed within a few hours of birth and treated with a special low phenylalanine diet (small doses of low-protein food and avoidance of high-protein food).

Congenital hypothyroidism

Congenital hypothyroidism (CH), or underactive thyroid disease, stems from thyroid hormone deficiency or absence, which slows physical growth and brain development. Affected infants often show respiratory distress, constipation, umbilical hernias, jaundice, late onset milestones, slowed mental and physical development, and oversized heads, tongues, and abdomers. Their temperature, heart rate, and blood count are usually below normal. Incidence is as high as 1 in 3000. If detected very early, treatment with oral thyroid hormone assures normal development, otherwise symptoms are permanent and many never learn to speak.

Congenital adrenal hyperplasia

Congenital adrenal hyperplasia (CAH) includes a group of disorders, each related to a deficiency of one of the enzymes necessary to transform cholesterol to cortisol. This deficiency leads to hyperfunction and increased size (hyperplasia) of the adrenals. Consequences include low blood sugar, salt-wasting (low body sodium levels), elevated blood potassium levels, acidosis (reduced alkalinity of blood and body tissues), and severe virilization (development of male sex characteristics in a female). Many infants die (9% mortality rate) if the disorder is not recognized. Those who survive a newborn adrenal crisis often have significant psychomotor handicaps from the associated acidosis and shock. The incidence of CAH is 1 in 19 000 and is treated with hormone replacement. Living with CAH requires special attention to common illnesses and stress-inducing situations, and lifelong surveillance by an endocrinologist.

Galactosemia

Galactosemia (GALT) is the absence of a liver enzyme required to convert galactose or milk sugar into glucose, a sugar that the body uses as energy source. GALT prevalence is 1 in 53 000. It may cause death in infancy, or long-term blindness and mental retardation. Treatment includes dietary supplements and the life-long diet-elimination of galactose (milk products).

Cystic fibrosis

Cystic fibrosis (CF) is an inherited disease that affects breathing and digestion. Advances in medical treatment have improved the outlook for affected children and adults, but there is currently no cure yet. While some die in childhood, most affected individuals survive into their 30s. The abnormal gene that causes CF was discovered in 1989 and led to the development of a carrier-screening test, which helps determine whether a couple is at increased risk of bearing a child with the disease. Infants of mothers with CF are not at risk of inheriting the disease, unless the father also carries the gene. More than 10 million Americans are genetic carriers and about 30 000 have CF. It is most common in Caucasians, though all racial groups are affected.

CF affects the normal movement of salt into and out of certain cells, including those that line the lungs and pancreas. Sticky mucus clogs the lungs, causes breathing problems, and provides a breeding ground for bacteria, which leads to lung infections and contributes to early death. Thick digestive fluids also clog the ducts from the pancreas to the small intestine, and cause digestive problems and slow growth.

CF is diagnosed with a sweat test or with gene tests using a blood sample or saliva. Many children with CF are now diagnosed within 6 months after birth. Since about 15–20% of newborns with CF have meconium ileus (greasy and bulky stools), this symptom calls for testing. Early diagnosis and treatment improves the growth of newborns and children with CF. Types of medications include mucus-thinners, bronchodilators, antibiotics, and anti-inflammatories. Many children with CF require daily respiratory therapy since infection severity increases with age, often leading to serious lung damage and death. Lung transplantation is increasingly successful in the most severely affected individuals. To improve growth, most children with CF also take medications containing pancreatic enzymes and eat a healthy, high-caloric diet supplemented with vitamins (A, D, E, and K) and curcumin, found in the curry spice turmeric, to help improve salt transport.

Maple syrup urine disease

Maple syrup urine disease (MSUD) is a disorder caused by a faulty gene that prevents appropriate metabolization of three amino acids (leucine, isoleucine, valine) essential for growth. These amino acids build up in the body and cause urine to smell sweet. MSUD may cause mental retardation, physical disability, and death. The incidence is 1 in 230 000. A diet that eliminates the amino acids may prevent detrimental outcomes.

Biotinase deficiency

Biotinase deficiency is a metabolic disorder in which the body fails to process the vitamin biotin (vitamin H). Without biotin, specific enzymes called carboxylases fail to process proteins, fats, and carbohydrates. The condition is inherited in an autosomal recessive pattern, which means two copies of the gene in each cell must be altered to yield the disorder. Most often, the parents of a child with the disorder are not affected but are carriers of one copy of the altered gene. The incidence is about 1 in 40 000–60 000. Symptoms include seizures, hypotonia, skin rashes, immune system impairment, hair loss, hearing loss, and mental retardation. Treatment includes oral biotin supplementation.

Homocystinuria

Homocystinuria, a hereditary error of metabolism, is due to the defective enzyme cystathionine synthetase, required to properly digest methionine, an amino acid necessary for normal development. The condition's incidence is 1 in 340 000. It leads to eye lens abnormalities, mental retardation, skeletal abnormalities, and abnormal blood clotting. Treatment with a special diet and vitamin supplements may prevent most of the problems.

Muscular dystrophies

The muscular dystrophies (MDs) are a group of muscle diseases, which are hereditary and cause progressive weakness in movement. Duchenne muscular dystrophy (DMD) and Becker muscular dystrophy (BMD) are the two most frequent types. Both are due to defects of the same gene, which assures that muscle fibers make a protein called dystrophin. DMD, in most cases, affects only males, and is usually diagnosed at 2–3 years of age. DMD causes impaired intellectual development and problems with joints, spine, heart, and lungs. Scoliosis (curvature of the spine), congestive heart failure, and arrhythmias are frequent complications. Typically, by 12 years of age, affected children are wheelchair-bound, and by age 25 years they die of complications of respiratory failure. BMD has similar symptoms as DMD yet is often less severely disabling, starts later, progresses more slowly, and is more variable. Cases may be recognized as early as 3 years or as late as age 70 years; mean age is 12 years. The effects of BMD on muscle strength, the joints, and lung function are mild compared with DMD. Scoliosis is rare since young persons with BMD are usually still in relatively good condition at the time of the pubertal growth spurt. Some walk into early adulthood, others well into advanced age. Survival varies from midlife to the 80s. In BMD, intellect remains intact.

A blood test of the amount of serum creatine kinase (SCK), an important chemical in muscle fibers, aids in diagnosis. In MD, SCK leaks out of the muscle fibers and increases in blood serum. The diagnosis should be confirmed by muscle biopsy or electromyography, an examination where a needle, inserted in the muscle, records the electrical activity generated when the muscle contracts. The incidence of MD is approximately 1 in 650 000. There are currently no known cures for MD. Treatment controls symptoms and maximizes quality of life.

Hemoglobinopathies

The most devastating, yet treatable, inherited blood diseases in the newborn include glucose-6-phosphate dehydrogenase deficiency (G6PD deficiency), sickle cell disease (SCD), and inherited vitamin K deficiency bleeding. G6PD deficiency is the lack of glucose-6-phosphate dehydrogenase, an enzyme normally present in red blood cells. Red blood cells carry oxygen in the body; G6PD protects these cells from natural oxygen chemicals that may build up during fever or with certain medications. Too many of these chemicals cause hemolytic anemia, in which red blood cells are destroyed faster than bone marrow produces them. Symptoms include skin paleness, jaundice, dark colored urine, fever, weakness, dizziness, confusion, intolerance of physical activity, enlargement of the spleen and liver, increased heart rate (tachycardia), and heart murmur. G6PD deficiency is inherited from females, who carry a copy of the gene on one of their X chromosomes. Boys who receive the gene have G6PD deficiency, and girls who receive the gene are carriers and generally symptom-free. G6PD deficiency is seen in about 10% of African–American males, and is also common in persons from Mediterranean countries or Asia. Treatment includes avoidance of certain medications (aspirin), foods (fava beans), and environmental exposures (mothballs).

Sickle cell disease is a hereditary disorder that mostly affects persons of African ancestry, yet also occurs in other ethnic groups, including those of Mediterranean and Middle Eastern descent. More than 70 000 Americans have SCD and about 2 million (1 in 12 African–Americans) have the sickle cell trait, meaning that they carry one gene but do not have the disease. SCD occurs when a person inherits two abnormal genes (one from each parent), which cause their red blood cells to change shape. Instead of being flexible and round, the cells become rigid and curved. SCD affects hemoglobin, a protein found in red blood cells. The differently shaped red blood cells may clog blood vessels and deprive tissues and organs of oxygen. Normal-shaped red blood cells last about 4 months; sickle cells break down after 10–20 days, and cause anemia. Symptoms include weakness, slow growth, and late onset of puberty. SCD-caused complications of blood circulation and immune response lead to a higher risk for infections, stroke, and acute chest syndrome. The blocking effect of blood flow may cause severe pain in the chest, stomach, arms, legs, and other body parts. Depending on duration and severity, the disease may be fatal. Treatment is symptomatic rather than curative and includes folic acid, which aids red blood cell production; pain medications; and antibiotics to control infection. In rare cases, bone marrow transplants help produce healthy hemoglobin.

Inherited vitamin K deficiency bleeding is a rare inherited disorder that results in deficient blood-clotting. Normal blood coagulation is a complex process that involves up to 20 different plasma proteins, known as blood coagulation factors. When certain coagulation factors are deficient or missing, the coagulation chain reaction is disturbed. This autosomal recessive trait occurs in approximately 1 in 10 000 infants. Symptoms include umbilical cord bleeding at birth, nose bleeds, abnormal menstrual bleeding in the mother prior to pregnancy, abnormal bleeding after delivery, and severe bruising. Inherited vitamin K deficiency results in a lifelong bleeding disorder. Many infants will die or sustain significant brain damage due to bleeding into the brain. If diagnosed promptly, such symptoms are almost completely preventable with vitamin K administration immediately after birth. Since vitamin K will correct the deficiency, without curing it, it has become commonplace to administer vitamin K to all newborns in order to reduce the risk of hemorrhage. Other treatments include infusions of plasma or concentrates of clotting factors for blood loss. Diagnosis of bleeding disorders is also critical for precautionary measures to be taken during any surgery.

Screening for Viral Infections of the Newborn

The ACOG and the American Medical Association (AMA) support mandatory testing of all pregnant women and newborns for human immunodeficiency virus (HIV), which causes acquired immunodeficiency syndrome (AIDS). About 2 in 1000 pregnant women are HIV-positive. If untreated, infants born to HIV mothers have a 25–30% chance of infection. About 20% of infants infected with HIV develop serious disease in the first year and die by age 4. The remaining 80% may develop serious symptoms of AIDS around school age or adolescence.

Infants may contract HIV during gestation, labor, delivery, and breastfeeding. Timely knowledge of the mother's HIV status makes prenatal intervention possible and may reduce transmission. Intervention includes elective Cesarean section, avoiding artificial rupture of membranes, medication, and abstaining from use of breast milk. Antiretroviral drugs reduce the transmission from mother to infant rate by two-thirds, slow the growth of the virus, and allow strengthening of the infant's immune system. If the mother's HIV status is not documented, newborns may be tested immediately after birth; administration of antiretroviral drugs at this stage may reduce any risk of HIV transmission (postexposure prophylaxis).

Legislation and Recommendations Concerning Newborn Screening

Despite the value of newborn screening in terms of prevention of death, lifelong illness, disability, and economic savings, federal screening law enforcement is still weak. Within the US, most is in the form of federal recommendations and/or is entirely left to the discretion of each state. The US Preventive Services Task Force, based on the evidence of death-and-disability-prevention, recommends newborn screening for three groups of disorders: PKU, hypothyroidism, and GALT. There are no other federal guidelines regarding which disorders should be included in state screening programs. Individual programs vary widely, including conditions included in newborn screening, parental consent, screening methods, thresholds for abnormality, result-transmission to parents and physicians, and methods and resources for follow-up and treatment of children with atypical results. The March of Dimes recommends that all newborns be screened for at least 29 disorders including hearing loss. The actual number of genetic and metabolic disorders included in state newborn screening ranges from four to 36; the average is eight.

Procedures for Recommended Newborn Metabolic and Genetic Screening

Many of the disorders are detected by blood test; the infant's heel is pricked to obtain enough blood for laboratory analysis. Blood specimen should be taken from every newborn before hospital discharge, usually within 24–48 h of birth. The AAP recommends taking a repeat specimen 1–2 weeks later to ensure accurate screening. Blood samples are tested with a method known as a tandem mass spectrometry (TMS). With TMS, the same blood sample may be tested for over 55 different disorders. Typically, the infant's blood specimen is sent to a state public health laboratory for testing; the healthcare professional responsible for the infant's care receives the findings. Blood sample analysis may take several days; results generally are available by the first well-infant check-up at 2 weeks after birth.

In the US, states maintain databases of newborn screening results and track patients presumed positive. After testing, collection cards with residual blood are stored. There is no consensus regarding appropriate storage duration, storage conditions, and appropriate long-term use beyond initial newborn screening, nor is there consensus concerning consent for storage or future use.

In over half of the states, statutes mandate that information collected from newborn screening remain confidential. However, some states permit information release without authorization by the parent. The most common provisions for information release are for research, healthcare facilities disease management, law enforcement, and billing. Most states mandate screening of all infants unless parents object, known as 'informed dissent'. Many parents fail to realize that their infant is screened, that they as parents were screened prenatally, and what screening might imply. Parent education about prenatal and newborn screening may ensure parents' comprehension of the risks of refusal, improve follow-up rates for abnormal screening results, and minimize the harm of false positive results. Furthermore, it will increase parents' autonomy in arranging for additional screening for varying conditions not part of their states' current screening program. Several states report that they provide information on how to obtain testing through private laboratories for additional disorders not covered by the state screening. Most states report that they provide parent education about newborn screening, but amount and quality vary widely.

Fees charged to parents are the largest funding source for most newborn screening programs. Fees, generally paid by insurance companies, range from $10 to $60. Since they do not cover the entire cost, individual states finance the differences in various ways, such as through federal grants and state health department funds. Financing of screening programs is based on the expectation that the benefits of testing, early detection, and treatment will equal or exceed the cost of testing.

Newborn Screening Controversy

Public pressure to expand newborn screening provides controversy among some healthcare providers and policy experts. Early detection and treatment creates positive outcome, such as budgetary savings, given prevention of severe cognitive and physical abnormalities. In 1975, the National Research Council issued a report, which concluded that mandated screening was justified only if there was evidence that screening and early detection prevents death or other serious harm. This approach was reaffirmed in 1994 by the Institute of Medicine's Report on Newborn Screening. At present, controversy remains over the disorders to be included in the screening process. Disorders without known cure, such as CF, MD, and HIV are questioned in terms of the balance of costs, resources, and priorities.

Current Practices of Newborn Screening and Prophylactic Treatment

Several practices, beyond the federally recommended genetic, metabolic, and teratogen screens, are widely adopted by practitioners. These include screening for blood glucose levels, congenital heart defects, hip dysplasia, hyperbilirubinemia, teratogens, car safety seat tolerance, and vaccinations.

Glucose levels

Blood glucose screening is frequently performed for infants at risk for hypoglycemia, including infants of diabetic mothers; SGA or LGA infants; hypothermic infants; and hypoglycemic or septic (infection) infants. Such infants may require additional therapy and testing, should their blood glucose levels diverge from normal with routine breastfeeding.

Congenital heart defects

Over 25 000 babies (1 in 115–150) are born each year with a congenital heart defect. Congenital heart defects affect how blood flows through the heart or through the blood vessels near the heart. Some defects may cause blood to flow in abnormal patterns, others may block blood flow. Suspicion of a heart defect is raised by the presence of feeding difficulties, tachypnea (abnormally fast breathing), sweating, subcostal recession (pressure and in-drawing of the chest), or severe growth impairment. Cardiac heart defects are diagnosed with blood tests, echocardiograms (ultrasound of the heart and aorta), and heart catheterization (measures of blood pressure in heart and arteries). Follow-up of infants with congenital heart disease is typical; administration of influenza and pneumococcal vaccines may vary.

Developmental hip dysplasia

Hip dysplasia refers to the presence of an unstable, subluxated, dislocated, or malformed hip. The incidence is 11.5 per 1000 infants. In 2000, the AAP recommended hip examination in the newborn period, referral to orthopedics, and repeat examinations.

Hyperbilirubinemia

Hyperbilirubinemia testing is important for the prevention of kernicterus, a type of brain damage that causes athetoid cerebral palsy, hearing loss, problems with vision and teeth, and possible mental retardation. In some cases, the liver of the newborn is too immature or inefficient to excrete the used-up blood cell breakdown products, characterized by a yellow pigment called bilirubin, which causes jaundice. Jaundice is common in the first few days after birth, and usually resolves as the infant feeds, becomes well-hydrated, and excretes the pigment. Excessive jaundice indicates a high level of bilirubin, which over time deposits in fatty tissues, including the brain, and causes kernicterus. The AAP recommends measuring total bilirubin levels of infants, who exhibit jaundice in the first 24 h after birth. Hyperbilirubinemia, if present, may be treated with phototherapy (exposure to ultraviolet light) and, as necessary, with exchange transfusions.

Teratogens

A teratogen is an agent that may cause embryonic or fetal malformations. While identification of maternal teratogen exposure before or during pregnancy would be ideal, this is not always possible and infant testing is necessary. Currently, there are no federally mandated guidelines on infant teratogen and drug-exposure testing. The decision rests with the doctor and hospital. Teratogen levels are easily detected in the newborn period by blood, urine, meconium, or hair testing.

The use of illicit drugs (marijuana, cocaine, amphetamines, heroin, methadone, lysergic acid diethylamide (LSD), opioids, among others) and licit drugs (nicotine, alcohol, caffeine) during pregnancy may influence maternal and infant outcomes. Prenatal drug exposure has been associated with placental abruption, premature labor, microcephaly, congenital anomalies including cardiac and genito-urinary abnormalities, necrotizing enterocolitis, cognitive disabilities, and central nervous system stroke and hemorrhage. Withdrawal symptoms, such as sweating, irritability, hypertonia, jitteriness, diarrhea, and seizures are often seen in infants after *in utero* exposure to drugs. The 2004 National Survey on Drug Use and Health, based solely on self-report of randomly sampled pregnant American women, estimated that 4.6% used illicit drugs during pregnancy. When a child is found to have been exposed to drugs *in utero*, healthcare providers are often required to notify social services for a discharge placement decision and family court determination of custody. However separation of mother and child in the newborn period has lasting implications for the mother–infant relationship and long-term development.

Lead exposure is an additional potent neurotoxin with primary effects on the nervous, hematopoietic, and renal systems. Lead inhibits enzymes in many biochemical pathways; high levels of lead exposure are associated with poor attention, aggression, lowered cognitive abilities, somatic complaints, antisocial behaviors, seizures, coma, and death. Adverse neurodevelopmental sequelae associated with even mildly elevated levels include reduction in auditory threshold, abnormal balance, poor eye-hand coordination, slowed reaction times, sleep disturbances, and impaired cognition.

Lead is readily transmitted through the placenta from the mother to the fetus. Maternal exposure to high environmental lead levels may be associated with spontaneous abortion, premature rupture of membranes (PROM), and preterm delivery. Children absorb lead more readily than adults; children's developing nervous systems are more susceptible to the toxic effects of lead. Even with treatment, it remains unclear to what extent the effects of lead exposure are reversible.

Currently, the primary sources of lead exposure are deteriorated lead paint, and the soil and dust it contaminates. The AAP recommends blood lead screening as part of routine health supervision for children between 9 to 12 months of age and re-screening at 24 months. It also recommends that children, pregnant women, and families be screened routinely by healthcare providers with community-specific risk-assessment questionnaires, which evaluate chances for lead exposure.

An estimated 890 000 children aged 1–5 years, or 4.4% of the US population in that age range, have elevated blood lead levels. Successful prenatal identification of lead-exposed women would allow for removal of lead, and a lead-free environment for newborns. Once exposed, treatment includes nutritional interventions (iron and calcium supplementation), a reduced-fat diet, and frequent meals. Use of chelating agents, which competitively bind lead and remove it from the body, may be necessary. Timely intervention prevents progression and improves outcome.

Car safety seat tolerance

Car safety seat tolerance testing is increasingly part of inhospital screening before discharge. The AAP recommends that all infants discharged from hospitals be transported in car safety seats that meet the Federal Motor Vehicle Safety Standard. Some infants have difficulty with oxygen saturation and hypoxia (lack of oxygen), while in the car seat. It is recommended that, at minimum all infants born under 37 weeks PMA or otherwise at high risk, receive a car seat test. There is no specific car seat screening test; however, the AAP recommends that each hospital monitor infants for possible apnea, bradycardia, or oxygen desaturation, while in the car seat. It also recommends that parents receive hands-on teaching including selection of the most appropriate car seat for their newborn, proper infant positioning in the seat, and car seat installation.

Vaccinations

While most vaccinations are administered at the 2, 4, 6, and 12 month well-baby visits, the immunization action coalition and the AAP recommend that the infant be protected from the hepatitis B virus immediately and that the first vaccine dose, determined to be highly effective, be administered at birth and no later than hospital discharge. Hepatitis B causes the most common serious liver infection in the world. The virus is transmitted through blood and infected bodily fluids, occurs through direct blood-to-blood contact, unprotected sex, use of contaminated needles, and from an infected woman to her newborn during delivery. In 95% of cases, the spread of hepatitis B from an infected mother to her fetus is preventable with the hepatitis B vaccine if given to the newborn within 12 h of birth. There is also concern that the newborn might be exposed to Hepatitis B after birth by another family member or caregiver; this occurs in two-thirds of childhood transmission cases. A simple blood test determines the newborn's hepatitis B status.

Neurological and Behavioral Evaluation of the Newborn

Medical examinations and blood tests are one kind of newborn screening. Of great importance is also the clinical neurological and neurodevelopmental behavioral evaluation of the newborn.

Neurological Evaluations

The neurological evaluation, often built into the pediatric examination of the infant, is helpful in the determination of the strengths and weaknesses of the newborn central nervous system. The goals of newborn neurological assessments are twofold: first, to arrive at a diagnosis of suspected neurological problems or pathological processes; and second, to develop a long-term prognosis for a newborn recovering from a neurological insult or judged at risk due to nonoptimal circumstances during pregnancy, labor, or delivery, and/or a diagnosed neurological problem. André Thomas and St. Anne Dargassies developed the first systematic neurological examination of the newborn, which was translated into English in 1960. It includes a survey of family history, pregnancy, delivery, placenta, and birth conditions. It focuses on the infant's normal responses including an assessment of tone, reflexes (obligatory, simple responses), and reactions (flexible, complex responses).

The Prechtl neurological examination of the full-term newborn infant is the most popular examination. It was developed by Prechtl and Beintema in 1964, revised in 1977. The first part consists of observation of resting posture, spontaneous motor activity, tremor, skin, respiratory rate, temperature, and weight, and examination of the skull, fontanels, head circumference, face, and eyes. A second section includes continued observation of state, posture, and movement in the course of a sequence of the standard elicited reflexes, some of which are taxing, such as the Moro. The examination takes approximately 20–40 min. Three summary parameters – reactivity, stability, and degree of asymmetry – are of particular value in the assessment of newborn integrative intactness.

Behavioral Evaluation of Low-Risk Full-term Newborns

Observable behavior as an expression of neurological status and brain function is systematically utilized to identify specific brain lesions and/or diagnose more diffuse brain compromise. Graham in 1956 developed the first newborn behavioral assessment with the goal of differentiating normal from brain-injured infants. The examination includes pain threshold; motor responses; visual attention; and integrative parameters such as irritability and muscle tension. Rosenblith's 1961 modification deleted the pain threshold test, added auditory and visual responses, and divided the test into motor and tactile scores. She rated best rather than average performance in an effort to overcome newborns' behavioral instability.

The Brazelton Neonatal Behavioral Assessment Scale (BNBAS or NBAS), developed by T. Berry Brazelton in 1973, distinguishes itself from other newborn assessments in its interventive usefulness with parents and medical staff. The success of the BNBA is related to its enhancement of the caregiver's perception of the newborn as a competent, autonomous being. The main goal is assessment of individuality in the spectrum of healthy full-term newborns. It focuses on motor integration, state regulation, attention-interactive as well as reactivity and consoling capacities. An assessment takes approximately 30 min.

Neurobehavioral Assessment of High-Risk Newborns

Tests, developed specifically for the assessment of preterm and high-risk infant functioning, include the Dubowitz Neurological Assessment of the Pre-term and Full-term Newborn Infants, 1981, which draws primarily on the Dubowitz Gestational Age Assessment (1970). The Dubowitz uses stick-figure drawings to facilitate scoring of 32 scale items. Test time is 10–15 min. Some items possess high demand characteristics, inappropriate for fragile infants.

The most recent combination of neurological, maturational, and behavioral items, the 2004 NNNS (NICU Network Neurobehavioral Scale) developed by Lester on infants exposed to illegal substances *in utero*, assesses a full range of infant neurobehavioral performance inclusive of stress, abstinence and withdrawal symptoms, neurological functioning, and PMA. The order of items is strictly specified; it is purposely not a relationship-based interactive assessment. This makes a fair assessment of the newborn more difficult, since it is social in nature.

The assessment of preterm infants' behavior (APIB), developed in 1982 by Heidelise Als, is a neurobehavioral assessment, which articulates behavioral organization constructs of modulation and differentiation of functioning. The specificity and organization of preterm and full-term infants' behavioral functioning is assessed by observation of the infant's threshold from balanced organization to disorganization, functional stability and competence to recovery from disorganization back to balance. Measured is the degree of differentiation and modulation of various behaviorally defined subsystems (autonomic, motor, state, and self-regulatory) of functioning in the course of a behavioral assessment sequence. The APIB uses the test items of the Brazelton Scale, organized into increasingly vigorous questions posed to the infant. A typical assessment takes approximately 45–60 min. Concurrent validity with MRI and electroencephalogram (EEG) as well as predictive validity have been established in a number of studies. The APIB currently is the most thorough and in-depth newborn assessment and most resembles the neuropsychological assessment of an older child.

Parental Support and Referral Services

Newborns with abnormal results on any of the assessments discussed should receive a longer-term process of monitoring, intervention, and treatment. Follow-up services may encompass a variety of care coordination and direct service activities, including parents and provider notification of test results, confirmation of diagnosis, treatment for specific disorders, monitoring of service provision, and evaluation of clinical care of individuals. Since states ultimately carry control and responsibility for the structure of newborn screening programs, they also must carry control and responsibility for the follow-up implementation pursuant screening. More is known about the specifics of screening mandates of individual states than about the types of follow-up services provided. Identification of a particular disorder is typically the first component of newborn screening; however, if infants with confirmed diagnoses do not receive timely and appropriate care for their conditions, mere identification serves little purpose. In 2006, a study by Hoff and Hoyt reviewed the follow-up services of all 50 states, including Washington DC, Puerto Rico, and the US Virgin Islands. The results are alarming in that half of the states revealed that they did not engage in any follow-up oversight or activities. Follow-up remains a seriously overlooked component of newborn screening. At this point, decisions rest with clinical care providers, hospitals, and pediatricians as to what kind of follow-up a child will receive.

There are a variety of voluntary resources available to parents of newborns at-risk for and/or diagnosed with special health and development conditions. These include foundations, internet sites, mailing lists, magazines, and support groups. Resources may provide parents with information, support, and encouragement to serve as their children's advocates. Sometimes hospitals may offer support and follow-up programs. Hospitals, community social workers, family physicians, and healthcare centers may serve as referral source for new parents as well as for parents of infants with special health and developmental conditions. Typically, the least privileged families will receive the worst services given the very poor resource availability. This is a serious public health concern for many nations.

Acknowledgments

This work is supported by grant sponsor: NIH/ NICHD; grant number: R01 HD047730 and R01 HD046855 (H.Als). Grant sponsor: US Department of Education/ OERI; grant number: H324CO40045 (H.Als). Grant sponsor: I. B. Harris Foundation (H. Als). Grant sponsor: NIH/ MRDDRC; grant number: P30HD18655 (M. Greenberg).

See also: AIDS and HIV; Auditory Development and Hearing Disorders; Birth Complications and Outcomes; Birth Defects; Depression; Developmental Disabilities: Cognitive; Developmental Disabilities: Physical; Endocrine System; Genetic Disorders: Sex Linked; Genetic Disorders: Single Gene; Healthcare; Neuropsychological Assessment; Newborn Behavior; Postpartum Depression, Effects on Infant; Safety and Childproofing; Screening, Prenatal; Vision Disorders and Visual Impairment.

Suggested Readings

Als H, Butler S, Kosta S, and McAnulty G (2005) The assessment of preterm infants' behavior (APIB): Furthering the understanding and measurement of neurodevelopmental competence in preterm and fullterm infants. *Mental Retardation & Developmental Disabilities Research Reviews* 11(1): 94–102.

Braddock D, Hemp R, Parish S, and Westrick J (eds.) (1998) *The State Of The States in Developmental Disabilities.* Washington, DC: American Association on Mental Retardation.

Cunningham G (ed.) (2006) *Williams Obstetrics*, (22nd edn. New York: McGraw-Hill.

Green N, Dolan S, and Murray T (2006) Newborn screening: Complexities in universal genetic testing. *Public Health* 96: 1955–1959.

Hobbins J, Aagaard-Tillery K, Adashi E, and Amon E (eds.) (2007) *Clinical Obstetrics: The Fetus and Mother.* Oxford: Blackwell Publishing.
Kaye C, Committee on Genetics, Accurso F, *et al.* (2006) Introduction to the newborn screening fact sheets. *Pediatrics* 118(3): 1304–1312.
Martin R, Fanaroff A, and Walsh M (eds.) (2005) *Fanaroff and Martin's Neonatal–Perinatal Medicine: Diseases of the Fetus and Infant,* 8th edn. St. Louis: Mosby.
Miller L (2002) Postpartum depression. *Journal of the American Medical Association* 284: 762–765.
Thompson D, McPhillips H, Davis R, *et al.* (2001) Universal newborn hearing screening: Summary of evidence. *Journal of the American Medical Association* 286: 2000–2010.
Waisbren S and Levy H (2004) Expanded screening of newborns for genetic disorders. *Journal of the American Medical Association* 291: 820–82.
William H, Taeusch R, and Ballard M (eds.) (2004) *Avery's Diseases of the Newborn.* Saunders: Elsevier.

Relevant Websites

http://www.excellence-earlychildhood.ca – Centres of Excellence for Children's Well-being, Early Childhood Development.
http://www.nidcd.nih.gov – National Institute of Deafness and Communication Disorders.
http://genes-r-us.uthscsa.edu – National Newborn Screening and Genetics Resource Center.
http://www.nidcap.org – NIDCAP Federation International.
http://www.postpartum.net – Postpartum Support international.
http://www.aap.org – The American Academy of Pediatrics.
http://www.acog.org – The American College of Obstetricians and Gynecologists.
http://www.cdc.gov – The Center for Disease Control and Prevention.
http://www.gao.gov – The Government Accountability Office.
http://www.marchofdimes.com – The March of Dimes.
http://www.unicef.org – UNICEF, Unite for Children.

Screening, Prenatal

T A Lenzi, Vanderbilt University Medical Center, Nashville, TN, USA
T R B Johnson, The University of Michigan, Ann Arbor, MI, USA

Glossary

Amniocentesis – An invasive prenatal diagnostic procedure whereby amniotic fluid is withdrawn from the amniotic cavity under ultrasound guidance between 15 and 20 weeks' gestation. Cells from the amniotic fluid (amniocytes) can be cultured for chromosome analysis or karyotype.
Aneuploidy – A chromosome number that is not an exact multiple of the haploid number. The normal human haploid number of chromosomes is 23. Since humans are diploid, the total number of human chromosomes is 46. Examples of aneuploidy include trisomy (a third copy of a chromosome, for 47 total chromosomes) and monosomy (a single copy of a chromosome for a total of 45 chromosomes).
Autosomal dominant – A pattern of inheritance characterized by affected people having an affected parent, equal number of males and females affected, recurrence risk for siblings of the affected of one in two, and the presence of male-to-male transmission. The latter distinguishes autosomal dominant from X-linked forms of inheritance. In autosomal dominant inheritance, only one mutant copy of a gene must be present to cause disease.
Autosomal recessive (AR) – A pattern of inheritance characterized by asymptomatic parents of affected offspring (carriers), males and females equally likely to be affected, and recurrence risk of one in four for each sibling of an affected person. In AR inheritance, both copies of the gene must be mutant in order to express the disease.
Chorionic villus sampling (CVS) – An invasive prenatal diagnostic procedure performed between 10 and 13 weeks' gestation. Placental tissue, or chorionic villi are withdrawn from the uterus by either the transabdominal or transcervical approach under ultrasound guidance. Once obtained, the chorionic villi can be cultured for chromosome analysis, or karyotype.
Chromosome – Threadlike unit of DNA contained within the nucleus of the cell. Humans have 23 pairs or 46 total chromosomes.
Congenital adrenal hypoplasia – An autosomal recessive enzyme deficiency resulting in cortisol deficiency. Symptoms might include masculinization in females due to excessive male hormones and dehydration due to salt wasting.
Diploid – The normal number of chromosomes in somatic (nongamete) cells. The diploid human chromosome number is 46. Gametes which are haploid contain 23 chromosomes.
Gametes – Reproductive cells with the haploid chromosome number. Female gametes are also

called ova, and male gametes are also called sperm. The haploid number of chromosomes in humans is 23.
Genetic anticipation – Progressively earlier onset and increased severity of a disorder with successive generations. Anticipation is frequently due to expansion of triplet repeats.
Karyotype – A standard arrangement of the chromosomes of an individual, often displayed in a photomicrograph.
Mean corpuscular volume (MCV) – A measure of the mean red blood cell volume. Normal values are typically 80–96 fl. An MCV less than 80 should raise suspicion for thalassemia in susceptible ethnic groups.
Meiosis – A form of cell division in which diploid cells divide to form haploid gametes. Meiosis is notable for genetic recombination, in which chromosomal segments are exchanged, resulting in nonidentical daughter cells, and is a source of genetic variation in humans.
Monochorionic – A type of placentation in twins in which the outer membrane or chorion is shared. Monochorionic pregnancies are at risk for complications such as twin-to-twin transfusion syndrome.
Nondisjunction – An error in meiosis resulting in abnormal chromosome number due to homologous chromosomes going to the same pole (and later same cell) instead of to opposite poles (and different cells).
Pedigree – A graphic representation of a family showing the relationship of family members to the proband, gender, and information about genetic disease and which family members are affected.
Polar body – A DNA containing structure within an ovum resulting from normal, unequal cell division during female meiosis. In female meiosis, the two-step cell division process produces only one ovum and two polar bodies (the first polar body is diploid, the second polar body is haploid). In contrast, male meiosis results in four sperm.
Proband – The first identified clinically affected member of a family.
Sickledex – A solubility assay which detects cells susceptible to sickling.
X-linked icthyosis – A deficiency of steroid sulfatase resulting in decreased placental estrogen production. Features include low levels of estrogen in affected pregnancies, and icthyosis, or dry scaly skin in affected males.

Introduction

Prenatal screening ideally begins prior to conception. Family history, patient ethnicity, and various screening tests (such as maternal serum screening and fetal ultrasound) help to identify patients at high risk for genetic disorders or congenital anomalies. Screening tests, which carry virtually no risk to the pregnancy, do not provide a definitive diagnosis for the disorder in question. Invasive, diagnostic tests such as amniocentesis and chorionic villus sampling (CVS) in contrast do provide a definitive diagnosis, but have the disadvantage of carrying a risk of pregnancy loss. It is the job of the provider to counsel patients in a nondirective way about the wide range of screening and diagnostic options patients have so they may make informed decisions.

Initial Genetic Screen

Introduction

Prenatal care has existed for over 100 years as an approach to improve maternal and newborn outcomes. Traditionally, risk factors such as family history, social and behavioral factors, and the identification of existing risk factors (sexually transmitted disease, anemia, blood incompatibility) and intercurrent problems such as hypertension, fetal growth restriction, and pre-term labor have been the core of prenatal care. With advances in knowledge and tools of modern genetics, a major emphasis has become prenatal and recently preconception screening of hereditable diseases. The goal of prenatal screening is to counsel patients about their screening and diagnostic options, to provide reassurance to patients at low risk, and to identify high-risk patients who may benefit from diagnostic or therapeutic procedures.

Patient and Family Histories

Genetic screening begins with a thorough medical and family history of the patient and her partner. The ideal time to perform genetic screening is prior to conception. At this time, as well as during early pregnancy, all reproductive aged females should be counseled that they should take folic acid at a dose of 400 μm (the dose in a standard prenatal vitamin), which has been shown to decrease the risk of having a child with a neural tube defect such as spina bifida. It is especially important to screen for genetic disorders in patients presenting for artificial reproductive technologies such as *in vitro* fertilization.

The family history is best represented in pedigree format, and should include at least three generations, including the pregnancy. As part of the family history, patients should be specifically asked about consanguinity (marriage between relatives), genetic disorders, birth defects and people in the family with a learning disability or mental retardation. Patients should also be asked about their ethnicity, and appropriate carrier screening should be offered as below.

All pregnancies are at risk for congenital anomalies, or birth defects which occur in 2–4% of the general population. A family history of congenital anomalies or a genetic disorder may increase risk above this baseline.

Ethnicity Based Screening

Carrier testing in Caucasians: Cystic fibrosis

Cystic fibrosis (CF) is the most common genetic disorder amongst Caucasians, with a prevalence of 1/3300 in the US. CF is a multisystem disease affecting primarily the lungs, digestive system, and reproductive system in males. Patients may present as children with failure to thrive, chronic cough or pulmonary infections, and malabsorption with loose stools. The median survival in the disease is approximately 30 years, but is significantly longer for those with normal pancreatic function. Cause of death is typically due to respiratory failure.

Approximately 1/25 Northern European Caucasians (and approximately 1/29 American Caucasians) are carriers for CF mutations. CF is inherited in an autosomal recessive (AR) manner which means that both parents must carry a mutation in order to have an affected child (**Figure 1**). When both parents are carriers of a CF mutation, they have a 25% chance of having an affected child. Carrier testing is clinically available and should be offered to high-risk groups including Caucasians and Ashkenazi Jews who are pregnant or planning a pregnancy. Information about CF carrier testing should be made available to other lower risk ethnic groups and those patients should be informed of the limitations of screening, mainly that detection rates with carrier testing are not as high.

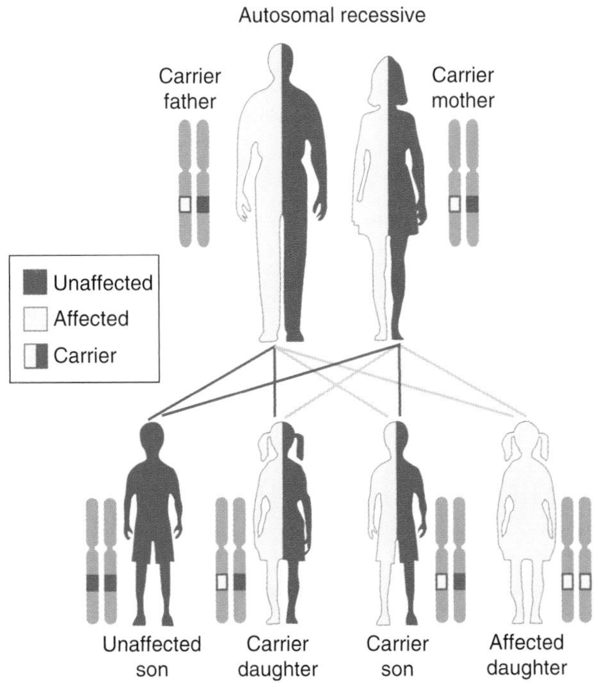

Figure 1 Autosomal recessive inheritance. From Genetics Home Reference (http://ghr.nlm.nih.gov/handbook/illustrations/autorecessive).

The CF gene encodes a chloride channel, called the cystic fibrosis transmembrane conductance regulator (CFTR). Mutations interfere with the transport of chloride in tissues, resulting in thick secretions which are responsible for many of the disease manifestations. Over 900 mutations in the CF gene have been described. A panel of 23 common CF mutations is available. Because this panel does not detect all mutations, only the most common ones found in Caucasians, detection rates are not 100%. Detection rates with carrier screening are highest in Ashkenazi Jews at up to 94%, followed by 88% in Caucasians, 72% in Hispanics, 65% in African Americans, and 49% in Asians (**Table 1**). Detection rates are lower in non-Caucasians due to the overall lower disease prevalence in these ethnic groups as well as less of an understanding of the molecular basis of disease in other ethnic groups. Therefore, a negative screen in non-Caucasians is less reassuring about the absence of a mutation.

In Caucasians, negative CF screening reduces the risk of being a CF carrier from 1/25 to approximately 1/200. In Ashkenazi Jews, who have a higher mutation detection rate, the post-test carrier risk is 1/400. Since carrier testing is not 100% sensitive, it does not guarantee that a couple will not have an affected child, but it can be used to provide a new risk assessment. As an example, an unscreened Ashkenazi Jewish couple has approximately a 1/2300 risk of having an affected child, assuming a carrier frequency of 1/24, and given that CF is an AR disease ($1/24 \times 1/24 \times 1/4 =$ approximately 1/2300). If one partner is screened and found not to carry a mutation, their new risk estimate for an affected child is approximately 1/38 000 ($1/400 \times 1/24 \times 1/4$). If both members of an Ashkenazi Jewish couple screen negative for CF mutations, their risk of having an affected child is approximately 1/640 000 ($1/400 \times 1/400 \times 1/4$).

If however, a patient has a family history of CF, it is helpful to obtain information about which mutation is present in the family. If the family carries an uncommon CF mutation not tested for in the common panel, then additional mutation testing and genetic counseling should be offered to the couple.

CF screening may be offered either as couple-based screening, or sequentially. In couple-based screening, both partners are screened simultaneously. This strategy may be preferable in high-risk ethnic groups, particularly if pregnancy is advanced and time is an issue. Others opt for sequential screening in which one partner is screened, and the other partner is only screened if the first is found to be a carrier. If this option is chosen, the person belonging

Table 1 Cystic fibrosis detection and carrier rates before and after testing

Racial or ethnic group	*Detection rate (%)*	*Carrier rate before testing*	*Carrier risk after negative test result (approximate)*
Ashkenazi Jewish	94	1/24	1/400
Non-Hispanic Caucasian	88	1/24	1/208
Hispanic American	72	1/46	1/164
African American	65	1/65	1/186
Asian American	49	1/94	1/184

With permission from the American College of Obstetrics and Gynecology. Update on Carrier Screening for Cystic Fibrosis (2005) ACOG Committee Opinion Number 325. American College of Obstetricians and Gynecologists. *Obstetrics Gynecology* 106: 1465–1468.

to the ethnic group with the highest detection rate should be screened.

Few genotype–phenotype correlations for predicting disease severity in an affected fetus exist. Some CF mutations are associated with pancreatic sufficiency, and therefore have a better prognosis. However, genotype is generally not helpful in predicting the severity of the lung disease which is the major cause of morbidity and mortality in CF.

Jewish carrier screening

A number of diseases are increased in frequency in those of Ashkenazi Jewish ancestry. Eighty percent of American Jews are of Ashkenazi descent, or originally from Central and Eastern Europe. This is in contrast to Sephardic Jews who originate mainly from the Mediterranean. Current recommended practice is to offer individuals of Ashkenazi Jewish ancestry carrier screening for four diseases including: Tay Sachs disease, Canavan disease, CF, and familial dysautonomia. Patients of Askenazi Jewish descent may inquire about carrier screening for other diseases increased among their ethnic group for which carrier testing is available including Fanconi anemia group C, Niemann-Pick disease type A, Mucolipidosis IV, Bloom syndrome, and Gaucher disease. All of these diseases can occur in the general population, but at a much lower rate. Because of the low prevalence of these diseases in non-Ashkenazi Jews, carrier frequencies outside of this ethnic group are often not known, and there is little benefit to carrier screening in other ethnicities unless there is a family history of one of these disorders.

Tay Sachs disease is a severe neurodegenerative disorder with early childhood death. Approximately 1/30 Ashkenazi Jews are carriers for Tay Sachs disease, which results from mutations in the enzyme hexosaminidase A. Deficiency of this enzyme leads to accumulation of toxic materials in cells. Like most enzyme defects, Tay Sachs is inherited in an AR fashion. Initial carrier screening for Tay Sachs disease may be accomplished with biochemical or molecular methods. Biochemical methods test the amount of enzyme activity using a synthetic enzyme substrate. If this enzyme assay is abnormal, further testing should be pursued, since 2% of Ashkenazi Jews carry a 'pseudodeficiency allele'. This allele produces an enzyme that functions normally *in vivo*, but does not process the substrate used in the assay. People with the pseudodeficiency allele are clinically unaffected in spite of the abnormal enzyme assay. The only way to distinguish the pseudodeficiency allele from a true carrier is to perform molecular analysis of the hexosaminidase A gene. Molecular DNA testing for the six most common mutations detects approximately 95% of Ashkenazi Jewish carriers.

Canavan disease, which is due to deficiency of the enzyme aspartoacylase, is another severe neurodegenerative disease that results in early death. Deficiency of this enzyme leads to accumulation of N-acetylaspartic acid (NAA) which may be responsible for the demyelination and neurodegeneration seen in this disorder. Canavan disease is also inherited in an AR fashion, and approximately 1/40 Ashkenazi Jews are carriers. Canavan may be diagnosed by the finding of NAA in a urine organic acid analysis. Enzymatic testing is not widely available, and generally not necessary since molecular DNA testing detects 97% of Ashkenazi Jewish carriers. However, if an at-risk couple has an unknown mutation, NAA measured in amniotic fluid can be used for prenatal diagnosis.

Approximately 1/32 Ashkenazi Jews are carriers for mutations in the *IKBKAP* gene which in the homozygous state results in the disease familial dysautonomia. This is a disease of the autonomic nervous system and may result in symptoms including feeding difficulties, vomiting, and temperature and blood pressure instability. Carrier screening by molecular DNA methods detects 99% of Ashkenazi Jewish carriers.

Genetic screening for hemoglobinopathies

Hemoglobin is the main oxygen-carrying protein in the blood. Normal adult hemoglobin is composed of two α- and two β-chains, and mutations can occur in either. Sickle cell anemia is the result of a mutation in the beta chain of the hemoglobin molecule characterized by abnormal red blood cells that form a sickle shape when exposed to low oxygen concentrations. These sickled cells do not easily traverse the smaller blood vessels and cause many of the ischemic complications of the disease including pain crises, infection and stroke. Individuals of African and Mediterranean descent should be offered carrier screening. Approximately 1/12 African Americans carries the sickle cell trait. Patients should be screened with a hemoglobin electrophoresis which is able to detect not only the abnormal hemoglobin S of sickle cell anemia, but also other abnormal hemoglobin variants which may cause disease. Solubility testing such as the Sickledex is not sufficient. Sickle cell anemia is inherited in an AR fashion.

The thalassemias are another form of AR anemias common in individuals of Southeast Asian, African, and Mediterranean descent. In fact, the word 'thalassa' is Greek for sea. The most common thalassemias are alpha and beta thalassemias, resulting from deletions or mutations in either the alpha or beta chains of hemoglobin respectively. Unlike sickle cell anemia which is due to a qualitative defect in hemoglobin, the thalassemias result from a quantitative imbalance in globin chain synthesis. In alpha thalassemia, deletions in the alpha chain result in decreased alpha chain production which results in excess beta chains which precipitate and damage the red blood cell. In beta thalassemias, mutations in the beta chain result in excess alpha chains which similarly precipitate and damage the red blood cell. Manifestations of the thalassemias vary from very mild alterations in red blood cell indices in asymptomatic carriers to severe transfusion dependent anemia, and in some cases fetal death.

Screening may be accomplished by determination of the mean corpuscular volume (MCV) of the red blood cell. A low MCV (<80 fl) may indicate thalassemia and should be followed by a hemoglobin electrophoresis. However, individuals of African and Mediterranean descent who are also at risk for sickle cell anemia and its variants should be initially screened with a hemoglobin electrophoresis in addition to an MCV. Beta thalassemia is diagnosed by an abnormal hemoglobin electrophoresis with elevated hemoglobin A2 levels >3.5%. Diagnosis of alpha thalassemia is somewhat more complicated. If an at-risk patient has a low MCV and a normal hemoglobin electrophoresis, iron studies should be done to rule out iron-deficiency anemia. If iron-deficiency anemia has been excluded in this situation, then molecular DNA-based testing for alpha gene deletions, as found in alpha thalassemia should be pursued.

A word about other ethnic groups

Ethnic groups that are relatively genetically isolated may also be at risk for certain disorders. Examples include French Canadians of the St. Lawrence river valley, Cajuns from Louisiana and the Amish of Pennsylvania who are also at increased risk of certain genetic diseases including Tay Sachs disease. Patients from these ethnic groups, or from other genetically isolated groups should be offered genetic counseling.

Other Genetic Screening

Fragile X syndrome

Patients with a history of developmental disability of unknown etiology, those with autistic features, and any patient with a family history of unexplained mental retardation should be offered screening for the fragile X syndrome. After chromosomal causes (see below), fragile X syndrome is the most common form of inherited mental retardation. Approximately 1/2000 males and 1/4000 females carry the full mutation. The name fragile X refers to a fragile site at the end of the long arm of the X chromosome where the DNA in the chromosome fails to condense properly. The actual fragile site can sometimes be seen with the microscope on a standard karyotype, however, this is not a sensitive enough test for diagnosis.

Fragile X is on the X chromosome, and X-linked disorders more frequently affect males because they have only one X chromosome. However, fragile X syndrome may also affect females who have two X chromosomes, although they are usually less severely affected. Approximately 50% of females with the full mutation have mental retardation in spite of another normal X chromosome. Affected males have a typical facial appearance consisting of a narrow face with prominent ears and jaw. Other features might include macroorchidism (or large testicles), autism and attention and behavioral problems.

Fragile X syndrome is due to an abnormal expansion of triplet repeats in the noncoding promoter region of the *FMR-1* gene. The triplet repeat expansion in the *FMR-1* gene consists of cytosine–guanine–guanine (CGG) nucleotides. Normal individuals have fewer than 50 of these CGG repeats. Those affected with fragile X syndrome have over 200 CGG repeats. This excessive number of repeats silences the gene by a process called methylation, which results in loss of gene function.

A premutation state exists where patients have an intermediate number of repeats (50–199). These patients may be normal; however, some have mild mental impairment. Other consequences of carrying a premutation include an increased risk of premature ovarian failure in women, and in men, an increased risk for fragile X ataxia syndrome later in life. Importantly, the repeats in premutation carriers can expand over generations, leading to affected children. This is also known as genetic anticipation, when a disease shows increased severity and/or earlier onset in subsequent generations. This triplet repeat is more likely to expand in female carriers of the premutation, therefore, sex of the carrier parent is important for genetic counseling. If a woman carries a premutation or a full mutation, each of her children has a 50% risk of inheriting the expanded mutation. The larger the premutation, the higher chance it will expand into a full mutation in subsequent generations. Parental testing and prenatal diagnosis for this expansion is clinically available.

Prenatal Genetic Screening

Screening vs. Diagnostic Tests

An important concept for this article and for patients is the difference between screening and diagnostic tests. Screening tests have the benefit of carrying virtually no risk to the pregnancy. Because of this, they are ideal tests to offer the general population. Examples of screening tests which will be discussed at length in future sections include maternal age, first trimester combined screening, second trimester serum screening, and second trimester fetal ultrasound. The downside of screening tests, however, is that they do not provide a definite answer about the presence of a chromosomal disorder, they can only provide a risk estimate. Screening tests may help delineate which patients are at high risk and should be offered invasive testing. Patients should be counseled prior to testing that a screen positive result does not mean the fetus is affected, rather it is a sign of increased risk for the disorder in question, and an indication for further testing. Alternatively, higher risk women, such as those with advanced maternal age with a negative screening test may decline invasive testing if their risk of aneuploidy seems sufficiently low. However, even with the most favorable screening result, the risk of a chromosomal disorder is never zero in the absence of diagnostic testing.

Screening tests must use cutoffs to define screen negative and screen positive patients. Screening tests are defined by detection rates and false positive rates. Certain cutoffs are chosen in order to optimize detection of the disorder while avoiding too many false positive results which may lead to unnecessary invasive testing, and procedure-related pregnancy loss.

Diagnostic tests on the other hand have the benefit of providing a definite answer about the presence of a disorder. Examples of diagnostic tests include CVS and amniocentesis. Since these tests carry varying risks of pregnancy loss, they are usually reserved for women at high risk. However, low-risk patients who request invasive testing should not be denied this opportunity, provided they have been thoroughly counseled about the risks and benefits.

Counseling patients for both screening and diagnostic tests should be done in a nondirective manner. Patients should not be told they 'should' or 'should not' have screening or testing. The role of the caregiver is to provide patients with the information they need to make a well-informed decision. Prior to accepting a screening test, patients and their caregivers should consider what they would do with a screen positive result. For patients who would not proceed with diagnostic testing due to the risk of the procedure, or if the results would not change the outcome of the pregnancy, screening may not be appropriate. For other patients who are either at high risk for the disorder, or for those who feel they need a definitive answer, invasive testing without screening may be the most appropriate next step.

Basic Genetics

Humans which are diploid or 2n have 23 pairs, or 46 total chromosomes. The chromosomes are numbered, with pairs 1–22 being the autosomes, and the 23rd pair being the sex chromosomes. Males have an X and a Y chromosome as their 23rd pair (46XY), and females have two X chromosomes as their 23rd pair (46XX). Chromosomes are ordered and represented as a photomicrograph as a karyotype.

Gametes, or oocytes and sperm are haploid (have a single copy of each of the 23 chromosomes), so that their union forms a diploid fetus. Gametes are formed by a special type of cell division termed meiosis. Occasionally, mistakes are made during meiotic divisions, resulting in extra or missing copies of chromosomes in a gamete. This is termed nondisjunction. Nondisjunction may occur in either the oocyte or the sperm, but is more common in oocytes as maternal age increases. When a cell contains any number of chromosomes that is not an exact multiple of the haploid number (which is 23 in humans), this is referred to as aneuploidy. A cell that has three copies of a chromosome is trisomic for that chromosome, and a cell with only one copy of a chromosome is monosomic for that chromosome. Most monosomies are lethal, however, certain trisomies are found in liveborn infants.

The three most common trisomies observed in liveborns are: trisomy 21 or Down syndrome, trisomy 18 (sometimes referred to as Edward syndrome), trisomy 13 (sometimes referred to as Patau syndrome), and sex chromosome aneuploidies. Down syndrome results from either an extra copy of the entire chromosome 21 (trisomy 21) or from translocations involving chromosome 21. Down syndrome is one of the most common chromosomal abnormalities with a birth prevalence of approximately 1/600. It is characterized by mental retardation, a characteristic facial appearance, low muscle tone, frequently cardiac defects, and other medical problems. Average survival for Down syndrome is 40–50 years, and medical complications that may occur include complications from congenital heart disease, hypothyroidism and an increased risk of leukemia and dementia. Trisomy 18 is a multiple malformation syndrome resulting from three copies of chromosome 18. Trisomy 18 is characterized by growth restriction, cardiac defects, clenched hands with overlapping fingers, and clubfeet. Survival is poor with approximately 50% miscarrying prior to birth and, most liveborns die within the first week of life, with a median survival of 4 days. Long-term survivors with trisomy 18 have been reported; however, this is rare. Trisomy 13 is characterized by multiple malformations including growth restriction, severe brain malformations, facial clefting, and cardiac defects. Survival for trisomy 13 is poor with most survivors dying in the first month of life, however as with trisomy 18, some long-term survivors have been reported.

Advanced Maternal Age

One of the simplest, yet nonspecific screening tests is maternal age. After age 35 years, the incidence of chromosomally abnormal fetuses begins to increase more sharply. The reason for this is not entirely known but may have to do with abnormal function of the meiotic spindle during female meiosis, resulting in nondisjunction. Unlike males who produce sperm frequently, females are born with all of their oocytes which remain suspended in a state of partial cell division until ovulation. This significant time lag makes oocytes prone to errors in cell division. The risk of aneuploidy may be reported as midtrimester risk, or risk of a term liveborn with that particular aneuploidy. Risks for a term liveborn are lower than midtrimester risks since a number of aneuploid pregnancies will be lost prior to term. For purposes of this article, we will quote risks of delivering a baby with aneuploidy. At 35 years of age, the risk that a woman will have a liveborn with any aneuploidy (or abnormal number of chromosomes) is approximately 1/204, and her risk of having a liveborn with Down syndrome is approximately 1/384.

Because the risk of having a liveborn with any chromosomal aneuploidy approximately equals the risk of pregnancy loss with invasive testing (0.5%, or 1/200), it is standard of practice to offer invasive testing to women who will be 35 years or older at the time of delivery. However, as we will see in upcoming sections of this article, additional screening tests may modify this risk sufficiently that invasive testing may not be warranted in some women over 35, and may be offered to younger women at high risk. When maternal age is used alone as a screening test, it would take approximately 140 invasive procedures to diagnose one fetus with Down syndrome (**Table 2**).

Table 2 Approximate risk of delivering a liveborn infant with any aneuploidy based on maternal age

Maternal age	*% Risk*
30	1/4
35	1/2
38	1
41	2
42	3
45	5

Recurrence risk for aneuploidy

If a patient has had a prior aneuploid pregnancy, her recurrence risk is approximately 1% until her age-related risk exceeds this (which is approximately the risk of a 38-year-old woman). One common aneuploidy, Turner syndrome or 45X, is not related to advanced maternal age, and does not modify *a priori* risk for future pregnancies. In fact, 45X is more commonly thought to be due to loss of the paternal X chromosome.

Advanced Paternal Age

Advanced paternal age which is a paternal age greater than 40–45 years at delivery is not associated with aneuploidy, or an abnormal number of chromosomes. Advancing paternal age does however carry some risk for the fetus, mainly, by increasing the risk for new autosomal dominant mutations. Examples of diseases that may be associated with advanced paternal age include achondroplasia, the most common form of dwarfism and Marfan syndrome, a connective tissue disorder. In addition, advanced paternal age may lead to spontaneous X-linked mutations that may be passed on to daughters who are only carriers who then transmit the disease to their sons. This has been called the 'grandfather effect'. Since the risk of paternal age includes many disorders, screening is generally not feasible; however, couples should be made aware of these risks and offered genetic counseling.

First Trimester Screening

The current standard of practice in the US is to offer second trimester serum screening to all patients, and to offer amniocentesis to women who will be over 35 years of age at delivery. However, screening earlier than the second trimester is becoming increasingly popular due to new methods with comparable detection rates for aneuploidy with decreased false positive rates. Furthermore, this screening can be done earlier in pregnancy, opening up the option of earlier diagnostic testing.

During the first trimester, between 10 and 14 weeks, thickening of an area behind the fetal neck (also called the nuchal translucency) is associated with an increased risk of chromosomal abnormalities and fetal cardiac defects (**Figures 2** and **3**). This fluid-filled area of the posterior neck normally resolves by the second trimester. A thick nuchal translucency may be due to abnormal lymphatic drainage due to delayed or abnormal development of the lymphatic or blood vessels. Accurate measurement of this very small area requires extensive training and monitoring. Nuchal translucency measurement alone detects 65–75% of Down syndrome.

Combined first trimester screening is as sensitive with lower false positive rates for detection of aneuploidy than second trimester serum screening, which is currently the standard of practice. Combined first trimester screening uses the nuchal translucency measurement and two serum analytes; pregnancy-associated plasma protein A (PAPP-A) and free beta human chorionic gonadotropin (β-hCG). PAPP-A has been found to be decreased in Down syndrome pregnancies when measured in the first trimester. Free β-hCG is increased in Down syndrome pregnancies in both the first and second trimesters. These measurements are combined to estimate the risk of carrying a fetus with Down syndrome (trisomy 21), and trisomies 13 and 18. As a screening test, first trimester combined screening does not provide a definite answer about the presence or absence of aneuploidy. Rather results are reported as a risk estimate. For the general population, first trimester combined screening detects approximately 87% of cases of Down syndrome with a 5% false positive rate. Detection and false positive rates differ by age. For women under age 35 years at delivery, combined first trimester screening detects approximately 75–80% of Down syndrome with a false positive rate of 5%. In women over 35 years of age at delivery, combined first trimester screening detects approximately 95% of Down syndrome with a 15% false positive rate.

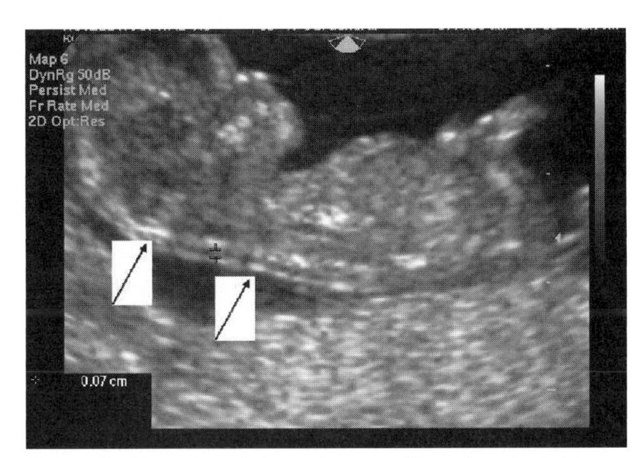

Figure 2 Normal nuchal translucency. First trimester fetal profile with normal nuchal translucency (arrows). The nuchal translucency appears as a dark area behind the fetal neck. The calipers indicate a measurement of 0.07 cm or 0.7 mm, a normal value. From Dr. Marjorie Treadwell, Professor of Obstetrics and Gynecology, the University of Michigan.

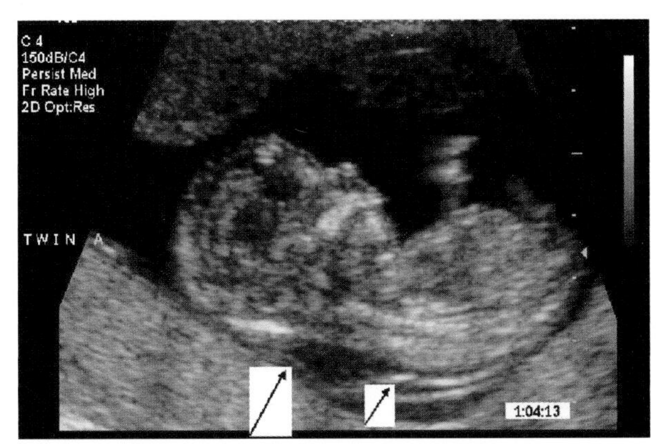

Figure 3 Abnormal nuchal translucency. First trimester fetal profile with an abnormally thickened nuchal translucency (arrows). The nuchal translucency in this image is much larger than in the fetus in Figure 2. From Dr. Marjorie Treadwell, Professor of Obstetrics and Gynecology, the University of Michigan.

First trimester biochemical screening alone with PAPP-A and free β-hCG (without measurement of the fetal nuchal translucency) may be offered if access to certified sonographers is not available. Detection of Down syndrome with this method is similar to second trimester serum screening at approximately 60% with a 5% false positive rate.

Additional benefits of nuchal translucency measurement is that it will identify some fetuses at increased risk of cardiac defects and other syndromes. Fetuses with a nuchal transclucency measurement greater than the 95th percentile should undergo a detailed second trimester ultrasound, in addition to a second trimester fetal echocardiogram to evaluate for cardiac defects. A thick nuchal translucency may indicate an increased risk for abnormalities in other systems such as skeletal dysplasias and neurologic abnormalities.

Second Trimester Serum Screening

Second trimester screening began in the 1970s using a single analyte, alpha fetoprotein (AFP) as a screen for neural tube defects, or spina bifida. Currently, second trimester serum screening such as the triple or quadruple screen are the standard of care for population screening. The triple screen measures maternal serum levels of three analytes: AFP, β-hCG, and estriol (E3). The quadruple serum screen adds inhibin-A to the above (**Table 3**). Second trimester serum screening may be performed between 15 and 20 weeks' gestation, but is most accurate between 16 and 18 weeks. The level of each analyte is reported as a multiple of the median (or MoM). As a screening test, it provides a risk estimate rather than a definitive answer.

Table 3 Pattern of quadruple serum analytes in neural tube defects and various aneuploidies

	AFP	*β-CG*	*E3*	*Inhibin A*
Down syndrome	⇓	⇑	⇓	⇑
Trisomy 18	⇓	⇓	⇓	⇓
NTD/AWD	⇑	N/A	N/A	N/A

AFP, alpha fetoprotein; AWD, abdominal wall defectes; β-CG, beta human chorionic gonadotropin; E3, estriol; NTD, neural tube defects. N/A, not applicable.

AFP is a fetal circulating blood protein similar in structure to albumin. AFP is produced by the fetus, but is transported across the placenta. Levels are highest in the fetal blood, followed by fetal urine (amniotic fluid) and maternal blood. High level of AFP are frequently associated with neural tube defects. Other possible causes of a high AFP include incorrect dates, previously undiagnosed multiple pregnancy, fetomaternal bleed, and other fetal malformations, such as defects of the abdominal wall. Low levels of AFP are associated with Down syndrome. An unexplained high level of AFP (high AFP level in the absence of a fetal malformation), is associated with an increased risk of adverse pregnancy outcome including pre-term delivery, maternal hypertensive disorders, fetal growth restriction, and even fetal death. This may be due to a 'leaky' placental barrier or other placental dysfunction. Any abnormal AFP measurement should be followed by a detailed fetal ultrasound.

Human chorionic gonadotropin or hCG is also known as the 'pregnancy hormone'. It is produced by the placenta very early in pregnancy. This hormone peaks early in pregnancy at 8–10 weeks. Levels are increased in Down syndrome, and decreased in trisomy 18.

Estriol is the dominant form of estrogen during pregnancy. This hormone is derived from precursors from the fetal adrenal that are processed in the placenta. Low estriol may be associated with Down syndrome. Other causes of a low estriol include absence of the fetal zone of the adrenal which may be found in anencephaly, the most severe neural tube defect characterized by absence of much of the fetal brain. Very low levels of estriol, less than 0.3 MoM may be associated with the syndrome Smith–Lemli–Opitz (SLO). This syndrome results from the deficiency of a cholesterol-producing enzyme 7-dehydrocholesterol reductase (DHCR7). This enzyme deficiency leads to buildup of cholesterol intermediates including 7-dehydrocholesterol (7DHC), and to lack of cholesterol which is used for many functions including cell membrane stabilization and production of steroid hormones. Features of this syndrome might include fetal growth restriction, cardiac defects, facial clefting, renal abnormalities, genital abnormalities, and characteristic facial appearance. Survivors typically have moderate to severe mental retardation. Diagnosis may be made by analysis of amniotic fluid 7DHC levels, which are markedly elevated in SLO, or by molecular testing. Other syndromes associated with low estriol include congenital adrenal hypoplasia, and X-linked icthyosis.

Inhibins are placental hormones that inhibit the secretion of follicle-stimulating hormone (FSH). There are two forms: inhibin A and inhibin B; however, only the former is found in pregnant women. Inhibin A has been found to be increased in Down-syndrome pregnancies, and has most recently been added as the fourth serum marker for second trimester screening.

Table 4 Detection and false positive rates of prenatal screening

	Detection rates (%)	*False positive rates (%)*
Nuchal translucency only	65–70	5
Combined FTS	82–87	5
Triple serum screen	70	5
Quadruple serum screen	80	5
For women over 35 years old		
Combined FTS	90	15
Quadruple serum screen	85–95	25

FTS, first trimester screening.
Data for table extracted from: Bahado-Singh R and Driscoll D (2007) Screening for fetal chromosomal abnormalities. ACOG Practice Bulletin Number 77. American College of Obstetricians and Gynecologists. *Obstetrics Gynecology* 109: 271–228; and the FASTER trial: Wapner R, Thom E, Simpson JL, *et al.* (2003) First-trimester screening for trisomies 21 and 18. *New England Journal of Medicine* 349: 1405–1413.

In the general population, the quadruple serum screen detects approximately 80% of cases of Down syndrome with a 5% false positive rate. As with first trimester screening, detection and false positive rates vary with maternal age (**Table 4**). In women over 35 years old, quadruple serum screening detects 85–95% of cases of Down syndrome with a 25% false positive rate.

For patients who opt for first trimester combined screening, second trimester screening, without consideration of results from first trimester screening results, is not recommended, because this results in a minimal if any increase in detection rates with an increased false positive rate. Screening protocols which incorporate both first and second trimester results to provide a single risk estimate are available, the details of which are beyond the scope of this article. Some authorities recommend a second trimester AFP measurement in patients who opt only for first trimester screening, since first trimester screening does not screen for neural tube defects. However, the sensitivity of AFP measurement alone for an open neural tube defect is 80–90%, while sensitivity of ultrasound at high-risk centers is 95–100%. In addition, serum AFP screening will not detect closed neural tube defects, and ultrasound may. This has led some to recommend second trimester AFP measurement after first trimester screening only if there is insufficient access to high-risk ultrasound.

Triple and quadruple serum screening, because it is based on measurement of analytes that vary with gestation, is very sensitive to gestational age. As a matter of fact, the most common reason for a positive screen is incorrect pregnancy dating. In addition, maternal age weighs heavily in the calculations employed for the risk estimate, therefore, false positive rates increase with maternal age. The overall screen positive rate for the triple marker screen, which includes both true and false positives is approximately 2.5% at age 20 years vs. 15% at age 35 years and 40% at age 40 years. Women of advanced maternal age should be counseled about the high screen positive rate prior to testing to avoid unnecessary anxiety in the event of a screen positive result.

Prenatal Screening in Multiple Gestations

The incidence of multiple gestations is increasing dramatically, most likely due to delayed childbearing and to increased use of assisted reproductive technologies such as ovulation induction and *in vitro* fertilization. The risk of aneuploidy in multiple gestations depends on zygosity. Dizygotic twins result when two different oocytes are fertilized by two different sperm. Dizygotic twins (sometimes referred to as fraternal twins) share the same amount of DNA as any sibling pair. The risk of aneuploidy with dizygotic twins is double the risk of a singleton, since each fetus has an independent risk for aneuploidy which must be summed. Because of the additive risk with dizygotic pregnancies, advanced maternal age in twin pregnancies with unknown zygosity is defined as 31 years of age at delivery. Monozygotic twins result from fertilization of a single oocyte by a single sperm, followed by early splitting of the embryo. Therefore, monozygotic twins are genetically identical and share 100% of their DNA. The risk of aneuploidy for monozygotic twins equals that of a singleton. Zygosity cannot always be reliably determined prenatally, which complicates screening in multiple gestations.

Biochemical screening in multiple gestations

Biochemical screening in multiple gestations is not as straightforward as it is in singletons. Levels of analytes are thought to be approximately twice as high in twins and three times as high in triplets. However, this assumes that each marker increases by the same amount in multiple gestations. Furthermore, serum screening in multiple gestations assumes equal contribution from each fetus, which may or may not be the case. Finally, an abnormal twin may be 'masked' by the analytes of the normal twin.

First trimester nuchal transclucency screening in multiple gestations has the advantage of being fetus specific, and not dependent on levels of analytes; however, detection rates are not as high as the combined first trimester screen. Nuchal translucency measurement alone detects approximately 70% of Down syndrome with a 5% false positive rate. Monozygotic twins have equal risk of being affected, so the nuchal translucency measurements are averaged to calculate a single risk estimate.

In dizygotic twins, the individual fetal risks based on the nuchal translucency are added. As with singletons, an increased nuchal translucency measurement increases the risk for cardiac and other organ system abnormalities. In addition, a thick nuchal translucency in monozygotic twins may be an early sign of twin-to-twin transfusion syndrome, a complication unique to monochorionic pregnancies. In this syndrome, one fetus, the donor, pumps blood to the other fetus (the recipient) which can result in heart failure and death of either twin if untreated.

First trimester combined screening in twins detects approximately 75% of Down syndrome with a 10% false positive rate, compared with detection of up to 87% of cases with a 5% false positive rate in singletons. Second trimester quadruple serum screening in twins detects only 50% of Down syndrome at a 5% false positive rate, vs. 80% detection in singletons with the same false positive rate.

As is the case for singleton pregnancies, patients with multiple gestations should think about what they would do with a screen positive result prior to proceeding. A screen positive result may warrant that both fetuses undergo invasive testing. In twins, this doubles the background loss rate for the procedure. Testing even one fetus increases the risk of loss of the entire pregnancy. Furthermore, if invasive testing shows one fetus is aneuploid and the other is not, this raises questions about what parents would do with the information. Selective termination of one fetus can be done in certain centers; however, this poses a 5–10% risk of loss of both fetuses.

Diagnostic Testing

In the first trimester, CVS may be performed between 10 and 13 weeks' gestation. The benefit of this testing is that results are available earlier in pregnancy; however, the risk of pregnancy loss with CVS is 1%, higher than second trimester amniocentesis which has a 0.5% risk of pregnancy loss. This procedure may be performed transcervically or transabdominally. The complication rate is not affected by the route. In the transcervical method, a flexible catheter is inserted through the cervix and posterior to the placenta under ultrasound guidance. Suction is applied and a small amount of placental villi are withdrawn. In the transabdominal approach, a needle is inserted through the abdomen and subsequently through the uterus. An appropriate sample consists of 5–30 mg of villi. Active cervical infection is a contraindication to performing the procedure. These cells are then taken back to the cytogenetics laboratory for analysis. In approximately 1% of CVS cases, chromosomal mosaicism, or detection of two or more cell lines on karyotype is found. In most cases, this is due to properties of early placental cells, or an artifact of cell culture, and does not reflect an abnormal karyotype in the baby. However, depending on the abnormality, amniocentesis in the second trimester may be required to clarify ambiguous results, and genetic counseling is indicated.

Amniocentesis

Amniocentesis is generally performed between 15 and 20 weeks' gestation, and carries a 0.5% risk of pregnancy loss. In this procedure, a needle is inserted into the uterus under ultrasound guidance, and approximately 20 cc of amniotic fluid is withdrawn. (The total amniotic fluid volume at this gestational age is approximately 200 cc) Amniotic fluid contains fetal fibroblasts, or skin cells with fetal DNA. The procedure of early amniocentesis (from 11 to 14 weeks) has been abandoned due to the higher fetal loss rate and an increased risk of limb reduction defects and clubfoot.

Flourescent in situ hybridization

Karyotyping of CVS or amniocentesis specimens typically takes 7–14 days since cells need to be cultured prior to analysis. Only dividing cells may be used for karyotyping since chromosomes are not visible in non-dividing cells. For patients who require faster results, or for testing of deletions of small areas of the chromosome below the level of resolution of a karyotype, flourescent *in situ* hybridization, (FISH) may be offered. There are FISH probes for chromosomes 13, 18, 21, X, and Y which may be used for rapid detection of aneuploidy prior to formal karyotyping. In addition, there are multiple FISH probes for areas associated with microdeletion syndromes such as DiGeorge syndrome resulting from deletion in chromosome 22 (22q11). However, FISH for aneuploidies does not replace standard karyotyping, since FISH will not detect chromosomal rearrangements such as translocations, inversions, or unspecified duplications or deletions.

Ultrasound Screening

It is controversial whether routine prenatal ultrasound should be the standard of care; however, most practitioners offer second trimester ultrasound screening for congenital anomalies. The ideal time to screen is around 20 weeks' gestation; however, because some patients might opt for invasive testing, ultrasound screening can be done as early as 15 weeks; however, resolution is not as high. Prenatal ultrasound is able to confirm viability, gestational age, fetal gender, and detect most fetal malformations. First trimester ultrasound is more accurate than later ultrasound for confirmation of gestational age, and may detect certain severe anomalies at an earlier point in gestation. Ultrasound is safe in pregnancy provided that it is used appropriately. **Figure 4** illustrates the resolution of fetal ultrasound.

Two to four percent of fetuses will have a major congenital malformation, or birth defect. The most common malformations are cardiac, followed by neural tube defects, such as anencephaly or spina bifida. When a major anomaly is found, it should prompt a detailed search for other anomalies.

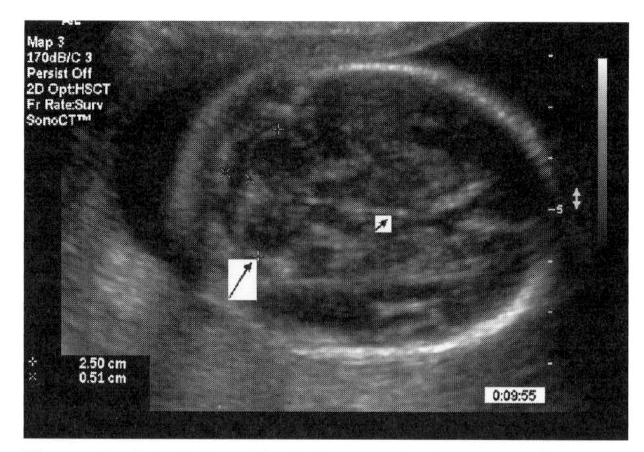

Figure 4 Resolution of fetal ultrasound – fetal head. Cross section of second trimester fetal head at the level of the cerebellum (large arrow). The small arrow indicates the falx cerebri, or midline of the head. From Dr. Marjorie Treadwell, Professor of Obstetrics and Gynecology, the University of Michigan.

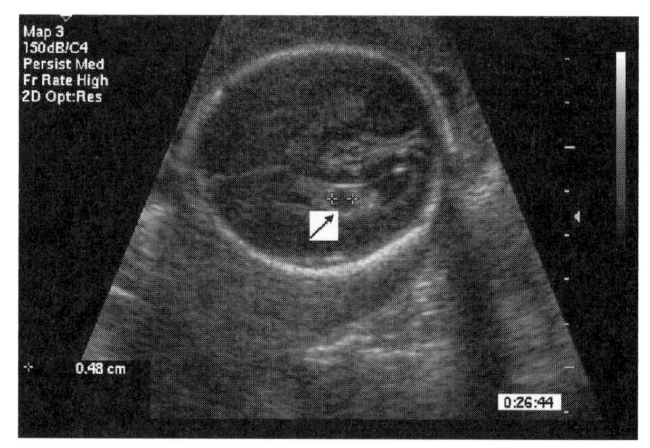

Figure 5 Choroids plexus cyst. Cross-section of second trimester fetal head at the level of the lateral ventricles. A choroids plexus cyst (arrow) is found in the choroid plexus of the lower lateral ventricle. From Dr. Marjorie Treadwell, Professor of Obstetrics and Gynecology, the University of Michigan.

At times, ultrasound will detect minor anomalies or population variants that happen to be more common in aneuploidy. These are called 'markers'. There are many markers of aneuploidy; however, we will focus on one, choroids plexus cysts, as an example (**Figure 5**). Typically, ultrasound markers do not have any functional consequence for the fetus, but should raise suspicion for aneuploidy. Choroid plexus cysts are located inside the cerebral ventricles in the choroid plexus, the tissue that forms cerebrospinal fluid. Choroid plexus cysts are easily detected with second trimester ultrasound. Because these were initially described in infants with trisomy 18, and since they are somewhat more prevalent in this disorder than in the general population, they are a marker for increased risk for trisomy 18. However, choroid plexus cysts are present in 1% of all fetuses, the vast majority of which are normal, and they have been found in a similar percentage of adult autopsies. The risk for trisomy 18 associated with a choroid plexus cyst is 1/374 for all ages. Because chromosomal abnormalities due to non-disjunction are more common with advanced maternal age, the risk does vary with maternal age. At a maternal age of 32 years, the risk of an isolated choroid plexus cyst approximately equals the risk of amniocentesis (0.5%); therefore, some would offer invasive testing to these patients. However, risk can be further modified by biochemical screening. If choroid plexus cysts are associated with other findings of trisomy 18 (such as growth restriction, cardiac defect, club feet or abdominal wall defect), then the risk for aneuploidy increases. There are numerous markers of aneuploidy, each of which is assigned a different likelihood ratio for the presence of aneuploidy.

Ultrasound may also be used as a screen for Down syndrome; however, only 50% of affected fetuses will have sonographic markers of aneuploidy. Therefore, a normal ultrasound decreases risk of Down syndrome by 50%. As an example, a woman with a 1/200 a priori risk of Down syndrome who has a normal fetal ultrasound has a new risk of 1/400.

Other ultrasound modalities include three-dimensional (3D) and four-dimensional (4D) ultrasound. These modalities may improve detection of fetal anomalies. An example of a 3D ultrasound output is shown in **Figure 6**.

When Fetal Anomalies are Found

Patients with fetal anomalies and/or aneuploidy should be dealt with in a sensitive way. Medical information is not always well absorbed by patients during emotional time periods, and multiple counseling sessions may be required. Patients should be informed of all of their options which might include fetal therapy or termination of pregnancy. As with invasive testing, counseling should proceed in a nondirective manner with respect for patients' personal beliefs and wishes. In the US, termination of pregnancy is legal until 24 weeks' gestation, at which time a fetus is considered 'viable', even though survival is poor and morbidity is high for fetuses born at this gestational age. Where available, grief counseling should be offered to patients.

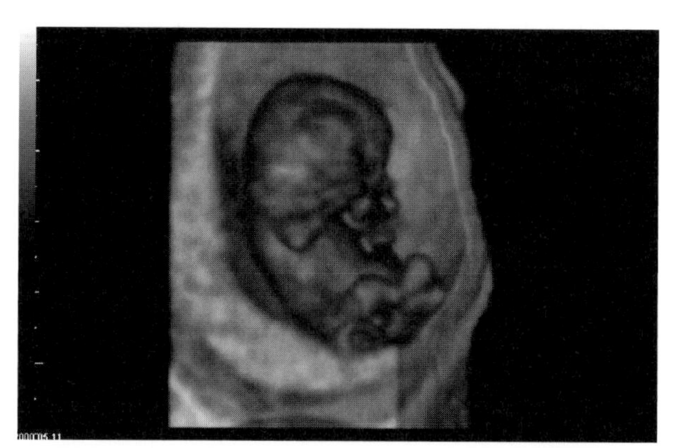

Figure 6 Three-dimensional surface rendering of a first trimester fetus. From Dr. Marjorie Treadwell, Professor of Obstetrics and Gynecology, the University of Michigan.

Advanced Topics in Prenatal Screening

Fetal Therapy

Certain fetal anomalies are amenable to prenatal therapy. One class of these anomalies is neural tube defects, such as spina bifida. The pathophysiology of this lesion is that the defect in the spine and neural tissue is thought to 'tether' the brain, leading to hydrocephalus. Depending on the severity of the defect, and the level of the lesion, many babies with spina bifida require shunts which drain excess fluid inside the ventricular system of the brain to the abdominal cavity (ventriculoperitoneal shunt). Shunts can malfunction, and infections are a serious problem.

A randomized, controlled trial of fetal repair of spina bifida called the management of myelomeningocele (MOMS) trial is ongoing. For patients randomized to the treatment group, open fetal surgery (meaning an incision is made in the uterus, and the fetus is exteriorized for surgery) to close the spinal defect occurs between 19 and 25 weeks of gestation. So far, fetal surgery for spinal neural tube defects (also called myelomeningoceles) has been found to decrease the need for shunting in children. This may correlate with better clinical outcomes; however, the trial and long-term follow-up are still ongoing.

Future Directions – Noninvasive Prenatal Diagnosis

Fetal nucleated cells and fetal DNA are found in the maternal circulation during pregnancy. Fetal cells however exist in low concentrations (1–2 cells per 20 cc of maternal blood), and are difficult to isolate and work with. Free fetal DNA on the other hand exists in high concentrations in the maternal plasma and is more easily isolated. Theoretically, fetal DNA could be used to diagnose any condition in which the mother and the fetus carry different mutations. In Europe, noninvasive fetal blood typing is commonly used for Rh disease. This disease is ideal for this use since Caucasian mothers who are Rh negative lack the D gene due to a gene deletion. Rh positive individuals carry at least one copy of the D gene. Therefore, if any DNA encoding the D sequence is found in the blood of an Rh negative mother, the fetus is Rh positive, and further surveillance of the pregancy is necessary. Clinical trials and quality assurance in the US have not yet taken place, but in the future Rh and other non-invasive genetic testing may be offered.

Conclusion

Pregnant women and their caregivers must understand and be able to make decisions about an ever increasing number of prenatal screening options, benefits, risks, and implications for care and practice.

See also: Birth Defects; Fragile X Syndrome; Genetic Disorders: Sex Linked; Genetics and Inheritance; Prenatal Care; Prenatal Development; Teratology.

Suggested Readings

ACOG (2004) ACOG committee opinion number 298: Prenatal and preconceptional carrier screening for genetic disease in individuals of Eastern European Jewish descent. *Obstetrics Gynecology* 104: 425–428.

ACOG (2005) ACOG Committee Opinion Number 325: Update on Carrier Screening for Cystic Fibrosis. American college of obstetricians and gynecologists. *Obstetrics Gynecology* 106: 1465–1468.

ACOG (2006) ACOG Committee Opinion Number 338: Screening for Fragile X syndrome. American college of obstetricians and gynecologists. *Obstetrics Gynecology* 107: 1438–1449.

Bahado-Singh R and Driscoll D (2007) Screening for fetal chromosomal abnormalities. ACOG Practice Bulletin Number 77. American college of obstetricians and gynecologists. *Obstetrics Gynecology* 109: 217–228.

Bianchi DW, Avent ND, Costa J-M, and Van der Schoot CE (2005) Noninvasive prenatal diagnosis of fetal Rhesus D. *Obstetrics Gynecology* 106: 841–844.

Jenkins TM and Wapner RJ (2003) Prenatal diagnosis of congenital disorders. In: Creasy RK, Reznik R, and Iams J (eds.) *Maternal Fetal Medicine,* 5th edn., pp. 325–380. Philadelphia, PA: Saunders.

Johnson MP, Sutton LN, Rintoul N, *et al.* (2003) Fetal myelomeningocele repair: Short term clinical outcomes. *American Journal of Obstetrics Gynecology* 189: 482–487.

Nussbaum RL, McInnes RR, and Willard HF (eds.) (2001) *Thompson and Thompson Genetics in Medicine,* 5th edn. Collingwood: W.B. Saunders Company.

Nyberg DA, McGahan JP, Pretorius DH, and Pilu G (eds.) (2003) *Diagnostic Imaging of Fetal Anomalies.* Philadelphia, PA: Lippincott Williams and Wilkins.

Wapner R, Thom E, Simpson JL, *et al.* (2003) First-trimester screening for trisomies 21 and 18. *The New England Journal of Medicine* 349: 1405–1413.

Williams JW (2007) Hemoglobinopathies in pregnancy. ACOG Practice Bulletin Number 78. American college of obstetricians and gynecologists. *Obstetrics Gynecology* 109: 229–238.

Relevant Websites

http://www.acog.org – American College of Obstetricians and Gynecologists.
http://ghr.nlm.nih.gov – Genetics Home Reference.
http://www.genereviews.org – GeneReviews, GeneTests.
http://www.marchofdimes.com – March of Dimes.
http://www.ncbi.nlm.nih.gov – OMIM, Online Mendelian Inheritance in Man National Center for Biotechnology Information, National Library of Medicine, National Institutes of Health.

Self Knowledge

A E Bigelow, St. Francis Xavier University, Antigonish, NS, Canada

Glossary

Ecological self-knowledge – Perceptually based knowledge of self within the local physical environment, for example, awareness of one's spatial relation to objects in the environment.
Episodic memory – Memory of a specific event that occurred at a particular time and place.
Generic event memory – Memory of a script for a routine event, that is, memory of the general sequence of what happens in the event.
Intermodal perception – The ability to integrate perceptions from different modalities, such that perceptions of an object from one modality allow recognition of the object in another modality.
Interpersonal self-knowledge – Perceptually based knowledge of self in interaction with others, for example, awareness that one's actions affect others' behavioral responses.
Joint attention – Child's ability to attend to an object or event and a social partner at the same time, knowing that the partner is also attending to the child and the same object or event.
Means-end understanding – The ability to combine actions, originally learned separately, to achieve new goals.
Secondary emotions – Emotions requiring the ability to sense how self-actions might be perceived by others, for example, embarrassment or pride.

Social contingency – Social responses to selected behaviors of a partner that immediately follow the behavior and match it in intensity, affect, and tempo.
Social referencing – Checking the emotional or behavioral cues of others to determine self-action in an uncertain situation.

Introduction

The development of self-knowledge is one of the oldest and most fundamental concerns in psychology. At the end of the nineteenth century, William James distinguished between the 'Me' and the 'I'. The 'Me' corresponds to the self-reflective sense of self that is identified and recalled. Traditionally within psychology, it is this sense of self that was the focus of study. During the second year of life, infants begin verbally to refer to themselves and they communicate their desires and feelings through language. At approximately the same time, they show recognition of themselves in mirrors. Such behaviors indicate children have begun to have a reflective concept of themselves.

During the past few decades, infancy research has had a resurgence of interest in the development of self-knowledge and has focused more closely on what is meant by the 'I'. The 'I' is the sense of self as a differentiated entity distinct from other objects and persons, yet capable of operating upon them. For example, in reaching for objects, infants express a sense of self as capable of acquiring objects that are perceived as graspable within a reachable distance. Such a sense of self does not require representational thought, conscious identification, or recognition, and as such it is present in preverbal infants long before children have a conceptual sense of themselves.

Humans share many aspects of the 'I' with other animals. Yet the 'Me', with its reliance on language or other representational systems and indications of visual self-recognition, may be uniquely human or shared only with few evolutionarily advanced species.

Although the development of the 'I' and the 'Me' may be independent, much of recent research on self-knowledge supports the notion that conceptual self-knowledge is rooted in earlier developing preconceptual knowledge of self. Infants' ability to sense themselves as objects of reflection and recognition does not develop suddenly in the second year, but rather emerges from earlier forms of self-understanding. By the second year, infants' sense of self has already evolved from simpler beginnings and self-knowledge continues to develop through early childhood and beyond. There is not one form of self-knowledge, or even two as James proposed, but many that build upon each other in complex ways.

What factors affect developments in early self-knowledge? Changes in the brain provide the foundation for these developments. Brain changes are rapid during infancy and early childhood and underlie cognitive developments important to self-knowledge, such as in visual processing, language development, and memory retention. There is debate about whether these brain changes are due to maturational factors, as traditionally thought, or are activity-dependent, that is, are based on the actions and perceptions of infancy that are universally experienced because of the similarity in human infants' environments. Whether critical brain changes are dependent on experience or not, experience plays a primary role in the development of self-knowledge. Theorists differ on the relative importance of experience in the physical vs. social environments for developments in self-knowledge. For early forms of preconceptual self-knowledge, some theorists propose that infants' engagement in the social and physical world have equal importance, but others support the dominance of infants' interactions with others because people tend to be particularly responsive and engaging with infants, allowing them more readily to notice the effect of their actions. For children with the ability to reflect upon themselves, self-knowledge is especially influenced by how others respond to them and help shape their emerging sense of who they are. Young children's experience in the world, perhaps particularly with others, is fundamental to their developing understanding of self.

Perceptually Based Self-Knowledge

Newborns spend much of their time caught up in physical states of sleep, drowsiness, fussiness, or crying that inhibit their focus on the external environment. The one exception is the quiet alert state, where infants are fully awake without excess distracting limb activity. In this state they can take in the surroundings visually, as well as through their auditory, tactile, taste, and olfactory senses. This perceptual information is the basis for infants' early self-knowledge. Essential to this self-knowledge is infants' ability to notice the relation between their own actions and perceived changes.

Ulric Neisser proposed that infants have access to two forms of perceptually based self-knowledge very early in life, probably from birth: the ecological self, which is self in relation to the physical environment, and the interpersonal self, which is self in relation to other people. These early perceptually based forms of self-knowledge do not disappear when other forms of self-knowledge are added; rather they remain reality-based sources of information about self in the physical and social world.

The ecological self is the sense of self within the local physical environment. Knowledge of the layout of the environment seen from the perspective of the self and knowledge of how that relationship changes with movement through space positions the ecological self in the environment. Young infants show evidence of the ecological self quite early. They react to looming objects by pulling back or moving away, which is not a simple reflex. When the object is a looming aperture, such as a framed window, infants as young as 3 months do not move away but rather lean forward to see what the window may reveal. When put in specially designed rooms that have walls that move, creating optic flow much like we see from windows of moving cars, infants make posture adjustments as if to maintain their position in the perceived moving environment. Such posture adjustments are clearly evident in crawling and walking infants, and also in the head adjustments of infants as young as 2 months. As infants' physical capabilities and knowledge of the world grow, infants' sense of their ecological self expands as well. For example, as infants develop locomotor abilities and increased strength, more objects are perceived as potentially attainable. Aspects of ecological self-awareness are shared with other species. Many animals with developed visual systems respond as young children do to the physical environment and to perceptual events in it, such as looming objects and optic flow.

The interpersonal self is the sense of self within the social environment and is manifested in actions such as mutual gaze and reciprocal responding. Such activities are clearly perceivable and no inferences to internal states being communicated are required. The interpersonal self is not necessarily embedded in a sense of relationship; rather it is based specifically on perceptual information. Like ecological self-knowledge, infants show evidence of interpersonal self-knowledge very early. When engaged in face-to-face interaction with a social partner who suddenly becomes still faced, that is, silent and unmoving, infants as young as 2 months, and possibly younger, react to the still face with less attention and decreased positive affect. When the partner reengages, the infants become happier and attentive again, indicating that they were reacting to the disruption in the social interaction rather than to boredom with a prolonged visual display. The replay effect is even stronger evidence for infants' interpersonal self-knowledge. To demonstrate this effect, infants engage in face-to-face interaction with a social partner over live video. Both the infant and the partner see and hear the other in real time over closed circuit television. The videotape of the social partner is then played back to the infant. In the playback, the infant-directed facial expressions and vocalizations of the partner are present as they were moments before except that the partner is no longer responding to what the infant is currently doing. Infants at 4 months, and in some studies at 2 months, show disinterest and less positive affect to the replay, similar to their reaction to the still face. When live video interaction with the partner is resumed, infants become engaged again, indicating that they are aware of when others' behaviors are responsive to their own.

Perceptions relevant to ecological and interpersonal self-knowledge can coexist in the same event, yet they are distinct. The two forms of self-knowledge are based on different information and can be salient on different occasions. Despite their early development, the coordination of ecological and interpersonal self-knowledge is thought to occur toward the end of the first year with the emergence of joint attention. In joint attention, infants are capable of attending to a person and an object at the same time, thus understanding that the object of their own focus is attended to by another person who simultaneously is also attending to them.

Evidence of the separate development of ecological and interpersonal self-knowledge comes from studies of children who have impairments or difficulties with acquiring one of these senses of self but not the other. Children with autism typically have difficulty with interpersonal self-knowledge but not with ecological self-knowledge. They have difficulty acquiring information from the behavior of others and understanding how others' behavior is affected by their own. Yet they have little trouble relating to the physical environment and objects in it. Children with autism also have problems engaging in joint attention, which in part may be due to the discrepancies between their development of interpersonal and ecological self-knowledge.

Children born totally blind show a pattern of disturbance in early self-knowledge that is the reverse of children with autism. To be sure, blind children's knowledge of their interpersonal selves is hindered. Many important avenues to the formation of interpersonal self-knowledge, such as mutual gaze, are absent in blind children. They have difficulty perceiving what others are attending to and, therefore, understanding the emotional reactions of others. Others also have difficulty knowing where blind children's attention is focused because there is neither visual orienting nor pointing, and their facial expressions are more neutral. Nevertheless, blind children's knowledge of their interpersonal selves can flourish if they perceive others' actions as contingent on their own behavior, a perception that is difficult but not impossible without vision. Tactile and vocal responses to the children's actions allow the children to sense the effect of their behavior on others. Interpersonal self-knowledge is attained as the children become aware that they can influence the actions of others in predictable ways.

Blind children's ecological self-knowledge is more fundamentally challenged. They cannot readily perceive the physical layout of their environment, the objects in the environment, the spatial relations among the objects, or the spatial relation of self to the objects and the physical space. Sound cues do not initially convey to blind infants an object's location or sustained existence. Their difficulty understanding their position within the physical environment and to objects in it delays reaching and locomotion, which further impedes the infants' interaction with and exploration of the environment. Blind infants' ecological self-knowledge is initially thought to be indicated by their reaching for objects on external sound cues. By their reaches, they convey their awareness of themselves as positioned within the physical world with objects to which they can gain access through their own actions. It is not surprising that blind infants' demonstration of joint attention, through acknowledgement that both they and another are sharing in the same event or object, occurs after their ability to search for objects on sound cues. Yet knowing where one is in physical space, where objects are in relation to each other and to self, and how these relations change with self-movement are lifelong challenges for blind children.

Bodily Awareness

Although very young infants can perceive the social and physical world around them, they are particularly interested in watching and discovering their own bodies. A distinguishing feature concerning perceptions of their own bodies vs. external objects, both animate and inanimate, is the perfect contingency between self-actions and perceived changes. With the exception of watching one's mirror reflection or live video image, perfect contingency is present only in self-actions on the self, such as sucking on one's own fingers or watching one's hand move; the perceptual feedback is consistent and simultaneous with self-action. From the beginning, infants show behaviors suggestive of an ability to differentiate self-actions from others' actions. Newborns show differential responding to their own hand spontaneously touching their cheek, generating double touch in that the hand feels the cheek and simultaneously the cheek feels the hand, and having another person's hand touch their cheek; they show rooting behavior to the latter but rarely to the former. They also show expectation of results of their actions on their own bodies. In moving their hands to their mouths, newborns open their mouths in anticipation of the hand entering. Young infants' familiarity with self-actions on the self may originate in prenatal experience. The fetus in the latter months of pregnancy has tactile contact with its own body and babies are often born with marks on their hands and arms from prenatal sucking. Newborns' differential responses to self vs. external actions may be attributed to reflex reactions built into the nervous system or to reinforced stimulus-response associations. But by 2 months of age, infants show active exploration of the effects of their own actions. For example, when given pacifiers which when sucked above a baseline pressure either produced sounds with pitch variations that were analogs to the pressure variations applied by the sucking or pitch variations that varied randomly, 2-month-old infants modulated their sucking to the pacifiers differently. Although sound from both pacifiers was produced by the infants' sucking, infants more actively explored the effects of their sucking in the analog condition.

Infants' capacities for intermodal perception facilitate their ability to distinguish self from other people and objects. Piaget thought that young infants experienced their perceptions from different modalities as unrelated and only gradually came to the awareness that perceptions from separate modalities can specify the same object, for example, mother's voice and her visual image originate from the same person. Research on infant development from the past several decades shows such thinking to be incorrect. From birth infants have the ability to integrate their perceptions from different modalities, such that they are able to perceive objects in one modality and recognize them in another. For example, 1-month-old infants who have sucked on, but not seen, a tactually distinctive pacifier visually discriminate that pacifier from a novel one when given a choice of looking at two different distinctively shaped pacifiers. Intermodal perception facilitates infants' understanding and organization of the external world, but also greatly aids in their awareness of their own bodies.

In the first few months of life, infants spend extended periods of time in self-exploration, for example, kicking, vocalizing, touching their bodies, watching their limbs move. These experiences are absorbing and do not include other people or objects. Such activities provide numerous opportunities for infants to experience intermodal perception of their own bodies and to notice the perfect match between their actions and perceived changes. When watching their hand move, infants see the movement as they proprioceptively feel the movement; when vocalizing, they hear sound as they feel air passing through their throat and mouth. Such actions help infants form their body schema; what belongs to their own body and what are its limits.

By 2–3 months of age, infants become more interested in the relation between self-action and external responses in the environment, both social and nonsocial, than in self-actions on the self, perhaps because effects of the latter have become familiar. External responses to infants' actions show high but imperfect contingency rather than perfect contingency. Imperfectly contingent responses occur immediately after self-action rather than simultaneously with self-action and do not occur in response to every self-action. Studies in which infants are given a choice of watching actions that are perfectly matched with their own bodies' movement, for example, live video displays of their legs kicking, vs. actions that are similar but not perfectly matched with their bodily movement, for example, video displays of another infant's legs kicking, indicate that infants over 3 months of age prefer to watch the displays that are not perfectly matched to self-actions, but younger infants do not. The shift to focusing attention on imperfect contingencies present in the environment or in others' social behavior rather than on intrinsic sensations is adaptive. Infants' ability to detect differences between perfect and imperfect contingencies is acquired early and may be one of the first ways they distinguish self from other.

Self-Efficacy

By noticing the relation between their own actions and resultant external changes, infants develop self-efficacy, a sense that they are agents of the perceived changes. Although infants can notice the effect of their behavior on the physical environment, it is in early social interactions that infants most readily perceive the consequence of their actions. People have perceptual characteristics that virtually assure that infants will orient toward them. They have visually contrasting and moving faces. They produce sound, provide touch, and have interesting smells. In addition, people engage with infants by exaggerating their facial expressions and inflecting their voices in ways that infants find fascinating. But most importantly, these antics are responsive to infants' vocalizations, facial expressions, and gestures; people vary the pace and level of their behavior in response to infant actions. Consequentially, early social interactions provide a context in which infants can easily notice the effect of their behavior.

Parents are generally infants' most frequent and consistent social partners and as such their behaviors are those that most profoundly affect infants' emerging sense of self-efficacy. The responses that are most effective in facilitating infants' early self-knowledge are socially contingent and reflect the infants' own behavior. In naturally occurring interactions with young infants, parental responses are primarily imitations of infants' actions. These imitations are not exact but rather match the infants' actions in intensity, affect, and tempo. Infants' early perceptual capacities allow them to recognize these imitative behaviors as mirroring their own. From the beginning of life, infants are aware of the matching quality of their behavior and that of others. Infants may more easily recognize the external effect of their behavior when the actions of others mirror the behavior the infants produce. Some theorists propose that in mirroring infant behavior, which exposes infants to external perceptual manifestations of what they are internally experiencing, parents facilitate infants' early understanding of their own experience.

Parents are selective in responding to infant behaviors. The infant actions that parents respond to tend to be those in which the parents perceive emotion that they, either with or without awareness, wish to reinforce, modify, or share with the infants. These emotions vary among parents because of the parents' own emotional histories and expectations regarding infants. Consequently there are individual differences in the range of parental social responsiveness. What is important for infants' sense of self-efficacy is that the presence of contingent responsiveness to them be such that the infants notice the effect of their actions on their parents' behavior. Thus, individual differences in parents' contingent responsiveness to infants' actions can affect infants' development of their self-efficacy.

The contingent responsiveness present in early parent–infant interactions has been shown to influence infants' subsequent sensitivity to various contingency patterns in others' behavior. Infants become accustomed to particular levels of contingency that they experience in their family interactions, creating optimal contingency levels through familiarization that are reflected in infants' responsiveness to new people. Maternal contingencies to infant behavior are relatively stable within mother–infant pairs but vary across the population. This stability within dyads and variability in the population is present in infants' first year, possibly by the time infants are 3 months old. Infants' detection of and preference for imperfect contingency at this age undoubtedly helps them orient toward people, but because people are imperfectly contingent to different degrees, infants are particularly oriented toward people whose levels of contingency are similar to the levels with which they have become familiar.

This principle goes against the intuitive expectation that infants should be increasingly responsive to increased social contingency because in such conditions the association between self-action and external consequences would be more evident, thereby facilitating infants' self-efficacy. Indeed, research does indicate that the more responsive parents are to infants, the more infants are able to rely on their own self-efficacy. For example, infants whose cries are readily responded to in early infancy cry less in later infancy. This contradicts learning theory, which would predict that responding to crying would reinforce the behavior and thus increase it. But infants' learning processes are complex. By having their cries responded to, infants learn that their own actions are effective in getting their needs met, increasing their sense of self-efficacy. Then at later ages when they run into difficulties, they are more likely to trust their ability to deal with the problems, often succeeding, and therefore needing to cry less. Infants whose parents are less responsive to their cries maintain higher levels of crying throughout infancy. Intermittent reinforcement has been proposed as an explanation, yet all infants experience some intermittent responsiveness from their parents, making this explanation inadequate. Parental responsiveness facilitates infants' understanding that they are effective agents in the world, which in turn influences infants' readiness to seek the effects of their self-actions. Yet infants develop sensitivities to particular levels of perceived social contingency based on past experience and, as a consequence, they are most responsive to other external stimulation that has similar levels of contingency.

Evidence for this principle comes from studies in which infants participated in face-to-face interaction with mothers and strangers. When infants interacted with strangers whose responsiveness to them was similar to that of their mothers, infants' responsiveness to the strangers was much like their responsiveness to their mothers. However, when strangers' responsiveness to the infants was dissimilar to that of the mothers, either by being more contingent or less contingent than the mothers, the infants were less responsive to the strangers relative to their mothers. Such evidence is depicted as a U-shaped curve when infants' responsiveness to mothers (Im) minus infants' responsiveness to strangers (Is) is plotted against mothers' responsiveness to infants (Mi) minus strangers' responsiveness to infants (Si). The significant quadratic trends shown for vocal contingency in **Figure 1** and for smiling contingency in **Figure 2** are from adult–infant interactions involving 4- to 5-month-old infants. Similar significant quadratic trends have been found for adult–infant interactions involving 2-month-olds, indicating that infants show a preference for familiar contingency levels from the time they first show an interest in imperfect or social contingency.

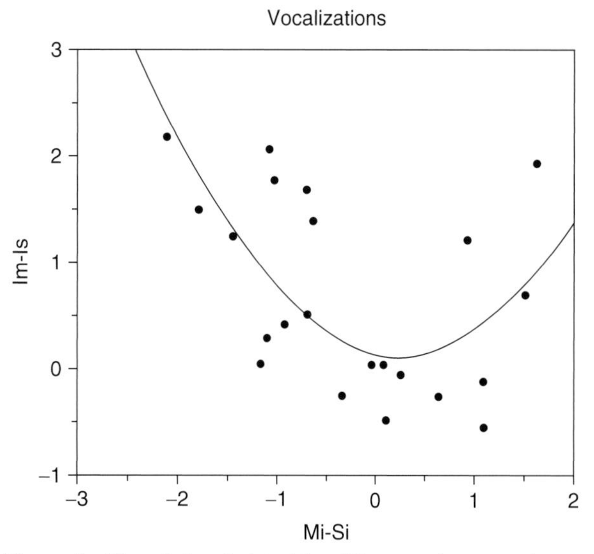

Figure 1 The relational plot of the differences between the infants' contingent vocal responsiveness to mothers and strangers (Im-Is) and the difference between mothers' and strangers' contingent vocal responsiveness to the infants (Mi-Si).Reprinted from Bigelow AE, Infants' sensitivity to familiar imperfect contingencies in social interactions. *Infant Behaviour and Development* 21: 149–162, Copyright 1998, with permission from Elsevier.

Individual differences in parental contingency levels also may influence infants' ability to regulate their levels of stimulation. Initially parents do much of the work in maintaining and regulating infants' emotional engagement in interactions. But infants can influence the level of engagement by averting their gaze when stimulation becomes too high and by reengaging with attention and positive affect when seeking more stimulation. Sensitive parents adjust their interactive behavior to the infants' current level of excitement, while also frequently arousing them to high but manageable levels of stimulation where the potential for learning is at its peak. Infants' experience with parents as regulators of interactions influences infants' ability to accommodate to wider ranges of stimulation and to self-regulate their own levels of engagement in the absence of the parents. In novel situations, the most arousing and interesting levels of contingency are those that are familiar. Infants with parents who respond to them at low levels of contingency may be most engaged in social situations in which low levels of responsiveness are present, and thus, they may have difficulty detecting the impact of their actions. Infants with highly contingent parents may be more sensitive to and interested in people who are highly responsive to them. In so doing they may learn more readily about their own effectiveness.

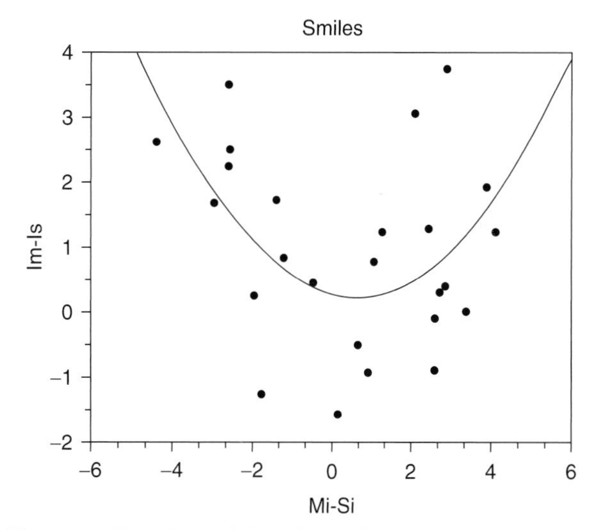

Figure 2 The relational plot of the differences between the infants' contingent smiling responsiveness to mothers and strangers (Im-Is) and the difference between mothers' and strangers' contingent smiling responsiveness to the infants (Mi-Si). Reprinted from Bigelow AE, Infants' sensitivity to familiar imperfect contingencies in social interactions. *Infant Behaviour and Development* 21: 149–162, Copyright 1998, with permission from Elsevier.

The sensitivity infants show to the social contingency levels in their parental interactions raises concerns for infants who are exposed to persistent low levels of parental responsiveness. It is not uncommon for periods of low parental contingent responsiveness to occur as a result of parental illness, grief, or other emotionally distracting circumstances. But such periods tend to be temporary; infants are compelling forces for reinstating parental attention. Yet for some infants, low levels of contingency persist in their most intimate interactions. Children of depressed mothers are such a population. Infants of depressed mothers are exposed to minimal contingent responsiveness and reduced synchronous behavior in their maternal interactions. Initially the infants attempt to engage their relatively unresponsive mothers, but by approximately 3 months of age, they tend to mirror their mothers' depressed activity and affect. When with nondepressed social partners, these infants continue to be relatively unresponsive, and interestingly, seem to elicit depressive behavior from these partners. Either with or without awareness, the nondepressed partners adopt lower levels of social contingency, perhaps because it is at these levels that the infants can be most engaged. The infants' familiarity with low levels of contingency within their maternal interactions generalizes to their interactions with others regardless of the contingency patterns provided. Thus the infants' experience with minimal contingent responsiveness in their social interactions may be easily perpetuated. Extended experience with low levels of social contingency may impair infants' ability to sense their self-efficacy, adding to the difficulties in cognitive, social, and emotional developments for which children of depressed parents are at risk.

Self-Reflective Awareness

Self-reflective awareness requires the child to take an outside perspective of self. Children's ability to take the role or perspective of another has a developmental trajectory that extends beyond infancy and early childhood, yet it is in this time period that the ability emerges. In the latter part of the first year, infants are no longer just engaged with the social and physical world through perception alone; that is, their sense of themselves is not limited to the immediacy of direct action and perception. Although younger infants can relate their actions to similar past experiences and, therefore, have expectations of the outcomes of their actions, infants at the end of the first year begin to act more intentionally with goals in mind. They start to use symbols to convey those goals to others and use tools as aids in acquiring those goals.

Infants achieve what Piaget called means-end understanding. They are able to differentiate goals from the means that bring them about and can choose among alternative means to achieve their goals. For example, infants may have an action pattern for reaching to retrieve objects and an action pattern for batting or striking objects to push them away. When faced with a desired toy that is partially blocked by another object, like a pillow, they can use the striking action, which was not associated with retrieving objects, as a means to remove the pillow in order to get the toy. Or if a desired toy is placed on a table out of reach but on a cloth that the infant can grasp, infants at the end of the first year will pull the cloth to get the toy, whereas younger infants tend simply to reach for the toy with growing frustration. Infants become able to combine actions with intention to achieve specific goals.

Infants also show intentional behaviors in their interactions with others and begin to treat others as beings with intentions that can be different than their own. Prior to the use of language, infants can use gestures to solicit help in obtaining desired objects. They point or reach for an object while glancing back and forth between the object and an adult. In so doing, infants not only are indicating their desire for the object but also are attempting to engage the adult's help; they are attempting to affect the adult's intention with their own.

In addition, infants can direct others' attention with the goal of sharing their interest in an object or event. Infants' gestures of pointing, showing objects, gazing, and accompanying affective expressions are used as directives for adult participation in object play. The goal is purely social and indicates infants' awareness that others' attentional focus can be different than their own but can be changed to match their own focus.

Although infants can use adults as social tools by following others' gazes to find interesting objects from about 6 months of age, beginning around 9 months of age, they engage in joint attention. They can actively coordinate their attention to both an object and a partner, knowing that the partner is attending to them and to the same object that they are. The prototype joint attention episode involves an infant and an adult playing with a toy and the infant looks from the toy to the adult's face and back to the toy. Initially infants are simply checking to see if the partner is attending to the object they are manipulating. Later in coordinated joint attention, they can show or give the object to the partner as a means of more actively participating in triadic interactions with adults and objects.

Infants' use of symbols increases during their second year. Knowledge that others' attention and intention can be different than their own facilitates infants' acquisition of language. They understand that novel labels used by adults generally refer to objects adults are focused on, which can be different from the objects on which the infants are focused. They also can reformulate their own communication when adults appear to have misunderstood them. Eventually, the use of symbolic gestures and language allows infants to move from a focus on the here and now to interactions that include multilayered temporal and spatial events.

In the second year, infants also can make inferences about others' intentions in their actions. For example, after watching an adult perform two actions in sequence, one of which is perceived to be intentional and the other as accidental, infants readily imitate the perceived intended action and tend to ignore the perceived accidental action regardless of which action came first. Perhaps even more impressive, infants who watch an adult perform a failed action on an object, for example, miss a bucket when attempting to drop a toy into it or unsuccessfully attempt to pull two objects apart, will complete the action for the adult. That is, infants read intention into the adult's action and can imitate the intended, but unwitnessed, action.

Around the same time, infants begin to use others to acquire emotional information through social referencing. When encountering a novel and uncertain situation, such as meeting a dog, a remote controlled toy, or a stranger, the infant will look to a trusted person, usually the parent, to see how that person has assessed the situation. Is the parent pleased, indicating encouragement for the infant to approach the new object, or is the parent wary, indicating retreat? In social referencing, infants show awareness that others have access to information that they themselves do not. Social referencing also indicates infants' knowledge of others' perceptual experience as different from their own. In order to ascertain whether the parent's emotional cues are related to the object of concern, the infant typically must turn away from the object to look at the parent and then must determine whether the parent is focused on the object in question. This involves a sophisticated knowledge of space and an awareness of where another's line of vision would intersect with their own if they themselves were looking at the object.

Thus, infants show intentional actions in their social encounters as well as in their encounters with the physical environment. They use adults' actions to change their own behavior and attempt to change adults' behavior with their own actions. Inherent in infants' use of communicative gestures, acts of joint attention, language use, imitation of intended goals, and social referencing is their awareness of intentionality in others' behavior. Whether infants' understanding of themselves as intentional comes before their understanding of others as intentional is debated. But it is likely that intention in self-actions comes first. Infants' experience of intentionality in self behavior, through formulating goals independent of actions and then pursuing them, prepares infants to understand others as intentional agents, whose attention to objects and events may be shared, followed, or directed. Integral to this understanding is infants' knowledge of themselves to be like others yet distinct from them.

During their second year, infants not only are objects of thought to themselves, but they also begin to realize they can be objects of thought to others. One way this is manifested is in the emergence of secondary emotions. Primary emotions involve a direct response to an event; knowledge of, or concern for, others' reactions is not necessary. Primary emotions include emotions such as joy, anger, and surprise. These emotions can be witnessed in infants during the first half year of life. Secondary emotions, sometimes called self-conscious emotions, involve a sense of seeing self from the outside, sensing how self-actions might be perceived by others. The emotions of embarrassment, shame, and pride involve a projected sense of self to another's perspective. In their second year, infants can show a marked sense of embarrassment, typically manifested when doing a task or a performance that can be evaluated by others, and sometimes in the context of protracted attention by others.

Incidents of secondary emotions increase in early childhood. Between 2 and 3 years of age, children begin to evaluate their actions against social expectations by holding in mind the standards of others and their own behavior at the same time. Significant others play a major role in the development of secondary emotions. How others respond to young children's actions influences how children evaluate their own behavior. Such self-evaluations are beginning points of self-esteem and can either enhance or injure children's growing sense of self-competence.

Visual Self-Recognition

How infants learn to recognize their own image as themselves is still an open question. Watching one's mirror reflection is a unique experience in many ways. The perceptual information pertinent to self-recognition is distinct from one's own body yet generated by it. Self is perceived from the perspective of an outside observer. Most theorists agree that visual self-recognition does not emerge suddenly but rather develops gradually, building on earlier aspects of self-knowledge.

Criteria for self-recognition vary among studies. Typically, baseline measures are taken of the infant's self-directed behaviors in front of a mirror or live video and then surreptitiously a mark is made on the infant's face or head, and subsequent self-directed behaviors to the marked area in front of the mirror or live video are noted. Significant increases in touching the marked area of the face or head indicate the infant knows the reflected image is of self. Such measures originated from studies showing self-recognition in chimpanzees. Alternative criteria for self-recognition include infants' self-labels of their reflected images, their coy or embarrassed behaviors in front of a mirror, and their turning to find interesting objects that appear behind them in the mirror. Although justifications, as well as criticisms, can be made for each of these criteria, the timing of self-recognition is quite similar by each of the measures, lending credence to them all. Self-recognition occurs for most infants near the end of their second year.

Although self-recognition occurs rather late in infancy, infants have an early interest in mirrors and other reflective surfaces. Initially, infants are more attentive to the reflected images of objects or other people rather than to their self-images, probably because they readily see that two identically looking objects or people seem to be present and this attracts their interest. Then, beginning around 3–4 months of age, infants' attention is directed toward the self-image. Smiles, vocalizations, touching the image, and even attempts to look behind the mirror become prevalent. Infants appear to treat the image in a social manner as if there were an interesting baby behind the glass, although studies of infants' responses at this age to their reflected image and to a socially responding partner show infants to be more responsive to the social partner.

Toward the end of the first year, infants' behavior toward their mirror image takes on a new dimension. Infants begin to test the correspondence between the action of the image and their own behavior. They study the movements of their reflections while systematically varying these movements. Most characteristic is repeated limb activity while observing the limb in the mirror image or a repeated bobbing, bowing, or bouncing while attending to the image, at times turning away and then quickly back to the image as if to try to catch it off guard. Movement testing behavior indicates that infants are exploring the uniqueness of their reflected self-image and its perfect match to their behavior. Movement testing behavior accelerates around the time of self-recognition. The realization that the movement of the self-image is perfectly matched to the infant's movement may be an initial cue to self-recognition. That is, the first recognition of the visual self-image may be the recognition of self-movement.

Figure 3 shows infants' movement testing behavior to different video conditions in a longitudinal study of the development of self-recognition beginning when infants were 18 months of age. On each monthly session, infants were shown a playback of a video of themselves taken at the beginning of the session (discordant condition), a live video of themselves (simultaneous condition), and a video of a similarly aged infant in the same setting (other child condition). The mean age of self-recognition in the simultaneous condition in this study was 22 months. Movement testing to this condition was clearly higher than in the other conditions and showed an increase prior to self-recognition.

Infants' interest in the movements of their mirror image may be due to advances in their imitative abilities and awareness. Around the time infants show an interest in movement testing with their reflected images, they show development in their ability to imitate novel behaviors not in their repertoire of actions and in their deliberate attempts to adjust their behavior to more accurately match that of a model. As infants' imitative ability becomes more precise, they may notice that the actions of their reflected images are unique. The images consistently, simultaneously, and perfectly match their own movements, unlike that of a social partner.

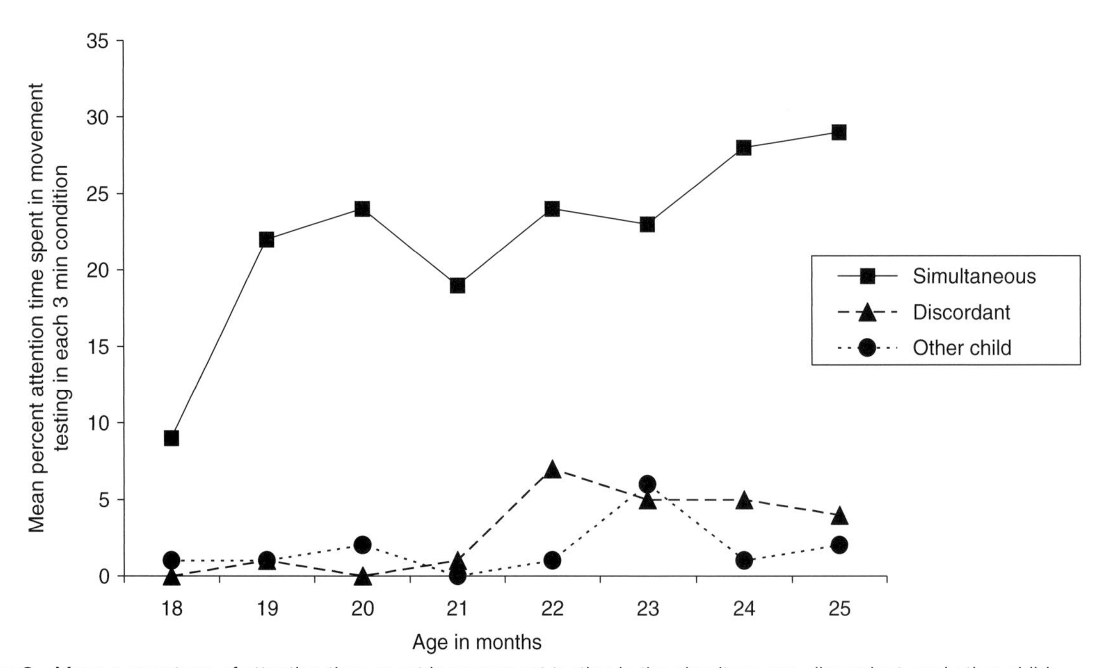

Figure 3 Mean percentage of attention time spent in movement testing in the simultaneous, discordant, and other child conditions from ages 18 to 25 months. Adapted from Bigelow AE (1981) The correspondence between self and image movement as a cue to self-recognition in young children. *Journal of Genetic Psychology* 139: 11–36, Copyright (1981), with permission from Heldref Publications.

Within a few weeks to a few months after infants can recognize themselves in mirrors or live video, they can recognize themselves in still images, such as picking out pictures of themselves from a series of photographs of babies, and on videotape that is not concurrent with their present movement. In the study depicted in **Figure 3**, self-recognition in the discordant condition occurred at a mean age of 24 months. Between self-recognition in the simultaneous and discordant conditions, movement testing increased in the discordant and other child conditions, although movement testing was virtually nonexistent prior to this time as can be seen in **Figure 3**. The infants may have been trying to identify the images in these conditions by means of the same process that facilitated recognition in the simultaneous condition, that is, by attempting to test for a correspondence between self and image movement. In these conditions, however, there was no visual feedback of a correspondence so the attempts were short-lived.

Infants eventually become aware that their reflected self-image has unique visual characteristics, that is, it is always the same-looking child who moves exactly like self. Once they understand that particular image to be of self, they can match that image to other self-images that do not have exact correspondence to their current movement. Thus, the process of self-recognition may begin with infants' interest in the correspondence between self and image movement, which leads to the realization that the image that shows such correspondence with self-movement is a self-image, and be followed by the children's development of mental representations of what they look like to which they can match the images they see.

Interestingly, studies of 2- and 3-year-old children's reactions to their delayed video images indicate that, although the children can recognize their delayed video images as self-images, they have difficulty recognizing the images as of themselves in the present unless the delay is less than 2–3 s. Young children's recognition of self-images in the present is dependent upon their ability to detect the temporal matching of their current action and the action of the self-image.

The temporal limits of recognition of self-images in the present correspond to the timing necessary for infants to detect socially contingent responses to self-action. The responses of others are perceived to be socially contingent only if the responses occur less than 2–3 s after the infants' own behavior. Adults show similar temporal limits to the perception of social contingency.

Experience with social interaction may be important for self-recognition. Such speculation is supported by findings that show chimpanzees raised in isolation, unlike those raised with other chimpanzees, do not perform self-directed behavior when watching their mirror reflection. Perhaps it is necessary to experience the contingency between self-actions and those of a socially responding partner before it is possible to become aware that the unique simultaneous matching between self and image action is an indication that the image seen is a self-image.

Early Autobiographical Self-Knowledge

Our autobiographical self-knowledge consists of our memories of important events in our lives that help define who we are to ourselves and others. There are large individual differences in the age of first memories, as well as the number of memories reported from early childhood. Rarely do people report memories from before 2 years of age. Most people have some sporadic memories from the years 2–4, with more accessible memories from middle childhood.

Freud labeled this phenomenon of little or no memory of early life infantile amnesia. He proposed the cause to be repression of memories that were too arousing for the ego, such as the child's early sexual desires. It is unlikely that Freud's explanation is the reason for the absence of self-memories from early childhood; all memories of very early childhood tend to be absent, not just those that are emotionally arousing or might be associated with the young child's sensual pleasures.

Piaget proposed a cognitive explanation. He thought that memories from early life are stored differently than memories from later childhood and adulthood, and therefore, the retrieval systems to those memories are not accessible or, at best, indirect. From a Piagetian perspective, thought in infancy is a product of the babies' ongoing perceptions and motor actions. Babies think about what they currently perceive and what they are doing. In later infancy, these sensorimotor processes connect to previous learning in new ways, as in means-end understanding. Yet infants still do not have representational thought. From the end of infancy at about 2 years of age through the preschool period, young children's thought is representational but is not yet logically organized, making access to memories fragmented. Thus, events that occurred in infancy and early childhood are not stored in ways that are easily retrievable by older children and adults.

More recently, cognitive theorists have proposed that until children have a concept of self as an individual with unique characteristics, as evidenced specifically by mirror self-recognition, there is no framework around which to organize their personal memories and formulate their autobiographical past. Thus, autobiographical memory depends on developments in specific self-constructs.

Developments in children's memory storage and retrieval systems and constructs of the self are important to children's ability to remember their own lives, but such developments may not fully account for the emergence of autobiographical memory. These theoretical positions cannot readily explain the large variation in age and number of early memories. Children across cultures develop neural cognitive structures relating to storage and retrieval of memories at approximately the same age, and visual self-recognition is acquired within a narrow age range even in cultures with little or no experience with reflective surfaces.

Social cultural theorists propose that autobiographical memory emerges gradually and is influenced by multiple factors that interact in a dynamic fashion. Important to autobiographical memory are advances in neural cognitive structures in the brain that facilitate encoding, consolidation, storage, and retrieval of memories; conceptual developments of the self that include a subjective view of how events make one feel and think, which has its basis in infants' understanding of intentionality in self and others; language development, especially in narrative skills; developments in temporal concepts, particularly of self in time; and conversations with others about events the children have experienced. The importance of conversations with others is particularly intriguing and may help explain variations in age and number of early memories.

There are individual differences in the ways parents and others discuss children's life experiences with them. Some parents are more elaborate than other parents in their discussions with children about events in their lives, both at the time of the events and in reminiscing about them. In trying to help children remember, elaborative parents provide verbal props, expand on whatever fragments the child contributes, and are detailed in their descriptions. Less elaborative parents tend to repeat their questions rather than become more expansive in their detail and are more pragmatic in their questioning about the past, for example, where did you put your sweater. The differences among parents' conversations with children about events in the children's lives are most evident when talking with 2- and 3-year-olds because children at this age tend to contribute little original information to conversations about past events, resulting in the discussion being carried primarily by the parents' comments. Although parents tend to become more elaborate as children grow older and acquire more narrative skills and parents tend to emphasize different topics with sons than with daughters, individual differences in how elaborative parents are in their conversations with children are robust. Parents' reminiscing styles correlate over time and show similar patterns with multiple children in the family. One of the reasons there are such large individual differences in age and number of early autobiographical memories may be due to individual differences in how parents discuss events in young children's lives with them.

How do conversations with children about events in their lives affect autobiographical memories? Autobiographical memories are episodic memories, which are memories of specific events that happened at specific times and places. Children as young as 2.5 years report episodic memories, but whether they have autobiographical memories is questionable. Not all episodic memories become autobiographical memories. For instance, yesterday's lunch may be remembered today, but unless the lunch was extraordinary for some reason, it is unlikely that it will become part of one's autobiographical self knowledge. In talking with children about events in their past, children are helped to reflect on the events, which may facilitate the consolidation of specific episodic memories into autobiographical memories.

To children of 2 and 3 years of age, routine events, rather than one time events, are particularly important. Young children are trying to figure out the world and themselves in it. Their particular interest is in how things are done and what to expect next. The scenarios of routine events are scripts or generic event memories, for example, bedtime scripts may involve taking a bath, getting into pajamas, getting a story read to you, having a glass of water, getting a goodnight kiss, hugging your teddy bear. When a novel event occurs, young children can hold it in their memories for a period of time. If a similar event occurs within that period, the event is remembered longer. Two-year-olds have been shown to remember an event for 3 months if it reoccurred within 2 weeks of the original occurrence. After an event occurs several times, it tends to become a generic event. For example, going to the zoo may be a memorable episodic event for a 2.5-year-old, but after several trips to the zoo, the child forms a script for zoo trips but does not remember what specific animals were seen on which trips. The underlying principle is that events must reoccur for young children to have sustained memories of the event, but those memories tend to get transformed into generic event memories.

But when parents, siblings, and others talk to the child about experiences the child has had, the experiences are reinstated; the child revisits the event in conversation with the other person. Unlike generic or script memories, the revisits are not similar actual events, but rather involve mentally reinstating the specific episodic event. All autobiographical memories may be products of mentally reinstating specific episodic events. The difference between the establishment of autobiographical memories in early childhood and in later childhood and adulthood may be that, for young children, the mental reinstating of episodic events is facilitated by others.

The influence of children's conversations with parents and others on children's memory implies that autobiographical memory is subject to social construction. What is salient to the parent from a particular event in the child's life may not be what was salient to the child at the time, yet the parent's version is what is discussed, especially in early childhood when information contributed by the child is minimal. Children's reports of private memories that do not involve discussions with others tend to become more prevalent in the late preschool years. Although this may be because of increases in children's narrative skills, it is also when children become more facile in using their thought processes to reminisce and reflect upon happenings for themselves, essentially reinstating the event in their minds without help from others. Yet social cultural theorists do not propose that conversations with others cause children's memories. Although children with parents who are elaborate in their discussions of past events report longer and more detailed descriptions of their past experiences, children with less elaborative parents do not necessarily have fewer memories.

From the perspective of social cultural theory, the frequency and manner of parents' reminiscing with children about events in the children's lives affect the development of several skills important to autobiographical memory. Parental conversation styles that are elaborate, both when events occur and when reminiscing about them, may help children organize their memories, which makes them more accessible. Parent–child conversations about the child's past may facilitate the child's understanding of self in time through focusing on the child's experience in temporally specified events. Potentially, such conversations also may allow more opportunity for the parent and child to disagree on the facts (e.g., whether talking to Santa was scary or not) and thus facilitate children's understanding of memories as representational and that self and others can have different perspectives of the past, allowing for the creation of a truly personal past. Children's discussions with others about their experiences help them distinguish specific episodic events as significant from other events in their lives and to integrate such memories into their life story. Parent–child conversations about the past influence the way children think about their lives, the sense they make of their experiences, and how they share their experiences with others.

Conclusion

Early forms of self-knowledge prepare the way for later more complex forms of self-knowledge to develop. Through experience with their own actions and perceptions, infants distinguish self-action from the actions of others or events in the physical world. They become aware of their own bodies and the effects their actions have on the physical and social environment. These effects become predictable and anticipated. Infants become intentional in their actions and begin to read intention in the actions of others. They become self-reflective, learn to recognize their own images, and begin to form their life narrative. In the first few years of life, self-knowledge progresses from simple beginnings to sophisticated forms of self-understanding that continue to develop throughout life.

Experience is crucial to early developments in self-knowledge. The child's experience when alone and when engaged with the physical environment provide the child with important information relevant to the self, but much of the experience most salient to self-knowledge occurs within social contexts. In early infancy, responding others facilitate infants' ability to distinguish self from other and to learn that they are effective in producing external changes. In later infancy, self-recognition may depend on children's awareness of the difference between the movements of their reflections and those of a socially responding other. The development of intentionality is enhanced through engagement with others by facilitating infants' understanding that their intentions and those of others are distinct yet can be changed through their own behavior. Others' communications with children influence how children begin to value their abilities and remember their own lives. Social encounters provide the fertile ground for young children to acquire self-knowledge. In early life, as well as throughout life, knowledge of self is embedded in interactions with others.

See also: Amnesia, Infantile; Emotion Regulation; Gender: Awareness, Identity, and Stereotyping; Milestones: Cognitive; Milestones: Physical; Newborn Behavior; Perceptual Development; Social and Emotional Development Theories; Social Interaction.

Suggested Readings

Bauer PJ (2007) *Remembering the Times of Our Lives: Memory in Infancy and Beyond.* Mahwah, NJ: Erlbaum.
Bigelow AE (1981) The correspondence between self and image movement as a cue to self recognition in young children. *Journal of Genetic Psychology* 139: 11–36.
Bigelow AE (1998) Infants' sensitivity to familiar imperfect contingencies in social interaction. *Infant Behavior and Development* 21: 149–162.
Carpenter M, Nagell K, and Tomasello M (1998) Social cognition, joint attention, and communicative competence from 9 to 15 months of age. *Monographs of the Society for Research in Child Development* 63. (4, Serial No. 255).
Lewis M and Haviland-Jones JM (eds.) (2000) *Handbook of Emotions,* 2nd edn. New York: The Guilford Press.
Neisser U (ed.) (1993) *The Perceived Self: Ecological and Interpersonal Sources of Self Knowledge.* New York: Cambridge University Press.
Nelson K (1993) The psychological and social origins of autobiographical memory. *Psychological Science* 4: 7–14.
Nelson K and Fivush R (2004) The emergence of autobiographical memory: A social cultural developmental theory. *Psychological Review* 111: 486–511.
Rochat P (ed.) (1995) *The Self in Infancy: Theory and Research.* Amsterdam: North-Holland/Elsevier.
Rochat P (ed.) (1999) *Early Social Cognition: Understanding Others in the First Months of Life.* Mahwah, NJ: Erlbaum.
Stern DN (2000) *The Interpersonal World of the Infant: A View from Psychoanalysis and Developmental Psychology.* New York: Basic Books.

Self-Regulatory Processes

C B Kopp, Los Angeles, CA, USA

Glossary

Emotion regulation – A multidimensional mental and/or behavioral regulatory process that draws upon cognitions and motivations to influence emotion states with respect to: self needs, demands relevant to information intake, and interactions that involve group goals, others' emotion states, and salient social conventions. Anticipatory forms of emotion regulation tend to be more effective than attempts to regulate highly elevated negative emotions.

Executive attention – A behavioral regulatory process that involves top-down, focused, or supervisory control of attention that is relevant for cognitive activities such as learning and problem solving, or engaging in social interactions that also necessitate the monitoring of informational content and emotional tone.

Executive functions (EF) – A constellation of behaviors that subsume adaptive decision making involving conscious reflection, planning, monitoring, and evaluations of goals typically related to complex social–emotional contexts or difficult cognitive problems. Underlying effective EF are executive attention, inhibition of actions, and working memory. EF is typically evaluated with a series of laboratory tasks that induce cognitive conflict, appraisal of competing stimuli, controlled inhibition, and planful strategies. EF is developmental in that age, experiences, and degree of growth of the brain's frontal lobes matter. Young children (3 years) are least successful in EF laboratory tasks despite age-related adaptations; in general, EF performance shows linear trends from childhood into adulthood. Recognize that some scientists debate the usefulness of the EF construct and measures used for its evaluation.

Inhibitory control – A behavioral regulatory process that involves cessation of concentrated activity or thoughts because they are irrelevant to a primary goal or undermine progress toward a goal whether set by the individual or designated by another.

Regulatory processes – Biological, physiological, and behavioral mechanisms that facilitate adaptations of metabolic processes, sensory and motor systems, attentiveness, emotion regulation, and activities in order to plan, adjust, and implement goal directed actions related to self well-being, learning and thinking, social interactions and demands, and cultural standards. Regulatory processes can be reactive or intentionally guided by a conscious self, a point that has age-related relevance in that conscious awareness soars during the second and third years.

Introduction

To be socially adept is to know the norms of one's group, to understand when and how norms differ, and to generate self-regulated strategies for managing one's behaviors particularly in complex social situations. To be cognitively adept is to know what one needs to learn, the kinds of learning required for different goals, and how to obtain relevant knowledge. Whereas knowledge gives us insight, how we behave typically draws upon regulatory processes such as inhibitory control, controlled attention, or emotion management for adapting our behavioral responses. Because behavioral fine-tuning is such an important human characteristic, it is not surprising that nascent forms of regulatory processes are observed in infancy. Ten-month-olds, for example, seem to realize if they make eye contact with another they can then direct the other's gaze to something else that interests them. Perhaps though the most essential role of regulatory processes involves facilitating 'executive functions': these are the often conscious, self-motivated, supervisory aspects of humans' planning, goal setting, monitoring, and evaluation whether involving an immediate or longer-term personal goal, facilitating teamwork to meet a competition, or planning a social event that includes fractious family members. Metaphorically speaking, a regulatory process such as controlled attention can narrow an individual's cognitive frame such that the person can fully concentrate on an issue that requires resolution. Research reveals that healthy, cognitively adept adults seamlessly integrate several regulatory processes preparatory to goal setting, organizing actions, predicting outcomes, monitoring progress, and instigating changes when necessary. In general, think of regulatory processes as underlying mechanisms that facilitate the realization of goals.

Conscious, intentional, self-directed modulation of regulatory processes begin to take shape during the end of the first year and are part of the constellation of distinctly human patterns of behavior that make their appearance during the toddler period (e.g., walking, elaborate forms of play, communicating with words, self-reflective awareness of agency and intentions, social imitation, verbalized self-awareness). These skills develop further because of children's own motivations, adequate nurturing from others, parents' socialization goals enacted with do's and don'ts, and, new connections within and across the brain's frontal lobes, specifically the prefrontal cortex. However as will be described in succeeding sections, the developmental growth of regulatory processes is neither straightforward nor trouble free. Several mitigating factors are involved. One, for example, involves the varied contextual demands made upon the young child's limited psychological resources. Consider as one example peer play, which tends to be exhilarating for young children. However, the maintenance of play demands cooperation while minimizing disagreements about personal possessions and roles. Cooperation in play is a matter of learning how to adapt and cope and in so doing enabling regulatory processes.

A second mitigating factor relates to the sheer magnitude of developmental change that occurs during the second year, and toddlers' impelling need to practice every developing skill; those that are most exhilarating such as walking and exploring are practiced the most. Karen Adolph's studies of relatively new walkers reveal numerous bouts of walking each day sometimes corresponding to lengths of many football fields. Data also suggest that although gross motor activities (walking, running, climbing) continue to be highly salient for young children, by the mid-toddler months they are better able to balance those activities with periods of small toy play that engage eye–hand coordination and attention. However, continued preoccupation with locomotion can have adverse implications for regulatory processes when parents negate the importance of toy play or do not intervene if a child has an exceedingly high activity level and engages in purposeless wandering.

A third mitigating factor relates to the differential amount of time that newly emerging skills become functionally competent. Findings reveal that walking expertise is achieved in a few months, whereas communicative skills (i.e., vocabulary, sentence use, narratives) that are useful for conversing about bothersome events may take a year of more to become functionally adaptive to different social contexts. What this means in the practical sense is that the language component of child agency can be severely constrained by limitations in communicating needs and goals to others, and also in talking to one's self and giving the self instructions. This developmental inequity is one reason that emotion regulation, which often requires self-issued reminders, is so difficult for most toddlers.

Despite these challenges, the toddler and early preschool years are also witness to growing competencies that continually influence all manner of social and object interactions, and the growth of regulatory processes. Expanding cognitions represent growth in semantic and episodic memory, causal reasoning sometimes associated with strategic-like behaviors, and consciousness, which often coincides with increases in different kinds of pretend play. With respect to language, for many children after about 18 months or so, there are substantial increases in comprehension of objects and people, as well as increasing ability to use ideas when communicating with others. Equally important is the child's growing sense of competence, which is tied to consciousness of an objective self, that is, a self represented by 'I' rather than only by a sense of 'me.' The former reflects a sense of personal agency, that is, "I can do ... I can jump ...," whereas the latter indicates a sense of awareness such as being warm, a girl, owning a toy, or feeling happy. Major patterns of change are typically observed between 18 and 24 months with clear differentiation of self from other, self as a 'being' who has preferences, and a self who can experience social emotions (e.g., an emotion akin to shame), again during the second and third years when language exchanges promote more defined reflective self-knowledge and increasing awareness of "I can ...," and between 3 and 6 years with autobiographical memory reflected in past and planned social interactions and in imaginary events. Although our human biological heritage provides an imprimatur for many early skills, their continuing development including the self as an agent, largely depends on a variety of social interactions.

With some exceptions, developmental scientists have seemed largely indifferent to developmental aspects of regulatory processes, and the component skills that are concordant with patterns of change. Rather there has been considerable effort to explore individual differences at one or another age. In part, this emphasis is due to concerns about preschool-aged children who have problematic behavioral controls, and school children who have difficulty controlling emotions. However, at times it is a challenge to more fully interpret individual differences in the absence of a broader developmental context; nonetheless, these studies have highlighted the adverse roles of poverty, unstable family environments, low parent education, and harsh parenting. Moreover, the data serve as reminders that the development of regulatory processes demands an incalculable number of appropriate caregiver-organized experiences, a fact that serves as an underlying context for the emphasis on age changes in regulatory processes that forms the rest of this piece. The regulatory processes that are the primary focus of this entry are inhibitory control, executive attention (also referred to as focused, or controlled), and emotion regulation. Before turning to specifics, it is useful to highlight what is inferred about general developmental trends in young children's use of regulatory processes.

Inferences: Developmental Issues and Regulatory Processes

First, as noted earlier there are indications that inhibitory control and controlled attention in nonemotional contexts are more evident in toddlers' and young preschoolers' behavioral repertoires than emotion regulation. A crucial reason is that any number of situations can elicit a highly charged emotion and any number of strategies can defuse a potentially disruptive emotion encounter. However, young children rarely have insights about the causes of disruptive social interactions, and even if they do, their cognitive limitations often restrict options for successfully forestalling distressing emotions. Complex psychological demands tax young children's psychological resources. This factor is one reason that the appropriate intervention of a parent greatly influences the young child's emotion regulatory competencies.

Second, young children's motivations matter, a factor often overlooked in research. Toddlers, for example, devote much psychic energy toward regulating their movements when the goal involves protecting their balance upon encountering changes in ground surfaces (a steep incline or drop). Sometimes toddler actions appear intentional as if guided by a prescient self and other times seem accidental. Whether intentional or not, experienced walkers (about 4 months of functional walking) appraise situations by determining relative safety or risk to themselves, try out different strategies to avoid risks and when necessary coordinate and use multiple strategies, and discover that anticipatory planning about risk avoidance is more effective than responding reactively. Despite growing expertise in negotiating locomotion, failures occur that at times relate to insufficient control of attention to contextual features. Overall, the multidimensional studies by Adolph and colleagues reveal how young experienced walkers construct a perceptually and cognitively driven strategically adaptive, regulated mobility system to avoid risks. The lack of across domain (cognitive, motor, social) longitudinal studies of contemporary toddlers makes it difficult to translate these findings to other aspects of regulated behavior. However, it is intriguing that toddlers' creative use of proactive walking strategies has an analog in anticipatory emotion regulation observed among children around the time of their second birthday. Whether encountering an obstacle while walking or hearing a parent say it is time to put toys away, children seem to sense that modifying the potentially upsetting situation before it actually occurs is more effective than trying to cope reactively. An anticipatory locomotion strategy might involve resorting to creeping in order to manage a flight of stairs, and for emotion regulation the strategy might involve using words to bargain for a few more minutes of play.

In addition to conditions and behaviors that foster the growth of regulatory processes, new competencies surface that raise challenges for toddlers' use of behavioral controls. These new achievements include a deepened awareness of one's own body and physical skills, stronger memories particularly related to salient events involving the self, and heightened cognizance of self-identity and personal possessions. Taken together, this burgeoning knowledge contributes to a sense of urgency to intentions, and when the child's intent is thwarted frustration and protest result. This behavioral pattern becomes evident between 15 and 30 months, has an inverted U-shaped pattern with a peak about 21–24 months and shows gradual declines thereafter. Accompanying behavioral attributes include heightened whining and crying, temper tantrums, anger, physical aggression, and negativism (No!), and are exemplified by howling for juice, screaming and hitting when a pen was moved beyond reach, biting a peer overpossession of a toy, and angrily jabbing a crayon at a parent. The intensity and frequency of these negative behaviors vary among toddlers, although in general, crying and negativism are more common than physical aggression. It is not clear why these behaviors fade. Possibly, somewhat older toddlers and young preschoolers gain skill in delaying an action in the service of self-directed emotion control because of improved communication skills, better memory of consequences with respect to do's and don'ts, and more concern about others' feelings. Whatever the reasons, behaviors associated with 'the terrible twos' diminish, and in the ensuing years preschoolers increasingly use regulatory processes for self-promoted learning, and in dealing with social situations that have the potential to be distressing. Even young preschoolers begin to negotiate conditions of play with their peers. It is interesting that during the period of relative developmental upheaval when very young children often seem out-of-control, predictions about later behavioral vulnerabilities tend to be problematic. Exceptions occur in the presence of serious risks (e.g., meager rearing environments; young children's persistent cognitive and language delays, heightened levels of irritability, and high levels of physical aggression).

Introducing the Study of Regulatory Processes

Regulatory processes are discussed in detail in the following sections, with greater emphasis on the toddler and early preschool years than earlier or later. The reasons are twofold. First, prefrontal neuronal activation is increasingly activated around the first birthday and is associated with regulatory processes that are gradually more conscious and more linked to burgeoning cognitions. Second, the magnitude of change between 1 and 4 years is uniquely transformative such that the young human transitions from a mostly dependent being to one who knows a self and individuality, is increasingly entrusted with some independence, and who is expected to learn how to balance self-goals with those of others. This developmental period represents another waypoint toward assuming an active role in social activities and groups.

In the following, the first section describes changes in brain functioning that occur during the early years and also summarizes information obtained with older children and adults about prefrontal cortex (PFC) activation, intrabrain interactions, and associated behavioral manifestations. The second section provides a figurative representation of the multiple factors and conditions that influence the development of regulatory processes including brain growth, parental and sociocultural influences, and child competencies. The goal is to emphasize the varied inputs and experiences that contribute to development. The third section draws upon selected cross-sectional and longitudinal studies to suggest various patterns in age trends in inhibitory control, executive attention, and emotion regulation, with particular emphasis on the years between 1 and 4. Indirectly, data support the notion that different regulatory processes make differential demands on the child's psychological resources. Yet again, note that inhibitory control seems to be less effortful than emotion regulation because the latter requires effort to evaluate a particular situation including who is involved, the cause of one's bothersome emotion, the potential resources available (another person), and, how to defuse the situation. The younger the child, the fewer the resources, a key reason for the crucial role of caregivers. Also, it will be apparent that it is easier for researchers to study controlled inhibition across a large age span than executive attention or emotion regulation. The reason is that task stimuli for the study of controlled inhibition can be more easily designed to be appropriate for a wide age range; this is not the situation for the other regulatory skills. This fact also has implications for the availability of data that extend across age groups. One last point needs emphasizing; the availability of multiple data points (cross-sectional or longitudinal) for across age comparisons during the toddler and early preschool years is markedly limited for emotion regulation.

The Brain: With Emphasis on the Prefrontal Cortex

The basic structural organization of the brain takes place during the prenatal period, and at birth the infant's brain looks like a miniature version of an adult brain. The newborn's brain differs in size, the number of its folds, and connections within and across lobes. Given a healthy uterine environment, the developing prenatal brain represents a conserved human system that is only minimally dependent on specialized experiences. As **Box 1** reveals, postnatal brain growth occurs first in the occipital and motor areas and then lastly, at about a year of age, crucial changes begin to occur in the frontal lobes. Evidence suggests that for very young primates (including humans), neuronal activations related to responses to certain visual stimuli and those related to control for postural patterns are subcortically innervated and then later cortically. In describing motor development, one prominent primate researcher suggests that "... primates appear to be forced to reconstruct on their own things that, paradoxically, may well be specified in their genes." In other words, primates must not only discover what they can do with their bodies, but must also build flexible, intelligent representations of those discoveries. This means that sensory and motor systems must become attuned, and stay attuned, to local ecologies including the family setting, and to social groups. Enter frontal lobe activation and initial glimmerings of regulatory processes. Consider again young human toddlers who walk hours each day and who try to maintain balance in the midst of changing conditions (e.g., light, spatial configurations, and floor surfaces). The more inexperienced the walker, the more likely the need to stop every so often to attend to the terrain beneath the feet, to look for support from a caregiver, and to take note of the caregiver's positive or negative responses to the walking activity. In other words, there is nascent behavioral inhibition, attention management, and sensitivity to caregiver expectations.

The human brain has a large number of neurons and high conduction velocity, which are associated with high information capacity and behavioral adaptability. Humans' frontal lobes are also large relative to brain and body size, and the PFC is larger and has a more complex structure than those of the great apes. Data indicate that the PFC is relatively young from an evolutionary standpoint probably evolving from nearby motor structures, and tripling in size in the past few million years. Overall, the human PFC contains a sophisticated neural architecture, interconnectivity within itself and across brain regions, and extended periods of neuronal firing that permit the coding, storage, and retrieval of long and complex sequences of behavior. Basically the PFC integrates information that is coming in, assesses the relative internal state of that individual, and facilitates the individual's assessment of what is necessary for an appropriate response. Thus in a very real sense, the PFC provides the potential to adapt to varied contexts, to realize individual and cooperative goals, to grow intellects, and to consciously enjoy meaningful and lasting social and emotional relationships. It is also crucially important in situations that are novel, ambiguous, demand self and intentionality, for integrating disparate kinds of information, and is invariably associated with 'top-down' conscious awareness across a period of time. Given the complexity of these processing demands, it is not

Box 1. The brain: early development, in brief

Nature provides a first draft, which experience then revises.
Gary Marcus

General: size, growth patterns, and volume. The newborn's brain is similar in structural organization to adult brains but differs in size (about 25% smaller), number of ridges and grooves (gyri, sulci), and connections within and across lobes. Postnatal brain growth occurs first in the occipital and motor areas, next in the temporal and parietal association cortices, and lastly in the lateral cortices and the prefrontal cortex. These regional patterns of growth are also reflected in relative rates of maturation with sensory areas maturing far earlier than the prefrontal cortex, which shows protracted growth into early adolescence. At about 6 years of age, cerebral volume is 90–95% of adult brains. Cerebral volume peaks at about 14 years for males and 11+ years for females. Although the peak in volume occurs during adolescence, the brain continues to be a dynamic structure. Connections continue to be fine-tuned and the process of myelination (of axons) continues into the adult years.

Cortical gray and white matter. Most neurons (gray matter) are formed before birth; however, some areas such as the hippocampus show neuronal growth after birth. Apoptosis refers to the programmed death of unnecessary or redundant neuronal cells that occurs during development. White matter refers to myelin, which is a fatty substance that surrounds a neuron's axis and hastens the transmission of impulses. Myelination refers to this process. By 3 years, major pathways are substantially myelinated with other pathways myelinated later on. In the broader context of development, gray matter decreases (likely due to synaptic pruning) and white matter increases with age. Wilke and colleagues' recent study of a large group of normally developing children and adolescents confirm and extend these findings, with details about age and gender differences; gray matter losses greater in parietal lobes and least in the cingulate and posterior temporal areas; virtually uniform increases in white matter volume. Of importance, the study of gender differences in the brain and related behavioral competencies is still in early phases.

Synaptic density. A rapid increase in synapse formation (connections made between axons and dendrites) occurs during the first year, and by the second year the increase in connections is 50% greater than synapses measured in adult brains. The peak period in growth of synapses is first observed in the area of visual cortex toward the end of the first year and into the second, and last in the prefrontal cortex between 2 and 5 years. In contrast, peak synaptic density in one of the layers of the motor cortex extends from a year of life to about 10 years. These increases in synaptic connections are one reason that brain growth occurs in the early years. However, synapse formation can occur through adult life. The periods of high synaptic density also result in far more synapses than can be used. Those that are not used gradually disappear ('pruned'). Synaptic growth and synaptic pruning are also dynamic processes. Taken together, the regressive and progressive changes that occur across development within the brain result in fine-tuning and strengthening connections.

surprising that the study of PFC functions first emerged from careful behavioral analyses of individuals who experienced frontal lobe injuries, often revealing impulsive and emotionally explosive behavior and minimal concern for social norms. With advances in technology, studies extended to PFC activation with nonhuman primates; then with the availability of increasingly sophisticated neural imaging techniques, neuroscientists studied PFC activation in laboratory settings using varied kinds of stimuli with healthy human adults, adolescents, and older children.

PFC activation is typically analyzed in relation to its subregions and interconnections, and also to connections to other brain structures such as the hippocampus (memory functions, particularly new memories), to the amygdala (regulation of emotions chiefly negative ones such as anger), and to the hypothalamus (regulation of endocrine and somatic functions). **Figure 1** shows major PFC regions as well as the anterior cingulated cortex and the amygdala, emphasizing the interconnections of these brain structures and emotions. In the figure, orbital PFC is distinguished from ventromedial PFC, both of which are associated with emotion, affective styles, and emotion control albeit the orbital PFC may be more linked to emotion control. One of the central debates in the study of PFC relates to exactly how its neural circuitry functions, and how best to characterize these functions.

Figure 2, from Wood and Grafman's discussion of PFC and its possible representations, provides a useful guide for highlighting the central interconnectivity of the PFC as a unit, while also differentiating connections of the dorsolateral PFC from those of the ventromedial PFC. The former is often more involved in top-down cognitive activities, whereas the latter is more often linked to emotionally laden situations that may also require cognitive inputs. The dorsolateral PFC supports decision making,

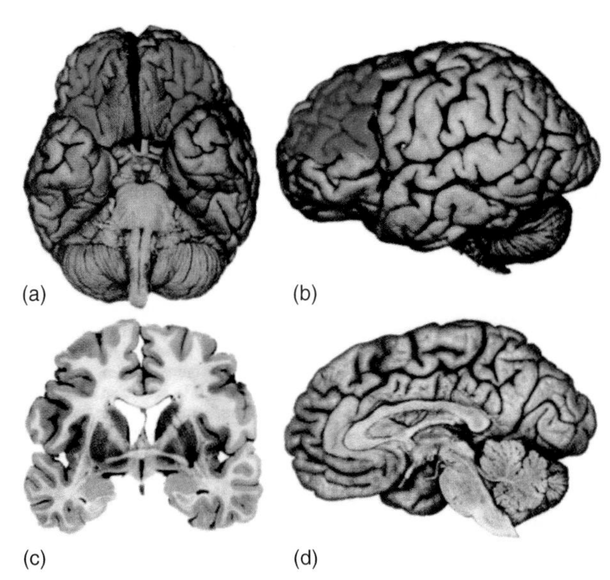

Figure 1 The prefrontal cortex (PFC) and two key areas of interconnections: (a) orbital PFC in green, and ventromedial PFC in red; (b) dorsolateral PFC; (c) amygdala; (d) anterior cingulated cortex. From Davidson RJ, Putnam KM, and Larson CL (2000) Dysfunction in the neural circuitry of emotion regulation – A possible prelude to violence. *Science* 289: 591–594.

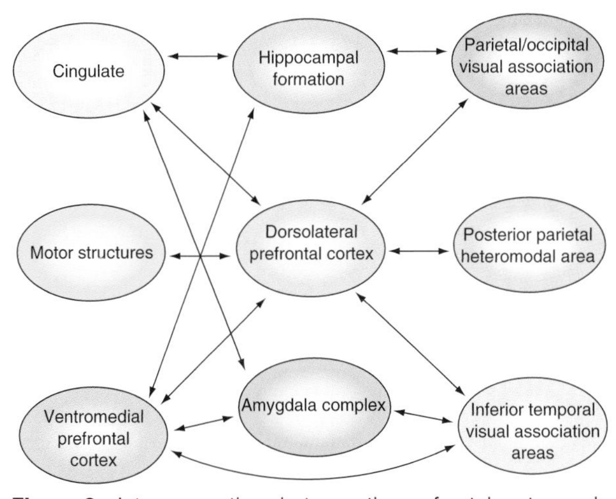

Figure 2 Interconnections between the prefrontal cortex and other brain regions. Adapted and reprinted from Wood JN and Grafman J (2003) Human prefrontal cortex: Processing and representational perspectives. *Nature Reviews Neuroscience* 4: 139–147.

the regulation of behavior and the control of nonemotional responses to environmental stimuli including motor control via the basal ganglia, premotor cortex, and supplementary motor area. It also has a role in performance monitoring via the cingulated cortex, as well as in higher-order sensory processing via the brain's association area and the parietal cortex. Ventromedial PFC supports functions involving emotion processing and emotion control, the integration of emotion and memory, and higher-order sensory processing via the amygdala, hippocampus, and the visual association areas. In addition to regional connections and functions, Wood and colleagues, as well as other neuroscientists, hypothesize that there are specific integrative roles for left and right, anterior, and lateral PFC that await research confirmation.

Among older infants and young children, evidence reveals PFC activation in some task situations, albeit measurement often lacks the precision that delineate links between PFC regions and other brain areas and behavior among older children, adolescents, and adults. Nonetheless, the potential for adaptive thinking and behavior begins to take shape at the beginning of the second year, with changes occurring again between 3 and 7 years, and then continuing well into adolescence, with activation increasing within and across the PFC to increasing connectivity with other brain regions. In general though, more mature PFC functioning is associated with less density of neuronal activation.

Increasingly, more sophisticated brain measurement tools should allow neuroscientists a better window into PFC connections, developmental changes in the brain, and behavioral analogs across early and middle childhood with respect to the organization of attention, memory storage and retrieval, the growth of complex cognitive activities, and emotion regulation. More precise measurement tools should also provide additional insights about behavioral sequelae subsequent to brain insults that occur during the first years of life, and for very young children who show extremely elevated levels of irritability or out-of-control behaviors suggestive of prefrontal cortex involvement.

Presumed Biosocial, Developmental, and Self-Linkages with Regulatory Processes

The preceding sections have introduced issues related to early behavioral development and regulatory processes, the varied roles involved in parental fostering of regulatory processes, and how brain growth is deeply embedded in behavior and development. Can these complex elements fit together into a coherent developmental picture? In the absence of relevant research, **Figure 3** represents a provisional overview of the multiple factors that have a role in young children's abilities to regulate their own behaviors, and, also serves as a reminder that development is a singularly complex process. The box on the far left distinguishes among the three legacies provided to all human children: our biological heritage provides a defined body shape, a central and peripheral nervous system, internal organs and systems, and functions related to sensory systems and limbs – all of which show developmental change in the early years due to varied postnatal experiences. Family inheritance refers to recent ancestral roots with respect to gene pool contributed by both parents, and

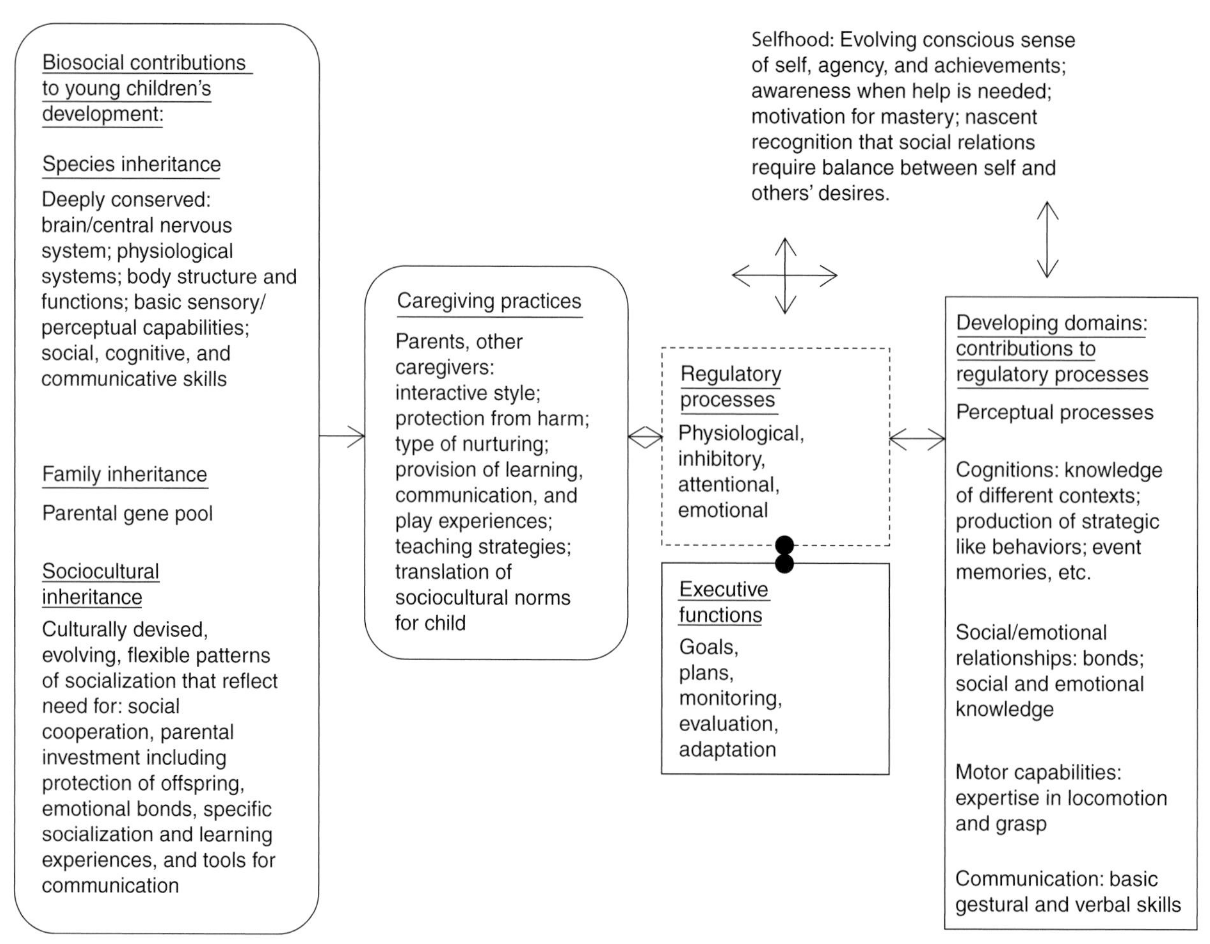

Figure 3 Contributors to young children's development of regulatory processes.

includes factors such as inheritance of skin color, hair texture, eye color, and potential size at maturity. To some degree, family inheritance influences temperament style such as sociability and activity level, as well as the potential for physical and mental health or illness. Humans' sociocultural inheritance is both ancient and modern. Our distant ancestors, for example, learned that survival of social groups depended on cooperation and both physical and emotional investments in offspring. Modern-day counterparts of parent investments are found in different cultures in terms of use of available healthcare, attention to diet, availability of playthings whether simple or elaborate, clothing, type of discipline, and specific socialization practices such as independence training and tolerance for a young child's self-assertion. The translation of sociocultural inheritance occurs through specific caregiving practices.

The right side of **Figure 3**, with its focus on the young child, highlights contributors to the growth of regulatory processes and thus to executive functions. These include the growth of competencies related to cognitions, social awareness, motor skills, and more, and the all important role of child selfhood. Consciousness of self and intentions and goals are fundamental to toddler and preschool development, and include attempts at self-directed learning, including how to regulate one's own behavior and to think strategically and planfully. Parental practices are at the nexus of legacies and the young child's developmental status and contributions to regulatory processes and executive functions. Parents and other caregivers provide the translation of legacies, along with emotional support, teaching, examples, and provision of specific socialization goals. The direction of parental influence is not one way; parents are influenced by children's goals, their developmental changes, individual child attributes such as personality, and sibling status. Thus the inter-connections of parents and children is an ongoing dynamic, and influences the nature and development of regulatory processes.

Three Regulatory Processes

Inhibitory Control

At 2.5 years, he was a precocious child already sounding out letters and a few words. He was also strong willed, often "working" his parents to achieve his goals. One dinnertime the child, his parents, and a guest sat around a small table enjoying a variety of foods. Mid-point in the meal, the father placed a piece of food on the child's plate. The boy removed the food, placing it on the table beyond his placemat. The father replaced the food on the boy's plate, which the boy again removed. This scenario was repeated several times with tension rapidly escalating between father and son. Suddenly the boy stopped moving; his body became rigid and his face contorted as he piercingly stared at a point on a nearby wall. The guest held her breath, waiting for an explosion. It did not occur. Instead after a minute or so the boy's body relaxed; he looked at his father and accepted the food. For a toddler, this was an unusual display of effortful and conscious inhibitory control in the service of emotion regulation.

Inhibitory control is a phrase that has multiple meanings including an inhibited temperament style, a culturally related behavioral style such that one group of children, for example, is more likely to be physically active than another group, and inhibitory control (IC), which involves the cessation of an ongoing activity or thoughts, that are irrelevant to or undermine the goal of an individual or to an essential activity designated by another. It is this kind of inhibitory control that is the focus here. IC reflects the inhibition of a prepotent (i.e., unaware, compelling stimulus) response such as acting impulsively, holding irrelevant thoughts, or being susceptible to interfering stimuli. Interest in IC is long standing, initially because individuals with frontal lobe damage often revealed impulsivity that was damaging to their thinking, social relationships, and emotion control. Although impulsivity had long been associated with toddler behavior, it was Alexander Luria, the great Russian neuropsychologist, who suggested that IC first emerged at about 4 years of age. Contemporary developmental research reveals that he underestimated young children's abilities, albeit IC is fragmentary and fragile in early development. Why is IC important? It is an essential co-condition for effective controlled attention, a precondition for working memory that temporarily 'holds' the contents of memory 'in mind' long enough to attend to, and then initiate an action that is related to a goal, and for the 'executive functions' involved in planning and evaluating the steps for pursuing a goal. Problems with inhibition are found among young children whose rearing environments are inadequate for their needs, and among children who have attention deficit hyperactivity disorder (ADHD), prenatal cocaine exposure, severe auditory limitations, gene-based disorders such as PKU, and chromosomal abnormalities such as Down syndrome. Note that some researchers consider IC a supervisory system, whereas others think of it in terms of a dimension of EF. However defined, IC seems to have different components in that sometimes it is the cessation of activity that is crucial and other times the task demand is to respond quickly to several competing stimuli selecting the most appropriate one.

Age trends

Clinical and research data indicate that IC improves across early childhood and into adolescence, given reasonably good childrearing environments. By mid-childhood and after, brain research reveals that IC is associated with bilateral dorsolateral PFC, inferior frontal cortex, and dorsal anterior cingulate cortex. Because IC is fragile in very young children, it is reasonable to conclude that frontal lobe connections are in their early stages. In the paragraphs that follow, evidence is marshaled to show general behavioral trends in IC; this is followed by laboratory studies in which children were asked to wait or to delay in relatively naturalistic settings. Then more recent data are summarized from research that used downward extensions of experimental procedures that involve presentation of two stimuli, one of which is highly salient but must be ignored in order to correctly follow task instructions.

Controlled cessation of an activity, an early form of IC, is clearly observed about 10 months when infants show wariness to unfamiliar adults or objects and cease their ongoing activity until reassured by an adult. IC is also evident at this age when infants pause in their activities when confronted with an unfamiliar situation, are uncertain about how to act and seek information from another's face to determine their course of action. This is called 'social referencing'; recent research reveals that infants often take their cues from adults' positive or negative facial expressions. With respect to IC research, the pioneering studies by Goldman-Rakic and Diamond with rhesus monkeys and human infants (7–12 months) unequivocally revealed that inhibition of actions was associated with dorsolateral PFC activation. Age-related data showed increases in inhibition times averaging about 2 s per month; these age findings mesh with those from other studies that used similar behavioral tasks. However, as will be seen below, depending on the IC task demand, response times may be seconds or minutes for toddlers and young preschoolers.

IC, measured by delay or waiting time, has been evaluated in behaviorally oriented laboratory studies in which toddlers and young preschoolers (seated alongside their mothers) were presented with a highly desirable toy, with a request not to touch the toy because experimenters had to leave for a brief period of time (180 s). Data revealed average waiting times of 10 s at 18 months, over a minute at 24 months, and close to 2 min at 30 months: half of 24-month-olds and more than half of 30-month-olds waited the full 3 min delay period. Toddlers who waited the longest often improvised strategies to help themselves wait: some turned to their mothers to gain her attention and converse with her, others sat on their hands, and still others turned away from the table that held the telephone. In a followup study, these delay strategies were studied more systematically, and findings again showed that keeping the goal out of sight or otherwise diverting attention helped keep the toy out of hand. The longer this strategy was implemented, the longer the delay. In an earlier decade, Walter Mischel and colleagues initiated a series of pioneering studies with preschoolers that involved self-imposed delay situations in which rewards varied as a function of length of children's ability to delay. Data unequivocally revealed that (1) delay was more likely to occur when rewards were obscured, or (2) if rewards could be seen, children were more likely to delay when offered control strategies or if they generated self-produced strategies to avoid looking at the desired reward. By the age of 6 years, findings showed that children who successfully delayed did so without need of overt strategic aids, probably relying on cognitively derived self-induced delay tactics. Interestingly, Mischel used a similar delay paradigm with 6–12-year-olds who had behavior problems and found that knowledge about control strategies was associated with longer delay periods. Later follow-up studies revealed that longer delays at the age of 4 years were associated with more social and cognitive competencies during adolescence. In all, studies that have simply asked young children to wait, under one or another study conditions, reveal the following: delay is very difficult for young toddlers, improves between 2 and 4 years, increases appreciably by the end of the fourth year, and by age 6 years is even better. Of equal importance is the finding that for children 4 years or younger, the use of strategic behaviors facilitates their waiting times.

What happens when delay tasks are modified so they place an additional psychological load on the inhibitory regulatory process such that both latency (delay) and erroneous responses to task instructions are measured? The classic Stroop test embodies such a task; here, words of colors are printed in the color of another word (the word red printed in green ink) with instructions to say the word not the printed color. IC responses are scored for number of errors (saying green instead of red), and for the amount of time taken to produce each correct answer. Numerous variations of Stroop task have been developed for toddlers and preschoolers, with the most interpretable and usable age-related data obtained with tasks that limit cognitive demands, task stimuli are interesting and appealing, and are suitable for younger and older children. In one study researchers used a computer presented Stroop-like IC task with a large group of participants who ranged in age from 3 years to mid-adolescence. The task involved naming drawings of animals (cow, pig, sheep, duck): some drawings showed a correct body and head (cow body and cow head), and other drawings with transposed heads and bodies (a pig body, a duck head). The researchers reasoned that humans of all ages are drawn to faces, and thus presentation of a stimulus that includes a friendly looking face makes it more likely that a person will respond to the face – unless instructed to do otherwise. Thus, the 'correct' response for participants was to name the animal's body and inhibit the prepotent response of naming the animal's head/face. **Figure 4** adapted from the study's data set shows age trends for response times and errors to incongruent stimuli (nonmatching head and body) across ages from 3 years into adolescence. Of particular interest are data from 3- to 7-year-olds. As can be seen, there are age-related changes in response times and errors with a steeper decline in the latter (from 3 to 5 years) than the former (from 3 to 7 years). Calculating the rate of reduction in both graphs and only comparing differences from age 3 to 5 years reveals a far greater improvement rate for error detection than response time.

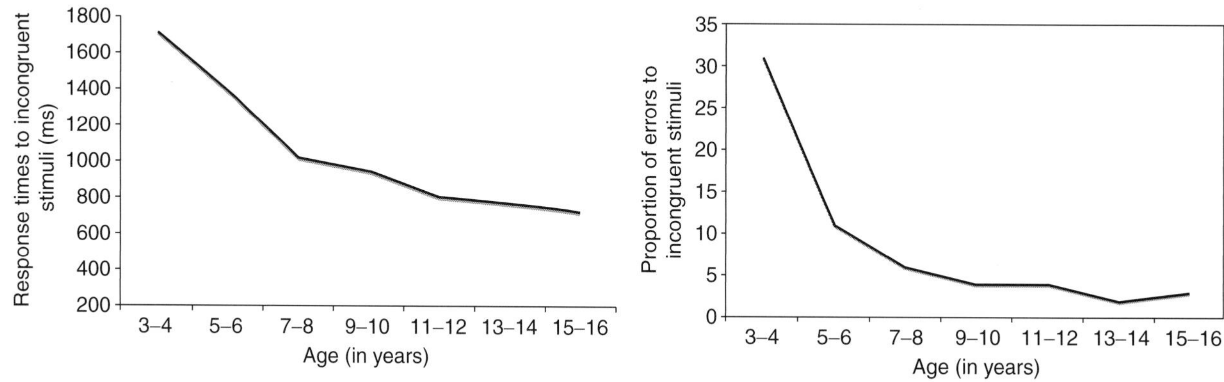

Figure 4 Across age response times and errors in an inhibitory control Stroop-like task. Adapted from Wright I, Waterman M, Prescott H, and Murdoch-Eaton D (2003) A new Stroop-like measure of inhibitory function development: Typical developmental trends. *Journal of Child Psychology and Psychiatry* 44: 561–575.

This finding suggests that the actual inhibition of a response may be more difficult for young children than detecting errors such as the noncorrespondence of an animal's body and head.

It is worth noting that this study protocol not only increased the psychological load for participants, especially the young ones, but also eliminated the opportunity to employ any kind of strategy to facilitate delay. Recall that in behavioral studies, young children often diverted their attention from a salient stimulus in the service of delay. What is not known as yet is when (at what age) and how child participants in the most challenging inhibition scenarios begin to generate rules that could guide their behavior. Recent data suggest that 'rule-like' strategies are more common among 5–7-year-olds than younger children, and moreover, recall that Mischel indicated that by the age of 6 years, children were able to delay without use of strategic behaviors presumably relying on internally generated (cognitive rule-based) commands. It is possible that the age period of around 6 and 7 years marks a turning point with respect to IC, perhaps due to self-produced cognitive activities. Other research shows several kinds of cognitive and social transitions occurring around 7 years.

Executive Attention: Managing One's Attention

At 36 000 feet, the jet's flight was smooth. A momentary glare from her seat's window drew her attention. The glare came from the sun shining on an abundance of snow-capped craggy peaks, some of which cast their shadows for miles on end. She immediately recognized New Mexico's terrain and scanned the landscape for a view of Santa Fe. Sitting back she thought of past pleasures visiting this historic city. She also vividly recalled the contrast of her emotions – awe at the majestic beauty of New Mexico and her distinct feelings of unease – when in an earlier year she and her husband flew a small airplane along a similar flight path albeit just a few thousand feet above the terrain. Inadvertently she had been alerted to a scene, oriented to it and scanned for landmarks, and then consciously turned her attention to memories representing mixed emotions. Alert, orient, and executive attention are current day conceptions of the possibly inter-related "attention trinity", proposed earlier by Michael Posner and colleagues.

The long and interesting history of attention research was recently reviewed by Raz and Buhl, with note made of significant advances made in understanding attention networks using imaging techniques, new measurement techniques, and current views of the anatomy of attention networks. In brief, alerting is associated with activation in frontal and parietal areas largely in the right hemisphere, orienting to a variety of areas (depending on the orienting processes) including pulvinar, superior parietal lobe, superior temporal lobe, temporoparietal junction, frontal eye fields, and more, and, executive attention with links between the anterior cingulate cortex and dorsolateral PFC with involvement of the locus coeruleus and dopaminergic areas within the ventral tegmental region. Executive attention (also labeled focused, selective, controlled, top-down, effortful) has all the earmarks of a regulatory process: it is involved with cognitive controls, planning, error detection, resolution of conflict, regulation of thoughts and feelings, and overcoming 'habitual actions'. Not surprisingly, cognitive-driven attention influences emotion states which at the level of brain shows interconnections between PFC and the amygdala, the structure deep in the brain that is key to emotions.

In contract to visual alerting and orienting, which has an extensive and distinguished history in developmental research, the study of focused/controlled/executive attention (note the terms are used interchangeably here) particularly with toddlers and young children is relatively recent with pioneering thinking and research by Mary Rothbart and Michael Posner, and by Holly Ruff. The former often address issues of temperament with executive or effortful attention or more recently with aspects of cognitive functioning. Their studies typically use variations of procedures used with older children or adults to tap executive attention. In contrast, Ruff has a more developmental emphasis on focused attention and its flip dimension, distractibility, often deploying a play scenario. Because focused attention is intrinsic to exploratory, functional, and pretend play, data obtained from these contexts can be useful in identifying age trends among young children. First, a step back in ontogenetic time to see how visual attention changes in the first year. Newborns show visual alertness most notably to patterns that are also characteristic of the contrast patterns of human faces, and their attention to human faces differs from attention to objects. Infants display other aspects of attention in their early months: they show obligatory attention at about 10 days, when they get visually locked onto an especially compelling nonhuman stimulus to the point of fatigue; they consistently produce eye-to-eye contact with their caregivers at about 2 months, which pleases parents; as they approach 3 months, infants spontaneously and consistently look at parents (and others) and smile broadly. This smile is both immediate and intense, and symbolizes a new form of psychological connection between infant and others. **Table 1** lists other developmental trends in visual attention during the first year of life: it also reveals the increasing integration of attention to other dimensions of development that are associated with more efficient and organized behaviors. In addition, note the important

Table 1 Developmental perspectives: visual attention in the first year of life

	Colombo	*Rothbart*	*Ruff and Rothbart*	*Behavioral linkages*
Conceptual approaches	Development of four inter-related aspects: alert state, spatial orienting, objects, endogenous control; neural substrates	Attention processes: temperament; links to neural substrates; focus on reactive vs. self-regulative attention	Adaptive to social/ physical environment, essential for learning; links w/ motivation; control and engagement	Linkages: key elements of organized, integrated, and efficient behavioral adaptations Examples below: visual attention
Birth–1 month	Newborns, minimal alertness; obligatory attention; increase alert state, 1 month	Reactive attention, with obligatory looking and difficulty with disengagement	Attention often directed to hairline and edge of face	
2–3 months	Changes in alertness, spatial orienting (the 'where' system), attention to objects (the 'what' system), flexible responses, disengagement		Eye contact with others, has social implications; 'active sampling of two objects'	w/ social: eye-to-eye contact w/ emotions: smiles to others w/ self: visual re-orienting when distressed
4–6 months	Inhibition of saccadic responses; better control spatial orienting; more sensitive object related form/color; sustained attention	Disengagement from stimuli; 'avoid overstimulation through self-regulation'	Acuity markedly better; increase in flexibility of attention, influences via experience, novelty	w/ social: uses eye contact to initiate social exchanges w/ memory: orients to novel stimuli w/ grasp: coordinates w/ vision
9–12 months, on	Relatively mature spatial orienting including disengagement; increase in endogenous attention	Effortful control, awareness of inputs; maintain focus: attention, executive control, planning	Decline in attention to static displays; increase in attention to toys; wariness to unfamiliar people; improved control of distractions	w/ social: joint attention; facial expressions; gestures w/ memory: landmarks; object characteristics w/ self: object preferences

changes in attention occur toward the end of the first year, not the least of which involves infant decisions about choices. An example is the older infant's conscious coordination of visual attention to the visual attention of another, which often signals a desire to share interest in an object, or to direct attention to an event. Not surprisingly, researchers have found frontal lobe correlates of joint attention using electroencephalogram (EEG) measures with young toddlers. Taken together, these findings point to the multiple roles of attention in learning and in social exchanges. It is likely that attention in general, and executive attention in particular, varies as a function of social relationships, emotional connections, and object interest.

Age trends

Holly Ruff and colleagues have studied various aspects of attention; however, one study in particular highlights different kinds of attention used in play scenarios with three age groups. The use of a play setting is a particularly good venue to study attention because play is another beloved and motivating activity for young children. The research was laboratory based and cross-sectional: the children were 10, 26, or 42 months of age. Three kinds of attention were defined: 'casual' was coded when children looked at toys but with limited engagement (akin to orienting), 'settled' was coded as a pause in casual attention in which the child looked steadily at a toy and manipulated it, and 'focused' attention reflected concentration, with an intent facial expression, minimal extraneous body movement, close visual inspection of the toy, or talking to self (akin to executive attention). Various toys designed to elicit the child's attention and the nature of play. Distracters were also introduced to determine effects on attention, and audio presented in varying intervals. **Figure 5**, adapted from study data, shows mean looking times by type of attention and child age when children were given multiple toys to play with, and, similarly within 2-min blocks of a 10-min period of play. With respect to duration of attention, 26 months marks a crossover time in which casual and settled begin to reverse positions, with casual a lower priority activity. The 2-min blocks reveal more a complex pattern of attention. At 10 months all forms of attention declined at mid-point in the period, perhaps a sign of fatigue, whereas at 42 months, changes occurred within the blocks perhaps

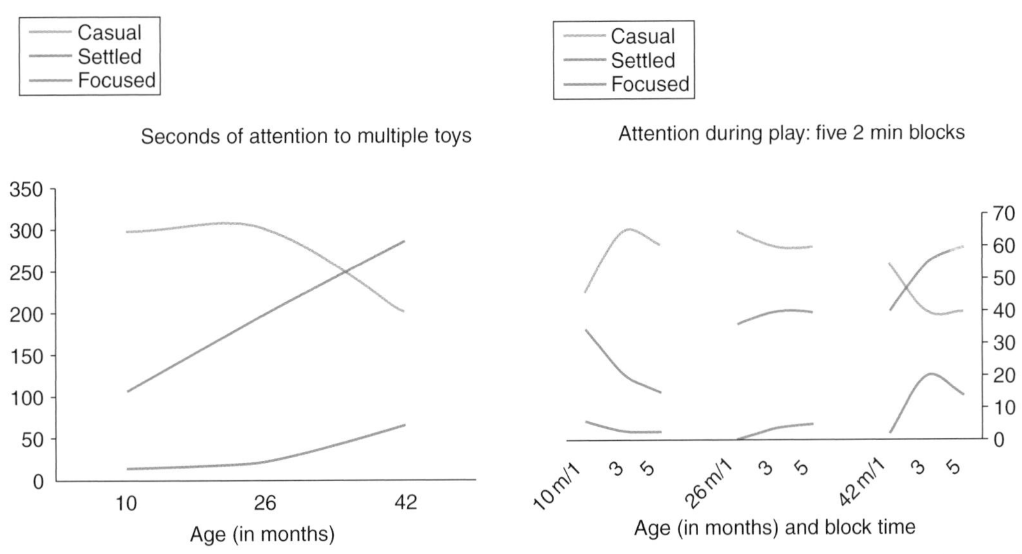

Figure 5 Casual, settled, and focused attention during play at 10, 26, and 42 months. Adapted from Ruff HA and Capozzoli MC (2003) Development of attention and distractibility in the first 4 years of life. *Developmental Psychology* 39: 877–890.

indicating changing interests in one or another toy and toward the end of the block decreasing curiosity about the toys.

Turning to distracters, research from another laboratory reveals that the tendency to look toward a distractor is related to the length of looks that occur before the distractor is introduced. Although not yet studied empirically, it is probable that distractors are less potent under conditions of executive/focused attention than more casual types of attention. In the Ruff study, age trends revealed that combined audio–visual distractors caused the most diversions at each age, with diversions dropping from 56% at 10 months to 14% at 42 months. This decline nicely parallels increases in settled and focused attention. Lastly, given the similarity of trajectories of settled and focused attention raises the question of whether these types of attention represent a continuum of controlled attention with settled representing somewhat less control and focused, more control. What this point suggests is that executive attention is not simply a process that is immediately 'turned on' but rather moves from a less heightened state to a more heightened one depending upon the nature of situational demands. If confirmed empirically, this gradual process might be more indicative of young children's attention management than that of more mature individuals.

What factors might influence changes in patterns of attention? Possibly, practice as part of young children's continuing interest in play, their increased curiosity and selectivity of toys and what one can do with toys (motivation), and vastly improved hand coordination that allows young children to concentrate less on controlling their fingers and thumbs and more on toy characteristics. Relatedly, an older study revealed that holding and manipulating objects enhanced visual attention, in contrast to just looking at an object placed on a surface. In terms of caregiving, it has been suggested that parents' use of everyday routines facilitates child learning because routines provide 'an invisible attentional structure' to the most salient things that need to be learned. Turning to problematic attention, especially executive attention, those factors (e.g., prenatal drug exposure, in some instances pre-term birth, ADHD) that interfere with IC also disrupt executive attention. Finally, there is a group of older toddlers who do not have diagnosed developmental disorders but who tend to be inattentive, show episodes of listless-type wandering, and have mild cognitive limitations; a small group of studies suggest that these children are at risk for later cognitive and social problems. These data give further credence to the developmental importance of focused attention during the early years.

Emotion Regulation

The family sensed the young toddler was becoming more difficult day by day, but they did not see the whole picture until months had passed. A fairly typical toddler, it was about 17 months when he began to be irascible and seemingly wired. He could not make up his mind, vacillating from one desire to the next. He rejected the old canister vacuum cleaner he had loved to roll along the floor. He became angry with his beloved grandfather, and one day hid from him behind a door. The door was glass. Exhausted, he refused to take naps. Whining was a daily event. Then at about 21 months, he began to change again. Better able to articulate annoyances, his pretend play also became increasingly rich, and his self-awareness in terms of preferences were more apparent – all of which reflected cognitive and language growth. Might these changes have contributed to his ER? The only fact that is certain is that among older children and adults cognition and successful emotion management are linked.

'Emotions', said famed neuroscientist Antonio Damasio, provide a natural means for the brain and mind to evaluate the environment within and around the organism, and respond accordingly and adaptively. Among adults, studies have revealed various patterns of medial and lateral PFC activity, along with activity in the anterior cingulate cortex and the amygdala depending on particular cognitions (e.g., expectations about an aversive emotional episode, changing an emotional situation) and ER. Much of this research is relatively recent and employs sophisticated brain imaging techniques along with well-controlled stimuli designed to elicit certain cognitive states – neither technique can be used with very young children. From a practical standpoint, this means that studying ER with young children requires different procedures along with different data collection goals.

Whatever the context, ER should be viewed as a vital, generative regulatory process in which children and adults use different constellations of mechanisms to adapt to their own physiological needs (managing arousal states), to maintain valued social relationships while also meeting social requirements, and to accommodate to their own goals such as learning. Unfortunately, at present there are major disagreements about defining ER, how to measure it, how to precisely identify causes of upsets and when ER occurs, the other processes involved in ER such as behavioral inhibition and attention, the specific contexts in which ER might occur, the constellation of domain competencies such as cognitions that contribute to ER, and how ER changes over time. These conceptual and methodological challenges are magnified because the study of ER in children is a recent occurrence in contrast to research on infants and toddlers' emotion expressions that extend back to the 1930s. Also contributing to research difficulties are obstacles involved in tracking individual and age-group increases and decreases in tantrums, aggression, and irritability, and interpreting the meaning of these patterns in relation to the child's other skills, the family environment, and culture.

Despite these unknowns and the challenges, the study of ER begs for developmental consideration. Indeed, some general age trends have been identified in infancy. For example, it has long been recognized that regulatory mechanisms such as thumb sucking are present at birth and offer some protection from variations in the immediacy of caregivers' attentiveness. Throughout the first year, infants engage in forms of distraction when they are lightly distressed, and when more deeply distressed they often signal caregivers with visual contact, gestures, and tears. However as noted earlier, what sets apart toddlers apart from infants is a burgeoning and explicit sense of mastery and of being agentic, the rise in 'collisions' with parents who are attempting to socialize the newly walking child with don'ts and do's, and the variety and display of negative emotions that may include intentional jealousy, physical aggression, temper tantrums, and resistance. In a very real sense, the cognitive growth that increasingly contributes to the toddler's sense of self and mastery also contributes to a sense of dismay or anger when self-motivated actions are restricted.

Utilizing data collected in a longitudinal study, **Figure 6** provides an indication of developmental trends in crying and refusals observed during home and laboratory visits in a study located in the US. Researchers noted instances of crying whenever it occurred in their presence, whereas they noted negative responses only at the end of laboratory visits when children were requested to put toys away. Crying and negativism were linked at 21 months, with 70% of criers also refusing to put toys away. The dramatic decrease in crying by 30 months still left a high proportion of children across older age periods who used words or deeds to utter "No" to a request. Although this negative behavior could be attributed to willful disobedience, it seems more likely to reflect cognitive limitations such being relatively clueless about parents' motivations along with an inability to figure out how to balance self-needs with those of others. Alternatively, developmental scientist Ellen Skinner questions whether the peak period of crying

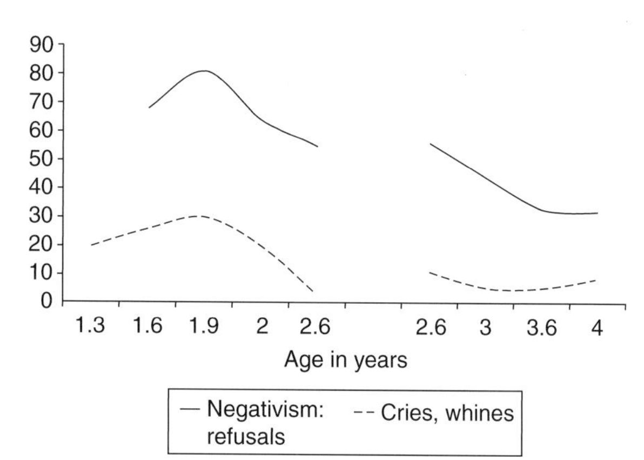

Figure 6 Developmental trends in crying and negative-resistive behaviors. Adapted from Kopp CB (1992) Emotion distress and control in young children. *New Directions for Child Development: Emotions. Motivation, and Self-Regulation* 55: 41–56; and Klimes-Dougan B and Kopp CB (1999) Children's conflict tactics with mothers: A longitudinal investigation of the toddler and preschool years. *Merrill-Palmer Quarterly* 45: 226–232.

and negativism represents "... a developmental moment in which toddlers' cognitive representations of what they want (to do, have, or not do) become durable enough that can persist even through the best efforts of caregivers to distract and divert them?" It may be, she continues, that it is the persistence of desires that often make 2-year-olds hard to handle, yet the fact that they can occasionally deal with their emotions represents major growth.

Age trends

Given the difficulties that young children have controlling their emotions, the fact that instances of negative emotions do decline, and the conceptual and measurement issues noted above, is there evidence of intentional, self-motivated ER during the toddler years? Yes: data from two cross-sectional studies suggest that between 18 and 24 months toddlers pursue efforts at self-distraction and intentional use of their mothers to reduce levels of emotion upset. This is representative of major developmental growth suggested by Skinner.

Drawing upon published and unpublished observations and comments from a variety of sources supports this view of ER. However, how can the data be organized to obtain a reasonable developmental view of ER? James Gross' process model of 'adult' ER provides a valuable tool as a point of deparure. By way of background, Gross demarcated five points in the emotion generative process in which ER can occur. Four of these are 'antecedent focused' ER, and include: (1) making a decision about a situation to attend or to avoid; (2) generating possible ways to modify a potentially difficult situation; (3) altering one's attentional deployment by using strategies (e.g., distraction); (4) using cognitive change mechanisms such as reappraisals (i.e., cognitively transforming a situation to modify its emotional impact). The fifth, 'response focused' ER, involves trying to decrease or suppress emotion expressions that have already begun. In general, Gross and colleagues' studies with adults reveal that antecedent focused (cognitive) controls are less psychologically and physiologically costly than response focused (behavioral) controls such as suppression. **Table 2**, adapted from Gross' ER model, suggests one form of antecedent ER adopted by children who ostensibly seemed to modify an emotion-arousing context into something less stressful. The specific entries in **Table 2** suggest that younger-aged children attempted to use their mothers as a multipurpose support system with particulars depending on context. In contrast, the older children either generated ideas to modify the situation on their own or accepted an adult directive while also protecting the self (putting toys away, choosing the sequence). Note too the role of language, which has been suggested as having a contributing role to ER. The fact that the table has empty cells and cells with only a few entries provides tentative evidence that some forms of ER may be especially challenging for young children. Although interpretative caution is warranted because the examples in **Table 2** may not be representative, they do appear to support Pamela Cole's thesis that ER can reflect a rapid response system especially among toddlers and young preschoolers who tend not to be intensely reflective thinkers.

Lastly in terms of caregiving, ER is as susceptible to adverse family and parenting conditions as are inhibitory control and executive attention. However, there may be specifics in the caregiving process that may be more relevant to ER than for inhibition and attention. For example, detached parenting (irrespective of social class or parent education) may be particularly detrimental for young children's ER because parental support is so essential to the developmental process. What comes to mind are uninvolved parents of toddlers and young preschoolers who show especially high levels of explosive behaviors including physical aggression. Finally, because ER itself, and its associated developmental trajectory, are so complex, it is essential to learn more about correlates with children's cognitive and language skills.

Summary

At the end of the first year, the frontal lobes show increasing activation, with subsequent growth largely a function of young children's experiences. The prefrontal cortex is implicated in executive functions such as conscious, self-directed activities such as goal setting, planning, and evaluation, and, the regulatory processes that contribute to executive functions. In a very real sense, the regulatory processes of controlled inhibition, executive attention, and emotion regulation facilitate all manner of learning and positive social interactions. Nascent forms of regulatory processes are observed during infancy. However, it is during the toddler years that conscious and intentional displays of regulatory acts can be identified. Although insufficiently documented, the growth of young children's cognition, language skills, and self-awareness contribute to more adaptive regulatory processes. Data also suggest that children are active in the growth of their regulatory processes, as for example, in controlling attention during play. Age changes in regulatory processes suggest growth is modest during the second year, and improves thereafter albeit slowly. By 4 years, there is evidence of relatively effective use of the regulatory processes of controlled inhibition, executive attention, and emotion regulation. However, the latter may be the most difficult for young children to begin to achieve, and thus far is the most difficult regulatory process for researchers to study.

Table 2 Indications of emotion regulation during the toddler and early preschool years

ER	*Age*	*Context*	*Observed behavior*
Antecedent *Context: avoid*	4 yr	Preschool setting	Child tells teacher he is upset, indicates he wants to go in another room to be alone
		Park	Child sees large dog on path; warily crosses to another
A – *Context: modify*	21 mo+	Home/laboratory	Child recognizes toy puzzle too difficult to solve, seeks help
	2 yr	Lab: toy cleanup	Mother asks child to put toys away: time to leave
			Child leaves play area, goes to nearby chair and sits, then tells mother she has to go potty
	2.5 yr	Study: home visit	Researcher (R) shows child toys: a small, wind-up spider frightens him. R takes toy outside and places on hood of her car. Conclusion of visit, mother and child accompany R to car. Child spies toy. Clutches mother, telling her to get toy and let it run on ground. He peers around her back, watching intently
	3.5–4 yr	Laboratory: toy cleanup	Child indicates will put toys away, but will make decision about how toys are put away (e.g., yellow toys first, using one shelf and not another)
	4 yr	Laboratory: child given a box, told contains gift. Box is empty.	Some children hid box under table; others use box as a drum; one child tapped finger on cheek, and said: "an empty box, an empty box, what can I do with an empty box? I know I can put my shoes in it."
A – *Distract self*	18 mo+	Home	Child uses object (e.g., piece of cloth, favorite toy) as soothing tool
	2 yr	Laboratory-delay and separation	Child finds toy to use as distraction, and is most effective when adult is present; separation is far more difficult and less successful regarding distraction than delay
A – *Cog. transform*			?
Response focused: *decrease*			?

Adaptation of James Gross' model of ER: examples of young children's ER.

See also: Attention; Brain Development; Brain Function; Cognitive Development; Emotion Regulation; Temperament.

Suggested Readings

Berger SE and Adolph KE (in press) Learning and development in infant locomotion. In: von Hoftsen C and Rosander K (eds.) *From Action to Cognition: Progress in Brain Research*. Amsterdam: Elsevier.

Brownell CB and Kopp CB (2007) *Socioemotional Development in the Toddler Years: Transitions and Transformations.* New York: The Guilford Press.

Calkins SD and Fox NA (2002) Self-regulatory processes in early personality development: A multilevel approach to the study of childhood social withdrawal and aggression. *Development and Psychopathology* 14: 477–498.

Colombo J (2001) The development of visual attention in infancy. *Annual Review of Psychology* 52: 337–357.

Davidson RJ, Putnam KM, and Larson CL (2000) Dysfunction in the neural circuitry of emotion regulation – A possible prelude to violence *Science* 289: 591–594.

Eisenberg N, Champion C, and Vaughan J (2007) Effortful control and its socioemotional consequences. In: Gross JJ (ed.) *Handbook of Emotion Regulation.* New York: The Guilford Press.

Gomez JC (2004) *Apes, Monkeys, Children, and the Growth of Mind*. Cambridge, MA: Harvard University Press.

Gross JJ (2007) *Handbook of Emotion Regulation.* New York: The Guilford Press.

Klimes-Dougan B and Kopp CB (1999) Children's conflict tactics with mothers: A longitudinal investigation of the toddler and preschool years. *Merrill-Palmer Quarterly* 45: 226–232.

Kopp CB (1992) Emotion distress and control in young children. *New Directions for Child Development: Emotions. Motivation, and Self-Regulation* 55: 41–56.

Marcus G (2004) *The Birth of the Mind: How a Tiny Number of Genes Creates the Complexities of Human Thought.* New York: Basic Books.

Mischel W, Shoda Y, and Rodriguez ML (1989) Delay of gratification in children. *Science* 244: 933–938.

Raz A and Buhle J (2006) Typologies of attentional networks. *Nature Reviews, Neuroscience* 7: 367–379.

Rueda MR, Posner MI, and Rothbart MK (2004) Attentional control and self-regulation. In: Baumeister RF and Vohs KD (eds.) *Handbook of Self-Regulation: Research, Theory, and Applications.* New York: The Guilford Press.

Ruff H and Rothbart MK (1996) *Attention in Early Development.* New York: Oxford University Press.

Ruff HA and Capozzoli MC (2003) Development of attention and distractibility in the first 4 years of life. *Developmental Psychology* 39: 877–890.

Tomasello M (1999) *The Cultural Origins of Human Cognition.* Cambridge, MA: Harvard University Press.

Wilke M, Krägeloh-Mann I, and Holland SK (2007) Global and local development of gray and white matter volume in normal children and adolescents. *Experimental Brain Research* 178: 296–307.

Wood JN and Grafman J (2003) Human prefrontal cortex: Processing and representational perspectives. *Nature Reviews Neuroscience* 4: 139–147.

Wright I, Waterman M, Prescott H, and Murdoch-Eaton D (2003) A new Stroop-like measure of inhibitory function development: Typical developmental trends. *Journal of Child Psychology and Psychiatry* 44: 561–575.

Semantic Development

J Bhagwat and M Casasola, Cornell University, Ithaca, NY, USA

Glossary

Agent – In linguistics, a grammatical agent is the recipient of an action that is carried out.

Bootstrapping – The idea that knowledge about one aspect of language (e.g. syntax) can help children learn about another aspect (e.g., semantics).

Count noun – A noun which can be used with a numeral (e.g. one ball, two dogs) and can occur in both singular and plural form, as well as with adjectives of quantity such as every, each, several, most, etc. (e.g. every ball, several dogs, most apples).

Intermodal preferential looking paradigm – (IPLP) In the standard IPLP, the infant is seated on a parent's lap in front of two laterally spaced video monitors. A concealed centrally placed audio speaker plays a linguistic stimulus that matches only one of the displays shown on the screens. The variable of interest is the total amount of time that the infant spends watching the matching vs. nonmatching screen.

Joint attention – Characteristic of certain interactions between child and adult wherein the child follows the focus of the adult's attention to a third entity or event in the environment. It may include the child's attempts to redirect the adult's attention to the entity of the child's interest. Joint attention is often achieved via eye-gaze, pointing, and verbal signals.

Mass noun – A mass noun cannot occur in singular/plural. This type of noun cannot be used with a number unless a unit of measurement is specified (e.g., two piles of sand, three bottles of water).
Mean length of utterance (MLU) – A measure of linguistic productivity in children. It is traditionally calculated by collecting 100 utterances spoken by a child and dividing the number of morphemes (a morpheme is the smallest linguistic unit that has meaning) by the number of utterances. A higher MLU is taken to indicate a higher level of language proficiency.
Patient – In linguistics, a grammatical patient is the participant of a situation upon whom an action is carried out.
Pragmatics (pragmatic) – The study of language as it is used in a social context. Pragmatics is concerned with how language meaning and language use are dependent on the speaker, the addressee, and other features of the context of utterance.
Referent – Any entity (including objects and events) that can be named or labeled. (Naming and labeling are used interchangeably throughout this article. The terms entity and referent have also been used interchangeably.)
Syntax (syntactic) – The study of the rules that govern how words combine to form phrases, and how phrases combine to form sentences.

Introduction

Broadly defined, semantic development describes how children learn the meanings of words. The term comes from the branch of linguistics called semantics: the study of the meaning system of language. Thus, semantic development could be defined as the acquisition of words and their meanings. To know the meaning of a word is to possess a certain mental representation or concept that is associated with a certain linguistic form.

However this process of mapping word to meaning is no easy task. Many of us have had the experience of being surrounded by a roomful of people speaking an unfamiliar tongue. Often, all one can perceive is a string of speech with few cues that tell us where a particular word begins and where it ends. Even after one has identified a word, there is the problem of determining the object or event to which the word refers. An often-cited example that beautifully illustrates the nature of this problem was first outlined by the linguist Willard V. O. Quine in 1960. Quine posited an imaginary linguist visiting a culture whose language bears no resemblance to the linguist's language. A rabbit wanders by and the native exclaims, "Gavagai!" The term gavagai could refer to any number of logically possible referents, including the rabbit, the name of that specific rabbit, all mammals, all animals or even all objects. It could mean white and furry, refer to one particular part of the rabbit's body, or alternatively refer to the act of running. Given that there many possible referents for a single word, how does a child solve this problem?

Word learning can be viewed in terms of steps that the child undergoes in arriving at the meaning of the word. The child must (1) identify the relevant entity from the ongoing stream of activity in the world, (2) parse or segment the relevant piece of sound from the ongoing stream of continuous speech, and (3) establish a mapping between the entity and that sound. Some researchers would add a fourth step: the child must develop an understanding that a word stands not only for the specific entity that it names, but also that it applies to other members of that category. For instance, knowing that the word 'dog' refers to a particular kind of domestic animal would imply knowing that the word 'dog' refers to all dogs and not simply an individual dog. The process or ability by which the name for an entity can be extended to other members that belong to that entity's category is known as generalization.

Others have broken down these steps further, particularly in terms of language comprehension. There is substantial evidence that children comprehend (i.e., understand) language earlier than they can produce it. Researchers have discriminated between different types of comprehension, such as recognitory comprehension, and symbolic comprehension. In recognitory comprehension, children form an association between a referent and a label. This type of comprehension is an early type of comprehension and is often considered a precursor to learning the meanings of words. Once children break away from this simple association between word and referent and begin to understand that a word does not merely co-occur with a referent but that the word stands for it or refers to it, they have acquired symbolic comprehension, a more advanced type of comprehension. Symbolic comprehension of the word 'dog' implies that the child understands that 'dog' does not merely refer to a particular dog but refers to the whole category of dogs. Thus, this definition of symbolic comprehension includes the aspect of generalization, described above. Some of the studies that will be discussed in this article examine recognitory comprehension, whereas others examine symbolic comprehension. Both are equally important in the broader study of semantic development.

First Words

Comprehension

Although infants in their first year produce few words, they nonetheless possess a sizeable receptive (i.e., comprehension) vocabulary. Numerous studies have shown that infants comprehend language earlier than they can actually produce it. Maternal reports document that word learning, both productive and receptive, begins at about 9–12 months. Similarly, naturalistic studies have shown that infants in this age range respond appropriately to verbal commands. However, the earliest traces of comprehension may begin as early as 4.5 months. Jusczyk and colleagues found that 4.5-month-olds listened significantly longer to repetitions of their own names than other names, and by about 6 months of age, they were able to recognize their own names in fluent speech. Six-month-old infants also demonstrate comprehension of the labels 'mommy' and 'daddy'. When shown side-by-side videos of their own parents, infants looked longer at the video of the named parent than the unnamed one (i.e., when hearing 'mommy' or 'daddy'). Thus, infants' comprehension of their own names and their caregivers' names is evident by 6 months. Comprehension of other labels has been shown to emerge by about 8 months.

In the infants' second year, comprehension continues to outpace production. Although 14-month-old infants, on average, produce only about 10 words in total, children of this age are reported by their parents to understand roughly 50 words. Moreover, by about 13–14 months of age, infants can learn to link words to objects under experimental conditions that provide only limited exposure to the novel labels and their referents. When the experimental condition involves an actual experimenter providing a label, this ability is evident by 13 months of age. For example, in one study by Amanda Woodward and colleagues, 13-month-old infants were shown two novel objects. One object was labeled nine times as 'dax'. The other object was not labeled, but the researcher drew equal attention to this nonlabeled object by using general linguistic phrases such as, "Ooh, look at that". When asked to find the 'dax' and put the 'dax' down a toy chute, infants chose the labeled objected more often than expected by chance. In contrast, when asked to simply 'pick one' to put down the chute, infants displayed no preference for the labeled object. These results provided some of the first evidence that infants can learn a new label after only nine exposures. Similarly, when the labels and objects are presented via video (without a live experimenter), infants of 14 months can form links between the labels and the objects. Infants of 12 months, however, have difficulty with this task, suggesting that infants develop the ability to quickly form associations between novel words and objects between 12 and 13 months of age. More recently, however, infants as young as 9 months of age have shown that they can quickly map a label onto an object, but only if the object is perceptually salient (i.e. interesting and attractive to the infants). Just as infants in their first year improve in their ability to quickly link words to objects, they also begin to learn that words hold a special status relative to other sounds. Whereas infants of 13 months are willing to accept a range of sounds, from words to whistles, as labels for objects, infants of 18 months accept only words as labels.

Production

At about 12 months of age, infants start producing their first words. These first words are usually single words, produced in isolation, giving this phase of language development its name: the 'one-word stage'. By the time they are 18 months, most English-learning toddlers have a productive vocabulary of about 50 words. During their second year, many children undergo a vocabulary spurt or naming explosion – a marked increase in the rate at which new words are added to their vocabulary. Even those children who do not show evidence of a marked increase in rate, still greatly increase the total size of their productive vocabularies during this time. By 24 months of age, children comprehend and produce hundreds of words and also start to combine them systematically to form phrases.

The very first words, at least for English-learning children, often include sound effects, such as moo and meow; words for routines such as peek-a boo, bath, bye, all gone; and names for people such as mommy and daddy. There is substantial evidence for significant individual differences between children in the single-word stage. Some children adopt what is known as a referential style. They begin by learning single words including a large percentage of common nouns or object labels in their first 50–100 words, and then begin combining them into phrases and sentences. Other children have more heterogeneous vocabularies including a number of rote-learned and unanalyzed multiword phrases, including strings of words for social and instrumental purposes such as 'thank you', 'go away', 'I want it', 'don't do it', and 'no'. This style has been called the expressive style. Similarly, there are certain patterns of word use that often are observed in the early productions of children. For example, children learning their first words often use a single word for several different referents, an example of overgeneralization. Thus, a child may initially use the term 'kitty' to refer to all animals or the term 'ball' to refer to all round objects, such as oranges, door knobs, or even the moon. The reverse phenomenon is undergeneralization wherein a child is conservative in his/her first uses of a word. For instance, the child may use car to refer to only the family car without generalizing it to other cars. Similarly, a specific word may be used only in a particular context, as in a child who only uses 'car' when watching cars move below the living room window.

Reasons for such generalization patterns remain unclear. It has been suggested that children may overgeneralize or undergeneralize even though they perceive differences in these referents. It is possible that their limited vocabulary compels them to use a single word for different referents. Alternatively, it is also possible their understanding of the world itself is limited. Whatever the reasons, all children eventually abandon these over- and undergeneralizations.

Learning Words: Theories and Mechanisms

Before launching into a discussion on the specific mechanisms and processes of word learning, it is worth noting that traditionally, most word learning theories have focused on how children learn the meanings of nouns. Although the reasons for this bias have also been hotly debated, some possible reasons might be that for children learning English, nouns tend to be more predominant in children's early vocabularies than other types of words (such as verbs), and nouns appear to be learned more quickly and easily than these other word types. At the same time, there have always been a few researchers, such as Lois Bloom and colleagues, who drew the attention of the field to the presence of other types of words in children's early vocabularies. Bloom's work set the stage for studies on how children learn verbs and other action words (see work by Michael Tomasello, Jane Childers, Diane Poulin-Dubois, and colleagues), adjectives (Sandra Waxman and colleagues), as well as cross-linguistic studies on how specific properties of a language can influence the way children learn that language (Melissa Bowerman, Soonja Choi, Twila Tardif, and colleagues). In the light of new findings, researchers such as Roberta Golinkoff, Kathy Hirsh-Pasek, and others have proposed more comprehensive and integrative theories of word learning, outlining not only how children learn to map words onto objects (as was the focus in many theories of early word learning) but also, actions.

In recent times, there is increasing consensus that children use multiple resources in order to hone in on the meanings of words. This complex network of resources comprises the child's own preferences (i.e., biases); the child's developing conceptual knowledge; social cues that are offered by communicative partners; as well as linguistic and grammatical cues that can be gleaned from the actual language that the child is learning. The theories that are discussed in the followings sections focus on one or more of these resources in order to explain early word learning by children.

Constraints Theories

Constraints theories, initially proposed by Ellen Markman and colleagues, offer a solution to the Quinean conundrum by proposing that children approach the word learning task biased to make certain assumptions about word meanings. These biases are also referred to as constraints, predispositions, expectations, or assumptions. Recall that the Quinean example suggests that children must venture different guesses in determining the referent of a new word. According to the constraints theories, rather than generating countless hypotheses about the possible meaning of a particular word, children are naturally predisposed to attend to certain aspects of the word learning situation. Traditionally, constraints have been viewed as specific expectations that children have about word meanings. Thus, these expectations are assumed to be specific to the domain of language learning. However, there is increasing evidence that suggests that constraints may be better viewed as default assumptions that the child relies on, in the absence of other social and linguistic cues, rather than viewing these expectations as absolute linguistic constraints. In the sections that follow, we discuss some of the different kinds of constraints that have been proposed to explain word learning.

The whole-object constraint

The whole-object bias, first proposed by Ellen Markman, predicts that children assume that new words refer to objects rather than their parts or properties. For instance, when provided with a novel object and a novel word, children often assume that the word refers to the whole object rather than parts of the object, or a property of the object (e.g., its color), or the substance that its made of. For instance, 2-year-olds were shown a novel object and were told that it was 'a zom'. They were then shown other novel objects, some of which matched the original object in form (i.e., they were identical in shape, size, texture and material, but not color), and others which matched the original only in color. Subsequently, when the children were asked to find 'another zom', they almost always chose the form match rather than a color match. However, when simply asked to 'find another one', children often chose the color match over the form match. The results suggest that a label plays a role in drawing attention to the whole object rather than a property of the object.

Taxonomic constraint

A second constraint, also initially proposed by Ellen Markman, is the noun-category bias that predicts that hearing a novel label actually leads children to form a category of objects. The taxonomic assumption predicts that children correctly extend object labels to members of a class (category) and not to thematically related objects. When presented with a novel label for dog, preschool-age children extend the label to other kinds of dogs and are thus more likely to put two toy dogs together in such tasks. In contrast, without a label, children are more likely to choose a thematically related object, such as placing a dog with a bone or a rabbit with a carrot. Even infants of 12 months seem to understand that count nouns refer to categories of objects. Indeed, infants of this age can use a novel noun to aid them in grouping objects into categories. In one study, infants were introduced to toys from two different categories (e.g., vehicles vs. animals). During a familiarization phase, infants were presented with toys from within a category (e.g., four different cars, belonging to the vehicle category) and the experimenter labeled each toy with the same novel label (e.g., 'avi'). Next, in the test phase, infants were presented with another toy from the same category (e.g., another car) and a toy from a different category (e.g., a plane or an animal). A control group of infants experienced the same procedure but no label was used to name the toys. Only the infants who heard the novel label during the familiarization phase discriminated between the categories of animals vs. vehicles, as measured by the time they spent attending to a toy from the familiar category as compared to a toy from another category. Thus, hearing the novel label drew infants' attention to certain commonalities between objects, leading them to form a category. This pattern was not evident when the infants were presented with the same toys without hearing a novel label, suggesting that infants of 12 months are developing an understanding that a count noun will refer to categories of objects.

Mutual exclusivity constraint

Another extensively studied constraint bias is the principle of mutual exclusivity. This bias predicts that children prefer a single label for an object or object category because children assume that a novel word will not label an already-named object, but instead, will label an unfamiliar object. In support of this view, several studies conducted by Markman and colleagues have demonstrated that when presented with a familiar object with a known label and a novel object, children tend to map a novel label onto the novel object rather than onto the familiar object. This effect has been demonstrated in infants as young as 15 months.

Sociopragmatic Theories and Cues to Word Learning

The sociopragmatic theories of word learning view the child as embedded in social networks and social contexts. These theories propose that children depend on communicative interactions with other people (usually adults) to provide cues about the possible meanings of words. Specifically, the child's earliest words depend on his/her ability to perceive and understand the actions of other persons as intentional. For instance, if an adult calls out the child's name and points to a referent in their common environment, the child understands that such pointing is purposeful and intentional – the act of pointing is an indication of the adult's intention to draw the child's attention toward that referent. This social understanding develops through the child's communicative interactions with others. Furthermore, such communicative interactions have been found to play a crucial role in the child's overall cognitive development and are not restricted to language learning. Thus, the sociopragmatists argue that word learning recruits general cognitive processes as opposed to cognitive processes that are specialized for language learning.

How does children's understanding of others' intentions aid them in word learning? Studies by Dare Baldwin and colleagues demonstrate that when learning new words, infants rely on a wide variety of social cues, such as direction of the speaker's eye gaze, head direction, body posture, pointing, source of the sound (whether the label is coming from a visible human source or coming from an disembodied voice with an unknown source), gestures, and facial expression. Some of these cues facilitate the creation of joint attention between the adult and the child, and provide information about the intentions of the speaker. Joint attention has been shown to facilitate word learning in several experimental and naturalistic studies.

Evidence from experimental studies

A series of experiments by Michael Tomasello, Nameera Akhtar and their colleagues have demonstrated that children use their understanding of others' intentions to learn new words. For instance, 2-year-olds and even 18-month-olds were able to use intentions and emotional cues to correctly infer the meaning of new words. Children observed as an experimenter expressed the intention to find an object, used a novel label for this desired object, and subsequently searched for the object. For some children, the experimenter did find the objects, whereas for other children, the experimenter failed to find the object. However, in both situations, children understood that an adult's intention to find an object and subsequent excitement at finding the object (or subsequent disappointment at not finding the object) suggested that the novel label referred to this specific object and not other objects that were also present and with which the adult also played.

As children become older, their understanding of the intentions and knowledge and beliefs of others becomes more sophisticated and they continue to recruit this expanding social understanding to learn the meanings of new words. For instance, 3–4-year-olds resist learning new words if the speaker displays signs of ignorance about the new words, but they readily learn the word when the speaker seems knowledgeable. Similarly, preschoolers prefer learning labels from an adult who has previously labeled an object correctly as compared to an adult who has been shown to label objects incorrectly in the past. In fact, although preschoolers usually assume that adults are better sources of information than their peers, children of this age sometimes consider another child as a more reliable source of information than an adult, if the child previously has proved to be reliable and the adult unreliable.

Parental input: Individual, socioeconomic and cultural factors

Both quality and quantity of maternal language input have been shown to play critical roles in children's early semantic development. Important studies by Michael Tomasello, Nameera Akhtar and their colleagues have found that some mothers engage more often in joint attention, by following their child's attentional focus rather than attempting to redirect the child's attention. Children of these mothers show more rapid vocabulary development and larger vocabularies than children whose mothers often attempt to redirect their attention. In fact, maternal following of the child's attention when the child was about 13 months old accounted for 60% of the variance in children's vocabulary at 22 months of age.

Those mothers who provide more language input overall also use a richer vocabulary, repeat the same words more times, and use longer utterances. Children of such mothers are found to have larger vocabularies than those whose mothers provide less input overall. For verb learning particularly, using several different sentence frames for each verb provides clues to the meaning of the verb and can thus aid verb learning. In fact, such mothers also tend to respond frequently and contingently to their children's vocalizations and these children often start talking sooner and reach the 50-word milestone at a younger age than children of less responsive mothers.

Furthermore, certain conversational settings such as book reading and meal times have been found to incorporate most of the above mentioned characteristics. In fact, time spent by children in book reading with an adult is found to predict vocabulary development. Children in families where mealtimes are used as opportunities for conversation, including extended narratives of family members recounting their days, have been found to show advantages in vocabulary development. Thus, the positive relation between verbal responsiveness and child language milestones could be an effect of engagement (i.e., responsiveness) as well as an effect of the amount and nature of the input.

Socioeconomic status has also been found to affect children's opportunities for communicative interactions and the availability of language input. An influential study by Betty Hart and Todd Risley in the mid-1990s found that socioeconomic status (SES) related differences in vocabulary-size in children were noticeable from the beginning of speech and they increased with development. Studies show that higher-SES mothers are much more likely to demonstrate all the input characteristics that have been related with advanced vocabularies in children, as compared to lower-SES mothers. When SES, input to children, and children's language development are all measured, it becomes clear that differences in input across SES account for the differences in children's language outcomes. Thus, differences of SES in children's vocabulary development reflect differences in experience and not ability.

Certain cultures do not consider infants as appropriate conversational partners and children are usually not addressed directly. Nonetheless, in these cultures, joint attention is often achieved by mother and child focusing on a common topic. In some cases, infants are held in such a way that they can see adults talking and see what adults are talking about. In such situations where children rely predominantly on overheard speech and thus do not get language that is segmented for their benefit, children begin talking by producing large memorized chunks of language, which they only later analyze into component words. Such patterns have been found among the Walpiri people of Australia, the Mayans in Mexico and the Inuit. In fact, this pattern of language acquisition is also found to be characteristic of children who find themselves suddenly immersed in a foreign language (such as children whose families move to a new country) and must rapidly learn this language without explicit instruction.

Similarly, Italian and Argentinean children are found to produce significantly more words for people (e.g., aunt, grandmother, cousin) than their US counterparts. These differences are thought to reflect differences in the amount of contact children have with extended family members. Nevertheless, it is important to note that these differences have been found in vocabulary composition and not vocabulary size.

Attentional Mechanisms

Recently, Linda Smith, Larissa Samuelson, and colleagues have offered a third perspective on the word learning problem. Similar to the sociopragmatic view, this perspective on word learning also argues for cognitive processes that are more general in nature, rather than specific to language. In this view of word learning, the earliest word learning can be best accounted for through attentional mechanisms. Children notice objects, events, and actions that are most perceptually salient in their environment. They associate the most frequently used label with the most salient candidate. Thus, a general cognitive mechanism such as attention is sufficient to account for how young children first map words onto referents. Furthermore, such an account also explains how different general mechanisms could combine in ways that would lead to more sophisticated word learning.

How exactly does an attentional mechanism account for word learning? Just as children tend to associate labels with whole objects, there is evidence suggesting that children attend to shape while learning new words (also known as the shape-bias). It is important to note that the shape-bias operates under the caveat of experience, so that children start attending to shape only after they have had sufficient experience with language. Whereas the very first words may be learned through a simple trial-and-error process, once the child has accumulated a vocabulary of about 50 words, the child has learned that names are usually associated with shape, that is, objects with very similar shapes usually have the same name. Thus, every time a novel word is heard, attention is drawn to the shape of the referent object. This association is the engine that propels word learning forward, leading to more and more complex associations between words and real-world referents.

To illustrate using a specific example, by about 2 years of age, English-learning children have been shown to extend novel labels on the basis of shape for objects with a rigid shape. Researchers introduced 2-year-olds to a novel object made of a distinctive substance (e.g., a circular piece of wood), while saying, "This is my blicket." This neutral sentence frame suggests that 'blicket' could refer to the whole object, or to the substance (e.g., wood). In the test phase, children were shown an object of the same shape but different material (e.g., a circular piece of clay) as well an object of the same material in a different shape (e.g., pieces of wood) and asked to 'find the blicket'. Despite the neutral sentence frame in the initial phase, children chose the object similar in shape (e.g., the circular piece of clay), rather than pieces of the original material (e.g., wood). However when the named entity was a nonsolid substance (e.g., sand), children of the same age were more likely to extend the name to other referents that were similar to the original in its material and color. Other studies have shown that when the named entity has properties that are typical of animate things – eyes, feet, limbs – slightly older children (2.5- to 3-year-olds) generalize the name to objects that match the named example in both shape and texture, presumably because they associate animate objects as having certain commonalities in texture, such as furry, scaly and so on. These findings demonstrate how increasing attention to a progression of commonalities across objects leads to the association of labels with these commonalities resulting in word learning. These findings highlight how a general cognitive mechanism such as attention can be shown to aid word learning.

Since the shape-bias is believed to be contingent upon sufficient experience with language, it is possible that specific properties of the language will influence the emergence of this bias. For instance, English makes a grammatical distinction between count and mass nouns (i.e., objects and substances). Specifically, English marks nouns as count nouns (e.g., a ball) or mass nouns (e.g., some water, bottle of water). Importantly, in English, entities having distinctive shapes are usually encoded as count nouns (e.g., balls, dogs, and most object labels) whereas entities that do not have distinctive shape are usually encoded as mass nouns (e.g., water, sand and most substance labels). This particular feature of English is thought to account for the shape-bias that is displayed by English-learning infants. English-learning children must learn that when a count noun is used (with count-noun syntax, such as 'this is a ball'), it is most likely to refer to an object, which has a distinctive shape. On the other hand, when a mass noun is used (with mass noun syntax, such as, 'this is some sand'), the label most likely refers to substances (e.g., water, sand). Thus, because English language syntax makes a distinction between count and mass nouns, English-learning children are more likely to attend to whether or not a novel object has a distinctive shape. However, they may be more likely to attend to substance, and ignore shape cues when mass-noun syntax is used.

By this reasoning, children who are learning a language that does not make a grammatical distinction between count and mass nouns (such as Japanese), should not show a preference to attend to either shape or substance. In a study with Japanese and American 2-year-olds, Mutsumi Imai and Dedre Gentner found that American 2-year-olds tended to extend novel labels for simple objects (e.g., a circular piece of clay) on the basis of shape. Specifically, when told that a circular piece of clay was 'my blicket' and asked to 'find the blicket' from a circular piece of wood and some differently shaped pieces of clay, American 2-year-olds were more likely to choose the circular piece of wood. In contrast, Japanese 2-year-olds did not show a preference to extend the name for a simple object on the basis of shape; instead, they were equally likely to choose other differently shaped pieces of clay and a circular piece of wood when asked to 'find the blicket' in Japanese. These findings suggest that specific characteristics of the English and Japanese language play a role in children's tendency to extend (generalize) novel names.

Combining Syntactic and Pragmatic Cues

Recall that in all the studies examining children's ability to learn novel labels for a referent, the novel labels were presented in a neutral sentence frame (e.g., "This is my blicket") so that children could not use syntactic cues in inferring the meaning of these labels. However, there is increasing evidence that by about 2 years of age, children are sensitive to syntactic or grammatical cues, and are even able to combine syntactic and pragmatic cues when deciding on the referents of novel labels.

For instance, D. Geoffrey Hall and colleagues found that when 2-year-olds were presented with a novel word in a syntactic frame that suggested that it was a proper noun (e.g., "This is Zav") in the presence of a familiar toy animal (such as a cat or a teddy bear), the toddlers assumed that 'zav' was a name for the animal. They were unwilling to extend this name to other similar toy animals, and preferred to restrict it to a particular individual. In contrast, when presented with a novel label in a syntactic frame that suggested that the label was a count noun (e.g., "This is a zav"), toddlers extended this label to other toy animals that belonged to the same category as the original animal, indicating that they interpreted the noun as a name for a category of animals such as all cats, rather than the name for a particular individual animal. However, this understanding was evident only for categories with which children were already familiar. If, instead of a toy cat, a novel animal such as a llama was labeled using proper noun-syntax (e.g., "This is Zav"), 2-year-olds assumed that the name labeled the entire category of llamas, and not just that particular llama.

Similarly, 2-year-olds have different expectations about the labeling norms for animate and inanimate objects. When an inanimate object was labeled using either a count noun- or proper noun-syntax, 2-year-olds did not show a systematic preference in the way they extended either label (i.e., 'Zav' or 'a zav'). Thus, children are able to use syntactic information (the sentence frames) as well pragmatic information (the fact that only animate entities typically have names and that each entity typically has just one name) in order to learn new words.

Hybrid Models of Word - Learning

In recent years, there is increasing consensus that children recruit a wide variety of cues and exploit multiple sources of information in order to learn their first words. The emergentist-coalition model of word learning, proposed by Roberta Golinkoff, Kathy Hirsh-Pasek, and George Hollich, is a hybrid model that outlines the diverse cues in the real world that children recruit in word learning. They argue that children use a combination of cues, such as attentional, social, cognitive, and linguistic to learn new words. Despite their availability, not all cues are equally utilized in word learning. Younger children may rely on only a subset of the available cues. For instance, although 12-month-olds are sensitive to speaker's eye-gaze, they do not appear to use this cue to aid them in word learning until they are about 18 months old. Rather, younger infants rely on perceptual salience of the object in order to decide on the referent of a new label. Older, more experienced learners rely on a wider set of cues and on some cues more heavily than others. Given these developmental changes, the emergentist model suggests that the word learning constraints may be better viewed as the products and not the root causes of semantic development. That is, word learning constraints may be expectations that emerge in the child with increasing experience with the world and the language that surrounds them.

Nouns vs. Verbs: Is there a Noun Bias?

A comparison of the findings on children's verb vs. noun learning has led many to note that many children, especially those learning English, seem to learn nouns (usually object labels) earlier and more easily than verbs. In one of the very few studies that directly compared the learning of novel nouns and novel verbs, Jane Childers and Michael Tomasello found that under a variety of conditions (where frequency of exposure was varied), 2-year-olds showed a more robust ability to learn nouns as compared to verbs. In fact, 2-year-olds in this study were able to remember and understand an action in a nonverbal task but still had trouble learning a name for it (i.e., a verb). What could be the reasons for these differences?

In two highly influential papers, Dedre Gentner and colleagues proposed that the answer may lie in the concepts to which these words usually refer. Nouns usually label concrete entities, whereas verbs and prepositions usually label events such as actions, motions, and spatial locations. These events tend to comprise components such as manner (the way in which something moves), instrument (the means by which it moves), path (the direction in which it moves), and result (the outcome of the movement). When a child sees a boy kicking a ball and hears, "Look, the boy's kicking the ball," the child must learn which component of the kicking action the adult refers to when saying 'kicking'. The question arises of whether the word 'kick' refers to the contact action, the trajectory, or the landing action.

Verbs are inherently relational. They often imply the presence of an actor to carry out that action and often have referents that exist only briefly. Nouns refer to an entity that is usually perceptually concrete and apparent as a whole unit, has distinct boundaries, is unchanging, and persists over time. These differences may explain why children seem to attach labels to objects more easily than actions. In fact, researchers have cited these differences to explain the whole-object bias. A novel label may heighten attention to a novel object over a novel action because objects are more perceptually apparent as distinct, whole units in comparison to an action, such as 'kicking' which may be observable for a brief time. It is important to note, however, that actions or relational concepts are not harder to understand *per se*. Evidence from experimental studies demonstrates that infants as young as 9 months are able to form categories of motion but are not able to map a verb onto these categories until much later.

An added difficulty with verbs, prepositions and other relational terms is that they often are encoded differently across languages (unlike most object labels). For instance, in English, meanings of motion verbs are usually centered around the manner of motion, with the path of motion encoded as a separate element (e.g., fly away, tiptoe across). In contrast, in romance languages such as Spanish and French, motion verbs often encode the path of motion with manner added as an optional separate element (e.g., *partir en volant* (to leave flying); *traverser sur la pointe des pieds* (to cross on tip-toes)). Consequently, a child who is faced with the task of mapping a label onto a verb must not only isolate the word, but must also learn the specific encoding patterns of his/her language.

In the light of these cross-linguistic differences, some researchers have proposed that the so-called noun bias may not be as universal as previously thought. Studies examining vocabulary development in children learning some languages other than English suggest that linguistic and cultural factors play a role in explaining the patterns of semantic development that are observed in children. The input to English-learning infants is characterized by frequent and salient object labels. Western mothers often focus on concrete objects and provide a higher proportion of nouns in their speech to their infants. During this early stage, mothers also tend to use grammatically simpler and shorter sentences in their speech. This kind of input is found to correlate with early vocabularies that start with single words, with a high proportion of object labels and nouns, and later start comprising novel combinations of those words. Some languages such as Korean and Mandarin are more verb-friendly (i.e., verbs are more salient and more frequent in the input). Korean and Mandarin mothers are less object oriented; their speech contains proportionately more verbs and fewer nouns, and the vocabularies of the children learning these languages are less dominated by nouns than their English-learning counterparts.

Verb Learning

Although much of the research has focused on children's learning of labels for objects, children's earliest vocabularies do contain words that refer to actions (verbs such as 'cry', 'kiss', 'bite', 'eat') and events, such as 'bye-bye' and 'all-gone'. Experimental studies have shown that at about 16 months, infants demonstrate comprehension of verbs such as 'wave', 'eat', 'bounce' and 'roll'. Observational and experimental studies have noted that children's early verbs are usually context-bound and that these verbs have restricted meanings as compared to adult uses of these verbs. Janellen Huttenlocher and colleagues, for example, noticed that many of children's first verb meanings referred specifically to self-involved actions and did not include actions produced by others. Similarly, Michael Tomasello and colleagues found that the youngest word-learners start out by learning verbs one at a time. Furthermore, each verb is initially associated with only certain sentence frames. For instance, 25-month-olds were taught a series of novel verbs, each of which was introduced in a limited set of sentence frames. Thus, one verb might be introduced in a frame with an agent but no patient (e.g., 'Ernie's gaffing'), another might be introduced with a patient but no agent (e.g., 'blicking Ernie') and another might be introduced with both (e.g., 'Ernie's ziking Cookie Monster'). When children's spontaneous productions of these novel verbs were recorded and analyzed, it was found that children of this age rarely used a verb in a sentence frame that they had not heard previously. These results, as well as findings from a diary study of a child's early verb acquisition, led these researchers to conclude that children are initially conservative in their use of verbs, restricting a given verb to a narrow range of sentence structures and usages.

In other studies, Diane Poulin-Dubois, James Forbes, and colleagues found that 18–20-month-olds generalized a familiar verb (e.g., 'kick') when the actor was different but not when the manner or outcome was different. For instance, infants perceived a video of a woman kicking three balls across the floor and into a box as being different from a woman who turned around and kicked the balls with her heels (a different manner). The first action also was perceived as different from an action wherein the woman kicked the balls and the balls bounced off an obstacle placed behind the box and rolled back in the direction of the woman (a different outcome). In contrast, older children of 26 months extended a familiar verb such as kicking to new actors and new manners. Nonetheless, neither age group extended these verbs when the outcome changed. Such findings and others suggest that young children's representations of familiar action verbs change from 20 to 26 months.

Sources of Information about Verb Meaning

As we have seen in the preceding sections, young children can recruit a wide variety of cues to learn new words, particularly object labels and other nouns. Not surprisingly, children similarly rely on several sources of information when learning the meanings of verbs. The following studies provide examples of some of the cues that children recruit in order to learn the meanings of novel verbs.

Sociopragmatic Cues

Children draw on their understanding of speakers' intentions in order to interpret new words (such as verbs) for actions. For instance, children use pragmatic cues to decide whether a new word is the label for an action or an object. When the action, as opposed to the object, was the new element in the communicative context, or when the experimenter made obvious preparations related to the novel action prior to introducing the new word, children interpreted the word as a label for the new action rather than an object label. Similarly, when shown video events of people performing certain actions, 2-year-olds are sensitive to the intention (via eye-gaze) of the actor in the event and can use this information to determine whether the novel label refers to the object or the action in the event.

Two-year-old children also understand that speakers usually label only intentional actions and not accidental ones. Similarly, children of this age understand that if the speaker uses a label while expressing an intention to perform an action, and then is not able to successfully perform that action, the label still refers to that unaccomplished action, presumably because the speaker expressed the intention to perform it.

Syntactic Bootstrapping

Researchers such as Lila Gleitman, Barbara Landau, and others have proposed that children use information from sentence frames as clues to verb meanings. The proposal that sensitivity to sentence structure guides the acquisition of verb meaning is known as syntactic bootstrapping. Thus, an understanding about the components of a sentence such as the agent and patient of the verb may help children in determining the meaning of the verb.

Findings from studies using the intermodal preferential looking paradigm (IPLP) have been used as evidence to support the argument for syntactic bootstrapping. For instance, Letitia Naigles presented 2-year-old children with a single videotaped event, involving a duck and a bunny. Each actor was performing two actions simultaneously. One action was causal (the duck pushed down on the bunny's head, causing the bunny to squat) and the other action was noncausal (both the duck and the bunny waved their arms in large circles). As children watched these events, they heard a novel verb. For some children, the verb was embedded in a transitive sentence ("The duck is gorping the bunny"), and for others the verb was embedded in an intransitive sentence ("The duck and the bunny are gorping").

After the introduction of the new verb, children were shown two video scenes simultaneously, each of which contained only one of the actions seen in the first video. Thus, one screen showed one character pushing the other into a squat. The other screen showed both characters moving their arms around in large circles. As these two events were presented, children were asked "Where's gorping?" and the amount of time they looked at each screen was recorded. Children who had heard the verb in the transitive frame looked longer at the causal action (pushing down) and the children who had heard the verb in the intransitive frame looked longer at the noncausal action (arm circling). Thus, the children inferred that a transitive sentence frame (e.g., "the duck is gorping the bunny") suggested a causal action and the intransitive frame (e.g., "the duck and the bunny are gorping") suggested the noncausal action.

A more recent study suggests that even 21-month-olds can use the word order of a sentence to interpret the meanings of novel verbs. Children watched two videos side-by-side. One of these videos depicted one cartoon character (e.g., a duck) performing an action on another cartoon character (e.g., a bunny). The other video depicted the reverse: the bunny performing an action on the duck. Half of the children saw these two videos and heard a sentence such as, "The duck is gorping the bunny", while the other half saw the same two videos and heard a sentence such as, "The bunny is gorping the duck". Those children who heard the former sentence (i.e., "the duck is gorping the bunny") looked longer at the video where the duck was performing an action on the bunny. The opposite was found for the children who heard the latter sentence (i.e., "the bunny is gorping the duck"). Further, when the same two videos were shown with sentences such as, "He is gorping the bunny" or "He is gorping the duck", children looked longer at the appropriate video. These results suggest that, even before the age of 2 years, children expect the subject of the sentence to refer to the agent of an action and they expect the object of the sentence to refer to the patient of the action. These results suggest that young children can use the sentence frame to inform them about the meaning of the verb.

Conclusion

Numerous experimental studies on children's semantic development have provided insights into the processes by which children learn how to map words onto real world referents. These processes include not only the sociopragmatic, linguistic, and contextual cues that children recruit but also the assumptions children make about the meanings of new words. Taken together, the evidence suggests that early word learning is a complex interplay of children's cognitive abilities, their emerging conceptual understanding of the world around them and their experience with their specific native language or languages. In any one situation, children are able to use multiple sources of information simultaneously in order to hone in on the meaning of a word.

Furthermore, early semantic development is also highly influenced by the child's environment. Factors as diverse as structural characteristics of the language, cultural influences, maternal sensitivity, and responsivity to children's needs and abilities, and socioeconomic status of the family are found to have powerful impacts on children's semantic development. In addition, these factors too combine and complement each other to predict language outcomes in children.

See also: Attention; Bilingualism; Birth Order; Categorization Skills and Concepts; Grammar; Language Acquisition Theories; Language Development: Overview; Parenting Styles and their Effects; Pragmatic Development; Preverbal Development and Speech Perception; Social Interaction; Speech Perception.

Suggested Readings

Bloom P (2000) *How Children Learn the Meanings of Words.* Cambridge, MA: MIT Press.
Bowerman M and Levinson S (eds.) (2001) *Language Acquisition and Conceptual Development.* Cambridge, UK: Cambridge University Press.
Hall DG and Waxman SR (eds.) (2004) *Weaving a Lexicon.* Cambridge, MA: MIT Press.
Hirsh-Pasek K and Golinkoff RM (eds.) (2006) *Action Meets Word: How Children Learn Verbs.* Oxford: Oxford University Press.
Hoff E (2006) How social contexts support and shape language development. *Developmental Review* 26: 55–88.
Woodward AL and Markman EM (1998) Early word learning. In: Damon W, Kuhn D, and Siegler RS (eds.) *Handbook of Child Psychology: Vol. 2. Cognition, Perception and Language,* 5th edn., pp. 371–420. New York: Wiley.

Sensory Processing Disorder

L J Miller, Sensory Processing Disorder Foundation, Greenwood Village, CO, USA
R C Schaaf, Thomas Jefferson University, Philadelphia, PA, USA

Glossary

Adaptive response – An appropriate action in which the individual responds successfully to a challenging demand.

Occupational therapy using a sensory integrative approach – The use of sensory-rich activities, tailored to individual needs, that are playful yet organizing, and elicit adaptive responses. Usually involves total body movements that are rich in vestibular, proprioceptive, and tactile input. The goal of therapy is to improve the way the brain processes and organizes sensations. Intervention is based on sensory integrative principles that guide the therapist's clinical reasoning skills. The intervention addresses the underlying substrates of dysfunction (e.g., neurological immaturity) rather than difficulties with specific skills. This intervention approach is most commonly utilized by occupational therapists.

Proprioceptive system – The sensory system that detects information from the muscles and joints and perceives sensation about the position or velocity of movement of body parts including force, tension and position. Proprioceptive input tells the brain which muscles are contracting or stretching, when they are doing so, and the amount of resistance on the muscles and joints. The receptors for the proprioceptive system include the muscle spindle, the golgi tendon organ, and the joint receptors.

Sensory modulation disorder (SMD) – This condition is the inability to automatically regulate incoming sensory information resulting in sensory over-responsivity, sensory under-responsivity, and/or sensory seeking/craving.

Sensory processing – The ability to detect information through the senses, organize that information, and interpret the information making a meaningful and appropriate adaptive response. For most people the process of sensory processing is automatic and unconscious.

Sensory processing disorder (SPD) – This complex disorder is a neurological condition that affects children and adults. People with SPD misinterpret everyday sensory information, such as touch, sound, and movement. They may feel bombarded by information, crave intense sensory experiences, be unable to discriminate the fine qualities of sensation, or have awkward responses to sensory input. To be classified as a disorder, the symptoms of SPD must be severe enough that participation in daily life activities is restricted.

Tactile system – Receptors for the tactile system are located in the skin and are responsible for the sense of touch.

Theory of sensory integration – This theory explains the relation between deficits in interpreting sensory input and learning, behavior, or motor difficulties. The theory recognizes brain–behavior interactions and focuses on the role of the senses in creating a foundation for higher level cognitive, emotional, and motor activities. The theory postulates that adequate detection, modulation, discrimination, and responses to sensory information are needed for normal adaptive behavior to occur.

Vestibular system – This sensory system responds to the position of the head in relation to gravity and to the acceleration or deceleration of movement. The receptors for the vestibular system are the semicircular canals and the utricle and saccule that are located in the labyrinth of the inner ear. These receptors detect the pull of gravity and movement of the head.

Introduction

What is sensory processing disorder? Sensory processing is our ability to take in information through our senses (touch, movement, smell, taste, vision, and hearing), interpret that information, and organize a meaningful response. For most children this process is automatic. When we hear someone talking to us or a bird chirping (auditory stimuli), our brain interprets this information as speech or an animal sound, and we respond to the information appropriately (e.g., turning our head to listen). When someone taps us on the shoulder (tactile stimulus) we turn our attention to that individual. When we are standing in a bus or train and it starts to move (vestibular stimulus), we automatically shift our weight so we do not fall. Individuals (both children and adults) who have sensory processing disorder (SPD) do not detect, regulate, interpret, and/or respond to sensory information accurately. SPD symptoms occur along a wide continuum from mild to severe and manifest in a variety of behavioral, motor, and social symptoms.

Seven sensory systems exist and SPD can occur in one or a combination of systems. The five well-known sensory systems are: visual, auditory, olfactory (smell), gustatory (taste), and tactile (touch). Two 'hidden senses' also exist, the vestibular and proprioceptive systems. The vestibular system detects information about the movement of the head in relation to the Earth's gravity through receptors in the vestibules (hence the term vestibular) located in the inner ear. The proprioceptive system detects information in the muscles and joints and provides information about the location and movement of the parts of the body (i.e., you can feel where your little toe is located without looking at it).

History

Dr. A. Jean Ayres, an occupational therapist (OT) and neuroscientist, pioneered the theory of sensory integration, expanded primarily in the field of OT. Sensory integration theory describes the underlying brain mechanisms hypothesized to cause SPD, defines a set of behavioral characteristics indicative of SPD, and also suggests intervention methods for remediating the disorder. Ayres called the disorder sensory integrative dysfunction and termed the intervention sensory integration treatment. Her theory discusses the relation among the neural processes of receiving, modulating, and integrating sensory input and the resulting output that Ayres called adaptive behavior. The theory postulates that adequate processing of sensory information is needed for normal adaptive behavior to occur.

Ayres developed two assessment batteries, the Southern California Sensory Integration Test in 1972 and the Sensory Integration and Praxis Test (SIPT) in 1989. The SIPT includes 17 subtests evaluating children ages 4 years 6 months to 8 year 11 months. It measures the ability to detect and interpret sensory information by responding to tactile, proprioceptive, vestibular, auditory, and visual stimuli. The results provide detailed information about underlying sensory factors that may affect a child's learning and behavior.

Although Ayres originally outlined the central theoretical tenets of the theory in her book *Sensory Integration and Learning Disorders* in 1972, she recognized that the theory would evolve and change as new scientific findings informed the field. This evolution is exactly what has happened over the 35 years since the original book was published. For example, Ayres originally identified six subtypes of sensory integration dysfunction: postural and bilateral integration dysfunction, developmental apraxia, form and space perception, tactile defensiveness, unilateral disregard, and auditory-language disorders. She later revised her theory and, based on new data, renamed some of the subtypes. However, as she predicted, new research has emerged and her theory has evolved. Thus, an update to Ayres' original taxonomy is presented.

Signs and Symptoms of Sensory Processing Disorder

The newest taxonomy encompasses and expands Ayres' original ideas based on new research. Dr. Lucy Jane Miller and colleagues note that delineating specific subtypes is crucial so that homogenous groups can be identified for intervention and research purposes. They have proposed a set of classic patterns with subtypes based on physiological research and behavioral studies. The new taxonomy utilizes the term SPD to identify the condition and includes all the subtypes identified by Ayres. The Ayres' classification scheme is reorganized into a new nosology that includes subtypes that were not labeled previously. The current diagnostic taxonomy is delineated in **Figure 1** Definitions and behaviors observed in each subtype follow.

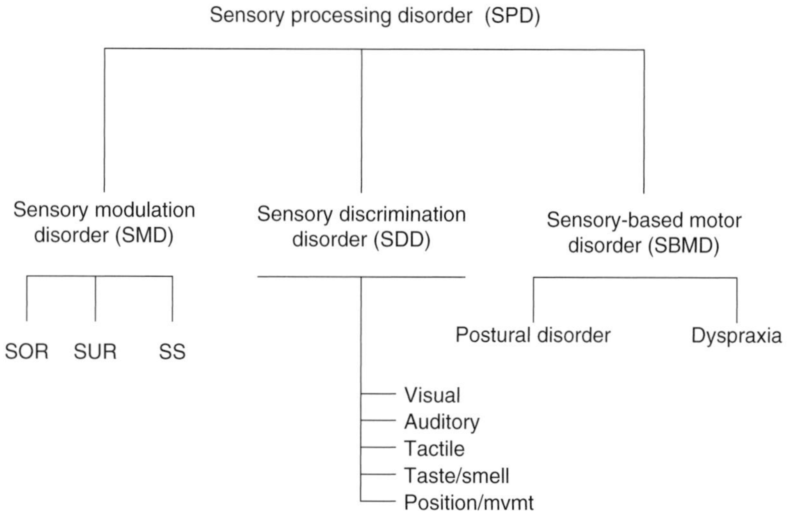

Figure 1 Current taxonomy of sensory processing disorder. SOR, sensory over-responsivity; SS, sensory seeking craving; SUR, sensory under-responsivity.

Sensory Modulation Disorder

The first classic pattern is sensory modulation disorder (SMD), defined as difficulty regulating and responding to sensory input in a graded manner. Almost all people experience SMD to some degree, at some point in their life. For example, when you get home after a long tiring day, any sensation can be 'too much' such as a loud radio or someone touching you. Because your stress level is high and your usual methods of coping with stimuli is poor, you experience normal levels of sensation as uncomfortable. However, poor modulation of sensation is a disorder only when it disrupts a person's ability to take part in daily life routines and self-care activities on a routine basis. Children and adults with the disorder demonstrate severe and frequent over or under-responsivity and/or sensory-seeking behaviors in response to levels of sensory stimuli in their environment that most of us would automatically process without effort.

Screening for SMD can be completed using parent, teacher, and self-report scales such as the 'sensory profile', the 'infant toddler sensory profile', and the 'adult sensory profile' developed by Dr. Winifred Dunn and colleagues, by the 'sensory processing measure' by Dr. Diane Parham and colleagues or by other similar report measures. Diagnosis of SPD also involves testing and observations by well-trained clinicians, usually OTs or other professionals with advanced training in sensory processing. In Miller's taxonomy, three types of SMD are proposed: sensory over-responsivity, sensory under-responsivity, and sensory-seeking.

Sensory over-responsivity

Children with sensory over-responsivity respond to sensation more quickly and intensely than most people. Their responses appear to be fight or flight reactions and are sometimes labeled sensory defensiveness. They often try to avoid or minimize sensations by withdrawing from the situation (e.g., covering their ears, pushing a person who touches them away, or closing their eyes) or they respond with aggressive behavior. For example, a child touched unexpectedly may punch the person who touched him. Many of the common sensory symptoms and the behaviors that accompany sensory over-responsivity are described by Miller. A few examples of the sensory symptoms and accompanying behaviors are shown in **Table 1**.

Sensory under-responsivity

Children with sensory under-responsivity do not respond to typical levels of sensation and, as a result, are lethargic and unaware of stimulation. They may seem oblivious to their environment and often do not respond to typical stimuli such as hearing their name called. Common behaviors associated with sensory under-responsivity are noted in **Table 1**.

Sensory seeking craving

A third type of SMD is sensory seeking craving. Children with sensory seeking/craving are hypothesized to have a high threshold to sensory stimuli, and compensate by constantly seeking stimulation that is more intense or prolonged than most children prefer. Children who seek sensation often take part in extreme activities or move constantly to provide the sensory input their brains seem to crave to feel normal. They may make unsafe choices in play such as jumping from the top of a slide, play music or talk very loudly, and/or constantly intrude upon other people's space, touching people, and handling their objects. Other behaviors associated with sensory seeking are noted in **Table 1**.

Many children have more than one type of sensory modulation problem and their symptoms include behaviors from several subtypes. To be diagnosed with SMD the child's responses to sensation must be extreme, well outside of the range typical responsiveness. The responses must be seen in a variety of settings such as school, daycare, home, and in the community. The child must exhibit these behaviors in 'ordinary' daily situations to receive a diagnosis of SMD (e.g., not just at the end of a tiring day or a long trip).

Table 1 Characteristics of sensory over-responsivity, sensory under-responsivity, and sensory seeking

Sensory over-responsivity
Sensory symptoms – Frequently bothered by
- Having his hair, fingernails, or toenails cut
- Food textures
- Noise in a restaurant, mall, or large gymnasium or loud, unexpected sounds
- Being upside-down, as when turning a somersault

Behaviors include being
- Aggressive or impulsive when overwhelmed by sensory stimulation
- Irritable, fussy, moody
- Unsociable; avoids group activities and has trouble forming relationships
- Upset by transitions and unexpected changes

Sensory under-responsivity
Sensory symptoms
- Does not cry when seriously hurt and is not bothered by minor injuries
- Nearly always prefers sedentary activities like computer time to active physical games
- Often seems unaware of what's going on around him (e.g., does not hear his name being called)
- Often seems unaware of body sensations such as hunger, hot or cold or need to use the

Behaviors include being
- Passive, quiet, withdrawn
- Hard to engage in conversation or other social interaction
- Apathetic and easily exhausted
- Exhibits no inner drive to get involved in the world around himself (e.g., uninterested in exploring games or objects)

Sensory seeking/craving
Sensory symptoms
- Is on the move constantly, crashing, bashing, bumping, jumping and rough-housing
- Constantly touches objects and/or intrudes on people
- Seems unable to stop talking and has trouble taking his turn in conversations
- Frequently fixates visually on objects such as reflections of the sun in the side-view mirrors of the car

Behaviors include being
- Described by others as hyperactive
- Angry or explosive when he is required to sit still or stop what he's doing
- Intense, demanding, hard to calm, excessively affectionate
- Prone to create situations others perceive as 'bad' or 'dangerous'

From Miller LJ (2006) *Sensational Kids: Help and Hope for Chi; dren with Sensory Processing Disorder*. New York: Putnam.

Sensory Discrimination Disorder

The second classic pattern is sensory discrimination disorder (SDD), difficulty interpreting sensory input. When a child has this problem, he or she can detect the stimuli but does not recognize the precise details of sensation, including the quantity, location, duration, size, and/or shape of stimuli. This interpretation of sensory qualities is needed to execute fine and gross motor skills. SDD can occur in visual, auditory, tactile, olfactory, gustatory, proprioceptive, and/or vestibular systems. Some children with SPD can respond adequately when only one sensory modality is presented; however, when two or more stimuli are present (as is the case in many typical daily activities), they are unable to organize appropriate responses. As a result, they have difficulty successfully participating in learning, play, and social activities. Tactile, vestibular, proprioceptive, and visual discrimination can be assessed using the 'sensory integration and praxis test' battery. Common sensory symptoms and behaviors associated with SDD are noted in **Table 2**.

Sensory-Based Motor Disorder

The final classic pattern type of SPD is sensory-based motor disorder. There are two types: postural disorder and sensory-based dyspraxia. Each is described below.

Postural disorder

Postural disorder includes problems with core body positions, for example, stability and mobility. Whenever the child is required to move against gravity (such as when lying on stomach and extending arms and legs into an airplane position, or lying on back and curling up into a ball or doing a sit up), the child with postural disorder has difficulty contracting muscles and using core stability.

Table 2 Characteristics of sensory discrimination disorder

Difficulties with these sensory tasks
- Distinguishing exactly what is touching him and/or where on his body
- Judging how much force is required for a task (e.g., how firmly to hold onto a pencil)
- Detecting whether he is in motion or not
- Identifying and distinguishing between different sounds
- Difficulty differentiating textures of food and smells

Behaviors include
- Difficulty following directions; gets lost easily
- Aversion to playing with puzzles or other visual games
- Frustration when unable to differentiate visual or auditory signals
- A need for directions repeated
- A need for more time than other children to perform assigned tasks

From Miller LJ (2006) *Sensational Kids: Help and Hope for Chi; dren with Sensory Processing Disorder*. New York: Putnam.

As a result the child may be slow to sit, crawl, walk, and run. This child frequently has difficulty using the two sides of the body in a coordinated manner, called poor bilateral integration. In addition, because they cannot contract the muscles needed for stability, they may exhibit poor balance. It is hypothesized that difficulty with these postural issues is related to poor detection of vestibular and proprioceptive stimuli resulting in poor muscle tone. Postural disorder is most frequently assessed using the 'clinical observations of sensory integration' by Dr. Erna Blanche, or by using a standardized motor development assessment that allows for observation of posture and balance. For example, the Miller assessment for preschoolers, The Miller function and participation scale, and the DeGangi-Berk test of sensory integration contain structured observations that are useful in the evaluation of postural disorder. The primary features of postural disorder are provided in **Table 3**.

Dyspraxia

The second type of sensory-based motor disorder is dyspraxia, also called motor planning problems. Children with this problem have difficulty utilizing tactile and proprioceptive information to plan and carry out motor activities. Dyspraxia is different from developmental coordination disorder, a diagnosis included in the Diagnostic and Statistical Manual (DSM)-IV because the core problem is based upon deficits in sensory awareness and planning. In contrast, the core issue in developmental coordination disorder is poor motor execution. Children with sensory-based dyspraxia appear clumsy and awkward in movements and are delayed in acquiring complex motor skills such as riding a bike or tying shoes. They have problems in particular with new motor actions or activities that require a series of motor steps to perform. The 'sensory integration and praxis test' battery provides an extensive series of subtests evaluating dyspraxia. Common characteristics associated with sensory-based dyspraxia appear in **Table 3**.

Table 3 Characteristics of postural disorder and dyspraxia (motor planning difficulties)

Postural disorder
Sensory symptoms
- Has poor muscle tone and/or seems weak compared to other children
- Often slumps over at a desk when writing
- Has difficulty crossing the middle of his body to complete a task (e.g., uses his left hand to write on left side of a piece of paper and his right hand for the right side of paper)
- Has poor endurance and gets tired easily

Behaviors include
- Appearing lazy, unmotivated, or indifferent
- Appearing weak and limp, tires easily
- Difficulty holding his own in competitive games like tug of war

Dyspraxia
Sensory symptoms
- Has difficulty with motor activities that require more than one step (e.g., opening a carton and then pouring a glass of milk)
- Has difficulty learning new motor skills, for example riding a bicycle, tricycle, big wheels
- Is clumsy, awkward, and/or accident-prone, tripping or bumping into other people or things
- Has difficulty keeping personal spaces such as a school desk or bedroom organized

Behaviors include
- Preference for fantasy games, talking or sedentary games rather than 'doing' things
- Messy or sloppy eating
- A disheveled appearance
- Frustration when unable to complete tasks due to poor motor skills

From Miller LJ (2006) *Sensational Kids Help and Hope for Chi; dren with Sensory Processing Disorder*. New York: Putnam.

Diagnosis and Diagnostic Classification of Sensory Processing Disorder

There is controversy regarding whether SPD is a valid diagnosis because, in the past, it was not listed in diagnostic classification references such as the DSM. Recently, however, it was accepted into two diagnostic classification resources. Both focus on one classic pattern of SPD, SMD, sometimes referred to as SPDs of regulation. While the differences in terminology may be confusing, important is that, for the first time, disorders of sensory processing are now recognized across professional disciplines. As a result, children with these problems have more formal justification for receiving treatment.

Research and advocacy efforts are underway to have SPD recognized by the DSM and the International Classification of Diseases (ICD). Only when SPD is formally recognized by these standard diagnostic manuals will third party payers likely be willing to consider benefits for children with this disorder. Formal recognition will also aide in efforts to receive federal funding to research this disorder.

Prevalence of Sensory Processing Disorder

Although clinicians and educators have speculated that a large number of children are affected by poor sensory modulation, prevalence data have been nonexistent until recently. Miller and colleagues recently conducted a survey to estimate rates of SPD in incoming kindergartners from one suburban US public school district. A conservative estimate of prevalence was made, assuming that all nonrespondents failed to meet positive criteria for SMD. This cautious estimate suggested that approximately 5% of the kindergarten enrollment met screening criteria for SPD. These percentages are consistent with hypothesized estimates published in the literature.

Other Clinical Populations of Children with Sensory Processing Disorder

In addition to children with SPD and no other diagnosis, children with other clinical disorders also have characteristics of SPD. These children are described in *The Nature of Sensory Integration with Diverse Populations*, a book by Smith Roley, Blanche, and Schaaf, as well as in other publications. These populations include children from 'at risk' environments or with low birth weight, cerebral palsy, visual impairments, fragile X syndrome (FXS), or autism spectrum disorder (ASD). Given the multiple and often complex nature of the needs of this group of children, treatment of their SPD provides an excellent complement to their comprehensive program of therapeutic and educational services.

Of particular note, children with ASD and FXS demonstrate a high incidence (80–90%) of SPD, contributing to their maladaptive behavioral profile and limiting their participation in daily life activities. They demonstrate significantly more sensory symptoms than typically developing children and children in other clinical groups. Their SPD leads to a restricted range of behaviors including self-stimulation, avoidance, or fearfulness. Children with autism often demonstrate stereotypic behaviors and repetitive behaviors that are sensory seeking in nature such as spinning, hand flapping, or tapping that limits their ability to participate in the activities with their family and peers. Recently, there has been a surge in research on SPD in ASD and FXS. Given the unique cluster of behaviors and their inherent heterogeneity of children with ASD and FXS, this research is challenging, yet it promises to provide useful data to improve behavior and learning in these children.

Children diagnosed with attention deficit disorders show a range of responses to sensory stimuli with about two-thirds of those studied demonstrating some symptomatology suggestive of poor sensory processing. SPD and attention deficit hyperactive disorder (ADHD) appear to be comorbid diagnosis in approximately 40% of children. Critics of the diagnosis of SPD comment that SPD is 'just another form of ADHD'. However, children with ADHD and SPD have been compared on physiological measures such as sensory habituation and response inhibition and found to differ significantly. Thus, evidence suggests that SPD and ADHD, while frequently co-occurring, are different conditions.

Proposed Mechanisms of Sensory Processing Disorder

Ayres' theory of sensory integration is based on principles from neuroscience, biology, psychology, and education. Noting that many children with learning disorders also demonstrated difficulty with perceptual-motor and sensory processing skills, Ayres theorized that their behavior and learning problems were, in part, due to faulty processing of sensory information and an inability of higher brain centers to modulate the information for lower brain sensory centers. In contrast to other learning-based theories, Ayres' theory was based on the relations among the underlying mechanisms and inadequate learning, behavior, and motor function. Ayres proposed that the integration of vestibular, proprioceptive, and tactile inputs provides a foundation for learning and behavior.

Ayres proposed that dysfunction occurred primarily in the brainstem, viewed as the primary integrator and modulator of sensory information. Specifically, she focused on the vestibular system and the reticular formation, an area in the brainstem, as centers for regulating responsiveness, for example, alerting, arousing, or suppressing sensory input. She believed that the cerebellum and the thalamus played major roles in sensory processing, the cerebellum through the processing of proprioception and the integration of sensory and motor stimuli, and the thalamus through integration of sensory information. Finally, Ayres viewed the limbic system as an important system that contributed to the emotions associated with sensory dysfunction. As her theory evolved, Ayres later included a focus on the role of the cerebral cortex in processing and integrating sensory information, particularly for praxis (motor planning).

Ayres' theory included a set of postulates about nervous system functioning that guided her development of an intervention model. She proposed that the nervous system has an innate drive to seek out the input that it needs for organized interactions with the environment, and that stimuli from one sensory system has the capacity to affect every other system. In addition, she outlined several key principles:

1. sensorimotor development is an important substrate for learning;
2. the interaction of the individual with the environment shapes brain development;
3. the nervous system is capable of change (plasticity); and
4. meaningful sensory–motor activity is a powerful mediator of plasticity.

Since Ayres outlined her theory of sensory integration, several advances in science have shaped the further evolution of the theory. Much of the evolution has been in the domain of SMD where significant scientific advances have occurred since the mid-1990s. Miller and colleagues completed a series of studies examining autonomic nervous system functioning in children with poor sensory modulation. The evidence suggests that children with severe over-responsivity to sensory stimuli have sympathetic dysfunction as evidenced by increased electrodermal activity compared to typically developing controls. Electrodermal activity is a psychophysiological measure that evaluates how much you respond to stimuli by measuring electrical changes in the skin. Your skin conducts more electricity because of eccrine sweat gland activity. Eccrine sweat glands are innervated by cholinergic fibers of the sympathetic nervous system. Thus, measuring electrodermal activity provides an index of sympathetic nervous system activity in the brain.

The research showed that children with sensory oversensitivity during functional activities in daily life also had significantly increased amplitudes, more frequent responses and less habituation of electrodermal responses compared to matched controls suggesting that SMD is associated with sympathetic overactivity. In addition, evaluation of parasympathetic markers suggests that children with SMD also have low parasympathetic activity.

Additional work on the mechanisms of SPD is being completed by two national workgroups: (1) the Sensory Processing Disorders Scientific Workgroup, a multidisciplinary group of established leaders in neuroscience and developmental psychobiology and (2) the Alpha research group, a national group of occupational therapy sensation processing researchers. Current research questions under study are noted in **Table 4**. Future studies will provide additional data about the mechanisms of SPD, the accurate identification of those with SPD and treatment of disorder.

Intervention for Individual's with SPD

The intervention for SPD is called occupational therapy with a sensory integrative approach. The goal of intervention is to improve the ability to process sensory information, providing a basis for improved independence and participation in daily life activities, play, and school tasks. The approach focuses on maximizing adaptive behavior and functional skills, and is most frequently utilized by OTs though some other professionals also have training in this intervention technique (e.g., physical therapists, speech/language therapists). Mastery of this intervention requires advanced clinical training that includes didactic coursework and mentoring as the trainee actively participates in supervised treatment.

Professionals who use the sensory integrative approach follow a set of principles, based on sensory integration theory, that guide their clinical reasoning skills. Clinical reasoning is a creative and flexible way of looking at a child's personal characteristics and context and then deciding what modifications will help the child function

Table 4 Research question and method

Research question	*Method*	*Primary researcher*
Do individuals with poor sensory modulation demonstrate metabolic differences compared to controls?	Proton magnetic spectroscopy study	Dr. Sinclair Smith Drexel and Temple Universities
Can physiologic correlates of early perceptual processing in individuals with poor sensory modulation determine subtypes of the disorder?	Auditory and somatosensory evoked potential study	Dr. Barbara Brett-Green University of CO Health Sciences Center
Does the sensory gating evoked potential (P50) discriminate children with over-responsivity from matched controls?	Auditory ERP study	Dr.Patricia Davies CO State University
Are there genetic factors that relate to the etiology of SPD?	A twin study	Dr. Hill Goldsmith University of Wisconsin at Madison
Is there a difference in dopamine D2 receptor binding availability, presynaptic dopamine synthesis and serotonin receptor availability in SPD?	A positron emission tomography (PET) study using a primate animal model	Dr. Mary Schneider University of Wisconsin at Madison
Are selective serotonin reuptake inhibitors and GABA agonists pharmacologic agents effective in affecting sensory gating?	Rat model	Dr. Edward Levin Duke University
Is low parasympathetic activity a marker of over-responsivity to sensation?	Vagal tone study	Dr. Roseann Schaaf Thomas Jefferson University
Do children with SPD show changes in cortisol levels during the Sensory Challenge Protocol?	Salivary cortisol study	Dr. Stacey Reynolds Virginia Commonwealth University
Can a reliable performance assessment be developed to characterize sensory over-responsivity?	Psychometric child and adult study	Dr. Lucy Miller and Dr. Sarah Schoen Sensory Processing Disorder Research Institute

GABA, gamma-aminobutyric acid; SPD, sensory processing disorder; ERP.

more successfully, in the moment. Rather than a rigid formula for what to do, clinical reasoning is an elastic way to think.

These principles are described in detail in several books that are designed to guide therapists through the clinical reasoning process using sensory integration theory. The primary principles of this intervention approach are described as follows: (1) the intervention is rich in sensory opportunities especially tactile, proprioceptive, and vestibular sensations; (2) activities are tailored to provide the 'just right challenge' for the child's developing skills; (3) intervention is 'child directed', for example, the therapist reads and follows the child's cues guiding him/her to seek the needed sensory activities; (4) intervention supports the child's arousal level, self regulation, and organization of behavior; and (5) the context of intervention is play; (6) the focus of intervention is on obtaining 'adaptive responses', identified by Ayres as a 'purposeful, goal-directed response to a sensory experience'. Therapy consists of fun activities that range from very simple (responds to passive stimuli or maintains organization during mulitsensory activities), to moderately challenging games (initiates and sustains an activity requiring familiar movements), to quite complex activities (initiates and executes a complex activity requiring unfamiliar complicated movements requiring exact timing and multiple adaptations). The focus on the adaptive response ensures that each activity is challenging (a little hard for the child) but also that the child succeeds (often with help or scaffolding from the therapist). These activities that meet these criteria provide the 'just right challenge', and provide the best chance of facilitating learning and development.

OT with a sensory integration approach is a unique intervention because it addresses the underlying substrates of dysfunction (e.g., neurological immaturity) rather than just difficulties with skill performance. The therapeutic environment resembles a huge playroom or gymnasium with suspended swings, pillows, mats and large balls, and the equipment taps into the child's inner drive to play. Therapy provides opportunities for engagement in sensory and motor activities rich in tactile, vestibular, and proprioceptive sensations. The therapist uses keen observation skills to detect and interpret the child's behaviors and interests, and then creates a constantly changing playful environment in which the child actively pursues achievable challenges. For example, occupational therapy using a sensory integrative approach for a child with over-responsivity to tactile and vestibular input might include an activity such as climbing up a rope ladder to access a hanging trapeze swing, swinging across the room while holding the trapeze bar, and then 'crashing' into a large ball pit (surrounded by mats and pillows for safety). During this activity, the child is enticed into play that is rich in vestibular (swinging), proprioceptive (climbing), and tactile (ball pit) input and thus through play his or her over-responsivity to sensory stimuli is modulated. The therapist focuses on the specific adaptive responses needed by each individual – evolving from tolerating the sensory demands, to adapting to the challenges by beginning to organize motor responses. Play serves as the medium to engage the child so that even though the child may be hesitant initially, the urge to play in a colorful, fun environment outweighs hesitation and encourages participation. Ayres called this 'the art of therapy' or the careful process whereby the therapist actively adapts activities to match the child's emerging skills always ensuring that the child has fun. Thus, the child is guided through challenging but fun activities designed that stimulate the sensory systems, challenge the motor system, and facilitate performance of cognitive, attentional, social, and emotional tasks. Ultimately, the child begins to process sensory information in more typical ways and this improved 'sensory integration' provides the foundation for more organized and competent play, self regulation, self esteem, learning, and participation in daily routines. In addition to direct intervention with the child, the therapist also collaborates with and educates the parents, teachers, and others who are involved with the child.

Recent developments in the field have advanced and refined the protocol for using OT with a sensory integrative approach in part because defining intervention in a manner that is replicable is required for treatment effectiveness studies. The existing literature that addresses the effectiveness of intervention is fraught with methodological problems that limit interpretation and utility including the lack of replicable intervention (e.g., a manualized approach). Recently, the collaborative multisite group of occupational therapy clinicians and researchers developed a 'Fidelity to Treatment' measure. This scale outlines the core principles and philosophy of the intervention, and also provides a mechanism to evaluate whether the intervention uses a sensory integrative approach. This tool will be useful in future studies examining the effectiveness of intervention.

Another effort to define the intervention in a replicable, valid manner is the work of Miller and colleagues who have operationalized the principles of the sensory integrative approach into an intervention protocol that guides therapist's clinical reasoning and parent education. This model, 'A SECRET', provides an organizational framework to guide treatment sessions.

A SECRET has seven elements:

A Attention
S Sensation
E Emotion regulation
C Culture
R Relationships
E Environment
T Tasks

The first three elements – attention, sensation, and emotion regulation – are the individual characteristics that influence children internally. The last four – culture, relationships, environment, and tasks – are the contextual elements that influence children externally.

Using 'A SECRET', the therapist tries out and then provides a 'toolbox' of strategies for the parent and child using the therapy 'secrets' that increase the child's performance, social participation, and self-confidence/esteem. Finally, other specific goals and priorities of the family are addressed.

Intervention by OTs and other professionals using this approach is not a quick 'fix'. It is a therapeutic program designed to improve the child's ability to neurologically process sensory information improving the quality of the child's life by enhancing his or her ability to learn and play. Treatment can take place in a number of settings: public schools, hospitals and outpatient clinics, and private practices. In all these settings, the role of intervention is to improve the child's ability to interact socially, to regulate him or herself, to maintain self-esteem, and to be independent in their daily living skills. Therapeutic methods in a school-based program compared to a direct service private therapy program are different. The child's treatment experience is significantly influenced by the setting of the therapy.

Evidence Evaluating Effectiveness of Intervention

Although controversy regarding the effectiveness of OT using a sensory integration approach exists, over 80 studies have been conducted that measure some aspect of the effectiveness of this approach to intervention. About half of the studies demonstrate some type of treatment effectiveness. Two meta-analyses and four research reports have been published summarizing the outcomes of these various studies; some of the syntheses conclude that the approach is effective and other syntheses suggest the intervention was equally effective as other approaches or not effective.

At this point in time, interpretation of the findings of these 80 studies is difficult due to three methodological limitations. The first limitation is defining the independent variable (the treatment) in a manner that is replicable. As this intervention approach is individualized (similar to the way psychotherapy is individualized), standardization of treatment has been a challenge to the researchers. With the development of the 'fidelity to treatment' measure and A SECRET, future intervention studies will be more able to adhere to a manualized treatment approach.

A second limitation is the outcome measures utilized. Previous research used outcomes not specifically related to the proposed changes from intervention. In addition, a quantity of research has been conducted on sensory stimulation rather than embedding it in the context of a full OT program as was originally intended. Ayres always used an 'occupational frame of reference' in providing intervention (e.g., the goals of therapy were functional abilities and routines, including the 'occupations' of childhood such as sleeping, eating, dressing, playing, interacting with others, learning, and active participation). Studies that do not use this frame of reference do not inform evidence-based practice related to OT using a sensory integrative approach.

Few studies establish a theoretical basis for their hypotheses, asking a global question instead, for example, 'does sensory integrative treatment work?' can be seen as a simplistic and atheoretical question. The last limitation of previous studies is that multiple outcome measures are utilized with no good explanation of how the outcomes relate to the suspected effects of treatment, for example, a 'fishing expedition' approach, hoping to find 'something' that might be statistically significant. This results in low power to detect significant changes.

The collaborative multisite occupational therapy research team that developed the 'fidelity to treatment' measure is also working on a systematic way to apply goal attainment scaling (GAS) as a primary outcome measure for effectiveness studies. GAS provides a means to establish intervention goals that are specifically relevant to individuals and their families and allowing comparison of achievement across diverse functional outcomes. GAS in combination with physiologic outcome measures is envisioned to provide a method of measuring effectiveness that will increase the integrity, strength, and replicability of effectiveness studies.

The final limitation relates to the homogeneity of the samples studied. Previous researchers have not defined a homogenous sample. The heterogeneity of samples in previous research increased the within group variability and again the probability of finding significant group differences was reduced. Now with the 'short sensory profile' and the physiologic paradigm, the 'sensory challenge protocol', highly selective inclusion criteria, can be utilized to select specific sensory processing subtypes for study samples. Building on this work, future studies can define samples in a manner that allows replication across sites.

The limitations in previous studies have resulted in a lack of consensus regarding the effectiveness of OT using an SI approach. Given the current constraints of research, diverse findings are not surprising. This inconsistency is predictable, given the variation in sample characteristics, intervention methods and duration, and outcomes measured. The knowledge base in this field is in its infancy and additional work is needed before valid conclusions about the effectiveness of this intervention approach can be derived.

Conclusion

In conclusion, significant progress has been made in defining homogenous subgroups for analysis, in describing a replicable treatment, and in choosing valid outcome measures. However, gaps exist in knowledge related to the effectiveness of occupational therapy in ameliorating SPD. Hence, a clear and exciting call to action exists. We and others are implementing a series of studies to elucidate the underlying mechanisms of the impairment, to define the phenotypic characteristics of the disorder, to discriminate the disorder from other developmental disorders (ADHD and autism), and to evaluate the effectiveness of OT in remediating the dysfunction. New research with stronger empirical standards is forthcoming. We are on the cusp of an explosion of knowledge in this area that will increase rigorous scientific data and move the field forward. Scientists and practitioners are collaborating to conduct research that leads to more specific diagnoses and more effective interventions, thereby improving the lives of children with SPD and their families.

See also: ADHD: Genetic Influences; Autism Spectrum Disorders; Developmental Disabilities: Cognitive; Fragile X Syndrome; Perceptual Development.

Suggested Readings

Ayres AJ (1972) *Sensory Integration and Learning Disorders.* Los Angeles: Western Psychological Services.
Ayres AJ (1979) *Sensory Integration and the Child.* Los Angeles: Western Psychological Corporation.
Bundy AC, Lane SJ, and Murray EA (2003) *Sensory Integration Theory and Practice.* Philadelphia: F.A. Davis.
Kranowitz C (2005) *The Out of Sync Child.* (Revised). New York: Penguin.
Miller LJ (2006) *Sensational Kids: Help and Hope for Children with Sensory Processing Disorder.* New York: Putnam.
Miller LJ, McIntosh DN, McGrath J, *et al.* (1999) Electrodermal responses to sensory stimuli in individuals with fragile X syndrome: A preliminary report. *American Journal of Medical Genetics* 83(4): 268–279.
Parham D and Mailloux Z (1995) Sensory integrative principles in intervention with children with autistic disorder. In: Case-Smith J, Allen AS, and Pratt PN (eds.) *Occupational Therapy for Children*, pp. 329–382. St. Louis, MO: Mosby.
Schaaf RC and SmithRoley S (2006) *Sensory Integration: Applying Clinical Reasoning to Diverse Populations.* Tucson, AZ: The Psychological Corporation.
Smith Roley S, Blanche E, and Schaaf RC (eds.) (2001) *Understanding the Nature of Sensory Integration with Diverse Populations.* San Antonio, TX: The Psychological Corporation.

Relevant Websites

http://www.abilitations.com – Abilitations.
http://www.aota.org – American Occupational Association.
http://www.icdl.com – Interdisciplinary Council on Developmental and Learning Disorders.
http://www.KIDFoundation.org – KID Foundation.
http://www.neurolearning.com – Neurological Concepts.
http://www.out-of-sync-child.com – Out of Sync Child.
http://www.sierf.org – Sensory Integration Education and Research Foundation.
http://www.sensory-processing-disorder.com – Sensory Processing Disorder Resource Center.
http://www.sensorycomfort.com – Sensory Products.
http://www.sensoryresources.com – Sensory Resources.
http://www.genjereb.com – Sensory Tools.
http://www.southpawenterprises.com – Southpaw.
http://www.spdnetwork.org – SPD Network.
http://www.seriweb.com – Special Education Resources on the Internet.
http://www.SIfocus.com – The international magazine dedicated to improving sensory integration.
http://www.spinkids.org – This site raises awareness of sensory processing disorder.

Separation and Stranger Anxiety

A Scher and J Harel, University of Haifa, Haifa, Israel

Glossary

Anxiety – The psychological and physiological reaction to an anticipated danger, real or imagined.
Distress – An intense negative reaction to adverse events. The reaction may be emotional and/or physical.
Person and object permanence – The understanding that people and objects continue to exist when they are not directly observed.
Separation anxiety – A distress reaction in response to separation from the primary caregiver.
Separation anxiety disorder (SAD) – Developmentally inappropriate and excessive anxiety concerning actual or anticipated separation from the caregiver, most often the parents.
Stranger anxiety – The fearful, distressed response that infants exhibit when approached by an unfamiliar person, in the second half of the first year.

Introduction

In the second half of the first year, infants show signs of distress when approached by an unfamiliar person and when their primary caregiver leaves. The study of these phenomena underscores the link between advances in the child's ability to mentally represent people and events, along with changes in the emotional tie to the caregiver. Separation anxiety is an important psychological construct within a number of emotional development theories. While the reaction is normative, some children develop a separation anxiety disorder.

Reactions to the Approach and Disappearance of People

The second half of the first year of life is a time of major cognitive and emotional discoveries and challenges. In this period, infants not only explore and manipulate the environment more actively, but they also start expressing clear social preferences and apprehensions. While infants happily exchange smiles with strangers during the first months of their life, in the second half of the first year they begin to exhibit a clear preference for specific social partners, typically their parents. Moreover, at this stage when parents leave the room, even for a short time, babies often become distressed and start crying. Another trigger for distress during this period is the approach of an unfamiliar person. Upon encountering strangers, infants of this age observe the unfamiliar face intently, turn their heads away, and sometimes cry. In the developmental literature, the emergence of these distress responses – to separation and to strangers – is considered a major developmental milestone. When describing the reaction to the approach of an unfamiliar person, researchers use the terms wariness, apprehension, distress, fear, and anxiety depending, partially, on the theoretical perspective they are using to explain the response. In psychoanalytic theory, the reactions to the disappearance of the familiar caregiver and to the approach of an unfamiliar person are conceptualized as anxiety: separation anxiety and stranger anxiety.

Stranger Anxiety

Around 6–8 months, when infants are approached by an unfamiliar person, a new response appears: the expression of wariness and distress. At this stage, infants react to encounters with unfamiliar people who try to engage them in ways they are not used to, including becoming sober and quiet, staring and frowning, lowering the gaze or turning the head away, getting a frightened expression, or even starting to cry or scream. These responses are particularly striking when they show up with family acquaintances or relatives who were greeted with smiles a month or so earlier. While there is variation in the form, intensity, and duration of the response, infants across diverse cultures show some degree of wariness toward strangers which tends to peak toward the end of the first year of life and generally decreases thereafter.

The contextual variables that affect the intensity of the stranger anxiety response include proximity and accessibility to the mother. More distress is shown when the mother is not present in the room; when the mother is holding the infant, the reaction is least intense. A sudden and abrupt approach of the stranger, as opposed to a slow warm-up period, also intensifies the distress reaction. Research on stranger characteristics is mixed, suggesting that infants react more favorably to child than adult strangers (presumably because children are perceived as more like themselves), while findings regarding stranger gender are inconclusive.

The emergence of the anxious response to strangers, which is widely acknowledged in child development textbooks and often discussed in the popular parenting media, was a topic of focused research during the 1960s and 1970s, but has received less attention in recent years. A review of the empirical studies reveals discrepancies and disagreement as to the prevalence of the behavior, the age at which it is first observed, and how it fades across time. In a number of reports, the reaction to strangers is described as emerging between 6 and 8 months or even earlier, while others conclude that the phenomenon is first evident only toward the end of the first year. There is also considerable discrepancy concerning the specific ages in which the response peaks (9–10 months according to some reports, 12–15 months according to others) and diminishes (toward the end of the first year vs. during the course of the second year). The different timetables described in these studies partially reflect differences in methodology. Still, a fairly consistent finding is that sometime in the second part of the first year infants display a noticeable new response to unfamiliar people – showing signs of distress when approached by strangers. What makes this response particularly interesting is that it underscores the important links between emotion and cognition.

Cognitive Advances Underlying the Response to Strangers

Object permanence

In the latter part of the first year infants are capable of evaluating situations and responding to them in a more complex way. Advances in sensory–motor capacities allow more regulated attention to relevant components of novel situations and more awareness of violated expectations. The examination of these evolving capacities is the hallmark of Jean Piaget's theory of cognitive development. Piaget was interested in how infants develop an understanding that objects are independent of themselves, occupy physical space, and continue to exist even when they do not see them. Piaget used the term object permanence to describe this capacity and suggested that the concept of people as permanent develops before the understanding of the permanence of objects. This is important for conceptualizing the infant's developing discrimination of the mother from the other. However, the prediction that the anxious reaction to strangers would occur only after the achievement of object permanence (typically around 12 months of age) is not supported, given that this phenomenon may appear as early as 6 months.

Research on the maturation of distance vision has indicated that it is not until 6 months of age that infants reach adult-like discrimination, allowing them to identify familiar faces from different angles and distances, and across a wide variety of situations. Nonetheless, we know that infants learn to recognize and differentiate between their parents and other people at a much earlier age; for example, it has been shown that newborns are able to identify the face, voice, and smell of their mothers already in the first weeks of life. Extensive research over the past few decades suggests that infants learn to recognize the invariant features of people and objects, as well as the concepts of appearing and disappearing and occupying different locations, earlier than Piaget claimed. Using internalized schemes and representations to bring past experience to bear on the present, young infants engage in detecting regularities and discrepancies in stimuli, and form expectations about events. Through repeated exposures during the early months, infants come to distinguish between the familiar and the unfamiliar. But why do they start expressing apprehension, avoidance, and distress when encountered by a less familiar or a strange person?

Incongruity between the familiar and the unfamiliar face

A number of investigators have argued that the reaction to unfamiliar people results from an incongruity between the stranger and the internalized schema of the familiar caregiver. Donald Hebb's cognitive theory, which links perception and behavior to the neuronal network, offers insight into infants' fearful response to strangers. Hebb argued that perceptual experiences establish memory traces in the form of neural circuits, and that these are activated when a new perceptual experience is sufficiently similar to a previous one. But when the new stimulus is not similar enough to maintain continued smooth transmission in the neural circuit, the ensuing disruption produces a distress reaction. According to this explanation, an approaching adult could seem somewhat familiar to an infant at first, but then turn out to be different from the well-established mental representation of the familiar caregiver, and this disruption stirs up emotional distress. The intensity of the reaction to novel experiences depends on the extent to which the child has developed an internal representation of the stimuli and the degree of discrepancy between the new situation and the internalized schema. According to the incongruity principle, it is the discrepancy between the novel face and the internalized standard (e.g., the caregiver) that is responsible for the distress reaction, not social interaction with the stranger *per se*. However, as noted earlier, infants can discriminate between their mothers and strangers already in the first weeks of life, but they do not show fear of strangers until 6 or 8 months of age.

Jerome Kagan, who has been studying the links between children's cognitive capacities and emotional reactivity for over 30 years, maintains that perceptual experiences and memory traces yield interest rather than fear in infants younger than 6 months; in older infants, who are better able to generate explanations about new and unexpected events, a discrepant event that they cannot explain generates emotional distress. This developmental account adds to the incongruity model in that it links the newly acquired capacity to explain the discrepancy between the familiar and the strange to distress when the explanation fails. Although this concept is plausible, it is difficult to test.

Brain maturation

During the latter part of the first year, the ability to retrieve knowledge from memory and use this information for performing tasks improves dramatically. Adele Diamond, who studied the development of memory functions and their neural basis, provided evidence that links the improvement in infants' search for hidden objects to the maturation of the prefrontal cortex, including the growing differentiation of gamma-aminobutyric acid (GABA), an inhibitory neurotransmitter known to play an important role in the regulation of anxiety and behavioral reactivity. Another critical development during this period is the integration of the limbic and endocrine systems into the memory networks. The capsula interna, which links the cerebal cortex with the amygdala, develops mature myelin around 10 months of age, allowing increased connectivity and efficient integration between the two systems. As the amygdala is also linked to the hypothalamic–pituitary–adrenal (HPA), or the stress axis, the improved connectivity between stimulation, interpretation, and emotional processing also increases the involvement of the stress axis in the processing of experiences.

Fear and Anxiety as Indicators of Emotional Advances in the First Year

The 8-month anxiety

Although distress reactions to strangers were described by the pioneers of infant observation at the turn of the nineteenth century, the first systematic study of the phenomenon was conducted by Rene Spitz. As a psychoanalyst working with infants in group care, he methodically observed and recorded behavioral patterns that marked the changing relations between infants and the social environment. The observations were documented in a film entitled *Anxiety: Its Phenomenology in the First Year of Life*, and discussed in a 1950 paper on the manifestation of anxiety in the first year. The naturalistic observations showed that between 6 and 8 months, infants no longer responded with smiles when unfamiliar visitors approached them, and instead showed apprehension and distress. While the specific behaviors of different children varied (e.g., turning the head away, covering the face, or screaming), the common denominator was an avoidant response, refusal to contact, and distress. Spitz called this pattern the 8-month anxiety and considered it the earliest manifestation of psychological anxiety.

According to Spitz, the 8-month anxiety is unique and differs from earlier expressions of fear, for instance, a fearful reaction to repeated inoculation. In reacting to a stranger, the infant is responding to a person with whom no previous unpleasurable encounters have been experienced. So why manifest wariness and anxiety? Using psychoanalytic reasoning, Spitz argued that the response to approaching strangers is triggered by the realization that, since the unfamiliar person is not the mother, mother has left. The anxiety results from an inference process involving the comparison of the stranger to an internal representation of the mother, and the fear of losing her. In attributing the 8-month anxiety to the infant's wish for the mother and the disappointment that the approaching person is not her, Spitz underscored the role of the infant's affective communication in the caregiving process, and attributed to the 8-month anxiety a major organizing role in the evolving psychological self.

Fearfulness as a marker of a new level of emotional organization

Inspired by Spitz's work, Robert Emde and colleagues conducted a longitudinal investigation of emotional development in the mid-1970s. Following a sample of 14 infants throughout their first year, at home and in the laboratory, the researchers collected an elaborate database that included naturalistic behavioral observations, interviews with mothers, structured tests, as well as EEG recordings. Emde, like Spitz, identified two organizing principles of emotional development that emerge in the course of the first year: the social smile and stranger distress.

Around 2 months of age, infants typically show the milestone of social smile, which is a marker for inquisitive, active engagement with their surroundings. At this age, infants' curiosity is on the rise as they develop and master new ways to maintain and increase interesting stimulation (e.g., shaking a rattle). Whereas Piaget viewed sensory–motor schemas of exploring and understanding the world (e.g., hand–eye coordination, mouthing) as the major organizers of experiences in the first year, Emde and colleagues emphasized the role of emotionality as a key organizer. The appearance of the social smile marks a new way of interacting with the world. Whereas crying, the key organizer in the first weeks of life, conveys an urgent need for change and a plea for alleviating discomfort, smiling signals positive engagement, an invitation for the continuation of a pleasurable exchange. Emde observed that by 2.5 months, infants smiled regularly in response to the faces of their parents, as well as the faces of unfamiliar individuals. By 4 months, the infants in the study showed more smiling and motor responsiveness in the presence of their mothers than with other people. At around 5 months, some infants curiously studied and compared their mother's face with that of strangers, and between 5 and 7 months, they stared soberly at strangers faces.

Around 8 months, the infants in Emde's study manifested a distress reaction to unfamiliar people which, according to his model, marks the second shift in emotional expression. While the average age was 8 months, considerable variation among the infants was observed; as to the duration of the response, 11 of the 14 infants manifested distress for 2 consecutive months and eight continued to show stranger distress into the third month. In their attempt to explain the roots of the fearful response to strangers, Emde and colleagues acknowledged the importance of the infant's changing relationship to the mother and the cognitive advances of the second part of the first year, but also suggested a new focus: the emergence of the capacity for fearfulness.

Evidence from numerous studies shows that around 7–9-month infants not only show distress to strangers and unfamiliar surroundings, but also start to manifest wariness of heights, mechanical toys, masks, etc. Before this age, distress was nonspecific, mostly a reaction to physical discomfort, whereas the new distress responses are linked to specific stimuli in the environment, as evidenced by the fact that infants look and evaluate before displaying distress. Cardiac measurements support the idea of a developmental shift in the capacity for fear. At 5 months of age, the approach of an unfamiliar person led to heart-rate deceleration in the infant, accompanied with a facial expression of delighted curiosity, but at 9 months, the stranger's approach was associated with cardiac acceleration, frowning, gaze aversion, and crying. Emde argues that from a social communication perspective, the fearful reaction to the approach of a stranger conveys a clear message to the mother: a preference for her company and a plea not to be left alone with unfamiliar people. This new message to the primary caregiver is linked to another major emotional milestone of infancy: separation anxiety.

Separation Anxiety

Sometime in the middle of the first year, when infants understand that people exist even when they are out of sight (person permanence), they react to the everyday recurring disappearances of their parents by attempting to maintain proximity through the behaviors available to them, including crying, cooing, and crawling. In manifesting these responses, infants not only indicate their desire to stay in proximity with the caregiver but also the development of ways to control distance and separation. During this stage, infants increasingly initiate interaction with their parents and actively protest when their primary caregiver departs, even for a moment. By the first birthday, behaviors that indicate separation distress are even more clearly detected, with infants tending to become agitated and upset upon separation.

The Normative Course of Separation Anxiety

Separation distress, signaled by crying in response to parental separation, may be observed as early as 4 or 5 months of age, but most accounts identify 8 months as the age when separation anxiety emerges. Distress from brief separations continues to characterize toddlers' behavior well into the second year of life; the normative response typically peaks around 12–18 months and then fades after 2 years of age. In diverse cultural contexts, such as the Kalahari Bushmen, the Israeli Kibbutz and Guatemala, infants display distress in response to separation from their mothers; this is considered a normative part of development and its emergence is viewed as a major milestone in the formation of the emotional tie between the child and primary caregiver. The reaction to separation from the mother appears to be a universal phenomenon; however, specific parenting practices and cultural experiences may impact the timing and the intensity of the response. For example, in cultural settings where infants experience constant physical contact with their mothers distress to separation was observed earlier than 8 months; Japanese, as compared to Western toddlers were found to express more intense reactions to separation from their mothers. The use of an inanimate companion such as a blanket or doll (also known as a transitional object) is one of the ways toddlers attempt to alleviate separation distress. While separation anxiety gradually fades for the majority of children after the second birthday, some children will continue to express extreme distress in the face of parental separation. In many cases, these children will be subsequently diagnosed as suffering from separation anxiety disorder (SAD), a psychological disorder briefly discussed in the final section of this article.

The role of cognitive and social factors

The emergence and decline of separation distress has been linked to the cognitive advances of the first and second year. As with stranger anxiety, object permanence has been suggested as one of the determinants of the response to the disappearance of the familiar caregiver. In a series of experiments on infants' early representational capacities, Chris Moore and colleagues demonstrated that while infants younger than 6 months are able to detect violation of identity of objects (characteristics of the objects), they only appear to understand the concept of permanency of objects at 9 months. However, Piaget suggested that understanding person permanence comes earlier, and Mary Ainsworth's observation of infants and mothers in Uganda revealed that around 4–6 months, when mothers left the infants and went out of sight, some of the infants appeared distressed and cried. Silvia Bell, who compared object vs. person permanency, confirmed that indeed the concept of persons as permanent objects appears before infants understand the permanency of inanimate objects.

The understanding that the parent continues to exist when out of sight, together with advances in motor control, are believed to shape the process of active searching for the caregiver (e.g., crawling). In the same vein, advances in cause–effect reasoning shape infants' responses; they begin to grasp that calling or crying increases the likelihood of the parent's reappearance. The establishment of an integrated and enduring representation of the caregiver plays a critical role in the formation of the emotional tie between the child and parent, but it is less clear why infants at this stage show distress when separated from their primary caregivers.

Drawing on the concept of discrepant event, discussed earlier with respect to stranger anxiety, Kagan maintained that the infant is likely to display separation anxiety when the sight of the mother leaving is a discrepant event which the child is unable to prevent and/or integrate with previous experiences. It was found that infants showed less distress in a home setting when the mother departed through a door she used frequently, compared to when she exited through a door she rarely used. The decline of separation distress in the latter part of the second year is believed to be associated with the toddler's increased cognitive capacity to understand the circumstances of the separation and maintain the expectation that the parent will return. For example, when the mother left the room through a door rarely used, it was found that some of the toddlers approached the door and engaged, on and off, in play with toys, but did not cry.

In the second half of the first year, as infants gain better control of posture and movement and become more active explorers of their environment, they appear to pay extra attention to the location of other people, both caregivers and strangers. Infants at this stage frequently monitor their relative proximity to the caregiver; while venturing away from their mothers, they tend to frequently look toward their mother's face. Social referencing, an active search for others' emotional expression as a source of information to help clarify uncertain events, begins around 8–9 months. At this age, infants can understand that facial expressions have emotional meanings and they make use of others' emotional expressions to guide their own behavior with reference to specific situations and events. By monitoring their parents' facial expression, infants obtain information as to the danger or safety of their planned actions. When infants encounter a potentially dangerous setting, such as a visual cliff (a glass-covered table with an illusionary deep drop), they make use of parents' facial information to regulate their actions; when mothers smile, infants typically cross the deep part whereas when mothers show fear, infants avoid crossing.

The Developmental Significance of Separation

In psychoanalytic theorizing, separation anxiety ininfancy is viewed as a consequence of, on the one hand, the capacity to mentally represent the mother, and on the other hand, the interpretation of her absence as 'losing' her. In other words, the cognitive ability to keep the mother in mind even in her absence not only triggers feelings of longing, but also stirs up the distress of separation. To understand the anxiety produced by separation, it is essential to conceptualize the significance of the absence and its implications from the perspective of the infant. When separated from the primary caregiver, infants lose a significant regulator of their needs, not only physical but, just as crucially, emotional.

Consequences of Separation in Animals

Significant insights into the formation of the emotional bond between infant and mother, and the detrimental consequences of maternal separation, come from studies of animal behavior, specifically the work of Harry Harlow and Stephen Suomi with monkeys, and Myron Hofer's studies with rats. For example, rat pups emit initial separation calls and their heart rate falls significantly after separation, regardless of supplemental heat. By studying a number of systems, such as those controlling sleep and arousal, activity level, and sucking, Hofer and colleagues identified changes in the activation of these systems that resulted from maternal separation and concluded that through ongoing interactions, mothers regulate their offspring, and that the loss of the maternal regulators has serious consequences, including a decrease in growth hormone secretion. In demonstrating the regulatory function of mother–infant proximity, animal models have significantly advanced our understanding of the neurobiological nature of separation distress, and provided important clues as to how proximity-maintenance shapes the well-being of mammals, including humans.

Physiological and Behavioral Correlates of Emotional Distress

Studying emotional distress among infants and young children presents many challenges of measurement and interpretation. Since fear and distress involve complex neural interactions and coordinated activities of psychobehavioral, physiological, and hormonal systems, measurement can take place at different levels. Facial expressions provide one avenue. Charles Darwin underscored the innateness, universality, and survival value of children's fear and distress responses when he documented, in a series of photographs, facial expressions displayed by different youngsters in circumstances of pain, hunger, and discomfort. Since then, a number of researchers have devised detailed measurement systems for coding facial expressions that index specific emotions (e.g., Izard's MAX coding system and Baby FACS, which is based on Ekman's Facial Action Coding System). In the MAX, for example, criteria of distress/pain expression include closed eyes and a squared and angular mouth, whereas in the fear expression, eyelids are lifted and the mouth corners are retracted straight back. Vocal response is another way to study the expression of distress, but there is still a debate whether infants cry distinctively when they are physically as opposed to emotionally distressed.

Measuring cortisol, a blood-borne hormone that increases under stress, has significantly advanced our understanding of children's responses to daily normative challenges, as well as the long-term effects of poorly regulated stress levels. For more than two decades, Megan Gunnar has been studying children's stress by measuring cortisol; she showed that the quality of the mother–child tie regulates levels of cortisol secretion. Children who experience secure relationships with their mothers show stable cortisol levels even when emotionally upset, whereas in insecure mother–child relationships, even minor challenges raise cortisol levels.

The way different children react to stress-producing stimuli has been studied within the conceptual framework of temperament. Kagan, who longitudinally studied children with different reactivity levels to unfamiliar stimuli, found that inhibited infants were more fearful as toddlers and were more likely to manifest symptoms of anxiety at school-age compared to uninhibited infants. Together with other studies, these findings point to a relative stability across time in children's reactivity. Temperamental disposition is one source of individual variability in the ways children cope with fearful events. Mothers' behavior is another determinant. For example, recent findings from Nathan Fox's laboratory show that infants who received insensitive caregiving display higher levels of right frontal electroencephalogram (EEG) asymmetry and fearfulness to unfamiliar stimuli compared to infants whose mothers were more responsive and sensitive in their daily caregiving behavior. The ways in which temperament, social learning, and caregiving variables jointly modulate stranger and separation anxiety during infancy have yet to be comprehensively investigated. The focus of the subsequent section is separation anxiety from the standpoint of the psychoanalytic and the attachment perspectives.

The Mother–Child Dyad and Separation Anxiety

Freud's description of his nephew playing with a reel of string is the first account in psychological literature describing a toddler coping with separation and anxiety. The child, in his crib, was throwing the reel and pulling it back again. Freud maintained that for the playing child, the reel represented his mother, who had to leave him several times. The play sequence helped the child gain control over his mother's disappearance and return, which in real life was an experience he endured passively, anxiously, and as beyond his control. Since then, many theoreticians have tried to describe children's reactions to separation and differentiate between the normative and disturbed variations.

The concept of separation is central to two influential theories of emotional development: John Bowlby's Attachment theory, and Margaret Mahler's Separation–Individuation theory. Both of these theories had a major impact on the way we understand separation reactions and separation anxiety today. Both these theories emphasize the relationship between the child and the parent (especially the mother) as the regulating factor of separation reactions, both normative and pathological.

Attachment as a window on separation anxiety

John Bowlby, the founder of attachment theory, was among the first to emphasize the human infant's biological disposition to participate in relationships, and proposed that the formation of the mother–child tie is controlled by mechanisms that evolved as a result of evolutionary adaptedness. This tie – the attachment relationship – is shaped through interactions in which proximity to the caregiver plays a significant role. In his book, *Separation: Anxiety and Anger*, Bowlby discusses the situations that trigger fear in children and lists four main categories: noise, strange people/objects/places, animals, and darkness. He also notes that being alone significantly increases the likelihood that fear will be aroused by these stimuli. In studies of infants' fear of strangers, the presence of the mother served as a moderator of the intensity of the distress: in the absence of the caregiver, infants were more fearful. It was found that the proximity to the mother was particularly significant around 12 months of age; Bowlby explains that as their emotional tie to mother becomes better consolidated, their knowledge of objects and situations becomes more sophisticated, and their ability to move in space becomes more skillful, infants are better able to coordinate moving away from a fearful situation toward the comforting proximity of the attachment figure, usually mother.

From an evolutionary perspective, proximity to the parent allows protection and thus provides a survival advantage; a predisposition to seek the protection of caregiver is particularly advantageous in times of danger and distress. According to Bowlby, attachment behavior – responses that aim to keep the caregiver in proximity to the baby – evoke caregiving behavior that promotes infants' sense of security. Attachment is a primary survival system, akin to other instinctual systems like feeding and sexual behavior, and is irreducible to other drives. Infants are born with the motivation and capacity to form emotional ties with their caregivers, and to use them as a source of comfort in times of danger and stress. During the first 6 months of life, the infant learns to prefer the primary caregiver as a source of comfort and security, thus creating an attachment bond. The attachment system is activated by external danger conditions (for instance, darkness, loud noise, sudden movements) and by internal conditions (such as illness, fatigue, pain). When the system is activated, the child seeks proximity to the caregiver to attain a sense of security. The caregiver can alleviate the child's distress by different means, depending on various factors including the child's age and the level of anxiety aroused. With young children, physical contact is the most effective response; with older children, more distal means like talking are also effective. When the danger is serious, even older children (and adults) may need physical contact to relieve the distress and anxiety.

Attachment theory explains why situations of separation or threats of separation arouse anxiety in people of all ages, but since children are more dependent on the protection provided by the caregiver, they suffer more intense separation anxiety. Bowlby and his coworkers described the sequence of typical reactions when young children are separated from parents. Children first protest, then show despair, and if the caregiver does not return, they subsequently show detachment. When the child perceives a threat of separation, she/he protests by crying, clinging, expressing anger, and looking for the parent; the protest is often expressed around sleep, at bedtime, and in the course of the night. When in despair, babies looks sad, move slowly and sometimes cry persistently, withdraw, and even act hostile. In the detachment phase, the child seems to return to normal behavior and is willing to accept comfort from unfamiliar adults. The problematic behavior shows up upon the parent's return: the child ignores the parent, or avoids and walks away. These behaviors might alternate with crying and extreme clinging, showing the child's suffering and anxiety regarding a possible future separation from the parent.

A key principle in attachment theory is the interrelation between the attachment, fear, and exploration systems. For example, the activation of the fear system generally heightens the activation of the attachment system and deactivates the exploration system. Bowlby maintained that the biological function of the fear system, like the attachment system, is protection. Because the two systems are inter-related, frightened infants increase their attachment behavior and seek protection; the fear not only triggers a desire to escape from the frightening stimulus but also a search for the anticipated security provided by the attachment figure. Separation anxiety occurs when attachment behavior is activated by the absence of the attachment figure, but cannot be terminated because the caregiver is not available to provide security. With the cognitive advances of the latter part of the first year, infants become capable of expectant anxiety in situations that seem likely to be threatening or in which the attachment figure is likely to become unavailable. As discussed, the presence or absence of the mother was found to attenuate or enhance the fear of strangers – in attachment terms, the proximity and trust in the availability of the attachment figure makes the infant less fearful. As the attachment and exploratory systems are linked, a child who is anxious about separation or does not have a secure relationship with the caregiver is expected to be inhibited in exploration and learning.

Separation anxiety in secure and insecure children

Attachment research identified different patterns of relationships between the infant and the attachment figure. Empirical studies, particularly those that use Ainsworth's Strange Situation procedure, differentiated between secure and insecurely attached infants. Secure children represent their relationship with mother as providing a sense of security, while insecure children encounter difficulties in attaining a sense of security, developing unique strategies to counteract this. Avoidant children tend to minimize their signals of needing mother, while anxious ambivalent children tend to exaggerate them; they have learned which strategies are most effective in eliciting caregiving from their mothers. The different attachment patterns are schematically represented in the child's mind as internal working models, guiding the child's behavior in relationships and specifically in stressful and emotionally charged situations. For secure children, the represented relationship with the attachment figure potentially provides security and alleviates anxiety, even in the absence of mother. Children with secure attachments are better equipped to cope with situations evoking negative emotions, including separation anxiety, than children with insecure attachments. For example, in Bell's study of person and object permanence, it was found that infants with secure attachment more actively searched for their mothers.

The separation–individuation process

Margaret Mahler was the first psychoanalyst to observe nonpatient mothers and infants as a source of information about emotional development, making her an innovator at a time when the accepted investigation method in psychoanalysis was the reconstruction of infancy from adult patients' narratives. In Mahler's opinion, the human infant's physical birth does not coincide with his or her psychological birth. The psychological birth involves a separation–individuation process, which is based upon the child's maturation and dependent not only on the child, but on the mother and eventually the father too. The process has two components which usually develop at the same pace: separation, the attainment of an experience of separateness from mother as opposed to nondifferentiation from mother (a different body), and individuation, the attainment of a sense of having specific, individual characteristics (being somebody).

Mahler describes several stages in the infant's journey from a state of nondifferentiation between infant and mother to a state of differentiated representations of self and mother, as well as in the attainment of differentiation between inner and outer worlds. Grasping these differentiations is an important step in the child's ability to function independently from mother without experiencing too much separation anxiety. The child who successfully goes through the separation–individuation process is one who can separate from the actual mother since he/she has an internally represented mother who is available to comfort the child when distressed, frustrated, and anxious.

The first two stages, labeled by Mahler as the 'normal autistic' and the 'symbiotic', span the first half-year of life. The infant's emergence from what Mahler referred to as 'symbiosis' marks the beginning of the separation–individuation process proper; the infant is 'hatching' from the mother–infant unit and turning his or her attention toward the world out there. In the differentiation phase, the infant, still in his mother's arms, starts exploring mother, pushing his body away from her and looking at her from a distance, pulling her hair, and fingering her face. The infant is comparing the mother who is known to the unfamiliar elements in the environment. The peek-a-boo game, much enjoyed at this age, is an exercise in separation, a way of facing this basic fear in a controlled, pleasurable atmosphere.

When the child is able to move away from mother (e.g., by crawling), the 'practicing' phase begins, peaking with the attainment of walking. With the achievement of this milestone, children are able to move further away from mother, and new cognitive abilities enable them to further explore the world outside them and enjoy new experiences. The child is at the height of feelings of omnipotence, in love with the world and with his or her own skills. Still, periodically the child will return to mother for emotional support when he momentarily becomes aware of being alone and anxious.

During the second half of the second year the toddler enters the phase of 'rapprochement' (approaching again) which lasts to about 2 years of age, considered one of the most sensitive, difficult periods of the separation–individuation process. During this phase, the toddler experiences the need to explore and function without mother, but at the same time, the need for mother is rediscovered because the growing awareness of separateness is anxiety-arousing. Reapproaching the mother is, on the one hand, a source of comfort to the infant, but it also triggers fear of regressing to earlier states of less differentiation and loss of independence and identity. Mothers find it difficult to adjust their behavior to the changing moods of the child who is clinging one moment and pushing her away the next. Mahler contends that both mother and toddler experience the loss of earlier ways of being with each other during this phase. The toddler experiences anger and sadness, and expresses these feelings by separation protest and temper tantrums. As the child explores separation from the mother, the father becomes a valuable alternative, a less conflicted caregiver figure for the child.

One of the main achievements of the rapprochement phase is the mastery of separation anxiety. Toddlers who have successfully resolved the conflicts of rapprochement enter the next phase, beginning around the third year of life: consolidation of identity and the beginnings of integrated self and other representations. The integration of the maternal representation, including positive and negative aspects of mother, establishes in the child's mind an 'internal mother' who is always with him/her and available to comfort the child when separated from his or her parents, or feeling anxious or distressed.

Although Mahler's theory, and mainly her first two subphases came under severe criticism, it is a rich source of insights and understanding of normative separation anxiety, as well as the more pathological separation reactions. Toddlers at risk for developing problems, including different degrees and forms of intense separation anxiety, are those with developmental limitations (e.g., regulatory disorders), those whose mothers have failed to respond sensitively to the child's needs during the separation–individuation process, and those experiencing an inordinate number of separations.

Separation anxiety as a marker of emotional development

Both Bowlby and Mahler underscored separation-related experiences and theorized about their developmental significance. Bowlby focused more on the observable aspects of the behavior, whereas Mahler emphasized the implicit, subjective experiences of the child. Both theories provide a detailed description of the child's development from a state of needing the actual, physical presence of the parent and experiencing distress and anxiety when separated from the parent, to a stage when the parent and the relationship with the parent are represented in the child's mind, consequently lessening the need for the parent's actual presence. In both theories, the representation of the caregiver takes the role of the comforting parent when anxiety is aroused. The qualities of the representation, and thus its effectiveness in reducing anxiety, are dependent on the child's experiences with the parent. Children who have had more positive experiences, whose parents are more attuned to their needs, are expected to form more positive representations of themselves, their caregivers, and their relationship. Whereas Bowlby gives more room to the real, objective aspects of the relationship, and assumes a closer correspondence between the real relationship and the child's representation of it, Mahler adds the child's subjective experience of the relationship, and the child's own drives and fantasies, as an additional formative factor of the representation. In both theories, the separation and reunion of the child and the caregiver, as well as the anxiety induced by the separation and its regulation, serve as key theoretical constructs for explaining child development in general, and emotional development in particular.

Maternal separation anxiety

The way in which mother and child negotiate separations has been a topic of continued developmental research. While separation anxiety has been typically addressed from the perspective of the child, mothers also experience distress when separation occurs. Bowlby postulated that caregiving is governed by a behavioral system which is reciprocal to attachment and is biologically predisposed to protect the child. The system is activated by the child's distress, for example, when separated from the parent, or by the caregiver's perception of danger to the child (e.g., at night); when the caregiving system is strongly activated, the parent seeks proximity to the child in order to insure protection. In situations of danger, real or imagined, when separated from the child, and the provision of care and safety cannot be maintained mothers experience anxiety.

Maternal separation anxiety has been studied by Ellen Hock, who defined it as an unpleasant emotional state that reflects concern and apprehension about leaving the infant. Maternal separation anxiety involves feelings of guilt, worry, and sadness that accompany short-term separation from the child. As mothers' separation concerns are likely to shape their tolerance of staying apart and their behavior upon return, it has implications for child behavior and development. For example, it has been found that high levels of maternal separation anxiety was linked to infants' sleep difficulties as well as to SAD in older children.

Separation Anxiety Disorder in Young Children

While SAD occurs most frequently after age 5 years (and is thus outside the age group addressed in this article), it is nevertheless important to include a brief description of the characteristics and correlates of the disorder as in some cases children as young as 2 years old are diagnosed. SAD is one of the most common disorders in childhood; prevalence estimates for SAD in community samples range from 3% to 13%. Though it is common and causes much distress to child and family, in most cases it is not severe and does not predict future emotional disorders. The clinical presentation of SAD includes a variety of signs of anxiety; it is not easy to differentiate between severe normal separation anxiety and the pathological variety, or among the different types of anxiety disorders (panic disorder and general anxiety disorder).

Differentiating Separation Anxiety Disorder from Normal Separation Reactions

SAD is suspected when the child expresses excessive anxiety upon actual or anticipated separation from the caregivers, most often the parents. Age is one criterion in diagnosing pathological separation anxiety. Although children older than 3 years are not supposed to show separation anxiety under regular circumstances, when ill, fatigued, or in a strange environment, they might exhibit signs of anxiety even at later ages. In diagnosing SAD, clinicians need to observe whether the child regresses to behaviors that were present at earlier ages; for example, children who stopped wetting the bed might begin bedwetting again as part of a SAD. An additional criterion in diagnosing SAD is the severity of the anxiety reaction. Children often cling, protest, and cry when separated from their parents and/or appear sad and distressed when their caregiver is away. However, children who throw up, cry for hours, and cannot be soothed, exhibit severe nightwaking and bedtime settling problems, and/or suffer from persistent depressive mood might be suffering from SAD. Another criterion often used in diagnosis is the pervasiveness of the reaction. Children who react anxiously or show physical distress in every situation unless they are in close proximity to their parents could be suffering from SAD. Some children express fears that something terrible might happen to them or to their parents, are afraid of being alone, refuse to go to sleep, or express a fear of monsters. Others complain of more diffuse feelings that are disturbing them and have difficulty describing why they are troubled. Children suffering from SAD try to coerce their parents not to separate and may react to separations with anger and aggression. Since some young children suffering from SAD are unable to verbalize their feelings and distress, it is important to look out for physical and somatic symptoms that may be signs of emotional distress. To assess separation anxiety in infants and very young children, the DC: 0–3R (Diagnostic Classification of Mental Health and Developmental Disorders of Infancy and Early Childhood) may be used. Although the DC: 0–3R is intended to diagnose children in the first 3 years of life, it is maintained that SAD is difficult to diagnose at this early age (for reasons we have delineated before).

Clinical and Etiological Consideration

While there is some evidence that secure attachment serves as a protective factor against psychopathology, the link between insecure attachment and anxiety disorders proved difficult to establish. Nevertheless, in the clinical literature on SAD, the child's and parent's failure to develop a secure realtionship is considered a key factor. It is assumed that this failure might arise for different reasons, including the child's temperament or parental mental problems that lead to compromised parent–child relationship. Normal anxiety reactions might become chronic or exaggerated by specific life events or circumstances. Children experiencing prolonged separations, death of a parent, traumatic events like war, as well as children living with anxious, overprotective, or neglectful parents are more vulnerable to SAD. In young children, even experiences such as vacations or illness might cause difficulties with separation. Bowlby stressed that separation anxiety might be heightened in children who are chronically exposed to actual separations or threats of separation, making them more vulnerable to normally occurring separation events. Clearly, not all children experiencing the above conditions and circumstances develop SAD. So far, risk factors rather than causes of the disorder have been identified. Although the causes of SAD are still unknown, parents who consult with professionals are often told that their own anxiety about separation negatively influences the child's ability to cope with separation. Informed by both the psychoanalytic and the developmental approach, many clinicians view sensitive parental responsiveness to the child's needs and attachment security as protective factors against SAD.

Finally, with respect to intervention and prognosis, clinicians maintain that children who are effectively and timely treated for SAD develop into mentally healthy individuals. When untreated, children with SAD may be at risk for depression and other anxiety disorders. In young children, sleeping and eating problems can be related to SAD; if not treated properly, more complicated problems in these areas might develop. Given the multiple contributing factors, difficulty in diagnosis, and different intervention approaches, there is a need for more research in the field, including longitudinal investigations of the antecedents and consequences of SAD, as well as intervention studies.

See also: Attachment; Emotion Regulation; Fear and Wariness; Independence/Dependence; Mental Health, Infant; Self-Regulatory Processes; Social and Emotional Development Theories; Social Interaction; Temperament.

Suggested Readings

Cassidy J (1999) The nature of the child's ties. In: Cassidy J and Shever PR (eds.) *Handbook of Attachment: Theory, Research and Clinical Applications.* New York: Guilford Press.
Eisen AR and Schaefer CE (2005) *Separation Anxiety in Children and Adolescents: An Individualized Approach to Assessment and Treatment.* New York: Guilford Press.
Emde RN, Gaensbauer TJ, and Harmon RJ (1976) *Emotional Expression in Infancy: A Biobehavioral Study.* New York: International University Press.
Fonagy P and Target M (2003) *Psychoanalytic Theories: Perspectives from Developmental Psychopathology.* London and Philadelphia: Whurr Publishers.
Spitz RA (1965) *The First Year of Life: A Psychoanalytic Study of Normal and Deviant Development of Object Relations.* New York: International Universities Press.
Witherington DC, Campos JJ, and Hertenstein MJ (2001) Principles of emotion and its development. In: Bremner G and Fogel A (eds.) *Blackwell Handbook of Infant Development*, pp. 427–464. Oxford: Blackwell.

Shyness

J B Asendorpf, Humboldt-Universität zu Berlin, Berlin, Germany

Glossary

Behavioral inhibition to the unfamiliar – Tendency to react with wary, inhibited, and sometimes fearful behavior to novel situations and strangers.
Modesty – Tendency to act in a reserved, modest, unassuming way in the presence of others.
Shyness – Tendency in social situations to show inhibited or modest behavior.
Social anxiety – Tendency to react with anxiety to others because of anticipated neglect or rejection.
Social isolation – Being alone because of social neglect or rejection.
Social withdrawal – Being alone because of shyness, social isolation, or unsociability.
Unsociability – Preference to be alone rather than with others.
Wariness to strangers – Wary, inhibited, in older children sometimes also coy behavior to strangers.

Introduction

Shyness is a term deeply rooted in everyday language that, when applied to infants and young children, refers to various forms of modest, reserved, wary, inhibited, anxious, or withdrawn behaviors in social situations, and to a temperamental personality trait. After discussing different facets of shyness (wariness to strangers, behavioral inhibition, social anxiety, and modesty) and distinguishing shyness from related constructs such as social withdrawal, social isolation, and unsociability, a simple developmental model for the development of trait shyness from infancy into early and middle childhood is provided. Finally, the evidence for the long-term outcome of early shyness in adulthood is reviewed.

Shyness: Social Behavior, Affective State, Temperamental Trait

In everyday discourse, 'shy' is used for describing (1) the subjective experience of uneasiness and discomfort in social situations ("I feel shy"); (2) observable modest, reserved, wary, inhibited, mildly anxious, or withdrawn behavior in social situations ("she reacts shy"); and (3) a recurrent tendency to experience shyness or to react with shyness frequently and intensely ("he is a shy person"). In developmental psychology, shyness in infants and young children refers to (1) an affective state in social situations, characterized by shy behavior and underlying physiological reactions, that may vary from bold disinhibition to a totally inhibiting phobic reaction, or (2) a temperamental personality trait that may vary from boldness to social phobia.

Around 8 months of age, nearly every infant starts reacting shy to adult strangers once in a while, and later most children react shy from time to time in particular situations. Both extreme shyness and the complete absence of shyness indicate problems with social–emotional adaptation. Interindividual differences in shyness to strangers do not show sufficient temporal stability over the first 18 months to be considered a personality trait; only later, they begin to show substantial stability, and this stability increases over childhood. Therefore, shyness can be considered a personality trait not before the second half of the second year. Because this trait refers to an affective state, it is part of children's temperament.

Facets of Shyness and Related Constructs

In this section, four facets of shyness and three psychological constructs that are related to shyness, but not identical with it (see also the glossary for brief definitions), are discussed. These different constructs are used in different research traditions, and the similarities and differences between the constructs are far from clear. Therefore, a careful discussion is in order to avoid confusion of similar but nonidentical constructs.

Wariness to Strangers

When infants and young children are exposed to unfamiliar people, they often react with a specific form of shyness that is called 'wariness to strangers'. Five stages of intensity are commonly distinguished: wary brow (a subtle movement of the eyebrow), wary averted gaze (wary brow plus gaze aversion), avoidance (body movement away from the stranger), cry face (distressed, fearful face without crying), and crying. Wariness to strangers is one of the earliest observable fearful reactions in infants (fear reactions to the visual cliff emerge even earlier). Wariness to strangers can be observed as early as 6 months of age although most infants begin to show this reaction around the age of 8 months.

Wariness to strangers is a normal reaction that peaks in intensity around 12 months of age, and generally lasts into the child's second year. Just as separation anxiety, it is an observable indication that infants are cognitively able to differentiate between familiar and unfamiliar people. Rather than indicating emotional difficulties, the emergence of wariness to strangers and separation anxiety in the second half of the first year is a milestone of mental development.

The setting and way in which the stranger approaches the child can influence how the child may respond. If the stranger approaches slowly when the caregiver is nearby, smiling and speaking softly, offering a toy, the infant will sometimes show interest rather than distress. Experimental variation of stranger characteristics has shown that stronger, more fearful responses are evoked by strangers who approach faster, are taller, and have lower voices. In an intriguing study, infants were exposed either to an unfamiliar adult, an unfamiliar peer, or an unfamiliar midget (small adult). Although the midget was the most unfamiliar type of person, infants responded strongest to the adult, with intermediate intensity to the midget, and with least intensity to the peer. Thus, it is not the discrepancy between a general mental image of human interaction partners and the stranger that evokes wariness of strangers, as assumed by the so-called discrepancy hypothesis, it is the unfamiliarity of the stranger paired with cues that signal danger (fast approach, body size, low voice).

The predominantly negative reactions to strangers in the first and second year of life are later followed by emotionally ambivalent responses that consist of both negative and positive components, particularly a coy smile. A coy smile is a smile during a wary averted gaze, signaling both approach and avoidance motivation. Ambivalent responses to strangers peak around the age of 3 years, and then decrease in intensity.

Detailed analyses of the videotaped behavior of the caretakers that accompany infants and children during encounters with strangers have shown that most caretakers also react with mild forms of wariness, particularly a wary brow, a coy smile, or a brief wary averted gaze. These studies support a 'social referencing' hypothesis according to which the caretaker's reaction is an important cue even for 8-month-olds on how to react to the stranger: The stronger the caretaker responds with wariness, the stronger the infant responds.

The intensity of wariness to strangers varies greatly among agemates. One source of inter-individual differences is the different developmental onset of the wary reaction. For example, some 8-month-olds will not show any wary behavior simply because they are not yet cognitively able to differentiate between familiar and unfamiliar people, and some 15-month-olds may react only slightly more because their wariness peaked already at 12 months, whereas some of their agemates just reached the peak of their responsivity.

If this source of interindividual differences is controlled in longitudinal studies that compare infants at their individual peak of responsivity, substantial inter-individual differences remain that are often considered as an early form of trait shyness or trait fearfulness. However, both the cross-situational consistency and the temporal stability of these inter-individual differences are so low that such a trait interpretation is not valid.

Shy behavior reaches sufficient consistency across different unfamiliar people and sufficient temporal stability, not before the end of the second year of life. At this age, it begins to show consistency not only between adult and peer strangers but also between unfamiliar social and nonsocial situations. For example, a 2-year-old who reacts with strong wariness to a stranger is expected to explore unfamiliar rooms rather slowly, even if no stranger is present. At this age, a first form of trait shyness can be observed which is called behavioral inhibition to the unfamiliar.

Behavioral Inhibition

'Behavioral inhibition to the unfamiliar' is a term introduced by Kagan and associates in 1984 that refers to a temperamental trait of young children. According to both parental reports and behavioral observations in the laboratory, approximately 15% of toddlers react with marked inhibition to novel situations or unfamiliar adults and peers. They cease their play behavior and withdraw to the proximity of their caregivers, remaining vigilant of the situation and rarely approaching novel objects or unfamiliar people.

Behavioral inhibition has been initially studied by comparing extreme groups of young children characterized by very high or very low inhibition. Later research in North America, Europe, and China has shown that interindividual differences in behavioral inhibition are gradually, continuously distributed and show moderate stability over childhood.

Building on neuroscience models of fear, Kagan suggested that high behavioral inhibition in infancy is due to an overactive amygdala, resulting in an enhanced fear response to unfamiliar situations. This hypothesis relates to early forms of behavioral inhibition that are mainly based on initial affective response tendencies. One prediction is that inhibited children should show higher heart rate and heart rate acceleration in response to novel stimuli, another prediction is that inhibited children should show higher salivary cortisol levels. Both predictions have only found mixed support, however.

Concerning precursors of interindividual differences in behavioral inhibition, behavioral inhibition after age 2 years shows only weak correlations with the intensity of wariness to strangers during the first 18 months of life. It seems that the many and profound changes in toddlers' cognitive ability during the second year affect also interindividual differences in reactions to novelty. It is assumed that the ability to understand social norms and rules and the ability to self-regulate one's affective responses according to such rules that both begin to emerge during the second year are important sources of interindividual differences that overlay the earlier developing interindividual differences in wariness to novelty.

Indeed, research on the development of self-regulation in infants and young children has described a gradual transfer of control over affective responses at both the behavioral and the neural level. Whereas infants' responses are initially governed only by affective response tendencies generated predominantly by the limbic system, with age and cortical development, cognitive control capacities such as response inhibition and attentional control increase, allowing for a greater cortical control over the initial response tendencies.

Concerning the later development of behavioral inhibition over childhood, children show an increasing repertoire of behaviors in response to novel situations and strangers, and despite a moderate stability of interindividual differences over shorter time periods, there is much evidence for long-term differential change in behavioral inhibition. Behavioral inhibition is by no means a fixed temperamental trait. The main reason seems to be, again, children's increasing ability to self-regulate their attention and initial affective responses.

For behaviorally inhibited children, the shifting of attention to a different aspect of a situation, or distracting oneself, can be an effective means of regulating their emotional distress in novel situations. Another means of coping with novelty that is more difficult to study in young children is the cognitive re-assessment of the situation as less dangerous or arousing. Indeed, there is increasing evidence that the emerging interindividual difference in self-regulation over childhood moderates the stability of the early temperament-based affective reactions to novel situations.

Research by Eisenberg and colleagues took up the hypothesis originally put forward by Rothbart and Bates that the development of 'effortful self-regulation' leads to important changes in children's temperament-based reactions. Effortful control is commonly defined as the efficiency of executive attention, including the ability to inhibit a dominant response and/or to activate a subdominant response, to plan ahead, and to detect errors. It involves abilities to focus or shift attention as needed, and to activate or inhibit behavior as needed. Eisenberg and colleagues distinguished effortful control from reactive control that is less under voluntary control, such as behavioral inhibition as an immediate reaction to unfamiliarity. They found some evidence that effortful control fosters the skills needed to get along with others and to engage in socially constructive behavior. Although effortful control seems to be most effective for preventing problems due to reactive undercontrol (high impulsivity), there is also some evidence that the ability for effortful control also helps children disposed to reactive overcontrol (high behavioral inhibition) in self-regulating their initially inhibited response to strangers.

Indirect evidence is also provided by a longitudinal study by Asendorpf who found that social competence as judged by preschool teachers and general intelligence as assessed by standard intelligence quotient (IQ) tests both moderated the long-term outcome of preschool inhibition: more competent and more intelligent children were better able to overcome inhibition in both laboratory and school settings. There is much evidence that more socially competent and more intelligent children are better able to self-regulate their reactivity, and therefore Asendorpf's finding may be interpreted in terms of the enhanced self-regulation ability of the more competent children.

Other studies have focused on interactions between behavioral inhibition and attachment to parents. There is some evidence that infants' early temperamental characteristics influence the development of both behavioral inhibition and anxious-ambivalent attachment. For example, in a 2-year longitudinal study by Fox and colleagues, observed distress to the withdrawal of a pacifier at 2 days of age was related to insecure attachment at 14 months, and reactivity to novelty at 5 months was related to inhibition at 14 months.

Furthermore, anxious-ambivalent attachment to parents may impede the self-regulation of behavioral inhibition. For example, in the above longitudinal study, anxious-ambivalent attachment at 14 months was related to behavioral inhibition at 24 months. In addition, a temperament by attachment interaction was found. Infants who were classified as anxious-ambivalent with their mother at 14 months and who had not cried to an arm restraint procedure at 5 months were the most inhibited at 24 months.

The few studies of attachment–temperament interactions over the first years of life suggest neither a main effects model for temperament (later inhibition is due to early temperament independent of attachment) nor a main effects model for attachment (later inhibition is due to early attachment independent of temperament). Instead, these studies suggest a transactional model such that early differences between infants in temperament, together with differences between parents in the sensitivity to their child's needs, give rise to insecure attachment to the parents which, in turn, interacts with infants' increasing self-regulation ability in unfamiliar situations.

More recently, behavioral inhibition has found increasing attention by clinical child psychologists because a few studies have shown that strong behavioral inhibition in early childhood is a risk factor for diagnosed anxiety disorders later in childhood and in early adolescence, particularly social anxiety disorders. Therefore, intervention programs have been developed that aim at reducing this risk. For example, Rapee and colleagues developed a short-term educational program designed to help parents of preschool-aged children with withdrawn/inhibited behaviors to better understand their child's problem and to better support the child in overcoming inhibition and anxiety. The children were randomly allocated to the education condition, or to no intervention. The children whose parents participated in the educational program showed significantly lower anxiety 1 year after the end of the intervention, as compared to the children in the control condition. However, no effects of the program were observed on measures of inhibition/withdrawal. This pattern of results suggests that the intervention affected children's subjective experience of anxiety but not their temperament.

Social Anxiety

As the more clinically oriented studies of behavioral inhibition show, behavioral inhibition is linked to social anxiety in childhood and adolescence. However, behavioral inhibition should not be equated with social anxiety for three reasons. First, behavioral inhibition is more general because it refers also to nonsocial situations. Second, it refers to observed behavior whereas anxiety refers to both behavior and subjective experience. One important consequence is that studies of social anxiety in older children sometimes include interview data or self-reports of their experience in social situations. Third, and most importantly, social anxiety is the more general concept for social situations because it includes fearful, anxious responses also in response to familiar people or situations.

Studies of social anxiety in adolescence and adulthood show that a main reason for anxious reactions in social situations are concerns of being negatively or insufficiently positively evaluated by others (familiar or unfamiliar). Asendorpf suggested the hypothesis that shy behavior in children might be linked to either behavioral inhibition (thus, to children's temperament) or to acquired fears of being negatively evaluated or ignored by others (thus, to social experiences).

He interpreted this two-factor model of shy behavior in terms of the temperamental theory of Gray. Based on his animal and psychopharmological research, Gray proposed the existence of a behavioral inhibition system at the neurophysiological level that mediates responses to three kinds of stimuli: novel stimuli, conditioned cues for punishment, and conditioned cues for frustrative nonreward. According to Gray, any such stimulus evokes behavioral inhibition, increased physiological arousal, and increased attention. Interindividual differences arise due to a different sensitivity (strength) of this behavioral inhibition system, and to interindividual differences in learning history (how many and which stimuli become cues for punishment or frustrative nonreward through conditioning).

Asendorpf applied this model to shy behavior in children (see **Figure 1**). According to this model, either strangers or cues for being rejected or ignored by others trigger the behavioral inhibition system in social situations. The resulting inhibitory tendencies are responsible

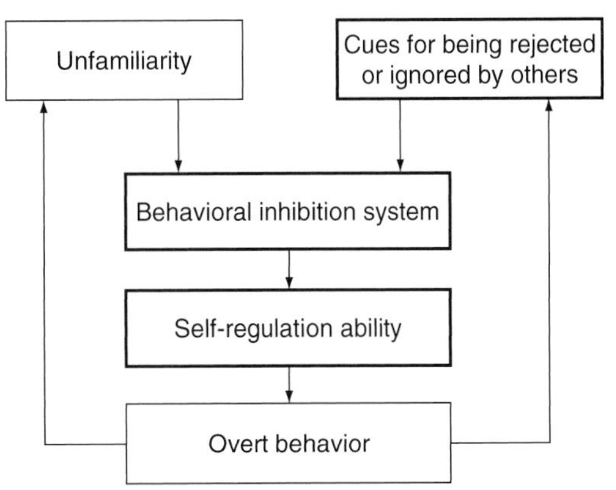

Figure 1 A three-factor model of shyness. Bold lines indicate sources of interindividual differences.

for the reactivity component of both behavioral inhibition to the unfamiliar and social-evaluative concerns.

Whether these inhibitory tendencies result in shy behavior depends on the child's self-regulatory abilities (see **Figure 1**). Furthermore, the child can modify the situation by both self-regulation ability (e.g., when a person that arouses fear is revaluated as being more friendly) and by overt behavior (e.g., by presenting oneself as modest and nonassuming in order to prevent criticism). These abilities to cope with inhibiting situations increase as children grow older and ultimately may be more important than their underlying temperament or earlier experiences with others.

According to this concept of shyness, a child may react shy to a particular person because of a temperamental disposition that may be genetically based or due to early caregiving, or because the child has been often rejected or ignored by this person (a parent, a sibling, or a familiar peer).

Because the second experiential source of shyness also triggers the behavioral inhibition system, it interacts with the temperamental source in a predictable way (amplification of response). Thus, a child with a 'weak' behavioral inhibition system that is often rejected by the parents may nonetheless not become shy whereas a child with a 'strong' behavioral inhibition system that is moderately rejected or ignored by the parents may nonetheless become shy in their presence. First evidence for this two-factor model of shyness in children was provided by Asendorpf in 1990. German children were observed in confrontations with adult and peer strangers in the laboratory, in their preschool and kindergarten peer group, and in play situations with a familiar peer in their familiar preschool. As expected, observed shyness was consistent between adult and peer strangers, but inconsistent between unfamiliar and familiar peers. Thus, a child who reacted with strong inhibition to an adult stranger in the laboratory tended to react also with strong inhibition to an unfamiliar peer in the same laboratory setting, but its shyness to a familiar peer was unrelated to its inhibition to peer or adult strangers.

Longitudinal analyses in the classroom showed an increasing influence of peer neglect or rejection on shyness in the classroom. Follow-ups of extreme groups with stable inhibition toward strangers vs. stable shyness in the more familiar peer group in the second and third year in preschool revealed that stable high inhibition toward strangers was unrelated to self-esteem up to age 12 years, whereas stable high shyness in the familiar peer group significantly predicted low social self-esteem between 8 and 12 years of age. Thus, shyness in the familiar peer group which was very likely due to social-evaluative concerns was a risk factor for internalizing problems throughout childhood but not inhibition toward strangers. In line with this finding, a more recent longitudinal study also showed that early peer neglect and rejection in preschool increased the risk of developing stable social anxiety and depression.

Because temperament is more likely stable than experiences of peer neglect or rejection across different peer groups, the consistency between inhibition to the unfamiliar and social-evaluative anxiety is expected to increase with age. This hypothesis was confirmed in another longitudinal study where inhibition to strangers was not correlated with negative peer relationships in late childhood, but in early adulthood. The bottom line of this developmental model of shyness in childhood is that shyness is the outcome of a continuous transaction of stable temperament and fluctuating social-evaluative experiences. During this transaction, the two initially independent factors become more and more correlated, and are hard to distinguish in adulthood. In early childhood, however, shyness due to the temperamental factor and shyness due to social anxiety can and should be distinguished. The former can be identified in its purest form in encounters with strangers, the latter in evaluative situations with familiar people.

Modesty

Shyness is not only used to describe children who react inhibited but also to describe children who act in a reserved, modest, unassuming way in the presence of others, without signs of fear or anxiety. As the model in **Figure 1** suggests, modesty can be an outcome of self-regulated inhibition, but this is not necessarily the case; children may be simply socialized to behave in a modest way. It depends then on the cultural norm for modesty – how often modesty is the outcome of self-regulated inhibition and how often it is the result of socialization favoring modesty.

This cultural influence became first obvious to developmental psychologists in a cross-cultural study by Chen who compared the peer reputation of shy-sensitive children, defined as shy, usually sad, and easily hurt by others, between Canada and mainland China in 1990. Whereas these children were less popular among their peers in Canada, they were above-average popular in China and showed superior school adjustment. The authors interpreted this result as the influence of the Confucian norm for modesty in China at the threshold of westernization. In line with this interpretation, studies carried out 8 and 12 years later could not replicate the Chinese results; instead, shy-sensitive Chinese children in large cities today are as low in peer popularity and school adjustment as in Western cultures.

These findings highlight the problem that shy behavior may be due to inhibition but also to self-regulation according to cultural norms favoring modesty, without underlying inhibition. The bottom line is that three different types of shyness in children can be distinguished: stranger shyness (behavioral inhibition to the unfamiliar), anxious shyness (behavioral inhibition to social-evaluative cues), and regulated shyness (self-controlled social restraint characterized by modesty and an unassuming demeanor).

Shyness vs. Social Withdrawal, Social Isolation, and Unsociability

It is important to distinguish shyness from social withdrawal, or solitary behavior, because solitary behavior can be due not only to inhibition and modesty but also to social isolation (sometimes also called social exclusion) and to unsociability, that is, a genuine preference for being alone rather than with others.

Social isolation occurs when children are rejected by their peers. Shy children are neglected by their peers rather than rejected (see also next section). Children are more often rejected by peers because of high aggressiveness. Aggressive-rejected children show a characteristic form of solitary behavior, often called solitary-active behavior, consisting of often-repeated sensorimotor activity and solitary dramatic play. For example, they move a play car back and forth for a long time, run around without any purpose, or pretend to be a famous movie star or a wild animal without interacting with others. Obviously, this would not be called shy behavior.

More difficult is the distinction between shyness and unsociability. Uninformed adults often believe that children are social by nature; therefore, they believe that children who spend much time with solitary behavior have some social or emotional problem. Research by Rubin and colleagues has shown, however, that solitary activity in early childhood is not necessarily problematic. Children's solitary-passive activity defined as exploratory and constructive solitary play in the presence of peers can be the outcome of a successful self-regulation of behavioral inhibition to the unfamiliar (if the peers are unfamiliar) or of social anxiety, of a norm for modesty (they would like to play with others but are socialized to wait until others approach them), or simply because they prefer to explore and play alone.

Indeed, children can be classified in terms of their dominant social motivation as being sociable (they prefer being with others rather than being alone), as being unsociable (they prefer to be alone rather than with others), as shy (they would like to be with others but do not dare to approach them because of inhibition or an internalized norm for modesty), or as avoidant (they avoid others because of experiences of rejection, without any motivation to approach them). From this motivational perspective, shyness is characterized by an approach-avoidance conflict rather than pure avoidance, and shyness is different from unsociability which is characterized by a lack of both approach and avoidance tendencies.

Development of Shyness: Infancy to Middle Childhood

Many cross-sectional and a few longitudinal studies have been conducted on the development of shyness from infancy to middle childhood. The major findings within a simple developmental model that borrows much from similar, more complex models by Rubin and colleagues (see **Figure 2**), are discussed.

Genetic and early environmental risks lead to an infant temperament that was described in the classic work by Thomas and Chess as 'slow-to-warm-up', and that is characterized in the second year of life by behavioral inhibition to the unfamiliar. In terms of the temperamental model shown in **Figure 1**, this early temperament is due to a strong behavioral inhibition system. Behavior genetic studies have supported that a substantial portion of the observed variability in behavioral inhibition in the second year of life is due to genetic differences, but currently the relevant genes are still unknown. Concerning early environmental influences on behavioral inhibition, only few specific pre- and perinatal risk factors are known.

Interestingly, one is the season of pregnancy. Studies have replicated for both North American and Australian samples that mid-pregnancy at the time of the year with the shortest daylight (December in North America, June in Australia) is a risk factor for behavioral inhibition. This might be less surprising as it seems because hormones such as melatonin and serotonin vary with daylight intensity, and play some role in neuroscience models of fear and behavioral inhibition.

As already discussed in the section on behavioral inhibition, this early temperamental trait, together with parental insensitivity, increases the risk for an anxious-ambivalent attachment to the parents and inadequate responses by the parents to the child such as overprotection or rejection. Anxious-ambivalent attachment as well as inadequate parenting, particularly involving rejection or neglect of the child, reinforce children's inhibitory tendencies, not only to unfamiliar situations but also to familiar social-evaluative situations, resulting at the end of the second year of life in a shy, somewhat socially anxious child who is sensitive to unfamiliar situations and criticism by others.

When such children enter the unfamiliar social world of preschool, they face the risk of being ignored (but initially not rejected) by their peers which, in turn, leads to reticent behavior such as long phases of just looking at others, being unoccupied without playing, and socially wary behaviors, and social-evaluative concerns of being insufficiently accepted by the peers.

Around second grade peers become more and more aware that these reticent children deviate from the age-appropriate pattern of social interaction which increases the risk that they now reject the reticent children. Such

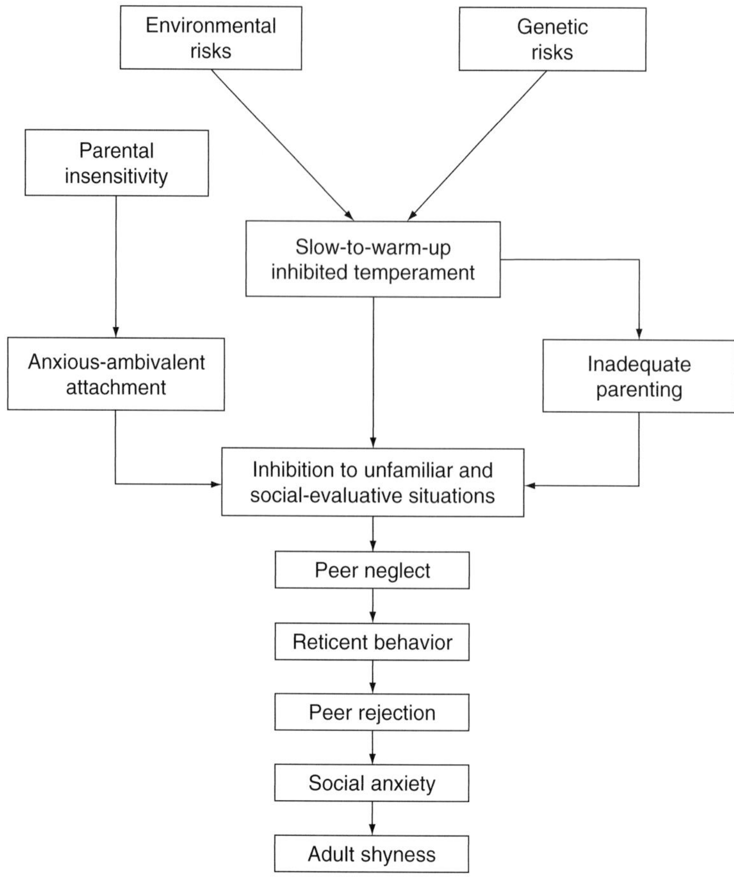

Figure 2 A developmental model of shyness.

peer rejection, in turn, increases social-evaluative anxiety and social withdrawal. If these children later during adolescence also face rejection by their potential dating and sexual partners, adult shyness likely results.

It is important to note that, in line with modern developmental psychology, this is a multifactor model of development where a single factor alone has little to no influence on development; what counts is the interaction between multiple risk factors. Also, personality traits such as early temperament alone are not sufficient for explaining later development; what counts is the transaction between personality and environment over age.

Long-Term Outcome of Early Shyness

The earliest evidence for a predictable long-term outcome of shyness in adulthood came from Kagan's analysis of data from the Fels Longitudinal Study where two measures of observed anxiety in unfamiliar social situations at ages 3–6 years were both significantly correlated with social anxiety in adulthood. The later extensive studies of temperamental inhibition by Kagan and associates did not result in reports about significant predictions from early inhibition toward the unfamiliar to adulthood personality or social–emotional adaptation. However, only a small number of children were followed into adulthood in these latter studies such that firm conclusions about the long-term effects of early temperamental inhibition cannot be drawn.

Much better evidence for the long-term outcome of early inhibition is provided by the Dunedin Longitudinal Study which follows a large, representative New Zealand birth cohort into adulthood. Based on behavioral observations in various situations, 8% of the sample were classified by Caspi and colleagues as inhibited at age 3 years and followed up until age 26 years. Compared to a control group of well-adjusted children (40% of the sample), the inhibited children reported more harm avoidance, less social potency, and positive emotionality at both ages 18 and 26 years, and at age 26 years were described by informants as lower in extraversion but not higher in neuroticism. Psychiatric interviews at age 21 years showed that the inhibited children were not more likely to have anxiety disorders of various kinds, including social phobia, but were more often depressed and had more often attempted suicide.

Thus, the evidence for internalizing disorders in adulthood for formerly extremely inhibited children was mixed. Importantly, social phobia was not related to early inhibition, neither we are aware of any other prospective longitudinal study into adulthood that has shown this, contrary to frequent claims in the clinical literature based on retrospective reports of adults. Thus, despite findings that early inhibition predicts social anxiety and phobia during childhood and early adolescence, early inhibition has not been found to be a risk factor for adult anxieties including social phobia.

With regard to life course sequelae of childhood inhibition, two longitudinal studies reported delays in social transitions for children classified as inhibited in middle childhood. In their reanalysis of the Berkeley Guidance Study, Caspi and colleagues found such delays only for inhibited boys at ages 8–10 years. These inhibited boys married 3 years later, became fathers 4 years later, and entered a stable occupational career 3 years later than the remaining boys. No such delays were found for the inhibited girls; instead, these girls became women who spent less time in the labor force and married men with higher occupational status. This should not be attributed to instability of female inhibition because inhibition as assessed in clinical interviews at ages 30 and 40 years correlated significantly with both boys' and girls' inhibition. The strong sex difference in the outcomes can be attributed to the traditional gender roles for this 1928 birth cohort that required action and social contacts, particularly from men.

In an attempt to replicate these life-course patterns in a 1955–58 Swedish cohort, Kerr and colleagues studied children who were rated as shy with unfamiliar people by their mothers at ages 8–10 years when they were 25 and 35 years old. Self-judgments of inhibition at age 35 years correlated with childhood inhibition significantly for females but not at all for males. Inhibited boys married 4 years later than controls and became fathers 3 years later; shy girls were educational underachievers, that is, reached a lower educational level after controlling for IQ. No effects on the number of job changes or monthly income were observed. Thus, this study replicated the delays for inhibited boys regarding marriage and parenthood as well as the absence of this effect for girls; unfortunately, the age at the time of beginning a stable career was not recorded.

In a recent follow-up of the Munich Longitudinal Study on the Genesis of Individual Competencies (LOGIC), Asendorpf and colleagues replicated the findings of delayed social transitions into adulthood not only for boys but also for girls, and also found a low stability of shyness between early childhood and adulthood. In this 19-year longitudinal study, the 15% most shy children at ages 4–6 years in a normal German sample were targeted by teacher judgments, and were compared with controls who were below average in preschool shyness. As adults, shy boys and girls were judged as shy by their parents and showed a delay in their first stable partnership and their first full-time job. This diminishing of a sex difference found in earlier generations was not unexpected because the LOGIC participants grew up in a culture characterized by more egalitarian gender roles than one or two generations earlier. Only the upper 8% in terms of shyness tended to show internalizing problems, including self-rated shyness; this tendency was of a similar effect size as in the Dunedin Longitudinal Study but not significant because of the smaller longitudinal sample.

Together, these longitudinal studies draw a consistent picture of the long-term consequences of early shyness. There is some stability of the core temperamental trait of inhibition to unfamiliar situations. This temperamental trait makes it more difficult for inhibited persons to cope with social life transitions where they are confronted with unfamiliar people. They are 'slow-to-warm-up' in such situations even as adults when they meet dating partners, enter new educational settings such as university, and apply for jobs which results in delayed social development.

This early temperamental core of shyness interacts so strongly with parental and peer influences over development that it is detectable in adults' self-judgments only in cases of extremely high childhood inhibition. Besides that, according to our present knowledge, early shyness does not lead to any identified psychological problems in adulthood, particularly not to social phobia.

See also: Attachment; Birth Order; Emotion Regulation; Exploration and Curiosity; Fear and Wariness; Friends and Peers; Nature vs. Nurture; Parenting Styles and their Effects; Social and Emotional Development Theories; Social Interaction; Temperament.

Suggested Readings

Asendorpf JB (1990) Development of inhibition during childhood: Evidence for situational specificity and a two-factor model. *Developmental Psychology* 26: 721–730.

Caspi A (2000) The child is the father of the man: Personality continuities from childhood to adulthood. *Journal of Personality and Social Psychology* 78: 158–172.

Chen X, Cen G, Li D, and He Y (2005) Social functioning and adjustment in Chinese children: The imprint of historical time. *Child Development* 76: 182–195.

Kagan J and Snidman N (2004) *The Long Shadow of Temperament.* Cambridge, MA: Harvard University Press.

Rubin KH and Asendorpf JB (eds.) (1993) *Social Withdrawal, Inhibition, and Shyness in Childhood.* Hillsdale, NJ: Lawrence Erlbaum.

Siblings and Sibling Rivalry

N Howe and H E Recchia, Concordia University, Montréal, QC, Canada

Glossary

Complementary interactions – Hierarchical exchanges in which one partner is invested with greater knowledge or authority as seen in parent–child interactions (e.g., teacher and learner roles).

Differential parental treatment – When parents' positive and negative treatment of their children is different for siblings in the same family.

Reciprocal interactions – Mutual and egalitarian exchanges typical of peer interactions, where both partners are invested with relatively equal levels of power and knowledge and can contribute to the interaction in fairly equal ways (e.g., during play).

Sibling rivalry – Siblings' resentment and jealousy typically associated with competition for parental affection, attention, and approval.

Introduction

Family systems theorists, in particular Salvatore Minuchin, have conceptualized the family as a system of reciprocally interactive and interdependent subsystems (marital, parent–child, sibling) that together form the whole family system. Although there is a large literature on the importance of the marital and parent–child subsystems to family functioning, considerably less attention has been devoted to the sibling system. Yet, more than 80% of children growing up in North America have at least one sibling and during the early years children spend more time with their sibling than any other family member. Nevertheless, parents (but most research has only included mothers) exert a strong influence on the quality of sibling relations. In addition, for most individuals, the sibling relationship will be their longest and most enduring relationship over their lifetime. Historically, the significant role of siblings in the lives of individuals and families is acknowledged by their prominent place in myths, biblical and classical stories, religion, history, autobiographies, and literature.

In the twentieth century, clinicians and family systems theorists, particularly those working within a psychoanalytic tradition, such as Alfred Adler and David Levy, wrote about the role of siblings (and rivalry) in family life and personality development. Sibling rivalry was believed to be the result of competition for parental attention after the second child's birth 'dethroned' the older sibling's position of importance in the family. Rivalry was manifested by jealous, agonistic behavior between the two children. This work was followed by research (mainly in the 1970s and 1980s, although there are still proponents of this approach today) emphasizing the role of structural variables (e.g., birth order, age, gender) in explaining why siblings differ from one another in their personality, temperament, intelligence, etc.

Since the 1970s or so there has been a shift away from examining the role of structural variables in sibling relations toward more process variables (e.g., understanding of the social world, relationship quality) with an emphasis on investigating types of interactions, the development of the sibling relationship in early childhood, and the influence of siblings on one another's development. As a case in point, research on the role of structural variables (birth order, number of siblings) in the development of children's theory of mind abilities is rather inconsistent; thus, more recent work has shifted to examining the role of process variables (e.g., relationship quality, pretend play) in explaining individual differences in theory of mind skills in early childhood.

Relationships Theory and the Sibling Relationship as a Context for Development

Theoretical work on the development of relationships, as articulated by Robert Hinde and Judy Dunn, informs much of the empirical literature. The basic premise underlying relationship models is that children's development occurs within the context of close, intimate relationships. Hinde argued that relationships can be described by their reciprocal and complementary features. Reciprocal interactions involve mutual and egalitarian exchanges, typical of peer interactions, whereas complementary interactions are hierarchical exchanges in which one partner is invested with greater knowledge or authority as seen in parent–child interactions.

Sibling relationships are uniquely characterized by both reciprocal and complementary features. Specifically, differences in siblings' ages and development dictate differential roles (e.g., caretaking, teaching) that define complementary interactions and are characterized by instrumental assistance, instruction, and guidance.

Complementary interactions have typically been considered via structural variables (e.g., age, birth order) rather than by examining children's behavior; however, recent research points to the significance of individual differences in the complementary features of exchanges. Proximity in age also promotes egalitarian exchanges (e.g., play) that define reciprocal interactions as illustrated by mutual understanding and companionship. Reciprocal interactions may provide key opportunities for facilitating development as siblings co-construct shared meanings during mutual and returned exchanges characteristic of play and conflict. Mutual engagement may facilitate emotional support, particularly in times of stress, because children are uniquely positioned to understand their sibling's perspective and experiences. The processes inherent in reciprocal exchanges (e.g., common interests, perspective-taking) may be important for promoting children's interpersonal and cognitive development. Thus, Dunn has argued that the reciprocal features of interactions are the building blocks of relationships because of the opportunities that they afford children for understanding self and others. Yet, the role of complementary interactions in children's development is not to be underestimated.

The distinction between reciprocal and complementary interactions provides a somewhat artificial dichotomy between different kinds of sibling exchanges, since most interactions probably contain both reciprocal and complementary features. This suggests some limits to the practical usefulness of this distinction. For example, during play children may engage in a series of reciprocal and equal exchanges as they develop a pretend scenario together (e.g., assigning roles, creating scripts); however, there may be opportunities for the older child to teach the younger (e.g., how to build a wooden barn, or that pigs eat corn). The degree to which reciprocal or complementary interactions predominate differs across dyads, and may illuminate our understanding of sibling dynamics and potential mechanisms of influence on development. Further, sibling-relationship quality and children's competencies may influence the balance between these two types of interactions and the patterns of individual differences evident in sibling interactions. Wyndol Furman and Duane Buhrmester delineated a four-factor framework for describing sibling-relationship quality, namely warmth, conflict, rivalry, and relative power. Warmth, conflict, and rivalry are hypothesized to relate to the reciprocal features of relationships and relative power to the complementary features. Since these four dimensions are considered to be independent of one another, children may exhibit seemingly ambivalent combinations of behaviors in the same relationship; for example, interactions may be both intensely warm and conflictual. Sibling-relationship quality may also exert an influence on children's socioemotional understanding and interpersonal problem solving. Thus, the sibling relationship provides an excellent window into studying young children's development.

Shared and Nonshared Environments

One important question regarding siblings concerns the extent to which children's experiences in the family serve to make them similar or different. Originally, the assumption was that children in the same family were predominantly influenced by their shared environment; that is, by virtue of growing up in the same family, any existing genetic similarities would be magnified to make siblings even more alike. However, contrary to this hypothesis, siblings tend to be quite different from one another. For example, the average correlation between siblings on personality variables is about 0.15; given that siblings share up to half of the same genes, this relationship is surprisingly weak. In fact, studies comparing adoptive and biological siblings, as well as identical and nonidentical twins reveal that most environmental influences on siblings are nonshared. For instance, they estimated that 40% of variance in personality is due to genes, 35% to nonshared environment, 10% to error, and only 5% to shared environment. So, for those who study siblings, the important question has become: what environmental factors exert their influence 'differently' for young children in the same family? First, though some experiences do differ consistently between families (e.g., neighborhood, divorce, socioeconomic status (SES)), it is likely that these experiences influence siblings in dissimilar ways. In fact, 69% of shared but unusual events during childhood are experienced differently by two siblings (based on their temperament, developmental level, birth order, etc.). Further, siblings engage in ecological niche-picking, and thus take on complementary nonoverlapping roles in the family. Other factors that contribute to differences between siblings include different relationships with parents, with peers and teachers, gene-by-environment interactions, and general idiosyncrasies of each child's experience. Finally, one important factor is siblings' differential relationships with each other. Whether one grows up with an older or younger sibling is associated with different experiences. Furthermore, there is no guarantee that siblings will be equally friendly or unfriendly with one another, and these inequalities will certainly contribute to children's differential experiences and later socioemotional outcomes.

Summary of the Introduction

Certainly, the sibling relationship is an integral part of most children's social worlds. Given their extended history of shared experiences including highly affectively intense prosocial and negative exchanges, siblings have an important socializing influence on one another's development. In early childhood, four major characteristics of the sibling relationship are prominent. First, sibling relationships are emotionally charged and defined by strong, uninhibited emotions of a positive, negative, and sometimes ambivalent quality. Second, sibling relations are defined by intimacy; since children spend large amounts of time together, they know each other very well. This long history and intimate knowledge translates into opportunities for providing emotional and instrumental support for one another, engaging in pretend play, in conflict, and for understanding others' points of view. Third, there are large individual differences in sibling-relationship quality. In addition, the age difference between siblings often makes the issues of power, control, and rivalry a source of contention for children. Fourth, environmental effects on children's development are mostly nonshared between siblings, and thus researchers are investigating the processes that serve to make brothers and sisters different. These characteristics sometimes make sibling relations challenging for parents to deal with on a daily basis, because of the emotional and highly charged nature of the relationship and the potential for differential parental treatment.

In the sections that follow, issues related to the birth of a sibling and the transition to siblinghood over the infant and toddler period are discussed. Then the features of sibling interactions over the preschool period, along with the influence of parents on these interactions are addressed. Finally, the limitations of current knowledge are discussed.

Birth of a Sibling and the Transition to Siblinghood

The birth of a second child launches a time of major changes in the functioning of the family system and the nature of interpersonal relationships between parents and children. Of course, this transition marks the beginning of the sibling relationship. The transition from one to two children, who are frequently close in age, signals a time of adjustment for all family members. Several longitudinal studies have charted the initial reactions and adjustment of the older child and the development of the sibling relationship over the infant, toddler, and preschool periods. Judy Dunn and Carol Kendrick conducted a naturalistic observational study of early sibling relations in British families beginning 1 month prior to the arrival of the new sibling, and again at 1, 8, and 14 months after the birth. Their findings form the backbone of our knowledge, which is complemented by other longitudinal studies, such as Robert Stewart's work on the transition to siblinghood.

Firstborn children generally have marked affective responses to the birth of a sibling, although individual differences in the range and intensity of affect have been noted. Compared to before the birth, firstborns exhibit a combination of positive (e.g., interest, affection, imitation of the baby) and negative behaviors (e.g., clingy, demanding, confrontational, distress), perhaps indicating their overall ambivalence to the event. Older firstborn siblings (age 3–4 years) engage in more mature behaviors such as greater self-help skills and assisting with the newborn, whereas younger firstborns (age 1–2 years) are frequently more distressed and clingy. Mothers report that at 1 month after the birth of the sibling, firstborns often have problems with toileting and sleeping, engage in baby talk, and are more confrontational and deliberately naughty, particularly when the mother is feeding or caring for the infant. Children may be jealous of the attention that the newborn receives by engaging in more negative behavior. Further, some boys respond by withdrawing after the birth of the sibling, whereas girls show more dependent behaviors (e.g., clingy, fussy, greater use of pacifier or bottle). Problematic behaviors are more evident in same-gender dyads. Certainly, mothers are less available to the older child once the baby arrives, but many mothers attempt to involve the older child in the care of the younger one, partly to ease this decrease in attention and involvement.

Yet, most firstborns respond quite positively to the birth of a sibling and, within several months, the more overt negative responses typically decrease significantly. The older sibling's initial confrontational behavior decreases by the time the younger sibling is 4 months old; however, at this time, firstborns show more anxious behaviors. By 8 and 12 months, firstborns' confrontations are more likely to be directed to their increasingly mobile and intrusive younger sibling than to the parents. The temporary nature of the more overt negative behaviors may be a response to a number of changes that the firstborn may experience after the birth of a sibling, including changes to their physical environment (e.g., new room, new furniture, or having to share a room); a decrease in maternal availability and her preoccupation with the newborn; the initial separation when mother is in the hospital and the presence of less familiar adults (e.g., grandparents, babysitters) who focus their attention on the newborn; the development of new family routines reflecting the dynamics of three vs. four members; and, helping the newborn to achieve a regular pattern of sleeping and eating.

The firstborn's initial adjustment to the birth of a sibling and the transition to siblinghood appears to be tempered by several factors, including their own level of cognitive understanding. Preparing the older sibling in advance of the birth is a frequent parental strategy and may include reading books about babies and families, having contact with other families with young infants, talking about the impending changes, and/or attending a sibling preparation class offered by a hospital or community public health program. Children who attend such classes are reported to exhibit fewer negative problems after the sibling's birth and mothers also coped more effectively with the child's negative behaviors, perhaps because they were also prepared for the range of the firstborn's possible reactions. Parental support is also critical for the firstborn's adjustment; maternal support for older sisters who exhibit high distress prior to the birth helps them to alleviate some of the stress following the birth. Fathers' support is also important, particularly after the birth when the mother may be preoccupied with the infant. Finally, having a strong friendship with a playmate who enjoys engaging in shared pretense may be a positive buffer for the older sibling's transition and acceptance of a younger sibling.

In sum, the empirical evidence is weak for the clinical (psychoanalytic) view of 'dethronement' of the older child after the arrival of the younger sibling as setting the stage for jealousy and sibling rivalry. In fact, as outlined below, the literature focusing on siblings' influence on each other and the development of their relationship suggests that other processes are equally relevant to children's development.

Development of the Sibling Relationship over the First 2 Years

Our knowledge of the early development of the sibling relationship has been greatly enriched by several longitudinal studies that have charted the processes implicated in the quality of sibling relations and the role of parents (especially mothers). Links between the older child's initial reaction and the development of the quality of the sibling relationship are evident over time; namely, friendlier sibling relations at 14 months are associated with firstborns who are initially interested (and not withdrawn) and who imitate the newborn.

Maternal interaction with the firstborn is also a critical factor associated with later sibling-relationship quality. Specifically, both (1) intense close relationships between mothers and older sisters at the time of the sibling's birth, and (2) between the mother and the secondborn at 8 months were associated with less friendly sibling relations at 14 months. Since we know that siblings direct less interaction to one another in the presence of a parent than when alone, these patterns may suggest that intense maternal closeness and very frequent interaction with the children does not allow youngsters the opportunity or emotional space to construct a positive and friendly sibling relationship on their own. In contrast, when mothers and daughters engage in frequent verbal confrontations after the baby's birth (but less frequent interaction), by 14 months the sibling relationship was positive and friendly. Thus, interestingly, a very close, nonconflictual relationship between mother and firstborn child does not seem to promote friendly sibling interaction, but rather the opposite. Related to this point, when mothers experienced fatigue and postnatal depression, by 14 months the sibling relationship was positive and friendly. This pattern suggests that in the absence of maternal attention or intimacy, siblings may have turned to one another as sources of interaction and interest, perhaps to buffer the lack of maternal emotional involvement.

On the other hand, some maternal behaviors are positively associated with the development of a friendly sibling relationship. For example, mother and firstborn's discussion of the newborn's internal states (feelings, desires, infant as a person) is positively associated with a friendly sibling relationship over time. Mothers who discuss internal states are also more likely to engage in pretense with the children, to enlist the older sister in caretaking, and to use language for complex purposes (e.g., comparisons, generalizations, explaining intentions and motives, and providing justifications in disciplinary situations). This maternal style may be a key process in helping older siblings to consider their younger sibling as a person with feelings, desires, intentions, and to be sensitive to their emotional needs and behavior. Apparently, siblings growing up in families where mothers employ such a verbal style are more likely to develop a friendly relationship, which is already evident by the time the younger sibling is 1 year old.

In sum, as younger siblings enter their second year, there are two critical features that highlight the nature of the sibling relationship. First, the salience of siblings for one another is apparent as seen in the younger sibling's high rates of imitation of the older's actions and language (27% of all interactions as reported in one Canadian study). These imitative acts along with frequent episodes of joint play suggest that siblings are often highly desired play partners for each other. Second, the marked affective tone of the interactions, particularly as the younger sibling becomes a more active and verbally skilled dyadic partner, cannot be missed. Sibling exchanges in the reciprocal (joint play, cooperation, affection) and complementary (comforting, teaching, helping) aspects of their relationship can be both positive and negative in tone. Some sibling relationships are characterized by frequent prosocial interactions, while others are more agonistic in tone; finally, some relationships are affectively mismatched (i.e., older sibling is more negative and younger child is more positive). Dunn reported that 22% of interactions when the younger sibling was 14 months old were defined by the older sibling's negative behaviors and the younger sibling's friendly behaviors. Clearly, the range of affective contexts that siblings co-construct may have an impact on the ways that they influence one another's development. The reciprocity evident in all of these interactions reflects how well siblings come to know each other and their pragmatic understanding of one another's likes, dislikes, how to tease and annoy one another, etc. During the second year, younger siblings engage in observer/follower roles, whereas older siblings are leaders during play situations and initiate invitations to play, create, and control pretense scenarios. As discussed below, distressed younger siblings may turn to older siblings (especially sisters) for comfort. The developmental implications of these two features of their relationship become evident as the younger sibling enters the early childhood period.

Sibling Relationships in Early Childhood

Clearly, sibling relationships are dynamic and reciprocal from their inception. Nevertheless, as younger siblings enter their third year of life, they become more active and interesting relationship partners for their older siblings. As such, at this age, mothers tend to withdraw from their mediating role in sibling interaction, and siblings spend more time interacting with each other than with their mother. During early childhood, there are various striking features of sibling dynamics. Research has typically focused on the negative aspects of sibling relationships, such as rivalry and conflict, given their implications for later development. However, sibling relationships are also characterized by play, prosocial behavior, caretaking, and teaching, which contribute in important ways to later social, cognitive, and affective development. Each of these features of relationships is discussed in turn.

Rivalry

As described above, the birth or arrival of a new sibling can precipitate strong negative feelings in their older brother or sister and in some cases, sibling rivalry continues into the early childhood years. To some degree, this resentment may be based on valid perceptions, as there is evidence that laterborn children tend to be somewhat favored by mothers. Mothers are more responsive, verbal, controlling, and emotionally expressive with their younger children, though they may be more consistent with same-sex pairs. In fact, about half of mothers in North American and British samples reported feeling more affectionate toward their younger child, whereas less than a quarter of mothers reported feeling more affectionate toward their older child. Although mothers may behave and feel differently toward their two children at any one particular time, they apparently behave in similar ways toward their two children when those children reach the same developmental age. In fact, paying more attention to the younger child makes sense, as they do require more care. However, only the older child is privy to the enhanced attention and affection that mothers show to younger children, and thus is selectively affected by this experience. Related to this point, parental differential treatment has negative effects only when children perceive differences in treatment as unfair. About 50% of children perceive that they are treated differently than their sibling (either better or worse). In this case, the degree of differential treatment during childhood is related to a number of negative outcomes, including concurrent internalizing (i.e., directed inwards toward the self such as depression, anxiety) and externalizing (i.e., directed toward others such as aggression, disruptive or argumentative behavior) problems as well as a diminished sense of self-worth. Differential treatment predicts self-worth even after controlling for initial differences between children, suggesting that though differential treatment may occur partly because children are different, it also contributes uniquely to adjustment. Furthermore, differential treatment (especially by fathers) is negatively associated with sibling-relationship quality. This is true for both siblings, even the child who is favored. However, as suggested above, when children perceive differential treatment as fair, this is linked to more positive sibling relationships. Finally, longitudinal studies reveal that differential treatment during childhood predicts maladjustment and delinquency in adolescence. Differential treatment may be especially problematic when children are insecurely attached or family stress levels are high.

Siblings of children with disabilities are especially likely to experience differential treatment, due to the special needs of their brother or sister. However, when children are cognitively sophisticated enough to recognize the need for differential treatment, there are no negative outcomes. In contrast, in two-child families, sibling rivalry is more pronounced than in families with three or more children. Children are also more hostile toward their sibling with a disability when their parents have ambivalent attitudes toward that sibling. Although siblings of children with disabilities may get less parental attention, they may also benefit in other ways. For instance, while mothers employ more power-assertive discipline techniques with their child with a disability, their siblings are more often the recipients of reasoning and compromise strategies.

In more general terms, competition and social comparison between siblings clearly occur from the beginning of their relationship. Older siblings may respond to as many as 75% of interactions between their mother and baby sibling (usually with protests or demands for attention). Similarly, beginning around 14 months of age, younger children pay close attention to interactions between their mother and older sibling. After their third birthday, younger children become increasingly adept at intervening in these conversations and turning them around to serve their own interests. Finally, when children describe conflictual events that occurred between themselves and their siblings, they tend to compare themselves favorably to their brothers and sisters. They often claim that their sibling engages in more harmful actions overall and provide more justifications for their own negative actions than those of their sibling. Furthermore, these relative differences in appraisals of self and sibling are at least partially due to children's deliberate attempts to manage the impressions of others. Naturalistic observations of sibling interaction support this claim, as children's lies tend to be self-serving in nature, and are commonly used to avoid responsibility and falsely accuse one's sibling. For preschool children, tattling is also a means to report selectively on sibling misdeeds. Thus, social comparison and competition between siblings are salient facets of the relationship.

Conflict

Sibling conflicts in early childhood are frequent, poorly resolved, and can sometimes be emotionally intense, aggressive, or violent. Estimates of the frequency of sibling conflicts during the preschool years vary from about 3 to 10 times per hour. When sibling conflict occurs, over 80% of disputes end either without resolution or with the submission of one child, typically the younger sibling. Thus, constructive resolutions such as compromises and conciliation occur infrequently.

However, sibling conflict is not necessarily aggressive and hostile, and has the potential to contribute positively to development, particularly if we consider the differences between constructive and destructive conflict-resolution strategies. Constructive strategies include reasoning, enhancing understanding between parties, and attempting to reach collaborative resolutions. Destructive strategies involve hostile or aggressive behaviors and becoming entrenched in one's own position, which result in conflicts being left unresolved. Thus, conflict resolution can be a useful context for learning skills critical to social competence. Specifically, when in conflict, children are faced with competing perspectives that are incompatible with their own. As such, divergent beliefs, goals, intentions, and motivations are made salient, helping children learn to differentiate their own perspectives from those of others. In support of this point, siblings often refer to internal states (goals, beliefs, etc.) while in conflict, which is linked to children's ability to develop shared meanings in other contexts (i.e., pretend play). Furthermore, sibling conflict may help children to improve their interpersonal relationships as they coordinate perspectives with those of others. Indeed, an intervention program aimed at improving understanding between siblings, promoting positive play interactions, and improving conflict-resolution skills resulted in friendlier sibling relationships with less rivalry and conflict.

Given the above, it is not surprising that sibling conflict is one of parents' biggest concerns about their children's behavior. There are competing arguments regarding the benefits and drawbacks of parental intervention into sibling conflict. On the one hand, it is important for children to develop conflict-resolution strategies on their own, as these skills have been found to have numerous later benefits including improved social understanding, relationships with friends, and school adjustment. For instance, there is evidence that siblings help children develop their use of justifications in the context of disputes; thus, parental interventions may deprive children of the opportunity to learn these skills. In fact, some parental interventions actually make disputes worse. When mothers are present, conflicts last longer and children may behave in more combative ways. Thus, intervening may provide positive reinforcement for attention-seeking conflictual behavior; however, other studies suggest that children are 'less' combative when mothers are present.

The proponents of intervention claim that parental involvement in sibling conflict may have numerous positive results. Parents usually intervene when conflicts are extended in duration, particularly aggressive, or when property has been damaged. Parental involvement under these circumstances, beyond simply keeping children safe, may help to reduce tension and uphold family rules. In addition, those who argue against intervention assume that siblings will learn and use positive conflict-resolution skills on their own, which is not necessarily the case. Given that there is an inherent psychological and physical power differential between siblings, older siblings may not learn that power-assertive strategies are an unsatisfactory way to resolve conflicts. On the other hand, intervening by consistently punishing the older child and supporting the younger may actually lead to 'increased' aggression. Thus, though results are somewhat mixed, parental socialization of positive conflict behaviors may be necessary. Indeed, more frequent maternal interventions are associated with a number of immediate positive changes in conflict behaviors by the children.

Clearly, beyond the question of whether parents should intervene into their children's conflicts, some types of interventions may be more beneficial than others. Maternal discussion of rules and feelings, other-oriented reasoning, and intervening (but leaving the final solution up to the children) are linked to children's later use of constructive conflict strategies. In contrast, self-oriented reasoning and punishment are linked to children's later destructive strategies. Thus, the nature of maternal interventions may be related in specific ways to children's later conflict-resolution styles indicating one way that parents influence siblings' behavior. Intervention studies involving mediation training for parents also provide concrete support for the notion that constructive parental interventions have a number of positive outcomes on siblings' conflict-resolution strategies. Siblings exposed to mediation talk more about emotions, are less negative during conflict negotiations, and have a better understanding of their sibling's perspective. In addition, secondborn children exposed to mediation are more likely to provide justifications and initiate solutions, suggesting that they have been empowered to participate more fully in the conflict-resolution process.

Beyond parental interventions into sibling conflict, other features of family relationships are related to the nature of sibling disputes. Specifically, parent–child and marital conflict, overcontrolling mothering, and insecure attachment are linked to sibling conflict. In contrast, parental alliances, positive marital relationships, and family cohesion are associated with less negativity in the sibling relationship. Individual characteristics of parents and children are also related to the quality of the sibling relationship; when parents exhibit more negative affectivity, sibling relationships are less positive and more negative. Further, children (especially older siblings or children with negative parent–child relationships) who have highly active, emotional temperaments and who do not adapt easily to change, engage in more sibling conflict. Temperamental mismatch between siblings is also associated with conflict, and fights are more frequent in same-gender dyads than in mixed-gender pairs, although this may be especially true of boys. Girls also tend to be more submissive in conflict than boys, consistent with literature suggesting that they are socialized to be less assertive.

Instances of sibling abuse and violence go beyond the normal range of conflictual behaviors between young children. However, unfortunately many cases of abuse go unreported as they are misperceived as 'normal' sibling rivalry. Extremely aggressive and hostile sibling conflict has been linked to later adjustment problems (e.g., conduct disorder), psychopathology (anxiety and depression), and academic problems, as well as later violent, aggressive, and delinquent behavior. This may be especially true for boys. In fact, sibling interaction can be a potent training ground for coercive behavior. Further, younger siblings seem to learn aggressive behavior from older siblings, though overall, older siblings are more aggressive than younger siblings. Sibling relationships tend to mirror other relationships later in life; children who are violent toward their siblings tend to be violent toward others as they get older, whereas children who are victimized by their siblings tend to be later victimized by their peers, but also themselves to be more aggressive toward others.

Sibling abuse and violence are more likely to occur when parents do not effectively monitor their children and are also linked to child abuse by parents, parental abuse history, maternal deprivation/rejection, extreme parental differential treatment, unhappiness, helplessness, children's medical illness, and parental condoning of abusive behavior. Sexual abuse occurs most frequently at the hands of a much older brother. The correlates of sexually abusive sibling relationships tend to be similar to those described above for physical abuse, but also include parental encouragement of a sexual climate in the home, family secrets, parental childhood sexual abuse, and rigid family rules regarding the denial of emotions.

To summarize, although sibling aggression and abuse is associated with negative outcomes, less extreme sibling conflict and negative affectivity are relatively normative aspects of this relationship, and may even contribute positively to children's development. However, the sibling relationship is also characterized by a number of positive features, to which we now turn.

Play and Prosocial Behavior

By the time the younger child is age 3, siblings turn to each other as play partners and spend more time playing with one another than with their mother. Prior to this, mothers are often actively involved as a partner in the children's play or support the children's playful and prosocial interactions through guiding, making suggestions, or talking about positive ways of interacting. However, as the younger sibling becomes more socially and cognitively competent, mothers take on a less directive and more supportive secondary role and allow the children greater opportunities to play by themselves.

Siblings are more desirable as play partners than mothers for several reasons. Older siblings probably experience greater intrinsic pleasure in playing, especially engaging in pretense, than do mothers. Certainly, friendly, cooperative behavior by the older sibling is reciprocated by the younger both contemporaneously and longitudinally over the preschool years, particularly in same-sex dyads. Older siblings (especially sisters) initiate about 65% of the prosocial behaviors, although younger siblings increase the frequency of these behaviors over this time period. In fact, when preschoolers direct cooperative behaviors toward their younger sibling, the latter are also more likely to be cooperative, conciliatory, but also to engage in more teasing behavior. Teasing certainly reflects the degree of intimacy between siblings and their shared history, because to be successful the teaser must be able to understand the sibling's point of view, have an awareness of his/her weaknesses, desires, and intentions, and be able to anticipate what will annoy the other. This knowledge apparently comes partly via close, frequent, and prosocial interactions. Thus, a warm and supportive sibling relationship provides a developmental context for promoting prosocial interactions such as sharing, cooperation, nurturing, teaching, comforting, good-natured teasing, and loyalty, which may foster emotional understanding, moral sensitivity, and understanding of the sibling's capabilities and point of view. Over early childhood, sibling friendliness and aggression are quite stable, particularly for older siblings, but interestingly it is especially the lack of a positive and warm relationship, even more than the level of conflict, that best predicts maladjustment in children. In sum, positive, friendly sibling relationships in early childhood are associated with adaptive functioning later in life.

Due to their shared history, siblings know each other intimately and have constructed a body of shared knowledge that makes them desirable play partners. Older siblings become quite skillful in creating scaffolds for enticing their younger sibling to enter collaborative play, partly due to their knowledge of their sibling's interests. For example, older preschoolers employ a range of complex strategies (e.g., invitations, descriptions, extending, building-on to ideas) to draw their sibling into and sustain their engagement in play, whereas younger preschoolers rely more on paralinguistic cues (e.g., play voice, sounds) and simple strategies (e.g., calls for attention, repetitions). Initially, the older sibling takes the lead in negotiating and enacting the role play; older firstborns are more likely to draw the younger sibling into the play than are younger firstborns. However, as the younger sibling's cognitive, linguistic, and cooperative skills increase after age 3, they begin to initiate more games and to take an active and sustained role in the creation of reciprocated play, particularly during pretense.

Many sibling dyads spend a considerable amount of time engaged in joint pretend play, although there are large individual differences in the frequency and sophistication of dyadic sibling pretense. In fact, sibling dyads who engage in frequent pretense appear to approach the play situation differently compared to dyads who are less interested in pretend play. The former employ a greater number of the sophisticated strategies described above to create shared meanings in the play. Frequent pretenders also engage in significantly more high-level negotiations regarding assignment of pretend roles, object transformations, and scaffolding ('Let's pretend...'). In contrast, dyads who engage in less pretend play focus on the set-up of the concrete play props (figurines, houses, animals), are more likely to become distracted, and are more interested in control issues, thus engaging in more frequent agonistic behavior. This is not an approach conducive for the development of sophisticated joint play; in contrast, dyads who engage in frequent pretense appear to use strategies reflective of sophisticated social cognitive skills.

In fact, the frequency of pretend play between siblings has been associated with the development of children's understanding of their social worlds. For example, dyads who engage in pretend play are more likely to use internal state language (references to emotional, mental states) during their pretense negotiations and while scaffolding. It may be that children who are adept at understanding other's internal states are effective play partners, because they are sensitive to the sibling's ideas, thoughts, and conceptions about the world, all of which create a context conducive for developing joint pretend scenarios. Moreover, individual differences in the propensity to engage in pretense with one's sibling are related to the development of greater social understanding (e.g., affective perspective taking) over the preschool period.

The evidence concerning the association between the frequency of sibling pretend play and sibling-relationship quality is inconsistent. Engaging in pretend play has been positively associated with both friendly and agonistic sibling relationships, while some authors report no associations or a negative association between frequency of play and negative affect expressed in the play context. More frequent sibling conflict appears to be negatively associated with the frequency of pretend play, suggesting that the nature of children's disagreements does not produce a context conducive for joint play.

Sibling Caretaking and Attachment

When laterborn siblings reach the early childhood period, elder children in the family often play important caretaking roles for their younger brothers and sisters. Though these roles are rarely formalized in Western industrialized societies, sibling caretaking is a critical childhood task in many other cultures. For instance, one study conducted in the 1970s found that in fewer than 20% of 186 societies, mothers acted as primary caregivers for their young children. In about 25% of societies, older children (mostly females) acted at least occasionally as caregivers for younger children. Cultural conditions associated with sibling caretaking include larger family size, lineal descent and residence patterns, an emphasis on family and community cooperation in tasks and chores, and a daily routine that results in the presence of child caregivers. Sibling caretaking is a valued task, not only because it frees parents to engage in work activities, but also because it prepares children, especially girls, for their later adult roles and may promote their sense of self-esteem, prosocial behavior, and interdependence. Although even very young caregivers (i.e., 3-year-olds) can be gentle and nurturant in their caretaking, they tend to largely imitate caregiving patterns of adults. As such, younger children may learn values, skills, and knowledge from their siblings in these contexts.

Though sibling caretaking in industrialized societies may occur less frequently (especially in the early years), it certainly exists, but may be a more informal and infrequent role for children. For instance, in one study of preschool-aged siblings, when their siblings were in distress, children only responded in a comforting way about 10% of the time (or 20% if they themselves were the cause of the distress). However, in unfamiliar situations (e.g., a university laboratory) preschoolers may be more likely to respond to their younger sibling's distress by approaching or hugging them, particularly when they have been talking about internal states with their younger sibling. In these cases, younger siblings may approach and seek comfort from their older brothers and sisters. In other unfamiliar settings (e.g., outdoor backyard), in the presence of their older siblings, infants left their mother sooner, explored more frequently and independently, and displayed less distress. As such, there is interesting evidence that at least some older siblings may be a secondary attachment figure for their younger brothers and sisters. In Western cultures, outcomes of caretaking are generally positive. Specifically, sibling caretaking is negatively associated with anxiety and depression in normative samples.

One final context in which sibling caretaking has been reported is for children of siblings with disabilities. Typically, these children engage in more helping, caretaking, and teaching behavior than children whose siblings are not disabled, which in some cases has been positively associated with their anxiety and depression. However, as opposed to quantity of caretaking, the quality of their sibling relationship and especially the degree to which their sibling with a disability is aggressive toward them may be more strongly associated with negative outcomes for the typically developing child. Furthermore, birth order, temperament, and gender, as well as parental marriage quality and attitudes appear to moderate the links between caretaking and children's adjustment. Thus, there is not a clear-cut relationship between caretaking for siblings with disabilities and children's adjustment, and children exhibit a great deal of variability in this regard. Overall, the meaning and outcomes of sibling caretaking likely depends on the frequency and context in which it occurs.

Sibling Teaching

The literature on sibling teaching has been largely guided by the work of the Russian psychologist, Lev Vygotsky. He believed that teaching and learning occurred within the zone of proximal development; namely, with the guidance and encouragement of a more skilled individual (usually an adult), the child is able to accomplish a task that he/she would not be able to do independently. The knowledgeable person guides or scaffolds the less knowledgeable child (e.g., provide hints, suggestions) so that this child can successfully learn to complete a task. In this respect, the pairing of an older and a younger child affords an excellent context for the younger, less-experienced child to acquire knowledge and develop skills. This may be true of both sibling pairs and mixed-age peers. Nevertheless, older siblings are particularly important socialization agents for younger children, given their history of collaborative interactions and the emotional intensity of the relationship. In support of this argument, younger children are more likely to solicit teaching from older siblings than from older peers and are more likely to participate actively in the teaching process. They also learn more from older siblings than from older peers, which may be partly due to the fact that the former provide more extensive explanations, feedback, and spontaneously instruct and correct their younger sibling more often than the latter. Apparently, older siblings are comfortable assuming the role of teacher, while younger siblings take on the corresponding role of learner during interaction.

The small literature on sibling teaching in a Western cultural context reveals considerable individual differences in children's tendencies to use strategies such as verbal instruction, physical demonstrations, control, and learner involvement in the task. To some extent, these differences are related to age and birth-order effects. Chronologically older sibling teachers use more verbal instruction and encourage learner involvement. However, older teachers also tend to be more controlling than younger teachers. Preschoolers tend to mainly demonstrate during instruction. Nevertheless, even preschool-aged sibling teachers (when supported by their mothers) are able to provide instruction to their infant sibling, to capture the younger child's attention and to modify instructions based on the infant's responses. In addition to developmental effects, birth-order differences in sibling teaching are also evident. Firstborn children use more frequent and varied strategies for teaching their younger siblings when the age gap is larger rather than smaller. Furthermore, secondborn teachers are more likely to involve the firstborn learner than vice versa. On the other hand, firstborn teachers tend to be more controlling. These results are consistent with the idea that placing a high-ability child in a novice role and a lower-ability child in an expert role may facilitate more collaboration and joint construction than in pairs where the lower-ability child is the novice.

The relationship between gender and sibling teaching is inconsistent; sometimes school-aged girls are more likely than boys to teach and use a positive style of guiding; however, sometimes there are no gender differences. Many older sisters in the early school years employ an inductive method (i.e., explaining rules, describing with examples), particularly with younger brothers. In contrast, older brothers employ a deductive method (i.e., providing examples for learners to deduct the rules on their own with varying amounts of teacher help). Interestingly, older sisters provide less feedback, perhaps because their teaching style is already more informative and responsive to the younger sibling's learning.

Unfortunately, we know little about how sibling teaching transpires naturalistically in the home setting, although there is some evidence to support the notion that it occurs, in particular that older siblings (but not younger) frequently engage in this behavior. Most of their teaching behavior involves instructing their siblings in procedural skills (e.g., for playing games or use of objects). However, older siblings also sometimes teach their younger brothers and sisters verbal skills and concept knowledge (e.g., labels, numbers).

Furthermore, during play children do not often engage in direct teaching, but it is clear that a great deal of socialization occurs in this context. Namely, older siblings engage in talk about social rules and expectations, direct attention, provide missing perceptual information, use nonverbal cues, and construct simple messages. As such, they may promote more advanced levels of play in their younger brothers and sisters. Older siblings are prone to emphasizing their own competence relative to their siblings and can be highly critical, hence providing clear and unambiguous teaching messages and making the younger child's incomplete knowledge salient. In contrast, adults tend to be more subtle and less critical. Thus, interestingly, it has been argued that when older siblings try to 'show off', they may be effectively socializing their sibling. In fact, children's interactive play with older siblings tends to be more sophisticated than with adults. Younger children pay close attention to their older sibling's cues, imitate frequently, follow directions, and request help, again suggesting the potency of the relationship for influencing siblings' development.

Cross-cultural research reveals that the form and content of sibling teaching varies as a function of cultural practices, beliefs, and values. For example, ethnographic research examining Mayan children's sibling teaching reveals that they teach their sibling important everyday tasks (such as making tortillas) using a distinct teaching style. This style consists of observational learning that incorporates scaffolding and contextualized talk, as well as physical closeness between teacher and learner, the expectation of obedience, and the possibility of multiple teachers. As such, verbal instruction is less important in this context than in Western culture or a formal school setting.

Limitations

There are a number of important limitations in the extant empirical literature on sibling relationships and sibling rivalry. First, the vast majority of research has been conducted on Caucasian, middle class, Western (British, Canadian, US) intact families. Unfortunately, we know little about the development of sibling relationships in other cultures or demographic groups. The nature of sibling relationships may possibly differ in more collectivistic cultures (e.g., Latin America) vs. the less collectivistic cultures of the industrialized West. Nor do we know much about how sibling relationships may vary within minority ethnic or linguistic populations in the West (e.g., Hispanic, French, South Asian), or rural or urban populations, etc. Only recently have researchers examined the quality of sibling relations between step- and half-siblings in nontraditional families (e.g., single parents, divorced). Second, researchers have not addressed the nature of sibling relationships in families with more than two children, thus there is no empirical evidence on the dynamics of families with three or more children. For example, the kinds of interactions that might exist between first- and thirdborn or second- and thirdborn siblings remain an open question. Third, in many studies the age gap between the children is confounded with the age of one of the siblings, thus we know little about the effects of this variable on the quality and types of sibling interaction. Fourth, although there is a small literature on the sibling relationships of children with a physical or intellectual disability, the impact of this experience on family and sibling functioning is a neglected area of research. Most studies rely on parental reports or employ questionnaire/interview methods and there are few naturalistic observational studies examining sibling interactions in these special populations.

Conclusions

In conclusion, the sibling relationship has been described as a natural laboratory for very young children to learn about their social worlds and social relationships. The sibling relationship is a safe and secure context in which to learn how to manage the positive and negative aspects of interaction with a partner who is close in age and with whom one has a shared, intimate, and affectively intense history. There are many opportunities to learn how to handle disputes in constructive ways and to regulate both positive and negative feelings in socially acceptable ways within the family context. In interaction with their sibling, youngsters develop an understanding of social relations with a partner who may be warm and affectionate one minute and nasty and aggressive the next. Certainly, the range and intensity of affection between siblings may be stronger than in any other relationship that young children experience. Further, the sibling relationship affords many opportunities for young children to foster their social cognitive skills to understand others' point of view, engage in prosocial behavior and play, imitate, teach, engage in caretaking and affectionate behaviors, and use their powers of persuasion. The positive benefits of constructing a warm and positive sibling relationship may last a lifetime, whereas more difficult or ambivalent early relationships appear to be associated with a poor developmental trajectory for children. The task for young siblings is to achieve a balance between the positive and negative features of the relationship as they develop over time.

See also: Attachment; Birth Order; Empathy and Prosocial Behavior; Play; Social Interaction; Temperament.

Suggested Readings

Brody G (1998) Sibling relationship quality: Its causes and consequences. *Annual Review of Psychology* 49: 1–24.
Dunn J (1983) Sibling relationships in early childhood. *Child Development* 54: 787–811.
Dunn J (2002) Sibling relationships. In: Smith PK and Hart CH (eds.) *Blackwell Handbook of Childhood Social Development*, pp. 223–237. Oxford: Blackwell.
Dunn J and Kendrick C (1982) *Siblings: Love, Envy, and Understanding.* Cambridge, MA: Harvard University Press.
Dunn J and Plomin R (1990) *Separate Lives: Why Siblings are so Different.* New York, NY: Basic.
Furman W and Buhrmester D (1985) Children's perceptions of the qualities of sibling relationships. *Child Development* 56: 448–461.
Hinde R (1979) *Towards Understanding Relationships.* London: Academic Press.
Stewart RB, Mobley LA, van Tuyl SS, Salvador MA The first born's adjustment to the birth of a sibling: A longitudinal assessment. *Child Development* 58: 341–355
Volling B (2003) Sibling relationships. In: Bornstein MH, Davidson L, Keyes CLM, and Moore KA (eds.) *Well-Being: Positive Development Across the Life Course.* Mahwah, NJ: Erlbaum.

Relevant Website

http://www.excellence-earlychildhood.ca – Centre of Excellence for Early Childhood Development.

SIDS

T G Keens, Keck School of Medicine of the University of Southern California, Los Angeles, CA, USA
D R Gemmill, California Sudden Infant Death Syndrome Advisory Council, Escondido, CA, USA

Glossary

Apnea – Stopping breathing. This usually refers to a breathing pause at least 20 s in duration.
Bedsharing – An infant sleeping in the same bed with one or more other people.
CHIME study – Collaborative Home Infant Monitoring Evaluation research project. This was a multicenter research study, funded in the National Institutes of Health in 1991–99. The study used custom-designed home monitors to study breathing, heart rate, and oxygen in over 1000 infants in their own homes during the first 6 months of life.
Electrocardiogram (ECG) – A diagnostic test to assess the rhythm and structure of the heart.
Home apnea–bradycardia monitoring – Commercial devices which monitor breathing and heartbeat, sounding a loud audible alarm when breathing stops for a designated time (usually 20 s) or heart rate falls below a designated rate. These monitors are designed to alert caregivers when a baby stops breathing or heart rate falls.
Hypercapnia – Abnormally elevated carbon dioxide levels in blood or tissues. Blood CO_2 is a measure of the adequacy of breathing, and hypercapnia indicates inadequate breathing or respiratory failure.
Hypoxia – Abnormally low oxygen levels in blood or tissues.
Intrathoracic petechiae – Pinpoint hemorrhages on the surfaces of organs in the chest. These are commonly seen in sudden infant death syndrome victims, but unusual in other causes of infant death.
Overlaying – Smothering an infant by lying on it during sleep.
Polymorphisms – Variations in gene structure that occur as variants in a normal population. These polymorphisms may be associated with quantitative variations in gene function that may predispose to disease.
Prone sleeping – Sleeping on the stomach.
Sudden infant death syndrome (SIDS) – The sudden unexpected death of an infant, under 1 year of age, with onset of the fatal episode apparently occurring during sleep, that remains unexplained after a thorough investigation, including performance of a complete autopsy, and review of the circumstances of death and the clinical history.
Supine sleeping – Sleeping on the back.

Introduction

> And this woman's son died in the night . . .
>
> 1 Kings, 3: 19 (~950 B.C.E.)

Sudden infant death syndrome (SIDS) is the sudden unexpected death of an infant under 1 year of age, with onset of the fatal episode apparently occurring during sleep, that remains unexplained after a thorough investigation, including performance of a complete autopsy and review of the circumstances of death and the clinical history. For 3000 years, it has been recognized that apparently healthy infants could die suddenly and unexpectedly during their sleep. Throughout most of history, it was believed that these infants somehow suffocated, either by maternal overlaying or by strangling in bedclothes. Although these explanations have largely been discarded, one infant per 2000 live births continues to die suddenly and unexpectedly from SIDS.

A typical clinical course for an SIDS death is that the parents or caregivers put their infant to sleep, either at night or during a daytime nap. They return at some later time to find that the infant has died unexpectedly. Usually, these infants were healthy prior to death, although some had evidence of a mild upper respiratory infection. SIDS deaths have occurred when parents or caregivers have placed their infants down for a nap, have been within hearing distance of the infant the entire time, and have returned as briefly as 30 min later to find that their infant has died. Yet, these parents report hearing no signs of a struggle. Thus, SIDS deaths appear to occur swiftly and silently.

By definition, the etiology of SIDS is not known. In approximately 20% of infants who die suddenly and unexpectedly, a conventionally accepted cause for the death is found at postmortem examination. These infants are not said to have died from SIDS, but rather from the cause of death found by the postmortem examination. The remainder, in whom no cause of death could be found, comprises the group called SIDS.

SIDS is the most common cause of infant death between the ages of 1 month and 1 year. During the 1980s in most Western countries, SIDS killed approximately 1.5 infants out of every 1000 live births, or approximately one in every 650 live births. Since 1990, the SIDS rate has steadily fallen, in conjunction with greater attention to the infant sleeping environment, and there were approximately 0.5 SIDS deaths per 1000 live births in 2003. SIDS rates for less developed countries are probably not accurate, since these countries have high infant death rates from respiratory, diarrhea, and infectious disorders, and many SIDS deaths may be lost in these statistics (**Figure 1**).

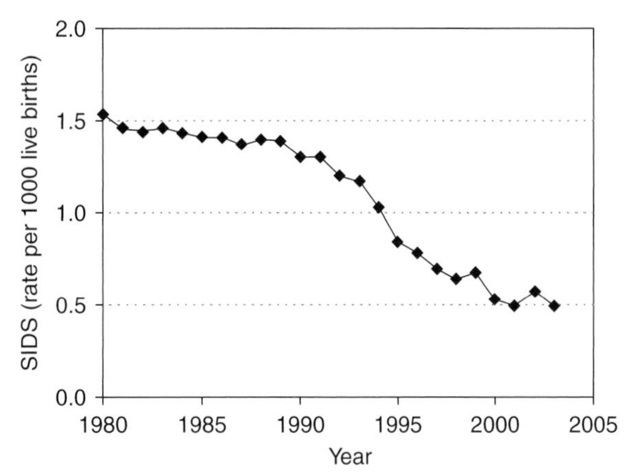

Figure 1 SIDS rates in the US. The SIDS rate per 1000 live births, is plotted for each year from 1980 through 2003.

By definition, SIDS occurs in the first year of life. The peak age is 2–4 postnatal months. SIDS is relatively less common in the first month of life, and 95% of SIDS deaths occur before 6 months of age. This is a unique age distribution, which differs from that of other natural causes of infant death, where the death rate is usually highest near birth and falls off with increasing age. SIDS tends to be more common in winter months than in summer months. The reasons for these distributions are unknown.

Diagnosis

The diagnosis of SIDS can only be made in an infant who has died. There is no known less severe form of SIDS in a living infant, and SIDS cannot be predicted in any infant prior to death. Many states and countries require that sudden infant deaths must be investigated to determine a cause of death. Ideally, in order to accurately diagnose SIDS, there should be an examination of the death scene performed by a qualified investigator, and an autopsy on the baby performed by a qualified forensic or pediatric pathologist. Death scene investigation protocols and autopsy protocols have been developed, and many authorities urge the use of these standardized protocols in order to improve the accuracy and consistency of diagnosis. The diagnosis of SIDS should be used as the cause of death when an infant meets this definition: (1) under 1 year of age; (2) death was sudden and unexpected; (3) death occurred when the infant was thought to be asleep; (4) examination of the death scene reveals no alternative cause of death; (5) autopsy reveals no identifiable cause of death; and (6) the case history does not indicate a medical problem which could have caused the death.

In some jurisdictions, medical examiners are reluctant to use the SIDS diagnosis if there is a question about other factors that may have contributed to the death, such as bedsharing or dangerous sleeping environments. In such cases, a diagnosis of undetermined cause of death is frequently used. Unless there is convincing evidence suggesting a cause of death other than SIDS, use of the term 'SIDS' is recommended, as this avails parents of SIDS supportive services and makes research dependent on these diagnoses valid.

By definition, an identifiable cause of death is not found at postmortem examination. The autopsy of an SIDS victim shows the absence of other serious illness that could contribute to the death, no signs of severe illness, and no signs of significant stress. However, common postmortem findings in the SIDS victim include:

intrathoracic petechiae; pulmonary congestion and edema; minor airway inflammation (not severe enough to cause death); minimal stress effects in the thymus and adrenal glands; and normal nutrition and development. The significance of the latter four of these findings is that these infants were generally healthy prior to death. Neither epidemiologic studies nor the postmortem findings have resulted in a generally accepted cause for SIDS. The cause remains unknown, though current research efforts are making advances in our knowledge, which may ultimately lead to this answer.

Epidemiology

Epidemiologic studies have been performed in an attempt to identify risk factors for SIDS. When a risk factor is found in a population, the statistical risk of SIDS occurring in those infants who have the risk factor is increased. However, risk factors are not causes of SIDS, although they may provide clues for researchers to the cause of SIDS. Therefore, they are important for research. However, no risk factor, singly or in combination, is sufficiently precise to predict the baby who will die from SIDS. Further, many SIDS victims had few, if any, risk factors prior to death.

Maternal factors associated with a statistically increased risk for SIDS include: cigarette smoking or substance abuse (specifically opiates or cocaine) during pregnancy, teenaged and older mothers, increasing birth order, short interpregnancy intervals, delay in initiating prenatal care, unmarried mothers, low blood pressure during the third trimester of pregnancy, and high or low hemoglobin during late gestation. SIDS is more common in lower socioeconomic groups. SIDS is more common in African Americans, and in indigenous populations around the world (Native Americans, Eskimos, Aborigines, Maoris, etc.). Although these studies do not point to a specific etiology, some investigators believe that they suggest that infants who had a suboptimal intrauterine environment may be at a higher risk of dying from SIDS.

Infant factors that are associated with a statistically increased risk for SIDS include: preterm birth, low birth weight, and multiple gestation (twins, triplets, etc.). Often, SIDS deaths are temporally associated with viral respiratory infections, though often when the infection appeared to be resolving. Recently, many factors associated with the infant sleeping environment have been associated with an increased SIDS risk. Some factors include prone sleeping; soft bedding, pillows, and stuffed toys in the bed; cigarette smoking around babies; overheating; and bedsharing. These risk factors can potentially be modified. Public health programs designed to modify these risks have successfully decreased the number of SIDS deaths by over half.

Epidemiological studies have been invaluable in helping to decrease the number of babies dying from SIDS. However, many infants who died from SIDS had few if any of these risk factors. Therefore, they are not the cause of SIDS.

Research on the Cause of SIDS

The cause of SIDS is not known. There are no tests that can be performed on living infants that will predict SIDS. SIDS appears to be the result of a natural process. SIDS deaths do not occur because of something SIDS parents did or failed to do. SIDS is probably not as simple as one abnormality in one physiological system. Filiano and Kinney suggested that SIDS is likely due to an interaction of: (1) a developmental window of vulnerability; (2) intrinsic physiological differences in infants affecting each one's vulnerability; and (3) environmental factors. An infant's vulnerability may lie latent until the infant reaches a developmental window of vulnerability and is exposed to an external stressor. Thus, it is likely that an understanding of the etiology of SIDS will require a new paradigm for understanding human disease (**Figure 2**).

Cardiac arrhythmias. When one thinks of sudden death, one usually thinks of heart failure or respiratory failure. Some investigators have described genetic abnormalities

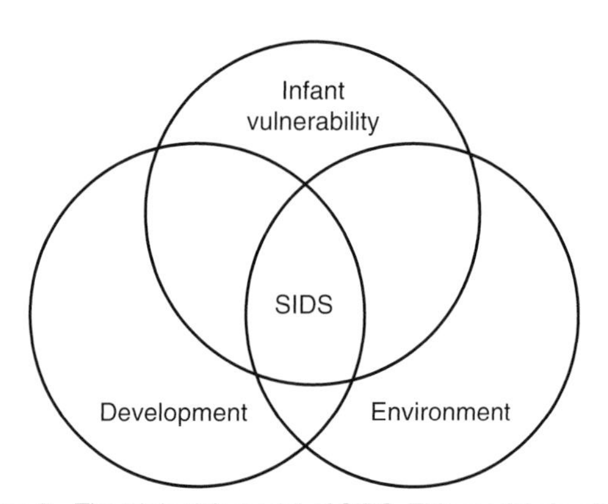

Figure 2 The triple risk model of SIDS. This model visualizes the concept that SIDS is likely due to the interaction of many factors. The risk of an infant dying from SIDS is represented by the area of overlap of all three circles. The top circle represents an infant's vulnerability. Different infants may have different sized circles based on genetic variations or other differences in physiology. The circle on the left is affected by age. Two-to-four months of age represent a developmental window of vulnerability, where the SIDS risk is highest, and the circle would be largest. It would be much smaller for a 1-week-old infant or an 11-month-old infant. The circle on the right represents environment. Prone sleeping, exposure to cigarette smoke, overheating, etc., increase the risk of SIDS. Modified from Filiano JJ and Kinney HC (1994) A perspective on neuropathologic findings in victims of the sudden infant death syndrome: The triple-risk model. *Biology of the Neonate* 65: 194–197.

of cardiac repolarization, which may predispose infants to the sudden development of fatal cardiac arrhythmias. These would not be able to be detected postmortem. However, a large study in Italy, by Schwartz and colleagues, suggests that the prolonged QT interval syndrome may cause a number of SIDS deaths. We now know that several genetic mutations, which can be detected in postmortem tissues by DNA testing, may have been present in some infants who have died. This research indicates that these types of cardiac abnormalities can cause sudden death, which is indistinguishable from SIDS. However, it is unclear if these rare genetic disorders comprise a substantial proportion of SIDS. Since it is not known if these disorders are frequent, there is not enough evidence to suggest that infants should be routinely screened with electrocardiograms (ECGs) to attempt to identify such abnormalities prior to death.

Apnea. Another possibility is that SIDS may be due to a sudden respiratory arrest, or apnea (prolonged breathing pause). This has been a popular hypothesis for many years, but more recently it has fallen from favor. There appears to be little evidence that an isolated apnea is the cause of SIDS. The use of home apnea–bradycardia monitors, which sound an alarm if an infant stops breathing for 20 s or longer or the heart rate drops below set levels, has not resulted in a drop in the SIDS rate, and it is not currently recommended as a strategy to prevent SIDS. Nevertheless, there are significant cardiorespiratory interactions, which may explain SIDS deaths through perturbations of the autonomic nervous system.

Brainstem dysfunction. Most researchers believe that the origin of the cause of SIDS lies in dysfunction of the portions of the brain involved in 'life support'. SIDS occurs during sleep. Sleep disrupts breathing, and this causes hypoxia, even in normal infants not destined to die from SIDS. The low oxygen resulting from an apnea is probably not sufficient to directly cause an infant's death. However, research from postmortem examinations of SIDS victims finds abnormalities in certain parts of the brainstem, which are thought to be important in the control of breathing and/or protective mechanisms when breathing fails. This suggests that many SIDS victims had abnormalities in the way their brains responded to environmental stresses, such as high carbon dioxide (CO_2) or low oxygen. High CO_2 and low oxygen can result from a prolonged apnea.

Arousal (waking up). Arousal is an important defense against danger-signaling stimuli during sleep, and many SIDS researchers believe that a failure to arouse in response to such stimuli may contribute to SIDS. Thus, a great deal of research has been done on a normal infant's ability to be aroused in response to a variety of stimuli, including respiratory stimuli. Infants in the first month of life are better able to be aroused in response to low oxygen than older infants. The decrease in this hypoxic arousal corresponds to the increased risk of SIDS at 2–4 months of age. It is possible that this brainstem-mediated hypoxic arousal response is lost with growth, as cortical development inhibits more 'primitive' brainstem responses. The late Andre Kahn and colleagues performed research sleep studies on thousands of infants in Europe, some of whom subsequently died from SIDS. Kato and Kahn found that those infants who subsequently died from SIDS had fewer spontaneous arousals during sleep than infants who did not die. Further, SIDS victims had more subcortical arousals, detected by electroencephalogram (EEG) criteria. However, these subcortical arousals failed to progress to cortical arousals that would allow an infant to fully awaken and respond to a potentially dangerous situation. Franco and Kahn found that infants with some SIDS risk factors had impaired arousal responses to sound. More research is required in this area. Nevertheless, these results suggest that infants with impaired spontaneous or induced arousals from sleep may be more vulnerable to an SIDS death. Many scientists now believe that anything that inhibits an infant's ability to arouse from sleep may increase the risk of SIDS.

Cardiorespiratory control. SIDS occurs at a peak age of 2–4 months. This is an age when infants are undergoing rapid and tremendous changes in brain development, particularly in cardiorespiratory control. From an engineering point of view, a system in rapid transition is intrinsically unstable. Thus, when the neurologic system controlling breathing is undergoing rapid change, it is also more likely to malfunction, and serious apnea can occur. However, in the 1990s, the Collaborative Home Infant Monitoring Evaluation (CHIME) Study did not find that prolonged apneas occur at the age when SIDS is most common. Thus, apnea alone is not likely to be the mechanism of death in SIDS. SIDS is not as simple as an infant simply stopping breathing during sleep.

Neurologic control of respiration and of cardiac function is linked. We now know that the autonomic nervous system, the life-support part of the central nervous system, links cardiac and respiratory function. Breathing has a profound influence on function of the heart, including its rhythm and blood pressure. The details of this relationship are beginning to be elucidated, but they are not completely understood. Nevertheless, we know that aberrations in breathing can alter cardiac responses to environmental changes. For example, adults with obstructive sleep apnea syndrome (OSAS), a disorder where there are repeated occlusions of the upper airway during sleep, have serious cardiac complications from their primary respiratory disorder, including high blood pressure, cardiac arrhythmias, and sudden death. Similarly, children with other abnormalities in respiratory control (such as congenital central hypoventilation syndrome) have abnormal cardiovascular responses to changes in breathing or in the environment. These are mediated by aberrations in the autonomic nervous system's coupling of cardiac and respiratory function. It is possible that respiratory abnormalities in infants may cause cardiovascular collapse through autonomic nervous system mechanisms, and this cardiovascular collapse may cause sudden death – SIDS.

Do respiratory problems cause cardiovascular collapse in all infants? Do infants need to have abnormalities in the brain in order to have these abnormal reactions? Can 'normal' mechanisms transform the brain to have aberrant cardiac responses to respiratory perturbations? Imaging studies of the brain's response to hypoxia or hypercapnia performed in children, using functional magnetic resonance imaging (fMRI), show that many parts of the brain are involved in these neural responses to cardiac and respiratory control, not just the brainstem. Harper and colleagues showed that the cerebellum has an important role in neural control of cardiorespiratory function. Similarly, midbrain areas, including areas in the limbic system, also participate in cardiorespiratory control. Thus, lesions or damage to many parts of the brain may affect autonomic function. Some of these areas may be more susceptible to damage from hypoxia than the brainstem, which was traditionally thought to be the anatomic site of cardiorespiratory control.

Hypoxia (low oxygen). Hypoxia may also play an important role in SIDS. The CHIME study showed that normal infants experience significant hypoxia in their own homes during sleep. The Purkinje fibers in the cerebellum are especially sensitive to hypoxic damage. In fact, pathologists often diagnose hypoxia at autopsy when they see damage to Purkinje fibers. These neurons modulate autonomic nervous system control of blood pressure and cardiovascular instability. If Purkinje fibers are damaged by hypoxia, the unchecked autonomic brain structures fire sporadically and erratically, causing highly varying cardiorespiratory function. Specifically, the cardiac response to respiratory perturbations may be unpredictable and potentially dangerous. Thus, hypoxia can make an infant vulnerable to abnormal, exaggerated, and/or life-threatening cardiovascular responses to respiratory stimuli. Removal of this cerebellar modulation of cardiorespiratory control can lead to physiologic crises, perhaps resulting in death. These studies suggest that SIDS may be due to a combination of a respiratory and a cardiac death, with the link being aberrant autonomic nervous system function.

Metabolic disorders. Metabolic disorders are inherited conditions, which decrease the body's ability to generate the energy necessary to sustain life from ingested food. There are thousands of metabolic disorders, but disorders of the β-oxidation of fatty acids are thought to be most relevant to SIDS. These disorders decrease the body's ability to make the energy, especially under conditions of fasting, fever, or other stresses. While some investigators believe that metabolic disorders may explain some SIDS deaths, the proportion of deaths so explained is not known, and most investigators believe it is a small proportion.

Genetic factors. Genetic factors may explain the increased vulnerability for SIDS in some infants. SIDS is not thought to be an inherited disorder. That is, there is no genetic mutation that has been shown to cause SIDS, or even to be present in a large number of SIDS victims. However, most genes have minor variations in structure (polymorphisms), which do not cause abnormal gene function. However, these polymorphisms may be associated with slight quantitative variations in gene function. For example, promoter polymorphisms of the serotonin transporter gene affect the amount of serotonin, a neurotransmitter thought to be important in cardiorespiratory control, which is available for signaling between neurons. There are two polymorphisms, a short and a long form. The long form metabolizes serotonin more quickly, leaving less available for neurotransmitter function. Narita and Weese-Mayer and their colleagues have found that the long promoter polymorphism of the serotonin transporter gene was more common in babies who died from SIDS than in controls. The long promoter polymorphism of the serotonin transporter gene does not cause abnormal function of the gene, which would cause a disease. Rather it simply promotes more serotonin metabolism than does the short promoter polymorphism of the serotonin transporter gene. Having less serotonin available as a neurotransmitter may make some infants less resilient to coping with environmental changes, or it may slightly alter physiologic protective mechanisms, such that some infants might be more susceptible to environmental or other challenges. Similarly, Weese-Mayer found mutations or polymorphisms in other genes thought to be important in development of the autonomic nervous system that were more common in SIDS victims than in controls. These studies do not prove that SIDS is a genetic disorder. However, such genetic variation may be a partial basis for why some infants are more vulnerable than others in Filiano and Kinney's triple risk model.

In summary, the cause of SIDS is not known. Investigations into the role of cardiac arrhythmias and metabolic disorders must continue. However, SIDS is generally not thought to be due to a single abnormality in a single physiologic system. SIDS is not thought to be due to an infection, environmental toxin, or nutritional deficiency. If there is a pre-existing abnormality in babies who die from SIDS, it must be subtle, as it has eluded identification by researchers for decades. It is more likely that small differences in infant vulnerabilities, such as those caused by genetic polymorphisms that predispose to autonomic nervous system instability, combined with an environmental stressor that occurs in a developmental window of vulnerability, all come together to cause an SIDS death.

Public Health Measures to Reduce the Risk of SIDS

Although the cause of SIDS is unknown, since the mid-1980s, epidemiologists have identified a number of potentially modifiable risk factors, which increase the risk of SIDS. In most cases, the mechanisms by which these risk factors operate are unknown. Nevertheless, a number of countries have established aggressive public health and public education campaigns to reduce the risk of SIDS. These have resulted in a fall in the SIDS rate to less than one-half what it was prior to these campaigns.

Prone Sleeping Position

Beginning in the 1980s, several investigators in several countries found that prone sleeping was associated with an increased risk of SIDS. The increased risk has been reported as being 10–20 times higher than in babies who sleep supine. The mechanism that underlies the danger of prone sleeping is not known. However, several epidemiologic studies from several countries leave no doubt that having babies sleep in the supine position decreases the risk of SIDS. Many countries have instituted public education campaigns to decrease prone sleeping and encourage supine sleeping (**Figure 3**). These campaigns have not only decreased prone sleeping, but they have also been associated with a decrease in SIDS deaths by over 50% (**Figure 4**).

Studies have shown that sleeping on the side is also associated with an increased SIDS risk of three to seven times higher than sleeping on the back, but not as high as prone sleeping. Therefore, all infants should be encouragedto sleep flat on their backs through the first year of life, as this carries the lowest risk for SIDS. Some infant developmental authorities were concerned that the promotion of supine sleeping would hinder infant development, as babies learn many developmental tasks in the prone position. There is no danger to having infants spend waking time in the prone position, where developmental tasks may be mastered. However, they should spend sleeping time on their backs.

Avoid Soft Bedding, Pillows, Stuffed Animals, etc.

Soft bedding, where a baby's head can be nestled in a small air pocket, increases the risk of SIDS. Especially dangerous are beanbags, water mattresses, sheepskins, soft pillows, quilts, comforters, and soft bedding placed under the infant. Studies show that placing pillows and soft objects in the crib with a sleeping infant is associated with a two to three times increased risk of SIDS. Further, infant crib mattresses should be firm, and only covered with a thin sheet. Studies show that soft mattresses are associated with a five-times increased risk of SIDS. Used crib mattresses may be dangerous. If these mattresses are soft and not firm from extensive use, they should be discarded.

Keep soft objects and loose bedding out of the crib. Bedding should be thin and placed in a way that the infant's head cannot be covered. Place the infant's feet at the foot of the crib ('Feet to Foot'). Thin blankets should be tucked so they

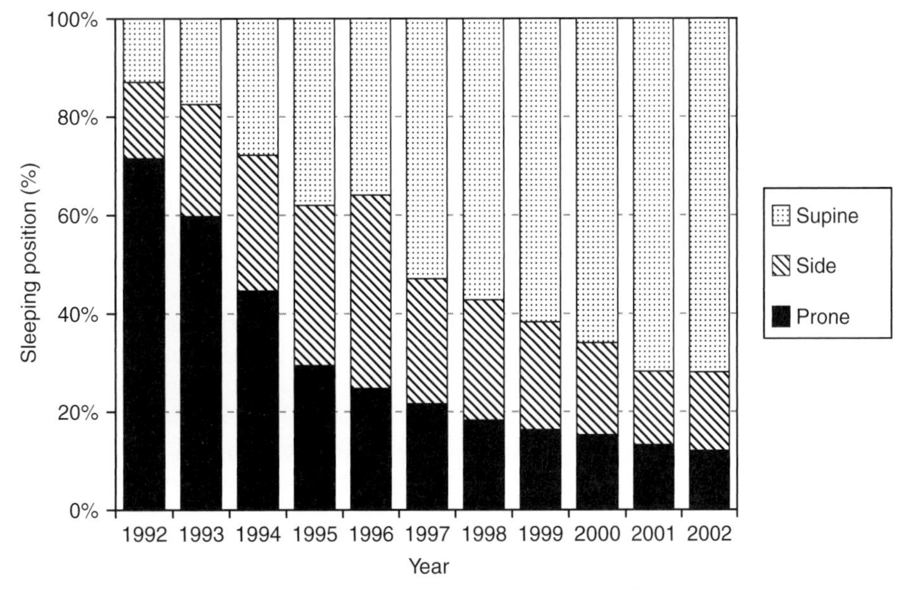

Figure 3 National infant sleep position study (US). The proportion of infants in the US who sleep in the prone, side, and supine positions are shown for each year from 1992 through 2002. There has been a marked drop in the proportion of infants sleeping prone in response to public health campaigns. Data obtained from the National Infant Sleep Position Study, and from Willinger M, Hoffman HJ, Wu K-T, *et al.* (1998) Factors associated with the transition to nonprone sleep positions of infants in the United States: The National Infant Sleep Position Study. *Journal of the American Medical Association* 280: 329–335.

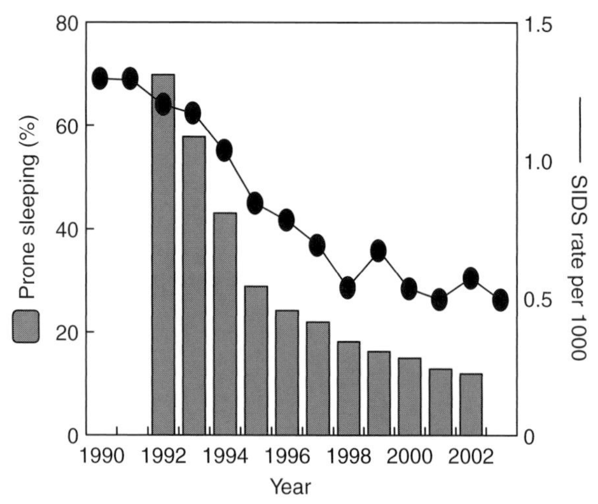

Figure 4 US prone sleeping and SIDS rate. For each year from 1990 through 2003 in the US, the proportion of infants sleeping prone is plotted with the shaded bars (Y-axis on the left); and the SIDS rate per 1000 live births is plotted with the circles connected by a line (Y-axis on the right). As the proportion of infants who sleep prone fell, so did the SIDS rate. Data obtained from the National Infant Sleep Position Study and from Willinger M, Hoffman HJ, Wu K-T, Hou J-R, *et al.* (1998) Factors associated with the transition to nonprone sleep positions of infants in the United States: The National Infant Sleep Position Study. *Journal of the American Medical Association* 280: 329–335.

can come up no higher than the mid-chest of the baby. Alternatively, one can use a sleep sack or one-piece clothing designed to keep the infant warm without the possible hazard of covering the infant's head. Additional blankets or covers are not needed with these sleep clothes. Stuffed animals should not be placed in a crib with a sleeping infant. Infants can play with them when they are awake.

Cigarette Smoking

Mothers should not smoke cigarettes during pregnancy. Infants of mothers who smoke 20 or more cigarettes per day face an eight-times increased risk of SIDS. The specific mechanism by which smoking increases the SIDS risk is not known. However, there are many studies of the harmful effects of maternal cigarette smoking on the fetus, including poor intrauterine growth, autonomic nervous system disturbances, and abnormal lung development. Further, infant exposure to cigarette smoking after birth is also associated with an increased risk of SIDS. No one should smoke cigarettes around any baby. No one should smoke cigarettes in a baby's room, even if the baby is not there. Infants exposed to 8 hours or more per day of environmental tobacco smoke face a tentimes increased risk of SIDS.

Bedsharing

Bedsharing has been the most common sleeping arrangement for mothers and infants for millennia, and it has increased in popularity among Western mothers. However, there has been fear that bedsharing parents could roll onto sleeping infants and smother them, also known as overlaying. The risk of maternal overlaying is thought to increase if the parents' ability to awaken (arouse) is inhibited, as with alcohol ingestion, drug use, or sleep deprivation. But, it is not known how frequently overlaying occurs. A definitive diagnosis of overlaying is difficult, and it can usually only be suggested by observation at the scene of death. Part of the difficulty in being certain about whether overlaying has occurred is illustrated by the following scenario. Suppose a baby is found dead in bed with an adult who has rolled over onto the infant. Did the baby die because the adult rolled onto it and smothered it? If so, why did the baby's movements not waken the adult? Or, did the baby die from SIDS, and the adult roll over on the lifeless baby, who did not move, and therefore did not awaken the adult? Neither a death scene investigation nor an autopsy can distinguish between these two scenarios with certainty.

Some investigators have suggested that bedsharing imparts protection or a survival advantage to the infant. It is clear that there is a great deal of behavioral interaction, which occurs, between a mother and infant during bedsharing. Breastfeeding is increased during bedsharing nights. However, no study has convincingly shown any protective effects of bedsharing on the infant.

A number of epidemiological studies have shown that the risk of SIDS is increased when infants bedshare the entire night. This is especially true if the parents are cigarette smokers, even if they do not smoke in bed. However, many studies show an increased SIDS risk from bedsharing even if the parents do not smoke cigarettes. Most studies indicate that the risk of SIDS with bedsharing is higher in young infants less than 4 months of age. Bedsharing on a couch or sofa is particularly dangerous, and has been associated with a 50-times increased SIDS risk. The issue is further complicated by the nature of the bedsharing. Some families choose to bedshare, but they possibly do so in a safe manner. That is, the mattress is firm, the infant is supine, there is no cigarette smoking, adults' arousal is not impaired, etc. Other families, usually in poor socioeconomic situations, bedshare because they have no choice. Bedsharing may occur in unsafe beds (soft mattresses) or crowded conditions, and there may be multiple bedsharers, including children. In these cases, there may be a number of other risk factors that increase the SIDS risk in addition to bedsharing, and it may be difficult to separate these effects from the effect of bedsharing alone.

Epidemiological studies also indicate that there is an increased risk for SIDS when infants sleep in a separate room from the parents. Therefore, the safest sleeping environment for infants appears to be room sharing without bedsharing. A crib placed in the same room as the parents has the lowest SIDS risk in several studies, and this is currently recommended. The crib should have a firm mattress and conform to safety standards. The baby may be brought into the bed for breastfeeding, but the infant should then be returned to the crib.

Despite this recommendation, many parents are still bedsharing. If parents choose this path, they need to understand that the mechanism for the increased SIDS risk is not known. Therefore, it is difficult to give advice on what to do or not do while bedsharing. However, it is clear that bedsharing is unsafe with: (1) cigarette smoking by the parents; (2) soft or unsafe mattress or bed; (3) quilts, pillows, or soft covers in the bed; (4) covering the infant's head with blankets; (5) prone or side sleeping; (6) parental alcohol or drug use; and (7) parental sleep deprivation, defined as less than 4 h of sleep on the previous night. As a baby frequently disrupts the sleep of new parents, this last condition may be particularly difficult to avoid. In summary, it would be very difficult to avoid all of the above while bedsharing. Therefore, room-sharing, without bedsharing, remains the safest recommendation for infant sleep.

Pacifiers

Pediatricians often discouraged use of pacifiers because it was believed that they caused dental problems and delayed or discouraged breastfeeding. However, a number of studies have shown a marked decrease in the risk for SIDS when infants use pacifiers in the first year of life. The mechanism for this protection is not known. Further, scientific evidence indicating that pacifiers cause dental problems or inhibit breastfeeding is absent. Therefore, it is recommended that infants be offered a pacifier for use during sleep in the first year of life. If an infant does not take the pacifier, it should not be forced. If the pacifier falls out of the infant's mouth during sleep, it need not be reinserted in order to achieve the epidemiologic protective effect. It is recommended that pacifier use be delayed until 1 month of age, so that breastfeeding can be established. There is little evidence that pacifier use will inhibit breastfeeding by this age. Pacifiers should not be coated in sweet solutions in order to avoid tooth decay. Honey, especially, should be avoided because of the risk of infant botulism.

Avoid Overheating

In some epidemiologic studies, there was evidence that SIDS infants were warmer than infants who did not die. SIDS infants were more likely to have more thermal insulation in clothes and blankets, have a heater in the room, use hot water bottles or electric blankets, and wear a hat, compared to controls. It is recommended that parents avoid overheating of infants. Infants should be lightly clothed for sleep, and the bedroom temperature should be comfortable for a lightly clothed adult. Infants should not be dressed so they feel hot to the touch.

Avoid Commercial Devices to 'Prevent SIDS'

A number of commercial devices have been developed and marketed 'to prevent SIDS'. These are designed to fix an infant in a certain sleeping position, or to provide a continuous flow of air through the mattress to make prone sleeping 'safe'. These devices have not been tested for safety or efficacy, and they are not recommended. When infants are placed flat on their backs to sleep, such devices are not necessary.

Home Apnea–Bradycardia Monitoring

Home apnea–bradycardia monitors are devices that monitor an infant's breathing and heartbeat. They sound an audible alarm if breathing stops for a period of time (usually 20 s) or if heart rate falls below a certain specified limit. Trained caregivers are then alerted to a potentially dangerous situation, and they do what is necessary to revive the infant. Although this sounds like a good idea, home monitoring has never been proven to prevent SIDS. Therefore, it should not be used as a strategy to reduce the risk of SIDS.

Breastfeeding

Breastfeeding has many benefits for infant health, and it should be encouraged for these reasons. However, breastfeeding probably does not have a specific effect on reducing the risk of SIDS. Many studies suggest that infants who breastfeed have a decreased risk for SIDS, but some studies show no difference. Many studies show that breastfeeding is associated with a reduced risk of SIDS by univariate analysis. However, when corrected for other co-varying risk factors by multivariate analysis, breastfeeding is not protective. This may reflect the fact that breastfeeding mothers are generally more likely to adhere to other practices known to reduce the risk of SIDS, such as supine sleeping, not smoking cigarettes, using safe bedding, etc. Thus, while breastfeeding should be encouraged for its general health benefits for infants, by itself, it does not appear to reduce the risk of SIDS.

It should be emphasized that none of these potentially modifiable risk factors are causes of SIDS. They have been shown, by epidemiological studies, to reduce the risk of SIDS. Infants without any of these risk factors continue to die from SIDS, and most infants with one or more of these risk factors will not die from SIDS. If an infant with one or more of these risk factors dies, it should not be concluded that these factors caused the infant's death. However, when viewed from a population perspective, adhering to these recommendations has been associated with a substantial decrease in the number of babies who die from SIDS. Therefore, they should be recommended to parents of infants in order to decrease the chances of their infant's dying from SIDS.

Parent Grief

The parents and families of a baby who died from SIDS are no less the victims of this tragedy than their babies. Although the death of any child is painful, SIDS deaths have some unique characteristics. SIDS deaths come quietly, suddenly, and unexpectedly. These babies were happy and healthy. They were usually tucked safely into their cribs for an overnight sleep or a daytime nap. Sometime during that sleeping period, they died. The death of any child is a devastating loss. The death of an apparently healthy child, with no symptoms or warnings, and no opportunity for SIDS parents to prepare or to say 'good bye', leaves parents with a unique grief.

Because medical professionals cannot tell a family how or why their baby died, parents often search the child's brief life for something they did, or did not do, which may have caused the death. The guilt generated by an SIDS death is tremendous, and it is generally more so than in infant deaths where the cause is known. One mother of an SIDS baby described her reaction: "Even after the autopsy ruled out all other causes of death, assuring us that we'd done nothing wrong, we found little comfort. Our son was dead. He was in my care when he died. Although part of me knew better, it was impossible to not blame myself. What had I missed? What if I had checked on him sooner? It was difficult to accept that my baby had died of no apparent cause."

The death of a child is certainly a stressful event in a family, and marriages are often strained. For many young SIDS couples, this is the first mutual experience with the loss of a loved one, and they are strangers to grief of this magnitude. In some cases, the parent who was with the baby at the time of the death may be blamed for the death by the other parent. Even if this does not happen, the loss of a child, and the individual ways of handling it, may magnify every personality difference between a husband and wife.

While not always the case, fathers (and sometimes mothers) often attempt to handle their grief by immersing themselves in work, sports, or other hobbies. Mothers report their need to discuss their child's life and death, to talk about the details, and to share their grief. This may lead to misunderstandings about one another's feelings, and assumptions about which parent is grieving 'correctly'. Couples may frequently find themselves at different places in their loss and feel worried that they might make each other sad on a 'good' day, and as a result avoid discussing their feelings. When, in the past, they may have been able to discuss most everything, even day-to-day things seem to create conflict.

There have been many unsubstantiated reports that most marriages dissolve following the death of a child from SIDS. This does not seem to be true now. While the sudden and unexpected death of a baby creates a great amount of stress on a family, access to a local SIDS parent peer support group or professional counseling is often a valuable help.

Although friends and family try to help SIDS parents cope with the death, they usually have no better understanding of SIDS than the parents. SIDS is as mysterious to them as it is to the parents. Most people know of SIDS as 'crib death', and many offer explanations based on things they have heard. The most helpful friends are those who sit and listen when parents need to talk, while the least helpful offer theories and advice about planning to have more children. It does not take long for SIDS parents to realize that they have worn out many of their family and friends.

In many families, there are other children in the family when SIDS strikes the youngest infant. Parents are not alone in their grief. The surviving children are suddenly in a family that is different. The parents look the same, but they act very differently. While it may be comforting and helpful for parents to know that their primary role as a parent is still in place, they may question every parenting decision they make. They know it is important to maintain daily routine and security for their surviving children, but at the same time it is difficult to not want to shelter and protect them from everything. Children have many questions that parents are forced to attempt to answer. Why did her brother die? Where was he now? Was she going to die during her nap? Because many young children are at an age where death does not seem final, they may want to know when the baby who died will be coming back. It does not take long for SIDS parents to realize that they are not just grieving parents, they are a grieving family. They often feel isolated, unable to explain or understand how apparently healthy babies can die in their sleep with no warning, and they worry that they will never be happy or whole again.

For most families of SIDS victims, the single best and most important resource is an SIDS parent support group. An SIDS mother said, "We might have drowned in our grief, had we not been put in touch with a local support group for SIDS families. We met with other families who had lost children in this same way, and for the first time, we felt that we were not alone. We found that other couples were grieving in similar ways, and that SIDS didn't have to mean the end of our marriage or our happiness. We were able to discuss current research, and to separate the facts from the myths. While we were unable to learn how or why our son died, we did learn some things that helped diminish our guilt and put us on a path of healing." SIDS parent support groups have SIDS parents who are available to speak with new SIDS parents at any time. While the immediate impact of the SIDS death is devastating to families, the ability to talk with someone who has been through it, who understands how they feel, and who has survived it, is reassuring.

SIDS changes a family's view of the world. One SIDS mother wrote, "It's safe to say that our son's death from SIDS changed the way we looked at everything in our lives. We questioned our marriage, our faith, our friendships, and our work. It felt easier to be cynical than fair, to be guarded rather than trusting. While we had once talked of having several children, we were now having serious disagreements about the possibility of another baby. My husband was unwilling to risk even the possibility of the death of another child. While I knew it was impossible to replace Tyler, I felt a deep need to mother another child, perhaps to prove to myself that I could, or perhaps simply to fill the empty hole that Ty's death had created. Looking back, I think I mostly just wanted to resume what I could of a normal life. I needed to be happy again. We needed to be happy again."

Many SIDS families do ultimately have subsequent babies, but this brings stress and anxiety that the SIDS death may be repeated. A subsequent child is often born to a still-grieving family, despite their efforts to pretend that everything is normal. This baby's parents may have been the same biological parents as his sibling's, but they certainly are not the same emotionally. They worry more, not just about SIDS, but also about things that had not crossed their minds with their previous pregnancies and babies. This is a time when many SIDS parents turn again to their SIDS support group friends to share their worries and fears. SIDS parents celebrate their subsequent child's first birthday with a big sigh of relief, but also with the quiet realization that, while life is good, it is missing an important member of the family.

Subsequent Siblings of SIDS Victims

When SIDS parents have a subsequent child, they are afraid that this new baby may also die. These SIDS siblings are not at increased risk for SIDS. They have the same risk of SIDS as the general population, which is a risk of approximately one per 2000 live births. There is no testing, such as sleep studies or ECGs, which can predict if a subsequent sibling of an SIDS victim is at increased risk for SIDS. Thus, such tests are not recommended. Nevertheless, SIDS parents frequently ask what they can do to reduce the risk of their subsequent baby from also dying from SIDS. Parents should do everything that any parent does to optimize the health of their baby. Once your baby is born, be sure to follow the 'Back to Sleep' recommendations. These recommendations have been shown to decrease the number of babies dying from SIDS. Find a pediatrician who is sensitive to the fact that you have had a previous baby die, and who will take your concerns seriously.

Summary

SIDS is the most common cause of death between the ages of 1 month and 1 year. It strikes approximately one out of every 2000 live births. The cause of SIDS is unknown. There are no tests currently available that can detect an infant who will die from SIDS. Reduction of SIDS risks for populations has been achieved by public health education, and SIDS rates have dropped by over 50%. Grief in SIDS parents is characterized by guilt. Based on our current understanding, SIDS is a natural cause of death, and there is nothing SIDS parents did, or did not do, to cause their baby's death.

See also: Brain Development; Brain Function; Mortality, Infant; Nature vs. Nurture; Newborn Behavior; Risk and Resilience.

Suggested Readings

American Academy of Pediatrics Policy Statement (2005) The changing concept of sudden infant death syndrome: Diagnostic coding shifts, controversies regarding the sleeping environment, and new variables to consider in reducing the risk. *Pediatrics* 116: 1245–1255.

Byard RW and Krous HF (2001) *Sudden Infant Death Syndrome: Problems, Progress, and Possibilities.* London, UK: Arnold Publications.

Filiano JJ and Kinney HC (1994) A perspective on neuropathological findings in victims of the sudden infant death syndrome: The triple-risk model. *Biology of the Neonate* 65: 194–197.

Ramanathan R, Corwin MJ, Hunt CE, *et al.* (2001) Cardiorespiratory events recorded on home monitors: Comparison of healthy infants with those at increased risk for SIDS. *Journal of the American Medical Association* 285: 2199–2207.

Willinger M, Hoffman HJ, Wu K-T, *et al.* (1998) Factors associates with the transition to nonprone sleep positions of infants in the United States: The National Infant Sleep Position Study. *Journal of the American Medical Association* 280: 329–335.

Relevant Websites

http://www.sidsalliance.org – First Candle/SIDS Alliance.

http://www.ispid.org – International Society for the Study and Prevention of Infant Deaths.

http://www.sidscenter.org – National SIDS/Infant Death Resource Center: Health Research and Services Administration, U.S. Government.

http://www.nichd.nih.gov/ – Research on SIDS. National Institute of Child Health and Human Development, U.S. Government.

http://www.sidsinternational.org – SIDS International.

Sleep

A Sadeh, Tel Aviv University, Tel Aviv, Israel

Glossary

Actigraph – A wristwatch-like device that records movements for extended periods. The information derived from actigraphy (activity-based recording) can be used to assess sleep–wake patterns. Actigraphy enables sleep assessment in the child's natural sleep environment.

Electroencephalogram (EEG) – Recordings of electrical signals from electrodes attached at different locations on the skull. The information represents brain activity, and wave forms from which sleep stages can be assessed.

Polysomnography (PSG) – A laboratory assessment of sleep including recording of electrical signals representing brain and muscle activity, eye movements, breathing patterns, and related information.

Quiet sleep – A sleep period that is characterized by relative tranquility, lack of gross body movements, and regular breathing.

Rapid eye movement (REM) sleep – Refers to the sleep state which is characterized by rapid eye movements, irregular breathing, twitches and jerky limb movements, and facial grimaces. This state is also called 'dream sleep' because it is assumed that most dreaming occurs during this period.

Settling – The sleep initiation process in infants and young children that includes overcoming problems such as bedtime resistance or difficulty falling asleep.

Introduction

The formation of sleep research as a unique scientific field has been associated with the discovery of rapid eye movement (REM) sleep in humans. Interestingly, this discovery, reported by Kleitman and Asherinsky in 1953, was based on observations of sleeping infants. This historic fact provides a special context for the interest in sleep in early development. Another important historical milestone was the publication of the manual for newborn and infant polysomnography (PSG) by Anders, Emde, and Parmelee in 1971.

The evolution of sleep–wake patterns is one of the most striking phenomena in early childhood and particularly in the first year of life. During infancy and early childhood, children spend more time in sleep than they spend in wakefulness. In infancy, the most prevalent parental concerns are related to feeding and sleep. Sleep problems in early childhood are very prevalent and disruptive to family life. The aims of this review are (1) to introduce the topic of sleep from a scientific perspective; (2) to describe the development of sleep–wake patterns; (3) to provide knowledge on factors influencing sleep and domains that are affected by sleep; and (4) to describe common sleep problems in early childhood: their effects and the means to manage these problems.

What is Sleep?

At first, the definition of sleep appears quite intuitive. However, scientific efforts to define sleep have led scientists to the realization that the definition of sleep is quite elusive. Definitions based on reduced awareness and responsiveness of the individual to the environment are appealing and are commonly used but they have their limitations. When we fall asleep, our awareness and responsiveness to the environment are indeed dramatically reduced. However, research has shown that when we sleep, our brain continues to process external information and our responsiveness to the environment is dependent upon the relevance and the intensity of the external stimulation. For instance, it has been shown that individuals are more likely to respond during sleep to auditory stimulation when their own name is used in comparison to other nonrelated words. Unique phenomena such as night terrors or sleepwalking also challenge these simple definitions, because they present mixed states of sleep and wakefulness. Therefore, it is not easy to sharply define the exact time when wakefulness ends and sleep starts and vice versa. Despite these limitations the reduced awareness and responsiveness to the environment are the core features of the definition of sleep.

The scientific definition of sleep is based on specific features manifested in electroencephalographic (EEG) recordings of brain activity. Specific EEG markers of brain activity have been associated with a sharp decrease in awareness and responsiveness to the environment and they are used to identify sleep stages.

Assessing Sleep

Parents are a very valuable source of information about their child's sleep–wake patterns. Young children usually require attention when they are awake and therefore parents usually know if their child is asleep or awake. Most of the research and the clinical work in this area are based on parental reports in the form of sleep questionnaires or sleep diaries.

However, research has shown that parental reports have serious limitations. For instance, if a child wakes up in the middle of the night and remains quiet his parents are less likely to know that their child was awake during the night. Considering this and other major limitations of parental reports, more sophisticated and objective methods have been developed to assess sleep–wake patterns. The gold-standard of sleep research and sleep medicine has been polysomnography (PSG). PSG is based on extensive assessment of sleep that includes attaching the child to multiple electrodes that document her brain activity, muscle activities, eye movement, and breathing efforts. These measures are required for assessing sleep stages, breathing patterns, and sleep disruptions. PSG is usually conducted in a sleep laboratory and not in the child's natural environment. It is therefore the most elaborate way to assess sleep, but this assessment does not necessarily reflect the child's natural sleep patterns.

In an attempt to capture sleep in a more naturalistic manner, additional methods have been developed. These methods include video recordings and activity-based monitoring, or actigraphy. The first method is based on video recording of infants in their crib and assessing sleep–wake patterns based on visual scoring of these recordings. Actigraphy is based on a small wristwatch-like device that can be attached to the child's ankle or wrist for extended periods (of days or weeks). The monitor records activity levels every predefined interval (e.g., 1 min) and stores them in its internal memory. Based on the unique characteristics of activity patterns during sleep and wakefulness, sleep–wake patterns are assessed in the natural environment of the child for extended periods with minimal disruptions. Based on video recordings and actigraphy it has been shown in different studies that infants often wake up during the night and resume sleep without signaling (e.g., crying) their parents. The findings of these studies revealed that self-soothing (the ability to resume sleep without crying) is a major developmental capacity that distinguishes infants reported to have sleep problems from those who do not.

The Main Rhythms of Sleep

Observation of sleeping infants led to the discovery of REM sleep in the early 1950s. As indicated earlier, this discovery was considered to be the starting point of the modern science of sleep research. Researchers interested in the phenomenon of eye movements observed that when babies fell asleep their eyes started moving rapidly and this phenomenon was associated with jerky limb movements, facial grimaces, smiles, and irregular breathing. After a short period this active sleep (the early infancy equivalent to REM) was replaced by different manifestations of quiet sleep, which is characterized by a very calm body, steady breathing, and the disappearance of REMs. These active and quiet periods of sleep alternate throughout the night in a cyclic manner. The active REM sleep was later associated with dream recollection and was also named 'dream sleep'. Furthermore, REM sleep has been associated with intense brain activity, information processing, and memory consolidation. The other type of sleep was later subdivided into four sleep stages, from stage 1 to stage 4, according to the depth of sleep and EEG correlates, where sleep stages 3 and 4 were defined as deep-sleep stages (slow-wave sleep), during which the individual is the least likely to respond to external stimuli or to wake up spontaneously.

The other major rhythm associated with sleep is the circadian rhythm that refers to the fact that sleep is a naturally recurring phenomenon, which alternates with wakefulness with a certain cyclic pattern. As diurnal animals, human sleep is mostly concentrated at night-time. The circadian rhythm relates to our internal biological clock and brain mechanisms that determine our preference to sleep at night and maintain wakefulness during the day. This repetitive 24-h cycle evolves during early childhood and is influenced by environmental and biological factors.

Development of Sleep–Wake Patterns

There are three main maturational changes in sleep–wake patterns across development. The first and most rapid maturational process is the concentration and consolidation of sleep during the night. The second change is the change in sleep architecture and mainly the significant reduction in REM sleep. The third developmental trend is the gradual decrease in total sleep time.

Consolidation of Nocturnal Sleep

Newborns spend an average of 18 h in sleep that is distributed into a number of sleep episodes (4–6) during the 24-h period (see **Figure 1**). This finding has been reported in studies over the last few decades with no substantial change. One of the most striking developmental features of the evolving sleep–wake system is the consolidation of sleep to one main episode during the night. This process is very rapid during the first 6 months of life, and in most infants, a clear preference

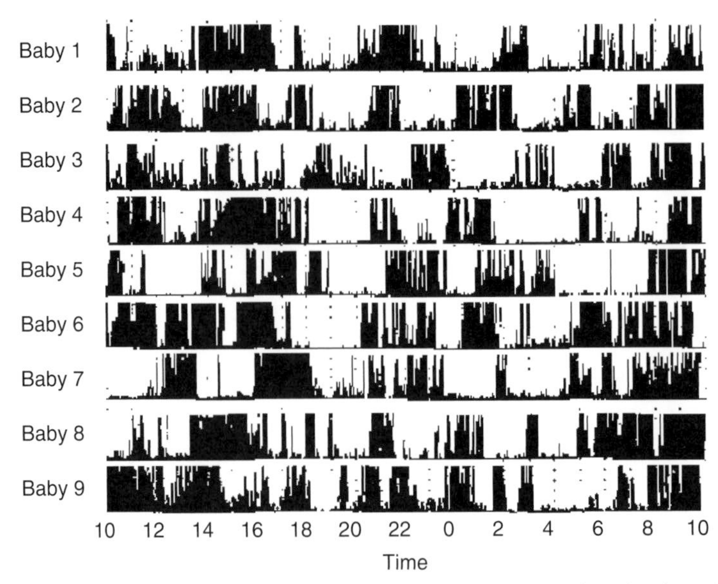

Figure 1 Sleep–wake patterns of newborn babies. The presentation is based on raw actigraphy data of nine babies. Each bar represents 24 h of specific baby. Dark lines represent activity level each minute. Dark condensed areas represent wakefulness periods. Areas with no activity or with very low activity levels represent periods of sleep.

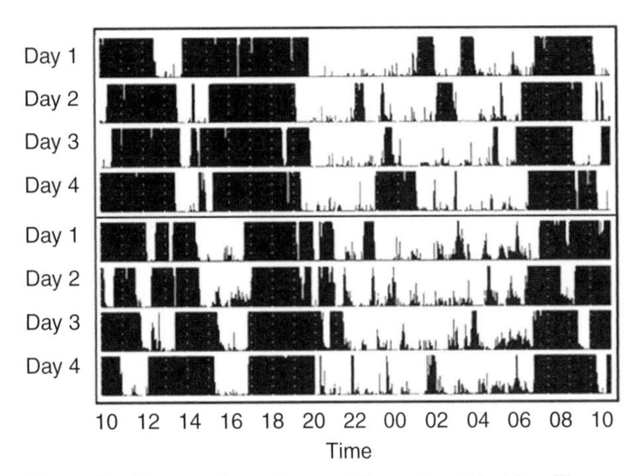

Figure 2 Sleep–wake patterns of 6-month-old babies. The presentation is based on raw actigraphy data of two infants, each for four consecutive nights. Each bar represents a 24-h period. Dark lines represent activity level each minute. Dark condensed areas represent wakefulness periods. Areas with no activity or with very low activity levels represent periods of sleep.

for night-time sleep is seen at 6 months of age (see **Figure 2**). It is estimated that by the end of the first year of life most infants are capable of sleeping through the night which means having a consolidated sleep period of at least 5–6 h at night (**Figure 3**).

As sleep becomes extended and consolidated during the night, daytime sleep decreases. As children grow they tend to have fewer and shorter naps. This trend continues until school age (5–6 years) when daytime naps become very rare. It should be noted however, that one mid-day nap (siesta) is a lifestyle choice in some cultures.

The consolidation of sleep during the night is significantly dependent on the environment. Caregivers usually encourage sleep at night by creating a quiet and dark environment for the infant and by discouraging and limiting night-time interactions. Biological processes also appear to play a major role in this process. The maturation of the pineal body in the brain during the first 6 months of life leads to adult-like secretion pattern of melatonin. Melatonin is a hormone secreted mostly during dark hours. Its secretion sharply rises in the evening hours and this rise is considered to be the time cue for other brain systems to prepare for sleep. It has been shown that daytime light exposure, and settings that provide an appropriate light–dark environment that is compatible with night–day differentiation, facilitate the consolidation of nocturnal sleep and circadian rhythms. Links between the sleep–wake system and melatonin secretion have been demonstrated. For instance, one study assessed the maturation of sleep patterns and melatonin secretion in 20 infants (age range: 26–37 weeks). Sleep was assessed using actigraphy for 1 week, and melatonin secretion was assessed by collecting samples of a metabolite of melatonin in the urine (saved in disposable diapers). Immature melatonin secretion patterns were associated with more fragmented sleep and an increase in evening melatonin level was associated with earlier bedtime.

Although the consolidation of sleep during the night is a very rapid and solid developmental trend, many infants exhibit difficulties in developing consolidated sleep. This topic is further addressed in the sleep problems section.

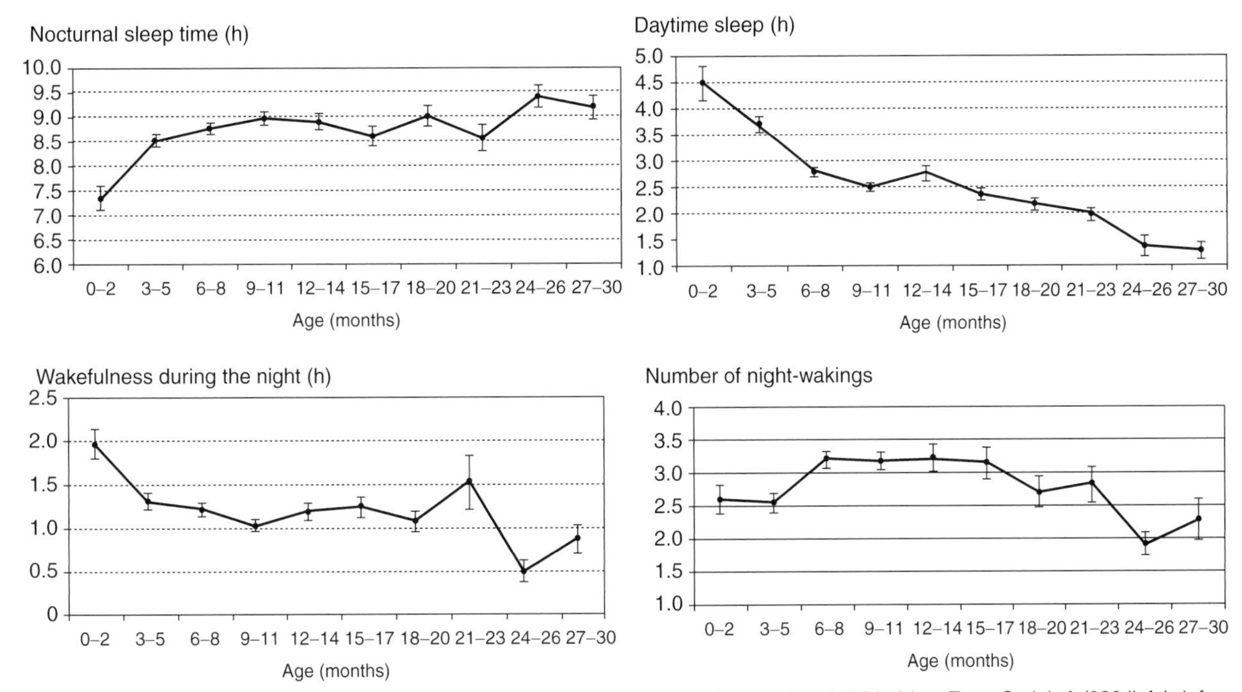

Figure 3 Sleep patterns across development: based on parental reports of more than 1000 babies. From Sadeh A (2004) A brief screening questionnaire for infant sleep problems: Validation and findings from an Internet sample. *Pediatrics* 113: e570–e577.

REM and Non-REM Sleep

Newborns spend about 50% of their sleep time in active sleep. This averages to about 8 h a day in REM sleep with its unique characteristics. During early development, the amount of time spent in REM sleep drops sharply. Actually, most of the developmental decrease in sleep time is related to the reduction in REM sleep.

Another phenomenon that is associated with the increased need for REM sleep in early infancy is that newborns and infants move directly into REM sleep as soon as they fall asleep. In later development the first REM sleep episode appears after the child spends some time in non-REM sleep stages. This delay between sleep onset and the first REM sleep episode is also called REM latency.

One of the most intriguing questions is what is the role of REM sleep in early development or why babies spend so much time in this unique sleep state. We know that during REM sleep the brain is very active although the infant is disconnected from the environment and is generally not responsive to external stimulation. From animal research, we know that there is a strong correlation between maturity of the newborn brain in each species and the amount of time that newborns of each species spend in REM sleep. Species born with a very mature brain (highly independent newborns) spend very little time in REM sleep in comparison to species born with immature brain (like the human newborn, born with about 30% of the adult brain size). Therefore, one strong hypothesis is that the intense activation of the brain during this early developmental period is needed for brain maturation, increasing the number and connectivity of neurons. Animal studies also suggest that during REM sleep, stereotypic behaviors are programmed and practiced. For instance, the famous French neurophysiologist and sleep researcher Michel Jouvet investigated what happens to cats when the area of their brainstem that is responsible for muscle paralysis during REM sleep is damaged. He reported that when these cats entered REM sleep they performed complex behaviors associated with sexual, aggressive, and explorative behaviors. The first smiles of the baby appear in REM sleep and demonstrate this activation of neurologically preprogrammed behaviors.

It has been shown in human adults and animal studies that REM sleep is directly related to information processing and consolidation of long-term memory. For instance, studies have demonstrated that selective deprivation of REM sleep led to compromised memory for new tasks learned prior to sleep. Modern research using brain mapping techniques has demonstrated that specific brain areas that were activated during a specific learning task in wakefulness turn on again during REM sleep episodes. Considering this, it appears reasonable to hypothesize that increased REM sleep time is needed in early childhood for the processing and absorption of enormous amounts of information that bombards the infant.

Decrease in Total Sleep Time

The maturational process is also clearly manifested in the total amount of time spent in sleep. From the newborn period, with an average of 16 sleep hours per day, to adulthood, with an average of 7–8 h, sleep time gradually decreases. This reduction in sleep time is mostly based on the disappearance of daytime sleep and the gradual delay of sleep onset time.

One of the common question that parents ask is "Do my child get enough sleep?" or "How long should she sleep considering her age?" Unfortunately, there is no simple answer to this question. Although information on average sleep times for different age groups exists, there are wide individual differences in sleep needs. For instance, some newborns spend 20–22 h in sleep during their first days of life, whereas others spend only 10–12 h in sleep at this time. When children get older these individual differences narrow, but they can still be quite significant, thus precluding a simple assertion as to how much sleep is appropriate for a given child at a given age. The decision is usually based on the evaluation of the child's daytime functioning. If a child is a short sleeper but functions well and does not show any signs of sleepiness or fatigue during the day, he is probably getting enough sleep. In contrast, if the child is a long sleeper but still shows signs of daytime sleepiness and fatigue he might be suffering from an undiagnosed sleep disorder that makes his sleep ineffective.

From a broader perspective, it has been claimed that because of changes in lifestyle, particularly in Western countries, including the long working hours of many parents and evening attractions such as television and the Internet, the length of sleep is gradually decreasing. Some experts suggest that the US, for instance, is a 'sleep-deprived nation' and that chronic sleep deprivation has become a common mode of living. Evidence for these claims exist for adults, teenagers, and school-age children; however, it has not yet been shown in younger children.

Factors Influencing Sleep in Early Childhood

The development of sleep in early childhood and its complex links to multiple factors could be considered from a transactional perspective. Many biological and environmental factors influence sleep but infant sleep patterns may also significantly affect the environment. **Figure 4** summarizes the transactional model proposed for infant sleep. The transactional model is based on systems dynamics and the notion that child development is influenced by bidirectional or multidirectional effects or transactions by which the parents influence their child and the child and her personal attributes affect her parents.

As demonstrated in this model, there are multiple distal and proximal factors that influence, or are influenced by, infant sleep in a transactional manner. Infant

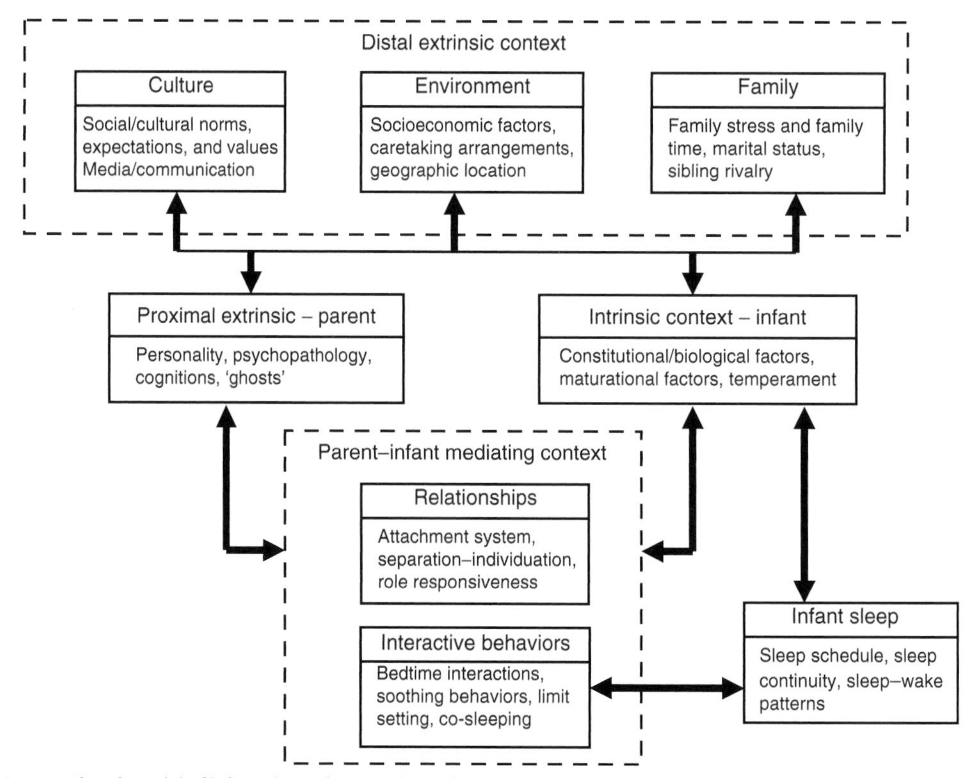

Figure 4 A transactional model of infant sleep: factors that influence and are influenced by infant sleep. After Sadeh A and Anders TF (1993) Infant sleep problems: Origins, assessment, intervention. *Infant Mental Health Journal* 14: 17–34.

sleep is influenced by infant factors such as temperament or biological and maturation factors. The parents play a role in shaping infant sleep by their sleep-related interactions with their infant (e.g., bedtime rituals, soothing techniques). Infant sleep could be a major source of family stress and shape parental behaviors in a reciprocal manner. Parental psychopathology and ghosts from their past (traumatic or stressful events) may underlie certain parental attitudes and behaviors that regulate infant sleep. For instance, parents who experienced traumatic neglect or abandonment in their childhood may be oversensitive to separation issues around bedtime and may overreact to the child. Such excessive involvement may lead to persistent sleep disruptions.

More remote factors play a more indirect role in shaping infant sleep. For instance, cultural traditions and expectations may determine what an acceptable bedtime routine or sleeping arrangement is. Co-sleeping with parents is a traditional and accepted choice in some societies (mostly in developing, non-Western, less-industrialized countries), whereas solitary sleep is the preferred choice in other societies (mostly Western industrialized societies). The socioeconomic status and the educational level of the parents appear to have significant effects on the way they address sleep-related issues and on their children's sleep. It also affects living conditions, including factors such as environmental noise level, home temperature, and sleeping arrangements, which can directly influence sleep.

The following sections address some of the factors that have been consistently associated with sleep in early childhood. In these sections, unless specified differently, the terms 'poor sleep' and 'sleep problems' usually refer to difficulty falling asleep (also addressed as settling problems) and multiple and prolonged night-wakings.

Medical and Biological Factors

Sleep is a very sensitive barometer to the physical well-being of the child. Even the most common colds or a congested nose may lead to significant sleep disruptions. Most of these conditions are transient and the associated sleep disruptions are usually resolved once the condition has run its course.

Many medical conditions have been linked to night-waking problems. Among the frequent ones are allergies, including cow-milk allergy, atopic dermatitis, colic, ear infection, gastroesophageal reflux. For instance, it has been shown that infants with persistent sleep problems, who fail to respond to behavioral interventions, suffered from cow-milk allergy. When these infants were put on a milk-free diet, their sleep improved significantly. Another study found that infants with a history of colic (excessive crying and fussing in infants, which is often associated with pain and muscle tightness) had poorer and shorter sleep compared to babies with no history of colic, between the ages of 4 and 8 months. It is quite clear that any medical problem that causes physical distress to the child is likely to interfere with sleep.

However, research suggests that some common problems or parental concerns may have been overemphasized as a potential source for sleep problems. Teething, for instance, is considered by many parents as a major cause for persistent night-waking problems. Nevertheless, studies on teething indicate that for most infants teething can cause distress for only a few days before and after tooth eruption. Therefore, it is unlikely that teething is a source of persistence and long-term sleep problems. Another major parental concern is that insufficient feeding and infant hunger are major causes for night-wakings. However, studies have shown that in normal, healthy infants, an enriched diet before bedtime does not improve sleep. Furthermore, excessive feeding during the night may serve as a reward and increase night-wakings and dependency on parents following night-wakings.

Temperament studies have suggested that perhaps infants who develop sleep problems have a certain biological vulnerability. For instance, studies have shown that children with poor sleep tend to have, according to their parents' reports, a difficult temperament, including a low sensory threshold. Low sensory threshold refers to the child's increased sensitivity to sensory stimulation, such as noise, touch, temperature, smells, and tastes. This link between poor sleep and reported low sensory threshold led to the hypothesis that this increased sensitivity of the child is the underlying cause for the sleep problem. For instance, if the child is hypersensitive to auditory stimulation he may have a difficult time falling asleep with background noise or wake-up more easily to external sounds during sleep. However, this hypothesis has never been supported by any experimental study or objective measures of both sleep and sensory reactivity.

In this context it is important to address swaddling – the technique of tightly wrapping the infant's body in tissue cloths, sheets, or light blankets. This old infant care practice is believed to reduce crying and improve sleep. Recent well-controlled studies demonstrated that indeed swaddling leads to reduction in crying and to a more consolidated sleep with fewer arousals. Another important finding was that swaddled infants required less intense auditory stimuli to arouse from REM sleep. This finding is in line with other research suggesting that sudden infant sleep syndrome (SIDS) is less likely to occur in swaddled infants.

Parenting and Infant Sleep

The most direct and consistent factor that has been associated with infant sleep is related to the parents. Poor sleep has often been associated with excessive parental involvement and interactions with the infant during the night.

Settling and night-waking problems in early childhood have been associated with specific parental characteristics and psychopathology. The most persistent finding is related to the links between maternal depression and sleep problems in early childhood. Infants and young children of depressed mothers are more likely to have sleep problems. Postpartum depression has been linked to infant sleep problems. Maternal depression also increases the likelihood of persistence of a sleep problem in early childhood. Maternal depression is also a predictor of persistence of sleep problems in young children. Studies have shown that interventions aimed at the prevention of infant sleep problems improve maternal well-being and reduce the likelihood of depression. Taken together, these studies suggest that maternal depression could be a factor in the development of sleep problems in early childhood. Furthermore, infant sleep problems may affect or exacerbate maternal depression because of the resultant maternal stress, sleepiness, and fatigue. It has been suggested that the toll of caring for a sleep-disturbed infant and the related exhaustion may make some mothers more vulnerable to postpartum depression. This area of research exemplifies how difficult it is to interpret cause and effect from findings of studies demonstrating associations between two domains. This is particularly true: there are good theoretical and intuitive rationales for both interpretations (infant sleep disruptions increase maternal depression and vice versa).

Parental sleep-related interactions with a young child appear to play a major role in determining sleep patterns. Going to sleep is a major separation for young children. During the day, the child is constantly attended to by his caregivers who are happy to respond to most of his wishes and needs. However, at night, the child is suddenly expected to separate from his attachment figures and social environment and go to sleep, often alone, in a separate dark room. As much as this separation is difficult for the child, it is often complicated for the parents to separate, and if the child protests and cries, they often feel like they are abandoning their child and this stimulates very intense and strong negative feelings. One of the measures used by many parents to alleviate this separation is the bedtime ritual. Bedtime rituals can include a bath, rocking, singing, storytelling, and other enjoyable activities around bedtime. These rituals make the transition to bed easier for many children and their parents. Studies show that in most cases, with maturation, children require less assistance to fall asleep. They usually develop their own self-soothing activities in bed and require less parental presence and assistance. However, many infants and their parents develop a falling asleep ritual that is very dependent on parental assistance. These infants fall asleep only if and while they are being nursed, rocked, held, bottle-fed or carried around the house. Research in this area has consistently shown that infants who require parental involvement to fall asleep are more likely to wake up more often during the night and require similar assistance each time they wake up. It has also been shown that the major difference between infants who are considered good sleepers and those defined as problematic is related to the infant's self-soothing capacity. Infants who possess the ability to sooth themselves to sleep do wake up during the night (2–3 times on average) but they are able to fall back to sleep without crying and requiring parental attention. Often, the parents are not even aware that their child wakes up at night and resume sleep without their involvement.

Another area of research has focused on parental attitudes, beliefs, and attributions regarding the child's behaviors and needs, summarized under the term parental cognitions. It is assumed that parental cognitions on topics related to the child reflect an underlying cognitive structure that drives specific parental behaviors and responses to the child. These, in turn, play a major role in shaping the child's behavior, development, and psychopathology. Translating this notion to developmental sleep research, it was found that infant sleep problems were associated with negative maternal sleep-related cognitions, including difficulty with limit-setting, anger toward the child, and doubts about self-competence. Another study that assessed both maternal and paternal cognitions found that when both parents have difficulties related to limit-setting, their infant is more likely to suffer from poor sleep. These correlational studies demonstrate the links between infant sleep and parental cognitions. These links are assumed to be bidirectional and further studies are needed to assess causal interpretations.

It is important to note that although most research findings relate to mothers, this does not necessarily indicate that fathers do not play a role in this area. This bias reflects the fact that most studies do not include fathers. This in contrast to the strong belief that fathers do play a significant role in child development and have influence on the child's evolving sleep patterns.

Culture and Co-Sleeping

Co-sleeping or bed-sharing with parents is a common practice in many cultures and societies. Anthropologists claim that sleeping together with parents is a more natural sleep mode in primates and in traditional human societies. In the Western industrialized world, solitary sleep has been encouraged and favored.

Co-sleeping could be a lifestyle choice favored by parents because of their cultural or family tradition or their emotions about the topic. Very often, parents who do not consider it as their preferred lifestyle choice resort to co-sleeping because they are too tired to cope with their sleepless child and the need to visit the child's room numerous times during the night.

Studies in the US reveal that co-sleeping is very prevalent in different sections of the culture. For instance, in an urban sample, co-sleeping was reported as a routine practice in 35% of the white families and in 70% of the black families. In both racial groups co-sleeping was associated with a parental approach that emphasized parental involvement and body contact.

Surveys on co-sleeping suggested that when it is the lifestyle choice of parents, co-sleeping is not necessarily associated with an increase in reported sleep problems. However, in societies that favor solitary sleep, co-sleeping is indeed associated with increased prevalence of sleep problems. As suggested above, it is not clear from these studies if co-sleeping is a cause or an exacerbating factor for the sleep problems or just a mere reflection of the efforts (or surrender) to solve the problems at night.

It has been suggested that co-sleeping could serve as a protective factor for SIDS (see later). This provocative claim has never been established. On the contrary, it has been demonstrated that co-sleeping is associated with fatal accidents and infant deaths because of trapping between or underneath parents, suffocation, and other accidents that tend to happen in parental beds (that are not appropriate for infant sleep). Recently, pediatric organizations have reached a consensus calling parents to refrain from co-sleeping with infants because of the increased risk for accidents and deaths. However, this does not mean that parents and babies should sleep in separate rooms. Infant sleeping in a crib in the parents' room does not pose a risk problem and many professionals encourage this arrangement, particularly during the first months of infancy.

From a scientific perspective, it is interesting to note that the issue of co-sleeping vs. solitary sleep was examined in sleep laboratories. These studies revealed that when infants sleep with their mothers in the same bed they sleep worse than when they sleep in separate beds. While co-sleeping, both mothers and infants wake up more often, and tend to stimulate and awaken each other.

Stress

The links between sleep and stress in early childhood are more complex than could have been expected. It is well established that stressful events produce a biobehavioral alarm response, mediated by the activation of the sympathetic adrenergic system, which lead to increased vigilance, arousal, fear, or aggression. This response is part of the preparation for coping with the source of stress and is incompatible with sleep. Indeed, sleep could be considered as the most unsafe behavior or state under dangerous circumstances.

Research on the effects of stressful events on sleep in infants and children reveals that indeed sleep can be disrupted under stressful circumstances. For instance, a few studies explored the impact of mother–child separation on the child's sleep patterns. The separations were either due to the mother's need to deliver another baby, or due to her business trips. These studies showed that in response to separation, young children exhibited increase in crying, negative affect, activity level, heart rate, and night wakings. When the mother returned, opposite trends were noted. These responses are compatible with the stress-activation theory that emphasizes the negative effect of stress on sleep. However, other studies in infants and children have shown that under diverse stressful situations, the effects of stress on sleep could be entirely different. For instance, studies in infants who undergo stressful event like circumcision or children exposed to prolonged stress periods have shown that under such unique circumstances children spend more time in deep sleep or they extend their sleep period. This response is compatible with the withdrawal-conservation hypothesis that suggests that under circumstances of uncontrollable, prolonged stress, it is best for the organism to preserve energy and to resort to inactivity or sleep. It has also been suggested that under such circumstances sleep is an escape from stress.

Studies on stress and sleep in adults reflect a similarly inconsistent picture. It has been suggested that these contradictions could be resolved if the nature of the stressor and the coping style of the individual are considered. Individual and maturational differences may be partly responsible for the biobehavioral strategy adopted to cope with stressors: the 'alarm' response, which lead to alertness, hypervigilance, and preparedness, or the 'escape' response, which leads to sleep. In accordance with stress theories, it is also conceivable that a sudden, intense stressor would lead to an 'alarm' response and alertness, whereas prolonged or chronic uncontrollable stress would lead to 'exhaustion' and to flight to sleep.

In summary, it appears that complex links exist between sleep and stress. These relationships are mediated by the type of stressor, its durability, the coping strategy of the child, and probably by other factors that are yet to be explored.

Sleep Problems and Related Interventions

Sleep problems are very prevalent during early childhood. Surveys suggest that 20–30% of all infants and young children suffer from sleep difficulties. As described in previous sections, many factors can disrupt sleep or cause severe sleep problems. Roughly, sleep problems may be divided in reference to the predominant causal factors: (1) medical/physical factors; (2) behavioral and psychosocial factors; and (3) different combinations of these factors.

The common medical problems that lead to severe sleep disorders in young children are those related to breathing difficulties during sleep. However, the most common problems are difficulty falling asleep and night-wakings that are mostly attributed to nonmedical factors. The following sections briefly review the most prevalent problems and common interventions.

Settling and Night-Waking Problems

The most prevalent sleep-related complaint during the first two years is related to night-waking. As sleep–wake patterns evolve, the child is expected to 'sleep through the night' which means having a consolidated and undisrupted sleep (of at least 5 h) during the night. However, despite a strong maturational trend in this direction, many infants exhibit significant difficulties in developing consolidated sleep during the night. This problem could be manifested in the form of multiple night-wakings, or in the form of extended night-wakings, or both. These night-waking problems are a source of great distress to the parents whose help is required repeatedly during the night. Based on surveys conducted in many countries, it is estimated that 20–30% of all infants suffer from some difficulties associated with night-wakings and difficulties falling asleep. With maturation, infants who have difficulty with sleep consolidation may overcome these problems. However, research has shown that these problems, if not treated, tend to be persistent in more than 50% of all children, when they are revisited 1 or 2 years later. It has also been suggested that the roots of chronic insomnia in adults could often be traced back to early untreated childhood sleep problems.

As indicated earlier, settling and night-waking problems have been repeatedly linked to family affairs and excessive parental involvement in sleep-related interactions with their child. These links are the basis for popular and effective interventions. The most common interventions for settling and night-waking problems are behavioral methods aimed at training infants and young children to fall asleep in their own bed and resume sleep in bed with minimal parental assistance. The parents are trained to convey the message to the child that they are near by, but wean the child from their intense involvement. If the child is old enough to understand, rewards and incentives are used to encourage the child to accept the new arrangements. It has been repeatedly demonstrated that most sleep-disturbed infants and young children improve their sleep rapidly and dramatically once their parents decrease their involvement and interaction with the child during the settling process and during night-wakings.

The use of objective means such as video recordings and actigraphy has significantly contributed to the understanding of important phenomena related to these problems and interventions. For instance, it has been demonstrated that many infants wake up during the night without their parents' awareness, because these infants are able to soothe themselves back to sleep without crying and requiring parental help. Furthermore, it has been shown that during behavioral interventions (such as those described above), many infants continue to wake up during the night but resume sleep without parental attention. As far as the parents are concerned, their baby learned to sleep through the night; whereas in reality, their baby may have learned to soothe himself back to sleep when he wakes up.

Sleep-inducing drugs are often used to help young children with settling and night-waking problems. However, studies have shown that although these drugs could be effective in improving sleep their effect is often limited to the period of administration. Because most parents and professionals share strong reservations about medicating young children for extended periods, medication is usually not a recommended treatment for common night-waking problems. The efficiency of behavioral interventions makes them the preferred treatment of choice.

Nightmares

Nightmares are very common as sporadic events during childhood. Studies indicate that more than 80% of all children report having scary dreams. When a young child is having a nightmare, she usually wakes up screaming or crying. The child usually responds to caregivers' attempts to console and relieve the fear. Verbal children can report a scary dream but young children may have difficulty in distinguishing between dreams and reality. When these episodes are infrequent and the child does not show any signs of stress or anxiety during the day, the practical advice is usually to calm the child during the event and help her restore sleep.

Clinical research suggests that repeated and persistent nightmares could be a sign of post-traumatic stress disorder (PTSD). Even minor stressful events or periods could lead to a surge in nightmares. Therefore, if the child suffers from very frequent and persistent nightmares, professional help should be sought for further psychological assessment and intervention.

Night Terrors

When a young child is having a night terror (pavor nocturnus), he usually wakes up with a piercing scream, he may sit in his crib with his eyes open (or closed). He looks like he is being tormented, his breathing is irregular, his heartbeat is racing, and he may be sweating. With this terror appearance, the child is not responsive to his caregivers' attempts to calm him down. He may actually struggle against such attempts. This episode can last minutes or up to an hour if not interrupted. Once the episode is completed, or the parents manage to fully awaken the child, he usually resumes sleep with no recollection of the event. It is important to reassure the parents that these episodes are normal during development and are usually not associated with any known disorder or negative consequences. The main parental role is comforting and reassuring the child if it helps in shortening the episodes.

Night terrors are disturbances of arousal and usually occur during quiet or non-REM sleep. Night terrors can occur in very young infants even during the first year of life. Usually, these events are sporadic and although they are very scary for the parents, they are considered normal phenomena with no known adverse consequences. If these events become frequent and persistent, they may indicate that the child is undergoing a stressful period and this issue should be further explored. Insufficient sleep can also contribute to an increased frequency of night terrors. Therefore, assessment of the child's sleep needs and trials of sleep extension could also serve as a measure to reduce them.

Rhythmic Behaviors and Head Banging

Most infants and young children use some forms of rhythmic behaviors for self-soothing while they calm down and fall asleep. These rhythmic behaviors can include body rocking, sucking, and head banging. It is assumed that these behaviors often replace parental rhythmic soothing techniques, such as rocking and tapping on the child's back. However, in some children these behaviors become very intense and even alarm the parents,who worry about possible physical damage, as in the case of intense head banging.

In most cases, it is assumed that rhythmic behaviors serve a positive purpose and therefore they should not be disturbed. Usually, as the child matures these behaviors are spontaneously discarded. In the event that these behaviors are very fierce and alarming, it is usually recommended to the parents to protect the child from possible self-injury (i.e., by putting a soft surface against which the child can continue her head banging).

There are no established clinical interventions for persistent and fierce rocking or head banging. However, these issues are often resolved by working with parents on issues related to developing alternative soothing techniques for the child.

Breathing-Related Sleep Problems

As described earlier, any cold, even a congested nose, can lead to difficulty breathing during the night that leads to sleep fragmentation, and to reduced sleep quality and daytime alertness. However, more serious and sustained problems are also common in children. These problems are associated with blocked airways due to enlarged tonsils and adenoids, due to the anatomy of the airways, the tongue, and other tissues, or because of some inflammation in these areas. During sleep, when muscle tone is reduced and breathing is under automatic control, blocked airways could lead to a reduction in oxygen level and to an arousal response initiated by the brain. In mild cases, blocked airways lead to greater breathing efforts, snoring and breathing with an open mouth during sleep. In more severe cases, they may lead to repeated arousals (sometimes dozens during each hour of sleep) and seriously compromise sleep and its revitalizing function. When there are significant breathing cessations during sleep, the disorder is defined as sleep apnea syndrome (SAS). Sometimes, SAS can result from a failure of some central brain mechanisms that control breathing during sleep. Young infants often have brief breathing pauses that are considered normal because of their immature control systems.

Snoring is very common in young children. Prevalence rates of snoring of up to 26% have been reported in infants. The older professional belief that snoring without apnea is a benign condition has been recently replaced by a more negative perspective. Snoring is associated with poorer sleep quality and reduced daytime alertness. A significant number of studies have demonstrated that children who snore are more likely to present symptoms of attention problems and hyperactivity as well as other neurobehavioral deficits. Snoring in infants has been associated with a bad mood.

There are two medical options for the treatment of sleep apnea and related disorders. One option is to eliminate the source of airways obstruction by surgically removing enlarged tonsils, adenoid, or other excessive tissue. These procedures are very common in young children and they are considered relatively safe and successful. Sometimes it is recommended to wait because the child is too young to have the surgery or some maturational changes are expected to potentially resolve the problem. An alternative treatment for severe cases is using a little compressor that creates positive air pressure that helps the air travel through the blocked airways. The child sleeps with a mask on his face and the airflow comes from a machine. This treatment does not solve the sleep apnea problem but it enables having a very reasonable sleep under otherwise very poor breathing conditions. This is a very common treatment for adults suffering from sleep apnea. For young children it is usually only a temporary treatment before other measures are taken to resolve the problem.

Sleep Schedule Disorders

Earlier the development of the circadian rhythm and the consolidation of sleep during the night were described as a strong characteristic of the early maturational process. However, these processes should not be taken for granted and there are specific disorders that reflect the disruption of these processes.

Sleep schedule disorders characterize individuals who are often good sleepers. Given the opportunity to go to sleep and get up when they want, their sleep quality is usually quite good. However, when these individuals are expected to adhere to normal environmental clock (i.e., a reasonable bedtime in the evening and rise-time in the morning), they have difficulty adjusting and are often unable to fall asleep when expected, or to stay asleep during night-time hours.

Typical sleep schedule disorder could be manifested in the form of delayed sleep phase syndrome that refers to the inability to fall asleep before very late hours after the age-appropriate bedtime. These children fall asleep very late at night and have serious difficulty waking up at a reasonable time in the morning. Another manifestation is the advanced sleep phase syndrome, which refers to the opposite picture of a child who falls asleep very early in the afternoon and gets up very early (sometimes in the middle of the night). Other manifestations of schedule disorders are related to a non-24 h sleep–wake schedule, which means that the child's biological clock is changing from day to day and 'permitting' sleep at a different hour every day.

The understanding of schedule disorders has evolved in the last two decades. It is still not very clear how these disorders evolve or interfere with the normal maturation of the biological clock. However, it has been shown that children who suffer from pervasive developmental disorders (with assumed underlying brain dysfunction) are more likely to develop sleep schedule disorders. Sleep schedule disorders are also affected by light exposure as daylight (or the light–dark cycle) is the major regulatory information for the brain vis-a-vis the 24-h sleep–wake schedule. It has been suggested that insufficient light exposure could also delay or interfere with proper development of the biological clock and the related sleep–wake schedule, in early childhood.

Sudden Infant Death Syndrome

SIDS refers to a sudden, unexpected death of a baby during sleep without an identified medical explanation. This is the major nightmare of many parents during infancy. Needless to say, this is not considered to be a sleep disorder but because it is a sleep-related event it does have significant impact on sleep research and sleep medicine. SIDS occurs during the first year of life, peaking in prevalence between 2 and 4 months of age. Intense research has focused on trying to understand and prevent these tragic events. The results of these studies have identified a number of risk factors. SIDS is significantly more likely to occur in babies sleeping in a prone position. Smoking (during pregnancy and after delivery), high room temperature, prematurity, and soft or loose bedding or objects in crib, are considered to be significant risk factors. The main risk factor established in the last decade has been the prone sleeping position. The Back to Sleep campaign that has educated caregivers to put babies to sleep on their back (and not on their tummy or side) has led to a significant reduction in the incidence of SIDS. Recently, it has been suggested that the use of a pacifier can also serve as a protective factor.

Because one of the underlying assumption in SIDS research is that SIDS victims have a problem with their arousal mechanism, research focused on evaluating the potential risk factors, often using the auditory arousal threshold paradigm to assess these factors. The arousal threshold paradigm is based on exposing infants to white noise at increasing volumes until they wake up. High arousal threshold relates to infants who require a high noise level to wake up. This may reflect a problem with their arousal response that is assumed critical for survival and SIDS prevention. Using this methodology, research identified that infants sleeping on their tummy have a higher arousal threshold which could be related to the increased risk for SIDS in this sleeping position. It has been found that the use of a pacifier may lower the arousal threshold and therefore may serve as a protective factor as well.

Sleeping in a supine position (on the back) appears to be a strong protective factor. However, research has validated parental experience that infants sleeping on their back wake up more often and are sometimes more resistant to sleep in this position. This may pose a difficulty for parents to adopt the 'back to sleep' recommendation. Nevertheless, in light of the strong data that supports this recommendation, it is mandatory to encourage parents to adhere to this practice. Since sleeping on the back may delay, to some extent, the ability of the infant to stretch and strengthen the neck and shoulder muscles, it is also recommended to put the infant on his tummy when he is awake, with supervision.

The Impact of Sleep Disorders and Insufficient Sleep

Sleep disorders that disrupt the restorative function of sleep, and insufficient sleep, may lead to significant functional impairments. Most of the experimental studies on sleep restriction and sleep deprivation have been conducted with adults. A few studies have been performed with school-age children. These studies have shown that sleep restriction leads to reduced alertness and compromised neurobehavioral functioning as manifested on attention, memory, and learning tasks.

Many studies have focused on the correlates of poor sleep quality and other sleep-related problems (e.g., snoring) in children. These studies have shown that poor sleep quality and sleep-related breathing problems are associated with reduced alertness, compromised cognitive performance, and behavior problems that have been associated with the diagnosis of attention deficit hyperactivity disorders (ADHD). These behaviors include restlessness and fidgetiness, poor concentration, poor sustained attention, and poor emotional regulation. Furthermore, it has been shown in research and case studies that when proper treatment resolves a major underlying sleep disorder, the negative behavioral correlates are alleviated.

In infants and young children, poor sleep has been associated with a difficult temperament. It has been argued that insufficient or poor sleep could compromise behavior regulation and therefore leads to a more moody child with a low frustration tolerance. The child is usually described as more difficult to manage. Research findings have not been very consistent but the overall picture does suggest that young sleep-disturbed children are perceived more negatively by their parents (usually their mothers) than their non-sleep-disturbed peers. It is not entirely clear if these findings indicate that these children present more problem behaviors because they are sleep deprived, or that their mothers have negative perceptions because the mothers themselves are sleep-deprived. In a study of children aged 4–5 years, poor sleep was associated with compromised behavioral adjustment in preschool.

There is very little information on the long-term effects of insufficient sleep or sleep disorders on child development. One study found that infants who suffered from reported sleep problems were more likely to be diagnosed with ADHD as they grow older. Other studies have shown that infants with delays in the maturation of sleep patterns are more likely to be diagnosed with other neurological disorders. Notwithstanding these studies, there is still insufficient knowledge how chronic insufficient sleep or sleep disorders interfere with brain maturation during the crucial years of early development.

Summary and Conclusion

Sleep–wake patterns evolve rapidly during early development and their development is determined by brain maturation and environmental influences. The evolution of sleep–wake patterns often involves difficulties and delays that are manifested in the form of sleep problems that may cause significant distress to the family.

Maturational trends and the significant individual differences in sleep needs and sleep patterns should be considered when questions like "Is my child getting enough sleep?" or "How many night-wakings are considered a sleep problem?" are asked.

A variety of cultural and parenting factors play a role in shaping children's sleep patterns. These factors should always be evaluated when a specific sleep problem is addressed.

Insufficient or disrupted sleep may have negative impact on other domains of child development particularly in the areas of behavior and attention regulation.

Some childhood sleep problems (e.g., night terrors, head banging) tend to disappear with maturation and usually require no intervention. However, other early childhood sleep problems (e.g., difficulty falling asleep, frequent night-wakings) respond well to brief behavioral interventions and therefore should be detected and treated as early as possible to improve the child's sleep and to alleviate parental distress.

See also: ADHD: Genetic Influences; Colic; Demographic Factors; Depression; Discipline and Compliance; Fear and Wariness; Imagination and Fantasy; Independence/Dependence; Newborn Behavior; Routines; SIDS; Stress and Coping; Temperament.

Suggested Readings

Acebo C, Sadeh A, Seifer R, Tzischinsky O, and Carskadon MA (2000) Sleep/wake patterns in one to five year old children from activity monitoring and maternal reports. *Sleep* 23: A30–A31.

Anders TF, Halpern LF, and Hua J (1992) Sleeping through the night: A developmental perspective. *Pediatrics* 90(4): 554–560.

Bates JE, Viken RJ, Alexander DB, Beyers J, and Stockton L (2002) Sleep and adjustment in preschool children: Sleep diary reports by mothers relate to behavior reports by teachers. *Child Development* 73: 62–75.

Kuhn BR and Weidinger D (2000) Interventions for infant and toddler sleep disturbance: A review. *Child & Family Behavior Therapy* 22(2): 33–50.

Lam P, Hiscock H, and Wake M (2003) Outcomes of infant sleep problems: A longitudinal study of sleep, behavior, and maternal well-being. *Pediatrics* 111(3): e203–e207.

Mindell JA (1993) Sleep disorders in children. *Health Psychology* 12(2): 151–162.

Mirmiran M, Maas YGH, and Ariagno RL (2003) Development of fetal and neonatal sleep and circadian rhythms. *Sleep Medicine Reviews* 7(4): 321–334.

Sadeh A (1996) Stress, trauma, and sleep in children. *Child and Adolescent Psychiatric Clinics of North America* 5(3): 685–700.

Sadeh A (2004) A brief screening questionnaire for infant sleep problems: Validation and findings from an Internet sample. *Pediatrics* 113: e570–e577.

Sadeh A and Anders TF (1993) Infant sleep problems: Origins, assessment, intervention. *Infant Mental Health Journal* 14: 17–34.

Thoman EB (1990) Sleeping and waking states in infants: A functional perspective. *Neuroscience and Biobehavioral Reviews* 14(1): 93–107.

Smiling

D Messinger, University of Miami, Coral Gables, FL, USA

Glossary

Anticipatory smile – A pattern in which a young child smiles at an object and then gazes at another person while continuing to smile, sharing positive emotion about the object.
Duchenne smile – Smile involving eye constriction (caused by orbicularis oculi, the Duchenne marker) involved in the communication of intensely positive emotion. Cheek-raise smile.
Joy – An emotional process characterized by pleasurable feelings of engagement, a desire for the engagement to continue, and action tendencies, such as smiling, that tend to continue the engagement.
Open-mouth smile – A smile involving a dropped jaw typically occurring during arousing play. Play smile.
Secure attachment – A categorization of infants and toddlers who are able to explore the environment, confident in their caregivers' emotional and physical availability should the need arise.
Simple smile – A typically weak smile that involves neither the Duchenne marker nor mouth opening.
Smile – The sideways raising of the lip corners caused by contraction of the zygomatic major.
Strong smile – Smile involving stronger contraction of the zygomatic major.

Introduction

Early smiles are a prototypical expression of joy and a window on the development of positive emotion. Smiles elicit positive emotion and engagement in others, a process that contributes to the development of joy and social competence in the young child. Infants express different intensities and qualities of positive emotion through alterations in the temporal and facial dynamics of their smiling and through the incorporation of other expressive actions such as laughter and jumping up and down. Through the first two years of life, infant smiles and laughter become increasingly social and affectively intense, and increasingly used in referential communications about objects; between 2 and 4 years, smiles reflect the social structure of peer interactions. Difficulties with smiling in early interactions reflect a variety of risk conditions, while emotionally positive and responsive interactions can index optimal developmental trajectories.

Historical Interest in the Study of Smiling

Early smiling is the quintessential physical expression of positive emotional engagement. Infant smiles appear to be direct behavioral expressions of joyful feelings (see **Figure 1**). This apparent link between behavior and meaning has motivated over a century of research on the emotional significance, causes, behavioral correlates, and developmental consequences of early smiling. Seminal figures in child development have concerned themselves with the meaning and causes of infant smiles. Freud regarded infant smiling as a signal of sensory pleasure and contentment, while Piaget considered the smile of mastery an index of pleasurable accomplishment. In his work on the expression of emotion, Darwin observed his own infants to determine whether their first smiles were expressions of joy.

This article begins with a review of contemporary theoretical perspectives on the emotional significance of smiling. It continues with an overview of the neurophysiology of smiling and common methods for measuring smiling in infants, toddlers, and preschoolers. The article continues with a discussion of smiling as a joyful process involving arousal regulation, a discussion which includes definitions of different types of smiling. A central section concerns the development of smiling from the neonatal to the preschool period. The penultimate section considers how smiling reveals deficits and competencies in infants with various disabilities. The final section documents the developmental continuity of smiling and its links with emerging social competencies.

Theoretical Perspectives on Early Smiling

Behaviorist Approaches

Social learning and behaviorist approaches suggest that the caregiver's contingent responsivity to the infant's actions produces increases in smiling. Smiling can, in fact, be reinforced. If an examiner contingently responds to an infant's smiling with standardized periods of smiling, talking, and tickling, the infant will initially smile at an increased rate. Infants, however, soon habituate to these

Figure 1 This 6-month-old infant's strong smile involves the Duchenne marker (eye constriction) and mouth opening.

reinforcers and smiling then declines precipitously. Behaviorism is one of the only theoretical approaches to divorce smiling from emotion. Behaviorist approaches to understanding smiling have been largely abandoned in favor of approaches that focus on the dynamic relationship of smiling to the infant's emotional engagement with the changing environment.

Cognitive Differentiation Theory

Cognitive differentiation theory maintains that joy is located in the meaning of the environment to the infant and young child. Infants' active cognitive understanding of events, and maybe even early awareness of their own pleasure, is thought to be necessary for the emergence of joy. Cognitive differentiation theory holds that joy and other emotions develop out of more diffuse states such as pleasurable positive valence. Early smiling, such as that triggered when recognition of a visual stimulus elicits a relaxation in tension, is held to index pleasure but not joy. Joy is thought to develop around 9 months of age and involve pronounced drops in cognitively mediated arousal and to be accompanied by particularly intense infant smiling and laughing.

Discrete Emotion Theory

In contrast to a cognitive differentiation perspective, discrete emotion theory proposes that infant joy is expressed in the infant's first waking smiles. Discrete emotion theory emphasizes the role of brain-based affect programs such as joy in organizing the output of multiple expressive systems in the infant. Smiles and other infant facial expressions are thought to directly express emotions produced by these discrete affect programs. By this account, smiles index an irreducible joyful feeling state throughout infancy, early childhood, and, indeed, the entire lifespan. Like other approaches, discrete emotion theory suggests that joy motivates infants to approach and interact in an affiliative fashion with caregivers and other social partners.

Functionalist Theory

While discrete theories locate joy within the infant, functionalist and dynamic theories locate joy in the relationship of the young child and his or her often social environment. Functionalist theoretical perspectives emphasize the adaptive role of emotions such as joy in the creation and maintenance of relationships with the environment, especially the infant's social partners. The infant's smiles and the infant's comprehension of the smiles of others are seen as part of the process of pursuing and attaining goals in the social world.

The functionalist emphasis on pursuing goals in relationships is not limited to human beings. Extensive ethological research, guided by a functionalist perspective, has painstakingly documented the communicative functions of smiles and similar expressions in young monkeys and chimpanzees. Attachment theory also borrows from functionalist theory to describe the function of smiles from an evolutionary perspective. From the ethological and functionalist perspective represented by attachment theory, early smiles are attachment behaviors that maintain the proximity of caregivers to the infant.

Dynamic Systems Theory

Dynamic systems theory conceptualizes smiles and other expressive configurations as constituents of infant emotional processes. The process of smiling is part of the infant's experience of joy as well as an element in the infant's emotional communication with others. Dynamic systems theory focuses on the bottom-up interrelationship between smiles and other constituents of social interactions. The theoretical approach focuses on the temporal dynamics of smiles and positive emotional processes. The idea is that the formation of smiles during social interaction can provide insights into the emergence of smiling developmentally.

Summary and Overview

These diverse theoretical perspectives offer different definitions of positive emotion and different arguments for the association between positive emotions and smiling. Despite their differences, there are clear areas of overlap between different theoretical perspectives. Cognitive differentiation theory's emphasis on engagement in the emergence of smiling, for example, exemplifies the dynamic systems emphasis on the bottom-up emergence of emotional expressions out of multiple interfacing constituents. Each perspective provides overlapping insights that will illuminate the presentation of the meaning and development of smiling in this article. Below, we review the anatomical and neurophysiological basis of early smiling, and methods used to measure smiling.

The Neurophysiology of Smiling

Definition of Smiling

Physiologically, the contraction of the zygomatic major muscle creates a smile by pulling the corners of the lips upward and laterally (see **Figure 1**). The zygomatic is innervated by the seventh cranial nerve, the facial nerve. The facial nerve emanates from the facial nucleus, a group of motor neurons located at the level of the pons in the brainstem.

Neurophysiology of Smiling

The facial nucleus receives inputs from two pathways. One pathway controls deliberate smiling and the other controls spontaneous expressive smiling. More deliberate facial actions may occur when a young child is asked to smile and involve pathways from the cortical motor strip through the pyramidal system. Spontaneous smiling predominates in infancy and early childhood. Spontaneous facial expressions involve an extrapyramidal pathway that involves subcortical structures such as the basal ganglia and amygdala.

Although spontaneous smiling is linked to joyful emotions, contemporary neuroimaging studies have not unambiguously identified structures that are activated by positive emotions. Candidate structures include portions of the anterior cingulate cortex as well as subcortical structures mentioned above such as the basal ganglia. The degree to which neurophysiological studies identify localized structures involved in positive emotion is of central importance to discrete emotion theory. This theory's hypothesized modular affect program for joy rests on the eventual identification of specific structures and pathways.

Robust evidence has been found for the association of joy with laterality differences in cerebral activation. Emotions involving an orientation or motivation to approach, particularly joy, are associated with greater left frontal cerebral activation than right. Laterality differences suggest a distributed cerebral basis for positive emotional processes and processing, one involving multiple networks of activation. This possibility is congruent with a wide range of theoretical perspectives such as cognitive differentiation and dynamic systems approaches.

Measurement of Smiling

Researchers typically measure the frequency and duration of infant smiling from videotaped records. Smiles and other emotional expressions are coded either with well-validated infant-specific coding systems, or according to study-specific criteria. These coding systems are also used to measure a set of smile-related actions such as eye constriction (the Duchenne marker) and other communicative actions such as changes in infant gaze direction. Researchers may also code vocal, gestural, and whole-body expressions of infant emotion, such as jumping up and down in joy, as well as the facial and other expressive actions of the caregivers and testers with whom the infant may be interacting.

Neonatal smiling is typically observed in hospital nurseries, laboratories, and homes where early infant smiling in response to experimentally controlled visual and vocal stimuli such as the static image of a human face and high-pitched tones has been carefully documented. Social smiling between 2 and 6 months of age is often studied during playful face-to-face interactions with a parent (see **Figure 2**). These interactions are typically videotaped in either the home or in a laboratory playroom and are usually between 2 and 5 min in length. Individual infants typically show a range of relatively stable levels of smiling in these face-to-face interactions. Level of smiling during these interactions is also associated with more general ratings of infant emotional valence over 2–3 h home observations.

Smiling is also measured during experimental procedures involving a period of parental nonresponsivity. The face-to-face/still-face (FFSF), for example, is an experimental procedure in which a period of face-to-face play is followed by a period in which the parent is asked to hold a still-face and not respond to the infant; this is followed by a reunion episode in which the parent is asked to renew play with the infant. Smiling typically declines precipitously in the still-face and rises in the reunion episode, though not quite to initial face-to-face levels.

Through 48 months of age, smiling is often observed during observations in the home, daycare settings, and preschools, and observations in laboratory playrooms. Naturalistic observations may be supplemented or supplanted with structured protocols carried out by a tester or parent such as tickling, peek-a-boo, and the presentation of standardized stimuli such as a jack-in-the-box used to document the development of positive emotion. These protocols have been incorporated into structured assessments which, along with parental reports of positive emotion expression, are also used to assess individual differences in infant temperament.

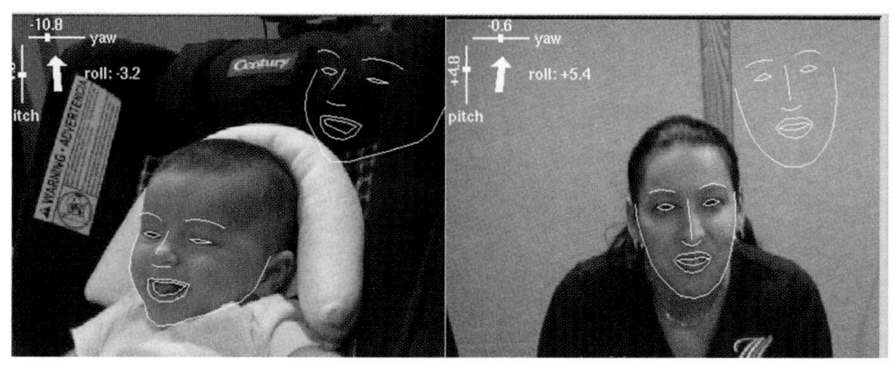

Figure 2 Four-month-old infant and mother smiling interaction as captured by Automated Face Analysis at the Carnegie Mellon University, Robotics Institute, compliments of Jeffrey Cohn, PhD. The infant and mother's faces are outlined to illustrate lip movement, mouth opening, and eye constriction.

Smiling, Joyful Positive Emotion, and Arousal

Smiles are simultaneously expressions of joy and indices of arousal modulation. Early discrete emotion theories held that the basis of positive emotion is a sharp reduction in neurally based arousal. Cognitive theories held that positive emotions involve active engagement with a challenging feature of the environment followed first by recognition and then by smiling. In support, infant heart rate – an index of arousal – is more rapid during smiling than during neutral expressions. Infants also accompany smiling with a variety of tension-reducing activities. Infants are likely to put their hands in their mouths while smiling and, after 3 months of age, tend to avert their gaze before ending a smile. Smiles may, in fact, be a mechanism for infants to maintain visual contact with arousing features of the environment for as long as possible.

The general role of arousal in smiling is also relevant to links between smiles and negative emotional expressions. When a period of engagement yields an experience that the environment is safe and interesting, positive emotion and smiling results. When engagement yields an experience of the environment as overwhelming and unsafe, negative affect results. This might occur, for example, when an interaction with a caregiver or parent becomes temporarily overstimulating for the infant.

Although related to the management of arousal, the smiles of infants and young children are also expressions of joy. Smiles, for example, are perceived as more emotionally positive than neutral expressions, even among infants with serious facial deformities. The smiles of infants and young children are part and parcel of a process of positive engagement with the environment. They occur during periods of interaction likely to elicit positive emotion and tend to elicit positive emotion on the part of others. Smiles, then, can signal a desire for arousing interaction even as they are part of a process or arousal modulation. We now turn to a discussion of different types of smiles and their role in the expression of positive emotion.

Different Types of Smiles

The smiles of young children have different forms. Some appear to be tentative, others appear to communicate a sense of personal connection, and yet other smiles appear to be part of hilarious outbursts. Infant smiles differ along a variety of dimensions. They can be stronger and weaker and can involve different degrees of eye constriction (the Duchenne marker) and mouth opening. In this section, we explore evidence suggesting that different types of smiling express different degrees and types of positive emotion.

Simple smiles

Smiles that are not particularly strong, and do not involve the Duchenne marker or mouth opening, are known as simple smiles. The types of situations in which infants produce simple smiles and ratings of those simple smiles indicate that even these smiles are more emotionally positive than neutral expressions. A functionalist view of facial expressions in nonhuman primates offers additional clues to the meaning of simple smiles. Chimpanzees (*Pan troglodyte*) possess a zygomatic major muscle active in producing a bared teeth display that is similar to simple human smiling. The bared teeth display was originally a signal of submission (I accept your dominance). It has come to be a signal of affiliation (I mean you no harm), which is frequently followed by behaviors such as holding out a hand. Likewise, simple infant smiles may signify a positive affiliation with others that may be a stepping stone for more positive engagement. Infant simple smiles occur, for example, during the warm-up phases of games and when infants are approached by an impassive stranger.

While simple infant smiles are emotionally positive, smiles involving stronger zygomatic contraction, eye constriction and/or mouth opening are more emotionally positive than simple smiles. Below, we review evidence that strong smiles, and smiles involving eye constriction and mouth opening are more likely to occur during periods of interaction likely to elicit positive emotion than are simple smiles and are perceived as more emotionally positive than other smiles.

Smiles involving mouth opening (play smiles) and smiles involving vocalizations

Infant smiles involving mouth opening caused by jaw dropping have a specifically social and excited quality. They tend to occur while infants gaze at their mothers' faces and are typically perceived as reflecting more positive emotion and arousal than closed-mouth smiles.

The open-mouth human smile is also morphologically similar to the relaxed open-mouth display of nonhuman primates. These displays develop in infant chimpanzee in the context of mock biting play with mothers. Like the open-mouth smiles of human infants, these displays communicate playful, aroused engagement. Relaxed open-mouth displays and infant open-mouth smiles are also related to laughter. Laughter is a rhythmic, smile-linked vocalization that appears to index intense positive emotion. More generally, infant vocalizations tend to be embedded within the time course of ongoing smiles such that the smiles are punctuated by the vocalizations. The vocalizations may serve both to recruit attention to the smile and to intensify the expression of joy.

Duchenne smiles

The Duchenne marker – eye constriction caused by orbicularis oculi, pars lateralis, which raises the cheeks toward the eyes – is perhaps the best known index of smiling intensity in infants. Infants tend to produce Duchenne smiles when their mothers are smiling and when they are approached by their smiling mothers. Infants also produce more syllabic sounds when Duchenne smiling, a potential marker of emotional intensity. Duchenne smiling is also associated with greater relative activation of the left than right frontal cerebral hemispheres, a pattern which suggests greater approach orientation and joy. Although smiles involving the Duchenne marker are often regarded as the only index of strong joyful emotion in adults, this distinction does not appear to be absolute in infants. In infants, smiles with and without the Duchenne marker often follow one another directly in time, suggesting that infant Duchenne smiles are more intense indices of positive emotion than smiles without the Duchenne marker.

Strong smiles

Smiles are continuous muscular processes in which the degree of zygomatic contraction determines the strength of the smile, the degree of lip corner movement. Strong smiles index more intensely positive emotion, the infant's positive emotional engagement with ongoing activities. More exciting parts of games elicit stronger smiling than the preparatory phase of the games. Tickling, for example, is accompanied by stronger smiling than getting ready to tickle or pretending to tickle. Smiles involving stronger zygomatic contraction are also perceived as more positive and joyful than weaker smiles.

Stronger smiling – involving greater zygomatic contraction – tends to be associated with eye constriction and mouth opening. Simple smiles without these features are the weakest while smiles involving both eye constriction and mouth opening are the strongest (see **Figure 3**). These intensity parameters vary together in time over the course of an infant smile. As the strength of an infant's smiles increase and decrease, the degree of eye constriction and mouth opening involved in the smile, also increase and decrease.

Combined strong, open-mouth Duchenne smiles

Infant smiles involving the Duchenne marker tend to involve mouth opening (and vice versa) (see **Figure 1**). These combined smiles – sometimes called duplay smiles – tend to occur during unambiguously positive period of interaction such as when young infants are gazing at their smiling mothers. Strong smiles involving mouth opening and eye constrictions are perceived as the most joyful of infant smiles. They occur in circumstances – such as while being tickled – which appear likely to elicit the strongest and most engaged positive emotion.

Conclusion: The meaning of different types of smiles

It is possible that Duchenne smiles are involved in reciprocating another's positive emotion, while open-mouth

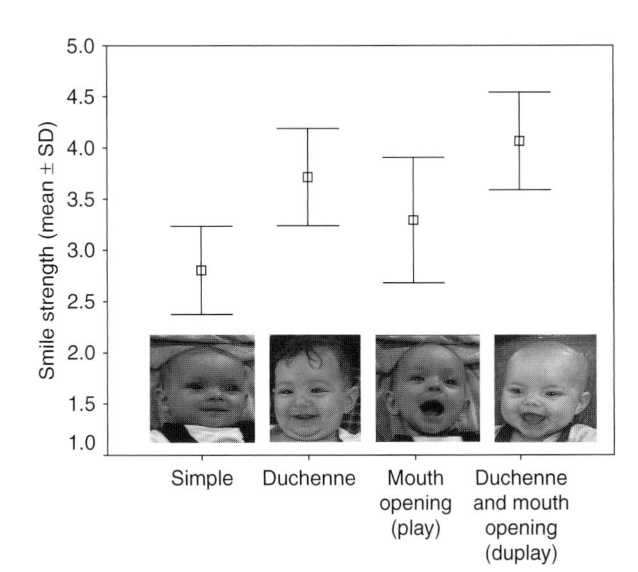

Figure 3 Mean smile strength of different smile types.

smiles involve a more aroused, playful quality of positive emotion. If different types of smiles have qualitatively different meanings, this would challenge the discrete emotion theory proposition that there is single affect program for joy. An alternate possibility – that different types of smiles express different degrees of a single dimension of positive emotion or joy – is consonant with a wide range of theoretical perspectives. Discrete emotion and cognitive theories are congruent with this dimensional perspective, although the dimensional perspective's emphasis on real-time changes in smiling intensity have been a more central concern of functional and dynamic systems approaches.

The Development of Smiling

Developmental Overview

The development of smiling reflects the emerging cognitive, social, and emotional competencies of the young child. Smiles first emerge during sleep during the neonatal period and rapidly become a centerpiece of face-to-face social interactions in the first half year of postnatal life. Between 6 and 12 months, infants begin to intentionally communicate desires and experiences about objects and events in the world to their communicative partners. Between 12 and 48 months, smiling and laughter within the parent–child dyad becomes more sophisticated and intricate. At the same time, the smiles of young children become essential features of their social interactions with peers. We review these developments below.

Neonatal and Early Smiling: 0–2 Months of Age

Neonatal smiling: 0–1 month of age

Neonatal smiles are an emotional puzzle. They are referred to as endogenous or spontaneous smiles because they are prompted by internal stimuli, suggesting they have no emotional content. Neonatal smiles occur more frequently in sleeping and drowsy states of rapid eye movement (REM) – about one smile every 5 min – than in other states. These smiles, however, do occur in other behavioral states, including states of alertness, suggesting the possibility that they are related to positive emotion.

The form of neonatal smiles suggests an association with positive emotion. Neonatal smiles can have a relatively mature form that involves strong muscular contractions and the Duchenne marker. These smiles occur against a backdrop of frequent lip and mouthing movements. Nevertheless, approximately one-third of these neonatal smiles are recognized by untrained observers, suggesting their potential signal value.

Neonatal smiling is unrelated to 'gas' as its frequency is unaffected by time since last feeding. Instead, neonatal smiling appears to have a subcortical origin, as evidenced by the observation of neonatal smiling in an infant with microcephaly. Infants born prematurely show more neonatal smiling than full-term newborns and the quantity of their endogenous smiling declines with age. These factors also suggest a subcortical origin for neonatal smiling, which may limit the emotional meaning of these smiles.

Theoretical perspectives differ on the meaning of neonatal smiles. While discrete emotion theory suggests that neonatal smiles – at least those occurring during waking states – are expressions of joy, a cognitive differentiation perspective regards them as physiological responses to internal or environmental stimuli. Neonatal smiles illustrate the dynamic systems emphasis on heterochronicity; that is, the neonatal smile appears to develop physically before it is integrated into patterns of cognitive engagement and social interaction that provide evidence for joyful emotion.

Early smiling and the transition to social smiling: 1–2 months of age

Over the first 2 months of life, smiling becomes gradually linked to environmental stimulation, which sets the stage for the emergence of social smiling. Infants first smile in response to auditory stimuli, and then respond to auditory plus visual stimuli, and finally smile in response to visual stimuli alone. Specifically, through 1 month of age, infant smiles often occur during states of drowsiness or even sleep when they are elicited by high-pitched tones including the human voice. After 1 month, smiles during alert states are increasingly elicited by visual stimuli such as gazing at a face or an upright image of a face. Infants become increasingly likely to smile to high-pitched auditory stimuli (such as the human voice) or visual displays (particularly static images of the human face) until about 3 months of age.

Cognitive differentiation theory maintains that while neonatal smiles involve a reduction in physiological arousal, the smiling of young infants involves a reduction in psychological or cognitively modulated tension. It is the emerging psychological meaningfulness of visual stimuli rather than their physical/perceptual properties that occasions smiling. In support of this proposal, as infants become more capable of rapidly recognizing more complex stimuli in the first months of life, latencies to smile decrease. This cognitive differentiation perspective is also relevant to the emergence of social smiling, to which we now turn.

Social smiling develops in a developmental period when infants are spending less time asleep and more time in periods of alert inactivity, awake but not fussing or crying. These states facilitate social interaction as infants spend increasing amounts of time gazing at the caregiver's face. The period in which social smiles emerge is also marked by the development of new patterns of visual attention between 1 and 2 months of age.

One-month-olds gaze alternately at the edge of the head and the eyes. Two-month-olds gaze between the edge of the head, the eyes, and the mouth. This more integrative pattern of gazing suggests attention to the facial expression of others which may also facilitate social smiling.

Social smiles typically first occur while gazing at the parent in the 4–6 weeks after birth. Age of social smiling appears to be contingent on a certain level of neurological maturity. For infants born prematurely, age of social smiling must be adjusted to account for the number of weeks the infant was born before due date. Maternal reports of the first social smile precede tester's first elicitation of social smiles by several weeks. Parents may experience infant's first social smiles as providing a sense of connection, fulfillment, and even reward ('my baby recognizes me') after the hard, sometimes sleep-depriving work of caring for a neonate.

In the first month of postnatal life, infants gaze at and away from mother's face without smiling. In the second month, the social smile emerges, heralded by periods of concentration. Several seconds of brow knitting and visual fixation of the mother's face are followed by relaxation of the brows, indexing apparent cognitive recognition, and a smile. This pattern links processes elucidated by cognitive differentiation perspectives to the emergence of social smiling. Dynamic systems approaches indicate – in complementary fashion – that the real-time occurrence of this attention-related smiling pattern may provide a window into the first developmental emergence of smiling.

The Development of Social Smiling in Face-to-Face Interaction: 2–6 months of Age

Social smiles develop during interaction. The period between 2 and 6 months is one of intense social interaction and rapid emotional development. During this period, infants become both increasingly responsive to the smiles of others and increasingly likely to initiate smiles to others. We begin this section with a discussion of general features of smiling in face-to-face interaction and then turn to the development of interactive smiling between 2 and 6 months.

General features of face-to-face interactive smiling

Overview of infant and parental activities during interactive smiling

Overall, infants smile for about 20% of face-to-face interactions and smiling typically occurs in bursts of smiles separated by periods without smiling. Infant interactive smiling is strongly linked to gazing at the parent's face and smiling tends to be associated with vocalizations that are also used to express positive emotion.

During face-to-face interactions, infant smiles are a high point of play with both mothers and fathers. Fathers tend to employ a more physical style of play with their infants (e.g., bouncing games) whereas mothers rely more on visual and vocal expressivity to elicit smiles. Although the term mother is often used in this article because of the preponderance of research findings on mothers, mothers and fathers are equally adept at eliciting smiles from their infants.

During interaction, parents both stimulate and entertain their infants, attempting to elicit engagement and expressions of positive emotion while at the same time attempting to prevent and modulate their infants' fussing and crying. In addition to smiling, parents hold, touch, and tickle their infants, move toward and away from the infant, and engage in high-pitched infant-directed speech. These rhythmic multimodal displays increase and decrease in emotional intensity over the space of several seconds in concert with and in reaction to infant smiles and other expressive actions.

Infant and mother responsivity to smiling

A key feature of interaction is the degree to which each partner influences and is responsive to the other. Mothers' smiles and vocalizations are typically necessary to elicit infants' smiles but may not be sufficient to elicit infant smiles. Mothers are optimally successful at eliciting infant smiles when they combine different communicative modalities with smiling such as vocalizing, leaning toward the infant, and smiling simultaneously.

Infant smiles are more likely to elicit mother smiles than mother smiles are to elicit an infant smile. An infant smile is typically sufficient to elicit a mother smile, usually within a relatively brief two second time interval. In fact, an infant neutral gaze at mother's face is often sufficient to elicit a mother smile, and mothers frequently initiate smiles in the absence of discrete infant behaviors. Infants, then, may experience parental contingency in the midst of a wide array of parental expressive behaviors.

Patterns of infant and mother smiling

As suggested by a dynamic systems perspective, infant and parent individual propensities toward smiling combine to create more complex dyadic patterns of interaction in time. Infant smiles typically occur when the infant gazes at the mother and the mother smiles. Once infants are smiling, parents will rarely cease smiling, which would break off a bout of mutual smiling. The young infant's experience of smiling, then, is, prototypically, smiling with a smiling parent.

Infant and mother also impact one another continuously in time. Stronger smiling on the part of the infant is likely to lead to stronger mother smiling. Stronger mother smiling may be mirrored by the infant or the infant may disengage, gazing away to regulate their levels of arousal. These levels of interactive influence vary among different infant–parent dyads. Generally, however, infant expressions of joy are mirrored and intensified by the parent. The infant responds to this intensification with either intensified engagement and positive emotional expression or disengagement, gazing away, and terminating smiling.

The exchange of smiling is a nonverbal dialogue whose topic is the shared experience of joy and the regulation of emotion. Prototypically, infants' experience of positive emotion as they smile is mirrored back in intensified form by the smiling parent. The infant perceives this increase in the parent's smile and simultaneously perceives his or her own increase in positive emotion that the parent's smile engenders. Sources of the infant's positive responsiveness to the parent's smile may be mirror neurons or related neurophysiological processes that produce feelings of sympathetic joy in the infant who perceives the smile of another.

Whatever the source, infants' awareness of their own changing feelings occurs in concert with their experience of their impact on the parent. The dynamic interplay that results suggests that one path to the development of joy involves experiencing the joy of another. The infant's simultaneous awareness of their own feelings and those of the parent is known as primary intersubjectivity. We now turn to the development of primary intersubjectivity and interactive smiling between 2 and 6 months.

Developments in interactive smiling between 2 and 6 months of age

As infants develop and increase their smiling around 2 months, there is a related increase in positive maternal expressions such as smiling. Infants appear to become accustomed to specific levels of positive responsivity such that 2-month-olds smile less at a stranger who is either more or less contingently responsive to the infant than the infant's mother. Early on, then, infants appear to show dyad-specific levels of interactive contingency that affect smiling levels. This may be one mechanism through which infants between 2 and 6 months increasingly differentiate between adults and come to reserve their smiling to a familiar attachment figure.

The development of smiling in face-to-face interaction occurs concurrently with changing patterns of infant attention to the caregiver's face. Between 2 and 6 months, infants spend decreasing periods of time gazing at their mothers' faces but become increasingly likely to smile when they are gazing at the mother's face. As infant smiles become more strongly coordinated with gazes at mothers' faces, patterns of gazing and smiling change. At 3 months, infants tend to begin and end their smiles within gazes at the parent's face; that is, infants' early expressions of positive emotion are dependent on visual contact with the parent. At 6 months, infants tend to gaze at mother's face, smile, gaze away, and only then end the smile.

Gazing away from the parent during smiling appears to be an early mechanism of emotion and arousal regulation. Five-month-old infants playing peek-a-boo tend to avert their gaze from the mother's face more frequently and for longer periods of time during stronger smiles and during longer-lasting smiles. This suggests that stronger and longer-lasting smiles involve more intense affectively positive arousal which infants regulate by gazing away from their parents' faces. In addition, smiles in which infants gaze away before the peak of the smile is reached may have a 'coy' quality which leads naïve observers to perceive some of these smiles as communicating shyness. These developmental patterns of gazing at and away from the parent's face are the context in which smiling develops during face-to-face interactions.

As infant smiling increases between 2 and 6 months, infants also become more active participants in smiling dialogues. Infants' tendency to smile in response to mothers' smiles increases with age as does infants' propensity to initiate smiles – even in the absence of a previous maternal smile. The age at which infants become reliably responsive to their mother's smiles and the range of responsivity between different infants and mothers is a topic of active research.

The development of different types of smiling

Considered as a whole, infant smiling during face-to-face interaction increases between 2 and 6 months. Different types of smiling, however, show different patterns of development. Simple smiles that involve neither eye constriction nor mouth opening show a nonspecific rise in different interactive periods (see **Figure 4**). By contrast, the more emotionally positive open-mouth smiles involving eye constriction show a specific developmental pattern. Between 2 and 6 months, infants become increasingly likely to use open-mouth Duchenne smiling to respond to their smiling mothers. These combination smiles decline in periods when mothers are not smiling and infants are gazing elsewhere. In sum, highly positive types of smiling become selectively associated with more positive periods of interaction. Infants' increasing tendency to engage their smiling mothers with open-mouth cheek-raise smiling appears to index their emerging capacity to fully participate in intensely joyful interactions.

The period approaching 6 months is one in which infants also become increasingly likely to gaze away from mother during the course of a smile in order to control their own arousal levels. As infants, then, become more capable of using very intense smiles to participate in highly arousing social situations they also begin to exercise more control over the direction in which they smile. Infants are increasingly controlling their own positive emotion by exercising control over their involvement in the interchanges that lead to this positive emotion.

Another clue to the emotional meaning of infant smiles is the infants' perceptions of the smiles of others. By 4 months of age, infants can visually match their mothers' smiles with a matching vocalization and, by 5 months, recognize the smile–vocalization pair posed by an experimenter. These abilities suggest the infant's appreciation of

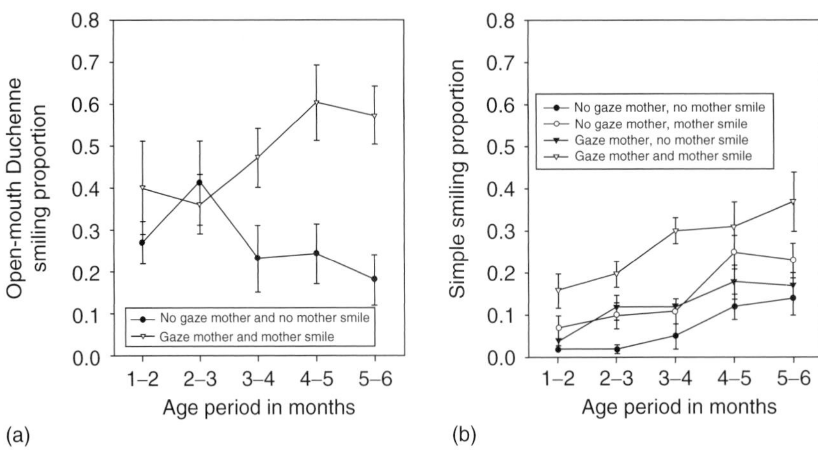

Figure 4 (a) Open-mouth Duchenne smiling increases when infants are gazing at their mothers' faces while their mothers are smiling. It decreases when infants are not gazing at their mothers and while their mothers are not smiling. (b) By contrast, simple smiling with neither characteristic tends to increase irrespective of where the infant is gazing and whether or not the mother is smiling. All smiles are positive, but some smiles are more positive than others. From Messinger D, Fogel A, and Dickson KL (2001) All smiler are positive, but some smiles are more positive than others. *Developmental Psychology* 37(5): 642–653.

the affective meaning of the smiles of others is blossoming in the same period in which the infant is able to more flexibly engage in his or her own intensely positive emotional expressions.

Smiling between 6 and 12 Months of Age: The Development of Referential Smiling

In the first half year of life, infant emotional expression during face-to-face interactions reflects a primary, nonreflective communication of immediate experience. In the second half of the first year of life, infant smiling takes on a qualitatively new form as smiling is integrated into intentional communications. We begin by reviewing the form of infant smiling and laughter during this period, examine smiles associated with walking, mastery smiles, and then turn to the development of smiling in intentional communications.

The development of different types of smiling, laughter, and mastery smiles

Between 6 and 12 months of age, strong smiles combining the Duchenne marker and mouth opening occur in the midst of positive and exciting periods of interaction such as physical play with a parent. Simple smiling without these features predominates both during the preparatory phases of active games (e.g., getting ready to tickle) and during slower-paced activities (e.g., book reading). While games such as tickle become more potent elicitor of smiles between 6 and 12 months, it is not clear if the relative frequency of different types of smiling – or their association with different types of elicitors – changes in this period. The conditions that elicit laughter, however, change developmentally.

Laughter is a smile-linked vocalization indexing intense positive emotion and arousal that becomes more common between 6 and 12 months. During this period, physical stimulation such as pat-a-cake remains potent elicitors of laughter even as infants become more likely to laugh in response to social games such as peek-a-boo. One factor in this development is that infants are become increasingly active agents in social games (e.g., moving the parent's hands in peek-a-boo and eventually hiding the parent) and eventually become full partners in producing their own smile- and laugh-inducing experiences.

Cognitive differentiation theory holds that mastery of a challenging task is intrinsically rewarding. In support, infants approaching 1 year of age engage in more smiling and laughing when engaging in newly acquired capacities such as pulling to stand than when engaging in more practiced tasks such as pulling to sit.

Smiling is linked to the developmental achievements of the toddler and young child. For early walkers (before 12 months), the onset of walking is associated with an increase in infant positive emotional expressions such as smiling. Walking onset is also, however, associated with a decrease in maternal expressions of positive affect to the early walker and increases in interpersonal struggles. This 'testing of the wills' may reflect the toddler's delight in the experience of increased mobility and the mother's work to ensure that the young toddler stays safe despite their increased mobility. The mischievous smile may develop around this age as toddlers gaze back at a parent from a distance while smiling to ascertain the level of prohibition or acceptance associated with a potential path of action. Such actions would reflect the toddler's developing secondary intersubjectivity, a topic to which we now turn.

Smiling in referential communication

Overview

In the period between 6 and 12 months, infants and parents increasingly integrate objects into their play. Smiles tend to occur in the context of coordinated joint engagement in which the infant actively shifts attention between a toy and a social partner. When initiating joint attention, infants use gestures and gaze to refer to objects and events outside the infant–partner dyad. Infant smiles are related to the communicative meaning of these gestures and gazes. Infants are more likely to smile during communications that show or share an object than they are to smile during communications that request an object or action. In sum, infants begin to smile at others with reference to particular objects or events in what is known as triadic communication.

The development of referential communications involving smiles

Between 6 and 9 months, infant initiation of joint attention by gazing between a toy and a responsive adult increases. Yet even among infants who gaze between the toy and an adult, the percentage who accompany this gaze with a smile rises between 6 and 9 months. This suggests that integrating a smile into a gaze at a responsive adult indexes a more complex communicative message than gazing alone. Such smiles index the infant's secondary intersubjectivity, the infant's awareness of the relationship between the adult and toy. An additional index of the infant's secondary intersubjectivity involves the sequence of smiling and gazing. The infant is aware not only of the parent, but increasingly aware of the parent's attentional state with respect to an object or event.

Anticipatory smiles involve a specific sequence of smiling and then gazing at a partner that appears to index the infant's secondary intersubjectivity (see **Figure 5**). Infants engage in anticipatory smiles when they smile at a toy or event and then turn to gaze at an adult while continuing to smile. The infant's smile anticipates social contact and communicates pre-existing positive affect with another person. It seems to communicate something like, "that was funny, wasn't it."

Infant anticipatory smiles increase between 8 and 12 months. An infant's likelihood of engaging in anticipatory smiling is associated with the infant's general capacity to engage in intentional communications and to understand means–end relationships. This suggests that anticipatory smiles index infants' emerging ability to understand and refer to the relationship of an adult and an object. From a dynamic systems perspective, the real-time process of smiling and then referencing an object to another suggests how positive emotion may motivate the development of early triadic communications.

Smiling between 12–48 Months of Age: Smiling among Toddlers and Preschoolers

As toddlers become more mobile and young children become more involved in play with peers, many researchers have neglected the observation of smiling, focusing instead on other dimensions of social competence. From 1 to 2 years of age, however, smiling and laughter remain revealing elements of play with parents during a period in which toddlers become increasingly aware of the social meaning of the parents' smiles Between 1 and 4 years, smiling is also an essential feature of the young child's developing peer play where it reveals emerging patterns of social affiliation. These two topics – smiling with parents and smiling with peers – are the focus of this section.

Toddler smiling and laughter with the parent

Infant comprehension of the smiles of others in social referencing paradigms provides evidence for the development of secondary intersubjectivity. In social referencing paradigms, infants are confronted with an ambiguous stimulus such as a moving mechanical object that might be interpreted as interesting or as threatening. Between 12 and 18 months of age, infants respond differentially to adult smiles (and associated vocalizations) than to fear and neutral expressions. Infant's interpret these adult smiles not as direct expressions of joy (primary intersubjectivity), but as referential signals that the ambiguous situation is nonthreatening (secondary intersubjectivity).

The toddler's developing understanding of pretense is also related to maternal smiling. Mother's smile more when engaging in pretend than actual versions of the same activity (e.g., pretending to eat vs. really eating a snack). Toddlers also give more clues that they understand that the activities are pretend – they participate more and smile more themselves – when mothers smile more. The 12–24-month period also involves developments in dyadic laughter. When engaged in play during this period, infants and mothers begin and end their laughs increasingly closer together in time. The members of the dyad appear to

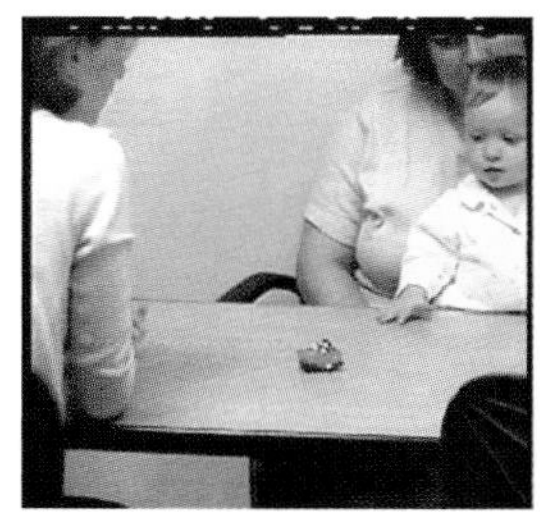
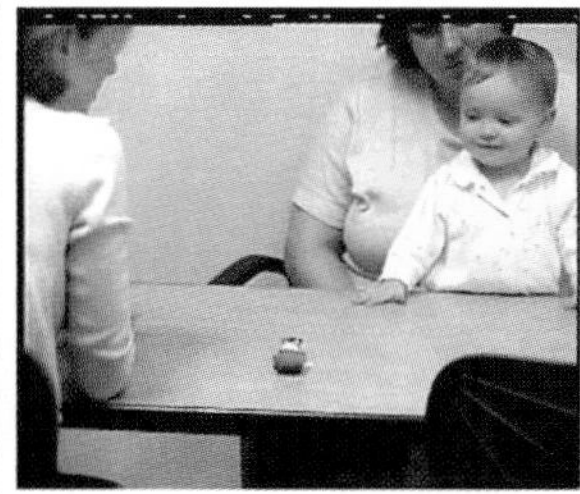
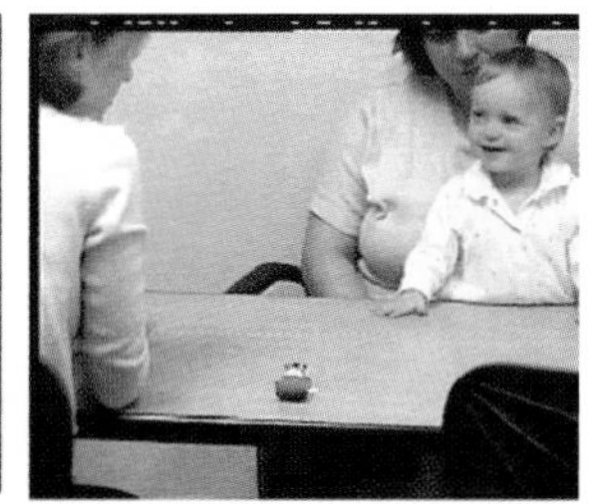

Figure 5 Anticipatory smile. A 12-month-old infant gazes at an object (left), smiles at the object (middle), and gazes at the experimenter while continuing to smile (right).

become increasingly responsive to the onset and offset of one another's positive communications, leading to the emergence of dyad-specific patterns of positive communication. Thus infant understanding of smiling as a social signal ('this is a pretend activity') develops at the same time as infants and mothers continue to evolve complex patterns of dyadic responsivity to each other's positive emotion expressions.

Smiling in peer play

Peer play is an increasingly important context for social development and smiling after 1 year. By 18 months, level of smiling is linked to increased interaction with peers, particularly when there is a relative absence of peer conflict. Additional evidence for the importance of peers involves three types of smiling identified among preschoolers.

A closed smile in which the teeth are covered that is likely related to simple smiling has been identified in preschoolers. Closed smiling predominates in solitary contexts and levels of closed smiling change little between 2 and 4 years of age. Upper smiles and broad smiles and open-mouth smiles show different patterns of occurrence and development. Upper smiles display the upper teeth and may include Duchenne smiles; broad smiles display both the upper and lower teeth and are likely to include open-mouth smiles. Upper and broad smiles occur in social situations and are increasingly used with same-sex peers between 2 and 4 years. Male children, in particular, are increasingly selective in directing broad smiles toward male peers and not to female peers. Different types of smiling may, then, reflect and reinforce developing patterns of social affiliation such as the increasing sex segregation of young preschoolers.

With respect to more recent typologies of smiles among preschoolers, by 3.5 years of age, stronger smiles are likely than weaker smiles to accompany success in a game. By 4.5 years, children tend to produce Duchenne smiles in games in which they produce – rather than simply being shown – an interesting display. Mastery, success, and failure during a given trial of a game are not, however, always accurate predictors of smiling. Gaze at the examiner – or whomever the child is playing with – remains a prepotent elicitor of smiling, whether the child has failed or succeeded at the game. In the preschool period, then, smiling continues to serve multiple masters. It expresses both joy at success and the happiness associated with interacting with a cooperative adult or peer.

Smiling as an Index of Developmental Risk and Disability

Individual differences in smiling are meaningfully related to concurrent risk factors. Levels of smiling differ between infants at risk for disturbed developmental outcomes and typically developing infants. We review evidence for differences in smiling associated with prematurity, maternal depression, and infants who are blind, infants with Down syndrome, and infants with autism spectrum disorders (ASD) – emphasizing how such differences shed light on the disorders and conditions in question.

Smiling in Premature Infants and the Infants of Depressed Mothers

Infants born prematurely spend less time than full-term infants engaging in relatively strong open-mouth smiles during face-to-face interactions and exhibit fewer strong smiles during peek-a-boo games with an experimenter. This likely reflects the difficulties of many premature infants in coping with high levels of even positive emotional arousal. Infants of clinically depressed mothers and mothers with high levels of depressive symptomatology also show reduced levels of smiling. This is likely to reflect a lack of maternal positive emotional initiation and responsivity to the infant. Effects are clearest when maternal depressive symptomatology is chronic rather than brief. Thus reduced smiling is likely to reflect physiological difficulties in premature infants and reduced opportunities for positive interaction among infants of depressed mothers.

Smiling in Blind Infants and Children

The impact of environmental influences is evident in the development of smiling in blind infants. Blind infants demonstrate social smiling in response to social events such as hearing a familiar voice and their smiling typically elicits a parental response. The frequency of these social smiles increases between 4 and 12 months. However, the smiles of blind infants are less regularly elicited and more fleeting than those of sighted infants. Blind infants, of course, cannot enter into mutually reinforcing visually mediated smiling exchanges with others, which may limit the duration of their smiling. Lack of contingent visual feedback to smiles is also likely to play a role in the decrement in smiling observed in blind infants after 2 or 3 years of age.

Smiling in Infants with Down Syndrome

Infants with Down syndrome – trisomy – show delayed development of positive emotional expressivity with the most substantial delays evident among the most cognitively delayed infants and the infants with the most flaccid muscle tone. Although levels of smiling are typically low in infants with Down syndrome, these infants do show mastery smiles consonant with their cognitive level. They also show the typical developmental pattern of smiling – first to auditory, then to visual and tactile, and then to social stimuli and activities.

Infants with Down syndrome show patterns of indiscriminate smiling whose cognitive and affective bases have not been adequately specified. Infants with Down syndrome direct open-mouth Duchenne smiles both to their mothers and to toys, whereas typically developing infants direct these smiles only to mother. Infants with Down syndrome also do not show decrements in smiling when their mothers adopt a still-face as dramatic as the decrements of typically developing infants. It remains to be seen whether such indiscriminate smiling is associated with the level of cognitive functioning of individual infants with Down syndrome.

Smiling in Children with Autism Spectrum Disorders

While children with Down syndrome show indiscriminate smiling, children with ASD show deficits in facial expressivity frequently including low levels of smiling. Low levels of smiling are associated with deficits in initiating joint attention and are particularly salient when children with ASDs are oriented toward an adult. These effects are evident as early as 12 months among infants who will later be diagnosed with an ASD. Even among infants at risk for autistic symptomatology because they are siblings of children with an ASD, levels of neutral affect are higher in early face-to-face interactions than among other infants. Smiling in children with ASDs reflects a deficit in the degree to which face-to-face contact with others is rewarding that may have cascading repercussions for the social development of affected children.

Developmental Continuity in Smiling: Predicting Social Competence

Individual differences in smiling are meaningfully related to subsequent developmental outcomes. This section is concerned with the continuity of early expressions of positive emotion and the association between early smiling and later indices of social competence. We begin with a discussion of smiling and security of attachment and other indices of social competence, turn to genetic and environmental influences on smiling, and end with a discussion of interactive smiling and its impact on socialization.

Smiling and Attachment

Infants who smile when their parent adopts a nonresponsive still-face have a tendency to develop socially appropriate relationships. They are perceived by their parents as having fewer externalizing behaviors (such as being loud and rough) 1 year later than infants who do not smile during the still-face, and may be more likely to develop secure attachments.

Infants whose level of smiling during face-to-face play with the parent rises between 2 and 8 months are more likely to be classified as securely attached than other infants. Similarly, smiling with the parent in play sessions around 18 months of age is associated with concurrent attachment security. It may be that regular smiling interactions in which the parent helps the infant modulate their level of positive arousal are a route to the development of a secure attachment relationship. This modulation involves not only responding positively to the infants' smiles but being responsive to the infant's need to look away after intense smiling bouts. This allows infants to calm themselves and then look back (and perhaps smile) at the parent.

Face-to-Face Smiling, Joint Attention Smiling, and Social Competence

Early social smiling in face-to-face interaction with a parent positively predicts 'anticipatory smiling', a tendency to communicate positive affect about an object to an adult tester. In addition, highly sensitive maternal caregiving predicts a more general measure of infant smiling at any point during an infant joint attention episode. It appears that infants' experience with early-rewarding social stimuli contributes to a later predilection to initiate positive communicative referencing with others.

Anticipatory smiling toward 1 year of age predicts parent-reported social expressivity and social competence scores at 30 months. Positive affect sharing indexed by anticipatory smiling may be a developmentally focal activity that is predicted by early social smiling and predicts subsequent social expressivity and competence. Likewise, infant Duchenne smiling during reunions with mother in the Strange Situation predicts parent ratings of extraversion and openness to experience when children are 3.5 years of age. In sum, positive emotion expression elicits positive responses from social partners that foster later sociability and social competence.

Smiling: Genetic and Environmental Effects

Parent reports on dimensions of infant temperament involving questions about infant smiling and laughter reveal the influence of both genetic and environmental effects. This contrasts with negative emotion expression, which showers higher genetic and lower environmental effects. Shared environmental effects in positive emotion expression point to possible socialization effects in factors that determine parent perceptions of level of smiling. This may mean that more emotionally positive infant–parent interactions influence future levels of infant smiling and positive emotional expression.

Developmental Continuity in Smiling

Infant reaction to standardized elicitors of smiling and other positive emotional expressions such as a puppet show and jack-in-the-box show moderate developmental stability between 1 and 3 years of age. Infants who engage in extremely high levels of smiling, positive vocalizations, and motor movement at 4 months in response to a mobile and auditory stimuli show different developmental patterns than infants who are nonresponsive or show more emotionally negative reactions. The infants who display earlier smiling are less behaviorally inhibited in unfamiliar situations over the first 2 years of life than the other infants. They continue to show a more exuberant temperamental style at 4 years when they are more likely to talk and engage with peers.

Concurrent Validity of Smiling to Social Stimuli

Infant smiles to social stimuli such as peek-a-boo games with examiners and infant smiles to nonsocial stimuli such as a jack-in-the-box appear to have different meanings. Only infant smiles to social stimuli are associated with infant positive emotion expression in the parent–child relationship and with parent ratings of their children's day-to-day positive emotion. Infant smiling in the parent–child relationship is in turn associated with later social competence.

Predictive Validity of Interactive Smiling

Through smiling in face-to-face interactions infants come to engage in simultaneous, reciprocal, and mutually enjoyable exchanges. Affecting and being affected by the positive emotional expression of the parent may lead infants to experience the happiness of others as essential to their own happiness. In support, shared infant–mother positive emotional expressions such as smiles – when they occur in conjunction with maternal responsivity to infant – are associated with two indices of social competence: children's internalization of social norms (obeying the rules) and committed compliance to maternal directives (cleaning up without reminders). In this way, experiences of affectively positive responsivity emerge from social interaction and shape the infant's developing social competence into childhood.

Conclusion

Early smiling has a relatively constant function. It expresses the infant and young child's positive emotional engagement with the environment even as it elicits positive emotional engagement in parents and peers. Yet smiling becomes more emotionally intense and multifunctional with age. From the first social smiles at 1 – 2 months to mischievous smiles at 1 – 2 years, smiling indexes increasingly complex cognitive engagement and social awareness as it becomes integrated into increasingly complex interactions involving objects, actions, and peers. The level and social specificity (appropriateness) of smiling is also sensitive to risk factors such as prematurity, maternal depression, and early psychopathology (e.g., Down syndrome). As such, smiling is a relatively stable index of age appropriate social communication and functioning in infancy and early childhood.

See also: Attachment; Autism Spectrum Disorders; Emotion Regulation; Humor; Imitation and Modeling; Intermodal Perception; Newborn Behavior; Self Knowledge; Social Interaction.

Suggested Readings

Aksan N and Kochanska G (2004) Heterogeneity of joy in infancy. *Infancy* 6(1): 79–94.
Barrett LF and Wager TD (2006) The structure of emotion: Evidence from neuroimaging studies. *Current Directions in Psychological Science* 15(2): 79–83.
Cohn JF and Tronick EZ (1987) Mother infant face-to-face interaction: The sequence of dyadic states at 3, 6, and 9 months. *Developmental Psychology* 23(1): 68–77.
Fox NA and Davidson RJ (1988) Patterns of brain electrical activity during facial signs of emotion in 10 month old infants. *Developmental Psychology* 24(2): 230–236.
Kochanska G (2002) Mutually responsive orientation between mothers and their young children: A context for the early development of conscience. *Current Directions in Psychological Science* 11: 191–195.
Messinger D, Fogel A, and Dickson KL (2001) All smiles are positive, but some smiles are more positive than others. *Developmental Psychology* 37(5): 642–653.
Sroufe LA and Waters E (1976) The ontogenesis of smiling and laughter: A perspective on the organization of development in infancy. *Psychological Review* 83: 173–189.
Striano T and Berlin E (2005) Coordinated affect with mothers and strangers: A longitudinal analysis of joint engagement between 5 and 9 months of age. *Cognition and Emotion* 19(5): 781–790.
Venezia M, Messinger DS, Thorp D, and Mundy P (2004) The development of anticipatory smiling. *Infancy* 6(3): 397–406.
Waller BM and Dunbar RIM (2005) Differential behavioural effects of silent bared teeth display and relaxed open mouth display in Chimpanzees (*Pan troglodytes*). *Ethology* 111(2): 129–142.
Weinberg MK and Tronick EZ (1994) Beyond the face: An empirical study of infant affective configurations of facial, vocal, gestural, and regulatory behaviors. *Child Development* 65(5): 1503–1515.

Relevant Websites

http://face-and-emotion.com – A site devoted to the human face, Dataface (contains information on the anatomically based Facial Action Coding System for the measurement of smiles and other expression).
http://www.psych.utah.edu – Alan Fogel's website.
http://www-2.cs.cmu.edu – Automated Face Analysis at the Carnegie Mellon University, Robotics Institute.
http://www.psy.miami.edu – Daniel Messinger's website.

Social and Emotional Development Theories

C R Thomann and A S Carter, University of Massachusetts, Boston, MA, USA

Glossary

Affordances – Learning opportunities and external supports.

Canalized – Behaviors that are likely to appear in development across a very wide range of environmental conditions.

Ecology – This term is used in Urie Bronfenbrenner's ecological systems theory and refers to the layers of contexts that influence and are influenced by children's development. These layers include the family, community, and culture.

Ethology – Ethological theories of development focus on the influence of evolution on development, proposing that caregiver–infant interactions are the product of environmental adaptation.

Goodness of fit – The match between a child's temperamental and other characteristics and the parent/caregiver's expectations and caregiving style.

Protective factor – Protective factors can exist within the individual, family, community, or culture, and improve an individual's response to a risk factor, creating a more adaptive outcome.

Psychopathology – Non-normative behaviors and emotions that are maladaptive for the child's developmental progress and that often cause distress to the child or family.

Risk factor – Most simply, risk refers to the probabilistic relationship between a predictor and an outcome. For example, individuals with poor literacy are at risk of being held back in school. A risk factor is a variable that, if present for an individual, increases the likelihood that a particular outcome will occur.

Scaffolding – This term refers to an approach to teaching children in which the adult adapts to the child's level of ability. The purpose of this approach is to promote independent functioning.

Social and emotional milestones – A set of behaviors with a normative developmental timing that can be considered universal.

Temperament – Individual differences in behavioral style usually thought to have a biological origin.

Zone of proximal development – A term pioneered by Vygotsky, referencing the gap between what individuals can do and what they have the potential to do. In child development, this is understood as the gap between what children can do independently and what they can do with adult assistance.

Introduction

We begin this article on social and emotional development in young children by sharing several definitions of emotion. Next, we briefly discuss some of the most widely held theories of early emotional development and the function of emotion in early development. Following a discussion of relevant theories, we turn our attention to important milestones in emotional and social development. In addition to interest in universal developmental patterns, or those social and emotional behaviors that unfold consistently across children living in very different circumstances, there has been a great deal of interest and attention to individual differences in social and emotional functioning. The largest body of research on individual differences in social and emotional functioning in early childhood has been in the area of temperament. Based on the importance of temperamental variation in children's social and emotional development, we briefly discuss several important dimensions of temperament and introduce the concept of goodness of fit. Finally, we discuss some of the ways in which children can manifest difficulties in the domains of emotional and social development in early childhood and some of the contexts that place children at risk for such difficulties.

What Are Emotions?

Many definitions of emotion have been offered over the centuries. Current emotion theories offer definitions that vary based, in part, on the relative emphasis placed on evolutionary and biological influences, the expression or communicative component of emotions, subjective experience, physiological activation of the parasympathetic and sympathetic systems, neuro-chemical activity in the brain, and the extent to which emotional experience is constructed in a psychosocial or relational context. Mainstream theories of emotion relevant to early childhood share the view that early emotions have evolved over time due to their importance in ensuring the survival of the human species. Thus, emotions, and in particular emotions that manifest early in life, are innately structured, biologically prepared abilities that serve alerting and organizing functions.

The term emotion can be used to refer to multiple levels of an organism's system, including the following: (1) the brain state association with the presentation or withdrawal of an incentive; (2) the subjective experience of a feeling state (e.g., butterflies in stomach); (3) the labels or meaning attributed to the feeling state (e.g., excited vs. anxious); and (4) a behavioral manifestation such as an action or facial expression (e.g., muscle tension, eyes widening). Scientific investigators utilize each of these levels to deepen understanding of emotional processes. However, it is critical to recognize that there tend to be small associations between measurements of these different ways of operationalizing emotion so that different conclusions may be drawn when different methods are employed. Moreover, there is dramatic individual variation across each of these systems, such that the appearance of joy may reflect multiple brain, feeling, and appraisal states (i.e., outside appearances do not necessarily reflect internal states). Moreover, although we talk about discrete emotions as if they are unitary constructs, the reality is much more complex. Feelings are better understood as members of sets and life's complexities often lead to complex or blended feeling states (e.g., feeling both angry and disappointed that one is unable to achieve a particular goal). A change in emotional state provides both an internal and communicative alerting signal that can facilitate or interfere with behavioral adaptation. Further, modern theories recognize that emotions influence cognitive processes, including how individuals perceive and appraise events and contexts. For example, an individual's emotional state can impact which features in the environment are salient or most noticeable and whether objects or events are appraised as threatening, neutral, or inviting. In addition to influencing perception and appraisal systems, emotions can also influence how individuals learn and remember information. Indeed, to the extent that you are enjoying this article you are more likely to remember its contents, as positive mood tends to promote learning.

It is important to recognize that emotions, like many phenomena, become more differentiated and complex with development. For emotion theorists who hold a social constructionist view of emotional development, socially constructed schemas can be viewed as mediating the relation between environmental or internal stimuli and emotional reactions. Thus, some emotion theorists argue that the subjective experience and expression of emotions depends on a social construction regarding when, where, and what is appropriate to feel as well as when, where, and how to behave. Within the social constructionist framework there are two general groups of human emotions. The first group emerges very early in development and can be seen in many different animal species. These emotions include joy, sadness, and fear. The second group of emotions is more complex, requiring cognitive attributions. Good examples of this second group of emotions are shame and guilt because it is only possible to feel shame or guilt if one has an understanding of right and wrong. It is this second group of emotions that are most likely influenced by cultural variations. The first group of emotions tends to be seen as more universal, or shared across cultures.

Theories

We present several theories of emotion to further deepen understanding of the concepts of emotion and social and emotional development. Ethological theory highlights the survival value of emotions while discrete emotions theory emphasizes the innate structure and universality of a core set of emotions. In contrast to discrete emotions theory, cognitive emotions theory proposes that the ability to experience and communicate discrete emotions is connected to the appraisal of internal and external events and therefore, the development of cognitive abilities. We also highlight the importance of the caregiver–child relationship, the primary context in which emotions develop. We conclude the section on emotion theories with the functionalist approach, which connects emotions to the goals of the individual. Finally, we conclude the section on theories with a very brief review of psychosocial theories highlighting the important contributions of social learning theory.

Ethology

Ethological theories of development focus on the influence of evolution on development, proposing that caregiver–infant interactions are the product of environmental adaptation. In contrast to many other species, human infants cannot survive without caregivers and have a relatively long period of dependence on their caregivers: For the first several years of life humans cannot feed themselves, find shelter, or protect themselves from harm. Thus, an effective infant– and toddler–caregiver relationship is essential to survival, and, ultimately, the survival of the human species. Ethology proposes that natural selection has given infants and caregivers an inborn set of behaviors that promote the development of a strong caregiver–child relationship and infant survival.

According to ethology, infants have instinctual behaviors and physical characteristics (e.g., large head, large eyes) that help keep caregivers nearby. For example, one function of the infants' cry is to signal distress that brings caregivers closer and motivates them to meet the infant's needs. As infants get older, they have a more complex set of behaviors to maintain proximity to their caregivers (e.g., crawling, walking, and running). Infants also encourage caregivers to stay close to them by making interactions fun through smiling, laughing, and making eye contact. Finally, when caregivers respond to a distressed infant and the infant subsequently becomes calmer, this serves as a sort of reward and promotes appropriate caregiving.

Attachment theory, which has generated hundreds of studies in developmental psychology, emerged from John Bowlby's adopting an ethological perspective on early human bonding behavior. Attachment theory is centered on understanding the manner in which children internalize and elaborate a working model of the history of their caregiving relationships. When the child's basic social and emotional needs are met within the parent–child relationship, the child develops a 'secure' attachment to the parent. A child's 'secure attachment' to the parent is viewed within attachment theory as a sign of healthy social and emotional development that will positively impact the development of future relationships. In contrast, there are several 'insecure' attachment styles, believed to reflect a failure within the parent–child system. These styles include an avoidant pattern, in which children learn to over-rely on themselves, a resistant pattern, in which children seek out assistance but are not easily soothed, and a disorganized pattern, in which there is not a coherent attachment style and atypical attachment behaviors may be observed.

Recent research has highlighted that children with different temperamental styles have different parenting needs. One dimension of parenting that has consistently been associated with positive outcomes, however, is parental sensitivity, a style that is characterized by responsiveness to the child's cues, warmth and emotional positivity, and acceptance of the child's range of emotional expression. Parenting dimensions that are associated with insecure attachment include intrusiveness, hostility, and detachment. In the infant/toddler period, studies have relied primarily on the strange situation, a series of play and separation segments involving the parent, child, and a novel examiner, to determine attachment status. In later childhood, adolescence, and adulthood, play- and interview-based narrative approaches have been utilized. The assessment of attachment security is somewhat controversial as different methods can yield different results.

Discrete Emotions Theory

Charles Darwin suggested that some fundamental emotions are inborn and universal in both animals and humans. He went on to propose that emotions are adaptive and important for survival in young children, as infants can use emotions to communicate their needs to their caregivers. Over time, these ideas developed into what is known as 'discrete emotions theory', which has been pioneered by Carroll Izard and Carol Malatesta. This theory proposes that infants are born with an innate ability to experience and express discrete emotions.

Discrete emotions theory states that each discrete emotion has three elements: (1) a neural element comprised of a particular pathway and area in the autonomic nervous system associated with the emotion; (2) a motor expressive element, which encompasses facial, vocal, and bodily expression patterns that give information to others about the intensity and quality of the emotion; and (3) a mental processes element, or the conscious and unconscious subjective feelings of emotion. The eight discrete emotions are happiness, sadness, interest, fear, contempt, anger, surprise, and disgust.

This theory further posits a developmental timetable for the emergence of these discrete emotions. At birth, the infant's emotional repertoire is quite limited, and includes only interest, a nonsocial reflex smile, distress, and disgust. By 4–6 weeks of age, a social smile that reflects happiness appears. By 3–4 months, one can observe anger, surprise, and sadness and shortly thereafter, fear emerges, including the presence of stranger anxiety in many infants. More complex emotions continue to emerge with all eight of the discrete emotions present by the end of the second year of life.

According to discrete emotions theory, the processing of emotion starts with a stimulus, such as a startling noise or a stranger's face. This stimulus triggers the neural component of the emotional system. Next, the nervous system communicates with the motor expressive component, creating facial, vocal, and bodily expression. The muscle contractions which create these expressions also activate the nervous system, which creates the subjective experience of emotion. The facial feedback hypothesis expands on this last step of the system, as the facial muscle contractions (e.g., smile, frown) send additional information back to the neural system. Thus, smiling when mildly distressed really can make one feel better, as the facial muscles associated with the smile send feedback to the neural system that influences subjective emotional experience.

Discrete emotions theory proposes that infants, regardless of age, express their subjective feelings of emotion though their facial expressions. For instance, a crying and fussing baby feels sad and distressed and a laughing and smiling infant feels happy. According to this theory, caregivers are able to discern and respond to their infant's subjective feelings of emotion simply by interpreting their facial, vocal, and bodily expressions. For example, facial and vocal expressions of pain might help a caregiver to attend to a too tight diaper, while an infant that smiles and laughs might encourage a caregiver to stay close and interact playfully. Importantly, as children get older and learn to mask their feelings (i.e., smiling when disappointed), there is no longer a 1:1 correspondence between facial display of emotion, neural systems, and subjective experience.

Cognitive Approaches

In contrast to discrete emotions theory, cognitive emotions theory proposes that an infant's ability to experience and communicate discrete emotions is connected to the development of cognitive abilities. Thus, although infants cry and have a nonsocial smile at birth, not all approaches accept that infants possess an innate ability to experience emotions. Rather, within the cognitive approach, the experience of distress and happiness emerges at 2–3 months of age, as cognitive skills develop.

Among the cognitive-centered approaches to early social and emotional development is Vygotsky's theory of social development. Vygotsky is best known for introducing concepts such as the zone of proximal development, which refers to the range of capacities and problem solving that the infant can achieve independently and those that the infant can achieve in collaboration with adult support and scaffolding, which refers to the behaviors that parents and other older interactive partners employ to enhance the infant's capacities. Central to Vygotsky's theory is the idea that infants develop new social and cognitive skills through interactions with older individuals. Vygotsky believed that, as an infant and caregiver participate in an activity, the adult begins by guiding and leading the experience (i.e., scaffolding the infant's experience), slowly giving more control to the infant. Vygotsky proposed that infants collect 'tools' to help them learn and grow. The older individuals in an infant's social network are some of these 'tools'. Thus, the older individuals in the child's world teach him or her not only about objects in the environment, but about the social context in which specific objects are employed and the kinds of social interactions that can be expected. Emotional experiences are interpreted within this social framework.

In his theory of early social development, Vygotsky highlighted the importance of 'all' social interactions. Not only are mother–child interactions important, but any older peer or adult influence can be significant. This is particularly relevant when considering the different models of caregiving found across cultures, as well as varied family constellations within cultures. For example, some cultures might emphasize interactions across generations, with grandparents filling the primary caregiver role. Other cultures might advocate community-centered caregiving, with infants and children spending time with many different members of the community. All of these relationships are thought to be essential to early social development.

The Context of Early Emotional Communication

The most central context for the development of emotional understanding and regulation in early childhood is primary caregiver–infant relationship. Caregiver–infant relationships are built on the multiple sequences of interactions that occur throughout daily routines. If infants and caregivers are able to accurately interpret each others' emotional expressions, these transactions are enhanced by greater mutuality and reciprocity. Research by Carroll Izard suggests that adults can identify many different emotions in infants. For example, in one of her studies, she showed adults pictures of 1–9-month-old infants exhibiting anger, fear, interest, sadness, surprise, happiness, and disgust. Adults were able to correctly identify these emotions at a high level of accuracy. Moreover, they became more accurate after being trained in the associations between certain facial expressions and certain emotions, suggesting that parents are learning to read their infant's emotional cues over time, rather than this being a completely innate ability.

Studies have also found evidence that infants can understand their caregiver's facial and vocal emotional cues. At 5 months, infants were able to distinguish between contrasting emotions by listening to only vocal cues. By 7 months, infants were able to distinguish between contrasting emotions by looking at caregiver facial expressions. This suggests that infants begin to understand emotional expression by listening to their caregiver's voice, and, eventually, learn which facial expressions match the tone of voice.

Infants also respond emotionally to their caregiver's emotional cues. For instance, one study found that 10-week-old infants tended to match their emotional expressions to their mothers' display of various emotions. For example, infants reacted to 'happiness' by smiling, to 'anger' by frowning, appearing angry, or freezing, and to 'sadness' with thumbsucking or other self-soothing behaviors. It appears that caregivers likely shape the way their infants express emotions. Carol Malatesta and colleagues also examined the way that mothers respond to the emotional expressions of their 3–6-month-old infants. Infants in this study displayed a broad range of emotions and changed their expressions every 7–9 s. Mothers reacted by trying to influence their infants' emotional expression, modeling, and imitating positive emotions and trying not to display negative emotions.

Functionalist Approaches

More recent views of emotional development connect emotion with the goals of the individual. From this 'functionalist' perspective, emotion is seen as a dynamic process coming from significant transactions between the individual and the environment. Within this functionalist framework, emotion is viewed as a process in which an individual marks the significance of a bodily or mental event. This approach focuses on the idea that (1) emotion is experienced in relation to adaptive goals; (2) emotional expression can be seen as 'social signals', not only indications of internal states; and (3) the physiological component of emotion can regulate and be regulated by social processes. In addition, it is not possible to determine an individual emotional response based on knowing what event preceded the emotion. Any eliciting event can cause multiple emotions depending on the manner in which an individual construes that event.

These theories represent a range of different understandings of social and emotional development. However, with few exceptions, it may be difficult for the average caregiver to apply these theories to daily interactions with children. Knowledge about universal aspects of social and emotional development, referred to as social and emotional milestones, may be more helpful in everyday life.

Psychosocial Theories

In addition to theories that focus on emotion, additional theories focus on social development. Psychoanalytic theory may be the earliest psychosocial theory and the first to adopt a developmental approach to the study of social–emotional phenomena, delineating both stages (e.g., oral and anal) and processes (e.g., fixation) in social and emotional development. Although psychoanalytic theory continues to have a presence, social learning theory has become more dominant in mainstream developmental research. Albert Bandura has been a leading advocate for social learning theory, which is concerned with the role of social context in learning. Early social learning theory focused on constructs such as observational learning and modeling (e.g., learning through watching others solve problems) and imitation. This theory highlighted that learning can occur without doing and what has been learned is not always reflected in observed behavior (i.e., the child may not show you what he or she knows). More recently, social learning theory has emphasized self-efficacy expectations, or an individual's appraisal of how likely they are to be successful at a given task, which, in turn, influences how likely they are to attempt the task. Gerald Patterson went on to employ social learning theory and behavioral principles to explain why parents and children escalate in negative coercive interaction cycles, as well as to explore how to use parent management interventions to break these cycles.

Social and Emotional Milestones

With increasing attention to the importance of social and emotional development, there is now general consensus regarding the normative developmental timing of a set of behaviors that can be considered universal. Indeed, recognizing the importance of early detection of children who may not be achieving these social and emotional milestones in a timely manner and may therefore be in need of early intervention, the US Center for Disease Control and Prevention has recently posted a set of social and emotional milestones along with milestones in other more traditional developmental domains. One can posit that the behaviors we call developmental milestones, or their developmental timing, are highly canalized, in that despite wide variation in parenting in the infant and toddler periods, these behaviors emerge in approximately the same time period and sequence around the world. These behaviors may also reflect qualitative shifts or behavioral reorganizations in infant and toddler behaviors, akin to the manner in which the motor milestone of transitioning from crawling to walking can dramatically change the affordances in the toddler's environment.

There is a dramatic behavioral reorganization in the infant at approximately 2–3 months that has been described as the infant waking up to the world. During this time, the social smile emerges and the infant begins to enjoy reciprocal interaction with a more skilled partner. Indeed, the infant may protest when an adult ceases interacting with the infant. The infant also becomes much more expressive and communicative at this time. The enjoyment of social interaction continues to develop. By 6–7 months of age infants clearly enjoy social play and are interested in exploring objects as well as their own image in a mirror. They are very sensitive to their emotional climate – responding to facial and vocal expressions of joy and becoming distressed or turning away in response to expressions of anger, fear and sadness. Although not universal, many infants will begin to exhibit stranger anxiety at approximately 6 months. For example, an infant may become extremely distressed when a loving grandparent, who has not visited since the infant was 3 months old, approaches to hug and kiss him or her.

Around the conclusion of the first year of life is another period of reorganization. At this time, the infant is transitioning into a toddler and should have a strong attachment to his or her caregivers, preferring to be held and soothed by the caregiver and looking to the caregiver for guidance when interpreting novel information. In addition to his or her caregivers, the toddler will have clear preferences for some people as well as specific toys and activities. The 12-month-old enjoys imitating other people in play and can express delight in mastering new skills. Depending on the demands and expectations placed on the toddler, he or she may also begin to feed him or herself (e.g., finger foods) and cooperate during routine caregiving activities (e.g., raising his or her arms when it is time to remove a shirt).

In the second year of life, toddlers become fascinated and excited by other children and babies. They are also becoming aware of themselves as independent agents in the world and may begin to test the limits of their own authority. Although labeled the 'terrible twos', challenging behaviors such as temper tantrums and 'testing' routinely begin to emerge at approximately 18 months of age. Although stressful to parents, these behaviors can be understood as a reflection that infants are sorting out the meaning of 'Me!' and 'Mine' in relation to you, yours, and ours. By the age of 2 years, there is also a clear interest in doing things independently and a greater awareness of success and failure. With greater cognitive understanding come more complex emotions, such as shame, which is evident in 2-year-olds who are beginning to grapple with learning what is permitted and what is not. Two-year-olds are typically very motivated to play with other children, although they are not very skilled at negotiating conflicts and therefore require adult supervision. Peer contact provides opportunities to practice social skills. The second year of life is also the time in which pretend play emerges. By 18 months of age, the toddler should delight in simple pretend activities such as feeding a stuffed animal.

By the time a child turns 3, they have strong preferences for particular playmates and have more elaborate play skills. For example, pretend play is more developed, such that they can now use a stuffed animal to be the active agent rather than the passive recipient of an activity (e.g., having the bear feed the baby). In addition, rudimentary turn-taking is possible and beginning inhibitory control permits appropriate responses to learning that an object belongs to another child. By this age children will often express their affection toward playmates and caregivers quite openly and can express and react to a wide range of emotions. At approximately the age of 2.5 years, many children begin to show a preference for doing things the same way, or having set routines. Some have argued that this is an effort to assert control over an increasingly complex environment that, with greater cognitive understanding, may provoke more fear responses. The child's ability to predict what is going to happen allows them to assert some control and minimize fear. Thus, having a specific routine, such as a bedtime routine that always involves the same activities (e.g., bath, pajamas on, brush teeth, read two books, backrub, sleep), can sometimes ease challenging transitions such as bedtime.

Throughout the preschool period, social skills with peers are increasing and pretend play is marked by increasing creativity and flexibility. Children use play to understand the complexities of their relational and physical world. One of the most salient developmental tasks for the preschooler is learning to negotiate the peer environment and make friends. It is important to recognize that early in the preschool years the boundary between reality and fantasy is not well understood. Thus, a 3- or 4-year-old may become quite frightened by monsters under his or her bed, and may have more difficulty sorting out fantastical images viewed on television or movies.

The study of social and emotional milestones has greatly informed parenting and professional practices, both in terms of the early detection of emotional delays and deficits as well as the development of prevention programs. For example, careful study of early crying patterns reveals that there is a significant peak in crying at approximately 2 months of age that is often characterized by long periods of inconsolable and unpredictable crying. Dissemination of this information to parents, along with specific strategies for soothing infants, has been shown to reduce the incidence of shaken baby syndrome, an early form of child abuse.

While social and emotional milestones are highly canalized, emerging in approximately the same period and sequence around the world, there is also great individual variation in how infants express emotions.

Individual Differences: Temperament

When discussing emotional and social development, it is essential to consider the way infants express emotions and their overall behavioral style when responding to environmental stimulation. These elements of infant personality are known as 'temperament'. Definitions of temperament vary on several dimensions. While most theorists believe that temperament is inherited, stable, and exhibited early in life, there is some variability. For example, some theorists also believe that temperament might be affected by the infant's environment (e.g., caregiving practices). Of note, no temperament style is inherently good or bad. Rather, some temperamental styles are better suited to some environmental conditions and others are better suited to other environmental conditions. Thus, in conditions of famine, children who are very quick to cry and cry intensely are most likely to survive. In contrast, in conditions of plenty, this same temperamental style is associated with heightened behavior problems and parenting stress. Thus, it is not a question of good or bad temperamental trait, but of good or bad fit with the environmental conditions. As children get older, they are able to have more control over their environments, engaging in what has been termed niche seeking, or pursuing environments that are a good fit for one's temperamental style.

Additionally, only some aspects of temperament have been found to be stable over time (for instance, negative emotionality, attention span, and activity level). Finally, there is some evidence that temperament begins to be exhibited in the uterus, as shown by heart rate and activity level, while other aspects of temperament do not manifest or are not measurable this early in life.

There are multiple approaches to the study and description of temperament, but all include dimensions of emotionality and sociability among the dimensions of behavior assessed. In their seminal New York Longitudinal Study, Alexander Thomas and Stella Chess developed the temperament categories 'easy', 'difficult', and 'slow-to-warm-up'. Approximately 40% of the infants studied by Thomas and Chess fell into the easy category, and were characterized by regular eating, sleeping, and toileting patterns. These infants adapted well to changing environments, were open to approaching novel people or objects, had generally low-to-moderate levels of reactivity, and were typically happy. In contrast, approximately 10% of the infants studied by Thomas and Chess fell into the difficult category, and were characterized by more unpredictable schedules. These infants had difficulty adapting to changing environments, often withdrew from novel people or objects, had generally high levels of reactivity, and often cried or fussed. Finally, approximately 15% of infants studied by Thomas and Chess fell into the slow-to-warm-up category, and while they often withdrew from novel situations and had difficulty adapting to changing environments, they also exhibited relatively low levels of activity and reactivity. The rest of the infants studied by Thomas and Chess did not fit into any of the categories, presenting a possible issue with the use of categorical temperament systems.

However, typologies are not the only way to measure temperament. For instance, the multidimensional, bottom-up approach used by Mary Rothbart in the children's behavior questionnaire (CBQ) offers an alternative. The CBQ assesses individual differences along 16 different dimensions, which cluster into three larger factors: 'extraversion/surgency', 'negative affectivity', and 'effortful control'. Children are not grouped into any one of these factors. Rather, they are measured on each factor, as well as on each of the 16 smaller dimensions.

Studies that tested and honed the scales of the CBQ supported the idea of a multidimensional view of temperament. For example, individuals who were high in negative affect were not necessarily low in positive affect, suggesting that at least two separate factors were needed to measure the emotional domain. By measuring individuals on multiple, hierarchical, dimensional scales (e.g., several different types of positive and negative aspects of emotionality), instead of simply grouping people based on a few temperamental attributes (e.g., easy, difficult, slow-to-warm-up), we gain the ability to detect more subtle individual differences.

Finally, Rothbart also looked for biological models to support her temperament dimensions. For example, 'effortful control', which works to regulate the more reactive aspects of temperament, is believed to be related to the anterior attention network, comprised of areas of the midprefrontal cortex, including the anterior cingulate gyrus and portions of the supplemental motor cortex. However, while Rothbart's model has a biological component and suggests that temperament is inherited, it also assumes that infants' caregivers and environments have a significant influence on their social and emotional developmental trajectories.

Early Emerging Psychopathology

Until fairly recently, all individual variation in social and emotional development in early childhood was discussed in terms of temperamental variation. There was little or no acknowledgement that some extreme behaviors reflected early emerging psychopathology, rather than an extreme normative variation in temperament. It is now recognized that some infants and toddlers exhibit patterns of behaviors that cause them or their families significant distress and that can impair their day-to-day life activities. Recognizing that a set of behaviors constitute psychopathology rather than normative variation is very challenging, and requires an examination of the frequency, intensity, duration, and quality of a set of behaviors. For example, although it is normative for 2-year-olds to have some temper tantrums, they may be part of a broader pattern of disruptive behavior when a child is having many temper tantrums each day with multiple caregivers. Temper tantrums are characterized by intense negative affect, aggression (e.g., kicking, biting, hitting parents) and/or destructiveness (e.g., breaking toys or household objects), last for over 15 min, and appear to have multiple triggers (e.g., fatigue, disappointment, frustration) or to appear without a trigger or 'out of the blue'. The child who spends 20 min multiple times each day having a tantrum because of simple frustrations (e.g., he cannot make the block tower in the way he envisioned it, he is asked to try a new cereal, a parent must run to the store to buy an ingredient for dinner unexpectedly, someone changed the television channel) is losing precious opportunities for learning a variety of social, emotional, and cognitive skills. Moreover, caregivers will be more likely to experience high levels of parenting stress and interactions are likely to be characterized as tense rather than positive.

Recent work demonstrates that parents and other caregivers are able to describe children's social and emotional problems and competencies in a differentiated and reliable manner on questionnaire assessments and interviews. Moreover, problem behaviors that emerge early in childhood tend to be as stable as those observed in later childhood and adolescence, with approximately half of children who show extreme scores continuing to show extreme scores one year later. Moreover, a significant percentage of children who parents and teachers rate as having significant social–emotional problems in kindergarten and first grade can be identified as having social and emotional problems before 3 years of age. Importantly, identifying problems in very young children does not suggest that the etiology or cause of the problems is isolated within them or that the intervention must be focused on the child. Indeed, as detailed in the next section, there are a variety of known risk factors that increase risk for psychopathology in young children and we believe that interventions must focus on child–caregiver relationships.

Risk and Protective Factors

Risk

Most simply, risk refers to the probabilistic relationship between a predictor and an outcome. For example, individuals who have difficulty reading are at risk of being held back in school. In other words, holding everything else constant, they are more likely than good readers to be held back. A risk factor can be an event (e.g., exposure to violence, separation from, or loss of, a caregiver), a condition, (e.g., having asthma or another chronic illness, living in poverty), or characteristic (e.g., being male, having a 'difficult' temperament) that increases the chance of the outcome associated with the risk factor happening. While risk factors may play a part in the etiology of a particular outcome, they are not considered causal factors.

Contextual risks: They come in clusters

Most children do not experience one isolated risk factor or stressor. As Bronfenbrenner, a proponent of viewing children in their ecological contexts, pointed out, risk factors usually cluster in the same individuals, and are present within many different systems in the child's ecology (e.g., the individual, the family, and the community). Further, stressors are often embedded within each other. For example, a parental job loss is often followed by increased parental stress, significant loss of income, and moving. Given that children frequently experience multiple risks and stressors, focusing on an isolated risk factor does not create an accurate picture of children and their contexts.

Multiple risks: The more risk, the greater the negative impact

There is substantial evidence that measuring the cumulative impact of multiple risk factors predicts child outcomes better than any one single factor. For example, in Rutter's study of 10-year-olds, risk for developing a psychiatric disorder was only 2% for families with zero or one risk factor. Risk increased to 20% for families with four or more risk factors. Risk factors examined were severe marital distress, large family size or overcrowding, maternal psychiatric disorder, paternal criminality, low socioeconomic status, and admission of the child to foster care. Other studies have included a wider range of risk factors such as the number of residence and school changes (with a higher-number conferring greater risk), low socioeconomic status, single parenthood status, marital separation or divorce, poor family relationships, seeking marriage guidance, young motherhood, low maternal cognitive ability, and maternal psychopathology. Across several studies there is strong evidence that single risk factors show small effects on child outcomes, when compared to an aggregate of the multiple stressors and risks that distinguish high-risk children. The more risks that are present in a child's life, the greater the negative impact on children's social and emotional functioning.

Protective factors

However, not all children who face significant risks experience problems in their social and emotional development. There is increasing interest in identifying factors that may serve as buffers, or protective factors, in the lives of children who face cumulative adversity. To develop effective prevention and intervention strategies to promote the social competence of children facing cumulative risk and to identify those children at greatest risk, it is imperative to explore these potential protective factors. In particular, it is essential to identify protective factors that are amenable to change and that can introduce positive shifts for children who are exposed to multiple risk factors.

Culture and Social and Emotional Development

In the study of social and emotional development, we often focus on individual characteristics (such as temperament) and relational components (such as parent–child interactions, attachment, and peer relationships). However, as Bronfenbrenner suggests, it is important to remember that both the individual and relational aspects of social and emotional development are held within a larger cultural macrosystem. Culture is an array of shared attitudes, beliefs, values, rituals, and behaviors that are transmitted across generations. Cultural attitudes and values can shape which individual characteristics are nurtured or suppressed and help determine the acceptability of particular interactions and relationships.

For example, child outcomes based on behavioral style vary depending on the cultural context. For example, Kenneth Rubin found that having a temperamental style labeled 'behaviorally inhibited', meaning the child responds with higher levels of 'wariness and fear' to unfamiliar people and situations, was associated with different outcomes for children living in Canada as compared with children living in the People's Republic of China. In Canada, behavioral inhibition was associated with having less positive peer relationships, low feelings of self-regard, and feelings of loneliness in adolescence. In contrast, shy-inhibited behavior is valued and encouraged in China, and children with this behavioral style developed positive social relationships and positive feelings about themselves. The way behavioral inhibition is understood and the meaning it holds for social interaction clearly varies across these two cultures. This is but one example of the myriad of ways in which culture can shape early social and emotional development. It also highlights the importance of cross-cultural studies for understanding both universal and culture-specific aspects of social and emotional development.

Summary and Conclusions

In this article, we explored several definitions of emotion and discussed some of the most widely held theories of early emotional development. We also explored universal milestones in social and emotional development as well as individual differences in social and emotional functioning. Finally, we discussed some of the ways children can manifest difficulties in the domains of emotional and social development and some of the contexts that place children at risk for such difficulties. Our attempt was to emphasize the importance and complexity of early social and emotional development. In particular, we hope that this article highlighted the importance of focusing not only on the individual child, but on the child's broader ecology, with respect to caregiver relationships, family, and community risk and protective factors, and the larger cultural context that critically influences social and emotional development.

See also: Attachment; Birth Order; Discipline and Compliance; Emotion Regulation; Empathy and Prosocial Behavior; Fear and Wariness; Gender: Awareness, Identity, and Stereotyping; Humor; Play; Postpartum Depression, Effects on Infant; Risk and Resilience; Separation and Stranger Anxiety; Shyness; Social-Emotional Development Assessment; Socialization in Infancy and Childhood; Temperament; Vygotsky's Sociocultural Theory.

Suggested Readings

Briggs-Gowan MJ, Carter AS, Bosson-Heenan J, Guyer AE, and Horwitz SM (2006) Are infant–toddler social–emotional and behavioral problems transient? *Journal of the American Academy of Child and Adolescent Psychiatry* 45(7): 849–858.

Carter AS, Briggs-Gowan MJ, and Davis NO (2004) Assessment of young children's social–emotional development and psychopathology: Recent advances and recommendations for practice. *Journal of Child Psychology and Psychiatry* 45(1): 109–134.

Cole PM, Martin SE, and Dennis TA (2004) Emotion regulation as a scientific construct: Challenges and directions for child development research. *Child Development* 75: 317–333.

Eaton W (1981) Demographic and social ecological risk factors for mental disorders. In: Regier D and Gordon A (eds.) *Risk-Factor Research in the Major Mental Disorders*, pp. 111–130. Washington, DC: US Government Printing Office.

Lieberman A (1993) *The Emotional Life of the Toddler.* New York: Free Press.

Malatesta CZ, Culver C, Tesman JR, and Shepard B (1989) The development of emotion expression during the first two years of life. *Monographs of the Society for Research in Child Development* 54: 1–2 Serial No. 219.

Rothbart MK, Ahadi SA, Hershey KL, and Fisher P (2001) Investigations of temperament at three to seven years: The children's behavior questionnaire. *Child Development* 72: 1394–1408.

Rothbart MK and Derryberry D (1981) Development of individual differences in temperament. In: Lamb ME and Brown AL (eds.) *Advances in Developmental Psychology,* vol. 1, pp. 37–86. Hillsdale, NJ: Lawrence Erlbaum Associates.

Rothbart MK and Putnam SP (2002) Temperament and emotion regulation. In: Pulkkinen L and Caspi A (eds.) *Paths to Successful Development: Personality in the life course*, pp. 19–45. New York: Cambridge University Press.

Rutter M (1979) Protective factors in children's responses to stress and disadvantage. In: Kent MW and Rolf JE (eds.) *Primary Prevention of Psychopathology: Vol. 3. Social Competence in Children*, pp. 49–74. Hanover, NH: University Press of New England.

Rutter M (1987) Psychosocial resilience and protective mechanisms. *American Journal of Orthopsychiatry* 57: 316–331.

Social Interaction

E Tronick, University of Massachusetts, Boston, Boston, MA, USA

Glossary

Developmental disorganization – A normal developmental process in which one well-organized behavior, capacity, or state of consciousness is disassembled in order to reorganize it in a more complex and coherent form.

Mutual regulation model – The bidirectional process of communicating and responding to the relational intentions and meanings of the other during social interactions.

Reparation – the process of changing mismatching affects and intentions to matching affects and intentions.

Resilience – The individual's ability to resist and regulate stress. Individual differences in resilience in part emerge from differences in interactive reparatory experience.

Still-face – An experimental manipulation during interactions in which one partner is instructed not to respond to communicative displays of the other.

States of consciousness – The psychobiological organization of one's self in relation to the world. It is one's sense of self in the world. It does not imply awareness.

Introduction

Infants' and young children's social engagement with other people, along with genetic and other experiential processes, is a fundamental process shaping a child's normal as well as abnormal development. Normal social interaction leads to positive emotions, curiosity about the world of things, the capacity to cope with stress, and the development of close relationships during infancy and in adulthood. An infant experiencing abnormal social interactions becomes sad or angry, hesitant and withdrawn, anxious and vigilant, unengaged with people, the relationships they do have lack emotional closeness, have a limited emotional range and may lack empathy. They are likely to disengage from acting on the world of inanimate things. Whether the interactions are normal or abnormal, social experience not only becomes part of the content of the brain, but may actually sculpt the brain. Though interactions the infant makes meaning about the nature of him or her self and his or her relation to other people and the world.

Infants must be seen as a component of a dyadic – a two part – communicative system in which the infant and adult mutually regulate and scaffold their engagements with each other and with the world of things. In interactions, they communicate their individual needs and intentions and respond to each others needs and intentions. They exchange their private meaning of themselves and the world and they create new meanings. The infant has capacities to express their intentions and sense of the world and capacities to respond to the expressed needs and intentions of the other person. Of course, the other person has to have the same capacities.

Macro-Development

Though the classic milestone charts make the sequence of development appear like a smooth progression, normal development is neither smooth nor steady. Development actually is characterized by periods of stable organization in one domain followed by periods of disorganization in which the old organization is disassembled followed by a period of reorganization out of which a new more complex organization emerges. Crawling is an effective way of getting around in the world but it is disassembled to allow for the emergence of walking. Crawling allows the hands to be used only when sitting and stationary, whereas walking frees up the hands to be used while being mobile. Yet taking apart crawling in order to put together walking is energetically costly. The process is also emotionally costly because intentions cannot be fulfilled. Crawling has become less effective but walking is not yet in place such that achieving goals is difficult and frustrating.

The sequence of organization, disorganization (sometimes referred to incorrectly as regressions, because the infant does not go back to an old form but rather takes apart the old), and reorganization into a more complex and coherent form of functioning characterizes the development of all systems (see **Figure 1**). Periods of disorganization are an 'inherent' characteristic of self-organizing systems which grow and develop greater levels of complexity. Adding to this complexity and costliness, the

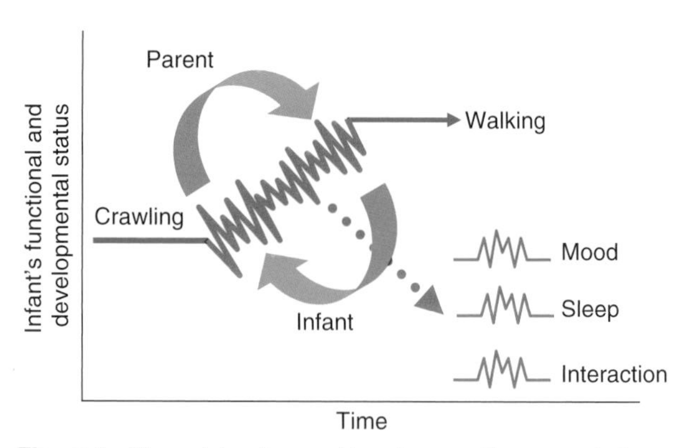

Figure 1 Normal development is not a smooth process but one characterized by organization, followed by disorganization and then reorganization. Disorganization in one system can disorganize other systems. The disorganization is regulated by a dyadic system made up of the infant and an adult.

disorganization of one domain can disorganize other domains. For example, the infant who is beginning to change from crawling to walking not only becomes disorganized motorically, but also is likely to become emotionally and diurnally disorganized. The regulation of this disorganization falls to the internal self-organizing resources of the infant. These resources are not trivial and include for instance brain processes that control the limbs and posture (motor cortex, vestibular mechanisms), and other areas that control wake-activity cycles (reticular formation). Yet some of the time for all developmental changes the infant's internal resources are inadequate to the task of controlling the disorganization. To overcome this limitation we have evolved a system to externally supplement the infant's internal resources – caretaking, or more formally a system of mutual regulation in which the infant is part of a larger dyadic system that includes an external regulator, an adult.

Under normal circumstances the combination of internal and external regulation is adequate and development moves forward. However, when the internal and external resources are inadequate development may be seriously disrupted. Disorganization increases and becomes long lasting, and in turn the development of new forms of organization fail or become compromised and coherence and complexity are lost. Note however, that a critical feature of the model is that disorganization is part of the 'normal' process. Disorganization is 'necessary' for development to move forward. It is only problematic when it exceeds the capacities of the dyad to regulate it.

Micro-Development: The Moment-by-Moment Process of Mutual Regulation

The infant is motivated to communicate with people, to establish intersubjective states, states in which there is mutual expression and knowing of the intentions and needs of oneself and of one's partner. This motivation is assumed to be a biological characteristic of our species. The child also is inherently motivated to act on and make sense of their place in the world – reach for objects to know what he or she can do with it. The accomplishment of motivated action on the inanimate world, however, is often dependent in the infant and young child on the establishment of intersubjective relationships. As is the case for *Homo sapiens*, children can only create meanings in collaboration with others. Their understanding of the world of objects, no matter how primitive, is dependent on establishing intersubjective states with others and the mutual creation of meaning. Though we are impressed with our ability to manipulate the world of things and create new technology the primary context in which the understanding of the world emerges is when we are in social relationships. Thus the child who successfully accomplishes communication with others, develops normally. Their understanding of themselves, others and the world expands. A child who does not engage the world in a culturally appropriate manner does not develop normally no matter what causes the failure – chronic or acute illness, congenital malformations, poor parenting, toxic exposures, or parental psychopathology.

Success or failure in accomplishing intentions is dependent on at least three critical processes among others. The first is the integrity and capacity of the child's physiologic systems and central nervous system to organize and control the child's physiologic states and behavior. The second is the integrity of the infant's communicative system including the central nervous system centers that control and generate messages and meanings and the motor system that makes the messages manifest (e.g., gestures and facial expressions). The earliest and continuing function of the communicative system is to express the child's intention for action to the caregiver and to communicate the extent to which the infant is succeeding or failing in fulfilling his or her intentions or goals. The third process, reciprocal to the second, is the caretaker's capacity to appropriately read the child's communications and willingness to take appropriate action. Therefore successful engagement with the world of people and things depends on the status and the effectiveness of the child–caretaker communicative system in facilitating the child's motivated intentions. These processes make up the process of mutual regulation – the capacity of each interactant, child and adult, to express their motivated intentions, to appreciate the intentions of the partner, and to scaffold their partner's actions so that their partner can achieve their goals.

The Mutual Regulation of Infant–Mother and Other Adult Social Interactions

Infant social interactions and emotions are also regulated dyadically. The principal components are the infant's central nervous system (e.g., primarily the limbic system) and the behaviors it controls (e.g., facial and vocal emotional displays) and the caregiver's regulatory input (e.g., facial expressions, gestures, vocalizations). Thus, the dyadic (collaborative) regulatory system is guided by communication between internal and external components, the infant and the caregiver (see **Figure 2** for one such example).

The Normal Individual and Cultural Variation of Social interactions

Interactions have been found to have enormous individual variation. In studies of normal mother–infant face-to-face interactions, expressions of positive affect by either the mother or the infant occur respectively about 42% for the mother and 15% for the infant. The standard deviation for positive affect for the mother varie from almost 0 to 80% or more. There is also variation between what mothers and fathers do with infants. Relative to mothers, fathers express positive affect with infants less often and spend a greater proportion of time in physical play with infants. During mother–infant interaction, infant arousal cycles between medium and low levels, and high positive affect appears gradually. In contrast, infants' arousal during father–infant interaction is high, sudden, and organized in multiple peaks that appear frequently as play progresses. For both mothers and fathers, positive affect predicted infants' positive affect at 6 months. Thus the 'what' and

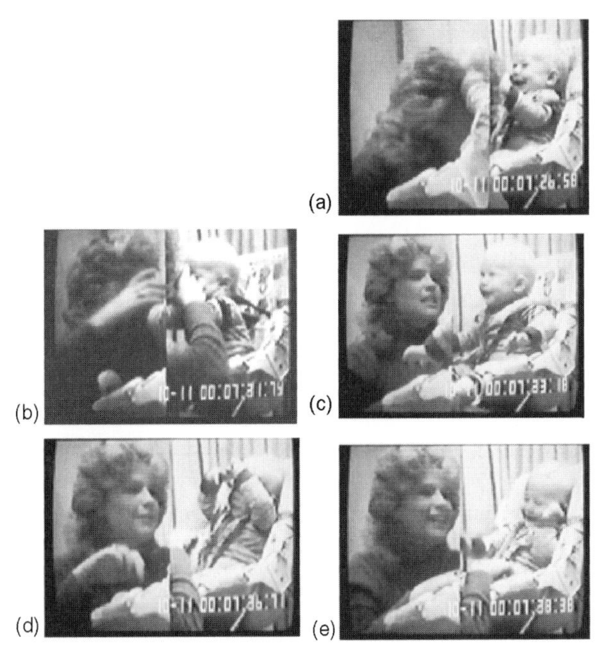

Figure 2 In (a) the infant is pulling on the mothers hair and in (b) she tries to disengage herself. In (c) she makes and angry face because it hurt as she disengaged. The infant reacts immediately and in (d) he places his hands in front of his face to defend himself. In (e) they have reestablished contact.

'how' of mothers and fathers interactions with their infants is different but neither is more optimal.

Another and particularly telling instance of normal variation are findings of gender differences in the affective and regulatory behaviors of normal 6-month-old infants as well as differences in interactive coherence between mothers and sons and mothers and daughters. Infant boys are more emotionally reactive than girls. They display more positive as well as more negative affect, focus more on the mother, and display more signals expressing change or stop, and demands for more contact than girls. Girls show more interest in objects, a greater constancy of interest, and better self-regulation of emotional states. Their message is more that they can do it on their own. Girls also evidence greater stability of sadness over time than boys. Sex differences in interactive coherence or matching have also been demonstrated with mother–son dyads evidencing more coherence than mother–daughter dyads. These gender differences reflect normal variants and highlight the range of affective expressiveness, regulatory behavior, and synchrony that occurs during normal interactions.

Cross-cultural findings further make the point that there is no single optimal form of interaction. Among the Gusii, an agricultural community in western Kenya, mothers turn away from their infants just as their infants become most affectively positive and excited. This maternal behavior presages the socialization of later restrictions on the expression of positive affect among different individuals (e.g., younger individuals do not look directly at older individuals especially when expressing strong affect). This looking away pattern is normative for the Gusii, but is quite different from that seen in the US. American middle income mothers respond to the infant's affective excitement with continued intense looking and heightened positive arousal. Looking away in a Gusii fashion by an American middle class mother would be seen as pathological. And in the US, it might be correct judgment, and it might also be correct that a American middle class gaze pattern by a Gusii mother might be pathological.

The Quechua of the altiplano of the Peruvian Andes have a pattern of child-care and interaction that if engaged in the US would be seen as bordering on neglect. Quechua mothers tightly swaddle and fully wrap their infants in blankets from head to toe and then carry them on their backs. There is no light inside the wrappings, sound is muffled, and the infants can hardly move because of how they are swaddled. In addition, though the infants are nursed, the duration between feedings may be several hours and it is done in a nurturing but perfunctory manner. Thus there is minimal nurturing interaction. According to some, this pattern would be 'abusive', because they argue it is necessary for the infant to experience affectively intense interactions to develop normally, yet somehow Quechua infants do develop normally, but of course as Quechua. Another perhaps dramatic example is the child rearing pattern of the Efe foragers of the Ituri forest. In this community, infants are with their mothers less than half of the time in the first year and regularly interact with many different individuals per hour. Even when the mother is in proximity, a crying infant is as likely to be calmed by someone other than the mother as by the mother. Moreover, infants are regularly nursed by individuals other than their mothers. There are playful interactions, more often with individuals other than the mother, but much of the time the infant is held or carried in a sling. Despite the fact that the Efe are foragers and live in the purported niche of evolutionary adaptation, the Efe pattern of care does not conform to a universalist evolutionary model, such as attachment theory, that postulates an evolutionarily given constraint that infants 'need' to be taken care of by one individual, usually the mother, or at most only a very few individuals, and that they are only able to develop other relationships slowly over the first years of life. Certainly, the Efe infant will be different than singularly (sometimes double) reared infant in an American or European middle class family, but neither is inherently more optimal the other. And if these examples from technologically simple societies seem too distant, one need only consider that in Japan many individuals from birth to death never sleep alone, or that many Italian families' children do not have a bedtime, but stay up or fall asleep while the rest of the family is awake and only get put to bed when the family goes to bed.

These findings make it clear that there is no singular universal optimal form of mother–child interaction from which deviations are considered pathological, as implied by the attachment model. Interactions vary among cultural communities (and the individuals in those communities) in culturally meaningful ways. On a daily basis, infants repeatedly participate in a culturated but variable set of interactions which results in their internalization of culturally accepted social–emotional interactive practices. Culturated interactive ways of being can be thought of as having a narrative structure, even though it is a narrative of communicative action and not words. The child comes to 'know' that "this is what is happening; this is what will happen; and this is how it will feel." This meaning system is established long before the child can engage in a narrative of words.

Matching, Mismatching, and Reparation

The typical mother–infant interaction is one that moves from coordinated (or synchronous) to mis-coordinated states and back again over a wide affective range (see **Figure 3**). The mis-coordinated state is referred to as a normal interactive communicative error. It is a bit of interactive disorganization or messiness. The interactive

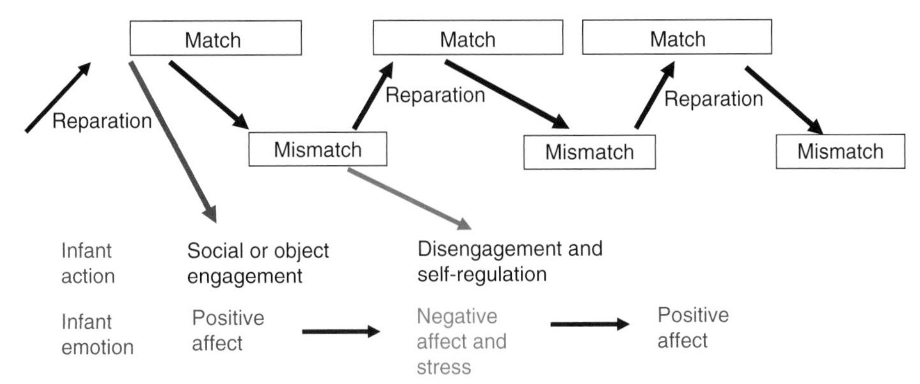

Figure 3 Normal interactions move between matching and mismatching states. Each state has different emotional consequences. The change from a mismatch to a match is a reparation.

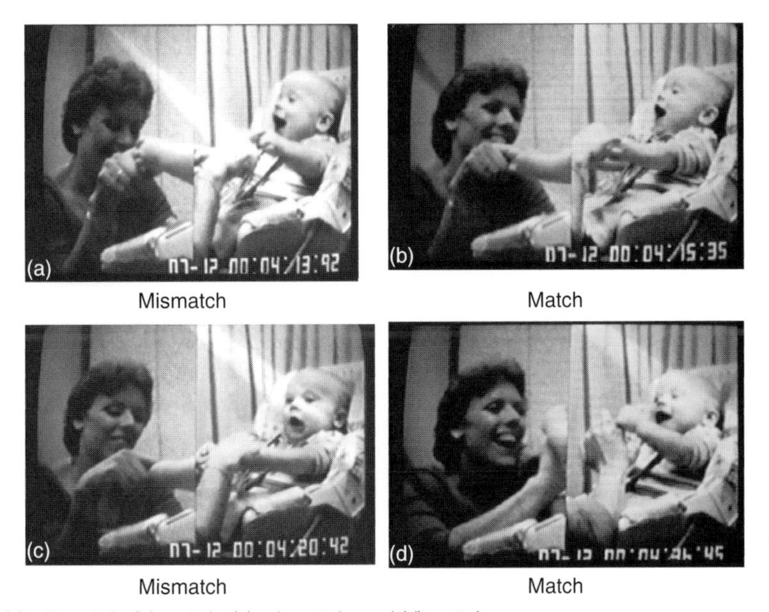

Figure 4 Sequence of (a) mismatch, (b) match, (c) mismatch, and (d) match

transition from a mis-coordinated state to a coordinated state is referred to as interactive repair. The process of reparation, like the dynamics of regulating homeostatic states, is mutually regulated. The partners, both infant and adult, convey their evaluation of the state of the interaction through their affective configurations (Stop! Continue.). In turn, in response to their partner's expressed evaluation, each partner attempts to adjust his/her behavior to maintain a coordinated state or to repair an interactive error. Critically, successful reparations and the experience of coordinated states are associated with positive affective states whereas interactive errors generate negative affective states. Thus the infant's affective experience is determined by a dyadic regulatory process. **Figure 4** presents a sequence of matching and mismatching states.

Interactive mismatches have a high rate of occurrence but they are quickly repaired. In studies of face-to-face interaction at 6 months of age, repairs occur at a rate of once every 3–5 s and more than one-third of all repairs occur by the next step in the interaction. Other studies using different analytic methods have found that maternal sensitivity in the mid-range, rather than at the low or high end, typify normal interactions. Mid-range sensitivity is characterized by errors and repairs as contrasted to interactions in which the mother is never sensitive, or always sensitive. In interactions characterized by normal rates of reparation, the infant learns which communicative and coping strategies are effective in producing reparation and when to use them. This experience leads to the elaboration of communicative and coping skills, and the development of an understanding of culturated interactive rules and conventions. Reparations are associated with positive affect and with the experiential accumulation of successful reparations and the attendant transformation of negative affect into positive affect, the infant establishes a positive affective core. This internal positive affective core is a resource that allows the infant to come to new situations feeling positive about him or herself and the unknown situation. The infant also learns that he or she has control over social interactions. Specifically, the infant develops a representation of himself or herself as effective, of his or her interactions as positive and reparable, and of the caretaker as reliable and trustworthy. These representations are crucial for the development of a sense of self which has coherence, continuity, and agency and for the development of stable and secure relationships.

The functional consequences of reparation from the perspective of mutual regulation suggest that when there is a prolonged failure to repair communicative messiness, infants will initially attempt to reestablish the expected interaction, but when these reparatory efforts fail, they will experience negative affect. To evaluate this hypothesis mothers were asked to hold a still-face and remain unresponsive to the infant. Thus, the mother fails to engage in her normal interactive behavior, carry out her regulatory role, and does not allow for reparations. The effect on the infant is dramatic. Infants almost immediately detect the change and attempt to solicit the mother's attention. Failing to elicit a response, most infants turn away only to look back at the mother again (see **Figure 4(a)–4(d)**). This solicitation cycle may be repeated several times. In more intense reactions when an infant's attempts fail to repair the interaction he or she may lose postural control, withdraw and self-comfort. The disengagement is profound even with this short disruption of the mutual regulatory process and break of intersubjectivity.

Reparatory Failure and Pathology

To examine the process of reparatory failure in natural settings the interactions of depressed mothers and their infants have been studied. It was hypothesized that maternal depression, like the still-face, disrupts the mutual regulatory process and constitutes a break in intersubjectivity. The break is brought about by the effects of depression on maternal affect and responsiveness. Depression compromises the mother's, and eventually the dyad's capacity to mutually regulate the interaction. Overall, depressed mothers look away more and express more negative, angry and sad affect than do nondepressed mothers. They engage in less play and use less motherese (exaggerated intonations in adult speech to infant). The infants of depressed mothers look away more, self-comfort more, and express more sad affect than do infants of nondepressed mothers. Depressed mothers and their infants share more negative dyadic states more often and positive behavior states less often than nondepressed mothers and their infants.

Depressed mothers with similar levels of depressive symptoms do not engage in the same interactive style. There are at least two interactive patterns (intrusive and withdrawal) and each disrupts the regulatory process. Importantly, in terms of the argument that development is shaped by social–relational experience each form has a different effect on the infant. One way depressed mothers act is to be 'intrusive'. These mothers engaged in rough handling, spoke in an angry tone of voice, poked at their

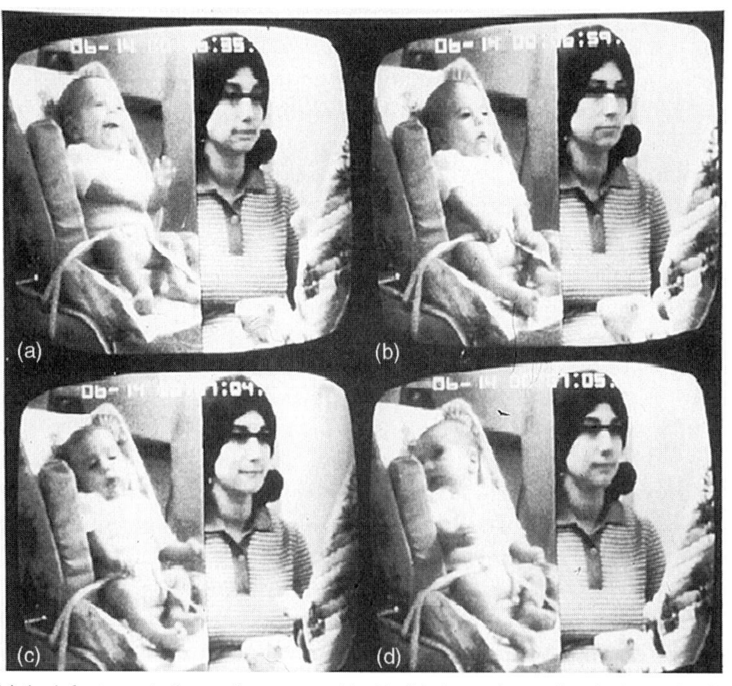

Figure 5 In the still-face (a) the infant greets the mother as usual but in (b) almost immediately detect her lack of response the change, and attempt to solicit the mother's attention. In (c) he looks away and in (d) turns fully away. Typically, the infant will then try to elicit the mother, much as in (a) and then cycle through (b) through (a) repeatedly.

babies, and actively interfered with their infants' activities. Withdrawn mothers, by contrast, were disengaged, unresponsive, affectively flat, and did little to support their infants' activities.

As a striking demonstration of the sensitivity of the infant to these different maternal ways of being with their infants, infants of intrusive mothers (re)acted one way, whereas infants of withdrawn mothers (re)acted another way. Infants of intrusive mothers spent most of their time looking away from the mother, and seldom looked at objects. They infrequently cried. Infants of withdrawn mothers were more likely to protest and to be distressed than the infants of the intrusive mothers, suggesting that maternal withdrawal may be particularly aversive to young infants.

These differential infant reactions are expected. The infants are reacting to and acting on different kinds of external social input; the affective reality they are regulating is different. Infants of withdrawn mothers are failing to achieve social connectedness because of the mothers' lack of response and their inability to repair the interaction. Initially, they may become angry. However, since they are unable to successfully cope or self-regulate this heightened negative state, they become dysregulated, fuss, and cry. This dysregulation, similar to the dysregulation associated with homeostatic failures, compels them to devote much of their coping resources to controlling their dysregulated state. With chronic exposure moment-by-moment, day after day they develop a disengaged and self-directed regulatory style characterized by self-comforting, self-regulatory behaviors (looking away, sucking on their thumb), passivity, and withdrawal as a way of coping with their state. To the extent that this coping style is successful in stabilizing their affective state, it is deployed automatically and becomes defensive. This self-directed style of coping is used in an effort to preclude anticipated negative emotions even in situations in which negative affect may not occur. This interpretation explains findings that infants of depressed mothers have less engaged and more negative interactions with a friendly stranger than do infants of non-depressed mothers. The infants of the depressed mothers are utilizing this strategy automatically without evaluating whether or not it is warranted. Eventually with the reiteration and accumulation of failure, these infants develop a negative affective core primarily characterized by sadness and anger, a representation of their mother as untrustworthy and unresponsive, and of themselves as ineffective and helpless.

The infants of hostile intrusive mothers must cope with a different regulatory problem. The mother's behavior prevents reparation of the interaction because she consistently disrupts the infants' activities. These infants initially experience anger, turn away from the mother, push her away, or screen her out. However, unlike the failure experience of the infants of withdrawn mothers, these coping behaviors are occasionally successful in limiting the mother's intrusiveness. Thus infants of intrusive mothers erratically experience reparation, such as a transformation of their anger into a more positive state. To the extent that these coping behaviors are successful in fending off the mother, these infants eventually internalize an angry and protective style of coping which is deployed defensively in anticipation of the mother's intrusiveness. These infants are easily angered when interacting not only with their mother but with others as well and are more easily frustrated when acting on objects.

More speculatively, these differences in infant reactions to maternal withdrawal and intrusiveness suggest an interpretation of differential effects associated with parental neglect and abuse. Infant failure to thrive, withdrawal and lack of motivation seen in situations of parental neglect, probably result in the lack of parental scaffolding leading to a constant demand on the infant to self-regulate. The infant is continuously required to control his or her own physiologic and affective states. This self-directed coping style compromises the infant's interchanges with the environment and motivation to engage with the world. By contrast, in the abusive situation, parental abuse leads to chronic physical defensiveness and anger as well as heightened vigilance, and fear.

These observations need to take into account gender differences in infant regulatory and affective styles. Boys are more affectively reactive and less able to self-regulate their affective states. This would make them particularly susceptible to the withdrawn style associated with depression because maternal withdrawal denies them the regulatory support that they need. On the other hand, girls, who are significantly more focused on objects and more able to maintain their own states than boys, may be more vulnerable to the intrusive style of depression which interferes with their self-organizing capacities. Combined with the findings that girls show more stability of sadness than boys, and boys show more stability of distancing and escape behaviors than girls, these gender differences in regulatory styles may be the first signs presaging the differential proportion of depression in girls and hyperactivity and aggressiveness in boys. Note, that it is not the case that girls are inherently depressed and boys inherently hyperactive. Each has different regulatory styles that in interaction with different caregiving styles make one or another outcome more likely.

This perspective also has implications for the higher rates of conduct and delinquency disorders in boys. We know from the literature on juvenile delinquency that boys commit many more crimes than girls. However, there is not a very good explanation for this phenomenon, but gender differences in infancy may already set the stage for this differential rate. The explanation, however, is not simply that boys are more aggressive than girls. Rather, it is that boys have greater difficulty controlling their emotional reactions. Because of this difficulty they are more likely than girls to fail to accomplish their goals. This failure generates frustration and anger and may lead to aggression. This may be exacerbated in those situations where parenting behavior is also compromised by, for example, depression.

Other at-risk populations have been studied and reparatory failure is at the heart of the interactive problems observed. Mothers with borderline personality disorder (BPD) have major emotional regulation difficulties during the social interactions and during the still-face procedure. Mothers with BPD are more intrusive and affectively negative. The infants of mothers with BPD exhibited more emotion dysregulation such as more hiccupping and spitting up. Prenatal cocaine and opiate exposure are also thought to subtly compromise social and emotional development. Mothers of cocaine-exposed infants showed more negative engagement than mothers of unexposed infants and showed higher overall levels of mismatched engagement states than nonexposed dyads, including more negative engagement when the infants were in states of neutral engagement. Infants exposed to heavier levels of cocaine showed more passive/withdrawn negative engagement and were more likely to engage in negative affective matching with their mothers than other infants. Though the effects are relatively small, cocaine exposure in general and heavy cocaine exposure in particular were associated with subtle patterns of negative affective interchanges, which may have a cumulative impact on exposed infants' later development and the quality of their relationship with their mothers. Similar effects have been for other *in utero* drug exposure as well as medical conditions such as low birthweight, small size for gestational age, gestational age, and white matter disorders.

Mutual Regulation, Brain Psychophysiology, and Resilience

One way to think about the long run effects of these risk conditions is to consider the interface and interaction between the nervous system and behavior. It is well established that there is a mutual influence of brain and behavior. Mother–infant interaction in animals and humans has long-term effects on the regulation of fearful behavior and on the systems regulating stress. The stress system of the human child appears to exhibit plasticity during development, which is mediated at least in part by social factors. During the first half of the second year, an infant who has been attended by highly responsive, sensitive, loving adult will exhibit a period of low cortisol responsivity. This is hypothesized to protect structures of the brain that are developing during that time from the deleterious effects of high cortisol. Moreover, individual differences in temperament can affect the likelihood that children will show increases in stress hormones as the quality of their care decreases. Children who exhibit more negative affect are more vulnerable to elevating cortisol as quality of care. In fact work with at-risk children has shown that the longer a child is neglected, the higher the degree of developmental delay. The longer a child experiences severe neglect, the less the hypothalamic, pituitary, adrenal (HPA) system recovers when conditions are improved.

Innovative research looking at the psychophysiology of relationships has made major advances and demonstrates that mutual regulatory processes not only regulate affect and behavior but physiology as well. Simultaneous recordings of cardiac responses and skin conductance have been carried out with infants aged 6 months and their mothers during normal interactions and in the still-face. The cardiac measure, heart rate and respiratory sinus arrhythmia index the parasympathetic nervous system which has an important function in downregulating arousal. Skin conductance, a measure that has been difficult to use with infants because of movement artifacts, measure the sympathetic nervous system that has a primary role in arousal. Findings suggest that maternal behavior and psychophysiology and infant behavior and psychophysiology are mutually related. Parasympathetic and sympathetic activity between mothers and their infants was found to be concordant as was infant negative engagement and parasympathetic and sympathetic activity. The finding on sympathetic activity may be of particular importance because sympathetic activity is related to the activity of the amygdala, a brain site intimately related to emotionality and reactivity. These results open up an area of relational psychophysiologic research that may deepen our understanding of mutual regulation, the development of relationships and the development of infant emotion regulation.

Conclusion

Social–emotional development is a critical process affecting all developmental domains. It leads to both the sculpting of the brain as well as its experiential content. The infant as well as the adult are active participants in the interaction. It is regulated by mutual regulatory processes. The mutual regulation of the interaction however is not smooth, but rather it is a messy process characterized by the matching and mismatching of affect and intentions. Reparation of mismatching to matching states powerfully affects the development of infants' sense of self and the emotional quality of their relationship with their partner(s). However, there is not an optimal universal form of interactions, but only interactions that are culturally appropriate resulting in the development of an culturated sense of self, even in infants. Nonetheless, interactions that produce unrelenting mismatches and failure of reparatory processes lead to withdrawal and a sense of helplessness.

Humans are makers of meaning and in essence, interactions are about making meaning – meaning about the infant's and adult's way of being together and what they want to do together. Successful interactions lead to shared states of knowing – dyadic states of consciousness – about the infant's and the adult's relation to each other and to the world. Meaning making during interactions is a creative process in which the uniqueness of the infant and adult generate new meanings out of the inherent messiness of interactions. When new meanings emerge there is a growth and expansion of the complexity and coherence of the infant's state of consciousness and infants are all about growth and development.

See also: Attachment; Autism Spectrum Disorders; Breastfeeding; Child and Day Care, Effects of; Depression; Discipline and Compliance; Emotion Regulation; Empathy and Prosocial Behavior; Family Influences; Feeding Development and Disorders; Friends and Peers; Gender: Awareness, Identity, and Stereotyping; Imagination and Fantasy; Independence/Dependence; Marital Relationship; Mental Health, Infant; Parenting Styles and their Effects; Play; Pragmatic Development; Self Knowledge; Semantic Development; Separation and Stranger Anxiety; Shyness; Siblings and Sibling Rivalry; Smiling; Socialization in Infancy and Childhood; Theory of Mind; Twins.

Suggested Readings

Nadel J and Muir D (eds.) (2005) *Emotional Development.* Oxford: Oxford University Press.
Tronick E (2007) *The Neurobehavioral and Social Emotional Development of the Infant.* New York City: Norton Press.
Schore A (2003) *Affect Regulation and the Repair of the Self.* New York City: Norton Press.

Social–Emotional Development Assessment

L Godoy and A S Carter, University of Massachusetts Boston, Boston, MA, USA
R Clark, University of Wisconsin, Madison, WI, USA

Glossary

Dimensional assessments – Type of assessment that characterizes social–emotional deficits, competencies, subthreshold manifestations of symptoms, and risk factors.

Emotion regulation – Refers to voluntary or automatic processes that help children control/manage their emotional reactions. For example, being able to sooth oneself by diverting attention away from distressing stimuli. The intensity and duration of emotional reactions can serve as indicators of emotion regulation abilities. Difficulties regulating negative emotions have been linked to social–emotional and behavioral problems.

Joint attention – When two individuals (e.g., parent and child) are focused on or engaged in the same activity or event.

Multigated or multistage screening procedures – A cost-effective, multistep screening process used to identify children exhibiting atypical behavior and psychopathology. Short, inexpensive screeners are first used to identify children at elevated risk for behavior problems from a larger pool of children and identified children are then referred for more comprehensive assessments.

Semistructured observational diagnostic tools – Specialized laboratory paradigms used to assess behaviors symptomatic of particular disorders. These assessments involve a variety of 'presses' designed to elicit behaviors relevant to a particular diagnosis that might not be commonly observed in an evaluation session.

Sensitivity – Proportion of a sample found to fall within a diagnostic category or the proportion of true positives.

Sensory sensitivity and reactivity – Hypersensitivity to sensory stimuli and difficulty regulating reactions to sensory stimulation. Oversensitive and overly reactive to sensory stimuli.

Social referencing – A form of emotional communication that helps young children learn about their environment through the emotional reactions of others. Children can use the emotional responses of adults to gauge their own affective responses in unfamiliar situations.

Specificity – Proportion of a sample not falling within a diagnostic category or the proportion of true negatives.
Story stems – An interviewing technique used with children as young as 3 or 4 years in which the child is introduced to a story through props and narration and is asked to complete the story by showing and telling what happens next. Responses are coded based on the coherence of children's narratives, their representations of adults as positive or negative socialization agents, and their use of coping strategies.

Introduction

Since the mid1990s tremendous progress has been made in the conceptualization of young children's social–emotional problems and competencies and psychopathology. Progress has been fueled by an emerging consensus, supported by both clinical case review and research, that infants, toddlers, and young preschoolers suffer from mental health disturbances and clinically significant dysregulated mood states, such as profound sadness, disruptive anger, and debilitating fears. Early emerging psychopathology frequently persists and is associated with child- and family-level impairments and delays in child social–emotional and academic competence. Failure to identify and address social–emotional and behavior problems early on likely leads to the exacerbation of problems and may diminish parents' sense of efficacy in the parenting role. In short, there is a growing body of work documenting the prevalence and persistence rates of psychopathology in early childhood that are comparable to that observed in older children and adolescents.

Recent Advances in the Field of Child Assessment

Research documenting early child psychopathology has only emerged relatively recently due to the historical neglect of young children's mental health issues. Previous disregard of children's mental health needs has multiple determinants, including general societal stigma associated with young child psychopathology, parental fear of blame for the child's difficulties, cultural differences in belief systems regarding both children's development and mental health service utilization, and, until a short time ago, a lack of developmentally appropriate instruments to assess early emerging psychopathology. There has also been reluctance to dispel the notion that early childhood is a 'sacred', happy time and to acknowledge the seriousness and persistence of psychopathology among very young children. Many individuals, including healthcare professionals, often minimize or dismiss parental concerns assuming that early problem behaviors are temporary (i.e., 'only a stage' or 'he'll grow out of it') and/or that the parent is overly anxious. Despite prior neglect of young children's mental health issues, recent empirical findings support the view that young children evidence significant social–emotional and behavioral problems and psychopathology and counter the notion that these early emerging problems are transient in nature.

Research contributing to recent shifts in our recognition of young children's mental health needs is in part due to significant improvements in the assessment of young children's social–emotional functioning and indications of psychopathology. Improved assessment techniques have allowed researchers to begin documenting the prevalence, persistence, and course of early disturbances in emotion and behavior, as well as competencies. In this sense, improvements and availability of assessment methods have fueled progress in our understanding of young children's mental health. At the same time, advances in the conceptualization of young children's mental health needs have contributed to improvements in assessment techniques. Acknowledgment of the complex and multifaceted nature of child development has made researchers and clinicians increasingly aware of the need to approach assessment in a manner that recognizes these complexities. For example, advances in our understanding of child development through concepts such as emotion regulation, social referencing, joint attention, and sensory sensitivity and reactivity, have contributed to more focused, developmentally salient, and empirically informed assessment techniques that are beginning to be validated through large-scale epidemiological studies. Thus, the relationship between our understanding of young children's social–emotional development and our ability to assess behavioral problems and competencies is bidirectional and advances in both these arenas over the past decade have underscored the importance of recognizing and treating the mental health needs of very young children.

A key improvement in recent years has been the broadened approach researchers and clinicians have taken to conceptualizing and evaluating children's social–emotional functioning. Traditional approaches have been limited by an overemphasis on diagnostic considerations focused on identifying whether a child is exhibiting prominent deviations from expectations in social–emotional functioning based on meeting criteria on a list of symptoms developed for use with older children, adolescents, and adults. Assessing extreme or deviant behaviors is critical to the accurate identification of disorders, but a more developmentally sensitive and dimensional approach to assessment provides a more comprehensive understanding of young children's social–emotional development. Such an approach not only characterizes social–emotional deficits but also subthreshold manifestations of symptoms and risk factors, as well as competencies. Assessments have also been broadened by evaluating patterns of strengths and weaknesses across multiple domains of functioning and by considering behaviors within a developmental framework that acknowledges the relevant ecologies that transact with the individual's functioning over time.

Difficulties Involved in Child Assessment

While dramatic improvements in the conceptualization and assessment of young children's social–emotional development have been made, it is useful to examine the inherent difficulties involved in evaluating very young children.

Caregiver Reporter Issues

Infants and young children have little or limited speech, which makes it difficult for them to convey their thoughts and feelings to their parents, other care providers (e.g., extended family members, daycare teachers), clinicians, and researchers. Even young children who have a better grasp of language lack the meta-cognitive ability to reflect on their experiences. Skepticism about the reliability of child report data, especially with very young children, has compelled researchers and clinicians to look elsewhere for reliable and valid sources of information about young children's social–emotional functioning.

Reports from adult sources, though considered more reliable than child report data, still pose considerable concerns due to potential biases and response style differences that can stem from a number of factors. Parental affective symptoms, especially depression and anxiety, can distort perceptions of child behavior. Often parental psychopathology increases negative reports of behavior problems as children's problems may seem worse when a parent has limited emotional resources for responding to a child's emotional needs, to state expectations clearly, to set limits, or to respond appropriately to problem behaviors. Alternatively, some parents under-report symptoms for fear of stigma or of involvement by outside agencies.

Varied response patterns can also emerge from differences in familial and cultural interpretations of child behavior. Families construct meanings of young children's behavior based on the history of interactions between the parents and child, the caregivers' prior relational or attachment history, and cultural values and beliefs. The interpretation or meaning attributed to the child's behavior influences the parents' level of concern about and responses to the child. Thus, the same set of child behaviors may evoke widely disparate reactions from different parents. This poses some problems in distinguishing children who have social–emotional/behavioral problems from those whose parents interpret typically developing behaviors as evidence of a problem.

Distinguishing Typical from Atypical Development

Discriminating typical from atypical development is complicated by the rapid pace of children's development. Behaviors considered normative at one stage of development may be cause for concern if exhibited at a later stage. For example, temper tantrums during toddlerhood are normative since oppositional behavior during this time signifies an emerging sense of self and an assertion of autonomy that reflects the child's understanding of their individual agency. However, tantrums that persist beyond the preschool years or significant anger outbursts in later childhood are most often evidence of atypical, or maladaptive social–emotional functioning.

In addition to considering the presence or absence of a particular behavior, the frequency, intensity, quality, and context in which the behavior emerges, as well as whether or not there is a broader pattern or constellation of problems is also important in distinguishing typical from atypical adaptation. For example, even during the toddler years, prolonged temper tantrums that cannot easily be assuaged, that occur multiple times a day across many different settings (e.g., home, daycare, supermarket) and that include hitting, biting, or destroying toys would be considered atypical. Characterizing typically occurring behavior problems, such as temper tantrums, by degree of intensity, frequency, or duration makes it difficult to establish the boundary between typical development and psychopathology.

Observational attempts to distinguish typical and atypical behaviors are made difficult by young children's changing mood states. Assessment of optimal functioning is state dependent and infants and young children's states change often and are affected by lack of sleep, hunger, and illness. Due to children's variability in mood states and behaviors across time and sessions, when assessing young children directly, it is important to schedule multiple assessments across several different sessions.

Given rapid developmental shifts in early childhood, creators of dimensional assessment tools have attempted to identify coherent clusters of problem and/or competence behaviors. Although it was once believed that it would not be possible to see differentiation of different types of social–emotional problems in early childhood, large-scale normative studies have demonstrated that parents can report about their children's problems in a manner that distinguishes children who are predominantly anxious or withdrawn from those who are aggressive or overactive from those who have problems with sleep, eating, or sensory sensitivities. Normative data about the clustering of behaviors and data about children with known psychopathology are used to establish cut-points that are then employed to assign caseness (e.g., clinical or at-risk status). Ideally, measures designed to assess young children's development rely on narrow age bands for comparison that gradually increase over the course of development. The need for narrow comparison groups is particularly salient for social–emotional behaviors, such as competencies, which change at a more dramatic rate throughout early childhood, when compared to problem behaviors.

Normative data are clearly needed to evaluate children's development, yet there is very limited epidemiological or national standardization data regarding very young children's expression of social–emotional/behavioral problems and competencies. Limited normative data makes it difficult to discern typical from atypical development, especially when symptom presentation is not extreme. Fortunately, with the development of new assessment tools, researchers are now able to conduct large-scale epidemiological studies to gather data on individual behaviors, symptom clusters, and disorders. Given that the absence of sufficient normative data likely contributes to the under-identification of psychopathology in young children, current epidemiological studies are providing the momentum needed to document young children's mental health needs and facilitate earlier identification of young children exhibiting early signs of psychopathology.

Assessing Children within the Caregiving Context

A final and critical difficulty in the assessment of young children's social–emotional development is the need to consider children within the context of their relationships. Young children's development is embedded within their caregiving relationships making it critical to examine child behavior, functioning, and impairment within these contexts. Caregivers structure children's environments through affective, regulatory, verbal, and physical support. Parents can therefore impact child problem behaviors and competencies through the quality of affective involvement and scaffolding they provide. For example, a caregiver who does not provide adequate responsiveness may elicit and/or reinforce problem behaviors that are not observed in other contexts. Alternatively, a child who has significant problem behaviors across several settings may appear well-regulated with a particular caregiver due to the unique sensitivity, accommodations, and affordances that s/he provides. In addition to evaluating the ways in which caregivers structure the child's environment, consideration must also be given to the match (or mismatch) between a child's temperament and developmental functioning and the situational demands and supports in his environment. Parents' perceptions of their child's behavior and of themselves in the parenting role is also important to assess in order to understand the nature of their interactions with their child. Thus, problem behaviors in a young child may reflect a mismatch between the child and the caregiving environment or caregiver capacities to meet the child's needs. In short, young children and their caregivers are inextricably linked, making assessment of the parent–child relationship critical to the evaluation of a child's social and emotional development.

Problem behaviors that occur across relationships are generally viewed as of greater concern than those that are limited to a single caregiver. Also of greater concern are behaviors viewed as impairing, including those behaviors that impede the acquisition of new developmental capacities and skills, interfere with relationships, or threaten adaptation to developmentally appropriate demands. For older children and adults, individual impairment is necessary for a diagnosis of psychopathology, but with very young children, individual markers of impairment may be absent despite the presence of risk or disorder, as caregivers may minimize demands that would illuminate the child's impairment. Moreover, since young children develop within their caregiving relationships, evaluations of impairment that consider both child and family individual and relational impairments may be more appropriate. For example, parental distress or indicators that the child's behavior interferes with the parent's ability to maintain family routines (e.g., eating together as a family in a restaurant), household activities (e.g., making a telephone call to family members or friends), or employment (e.g., stopping or changing work settings because of difficulty obtaining appropriate child care) could be considered an appropriate gauge of impairment for young children. From a developmental–contextual perspective, it is therefore important to evaluate the functioning of both the child and the family in determining level of impairment.

Evaluating the family context requires first characterizing basic features such as who is considered a member, how many members make up the family, and the gender and age of each family member. In addition to descriptive features of the family context, broader characteristics of family climate and relationships should be assessed, including communication styles, affective tone and expressiveness, sensitivity, warmth and responsiveness, cohesion, mutuality, reciprocity, and adaptability. These characteristics, which can be assessed with questionnaires and observational methods, have been shown to influence cognitive and social–emotional outcomes for children.

Race, Ethnicity, Culture, and the Caregiving Context

Critical to evaluations of the family context is an understanding of families' racial, ethnic, and cultural backgrounds.

Though not unique to child assessment, considerations of race, ethnicity, and culture are fundamental to the mental health evaluation process and thus deserve considerable attention. Race is a socially constructed classification system based on physical traits. From a population genetics perspective, there are no discrete boundaries between racial groups. Culture refers to shared values, beliefs, and practices that are transmitted across generations within a group. It is critical to recognize that culture is not a static entity, but is dynamic and responsive to the settings and conditions to which the family must adapt. Ethnicity is used to denote a particular kind of culture, which is usually associated with a common geographic region, or national origin. Distinctions between culture, ethnicity, and race are often ignored, yet families of color face unique challenges associated with societal racism and stereotyping. Thus, the caregiving context may be influenced by race, independent of the contribution of culture and ethnicity.

Considerations of culture, race, and ethnicity are vital to sensitive evaluations of the caregiving context. Yet, understanding the role of culture in development is becoming more complex in part because families are increasingly multiethnic, cultural, and racial. There are also wide variations in acculturation patterns within and across ethnic, cultural, and racial groupings and generations. Thus, researchers and clinicians should talk with families about their cultural formulations/expectations of caregiving and child behavior. Specifically, parents can evaluate the child's behavior relative to other child behavior in their cultural group(s) and they can discuss cultural explanations for the child's difficulties or distress. With a clearer understanding of a family's worldview, clinicians and researchers can better evaluate the child's behavior and the context in which it emerges and is understood by the family. Increased awareness of differences between the evaluator and the child's family should improve the gathering of reliable and valid data about child and family functioning.

In addition to determining cultural explanations for child behavior, it is critical for researchers and clinicians to engage in a continual process of self-reflection and awareness about their own background and worldview in order to avoid biases that could lead to over- or underpathologizing the child or family practices. In short, cultural proficiency is central to gathering reliable and valid information about child behavior, the caregiving context, and the way in which the family understands the child's behavior.

Summary: Difficulties Involved in Child Assessment

In attempting to evaluate children's social–emotional functioning, researchers and clinicians face several challenges. Some of these challenges, such as limited meta-cognitive abilities and rapid developmental shifts, are unique to the process of child assessment, but several of these challenges, such as the need to consider contextual factors, are faced by researchers outside of the field of child development. Acknowledging the difficulties inherent in the evaluation of children's social–emotional development is vital to conducting competent assessments. Moreover, advances in the field of child psychopathology and in the assessment of social–emotional development have the potential to address several of the difficulties currently faced by investigators.

Types of Assessment

Several assessment techniques exist with which to examine young children's social–emotional functioning, each differing in terms of advantages and drawbacks. Having an understanding of each technique allows for a more thoughtful and appropriate approach to assessment. Whenever possible, multiple techniques are combined to develop a more comprehensive understanding of the child and family context.

Caregiver Report: Rating Scales, Questionnaires, and Interviews

Rating scales and questionnaires are the most commonly employed assessment tools in research applications as they are inexpensive, quick, and easy to administer to a large number of individuals in a flexible manner (i.e., in person, via mail, online). Parents or primary caregivers are the most frequent reporters on questionnaires about young children's development, but other caregiver (e.g., daycare providers) can contribute valuable information as well, particularly to gain an understanding of the pervasiveness of problems and competencies across caregiving relationships and contexts. The response format of questionnaires typically requires the person completing the questionnaire to consider certain characteristics or behaviors and evaluate the extent to which these behaviors are representative of the target child and/or how often they occur. Likert scales are commonly employed ranging from never/uncharacteristic to often/very characteristic. Thus, questionnaires often cross ratings of the frequency of a behavior with ratings of whether the behavior is typical of the child. Although this is sufficient for identifying children at elevated risk for psychopathology, it does not yield information that is sufficient for determining clinical diagnostic status. To determine whether or not a child meets criteria for a diagnosis, information about onset, duration, and intensity of behaviors, as well as the extent to which they are impairing the child's development is required. Moreover, questionnaires often exclude behaviors that are rare in the population or that have very low base rates of occurrence because their inclusion compromises psychometric sufficiency (i.e., reduces internal consistency). These rare behaviors may be very informative clinically and may also be elements in diagnostic criteria for specific childhood diagnoses.

Structured or semistructured interviews with parents or caregivers, commonly employed in clinical assessments, allow for a more in-depth examination of child problems and competencies than do questionnaires. Interviewers can obtain specific examples of child behavior and inquire about the onset, offset, frequency, duration, intensity, quality, and context of occurrence through follow-up questions and probes. Thus, interviews allow for a more comprehensive understanding of the child's behavior and they permit diagnostic determinations. Unfortunately, structured and semistructured diagnostic interviews are too rarely administered because of time constraints and training issues.

The use of both questionnaires and interviews often yield information about areas that a parent is not worried about but that the clinician determines to be an area of clinical concern. Thus, gathering information about multiple aspects of children's social–emotional and behavioral functioning, whether through questionnaires or interviews, is an important component of best practice for young child evaluation.

Obtaining information from the child's primary caretaker through questionnaires and interviews is beneficial because caregivers have an intimate knowledge of their child's development. Parents are familiar with their child's behaviors, temperament, and routines. Moreover, unlike observational techniques that only provide information about a moment in the child's development, parents can provide a historical account of the child's development, can report on how the child's behavior has changed, and can explain the context of the child's current and past behavior. For example, a parent is in the unique position of being able to report on the number of temper tantrums a child has per week, whether there has been an increase or decrease in the tantrums, what normally triggers the tantrums, how long they last, and what supports the child needs to help him or her calm down. In sum, parents can provide information about the child's current and past behaviors that is informed by a rich developmental and contextual knowledge of the child.

Parents are attractive reporters because they know the most about a child and that child's development. Moreover, research has demonstrated that parents can describe their young children's social–emotional and behavioral problems and competencies in a differentiated manner, distinguishing between problems and competencies in various domains. However, as discussed above, parents vary in their explanations of child behavior, which poses difficulties to the interpretation of parent reports. Additionally, parents can be biased reporters and poor historians making sole reliance on parent reports questionable. Thus, information obtained from parent interviews and questionnaires should be considered in light of potential biases and differences in responding and should be supplemented, whenever possible, with additional sources of information.

Child Report: Puppet Interviews and Story Stems

Innovative interviewing techniques targeting children are one possibility for obtaining supplemental information. For example, puppet interviews have been devised in which puppets are employed to ask children a series of questions about their perceptions of their family, school, and emotional states. The interviewer has two puppets, each endorsing a different statement. The puppets then ask the child which statement he or she would endorse (e.g., Puppet 1: "My parents fight a lot"; Puppet 2: "My parents don't fight a lot. How about your parents?") Puppet interviews elicit self-report information that may not emerge naturally in laboratory settings. Young children feel more comfortable expressing their perceptions of their lives and their feeling states to puppets rather than to unfamiliar clinicians.

Another method that has been shown to be very useful with young children is the introduction of story stems that the child is asked to complete. Specifically, the child is introduced to characters in the story, shown a series of props, and then the interviewer will narrate the beginning of a story while using the props (e.g., "Johnny and his friend Tommy are playing soccer. Johnny's little brother walks up to them and says: 'Can I play?' "). The child is then asked to "Show me and tell me what happens next." Coding systems have been developed that focus on the coherence of children's narratives, their representations of adults as positive or negative socialization agents, and their use of coping strategies. These codes are associated with a range of children's social–emotional and problem behavior outcomes.

Puppet interviews and story stems conducted with children as young as 3 or 4 years have been shown to be reliable and valid assessment instruments. Although these new child interviewing techniques appear promising in their ability to provide valuable information about child social–emotional and behavioral functioning in both the family and school context, doubts about reliance on child reports (noted above) remain.

Observational Techniques: Semistructured Diagnostic Tools and Parent–Child Interactions

One promising avenue in the evaluation of children's social–emotional functioning that can be used to supplement questionnaires and interviews is the development of semistructured observational diagnostic tools. Observational assessments are currently available to evaluate autism spectrum disorders and disruptive behavior disorders in young children. The assessments involve a variety of 'presses' designed to elicit behaviors relevant to a particular diagnosis (e.g., autism, oppositional defiant disorder) that might not be commonly observed in an evaluation session where the setting and examiner are unfamiliar to the child. For example, to address oppositionality, frustration is elicited by having children attempt to use a broken toy without the child knowing that the toy is broken. Though useful in identifying behaviors symptomatic of particular disorders, these instruments are quite specialized. In other words, observational techniques that use presses are most relevant when the evaluator has targeted a particular diagnostic category.

Given the centrality of parents in young children's lives, observing parent–child interactions proves vital to the assessment of children's social–emotional development. A number of laboratory paradigms exist with which to evaluate parent–child interactions, including separation/reunion, feeding, free play, and structured tasks (e.g., building a tower or completing a puzzle). Segments typically last a couple of minutes and the interactions are videotaped and later coded using standardized coding systems that evaluate child behavior, parent behavior, and parent–child interaction quality. Consistent with interview, rating scale, and questionnaire data, observational methods vary along a continuum of structure and the level of inference required to evaluate the constructs of interest. In addition, observational data add the dimension of time, and decisions must be made regarding the timeframe of the analysis (e.g., continuous vs. time or event sampling). The unit of analysis in terms of a micro-analytic or macro-analytic focus must also be considered. Such decisions will be driven by the constructs under study.

Use of a standardized protocol and coding scheme allows evaluators to assess child behavior and parent–child relationships free from reporter biases. In this sense, observational techniques are more objective than questionnaires or interviews, which rely on information from parents who will vary in their perception of child behavior problems. Though observational techniques avoid parent subjectivity and biases, coding schemes and decision making are inherently subjective and culturally biased. Thus, it is important to acknowledge the intrinsic subjectivity of all evaluation techniques, including observations. One complement to observational ratings is to involve the parent in viewing the videotape to capture their perceptions of their child's behavior in the observational paradigm, as well as their perceptions of themselves in the parenting role. Selecting segments of the interaction and viewing these with the parent can help to engage them in 'wondering along' about who this child is for them, who he/she may remind them of, and how they are interpreting their child's behavior. This can both allow the parent(s) to be part of the assessment process and help to inform our understanding of their responses or difficulty responding to their child's needs.

In addition to the difficulties involved in creating an objective coding scheme, observational techniques have other drawbacks as well. Observations are only able to capture a snapshot of the child's behavior and quality of the parent–child relationship at one point in time. Thus, unlike parent reports, observational techniques may be less able to put the observed behaviors into context developmentally. Laboratory observations also do not provide contextual information about the antecedents or consequences of behaviors in everyday life. Situational-specific behaviors (i.e., problems that only occur while at preschool) may not be exhibited or may be displayed differently during observational assessments. Observations are also more expensive to employ than questionnaires and interviews due to time needed to train staff, administer the paradigm, and code the videotapes.

Summary: Assessment Techniques

Clinicians and researchers evaluating children's social–emotional development can choose from an array of assessment techniques. These tools vary with respect to who provides information about the child, the method of assessment employed (e.g., questionnaire, interview, or observation), the timeframe that is covered (e.g., last 2 weeks, last year, lifetime), and the type of information that is gathered. Given the spectrum of assessment tools and the pros and cons of each, the most comprehensive approach to child assessment involves the use of multiple techniques that gather information from various respondents. Multimethod, multi-informant assessment approaches are especially important for the evaluation of young children due to young children's inability to provide self-reports and the embedded nature of children's development in their caregiving contexts.

Evaluating Assessment Techniques

Regardless of the assessment approach taken, the psychometric properties of the instruments should be evaluated. With respect to reliability, the more structured the assessment format, the easier it is to obtain adequate test–retest and inter-rater reliability coefficients. Similarly, the lower the inference level required to make ratings (either for the informant or the evaluator), the greater the probability that adequate reliability can be obtained. With respect to validity, an assessment's underlying traits or constructs should be confirmed using factor analytic or item response theory methods within a developmental framework to ensure that the measure has the same structure and measures the same traits/constructs over development. In addition, because it is rare to obtain appropriate within ethnic group reliability and validity data, investigators who are working with minority populations are encouraged to report internal consistency statistics when presenting findings. It is not appropriate to assume that the internal consistency or factor structure obtained in a dominant culture population will be comparable when a scale is employed with ethnic/racial minority groups.

Although an assessment tool may be a reliable and valid measure of an underlying construct or behavior, there is still an issue of how useful it might be for a given diagnostic or classification purpose (e.g., meets criteria for oppositional defiant disorder, is peer rejected, has a relationship disturbance that warrants intervention). The measures of sensitivity (proportion of a sample found to fall within a diagnostic category) and specificity (proportion of a sample not falling within a diagnostic category) help to determine how well any test can be used for a specific diagnostic purpose. Specificity should be high for assessment tools designed to aid specific diagnoses (e.g., structured clinical interviews, structured observational diagnostic tools). However, for assessment tools aimed at screening large samples and identifying at-risk individuals regardless of their diagnostic status, it becomes more challenging to maintain a balance whereby a sufficient proportion of children with problems are detected while maintaining an acceptable rate of false positives.

If the scoring threshold is too high, then too few true 'cases' (e.g., meets criteria for a psychiatric disorder) will screen positive and the screener will have low sensitivity. Yet, the screener will likely have high 'specificity', meaning it will identify a low proportion of 'non-cases' as screen positives. In contrast, if the threshold is set too low, sensitivity will be high, but specificity will be low, potentially flooding the service system with unnecessary costs for assessing false positives. Also of concern is the problem of misclassification and its impact on the child and family being evaluated. Thus, it is important to achieve a balance between identifying a sufficient proportion of 'cases' to effectively improve early detection, while minimizing false positives. It is therefore necessary to document that assessment tools are sufficiently sensitive to clinically significant social–emotional/behavioral problems (detecting a minimum 80% of cases), yet maintain false positive rates that are low enough (20% or lower) that service systems are not overwhelmed unnecessarily. Additionally, one should not expect any test to have stable sensitivity and specificity for a particular diagnostic decision across the developmental spectrum, especially with diagnostic conditions that might have different base rates at different ages (e.g., speech disorders).

Psychometric concepts are frequently given only passing attention in clinical practice or research, when time and ease of administration are often the first priorities, but conceptual issues, such as a test's factor structure, are critical considerations for assessing the development of an individual or group. A developmentally informed comprehensive perspective on psychological assessment can only be achieved with a basic understanding of psychometric and methodological issues.

Conclusion: Remaining Gaps and Future Directions

The range of assessment techniques available to clinicians and researchers evaluating children's social–emotional development has increased dramatically over the past 10–15 years. The versatility and quality of these methods will continue to grow as more questionnaires and rating scales become available with appropriate normative information, and as clinical interview methods and observational paradigms are standardized. Several challenges to the assessment of children's social–emotional development persist and warrant consideration in future research.

A major existing difficulty is determining appropriate methods for integrating data across different methods and sources. Data integration is further complicated when multiple informants provide conflicting information. However, conflicting data are often informative and contribute an added dimension to the assessment, especially in terms of understanding the systems in which the individual functions. As informants may have access to different samples of behavior in multiple settings, conflicting information may reflect true variability in current functioning. On the other hand, conflicting information may be a function of observer or interviewer biases. Additional research on how best to synthesize information from multiple sources is clearly needed.

A current challenge to assessment that is in the process of being addressed is the lack of normative data. Several large-scale, longitudinal, epidemiological studies are currently underway and their findings will be critical to disentangling the continuities and discontinuities in normative and atypical development. Large, representative samples also permit cross-group validation, which will allow much needed examinations of the cultural, racial, and/or ethnic appropriateness of assessments. Sadly, at this point in time, very few psychological tests, scales, or interview assessments have undergone such scrutiny, even for the largest racial/ethnic groups within the US population.

A potentially complicated issue related to culture is that of assessing multilingual individuals. It is inadequate to employ a measure that has been translated into the target population or client's native language because the translation may not be appropriate for the population under study or the family seeking treatment. Differences in language or contextual understanding of behaviors and emotions must be examined and efforts made to minimize miscommunication. Furthermore, translation and back-translation do not guarantee that the psychometric properties of the instrument will remain stable across cultural, racial, or ethnic groups. Thus, researchers and clinicians must evaluate the cultural and linguistic appropriateness of assessment techniques being used and work toward the development of more suitable measures.

The role of race, ethnicity, and culture in the assessment of young children's social–emotional development should be a central focus of future work given the increasing diversity of the US population and prior neglect of these issues within the field of child development and assessment. Research initiatives designed to improve assessment techniques for diverse populations are therefore critical. Increased awareness of parents' understanding of child behavior will be vital to these initiatives. Since assessment is linked to diagnostic and treatment decisions, advances in cultural conceptualizations of assessment have the ability to encourage culturally sensitive diagnostic guidelines and treatment recommendations. Additionally, during assessments investigators and clinicians can take a more proactive role by inquiring about parents' experiences with and preferences for treatment.

Given the emerging body of work documenting psychopathology among very young children and the increasing number of assessment instruments available, more effort should be made to increase widespread assessment of children's social–emotional behavioral development. Screening and diagnostic measures remain under-utilized even though measures of social–emotional development have proven reliable and valid and behavioral screening has been introduced successfully into a number of settings, including the primary care pediatric office. Reluctance to screen is in part due to continued resistance to acknowledge psychopathology in young children, knowledge barriers about the seriousness of early emerging psychopathology, resource limits regarding the availability of appropriate mental health services for young children and their families, short-term costs, and lack of trained professional evaluators. As child assessments become more widespread, the need for trained professionals knowledgeable in assessment techniques for young children will only increase. Training should cover basic knowledge about social–emotional developmental expectations of young children, as well as skills for working with young children and their families in an assessment context. For example, evaluators should be trained to spot the toddler who has trouble waiting and find ways to respectively engage both the parent and the young child and to move quickly through the assessment process. However, lack of available referral services remains the largest barrier to screening. That the overwhelming majority of children whose parents report social–emotional/behavioral problems do not receive services highlights the need for enhanced screening and intervention efforts.

Multigated or multistage screening procedures offer a cost-effective means for screening large groups of children. The first step in the process involves utilizing a short and relatively inexpensive screening assessment tool to identify children at elevated risk. Pediatric visits are an ideal venue for such first-stage screening. Children who are identified as at elevated risk can then be referred for a second, more comprehensive screening that might involve a longer parent report instrument about the child's behavior, the parent's degree of concern about the behaviors, and the presence of any impairment as a function of the child's social–emotional behaviors. The meaning of the child's behavior and cultural considerations are central foci of the comprehensive second-stage assessment. Depending on available resources, the third stage of screening could involve observations, collateral informants, and/or referral for more intensive diagnostic evaluation. Ideally, this third-stage evaluation would be conducted at a site that can also provide intervention services. Routine social–emotional screening and follow-up assessments, especially in a primary care pediatric setting may play an important role in ensuring that the needs of young children with early-emerging difficulties are addressed.

Research documenting the prevalence of child psychopathology and the persistence of early behavior problems may provide the thrust necessary to create systemic changes in the assessment, diagnosis, and treatment of very young children exhibiting social–emotional and behavior problems. The availability of assessment tools can bolster this research and improve studies that focus on the clinical efficacy and effectiveness of screening, prevention, and early intervention programs designed to promote positive mental health. Ideally, such studies would encourage the implementation of the assessment and prevention practices being evaluated, as well as the training of professionals who have the competence to both assess and treat young children and their families.

Thus, in helping to document the prevalence and consequences of early emerging psychopathology, as well as the benefits of early identification and intervention, high-quality assessment techniques have the potential to improve mental healthcare systems for very young children. Children and families currently underserved by current healthcare and mental healthcare systems, who also happen to be the most vulnerable in terms of being exposed to multiple contextual risk factors, may gain the most from this line of assessment research.

See also: Social and Emotional Development Theories.

Suggested Readings

Canino G, Costello EJ, and Angold A (1999) Assessing functional impairment for child mental health services research: A review of measures. *Journal of Mental Health Serivces* 1: 93–108.
Carter AS, Briggs-Gowan MJ, and Davis N (2004) Assessment of young children's social–emotional development and psychopathology: Recent advances and recommendations for practice. *Journal of Child Psychology and Psychiatry* 45: 109–134.
Carter AS, Marakovitz SE, and Sparrow SS (2006) Comprehensive psychological assessment: A developmental psychopathology approach for clinical and applied research. In: Cicchetti D and Cohen DJ (eds.) *Developmental Psychopathology Vol. 1: Theory and Method,* 2nd edn, pp. 181–210. Hoboken, NJ: Wiley.
Clark R, Paulson A, and Conlin S (1993) Assessment of Developmental Status and Parent–Infant Relationships. In: Zeanah CH (ed.) *Handbook of Infant Mental Health,* 2nd edn, pp. 191–209. New York: Guildford Press.
Clark R, Tluczek A, and Gallagher K (2004) Assessment of Parent-child Relational Disturbances. In: Del Carmen-Wiggins R and Carter AS (eds.) *Handbook of Infant,Toddler, and Preschool Mental Health Assessment*, pp. 25–60. New York: Oxford University Press.
Crowell J and Fleischmann MA (1993) Use of structured research procedure in clinical assessments of infants. In: Zeanah CH (ed.) *Handbook of Infant Mental Health,* 2nd edn, pp. 210–221. New York: Guilford Press.
Del Carmen-Wiggins R and Carter AS (eds.) (2004) *Handbook of Infant, Toddler, and Preschool Mental Health Assessment.* New York: Oxford University Press.
Glascoe FP (2000) Early detection of developmental and behavioral problems. *Pediatric Review* 21: 272–280.
Task Force on Research Diagnostic Criteria: Infancy Preschool (2003) Research diagnostic criteria for infants and preschool children: The process and empirical support. *Journal of the American Academy of Child and Adolescent Psychiatry* 42: 1504–1512.
Weston DR, Thomas JM, Barnard KE, *et al.* (2003) DC: 0–3 Assessment Protocol Project: Defining a comprehensive information set to support DC: 0–3 diagnostic formulation. *Infant Mental Health Journal* 24: 410–427.

Relevant Website

http://www.zerotothree.org – Zero to Three, National Center for Infants, Toddlers and Families.

Socialization

R D Parke, M S Leidy, T J Schofield, M A Miller, and K L Morris, University of California, Riverside, Riverside, CA, USA

Glossary

Co-parenting – The patterns of cooperative or noncooperative alliances that mothers and fathers assume in their parenting roles.
Family systems theory – The view that various subsystems such as the parent–child dyad, sibling, co-parenting, and marital units are interdependent.
Socialization – The process by which an individual's standards, skills, motives, attitudes, and behaviors change to conform to those regarded as desirable and appropriate for his or her present and future role in any particular society.

Introduction

Socialization is the process by which infants and children acquire the standards, skills, motives, attitudes, and behaviors that are appropriate for a particular society and culture. Currently, ecological systems theory is the central framework for understanding socialization. According to this perspective, many agents play a role in the socialization process including families, peers, media, neighborhoods, schools, and religious institutions. Within families, various subsystems are recognized, including the parent–child dyad, the co-parenting, marital and sibling subsystems as well as the family unit itself. Families, in turn, are embedded in a variety of extrafamilial socialization systems (e.g., peers and schools) and they operate together with families rather than independently. A variety of factors such as child characteristics including genetic differences, personal parental resources, contextual factors, and ethnicity modify the operation of these socialization influences.

Socialization in Infancy and Childhood

Socialization is the process whereby an individual's standards, skills, motives, attitudes, and behaviors change to conform to those regarded as desirable and appropriate for his or her present and future role in any particular society. Many agents play a role in the socialization process including families, peers, neighborhoods, the mass media, schools, and religious institutions. It is assumed that these various agents function together rather than independently. Families have been recognized as an early pervasive and highly influential context for socialization. Infants and children are dependent on parents for nurturance and support from an early age, which accounts, in part, for their prominence as a socialization agent. We next consider peers, mass media, and neighborhood socialization influences. In this article, we will focus on parents, as well as sibling, co-parenting, and marital subsystems as contexts for socialization. Next, we will examine the determinants of parental socialization strategies. Finally, we examine the socialization roles of a variety of extrafamilial influences (e.g., peers, media).

Contemporary Perspectives on Socialization

Several themes are evident in current theoretical approaches to socialization. First, the rise of systems theory has transformed the study of socialization from a parent–child focus to an emphasis on the family as a social system. To understand fully the nature of family relationships, it is necessary to recognize the interdependence among the roles and functions of all family members. Second, it is being increasingly recognized that families are best viewed as social systems. Consequently, to understand the behavior of one member of a family, the complementary behaviors of other members also need to be recognized and assessed. For example, as men's roles in families shift, changes in women's roles in families must also be monitored.

Third, different units of analysis are necessary in order to understand families. While the individual level – child, mother, and father – remains a useful and necessary level of analysis, recognition of relationships among family members as units of analysis is necessary. The marital relationship, the co-parental relationship, the mother–child, the father–child relationship, and the sibling–sibling relationship require separate analysis. Finally, the family as a unit that is somewhat independent of the individual or dyads within the family requires recognition.

Fourth, contemporary work on socialization recognizes the importance of considering the wide range of forms that families assume in our society. While our focus will be largely on intact, two parent families, many children are raised in a variety of nontraditional family structures including single parent households, same gender parent families, extended families in which grandparents or another relative are the primary caregivers, families formed through the assistance of new reproductive technologies, and adoptive families. Many children are also reared in stepparent or divorced families with varying custody arrangements. While care needs to be taken in generalizing from research on socialization of children in traditional family arrangements to other family forms, many of the issues that we address in this article are relevant for understanding socialization in other family structures as well.

A fifth conceptual shift is from unidirectional to transactional models of relationships among family members. There have been various phases in the conceptual thinking in this domain. In place of the unilateral model, a bilateral model has emerged as the dominant paradigm for guiding research in the parent–child relationship domain. In contrast to the unilateral model, the direction of causality between parents and children is bidirectional, equal agency on the part of parents is assumed, and power relations are characterized by 'interdependent asymmetry'.

Sixth, under the influence of Urie Bronfenbrenner's ecological theory, recognition is being given to the embeddedness of families within a variety of other social systems, including both formal and informal support systems as well as the cultures in which they exist. These include a wide range of extrafamilial influences such as extended families, informal community ties such as friends and neighbors, work sites, as well as educational, religious, medical, and other social institutions.

A further shift over the last two decades is the challenge to the universality of our theories of parent–child relationships as well as peer relationships. This challenge takes a variety of forms. First, as cross-cultural work has accumulated, it has become evident that generalizations from a single culture (e.g., American) may, in fact, not be valid in other cultural contexts. Second, studies of social class differences in socialization challenged the generality of findings even within one cultural or national context. Currently, there is an increased awareness of the importance of both recognizing and studying variations in socialization strategies in other cultures as well as across ethnic groups within our own culture.

An eighth and closely related theme involves the recognition of the importance of the historical time period in which the family and peer relationships are taking place. Historical time periods provide the social conditions for individual and family transitions: examples include the 1930s (the Great Depression) or the 1980s (Farm Belt Depression). Across these historical time periods, family interaction may, in fact, be quite different due to the unique conditions of the particular era.

Ninth, in order to understand the nature of parent–child relationships within families, a multilevel and dynamic approach is required. Multiple levels of analysis are necessary in order to capture the individual, dyadic, and family unit aspects of operation within the family itself as well as to reflect the embeddedness of families within a variety of extrafamilial social systems. The dynamic quality reflects the multiple developmental trajectories that warrant consideration in understanding the nature of families in infancy and childhood. Distinctions among different developmental trajectories, as well as social change and historical period effects, are important because these different forms of change do not always harmonize. For example, a family event such as the birth of a child may have more effects on a man who has just begun a career than on one who has advanced to a stable occupational position. Moreover, individual and family developmental trajectories are embedded within both the social conditions and the values of the historical time in which they exist. The role of parents as socialization agents is responsive to such fluctuations.

Tenth, a major change in the study of parent–child relationships, is the renewed interest in the role of biological factors in shaping this dyadic relationship. The recent work on genetics has produced not only a more sophisticated understanding of the potential role that genetics can play in the onset of certain behaviors, but in the unfolding of behavior across development. Specifically, there is more interest in genotype by environment interactions by which the impact of a particular gene will depend on the specific environment to which the child is exposed (see section titled 'Child characteristics'). Moreover, Robert Plomin's reformulation of genetic questions has led to studies of the effects of nonshared family environment on children's development. A second focus is found in studies of hormones and behavior especially during infancy and adolescence. Third, the increased use of psychophysiological assessments as well as brain imaging techniques with families represents a further instance of how biological processes are changing studies of parent–child relationships. Fourth, the resurgence of interest in the use of evolutionary approaches to the study of families is producing new and provocative hypotheses and research directions.

It is not simply that there is more recognition of biological markers and individual differences among infants and children in genetic and biological predispositions such as variations in temperament that has shifted. Our views of the parent–infant dyad have moved from a static to a dynamic and mutually influential one in which we recognize that infants are 'biologically prepared' to play an active role in their own socialization. New appreciation of infants' perceptual-cognitive competence by which they show early responsiveness to a variety of social stimuli, such as human faces and voices, as well as human odors, suggests clear evidence of preparedness for social interaction. In addition, through a variety of signaling systems, such as crying and smiling in the early months of life, as well as crawling and walking in later infancy, the infant can control to some degree the actions of their caregivers (see our discussion of attachment theory below). In short, infants clearly share the work of socialization with their caregivers through their own biologically based readiness to respond to social cues and to become active social partners.

Finally, affect is increasingly viewed as a central family process. Under the guidance of such researchers as Suzanne Denham, Nancy Eisenberg, and Carolyn Saarni, the study of affect has assumed a variety of forms including the development of emotion regulation, the development of emotional expression and understanding, as well as the role of emotion in the enactment of the parenting role. Cognition is viewed as central to socialization as well. As Jacqueline Goodnow has reminded us, the ways in which parents perceive, organize, and understand their children's behaviors is important for appreciating how parent–child relationships are regulated and change. In current work on parent–child relationships there is the recognition that cognitive and affective processes are interdependent, mutually influencing each other.

Quantitative and Qualitative Assessments of Mother and Father Involvement

In spite of current shifts in cultural attitudes concerning the appropriateness and desirability of shared roles and equal levels of participation in routine caregiving and interaction for mothers and fathers, the changes are modest in the majority of intact families. Fathers spend less time with their infants, children, and adolescents than mothers not only in the US but also in other countries such as the UK, Australia, France, and Belgium.

Fathers participate less than mothers in caregiving but spend a greater percentage of the time available for interaction in play activities than mothers do. The quality of play across mothers and fathers differs too. With infants and toddlers, fathers play more physically arousing games than mothers. In contrast, mothers play more conventional motor games or toy-mediated activities, and are more verbal and didactic, although fathers in several other cultures, such as Sweden, India, and Central Africa, do not show this physical play style. As children develop, fathers become more involved in physical/outdoor play interactions and fixing things around the house and garden, where mothers are more actively involved in caregiving and household tasks, in schoolwork, reading, playing with toys, and helping with arts and crafts. In adolescence, the quality of maternal and paternal involvement continues to differ. Just as in earlier developmental periods mothers and fathers may complement each other and provide models that reflect the tasks of adolescence-connectedness and separateness. Recent evidence suggests that fathers may help adolescents develop their own sense of identity and autonomy by being more 'peer-like' and more playful (joking and teasing) which is likely to promote more equal and egalitarian exchanges.

Why do mothers and fathers play differently? Both biological and environmental factors probably play a role. Experience with infants, the amount of time spent with infants, the usual kinds of responsibilities that a parent assumes – all of these factors influence the parents' style of play. The fact that fathers spend less time with infants and children than mothers may contribute as well.

Fathers may use their distinctive arousing style as a way to increase their salience in spite of more limited time. Biological factors cannot be ignored in light of the fact that male monkeys show the same rough and tumble physical style of play as American human fathers. Perhaps predisposing biological differences between males and females may play a role in the play patterns of mothers and fathers. At the same time, the cross-cultural data underscore the ways in which cultural and environmental contexts shape play patterns of mothers and fathers and remind us of the high degree of plasticity of human social behaviors.

Assessing Parent–Child Interaction: Three Approaches to Socialization

Three approaches to understanding the impact of parent–child interactions on children's socialization outcomes have been utilized: (1) a typological approach which focuses on styles of child-rearing practices; (2) an attachment approach to parent–child relationships; and (3) a social interaction approach which focuses on the nature of the interchanges between parent and child.

The Typological Approach

The most influential typology has been offered by Diana Baumrind who distinguished between three types of parental child-rearing typologies: authoritative, authoritarian, and permissive. Authoritative parents were not intrusive and did permit their children considerable freedom within reasonable limits, but were firm and willing to impose restrictions in areas in which they had greater knowledge or insight. In general, high warmth and moderate restrictiveness were associated with the development of self-esteem, adaptability, and social competence. In contrast, the authoritarian parents were rigid, power-assertive, harsh, and unresponsive to the children's needs. This results in the unhappy, conflicted, neurotic behavior often found in these children. Finally, in spite of the permissive parents' reasonably affectionate relationship with their children, their excessively lax and inconsistent discipline, and encouragement of the free expression of their children's impulses were associated with the development of uncontrolled, impulsive behavior in their children.

Baumrind has followed these types of parents and their children from the preschool period through adolescence. She found that authoritative parenting continued to be associated with positive outcomes for adolescents as with younger children and that responsive, firm parent–child relationships were especially important in the development of competence in sons. Moreover, authoritarian child rearing had more negative long-term outcomes for boys than for girls. Eleanor Maccoby and John Martin extended the Baumrind typology and included a fourth type of parenting style which is characterized by neglect and lack of involvement. These are disengaged parents who are motivated to do whatever is necessary to minimize the costs in time and effort of interaction with the child. In infants such a lack of parental involvement is associated with disruptions in attachment; in older children it is associated with impulsivity, aggression, noncompliance, and low self-esteem.

This typology approach has been challenged on several fronts. First, questions remain concerning the processes that contribute to the relative effectiveness of these different styles. Second, it is unclear whether parenting styles are, in part, in response to the child's behavior. Placing the typology work in a transactional framework would argue that children with certain temperaments and/or behavioral characteristics would determine the nature of the parental style. A third concern is the universality of the typological scheme. Recent studies have raised serious questions about the generalizability of these styles across either socioeconomic status (SES) or ethnic/cultural groups. In lower SES families, parents are more likely to use an authoritarian as opposed to an authoritative style but this style is often an adaptation to the ecological conditions such as increased danger and threat that may characterize the lives of poor families. A second challenge to the presumed universal advantage of authoritative child-rearing styles comes from cross-ethnic studies. In Ruth Chao's study of Chinese families, authoritarian styles of child rearing are more common and some have argued that the application of these stylistic categories to Chinese parents may be 'ethnocentric and misleading' since these child-rearing types represent an American perspective emphasizing an individualistic view of childhood socialization and development. Contextual and cultural considerations need to be given more attention in typological approaches to child rearing.

The Attachment Theory Approach to Parent–Child Relationships

Attachment theory, developed originally by John Bowlby, offers organizing principles for understanding various aspects of relationships. The comprehensive theory has guided researchers in diverse areas of psychology including social, clinical, and developmental psychology. As Alan Sroufe, Byron Egeland, and colleagues have shown, securely and insecurely attached youngsters developed very different social and emotional patterns. At 4–5 years of age, teachers rated securely attached children as more socially competent and socially skilled and as having more friends than other children. Moreover, their classmates considered them more popular than others.

At 8 and 12 years of age, the securely attached children continued to be rated as more socially competent, more peer oriented and less dependent on adults. Moreover, they were more likely to develop close friendships than their less securely attached peers. At age 19 years, the socioemotional functioning of those adolescents with a history of secure attachment was rated higher as well. In comparison with peers who had a history of insecure attachment, these young adults were more likely to have close family relationships, long-term friendships, sustained romantic involvement, higher self-confidence, and greater determination regarding personal goals.

Just as John Bowlby argued, the links between attachment and social outcomes are forged by children's internal working models. In a longitudinal study, Alan Sroufe and colleagues assessed children's cognitive working models of relationships at various times throughout childhood and adolescence. For example, in the preschool years, these researchers evaluated children's relationship expectations, attitudes, and feelings. Securely attached children's relationship models were characterized by expectations of empathy between play partners, a high expectation of sharing during play, and constructive approaches to conflict resolution (e.g., take turns, seek adult acceptance, get another toy). During adolescence (age 12 years) securely attached children construed their friendships as close, emotionally connected, and skilled in conflict resolution. These investigators showed that cognitive working models and social behavior mutually influence each other across time. In other words, cognitive representations in the preschool period predict social behavior in middle childhood; in turn, the representations in middle childhood predict social behavior at 12 years of age, and these cognitive models predict social outcomes at 19 years of age. Moreover, across time, social behavior at one point predicts later cognitive representations. For example, social behavior in middle childhood is related to a child's cognitive working models in early adolescence. Together, these studies illustrate the interplay among attachment, cognitive understanding, and children's social outcomes. Clearly, the attachment approach to parent–child relationships has been an important theoretical framework.

What is the current status of this theory? First, this approach continues to evolve and has been successfully applied to other relationships beyond the parent–child dyad, including dating and marital relationships. Second, as the longitudinal studies of attachment mature there is increasing examination of cross-time and cross-generational linkages. These studies provide evidence for both continuity and discontinuity and underscore the dynamic and changing nature of attachment relationships in response to shifting socioemotional experiences. Third, more attention to mechanisms that account for the long-term effects of early infant–parent attachment, such as emotional antecedents and cognitive factors, are evident. These efforts will help reconcile this approach and the social interaction approach that we review in the next section. Fourth, cross-cultural examination of the generalizability of attachment patterns is yielding new insights concerning how culture-specific experiences shape the nature of dominant attachment patterns in different cultures. Fifth, recognition of the fact that infant–parent attachment is most profitably viewed from a family systems perspective is needed in order to more fully appreciate the ways in which mother, father, and sibling attachment patterns coordinate with each other in affecting children's developmental outcomes.

The Parent–Child Interactional Approach

Research in this tradition is based on the assumption that face-to-face interaction with parents may provide the opportunity to learn, rehearse, and refine social skills that are common to successful social interaction with other social partners. The style of the interaction between parent and child is linked to a variety of social outcomes including aggression, achievement, and moral development. Parents who are responsive, warm, and engaging are more likely to have children who are more socially competent. In contrast, parents who are hostile and controlling have children who experience more difficulty with age mates. Moreover, these findings are evident in the preschool period, middle childhood, and adolescence. Although there is an overlap between mothers and fathers, fathers make a unique and independent contribution to their children's social development. Although father involvement is quantitatively less than mother involvement, fathers have an important impact on their offspring's development. Both quality and quantity of parent–child interaction are important predictors of cognitive and social development.

This approach is especially useful for understanding socialization processes. In fact, within this tradition, a variety of processes have been suggested as mediators between parent–child interaction patterns and children's social and cognitive outcomes including emotional encoding and decoding, emotional regulatory skills, cognitive representations, attributions and beliefs, problem-solving skills, and attentional regulatory abilities. As in the case of the attachment model, this approach is profitably cast in a family systems framework to understand how mothers' and fathers' unique styles of interaction combine to alter children's socialization outcomes. Finally, more work on how parent–child interaction patterns change across development and especially how parent and child power shifts toward more equality and mutual influence and a shared understanding of the relationship is needed.

Alternative Socialization Pathways

Parental Instruction, Advice Giving, and Consultation

Learning about relationships through interaction with parents can be viewed as an indirect pathway since the goal is often not explicitly to influence children's social relationships with extrafamilial partners such as peers. In contrast, parents may influence children's relationships directly in their role as a direct instructor, educator, or advisor. In this role, parents may explicitly set out to educate their children concerning appropriate ways of initiating and maintaining social relationships and learning social and moral rules.

As Alan Russell has found the quality of advice that mothers provided their children prior to entry into an ongoing play dyad varied as a function of children's sociometric status. Mothers of well-accepted children were more specific and helpful in the quality of advice that they provided. In contrast, mothers of poorly accepted children provided relatively ineffective kinds of verbal guidance, such as 'have fun' or 'stay out of trouble'. The advice was too general to be of value to the children in their subsequent interactions.

As children develop, the forms of management shift from direct involvement or supervision of the ongoing activities of children and their peers to a less public form of management, involving advice or consultation concerning appropriate ways of handling social problems.

Parents as Managers of Children's Socialization Opportunities

Parents influence their children's social relationships not only through their direct interactions with their children, but also function as managers of their children's social lives and serve as regulators of opportunities for social contact with extrafamilial social partners. This parental role is of theoretical importance in light of the recent claims by Judith Harris that parents' impact on children's development is limited and peer group level processes account for major socialization outcomes. In contrast to this view, we conceptualize the parental management of access to peers as a further pathway through which parents influence their children's development. From infancy through middle childhood, mothers are more likely to assume the managerial role than fathers. In infancy, this means setting boundaries for play, taking the child to the doctor, or arranging daycare. In middle childhood, it was found that mothers continue to assume more managerial responsibility (e.g., directing the child to have a bath, to eat a meal, or to put away toys).

Beyond the Parent–Child Dyad: The Sibling, Co-Parenting, and Marital Subsystems as Contributors to Children's Socialization

Children's experiences in families extend beyond their interactions with parents. Evidence suggests that children's understanding of relationships is also shaped through their active participation in other family subsystems (e.g., child–sibling) as well as through exposure to the interactions of other dyadic subsystems (e.g., co-parenting subsystem; marital relationship).

The Sibling Subsystem

Siblings play a critical role in the socialization of children. Most children are likely to spend more time in direct interaction with siblings than parents and this array of interactions between siblings have been found to be typified by greater emotional intensity than the behavioral exchanges that characterize other relationships. As Judy Dunn has noted, sibling relationships contribute to children's socialization in a number of significant ways. Through their interactions with siblings, children develop specific interaction patterns and social understanding skills that generalize to relationships with other children. Relationships with siblings may also provide a context in which children can practice the skills and interaction styles that have been learned from parents or others. Older siblings function as tutors, managers, or supervisors for their younger siblings. Also paralleling the indirect influence that the observation of parent–parent interaction has on children, a second avenue of influence on children's development is their observation of parents interacting with siblings. These interactions may serve as an important context in which children deal with issues of differential treatment and learn about complex social emotions such as rivalry and jealousy.

The Co-Parenting Subsystem

Recently there has been an increasing focus on co-parenting in recognition that mothers and fathers operate as a parenting team as well as individual parents. Much of the research about co-parenting is based upon Salvador Minuchin's structural family theory. James McHale has identified a variety of forms that co-parenting alliances can assume, including antagonistic and adult-centered or hostile-competitive co-parenting, a pattern marked by significant imbalance or parenting discrepancy in levels of parental engagement with the child, and a pattern reflecting cooperation, warmth, cohesion, and child centeredness or high family harmony. These patterns have been observed across a range of studies with infants, preschoolers, and school age children and in both European American and African American families.

Of course, the family unit expands past a triadic (mother–father–child) unit when a second child is involved. Looking beyond the triadic level of interaction, research on co-parenting suggests that the co-parenting system may undergo radical modification when there are two or more children in the family. Studies of two-child families support that each parent engages with one child at a time, and that the four members of the family varied in interactions and amount of unity depending on outside influences such as siblings' gender, age differences, and temperament. Moreover families do not stop at the nuclear unit, and the extended family in which the nuclear unit is embedded has unique influence, context, and consequence, as does the society and culture in which the entire family exists.

Co-parenting accounts for unique variance in child measures and clearly needs to be distinguished from traditional parent–child and marital-level processes. Less is known about the processes that control these various patterns of co-parenting, but recent work on gate-keeping that focuses on ways in which couples facilitate or hinder the involvement of their partner's interactions with their children is promising. The similarities and differences of the co-parenting relationship among both intact and nonintact (divorced and single-parent) families are only poorly understood.

The Marital or Partner–Partner Subsystem

Considerable evidence indicates that marital functioning is related to children's short-term coping and long-term adjustment. Children exposed to marital or partner–partner discord are likely to have poorer quality of interpersonal relationships, including internalizing and externalizing behavior problems, and changes in cognitions, emotions, and physiology. Two alternatives, but not mutually exclusive models, have been proposed to account for the impact of marital relations on children's developmental outcomes. One theoretical framework conceptualizes marital discord as an indirect influence on children's adjustment that operates through its effect on family functioning and the quality of parenting. A second model focuses on the direct effects of witnessed marital conflict on children's outcomes rather than on the indirect effects. Both of these models have received empirical support.

The Family Unit as a Contributor to Children's Socialization

Parent–child, marital, and sibling influences are clearly the most well-researched aspects of family socialization. However, consideration of these units of analysis alone is insufficient because they fail to recognize the family unit itself as a separate and identifiable level of analysis. Consistent with a systems theory perspective, the properties, functions, and effects of the family unit cannot necessarily be inferred from these smaller units of analysis. The family as a unit changes across development in response to changes in the individual members, life circumstances, and scheduled and unscheduled transitions. Families develop distinct climates, styles of responding to events, identities and distinct boundaries, which provide differing socialization contexts for the developing child. Several investigators have argued that the family regulates the child's development through a range of processes, including myths, stories, and rituals. Recent evidence suggests the potential importance of these family level processes for understanding socialization in the family.

Myths refer to beliefs that influence family process, provide continuity across generation, and are generally not open to discussion or debate. Family myths influence mate selection and marital satisfaction. Individuals can set aside destructive family myths by marrying a person with different and perhaps a healthier history of family myths. To date, there is little direct evidence of the impact of family myths on children's development. Family stories have received more attention as vehicles for socialization of young children. Family of origin experiences may be transmitted across generations through stories and shared memories, and shape contemporary interaction between family members. Barbara Fiese has provided a useful framework for studying family stories by focusing on three narrative dimensions: (1) narrative coherence, (2) narrative styles, and (3) relationship beliefs that characterize the form that the content of family stories assumes. This approach yielded important insights into child functioning attitudes toward open vs. closed adoption, marital satisfaction, and diagnosis of depression. Stories are related to family interaction patterns and are linked to children's social competence as well.

Rituals have been recognized for decades as an important aspect of family life, but only in the last decade has the socialization function of rituals and routines become apparent. As Fiese suggested, routines typically involve instrumental communication in conveying information that is 'what needs to be done'. Rituals, in contrast, involve symbolic communication and convey this is 'who we are as a group'. Failure to attend an important family event, such as a wedding, often indicates a shift in family alliances and definitions of who is in or out of the family. Family routines are associated with better child health and better behavioral regulation in intact families. Similarly, routines serve a protective function and are linked to better adjustment for both parents and children in single-parent, divorced, and remarried households. Rituals, serve a protective function such that children who came from families who were able to preserve family rituals, such as holidays and routines, were less likely to become alcoholic adults. Other studies report that families who attach more meaning to their rituals have adolescents who are higher in self-esteem. In sum, routines and rituals are a powerful index of family functioning and may serve as a protective socialization influence on the child.

Determinants of Family Socialization Strategies

One of the major advances in the field has been recognition of the importance of understanding the determinants of parenting behavior. Jay Belsky proposed a three-domain model of the determinants of parenting, which included characteristics of the child, personal resources of the parents, and contextual sources of stress and support (i.e., social capital) which has been an influential guide to this issue.

Child Characteristics

Child characteristics take two forms: universal predispositions that are shared by all children and individual differences in particular characteristics. Infants are biologically prepared for social, cognitive, and perceptual challenges and these prepared responses play a significant role in facilitating children's adaptation to their environment. Under the influence of recent advances in behavior genetics, there is increasing recognition of the role of individual differences in temperament on parenting behavior. Although debates about the relative contributions of genetic and experiential factors to the emergence of individual differences in temperament continue, temperament clearly is a determinant of parental socialization tactics. Children who are more difficult may elicit increasingly coercive strategies from parents. In contrast, fearful children may respond optimally to subtle parental socialization strategies such as reasoning or re-direction rather than harsh, punitive, or coercive tactics. Infants with difficult temperaments elicit more arousal and distress from caregivers than less difficult infants. The impact of these individual differences on parental socialization behavior is not independent of environmental conditions. As Susan Crockenberg has shown, the impact of a difficult infant temperament on the parent–infant attachment relationship varied as a function of the degree of social support available to the mother, which underscores the potential modifiability of temperament-based influences. Other characteristics, in addition to temperament, have been examined, including activity level, social responsiveness, and compliance level. In general, the more active, less responsive, and more noncompliant child elicits more negative parenting and more negative parental arousal and affect.

More recently, under the guidance of scholars such as Robert Plomin, Michael Rutter, and their colleagues, gene–environment interaction models for understanding the interplay between genetics and child-rearing contexts have gained prominence in our theories of socialization. In such research, specified genetic variations in combination with particular environmental circumstances can reveal associations with child outcomes. With respect to adverse outcomes, such genetic variations can be thought of as susceptibility factors whose impact depends on the type of environments to which the child is exposed during socialization. For example, Avshalom Caspi and colleagues found that men with a variant of a normal but low active gene that is associated with inhibition of aggression (*MAO-A*), and who were exposed to severe abuse were more violent as adults than individuals exposed to the same abuse but had a more active aggression inhibitory gene. Similarly, Marian Bakermans-Kranenburg and Mariunus Van IJzendoorn from the Netherlands recently found that maternal insensitivity was associated with externalizing (oppositional, aggressive) behavior but only in the presence of a specific gene (seven repeat *DRD4* polymorphism), a part of the dopaminergic system. As these studies illustrate, contemporary researchers emphasize a model of 'gene environment interplay' as a framework for understanding development in which both behavioral predispositions, such as temperament and specific genes, interact with parenting strategies in determining socialization outcomes.

Personal Parental Resources

A variety of studies support the prediction that personal resources – conceptualized as knowledge, ability, and motivation to be a responsible caregiver – alter parenting behaviors. Particularly striking are recent studies of how parental psychopathology, such as depression, will alter parenting behavior. When interacting with their infants, depressed mothers show flat affect and provide less contingent stimulation than nondepressed mothers; in turn, their infants showed less attentiveness, more fussiness, and lower activity levels. Differences are particularly evident when depression is protracted and not merely transient.

Social Capital

Recognition of the role of the community and community agents as modifiers of family interaction is necessary for an adequate theory of socialization. The concept of social capital is useful for understanding the links between families and the wider set of community institutions. According to James Coleman, social capital is both the flow of information and the sharing of norms and values that serve to facilitate and constrain the actions of people who interact in a community's social structures (e.g., schools, religious institutions, or business enterprises). Recognition of the embeddedness of families in a set of broader social systems such as community and culture is only a first step. The next task is to articulate ways in which these other levels of social organization affect family functioning and explore the way in which these influence processes take place. Social capital can be either positive or negative, since a high degree of connectedness with community resources is not necessarily positive. In addition, the relationship between communities and families is bidirectional and varies across development. Moreover, the influence of support systems on families may either be direct or indirect in its effects. Finally, both availability and utilization need to be separately considered. While the availability of social capital is potentially valuable to families, especially in times of stress, families may have friends, relatives, and neighbors available, but fail to utilize these members of their informal social network in times of stress or crises or even on a day-to-day basis.

Socioeconomic Status

There is a long history of research concerning the links between SES and/or social class and parenting beliefs and practices. In contrast to traditional assumptions that SES is a static state, SES is a dynamic concept. Over the course of childhood and adolescence, families change social class and change is greatest in the youngest ages. Over 50% of American children change social class prior to entering school. In spite of the controversies surrounding this variable, there are SES differences in parental socialization practices and beliefs. Lower SES parents are more authoritarian and more punitive and controlling than higher SES families. Second, there are more SES differences on language measures than on nonverbal measures with higher SES mothers being more verbal than low SES mothers. Some SES differences are independent of race and poverty. In China, where there are relatively small differences in income across groups who vary in terms of education, less educated parents used more imperatives with their toddlers than better-educated mothers. Similarly, studies of cognitive socialization found clear SES differences in African-American lower class and middle class families.

Ethnicity

Recent cross-cultural and intracultural theories have emphasized the importance of socialization goals, values, and beliefs as organizing principles for understanding cultural variations. In contrast to the older cultural deficit models of socialization, the more recent models emphasize how ecological demands shape values and goals. In the past, cultural deficit models were popular explanations for the socialization and child outcome differences observed between ethnic minorities and Euro-Americans. The focus on ethnic minority families has shifted away from majority–minority differences in developmental outcomes and more toward an understanding of the adaptive strategies ethnic minorities develop in response to both majority and minority cultural influences on their development. The parents' individual history of interaction with the larger sociocultural context, including their awareness of their ethnic group's history within the larger society, affect the manner in which they socialize their children. An important dimension of socialization in ethnic minority families is teaching children how to interact effectively in dual cultural contexts; the context of their ethnic group and the context of the larger Euro-American society. Scholars, such as Raymond Buriel and Cynthia Garcia-Coll, have adopted an ecological orientation to explain the diverse environmental influences that contribute to the socialization of ethnic minority children. They conceptualize the socialization of ethnic minority children in terms of the interconnectedness between the status of ethnic minority families, adaptive strategies, socialization goals, and child outcomes. Emerging out of the adaptive strategies of adults are the socialization goals that they endeavor to inculcate in children to help them meet the ecological challenges they will face as ethnic minorities in a class and race conscious society. Ethnic pride and interdependence are two important socialization goals that enable ethnic minority children to function competently as members of both their minority culture and the larger society.

Research needs to take into account the acculturation level of parents and children in recent immigrant families and the effects it has on family processes and child outcomes. Intergenerational differences in acculturation can create role strains between parents and children that have implications for child rearing styles, disciplinary practices, and overall parent–child relations. Together with acculturation, recognition of biculturalism as both an adaptation strategy and socialization goal is important. The effects of prejudice and discrimination on ethnic minorities, in such areas as social and emotional development, ethnic identity, and achievement motivation, deserve more attention. Language development research should also give greater attention to second language acquisition (usually English) and bilingualism and its relation to cognitive development and school achievement. More attention must also be given to the role of ethnic minority fathers, grandparents, and extended family members in the socialization of children.

The Impact of Social Change on Socialization

Families are not static but dynamic and are continuously confronted by challenges, changes, and opportunities. A number of society-wide changes have produced a variety of shifts in the nature of family relationships. Fertility rates and family size have decreased, the percentage of women in the workforce has increased, the timing of onset of parenthood has shifted, divorce rates as well as rates of remarriage and stepfamily formation have risen, and the number of single parent families has increased. These social trends provide an opportunity to explore how families adapt and change in response to these shifting circumstances and represent 'natural experiments' in family coping and adaptation. Moreover, they challenge our traditional assumptions that families can be studied at a single point in historical time since the historical contexts are constantly shifting. Our task is to establish how socialization processes operate similarly or differently under varying historical circumstances. In both the US and other parts of the world, a variety of changes, including the timing of parenthood, increases in women's employment, and increases in rates of divorce and remarriage, have taken place. These social changes can have a major impact on children's socialization. For example, some divorce experts such as Mavis Hetherington suggest that approximately 25% of children in divorced and stepparent families are at risk for developmental problems, in part, as a result of changes in socialization practices accompanying these shifts in family structure. However, the majority of children adapt and function well in a variety of family arrangements including divorced-single parent families and stepfamily households. To date, societal changes, such as shifts in the timing of parenting, work participation, or divorce, have been treated relatively independently, but, in fact, these events co-occur rather than operate in any singular fashion. Multivariate designs which capture the simultaneous impact of multiple events on family socialization strategies are necessary.

Extrafamilial Socialization Influences

Peers

Peers, in addition to parents, play important socialization roles. Peers play a central role in children's socialization, beginning in infancy. Especially in view of the growing number of infants and children who spend time in out of home child-care, the role of peers as socialization agents has assumed major importance. From the first year of life infants are responsive to peers and by the second year engage in mutually responsive social exchanges. Learning to interact in a socially skilled manner with peers is a central task of early socialization. Children with different temperaments or with cold, unresponsive parents or who have developed insecure infant–parent attachment have more difficulty interacting in a harmonious way with their peers. Of importance is the fact that toddlers with poorly developed social skills are more likely to be disliked and rejected by their peers. In turn, children with this history of poor peer relationships are more likely to experience academic failure as well as socioemotional problems (i.e., loneliness, depression, externalizing behaviors) in the elementary school years and in adolescence. Clearly, peers are an important part in the socialization saga.

However, peers and parents do not make independent socialization contributions; instead, these two sets of socialization agents are best viewed as independent and mutually influential. For example, parental interaction patterns, advice giving, and monitoring play central roles in the nature and quality of children's peer relationships. Similarly, children develop attitudes, norms, and values as a consequence of their extrafamilial peer relationships that, in turn, can modify the nature of their relationships with their parents and siblings in either a positive or negative way. Although it is clear that peers play an increasingly important role as children develop, family values and control strategies continue to play an important role in shaping children's ties with peers.

Mass Media

In our increasingly technological era, the mass media in the form of television, movies, computer-based educational programs, and video games play a role in infant and child socialization. Even in infancy, parents expose their offspring to videotapes, television programs, and other forms of mass media that is facilitated by the fact that a large percentage of infants and toddlers have a television and/or video player in their rooms. Some types of media exposure are clearly beneficial, such as educational programs (e.g., Sesame Street and Mr. Rogers) can increase young children's cognitive development as well as their prosocial behavior. In contrast, there is abundant evidence that violent cartoons and programs watched by children can have detrimental socialization effects including desensitization to witnessed violence, greater acceptance of aggression as a solution to social problems and, for some children, an increase in aggressive behavior. Moreover, the impact of a high diet of violent television exposure has long-lasting effects; first grade children who watch a great deal of violent programs have more antisocial and unlawful behavior in early adulthood. As in the case of viewing aggressive television, violent video and computer games have been found to produce similar negative effects such as increased aggression. Again, parents play a major role in their regulation of access to mass media including the amount of exposure and the types of programs that children watch. Moreover, parents can help children better understand television plots and programs (i.e., highlight negative consequences of violent actions) that, in turn, can reduce the negative effects of exposure. Often parents fail to exercise this regulatory responsibility.

Neighborhoods as Socialization Contexts

Neighborhoods are important socialization contexts as well. Children who grow up in poor and dangerous neighborhoods have more academic and social problems. High-risk neighborhoods expose children to violence, limit their access to safe play spaces and often encourage aggressive strategies in order to function effectively in these contexts. Moreover, as children develop, they are prone to more negative peer influence (i.e., gangs) and lawlessness (drug use; drug dealing; vandalism). The impact of the quality of neighborhoods is illustrated by studies in which children change neighborhoods; those that move to higher quality neighborhoods improve in both achievement and social behavior, while those who move to poorer-quality neighborhoods show declines in academic and social outcomes. Nonexperimental studies show these patterns but experimental policy-based planned shifts in neighborhood quality show short-term but not long-term effects. This suggests that 'neighborhoods' can be viewed as an additional level of socialization influence. Again it is critical to underscore that 'neighborhood effects' are often achieved through changes in parenting behaviors in response to aspects of neighborhood, such as perceived dangerousness, or through the types of peers and/or peer related activities afforded by the neighborhood.

Schools

Parents choose not only neighborhoods but also, for middle-class families, the type and quality of day care and elementary schools that their children will attend. These choices make a difference to children's later development. As studies of child care have shown, the quality of and, to some extent, the amount of time in care are linked to children's cognitive and social development. Higher quality of child care is associated often with higher cognitive functioning. Social behavior, despite the opportunity to have increased peer contact, is less consistently linked with day care quality. Some evidence suggests that children who are in day care for more than 40 h per week may show some increases in aggression. As children develop, parents select neighborhoods as a function of the quality of the schools that are available. However, these choices are limited by social class and economic resources and are mainly available to middle-class families. Moreover, the ability to choose is not inconsequential because exercising the ability to choose a school has been linked to adolescent academic outcomes. As a reminder that children can play a role in the process of school choice, there is some evidence that children's behavior in school – their successes and failures in both social and academic domains – influence the nature of the parent–child relationship. Children's positive and negative experiences at school during the day alter the nature of the parent–child interaction in the home after school.

School choice is not the only way in which families and schools are linked. The extent to which parents are involved in school-related activities (e.g., parent–teacher associations or school conferences) is positively related to children's academic outcomes. Practices of partnerships between parents and schools decline across child development. Parents of children in elementary school are more likely to volunteer, attend parent–teacher conferences, and supervise children's homework. In recognition of adolescents' need for autonomy and independence, parental involvement decreases in high school, but young adolescents still want their families to support their learning and activities at home. Even older adolescents endorse parent involvement in school, but in different ways than in earlier school grades. These developmental changes can be interpreted as evidence of the child's role in shaping the form that the parent–school partnership will assume at different points in the child's educational career.

Religious Organizations

Parental facilitation of children's involvement in religious institutions is another potentially important way which parents socialize their children. It is important to distinguish between the issue of involvement in religious institutions and religious beliefs because these two aspects of religion may have partially independent effects on family functioning and child outcomes. In their book, *Children of the Land*, Glen Elder and Rand Conger argue that church involvement is a family affair. When both parents attended church on a regular basis, children were more likely to be in involved in religious organizations. Similarly, actively involved grandparents tend to have actively involved grandchildren. Church attendance involved more than contact with a broadened network of adults who share similar family and religious values; it also involved exposure to a network of age-mates with common beliefs and values. Involvement in church activities was associated with higher endorsement of not only church but also school, good grades, and – especially for boys – community activities. For those who were less involved in religious activities, athletics, and school were given high priority. Religiously involved youth perceived their friends to be less likely to encourage deviant activities, viewed their friends and themselves as less involved in deviance, and were less likely to see friends that their parents disapproved of. Religious involvement in the eighth grade was predictive of competence by the 12th grade in grades and peer success. Moreover, adolescents who become more religiously involved by the end of high school tend to rank higher on a variety of competence dimensions – from academic and peer success to self-confidence and relations with parents. A reciprocal influence model best accounted for those findings. Although the primary flow of influence moved from religious activity and socialization to individual competence in achievement, some adolescents who were successful academically and socially, and became more involved in religious activities, further enhanced achievement. Similarly, it is likely that both parents and children are active players in the process of involvement in religious activities. Although parents – through their own involvement and through their introduction of the child to religious beliefs and functions – play an important initial role, children, and especially adolescents, themselves are central agents in choosing to continue their regular participation in religious institutions. Finally, parental religiousness (frequency of church attendance and importance of religion) is associated with better child adjustment as well. Specifically higher maternal and paternal religiousness is associated with less externalizing problems among 9- to 12-year-olds. The effects were mediated by family cohesiveness and lower marital conflict. However, the relative importance of beliefs or involvement in organized religious activities in accounting for these effects is unclear.

Summary

Socialization is a multiply determined process; while families have traditionally been viewed as central socialization agents, we argue that it is important to recognize the roles of social agents such as peers, neighborhoods, schools, religious institutions, and the mass media in this process. A fuller understanding of socialization will come from more attention to the interplay among these diverse agents and how biological, including genetic factors as well as cultural and ethnic backgrounds, influence socialization practices and outcomes.

See also: Attachment; Demographic Factors; Discipline and Compliance; Family Influences; Friends and Peers; Marital Relationship; Parenting Styles and their Effects; Routines; Siblings and Sibling Rivalry; Social and Emotional Development Theories; Social Interaction; Television: Uses and Effects; Temperament.

Suggested Readings

Bugental DB and Grusec JE (2006) Socialization processes. In: Damon W, Lerner RM, and Eisenberg N (eds.) *Handbook of Child Psychology: Vol. 3. Social, Emotional, and Personality Development,* 6th edn., pp. 366–428. New York: Wiley.

Damon W and Lerner RM (eds.) (2006) *Handbook of Child Psychology: Vol. 3. Social, Emotional, and Personality Development*, 6th edn. New York: Wiley.

Grusec J and Ungerer J (2003) Effective socialization as problem solving and the role of parenting cognitions. In: Kuczynski L (ed.) *Handbook of Dynamics in Parent–Child Relations*, pp. 211–228. Thousand Oaks, CA: Sage Publications.

Kuczynski L (ed.) (2003) *Handbook of Dynamics in Parent–Child Relations.* Thousand Oaks, CA: Sage Publications.

Ladd G (2005) *Children's Peer Relations and Social Competence.* New Haven, CT: Yale Univesity Press.

Parke RD (2004) Development in the family. *Annual Review of Psychology* 55: 365–400.

Parke RD and Buriel R (2006) Socialization in the family: Ecological and ethnic perspectives. In: Damon W, Lerner RM, and Eisenberg N (eds.) *Handbook of Child Psychology: Vol. 3. Social, Emotional, and Personality Development,* 6th edn., pp. 429–504. New York: Wiley.

Parke RD, Simpkins S, McDowell D, *et al.* (2002) Relative contribution of families and peers to children's social development. In: Smith PK and Hart CH (eds.) *Blackwell Handbook of Childhood Social Development*, pp. 156–178. Oxford, UK: Blackwell.

Special Education

J J Gallagher, University of North Carolina at Chapel Hill, Chapel Hill, NC, USA

Glossary

Class action suits – Legal cases whereby the decision affects not only the particular case but also all of the members of a particular class of people (e.g., children with mental retardation) and therefore has had a major impact on education and society.

Developmentally appropriate practices – Curriculum designed to match the level of developmental progress of the child approved by early childhood professionals.

Down syndrome – A chromosomal abnormality that leads to mild or moderate mental retardation and a variety of skeletal, hearing, and heart problems.

Fetal alcohol syndrome – Limitations in a child's development as a result of the mother's heavy use of alcohol during pregnancy.

Fragile X syndrome – A restriction at the end of the X chromosome that may lead the newborn child to mental retardation and various learning problems.

Functional behavioral assessment – Evaluations of negative behavior that attempts to explain why the behavior occurs, describes where and when the behavior is present and how the behavior impacts the child and his/her surroundings.

Human Genome Project – An ambitious research project which involves many scientists and research institutes attempting to identify the genes on every chromosome and their influences on human development and performance. Beginning to identify the genetic influences on various disabilities.

Individual education program (IEP) – A plan mandated by law to be developed for every child with disabilities which describes the child's current performance and the goals for the school year, the special education services to be delivered, and procedures by which the outcomes are evaluated.

Individual family service plan (IFSP) – A plan mandated by law for children with disabilities under school age. It identifies family needs and sets forth a plan to meet these needs and charts the progress of the plan.

Mobility training – A special set of skills applied by specially trained educators to aid children with visual disabilities to be able to navigate their physical environment and increase their self confidence.

Special education – A branch of education focusing on children with disabilities or special talents. It stresses the assessment of individual needs and differential programming to meet these needs. Such services are provided by specially trained personnel.

Total communication method – A method of teaching deaf children that combines finger spelling, signing, and speech reading and auditory amplification.

Wraparound approach – An intervention approach for children with disabilities that includes multidisciplinary approaches such as counseling, medical services, and social services in addition to special education. A design of a total program.

Introduction

Special education has been a significant force in American education for over a half century. It is a branch of education characterized by concerns for the assessment and programming for students with disabilities, and those with special talents. An emphasis is placed upon formal plans for individual programming of students with disabilities by specially trained, multidisciplinary, personnel.

These individual plans are mandated by federal legislation and have been known as the individual education program (IEP) and the individual family service program (IFSP) for younger children with disabilities. In each plan, the students' current performance and the education goals for the year are stated, the special education services that will be provided to help meet those goals, and the methods used to evaluate the level of success attained. The IFSP places greater emphasis on the family participation in the treatment program.

The field of special education has a long history of interest and attempts at study and intervention in early childhood. From the mid-twentieth century to the present day there has been a recognition that remediation and treatment should begin in early childhood for a variety of conditions that lead to children with special needs. The primary disciplines of medicine and special education have followed the principle that "The earlier in the development of the child one starts treatment and remediation the better. If one starts earlier we can expect more positive results with less expenditure of professional energy." This article will document the variety of activities in early childhood for the specific areas of childhood disabilities and for the broad field of education of exceptional children.

Traditionally, the field of children with disabilities has been subdivided into diagnostic categories. Early childhood special education has modified this approach by focusing on developmental delay as the key educational dimension deserving attention regardless of the original cause. Since much of the literature is based upon categorical divisions, this article will follow that pattern.

Mental Retardation (Intellectual Disabilities)

Mental retardation is an umbrella term for a condition that may have many different causes but is characterized by significant limitations in intellectual functioning (often identified through intelligence tests) and social adaptation (identified through observation). It has been described both by its causes and by the intensity of impairment. 'Mild' would describe those who, with good education, can become self-sustaining in adulthood, 'moderate', those children who can be partially self-sustaining in adulthood with assistance, and 'severe', those who will be dependent on others for the rest of their lives. The conditions can also be described by the intensity of support needed to allow the individual to operate efficiently: 'intermittent', 'limited', 'extensive', and 'pervasive'.

Some of the genetic disorders resulting in mental retardation are Down syndrome, caused by failure of chromosomes to divide properly, fragile X syndrome, resulting from the mutation on the long arm of the X chromosome and phenylketonuria, an inborn error of metabolism which can be treated with a rigid diet. A screening program at infancy has been established in the US so that children with phenylketonuria can be started on a nutritional regime at the earliest time.

One major toxic agent that results in mental retardation is fetal alcohol syndrome resulting from alcohol ingestion by the mother during pregnancy. Public information campaigns have been initiated to teach key facts: such as when a pregnant woman drinks, so does her baby; the baby's growth can be altered or slowed; and the baby may suffer lifelong damage. Another toxic agent is lead which is found in gasoline and in paint. Legislation has been passed in the US to limit the lead in gasoline and remove it from paint, but old buildings where paint was used before the ban on lead can still be a risk factor for young children.

Finally, environmental factors such as poverty, or child abuse and neglect, are identified as creating unfavorable environments for the development of intelligence and of socially adaptive behavior.

What all of these children have in common are special needs requiring differentiated programming in the education system and some special multidisciplinary personnel with unique training to enhance the child's development. This, in turn, requires additional fiscal resources and personnel to carry out such assistance.

Although there has been a general assumption that the condition of mental retardation is a permanent one, there is some evidence available that intensive early intervention can ameliorate the condition in its milder form. It is important that the conditions of mental retardation are recognized and intervention begins early in the child's lifespan.

Autism Spectrum Disorders

Children with autism spectrum disorders display a common set of symptoms that identify it. Michael Rutter has listed the three conditions that distinguish these children from children with other disabilities:

1. failure to develop social relationships;
2. language retardation with impaired comprehension; and
3. ritualistic or compulsive behaviors.

The interest in this condition of autism is only decades old with many of these children earlier classified as mentally retarded. The prevalence of the condition is steadily increasing but many scientists suggest that this increase is merely due to our only now discovering a condition that previously had been identified as something else. Estimates now place the prevalence of autism at one in every two hundred children whereas early estimates were one in a thousand.

These conditions lead to serious educational impairments and social adaptation problems. They require early identification and intervention on an intense scale. Fortunately, there are tests now available that can identify such children with autism by the age of 18–24 months.

The cause of the condition is still not finally identified although there are clear indications of a genetic link. Many other causal suggestions, such as a cold and unfeeling mother, food additives, vaccines, etc., have been dismissed for lack of evidence.

Early intervention is often done in multidisciplinary clinics and focuses on the family as a bulwark of help and assistance. Parents are taught how to stimulate language and teach the social skills that other children learn automatically, whereas autistic children must learn them in a structured environment with clear procedures followed. The parents' use of effective teaching methods for their child with autism has shown a measurable impact on stress reduction in the family.

The IFSP almost always includes extensive attention to communication and language development plus opportunities to learn social skills. This is not a condition that a child will 'outgrow' and will need continuing attention throughout the school years.

Behavior and Emotional Problems

Children who are manifestly unhappy, or who create unhappiness in others through their behavior, are an inevitable group included under the term exceptional children. The growing number or longitudinal studies linking childhood with adulthood has revealed important facts such as children with serious behavior problems in early years will often carry forward those problems into adulthood.

Such information calls for early intervention to prevent or ameliorate the forces leading to such behavior. Although poor environment has been given the responsibility for much of this problem, recent evidence strongly suggests an interaction between genetics and environment in creating what we see as 'problem children'.

The clashes of cultures in many urban schools can be another factor leading to disaffection of the child with his/her school and society. Such clashes also seem to weaken the academic performance particularly with children in these categories.

There have been a number of intervention strategies suggested by research and clinical experience and, once again, the earlier they are applied the more effective and efficient would seem to be the results. Functional behavioral assessment means an attempt is made to understand the motivation behind deviant behavior and to reduce the need for the expression of antisocial or nonfunctional behavior by dealing with the more basic cause.

Positive behavior supports refer to strategies used to enhance positive behavior for the entire classroom. An example would be the posting of what is acceptable and what is unacceptable behavior and a class discussion of these rules and the consequences for violating them. Such a strategy is designed to make students secure in their understanding of classroom rules.

However, some children, particularly those with emotional or behavioral problems, may need individual attention and planning to help them toward acceptable behavior. Positive behavior supports are expected to create a positive atmosphere in the classroom which will make it easier for the teacher to adapt to behavior outside the limits.

A current instructional model is to ignore behavior that is nonfunctional (if it is not too serious) and reward behavior that is socially and personally acceptable. The deliberate teaching of social skills is often a part of the program. Modeling, role playing, and generalization of social skills becomes a part of daily instruction and interaction with the child. If possible, a variety of professional skills can be added to the planning and treatment. Such multidisciplinary planning and treatment is often referred to as the wraparound approach meaning that many different aspects of the child's life are being addressed simultaneously.

A combination of psychological therapy combined with drug therapy has been found to be useful for many hyperactive and attention deficient children with the *proviso* that they are administered by qualified professionals.

Children with Hearing Problems

It is extremely important that children with hearing loss become identified at the earliest possible time and begin language development and training as soon as feasible. This is so critical that various newborn screening proposals are being considered in some states.

While a child with normal hearing learns how to speak by listening to others, and also learns language the same way, children with hearing loss are at an important disadvantage. Two quite distinctive educational approaches are provided for such children. For those with a mild or moderate loss, sound amplification through hearing aids and other devices seems to be the method of choice. With sound amplification and special training, the young child with moderate hearing problems can master language in a similar fashion to the hearing child.

For the child with more severe hearing loss, the child may be taught through systems of gestures. Sign language such as the American Sign Language is a distinct language with its own grammar and syntax and is in common use in the 'deaf community'.

Another method of communication for the child with severe hearing loss is finger spelling, literally writing in the air. The child spells out words as part of the communication. The total communication method combines finger spelling, signs, speech reading, and amplification. The child uses both speech and the manual method and this total communication appears to be the most common method in use in the public schools.

The importance of an early start and bringing the family into the treatment program as early as possible have been noted by many professional observers. Early education is an essential for such children. Later on, various technological advances can be brought into play to additionally aid communication such as assistive listening devices (ALDs) which increase the volume of voice received and reduce other environmental sound, frequency modulated (FM) systems in which the teacher wears a microphone that sends a direct signal to the child's hearing aid, and a variety of speech-to-print systems that can aid the child to use the telephone and print messages.

Children with Visual Impairments

The special education challenge for children with visual problems is to help them with their spatial problems (How high is the mountain? How wide is the ocean?) and to develop an alternative to reading as a communication channel for learning. Since their hearing is likely to be intact they do not have the problem of language development as do the hearing impaired children.

There are two additional problems for young children with visual problems. Their prevalence in the society is very small, perhaps four in a thousand (if the visual problem is correctable with glasses it is not considered an educational problem), so clustering these youngsters together for learning or instruction is difficult. Additionally, more than half of children with these problems also have additional problems (cerebral palsy, cognitive limitations, etc.) which complicates the educational programming.

Much of the focus of instruction is in helping the child to be self-sufficient and not fall into a passive mode where everything is brought to them. Mobility and orientation training should start early so the young child can move around his/her environment. Learning environments have to be designed so that the child is responsive to stimuli and seeking experiences. Parental assistance in creating a responsive environment is important.

The Braille system of feeling dots representing letters has helped many generations of children who are blind, to begin reading. Specially trained teachers are necessary to help the child get a strong start in life and to help the parents be active in the child's experiential development. The wide range of visual problems and individual differences in this group make it important that individual planning through IFSPs and IEP be utilized.

Although children with hearing problems can be successful in school, it takes a strong effort on the part of the child, family, and the persons providing them with assistance to be successful. Those that begin special training before 2.5 years appear to be more able to be successful in their academic programs.

Children with Learning Disabilities

By far, the largest number of children in special education in the US (almost half of the total disability population) are classified as children with learning disabilities. This is currently an amorphous category including children who are having difficulty learning despite adequate instruction.

The category itself emerged from a concern with children with minimal brain injury which seemed to result in large intraindividual differences in development which caused the student to have difficulty in learning. That is, the child might be learning through the auditory channel at age 8 years and through the visual channel at age 4 years. The distinguished special educator, Sam Kirk, introduced the term children with learning disabilities in 1963 meaning children with intraindividual differences. Since that time, the definition has been transformed into a child who differed in intelligence quotient (IQ) scores and achievement scores, a decision which resulted in a major leap in prevalence figures. Children with learning disabilities now comprise between 4% or 5% of the school population. When the category was first introduced there was an expectation of a prevalence of less than 1%.

Until recently, the preschool and pre-kindergarten programs were not deeply concerned with such children since their learning disability was not obvious prior to their entry into school, at which time they responded poorly to the school program and identified themselves. In recent years there has been an attempt to develop screening tools and methods which would find these youngsters in the preschool years, again because of the importance of beginning remedial work early. At the present time, specific remedial work with children with learning disabilities at the early childhood level is still just being started.

Multiple Handicapped

The advancement of medical science has led to an increasing number of children who have survived crises early in life but whose survival has been accompanied by a multitude of developmental problems. A child may be both blind and deaf, for example, or can have cerebral palsy with hearing problems accompanied by cognitive delay problems, or any number of variations of multiple disabilities. These create serious problems for the child, the family, and for those special educators who have the responsibility of helping them cope with their special issues.

These children, in particular, need a carefully crafted IFSP as a basis for productive intervention. Most of the special educators who deal with young children with multiple handicaps have had training in one or the other disability (they may have been trained to work with deaf children) and have expanded their knowledge and skills to deal with children with various problems. It is especially important that these professionals learn how to counsel parents and provide them with meaningful tasks so that they have a positive feeling about their child and optimism that they can play a positive role in their child's development.

Mobility and language become especially important set of skills to help develop in these young children so that they can interact with those around them.

Societal Changes and Early Childhood

Brain Development

Over the years we have learned a great deal more about the development of young children and those discoveries have had a major impact on our institutions and practices. One of the areas of development has been our understanding of how the human brain was mainly directed by hereditary influences which help to shape the maturation process by which an infant brain became an adult brain.

We now realize that the final emergence of the adult brain depends, in part, upon the experiences that that child has over time. Sections of the brain with stimulation can develop in a more complex fashion than those areas that were not interactive with the environment. This important discovery obviously places more importance on the experiences the child has in his/her early years. Brain growth and environmental interaction has become one of the scientific arguments for early intervention for all children but particularly for children with special needs.

A second major development has been the Human Genome Project which hopes to catalog and map all of human genes and to identify what parts of human development have been related to which genes. A related discovery is that only a small proportion of genes participate in the developmental process. A change in environment and experience can activate genes that had not been previously involved, thus changing the behavioral phenotype. The continued and sequential interactions of experience and genetics is one more powerful argument for paying attention to the very young child since the early experiences cast long shadows into the future with the help of the genetic make-up of the child.

Cultural Changes

There are many changes taking place in the society that also have an impact on young children with disabilities. One of the most important has been the rapid shift in the number of mothers in the work force in a period of two to three generations. From post-World War II where the number of mothers with young children in the work force was less than 10% to the current figure of over 50% this shift has caused many readjustments.

There appears to be two reasons for the shift. First, there is an attempt to use 'women in the workforce' as an equity issue for women but there is also an economic issue that two incomes may be needed in the family to support the lifestyle that the family wishes. This increase in mothers working also raises issues such as who cares for the young child when the parents are at work? This is particularly true when the child, in question, creates many problems for the caregiver. Sometimes the mother of a child with disabilities is forced to give up her work to care for the child at home creating additional psychological and economic consequences.

These issues are complicated by the large number of one-parent families in the US society. The number of divorces obviously create one-parent families but there is a growing number of one-parent families where there never was a marriage in the first place and where the biological father appears to take no significant role. One of the clear consequences of the one-parent family is poor economic circumstances. Many of these families are at or near the poverty line which would make expensive care for a child with special needs either unlikely or unfeasible. So during the developmental period when the child most needs special help he/she is least likely to receive it.

A disproportionate number of such families come from racial or ethnic minority backgrounds where the knowledge of these children with special needs may be limited. The recent public policy movements to welfare reform have forced many mothers into the workforce again but do not provide an answer for their child with special needs.

There are positive forces trying to cope with these problems. There is a rapidly growing trend toward the establishment of pre-kindergarten programs in the public schools in the US (over 40 states now have publicly supported pre-kindergarten) that will allow the child with special needs to be identified at age four or even three and receive important care earlier. There also is the establishment of a diverse set of child care or day care programs to try and meet the needs of the working families. It is important that such programs are of high quality to meet the needs of children with disabilities. There is current evidence available that, all too often, the quality of child care in the US is not high. Studies involving multiple states have revealed many centers not reaching minimum standards.

The result of an uneven care for young children is that the number of children who enter kindergarten not prepared for the experience is too large and the consequences for increased school failure become predictable.

Court Decisions

Court decisions have been very important in defining the rights of children with disabilities within the education community. Many of the cases were called 'class action' suits which meant that the decision affected not only the child or family in question, but all other children of a similar class. Therefore a court decision affecting one mentally retarded child would affect all mentally retarded children in that jurisdiction.

One of the key decisions, for example, was Pennsylvania Association for Retarded Children (PARC vs. Commonwealth of Pennsylvania, 1972). Preschool children who were mentally retarded were being denied the right to attend school until they passed a test which presumed to declare them eligible for school. The parents complained that this violated the Pennsylvania constitution which declared a free public education for all children. The courts decided in the parents' favor and this decision affected all mentally retarded children in the state.

One of the key court decisions was Brown vs. Board of Education (1954) which declared the 'separate but equal' racial segregation concept unconstitutional and this decision opened the door for many families with children with disabilities to seek similar protection.

Scores of decisions followed detailing the proper position of children with disabilities in the educational enterprise. One other decision which placed parameters around the rights of children with disabilities was the Hendrick Hudson School District vs. Rowley (1982). The school had provided a variety of aids for Amy, a deaf student, to aid her in communicating but refused to provide a personal interpreter in the classroom. The Supreme Court ruled that an appropriate education, which guarantees positive development, need not mean the best possible education since no student receives the best possible education. This decision was an antidote to decisions asking schools for more and more services for exceptional children.

The number of class action suits has been limited in recent times and this has diminished the immediate effect of any court decisions on children with disabilities. Nevertheless, the courts have been a strong stabilizing force in upholding the rights of young children.

Public Policy

The interest in young children in the US has been translated into public policy through a number of different channels. There are four major players at the national level each with their own legislative authority and programs designed to aid young children. As can be seen in each of these programs, the emphasis has been in aiding low income families.

Child Care

Federally supported child care was established through the Social Security Amendments of 1935 and currently is comprised of two major funds: the Child Care and

Development Block Grants which distributes money for the states to aid them in their child care efforts in child care homes etc. and the Temporary Assistance to Needy Families (TANF) designed as part of the welfare program. It serves an estimate 1.7 million children with $5.4 billion (fiscal year (FY) 2001 figures) and is administered by the Federal Administration for Children and Families.

Head Start

Head Start was a program begun in the mid-1960s for 3- and 4-year-olds from disadvantaged families as part of the Economic Opportunity Act of 1964. It was designed to help children born into poverty to become ready for school by promoting good health, social skills, and cognitive growth. In FY 2007 it serves over 900 000 children with $6.8 billion and is administered by the Head Start Bureau in US Department of Health and Human Services.

Preschool Education

These programs were established through Title I of the Elementary and Secondary Education Act of 1965 (PL 89-10) to target children in schools with a high incidence of poverty to prevent school failure. The amount spent in FY 2001 was about $704 million and is administered by the US Department of Education. In addition, the states have been rapidly developing pre-kindergarten programs to serve 4- and sometimes 3-year-olds.

Children with Disabilities

Federal programs for preschool children with disabilities were established with a small demonstration program in 1968 and extended through the Education for All Handicapped Children Act in 1975 (PL 94-42) and finally included infants and toddlers in the Education for the Handicapped Amendments of 1986 (PL 99-457). These laws were mandates requiring services to eligible children and resulted in major state actions to extend their programs for these children. The program is administered by the Office of Special Education Programs in the US Department of Education. State and federal programs cost over $4 billion per year.

Each of these four programs were established at different times for different purposes and administered by different agencies. The problems of coordination and collaboration for these four programs are quite serious and complicated by distance and professional rivalries. A number of states have established mechanisms to aid such coordination. For example, several states support joint teacher certification programs between early childhood education and special education.

A comprehensive system of early childhood care would probably include joint efforts at personnel preparation, technical assistance, program evaluation, data system, planning, and the establishment of joint standards. The legislative and administrative actions necessary to bring such a comprehensive system about remain to be completed.

The need for special resources to meet the particular needs of young children with disabilities raised the issue of where such resources would be coming from. Public policy has been defined as 'the rules and standards by which scarce public resources are allocated to meet almost unlimited social needs'. Such situations mean that those issues with the highest public priority would be the ones who received the resources.

In the US the organization of parent groups such as the National Association of Retarded Citizens (now called the ARC) became a powerful stimulus for public action. They pursued some of the key engines of social change: 'legislation' and 'court actions' to institutionalize the channeling of resources to the help of their children.

One comprehensive piece of legislation (PL 94-142) known as the Education for All Handicapped Children Act provided in 1975 the base for federal help for special education. However, this legislation was misnamed. It was not for 'all' handicapped children, only for children of school age. Few of its resources went to young children.

It did embody the six principles that have been at the heart of legislation for children with disabilities since: (1) 'zero reject' – all children with disabilities shall be provided a free and appropriate public education; (2) 'nondiscriminatory evaluation' – the tests used in diagnosis shall be appropriate to the child's cultural and linguistic background; (3) 'least restrictive environment' – children with disabilities must be educated with children without disabilities as much as possible; (4) 'due process' – a set of legal procedures to ensure the fairness of educational decisions; (5) 'parental participation' – parents must participate in the development of the 'individual education plan' of their child; and (6) 'Individual Education Program (IEP)' – each child shall have a plan designed to meet his/her needs.

Earlier in 1968 (PL 90-538), a small but influential demonstration program was passed, the Handicapped Children's Early Education Act, designed to illustrate best practices for infants and toddlers and preschoolers with disabilities. This program, initially funding 20 programs of various types of special needs young children, was well received and quickly expanded across the US. It provided the base for subsequent legislation for young children with disabilities.

A major addition to this effort for preschoolers was the Infants and Toddlers with Disabilities Act (PL 99-457) which tried to complete the work of the earlier Education for All Handicapped Children Act by providing services from birth on. Although each of the 50 states were given the option to participate or not in this act (since they would be paying most of the funds), all of the states eventually agreed to do so.

This law for infants and toddlers was substantially different in several respects from the earlier legislation. First, it stressed the importance of the family as a crucial part of the treatment program. The IEP became the IFSP, stressing family needs as well. There was less attention paid to formal diagnosis and more to the developmental level of the child, and an expectation of multidisciplinary planning and execution. All of the above legislative initiatives are now incorporated in IDEA (Individuals with Disability Education Act of 2004).

Intervention

One of the significant issues addressed in the last few decades is the extent to which early intervention could improve the development of young children, particularly children with special needs or limited environments.

A number of major projects were initiated in the 1960s and 1970s that identified children in the preschool years and continued to follow their progress for a decade or more. In each instance a quasi-experimental design was used with a treated and nontreated group whose progress could be followed periodically to attempt to answer the question whether intervention makes a difference. With minor variations, the results seem to be roughly similar in scope. There were modest improvements in academic performance and IQ scores and some gains in the social areas as well.

The Perry project at Ypsilanti, Michigan reported that, children who were provided a stimulating curriculum at ages 4 and 5 showed tendencies for better academic performance and social adjustment at teenage with a marked drop in incarcerations at that time compared to their untreated comparison peers. Such a finding increased the cost-benefit of such early programs dramatically because of the high cost of incarceration.

The minority high-risk children who comprised the Abecedarian project in Chapel Hill, North Carolina, displayed similar gains for its experimental group over two decades with their improving in their academic programs, with fewer retentions and fewer referrals to special education, and modest gains in achievement and IQ scores. The rate of incarceration at later ages did not change in the way that the Perry project had indicated.

The Milwaukee project showed gains for the experimental group in IQ scores from the mentally retarded range to normal or near normal. Their academic advancement continued to be spotty and their behaviors remained a problem at teenage.

A series of later intervention programs focusing on students with particular disabilities have resulted in the following summary statement:

1. Early intervention programs can give children with mild retardation developmental gains and they can often enter the regular classroom.
2. Speech and language therapy can be effective in eliminating a broad spectrum of communication disorders or minimizing their impact on later speech and language.
3. Deaf infants who are taught a manual communication system in the first years of life communicate better as adults than those taught later in life.
4. Social and behavioral problems can be modified with systematic intervention techniques.
5. Motor problems can be improved with systematic interventions.

Although the results of these interventions are modest, they are meaningful to the child and family and teacher.

Surveying this body of literature, Michael Guralnick announced that the answers to the first generation of questions have been established ("Could we intervene to the benefit of young children?" The answer was, "Yes"). The second generation of questions therefore became, "what are the factors that can be introduced that can maximize the gains that can be obtained?"

The nature of the intervention focuses on where the child is placed, what the content of the program is, and the nature of the instruction received. Inclusion, or the practice of including children with disabilities with children without disabilities, has been stressed in many preschool programs as a way of providing proper models of language and behavior. Guidelines called the 'developmentally appropriate practices' have been published by the National Association for the Education of Young Children to guide early childhood teachers. They include encouragement of exploration, parental involvement, and matching early childhood practices to the ways children learn. A great increase in the programmatic design in cognitive and social development for young children is currently underway, matching the political pre-kindergarten movement. In the last decade, the majority of states have established publicly supported pre-kindergarten programs for some or all preschool students in that state.

International Perspective

While most of the writing and research on this topic has been done in English-speaking countries, the issues of early childhood are faced by all cultures. In 1998, the Organization for Economic Co-operation and Development (OECD) undertook a survey of 12 countries on how they dealt with Early Childhood Education and Care (ECEC).

Each of the 12 countries embarked on a self-study and were visited by a multinational team for about 10–12 days for discussion, observations, etc. Ten of the nations in the study were European plus US and Australia. A report was made for each country and an overall report was compiled.

Table 1 Key elements of successful OECD policy

- A systematic-integrated approach to policy development and implementation
- A strong and equal partnership with the education system
- A universal approach to access, with particular attention to children in need of special support
- Substantial public investment in services and the infrastructure
- A participatory approach to quality improvement and assurance
- Appropriate training and working conditions for staff in all forms of provision
- Systematic attention to monitoring and data collection
- A stable framework and long term agenda for research and evaluation

Adapted from Organization for Economic Cooperation and Development (2001) Starting strong: Early childhood education and care. *Report of the Organization for Economic Cooperation and Development*, Paris, France.

Table 1 summarizes the essential components that the participants felt were necessary for an effective early childhood education and care effort in any nation. One of the key elements was the necessity of an integrated and coordinated policy from birth to school age with linkage to the school systems, families, social agencies, etc.

Curriculum frameworks that bridge preschool and school age programs are desirable as are joint in-service training for early childhood and primary school personnel to reinforce the continuity.

One goal has been to provide access to a quality place and an affordable cost for all children who need it. Maternal and paternal leave policies might be considered as an aid to support working parents.

The OECD report also stresses the value of inclusion in the programs for children with special needs whenever possible together with the trained staff and family support necessary to make such inclusive policies work. All of this requires substantial public investment in services and infrastructure to ensure equity in the delivery of services to low-income families.

The development of program and personnel standards is a way of gaining quality improvement and assurance to the public that their investments have been positively realized. These programs should have a system of monitoring that supports staff, parents, and children.

One of the more obvious needed elements is the appropriate training and working conditions for staff who should reflect the diversity of the community being served. Finally, an emphasis on continued research on how to enrich environments and improve curriculum and cope with children's special needs requires to be carried out.

These broad standards are widely recognized and accepted in the US but their execution requires scarce resources to be allocated and a degree of political acceptance that is not always in place.

Future Trends

There are a number of trends noted here that can be expected to continue in the near future. First, an increasing emphasis within special education on the birth to 5 years in attempts to identify early and remediate where appropriate. There is an increasing appreciation of the importance of the environmental–genetic interaction in young children that pushes this emphasis.

The approach to inclusion with children with disabilities should continue, particularly with younger children with disabilities and there will be additional attempts to include the educational needs of children with disabilities as an emphasis in personnel preparation of day care and school personnel. There should be an increased use of multidisciplinary teams in planning for children with special needs.

Identification should be anticipated to be done with multiple methods, particularly with the younger children. Observation and ratings will be added to the standard measures of assessment and technology innovation, particularly for those children with sensory or motor problems, should increase and become more sophisticated.

All of these trends depend upon the availability of financial resources which have been strained by increased demands by the military and other segments of American society.

See also: ADHD: Genetic Influences; Auditory Development and Hearing Disorders; Autism Spectrum Disorders; Brain Development; Down Syndrome; Fetal Alcohol Spectrum Disorders; Fragile X Syndrome; Lead Poisoning; Learning Disabilities.

Suggested Readings

Cryer D and Clifford R (eds.) (2003) *Early Childhood Education and Care in the USA.* Baltimore, MD: Paul H. Brookes.

Gallagher J (2006) *Driving Change in Special Education.* Baltimore, MD: Paul H. Brookes.

Guralnick M (1997) *The Effectiveness of Early Intervention.* Baltimore, MD: Paul H. Brookes.

Kirk S, Gallagher J, Anastasiow N, and Coleman M (2006) *Educating Exceptional Children,* 11th edn. Boston, MA: Houghton Mifflin Co.

Organization for Economic Cooperation and Development (2001) Starting strong: Early childhood education and care. *Report of the Organization for Economic Cooperation and Development,* Paris, France.

Speech Perception

G W McRoberts, Haskins Laboratories, New Haven, CT, USA

Glossary

Acoustic invariance – A single, unique acoustic form for a category of speech sounds; phonemes in speech generally lack acoustic invariance across speakers, or within speakers across phonetic context or rates of speech.

Acoustic resonance – Physical properties of closed chambers or cavities, which strengthen the intensity of some frequencies of sound, while dampening other frequencies.

Coarticulation – Simultaneous or overlapping movement of articulators during speech production.

Contingency – The dependency of one event on another; in infant perceptual testing, a temporal contingency is established between sound presentation and a behavior under the infant's control; for example, sound may be presented only when an infant fixates a visual target, and fixation must be maintained for continued sound presentation.

Discriminate – The ability to distinguish or notice the difference between two speech sounds.

Fundamental frequency or F0 – The base frequency of a voice, determined by the rate of opening and closing of the vocal folds; it is the physical correlate of the perceptual quality of pitch.

Habituation – A reduction in behavioral response to a repeated stimulus.

Infant-directed speech – A register or style of speech used when adults speak to infants (infant-directed speech, or IDS) or young children (child-directed speech, or CDS); differs from speech directed to other adults (adult-directed speech, or ADS) prosodically, linguistically, and in discourse features.

Morpheme – Minimal distinctive unit of grammar, of which there are two types: free morphemes can occur as separate words, and bound morphemes cannot occur separately, but must occur as affixes to words.

Phoneme – The smallest unit in the sound system of a language.

Pressure transducer – A device that converts variations in pressure into a voltage that can be measured; attached to a nipple, it allows the strength and frequency of infant sucking to be recorded and used to control sound presentation in a discrimination test.

Prosody – Variations in pitch, loudness, rhythm, and rate of speech.

Introduction

Speech perception refers to the ability to perceive linguistic structure in the acoustic speech signal. During the course of acquiring a native language infants must discover several levels of language structure in the speech signal, including phonemes (speech sounds) which are the smallest units of speech. Although phonemes have no meaning in themselves, they are the building blocks of higher-level, meaningful linguistic units or structures, including morphemes, words, phrases, and sentences. Each of the higher-level units are composed of units at the next lower level using rules that are specific to each language (i.e., morphology, grammar, or syntax). Thus, sentences are made up of phrases, phrases are composed of words, and words are made up of morphemes. Each of the meaningful units are composed of one or more phonemes. In a very real sense, the ability to perceive differences between and categorize phonemes provides the underlying capacity for the discovery of the higher levels of language structure in the speech signal. In this way, infants' speech perception abilities play a fundamental role in language acquisition. Although infant speech perception has traditionally focused on discrimination and categorization at the phoneme level, research over the past two decades has shown that infants are also beginning to become sensitive to a variety of higher-level linguistic structures in speech. This article outlines the current state of knowledge about how infants begin to perceive linguistic structure in speech during the first year of life, and the methods used to study infant speech perception.

Why Speech Perception Is Difficult

Infants' discovery of language structure in speech is not a trivial task because phonemes lack acoustic invariance. That is, the acoustic properties of specific phonemes in fluent speech can vary dramatically based on several factors. The acoustic characteristics of speech sounds that listeners use in perception directly reflect the acoustic resonance properties of the vocal tract, which in turn are determined by moment to moment changes in the shape of the vocal tract during speech production. In addition, because the size and shape of speakers' vocal tracts vary, so do the specific acoustic properties of any particular phoneme. The rate at which speech is produced also introduces variations in the characteristics of speech sounds. In particular, as the rate of speech increases, speakers' articulatory gestures (the movement patterns of articulators, such as the tongue tip) fail to reach the positions attained with slower rates of speech. This means that the vocal tract shape associated with a speech sound varies as a function of speech rate. Finally, although speech unfolds over time, speech sounds are not produced in a strictly serial manner. Rather, the production of speech sounds overlaps in time due to a phenomenon referred to as coarticulation. One example of coarticulation can be seen when the word 'two' is spoken. The vocal tract movements for the vowel /u/ in 'two' includes a lip movement called rounding. However, it is common to see this lip movement occur throughout the word. Lip movement occurs during the /t/ even though it is not a normal part of the production of that phoneme, nor is it necessary, since the word 'two' can be produced without lip rounding during the /t/. One result of this coarticulation is that the sound of the /t/ is different when the lips are rounded compared to when they are not. In general, because coarticulation is common in fluent speech production, the acoustic information that specifies any particular speech sound is highly context dependent. That is, the acoustic properties of speech sounds can depend significantly on the preceding and following speech sounds. These, and other, sources of variation in the speech signal mean that there is no absolute acoustic signature (acoustic invariance) for any speech sound. In language acquisition, this lack of invariance in the acoustic specification of speech sounds is a complicating factor in speech perception. Additionally, it must also complicate the development of speech production, because infants' and young children's vocal tracts cannot physically produce many of the specific acoustic patterns they hear in adult speech.

Methodologies for Studying Infant Speech Perception

The limited behavioral repertoire of infants kept their ability to perceive speech unstudied until appropriate methods were developed beginning in the late 1970s. Unlike the case of vision, where observable behaviors, such as direction of eye gaze, are reliable indicators of perception, there is no overt behavior that indicates listening. Researchers interested in infants' auditory and speech perception capabilities had to develop methods that used behaviors infants had under their control as indirect measures of perception. For example, by coupling the presentation of speech (or other sounds) to behaviors that infants can control, such as fixating a visual target or sucking at a certain rate or pressure, these behaviors can be used as indices of infants' interest in the sounds. When infants look at a visual target more to make one sound play longer than another, it is inferred that the greater looking is related to more interest in the sound. Thus, the duration of looking (or the amount of sucking) is used as an index of infant listening or attention to the sounds. Procedures that use contingencies between infant behavior and sound presentation are sometimes referred to as 'infant-controlled' procedures because the infant controls the duration of sound presentation on each trial. There are other procedures used to study infants' speech perception that do not use contingencies, and thus are not infant controlled. However, these procedures still require infants to produce an observable behavior, such as turning their head in a particular direction to either choose between two sounds, or to indicate they heard a change in the sound that was playing.

The focus of this article is on two aspects of infant speech perception: (1) infants' ability to discriminate between different speech sounds or categories of speech sounds; (2) infants' preference to listen to some forms of speech or speech with specific types of structure over others. Both sucking and gaze patterns have been used as behavioral indices in each of these approaches to infant speech perception. The next section describes several approaches to infant speech sound discrimination. A later section describes infant speech preference procedures and their uses in studying the development of speech perception.

Infant Speech Discrimination Procedures

Infants' ability to discriminate or categorize speech sounds has often been studied using procedures that involve habituation. These procedures are typically divided into two phases, habituation and test. Early studies of infant speech perception exploited infants' sucking reflex as a response measure in the high-amplitude sucking (HAS) procedure. In this procedure, infants suck on a non-nutritive nipple attached to a pressure transducer, which measured the amplitude of the sucking. Spontaneous sucking levels without sound presentation are measured during an initial period to establish each infants' baseline sucking amplitude. After the baseline is established, the habituation stimulus is presented contingent on the infants maintaining a sucking amplitude greater than the mean of the baseline period. More recent studies have tended to use infants' gaze as a response measure. In this case, infants are presented with a simple image, such as a checkerboard, as a visual target. When the infant fixates the target, the habituation stimulus is presented contingent on the infant maintaining fixation. When the infant breaks fixation for a period greater than 1 or 2 s, stimulus presentation stops and the trial ends.

For both sucking and gaze measures, a criterion is used to determine when infants have habituated. When the behavioral response is sucking, the criterion is typically a decline in the sucking rate by 20% for two consecutive minutes. When gaze is the behavioral response, the habituation criterion is usually set at 50% of average looking on the first two trials, or the two longest trials. Habituation occurs when the behavioral response is below the criterion (e.g., 50% of the average of the first two trials) on two consecutive trials. Once the behavioral response indicates habituation, the habituation stimulus is changed to the test stimulus on the subsequent trial.

Consider an example in which a researcher wishes to test infants' ability to discriminate between two syllables differing in their initial consonant, such as [ba] and [pa], using the visual habituation procedure. During the habituation phase, infants would be presented with either a single token or multiple tokens of the habituation stimulus (e.g., [ba]) repeated at a short interval (e.g., 500 ms). When the infant fixates the visual target, the habituation stimulus is presented. Typically, a trial continues until the infant stops the target behavior for a specified duration (e.g., looks away for longer than 1 s) or the trial reaches a maximum time (e.g., 20 s). Because stimulus presentation is contingent on the infant maintaining fixation, the duration of the trial is taken as an index of interest in the stimulus being presented. Over several trials the infant becomes more familiar with the stimulus and habituation occurs, resulting in less looking at the visual target. The looking time on each trial is compared to the predetermined habituation criterion. When the criterion is reached on consecutive trials, the test phase begins and the test stimulus (e.g., [pa]) is presented on the next trial. The number of trials in the test phase varies. Often only two or three trials are presented, but testing can also continue until the infant is habituated to criterion on the test stimulus.

Usually 18–24 infants are tested per age group in discrimination experiments. Mean looking times for the last two habituation trials and the test trials are calculated for each group of infants. If infants notice the difference between the habituation stimulus and the test stimulus, the expectation is that they will look (or suck) more to hear the novel (unhabituated) stimulus. An increase in looking during the test phase relative to the end of the habituation phase indicates response recovery or dishabituation. To establish that discrimination did or did not occur, a comparison is made between the last two trials from the habituation phase and the first two trials from the test phase. If looking during the test phase is statistically greater than during the last trials of the habituation phase, discrimination is inferred. If the difference is not statistically different, failure to discriminate is inferred. Because infants can exhibit some degree of spontaneous recovery after several short stimulus presentations, such as the final trials of the habituation phase, a no-change control group is often employed. Infants in the control group continue to hear the same stimulus after reaching habituation criterion. Thus a second important comparison is between the test trials of infants in the test and control groups. To rule out the possibility that infants in the test group exhibited spontaneous recovery, their looking times in the test phase must be statistically greater than the no-change control group, as well as their own final habituation trials.

The visually reinforced head turn (VRHT) procedure differs from the HAS and infant gaze procedures in that it does not involve habituation and is not infant controlled. Rather, it requires infants to notice a sound change in a continuous stream of recurring syllables and look toward a visual reinforcer within a brief time window after the sound change. This procedure typically involves two sessions. In the first session, infants are trained on the procedure, and in a second session they are tested on the stimulus for comparison of interest. During the training phase, a visual reinforcer, usually an animated toy in a smoked plexiglass box, is used to train infants to produce a head turn when a change occurs in a repeated background sound (e.g., from a high tone to a low tone). During training, the visual reinforcer is activated just prior to a sound change. Over the course of training, the interval between the sound change and activation of the reinforcer is reduced and finally reversed, so that activation occurs after the sound change. When the infant reliably anticipates activation of the reinforcer by turning toward the reinforcer after a sound change, but before the reinforcer is activated, the testing phase can begin with the stimuli of interest. During a second session, usually on a separate day, a procedure refresher may occur prior to testing to establish that the infant still looks to the reinforcer within a brief time window after the sound change. Testing then occurs on the stimulus comparison of interest. During testing, the infant is distracted from the visual reinforcer by a research assistant displaying an interesting object. This reduces false positive responses, in which the infant looks to the reinforcer when no sound change has occurred.

Each of these procedures has both advantages and disadvantages. The habituation approach works well from the neonatal period into the second year of life. However, the sucking measure works best with infants up to 4-months of age, after which infants are prone to rejecting the nipple. The visual fixation method works well across a wide range of infant ages and is now the generally accepted method of choice. The VRHT procedure requires adequate head, neck, and postural control from the infant, and therefore does not work well with infants younger than about 4 months. In addition, some subjects are usually lost because they do not reach criterion during the training phase. However, this procedure has the advantage of providing reliable data for individual infants, while the habituation procedures can only be used for group comparisons. Although it may be possible to modify habituation procedures to provide individual data, attempts to do so have not proved successful at this time.

Infants' Phonetic Discrimination

In order to understand important issues involved in the study of infant speech perception, it is helpful to have a bit of background on how speech sounds are made and classified. Speech sounds are produced by complex coordinated interactions among the components of the vocal tract. During speech production, air from the lungs induces the vocal folds to vibrate, producing a buzz-like sound source that is filtered by passing through several cavities in the vocal tract, including the pharyngeal, oral, and nasal cavities. Speech production involves movement of the vocal tract articulators, including the tongue, velum, and lips, which change the sizes and shapes of the cavities, altering their resonance properties. It is the resonance properties of these cavities that filter the sound source and account for most of the differences in the sounds used in speech.

Phonetics, the study of how speech is produced and perceived, generally distinguishes between two classes of phonemes, consonants and vowels. One basis for this distinction is related to differences in how these sounds are produced. Vowels are produced with a relatively open and unobstructed vocal tract, which allows air and sound to move freely through the vocal tract. Changes in the height and front–back position of the tongue, along with rounding or spreading of the lips, produce most of the differences in vowels in English. Other languages also distinguish vowels based on whether air flows only through the oral cavity, or through the nasal cavity, which results in a nasalized sound.

In contrast to vowels, consonants are produced by introducing a constriction of the airflow. Consonants can be classified by the type and location of the vocal tract constriction used in their production. Many types of constrictions, or manners of articulation, are used in languages around the world. The most common types involve a complete closure or one of several kinds of partial closure. Stop consonants (e.g., /p/ or /d/), are produced with a full closure of the vocal tract that results in a complete stoppage of air flow, whereas fricatives (e.g., /s/) involve a less-than-complete degree of constriction that results in a turbulent air flow. There are several other manners of articulation, some of which are not used in English. Two manners of articulation not used in English are click and ejective. Clicks are used in Zulu and some related languages in Southern Africa. Production of clicks involves a suction type closure and release. Another common manner of articulation is called ejective. Ejectives are produced using a closure of the vocal tract in the mouth and also squeezing the vocal folds together. Air that is trapped between the vocal tract closure and vocal folds is compressed by moving the larynx upward. When the closure in the oral cavity is released, the built-up air pressure is released with a distinctive sound.

Each manner of articulation can be produced at various places within the vocal tract and can involve the tongue, lips, teeth, hard and soft palate, as well as other parts of the vocal tract. One common constriction location involves a closure at the lips, and is referred to as bilabial. Examples of other common closures involve the tongue and any of several locations along the roof of the mouth, including the teeth (interdental), the ridge behind the teeth (alveolar), the hard palate (palatal), or the soft palate (velar).

Consonants are also classified as being either voiced or voiceless. Voiced means vocal fold vibration occurs during the constriction or constriction release. This contrasts with voiceless (or unvoiced) consonants, where vocal fold vibration begins some time after the constriction is released. The difference in when the vocal folds begin to vibrate is referred to as voice onset time (VOT), or the time from when the constriction is released until the vocal folds begin to vibrate. In English, voiced consonants have a VOT from about 0 to 40 ms, meaning the onset of vocal fold vibration can be simultaneous with, or up to 40 ms after, release of the closure or constriction (e.g., /b/ or /z/). In unvoiced consonants, vocal fold vibration begins from about 60 to 100 ms after the constriction is released (e.g., /p/ or /s/). Thus, the consonant inventory of a language is dependent on which combinations of articulatory features, including voicing, manner of articulation, and places of articulation, are used. The phoneme inventory of languages differ substantially in the number of vowels and consonants that are used. Anyone acquiring a language must be able to distinguish among the phonemes, as well as produce them.

Infants' Discrimination of Phonemes

Early research on infant speech perception focused mainly on the ability of young (e.g., 1–6 month old), English-learning infants to categorize and discriminate between pairs of speech sounds from the phonetic inventory of English. These early studies established that young infants are very good at discriminating a wide variety of speech sounds. Later research investigated how infants perceive speech sounds that do not occur in their native language, the discrimination of longer segments of speech, and the role of visual information in infants' speech perception.

In 1971, Peter Eimas and colleagues reported the first study of infant speech perception. This study used the HAS method described previously to show that infants between 1 and 4 months of age were able to discriminate between two stop consonants that differed in VOT ([ba-pa]). Additional studies by Eimas and others investigated infants' discrimination of sounds differing in place of articulation. These studies showed infants discriminated [ba]-[ga], [bae]-[dae], [fa]-[øa], [va]-[øa], and [ma]-[na]. Infants were also shown to discriminate between sounds that differ in the manner of articulation, including [ra]-[la], [ba]-[wa], and [ba]-[ma].

After several early studies demonstrated that infants could discriminate various consonant contrasts, other researchers investigated infants' perception of vowels. These studies showed that 1–4-month-old infants also discriminate among a variety of vowels, including [a]-[i] (e.g., hod vs. hid), [i]-[I] (e.g., hid vs. heed), [a]-[aw] (e.g., hod vs. hawed). Thus young infants also appear to be very good at discriminating among vowels. As noted earlier, the lack of acoustic invariance in speech sounds is a potential problem in discrimination, since the same sound produced by different talkers will have different acoustic characteristics. Several experiments by Patricia Kuhl and colleagues have shown that infants are able to categorize and discriminate among vowels, even when they are spoken by different speakers (e.g., males and females), or have irrelevant acoustic variation (e.g., pitch contour).

Overall, these early studies established that young infants up to about 6 months of age are able to perceive the differences between consonants that differed along articulatory dimensions including VOT, place of articulation, and manner of articulation, as well as discriminate between many vowels. Initially, infants' discrimination of consonants was tested with syllables that differed in their initial consonants (e.g., [ba]-[pa]). Other studies showed that infants could also perceive differences between syllables that differed in their final consonants, or when consonants were between two vowels, and in multisyllable contexts. For example, young infants were shown to discriminate consonants in syllable-final position (e.g., pat vs. pad), between two vowels (e.g., [aba] vs. [apa]), and in two-syllable sequences (daba vs. daga). In order to more closely approximate natural speech, discrimination of consonants embedded in longer stretches of speech was also investigated. In these studies, 1–4-month-old infants were shown to discriminate between sequences of three syllables when only a single consonant differed (e.g., [marana] vs. [malana]).

Categorical Perception

As noted earlier, the acoustic properties of the same speech sound can vary significantly when produced by different speakers, or by the same speaker in different phonetic contexts. Faced with this variation, human perceivers 'categorize' speech sounds. That is, they are able to ignore irrelevant acoustic variation and focus on the properties that identify a phoneme as a member of a specific speech sound category. Because attention is focused on similarities among items of the same category, discrimination of different tokens or versions of a speech sound that are within a single category is usually difficult compared to speech sounds that are from different phonetic categories. That is, two spoken versions of [ba] sound more alike and are thus more difficult to discriminate than a [ba] and a [pa].

The sounds [ba] and [pa] in English differ in many ways, but one of most prominent differences is VOT. When producing [ba], the vocal folds begin to vibrate almost simultaneously with the opening of the lips, whereas with [pa] there is a noticeable lag in the onset of vocal fold vibration. It is possible to produce a VOT continuum of equal steps (e.g., 10 ms) from 0 (i.e., vocal fold vibration simultaneous with lip opening) to 80 ms (i.e., vocal fold vibration starts 80 ms after lip opening). On such a continuum, the endpoints (i.e., 0 and 80 ms) are heard clearly as [ba] and [pa], respectively. When native English-speaking adults are asked to label each token from the continuum, they typically show a rather abrupt shift from one category to another rather than a gradual change. That is, they may label items up to 40 ms as [ba], and items over 60 ms as [pa], while items at 50 ms might be labeled as [ba] half the time and [pa] half the time. Thus, a category boundary appears to exist between 40 and 60 ms. If asked to discriminate between pairs of sounds at 20 ms intervals along the continuum, it will be difficult to distinguish between two tokens on the same side of the category boundary, such as +10 and +30 ms, but easy to discriminate tokens that are from different sides of the boundary, such as +40 and +60. In other words, discrimination is poor within categories (e.g., two [pa]'s or two [ba]'s), but good when the pairs cross a category boundary (i.e., one [ba] and one [pa]), even when the physical difference between the items in the two pairs is equal. The degree to which native-language phonemes are perceived categorically varies. For example, stop consonants are usually perceived very categorically, while vowels are perceived less categorically.

Early studies showing young infants' ability to discriminate among various speech sounds were often followed by studies of categorical perception of the same sounds. These studies suggest that young infants, like adults, have categorical perception of consonants that differ in VOT, place of articulation, and manner of articulation. However, it should be noted that the procedures for establishing categorical perception are necessarily somewhat different for adults and infants, because infants are unable to directly identify speech sounds. Thus, the conclusion that infants perceive speech categorically relies on results showing that infants have more difficulty discriminating items that are within the adult categories than items that fall across category boundaries.

Audio-Visual Speech Perception

Speech is usually considered to be an acoustic event, and speech perception is typically seen as perceiving the acoustic structure of speech. However, there is strong evidence that under some circumstances visual information from the face of a speaker can influence the perception of speech. Two kinds of influences of visual speech information have been studied in infants. In some studies infants have been shown to look longer at a video of a speaking face that matches a speech sound than at a face that is mismatched. For example, 6-month-old infants have been shown to look longer at a matching face for some consonant–vowel syllables. Four-month-old infants have been shown to look more to a face that matches some vowels from the native language, and perhaps non-native vowels. Some studies suggest the ability to match visual and acoustic speech information may be present at birth or very early in the postnatal period.

Another way visual information can influence speech perception is to alter how speech sounds are perceived. When a video of a speaker's face saying [ba] is combined with audio [ga], many (though not all) adults and children perceive [da] or [tha]. Thus, the auditory and visual information have been integrated to form a novel percept. Other combinations are also possible. This phenomenon was first demonstrated by Harry McGurk and John MacDonald in 1976, and is referred to as the McGurk Effect.

A fascinating study by Larry Rosenblum and colleagues demonstrated that 5-month-old infants also appear to show the McGurk Effect. Rosenblum and colleagues habituated infants with video clips that contained a matched face (visual) and voice (auditory) saying [va], and then tested them on three kinds of trials that paired different auditory information with the original visual [va]: (1) the original auditory [va]; (2) auditory [ba]; and (3) auditory [da]. Infants differed in the rate at which they habituated to the three test stimuli. They were slower to habituate to audio [da] paired with visual [va] (perceived as [da] by adults) than when either auditory [va] or [ba] was paired with the visual [va] (both perceived as [va] by adults). These results suggest that the infants perceived the auditory [da] with visual [va] as different from either of the other two. That is, it appears the infants heard the visual [va] and auditory [da] as something other than [va], just as adults do, though it is unclear from these results that they heard the same [da] that adults hear. Other studies have confirmed these results in showing that infants appear to be susceptible to the McGurk Effect. Thus, this form of auditory–visual speech perception appears to emerge early in infancy. However, recent studies suggest that there may be large individual differences in infants' integration of auditory and visual information for speech, just as there are for adults.

Infants' Perception of Non-Native Speech Sounds

The early studies of infant speech perception clearly demonstrated that infants are quite adept at discriminating and categorizing a wide range of speech sounds. As a wider range of phoneme contrasts, language environments, and ages of infants were studied, it became clear that infants did not always discriminate all speech contrasts. For example, several studies suggest that infants have difficulty distinguishing between some fricative sounds, and even some vowel contrasts that are present in their native language. Other studies show that some speech contrasts were discriminated by infants from one language environment but not another. Still other studies clearly show that infants can discriminate between some speech sounds not present in their ambient language environment which adult speakers of their native language could not discriminate. Thus, the accumulating evidence suggested that the speech perception abilities of young infants must eventually become attuned to their native language. Beginning in the 1980s, the issue of how infant speech perception develops from a language-general ability that prepares infants to acquire any language to a language-specific ability became a central theme of research.

In a seminal series of experiments, Janet Werker and colleagues showed that infants' attunement to their ambient language environment begins by the end of the first year of life. Werker and colleagues tested English-learning infants between 6 and 12 months of age on a native-language phonetic contrasts ([ba] vs. [da]), as well as two non-native phonetic contrasts that adult and child native-English speakers could not discriminate. One of the non-native contrasts included two stop-consonants from Hindi. The phonemes were [ta], with a dental place of articulation (similar to English [ta]), and [ṭa] which has a more posterior place of articulation referred to as retroflex. Also included was a velar-uvular ejective contrast, [k'ae] vs. [q'ae], from the Native American language Nthlakapmx (also referred to as Puget Salish). The 6–8-month-old English-learning infants discriminated all three contrasts. However, the 8–10-month-olds discriminated the non-native sounds less well than the younger infants, and the 10–12-month-olds were generally unable to distinguish the non-native sounds. Both groups of older infants retained the ability to discriminate the native-language [ba]-[da] contrast. This showed that infants' sensitivity to at least some non-native speech contrasts declines significantly by 10–12 months.

These findings initially seemed to suggest that the decline in discriminability was due to a lack of experience with the speech sounds. That is, while young infants could discriminate speech sounds that did not occur in their native language, exposure or experience with the speech sounds seemed to be necessary to maintain that ability.

However, research by Catherine Best and colleagues showed that the decline in perceptual sensitivity at 10–12 months only occurred for some non-native speech sounds. In one study, English-learning infants from 6 to 14 months of age, and English-speaking adults were tested on their ability to discriminate click contrasts from the Zulu language. The Zulu click sounds are very different from anything in the inventory of English speech sounds, and thus represent an example of speech sounds that English-learning infants and English-speaking adults would never experience in a speech context. The results of this study showed that native English-speaking adults were able to discriminate among several click consonant contrasts. Both older and younger infants were tested on a subset of the clicks the adults discriminated and were also able to discriminate the clicks. Thus, while it seems clear that exposure to language influences the development of speech perception, the results with the Zulu clicks demonstrated convincingly that it is not necessary to have experience with specific speech sounds in order to be able to continue discriminating them. The results of this study reframed the issue of the development of speech perception to why discrimination of some non-native speech sounds declines, while others continue to be well discriminated.

Best and colleagues have investigated this question in a series of studies, in which the discrimination abilities of younger and older infants were compared to that of adults on a variety of non-native speech contrasts. In these studies, the discrimination pattern for adults is usually established first, followed by infant tests. To establish the pattern of discrimination ability, each infant is usually tested three times, using two non-native phonetic contrasts, and a native-language contrast. Across several studies, English-learning infants and English-speaking adults have been tested on a wide variety of non-native sounds, including several additional Zulu contrasts (lateral voiced-voiceless fricatives [ɮa]-[ɬa]; voiceless aspirated velar stop-ejective [k'a]-[k'a]; plosive-implosive bilabial stop [b]-[ɓ]), a bilabial-alveolar ejective distinction from Tigrinya (Ethiopian) ([p'a]-[t'a]), the Nthlakapmx velar-uvular ejective contrast [k'ae] versus [q'ae] from Werker's earlier study, as well as English bilabial-alveolar stop consonants [ba]-[da] and English alveolar voiced-voiceless fricatives [sa]-[za]. Younger infants discriminated all of the non-native contrasts. Older infants discriminated the clicks and fricatives from Zulu, the Tigrinya ejectives, and the stop-consonants and fricatives from English. They failed to discriminate the Nthlakapmx velar-uvular ejective contrast, confirming Werker's earlier results. However, even among the contrasts that were discriminated at both ages, the younger infants performed better than older infants on all tests except the Tigrinya [p'a]-[t'a] and the English [ba]-[da], which were discriminated equally well at both ages.

Infants' perception of non-native vowels has been studied less than non-native consonants. However, the studies that have been done suggest the development of vowel perception proceeds differently from the pattern seen for consonants. One difference is that the influence of the native-language environment on vowel perception may occur as early as 6 months of age, whereas similar effects for consonants do not emerge until 10–12 months.

In addition, there appear to be directional asymmetries in vowel discrimination that are not commonly reported with consonants (but may nonetheless exist). These asymmetries reflect the fact that infants discriminate better when they are habituated to one vowel (e.g., vowel A) and tested on a second vowel (e.g., vowel B), than when habituated to vowel B and tested on vowel A. As described earlier, different English vowels are produced by changing the height and front–back position of the tongue, as well as rounding, protruding, or spreading the lips. A vowel space can be defined based on the extremes of tongue and lip positions. For example, for /i/ (as in 'heed') the tongue is high and to the front of the oral cavity, and the lips are spread. The vowel /u/ (as in 'who'd') is produced with the tongue high and to the back of the oral cavity, with the lips rounded and protruded. The vowels /ae/ (as in 'had') and /a/(as in 'hod') are produced with the tongue low (on the floor of the oral cavity), and more to the front and back of the oral cavity, respectively. Other vowels are produced with less extreme positions. The vowels /i/, /u/, /ae/, and /a/ define the limits of the English vowel space, and are thus considered most peripheral (i.e., nearest the periphery) in the space. There is some evidence that the asymmetries in vowel discrimination are related to the degree of peripherality within this vowel space. Vowels that are more peripheral in the space appear to act as reference points, so that discrimination is easier when infants are habituated to vowels that are less peripheral in the space and then tested on more peripheral vowels.

Several theoretical models have been proposed to account for the results of infant non-native speech perception studies. The model that most adequately accounts for the results, especially with non-native consonants, is Catherine Best's perceptual assimilation model (PAM). This model assumes listeners hear non-native speech sounds in terms of their native-language phonetic categories whenever possible. This is called perceptual assimilation. Within PAM, listeners can assimilate non-native phoneme contrasts into their native categories in several ways. Two contrasting non-native speech sounds can: (1) be assimilated into a single native-language category (single category, or SC assimilation); (2) be assimilated into two different native-language phonetic categories (two category, or TC assimilation); (3) be assimilated into two native-language categories, but with different degrees of goodness (category goodness, or CG assimilation); and (4) fail to be assimilated into any native-language category (nonassimilable, or NA). Based on the earlier discussion of categorical perception, it should be clear that discrimination for SC assimilation will be very difficult (at or near chance levels) under most circumstances, but discrimination will be quite easy (near ceiling levels) in TC assimilation. In the case of CG assimilation, discrimination is intermediate between SC and TC. Finally, when non-native speech sounds are so different from any native-language phoneme that assimilation does not occur (NA), discrimination will be very good because the sounds will be perceived as nonlinguistic, allowing perceivers to compare them on acoustic dimensions that would be irrelevant or unavailable in phonetic perception. Predictions from PAM about the degree of discriminability of non-native sounds (especially consonants) have been tested extensively with English-speaking adults, who have also provided descriptions of their assimilations of non-native phonemes into native-language categories. In general, the predictions have been upheld. Although older infants often show the same pattern of discrimination as adults, Best and colleagues believe that infants' speech sound categories are not fully developed by the end of the first year. Rather, they suggest that infants' perception of speech sounds becomes increasingly sensitive to information about how the sounds are produced (i.e., phonetic or articulatory information). Thus, near the end of the first year of life, infants are beginning to perceive many, but not all, of the details that specify how native-language speech sounds are produced. Therefore, their pattern of discrimination (assimilation) of non-native speech sounds becomes increasingly adult like, but further development occurs as access to more fine-grained detail is achieved through infancy and into early childhood.

In conjunction with earlier studies, research on the perception of non-native phonemes shows that infants enter the world as 'language-general' speech perceivers, able to discriminate among most of the speech sounds of the world's languages, and over the first year or so of life, become attuned to many of the specifics of their language environment to become 'language-specific' speech perceivers.

Speech Preferences in Infancy

The research on phonetic discrimination abilities provides clear evidence of infants' underlying speech perception capabilities, as well as the timeline of some of the developmental processes involved in acquiring a native-language phonology. The development of infants' speech perception from language general to language specific over the course of the first year focuses attention on the early influence of the ambient language environment on language development. One question of interest is whether infants attend preferentially to some aspects of the language environment over others. The auditory preference procedure has been used to address this question. Whereas discrimination procedures assess infants' ability to detect differences between smaller units of speech, such as phonemes or syllables, preference procedures allow researchers to study how infants respond to longer samples of speech that more realistically approximate what they normally hear. As a result, studies of infant speech preferences have taken a significant role in research on the development of speech perception and language development. Early studies of speech preferences focused on infants' preference to listen to speech over nonspeech sounds, and infant-directed speech (IDS), or child-directed speech (CDS) over adult-directed speech (ADS). More recent studies have used speech preferences to investigate the development of sensitivity to various aspects of native-language structure in speech.

Auditory and Speech Preference Procedures

Auditory preferences in infants were first demonstrated in 1968 by Bernard Freidlander. The procedure involved an apparatus with two large knobs, a speaker, and an activity recorder. By manipulating the knobs, infants could activate one of two recorded audio samples. The activity recorder collected the amount of time each sample was played. Infants aged 11–15 months showed a preference by listening more to some sounds, such as their mothers' voice, more than other sounds, such as simple musical passages. Friedlander's apparatus was later modified for use with younger, less mobile infants. A related procedure was developed for use with young infants by Anne Fernald. Fernald's procedure required only a head-turn response to activate sounds that played from speakers located to the infant's right or left. No contingency was required to continue sound presentation. Eventually, infant-controlled variants were developed using both gaze and sucking.

Two versions of the auditory preference procedure are in common use today. Both are infant-controlled procedures that use gaze as the behavioral measure. In one variant, a single visual target is located directly in front of the infant (central fixation preference). The other approach is a direct descendent of Fernald's procedure, and requires a head turn to one of two visual targets located on the infant's right or left (head-turn preference). In the central fixation procedure, infants fixate a centrally presented visual target, such as a checkerboard. Stimulus sounds are played through a speaker located directly below the visual target. Sound presentation on each trial is contingent on the infant maintaining fixation of the target. When fixation is broken for more than 1 or 2 s, the sound ends, the visual target is removed, and the trial ends. After a brief delay, the visual target returns, signaling the availability of the next trial.

The head-turn procedure is somewhat more complicated than the central fixation procedure. It uses two speakers, each 90° to the infants' right and left. Small red lights are usually placed near the speakers, and directly in front of the infant. A test typically begins with several presentations of stimuli from each speaker to familiarize infants with the procedure and train them to turn toward the lateralized lights and speakers in order to initiate a trial. Trials begin with the central red light flashing. When the infant orients to the flashing light, it is extinguished and one of the lateral lights blinks to indicate a stimulus is available. Stimulus types can be associated with a specific side, or can be randomized to either side. Infants are required to make a criterial head turn (e.g., at least 45°) to initiate a trial, and they must maintain the head turn to continue sound presentation on each trial.

Both procedures are infant controlled, and typically use 12 trials, evenly divided between two types of speech presented on alternate or randomized trials. As in the discrimination procedures discussed previously, fixation time on each trial is used as an index of interest or listening. Fixation times are averaged across trials of each stimulus type, resulting in a mean for each stimulus type.

While both procedures are in current use, the central fixation procedure seems to have several advantages over the head-turn procedure: (1) it eliminates the effects of lateral biases evident in some infants; (2) it does not require training or familiarizing infants with head turning to initiate trials; and (3) observers are not required to judge whether infants maintain a sufficient degree of head turn to continue a trial.

Infants' Speech Preferences

The first study to address young infants' speech preferences was performed by Anne Fernald, who investigated 4-month-old infants' listening preference for IDS by female speakers compared to speech by the same speakers to another adult, or ADS. Fernald used the noncontingent head-turn procedure described earlier. Her results showed that infants turned to the side that activated the IDS speech samples more often than the ADS speech samples. In other studies infants have showed more positive affect when listening to IDS than ADS.

Other studies have explored a variety of aspects of infants' preference for IDS over ADS. For example, it appears that infants' preference for IDS is present from very early in the postnatal period. And while some studies suggested that the preference for IDS might decline or disappear in older infants, more recent studies show that infants as old as 16 months of age continue to show a preference for IDS over ADS. Still other studies have demonstrated that infants will attend to IDS in an unfamiliar language over ADS from the same language, and also prefer male speakers' IDS over the same speakers' ADS.

The acoustic basis for infants' preference for IDS over ADS has been somewhat in dispute. One early study showed that 4-month-old infants listened more to sine-wave analogs of the F0 contours of IDS than ADS, but not to sine-wave analogs of the amplitude envelope or temporal structure of IDS. Thus it appeared that the higher F0, wider F0 range, and expanded intonation contours typical of IDS were the acoustic basis of infants' preference. Several recent studies have noted that early studies of IDS preference often confounded the prosody of IDS with affect, because IDS typically contains expressions of positive emotion. These studies have shown that IDS prosody by itself, in the absence of expressions of positive affect, is not sufficient to result in a preference by infants at 6 months of age. In addition, when prosodic factors such as F0 range are controlled, infants prefer to listen to ADS containing positive affect over IDS that does not contain positive affect. Thus, it appears that by 6 months of age, infants may be attending more to the positive affective expressiveness of IDS, even if other prosodic characteristics of IDS are absent. Nonetheless, in spontaneous interactions with infants, the typical prosodic characteristics of IDS, including higher F0 and wider F0 range, will normally be highly correlated with positive affect.

Beyond establishing infants' preference to listen to IDS over ADS, auditory preference procedures have been used to study infants' detection of a wide variety of linguistic structures in speech, such as patterns of lexical stress (e.g., pres'-ent vs. pres-ent'), locating words in sentences, native-language phonotactics (the legal sound patterns that can make words in a language), and repeated utterances. These studies have provided important insights into how infants become attuned to the properties of their native language. One example is infants' ability to perceive differences between languages based on prosodic patterns. Several studies have shown that very young infants will listen longer to speech from languages that have rhythmic patterns that are similar to their ambient language (e.g., French) over languages with different prosodic patterns (e.g., Russian). However, not until 6 months do they show a preference for their own language over other languages with similar prosodic structure (e.g., English vs. Dutch).

Another use of the preference procedure is to pair it with familiarization to stimuli for which infants initially have no preference. Peter Jusczyk and Richard Aslin used this procedure in a landmark study showing that by 7.5 months of age, infants begin to segment words from fluent speech. In their initial study, infants were familiarized with a repeated list of single words spoken in isolation (either cup or bike). The infants were then tested for a listening preference with sentences containing the familiarized word and similar sentences containing the unfamiliar word. Although 6-month-old infants showed no preference, 7.5-month-old infants had a preference for the sentences containing the familiarized word. Follow-up studies reversed the procedure, familiarizing the infants with the sentences that contained the word, and then testing on the familiarized word repeated in isolation vs. the unfamiliar word. The outcome confirmed the initial results, showing that infants listened longer to the familiarized words. Additional studies showed that infants failed to prefer words that differed from the familiarized target by one phoneme, such as 'gike' instead of 'bike'. Taken together, these results provide evidence that infants are able to remember phonetic strings that occur in running speech soon after the middle of their first year of life.

See also: Grammar; Language Development: Overview; Preverbal Development and Speech Perception; Semantic Development.

Suggested Readings

Best CT (1995) A direct realist perspective on cross-language speech perception. In: Strange W and Jenkins JJ (eds.) *Cross-Language Speech Perception*, pp. 171–204. Timonium, MD: York Press.

Best CT and McRoberts GW (2003) Infant perception of non-native consonant contrasts that adults assimilate in different ways. *Language and Speech* 46: 183–216.

Eimas PD, Jusczyk P, and Vigorito J (1971) Speech perception in infants. *Science* 171: 303–306.

Fernald A (1992) Maternal vocalizations to infants as biologically relevant signals: An evolutionary perspective. In: Barkow JH, Cosmides L, and Tooby J (eds.) *The Adapted Mind: Evolutionary Psychology and the Generation of Culture*, pp. 391–428. Oxford: Oxford University Press.

Jusczyk P (1997) *The Discovery of Spoken Language*. Cambridge, MA: MIT Press.

Jusczyk P and Aslin RN (1995) Infants' detection of sound patterns of words in fluent speech. *Cognitive Psychology* 29: 1–23.

Kuhl PK and Melzoff AN (1984) The intermodal representation of speech in infants. *Infant Behavior and Development* 7: 361–381.

Polka L and Bohn O (2003) Asymmetries in vowel perception. *Speech Communication* 41: 221–231.

Rosenblum LD, Schmuckler MA, and Johnson JA (1997) The McGurk effect in infants. *Perception and Psychophysics* 59: 347–357.

Werker J and Tees RC (1984) Cross-language speech perception: Evidence for perceptual reorganization during the first year. *Infant Behavior and Development* 7: 49–63.

Stereotypies

J T Rapp, St. Cloud State University, St. Cloud, MN, USA
J Pinkston and S Fowler, University of Kansas, Lawrence, KS, USA

Glossary

Automatic reinforcement – A type of reinforcement that is directly produced by one's engagement in a behavior; it does not require consequences from another individual.

Basal ganglia – A set of subcortical regions of the brain important in the sequencing and control of voluntary movement. It is composed of four main structures: (1) the striatum, (2) the subthalamic nucleus, (3) the globus pallidus, and (4) the substantia nigra. Also called the extrapyrimidal motor system.

Environmental enrichment – An arrangement wherein an organism's environment contains an abundance of activities and modalities of stimulation with which the organism can interact.

Focused stereotypy – Primarily studied in rodents, focused stereotypies occur in response to high doses of compounds that enhance the action of dopamine in the brain. The stereotypies are characterized by highly repetitive head movements and a lack of locomotion.

Motivating operations – Are events that either increase the value of stimuli (establishing operations (EOs)) or decrease the value of stimuli (abolishing operations (AOs)) as consequences for behavior. Both EOs and AOs influence operant conditioning.

Neuron – Sometimes called nerve cells, neurons are specialized cells in the nervous system that can change in excitability and allow different parts of the body to work together. A neuron receives signals from other sources, like sensory organs or other neurons. When appropriately stimulated, a neuron may send its on signal to other neurons or organs and alter their function.

Neuroplasticity – Adaptive changes that occur in brain function and persist for long periods of time. Such changes are reflected in both long-term

sensitivities of particular brain regions to stimulation and the ability to effect action.
Operant conditioning – Procedures that involve increasing or decreasing the rate or duration of behavior by altering the antecedents (events that occur before a target behavior), the consequences (events that occur after a target behavior), or both.
Proprioceptive – Stimulation that is generated by the movement of the body or movement of body parts.
Punding – Prolonged, stereotyped behavior patterns, such as hoarding, manipulating, and even taking apart and reassembling items that can emerge with use of drugs acting on the dopamine system of the brain.
Tardive dyskinesia – A disorder characterized by oral and facial tics and movements that can develop after prolonged treatment of typical antipsychotic drugs.

Introduction

Researchers from disciplines such as psychiatry, neurobiology, developmental psychology, behavior analysis, and behavioral pharmacology have studied behavior that has been categorized as stereotypy or stereotyped. Consistent with breadth of the experimental interests within these areas, there has been considerable variability in the behavior described as stereotypy and the methodologies employed by researchers from their respective disciplines. Although we summarize the work of our colleagues in neighboring fields, it is perhaps worth noting that the authors may be best described as behavior analysts and behavior pharmacologists. Suffice it to say, we have studied many of forms of behavior that have been called stereotypy.

Definitions

For the purposes of this article, the term stereotypy will be discussed primarily with respect to definitions used to study stereotypy displayed by humans; however, considerable attention will also be given to the study of stereotypy displayed by nonhumans. In general, behaviors that are ultimately categorized as stereotypy typically share the dimensions of movement repetition and invariance. Such behavior is often displayed for extended periods of time and serves no clear social function. In addition to the persistence across time, studies show that stereotypy often persists across a variety of environmental conditions (e.g., even when stimulating activities are available). At one time, this pattern led some researchers to conclude that stereotypy was immutable; however, research from the past two decades has largely undermined this position.

Some forms of stereotypy may also be described as rhythmic, which is a term that connotes regularity in frequency of occurrence or periodicity (i.e., systematic front-to-back movement) or a sequence of behaviors (e.g., staring at the hand, then flapping the hand). As a whole, the proportion of time the respective individual engages in stereotypy is probably the most problematic dimension of this behavior and is ultimately the impetus for treatment. Studies suggest that engagement in stereotypy interferes with the acquisition of adaptive skills. Studies also suggest that individuals who display repetitive behavior such as stereotypy are viewed negatively by others in their environment. Specifically, individuals whose behavior (e.g., hand flapping) is salient to observers are viewed as less normal or natural. In turn, negative social perceptions may decrease the likelihood that other persons will interact with individuals who display repetitive behavior. A number of researchers have also distinguished between motor stereotypy (i.e., behavior involving repetitious body movement) and vocal stereotypy (e.g., acontextual speech, echolalia, and repeated words or sounds). For the purpose of the article, behavior from both of the subcategories will simply be referred to as stereotypy.

Population Characteristics

In humans, stereotypy commonly takes the form of body rocking, hand flapping, object spinning, and other repetitive movement of body parts or objects (e.g., spinning toys). Various forms of stereotypy are displayed by children and adults who are diagnosed with developmental disabilities (DD) and stereotyped movements are one of the defining characteristics of autism spectrum disorders. Studies on the prevalence of repetitive behavior indicate that as many as two-thirds of individuals with DD residing in institutionalized care settings and nearly one-fifth of children with visual impairments who reside with their families display such behavior. Stereotypy is typically viewed as problematic when it is displayed by individuals beyond a certain age (i.e., in early childhood) and it interferes with the individual's ability to learn new skills. Although stereotypy is currently viewed as a behavioral disorder, research from multiple disciplines indicates that many of the behaviors that were ultimately studied or treated as stereotypy were, at one time, exhibited by individuals during the course of normal or typical development. Thus, both the age of an individual and the amount of time typically allocated to a stereotyped response are factors when determining if intervention is warranted.

A recent study by MacDonald and colleagues compared the percentage of time children with typical development and children diagnosed with autism engaged

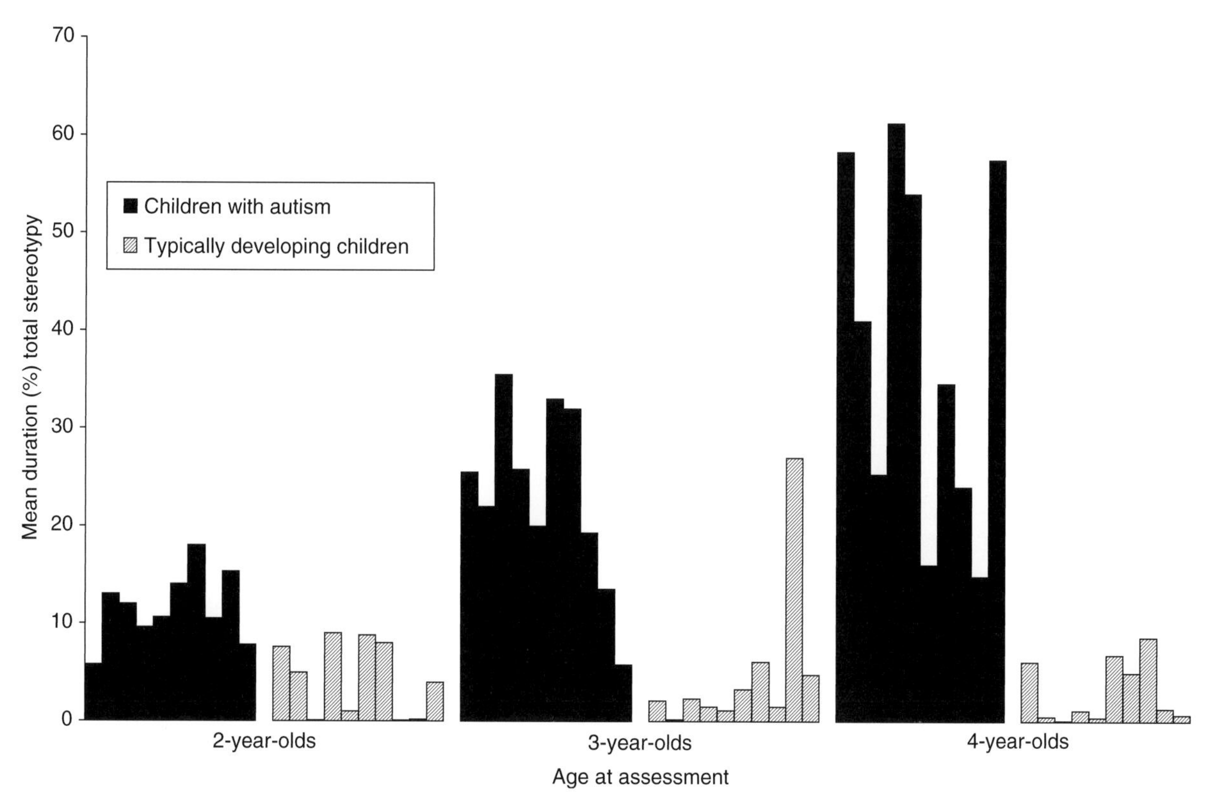

Figure 1 Mean duration for which children with autism and typically developed children engaged in all forms of stereotypy across age groups. Reproduced from MacDonald R, Green G, Mansfeild R, *et al.* (2007) Stereotypy in young children with autism and typically developing child. *Research in Developmental Disabilities* 28: 266–277, with permission from Elsevier.

in motor and vocal stereotypy during 10 min behavior samples. **Figure 1** shows that although not all typically developing 2-year-olds displayed stereotypy, children in both groups displayed some form of stereotypy approximately 10% of the observation time. The data, moreover, show that the percentage of time children diagnosed with autism engaged in stereotypy increased with age whereas the converse was true for children with typical development. There is also some evidence to suggest that some forms of stereotypy (e.g., hand flapping) may evolve into forms of self-injurious behavior; however, the reason for the relation is not yet clear. It is important to note that the conditions under which stereotyped behavior initially emerges in an individual's repertoire may bear little resemblance to the conditions that sustain such behavior throughout the individual's physical development and maturation. For example, a child may initially engage in body rocking as he gains control of the use of his abdominal muscles; however, thereafter, he may continue to body rock because it produces proprioceptive stimulation.

As previously noted, stereotyped behaviors are frequently displayed during the course of typical development; however, it appears that some individuals are more receptive to stimulation that is generated by engagement in such behavior, less receptive to stimulation that is available for engaging in other behavior (e.g., interacting with peers), or both. Based on over 30 years of assessing and treating stereotypy displayed by children with autism, researchers have concluded that different forms of stereotypy generate different types or modalities of stimulation. Research suggests that the stimulation generated by each form of stereotypy functions as 'reinforcement' for the repetitive behavior.

Operant Conceptualizations

Since the 1970s, behavior analysts have provided treatments for a wide range of behavior problems displayed by individuals with DD. As a discipline, behavior analysis focuses on environmental events that are correlated with problem behavior in order to identify variables that make such behavior more or less probable. Events that are present before a given behavior occurs are referred to as antecedents and events that are changed following the exhibition of a behavior are referred to as consequences. Together, antecedents, behaviors, and consequence are referred to as the ABCs or the three-term contingency. The three-term contingency can be used to describe processes related to reinforcement, punishment, and other empirically supported behavioral processes. In operant conditioning, the descriptor 'positive' connotes the addition of a stimulus that follows the occurrence of behavior, whereas the descriptor 'negative' connotes the removal of a stimulus following behavior. For example, the delivery of parental attention may serve to increase the frequency of tantrums by a child who is perhaps feeling ignored (addition of stimuli), but these same tantrums may also be increased by getting out of doing a chore (removal of stimuli). In both cases, the behavior of interest is strengthened by reinforcement, the former by positive reinforcement, and the latter by negative reinforcement. The process of reinforcement, thus, occurs when the frequency or duration of a behavior increases following the addition or removal of a stimulus. Extinction is considered a reciprocal process to reinforcement. Extinction is procedurally arranged when a stimulus is no longer provided (for positive reinforcement) or removed (for negative reinforcement) following a behavior. In terms of process, extinction is said to occur when, after withholding the consequent event, the behavior in question decreases and ultimately abates.

Stimuli that produce reinforcement effects are generally categorized as social or nonsocial. Social reinforcers are typically delivered by a person or change agent. Examples of social reinforcers include attention and physical contact. By contrast, nonsocial reinforcers are not controlled by a change agent. Instead, nonsocial or automatic reinforcers are produced directly by the behavior that is reinforced. Researchers have also referred to stimulation produced by repetitive behavior as proprioceptive (stimulation generated by body movements) and have further subcategorized such stimulation as interoceptive (occurring within the individual) and exteroceptive (occurring outside the individual). For the purpose of the article, all of these events will be subsumed into the descriptive category of automatic reinforcement.

Examples of automatic reinforcers include the production of auditory stimulation by an individual who hums or whistles and hears his or her sounds or the production of visual stimulation by an individual who rapidly rolls his head from side-to-side. In such cases of automatic reinforcement, the stimulation generated by the behavior also reinforces the behavior. In this sense, many forms of stereotypy are viewed as automatically reinforced behavior. For example, an individual may stare at his hand while engaged in hand flapping. The visual stimulation produced directly by hand flapping functions as an automatic, positive reinforcer for hand flapping. In the case of stereotypy, it is typically assumed that the stimulation generated by the respective behavior (and sensed by the nervous system) is relatively valuable.

Conceptually, it is also possible that some forms of stereotypy are elicited by stimulation in the environment. For example, when a loud noise (a potential unconditioned stimulus) is presented, a child engages in hand-flapping (a potential unconditioned response). In this way, the stimulation generated by engagement in the stereotypy does not reinforce the behavior. Instead, the behavior is directly controlled by a stimulus in the environment. Although it remains an interesting possibility, to our knowledge no applied studies have experimentally demonstrated such a relation.

Behavioral researchers have repeatedly demonstrated that reinforcers are influenced by motivational variables. For example, water becomes a more effective reinforcer of an individual's behavior when that individual has been deprived of water. Conversely, water becomes a less effective reinforcer for an individual after he or she consumes copious amount of water. In this example, deprivation from water is referred to as an establishing operation (EO), which increases the value of water, whereas access to large amount of water is referred to as an abolishing operation (AO), which decreases the value of water. Results from a handful of recent studies suggest that various forms of stereotypy are also affected by motivating operations.

A recent review of the behavior analytic literature yielded five sources of evidence that, together, strongly suggest that response forms that are appropriately categorized as stereotypy are most often maintained by automatic, positive reinforcement. As indicated above, the first source of evidence is the persistence of stereotyped behavior in the absence of social consequences. Such persistence indirectly suggests that the behavior generates its own reinforcing stimulation. The second source stems from studies which show that environments rich with alternative sources of stimulation (i.e., reinforcement) often produce the lowest levels of stereotypy. That is, when stimulation from other sources (besides stereotypy) is available, many individuals will engage in behavior (e.g., toy play) to obtain the alternative stimulation. The third source arises from treatment studies that used procedures to directly block or attenuate the stimulation produced by stereotypy. For example, one study demonstrated that tactile stimulation generated from stereotyped hair manipulation was blocked or prevented by having the respective individual wear a rubber glove. In this way, hair manipulation no longer produced reinforcing stimulation and the behavior was temporarily extinguished.

A fourth source of evidence stems from studies showing that access to stereotypy can be used as a reinforcer for appropriate behavior (e.g., academic engagement, requests). Such studies are particularly compelling because they directly demonstrate that the stimulation generated by stereotypy can function as a reinforcer for other behavior. Finally, as noted above, a handful of studies show that various forms of stereotypy are sensitive to EOs, AOs, or both. In regard to EOs, studies have shown that restricting stereotypy below free access levels temporarily increased that behavior once it is permitted, much as, drawing a parallel from above, water restriction increases the likelihood of drinking water. **Figure 2** shows

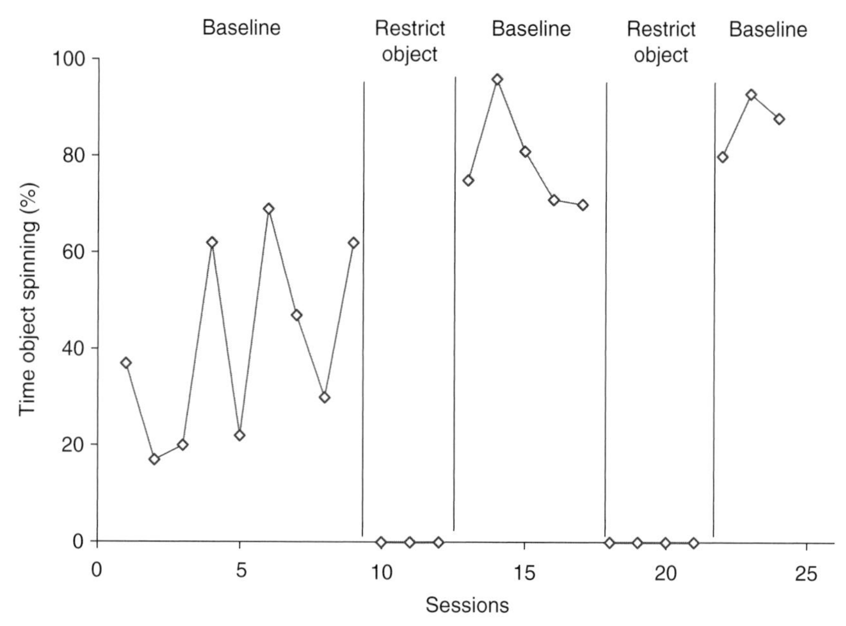

Figure 2 Percentage of time the individual engaged in object spinning during baseline and restrict object conditions across sessions. Reprinted from Rapp JT, Vollmer TR, Dozier CL, St. Peter C, and Cotnoir N (2004) Analysis of response reallocation in individuals with multiple froms of stereotyped behavior. *Journal of Applied Behavior Analysis* 37: 481–501, with permission from Society for the Experimental Analysis of Behavior, Inc.

the effects of restricting an individual's access to stereotyped object spinning. Object spinning was displayed at moderate levels during the first baseline; however, after it was restricted (the object was simply withheld for several sessions), the behavior increased above prior levels during the subsequent baseline conditions. Conversely, a few studies have also shown that providing long periods of free and uninterrupted access to stereotypy may subsequently decrease the amount of time an individual engages in stereotypy, though only temporarily. Thus, although stereotypy is typically automatically reinforced behavior, the behavior patterns produced by either restricting or permitting access to stereotypy (i.e., manipulating of motivating operations) are comparable to those produced by manipulating events for socially reinforced behavior.

Behavior analytic studies of how motivational operations may influence stereotypy require extensive observation and analysis of single individuals. For example, **Figure 3** shows the percentage of time an individual engaged in stereotypy during two daily 30 min sessions: one conducted in the morning and one conducted in the afternoon. The data for each day show that stereotypy was almost always lower in the afternoon session than in the morning session, suggesting that the prior access to stereotypy in the morning decreased the value of stereotypy in the afternoon. Arrows within the figure indicate where session times were altered to control for possible 'time of day' effects. Specifically, the first session was conducted when the second session was typically conducted and the second session was conducted 3 h after the first session. As a whole, studies from the five areas described above strongly suggest that many forms of stereotypy are operant behaviors that are automatically reinforced by stimulation generated directly by the respective behavior.

Behavioral Assessment

The methods used to collect data on occurrence of human stereotypy have drawn recent attention from researchers. Although studies have evaluated stereotypy using a variety of indirect (e.g., rating scales) and direct (e.g., rate or duration) measures, the percentage of time engaged in the stereotyped response is typically the dependent measure of interest. The percentage of time measure is determined by collecting data on the duration of time an individual engages in stereotypy within an observation period and dividing that number by the total number of seconds of the observation period and multiplying by 100%. This method is sometimes referred to as continuous duration recording (CDR). Given the labor intensity of this method of data collection, many clinicians and researchers prefer to use time sampling or interval methods to evaluate stereotypy.

One time-sampling method that generates very accurate estimates of the duration of events such as stereotypy is momentary time sampling (MTS). This method involves breaking an observation period into equal intervals and recording the occurrence or nonoccurrence of the behavior during the last second of each interval. For example, a 10 min (600 s) observation period can be divided into 60 intervals of 10 s. Using 10 s MTS to score

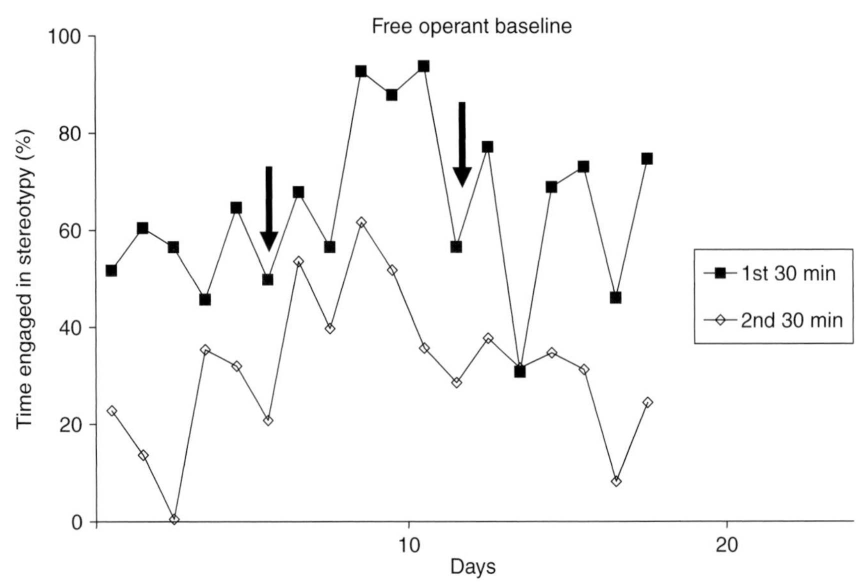

Figure 3 Percentage of time the individual engaged in stereotypy during the first and second daily 30 min sessions across days. Arrows indicate where the time of the two daily sessions was altered. Reproduced from 'Effects of prior access and environmental enrichment on stereotypy', *Behavioral Interventions* 19: 287–295, Rapp JT, (2004) © John Wiley and Sons Limited. Reproduced with permission.

stereotypy, an observer scores the occurrence of target behavior during only the last second of each 10-s interval. The number of intervals with the occurrence of the target behavior is divided by the total number of intervals and then multiplied by 100% to arrive at the percentage of intervals the individual engaged in the target behavior. As a whole, the literature suggests that data collected using 10-s MTS are comparable to data collected with CDR.

In behavior analytic studies, data on specific forms of stereotypy are individually collected and the effects of environmental events (e.g., potential interventions) are typically evaluated using single-subject experimental designs such as an ABAB reversal design or a multielement design. An ABAB reversal involves two conditions wherein 'A' is a baseline or no-intervention (or no manipulation) condition and 'B' is an intervention condition. Observations of a specified length (e.g., 15 min) are first conducted under the baseline condition. After a minimum of three observation sessions are conducted, and relatively stable levels of behavior are observed, the intervention phase is implemented. This phase is also conducted for a minimum of three sessions and until behavior levels stabilize. Once stable behavior is observed, the intervention phase is withdrawn and the process is repeated. A multielement design is similar to a reversal design except that a baseline condition is typically compared to one or more interventions denoted 'B', 'C', 'D', and so on. In addition, instead of conducting the same condition until stability is achieved, the conditions are rapidly alternated in a random or quasi-random order.

Operant interpretations of stereotypy are derived, at least in part, from data obtained via functional analysis methodologies, which were pioneered by Iwata and colleagues in the early 1980s through the mid-1990s. Functional analysis procedures that are used to evaluate the operant function of stereotypy involve systematic manipulations of both antecedents (e.g., presence of a task) and consequences (e.g., attention from a parent). Manipulations are made within specific environmental conditions to isolate events that may be correlated with the presence or absence of stereotypy. In that light, functional analysis represents a broad spectrum approach to identifying behavioral function. Much like an allergist applies many different sample materials to an individual's skin to assess his sensitivity to potential allergens, functional analysis places behavior in a variety of contexts to assess the individual's sensitivity to potential reinforcers. The effects of different environmental conditions are evaluated using single-subject experimental designs similar to those described above. Numerous studies involving a variety of problem behaviors (e.g., self-injurious behavior, aggressive behavior, habit behavior) have shown that data collected via functional analysis methodologies lead to the development of more effective behavioral interventions than interventions that are developed without such assessment.

Figure 4 shows two typical behavioral patterns produced by a functional analysis with a multielement design. Both patterns are indicative of behavior that is automatically reinforced. The top panel of **Figure 4** shows low levels of stereotypy in each condition except the alone condition. In addition to showing that stereotypy persists in the absence of social consequences (i.e., stereotypy is automatically reinforced), these patterns demonstrate that stimulation within the other conditions effectively

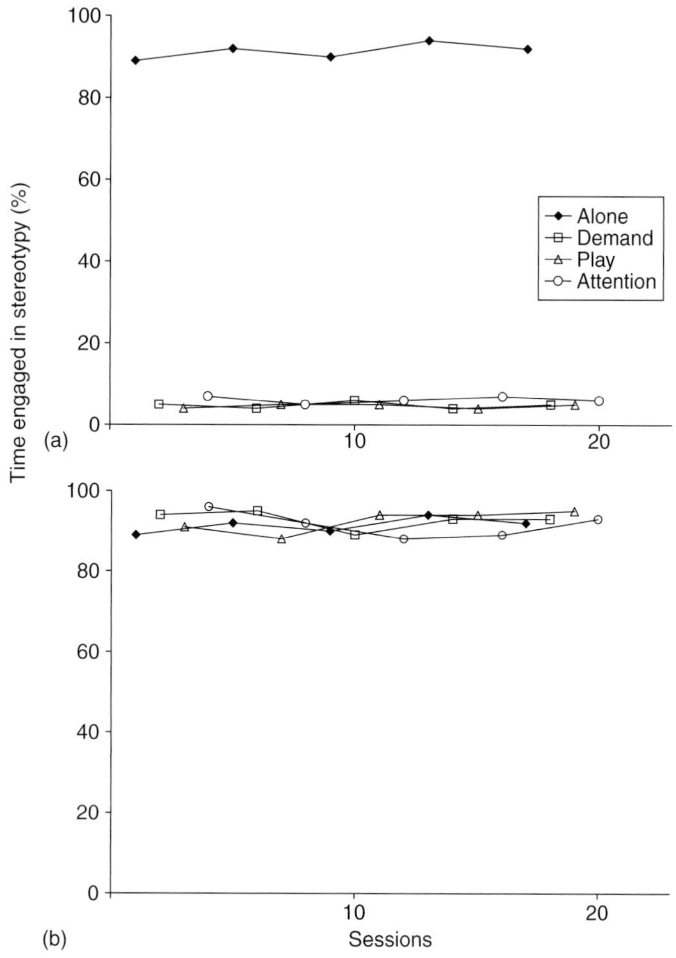

Figure 4 Sample graphs of functional analysis results indicating: (a) high levels of stereotypy in the alone condition only and (b) high levels of stereotypy across all experimental conditions.

competes with stimulation generated by stereotypy. The bottom panel of **Figure 4** shows a pattern wherein levels of stereotypy are elevated and undifferentiated across conditions. As before, this pattern suggests that stereotypy is automatically reinforced; however, it also demonstrates that stereotypy is immutable or insensitive to ongoing environmental events. Thus, even though both graphs provide the same conclusion about the function of stereotypy, the latter graph strongly suggests that stereotypy may be resistant to treatment. In general, researchers have found that behavior maintained by nonsocial or automatic sources of reinforcement is typically more difficult to treat than behavior maintained by social sources of reinforcement (e.g., attention from caregivers).

Behavioral Interventions for Stereotypy

A variety of consequent- and antecedent-based interventions have been used, alone or in combination, to decrease various forms of stereotypy. Interventions categorized as consequent-based are those that involve the delivery of: (1) potentially undesirable or aversive events following the exhibition of stereotypy or (2) preferred or desirable events following the exhibition of appropriate behavior that is topographically incompatible with stereotypy. Conversely, interventions categorized as antecedent-based are those that involve provisions of alternative sources of reinforcing stimulation. The alternative stimulation is intended to compete with stimulation produced by stereotypy. That is, if the respective individual engages appropriately with the alternative stimulation, then stereotypy will be indirectly decreased.

Prior to implementing either type of intervention, empirically based preference assessments are typically conducted to identify items to compete with stereotypy or that may be provided as consequences to increase other behavior. For example, with a free operant preference assessment, an individual is given free access to seven or eight items for 15 min. An observer then records the amount of time the individual manipulates each of the objects; the item that is manipulated for the greatest amount of time is presumed to be highly preferred and is then used in the interventions that are described below. The following is an overview of antecedent and consequent interventions for stereotypy.

Antecedent Interventions

The effects of noncontingent access to preferred items (identified by stimulus preference assessment) for decreasing various forms of stereotypy and other automatically reinforced behavior have been robustly demonstrated by behavior analytic researchers. In this sense, the mere availability of alternative stimulation may be sufficient for decreasing stereotypy that is exhibited by some individuals. Although the effects vary across individuals, free access to visual, auditory, tactile, and vibratory stimulation, alone or in combination, has been shown to decrease stereotypy. For example, the top panel of **Figure 5** shows the percentage of time an individual engaged in stereotyped vocalizing during baseline and music conditions. Each experimental condition was conducted for 30 min (on a separate day) and divided into three, 10-min segments.

During the baseline condition, no music was provided and no consequences were provided for vocal stereotypy. During the music condition, continuous access to music was provided during only the second 10-min segment (regardless of the occurrence of stereotypy) and, again, no consequences were provided for stereotypy during any of the segments. The data show that vocal stereotypy was

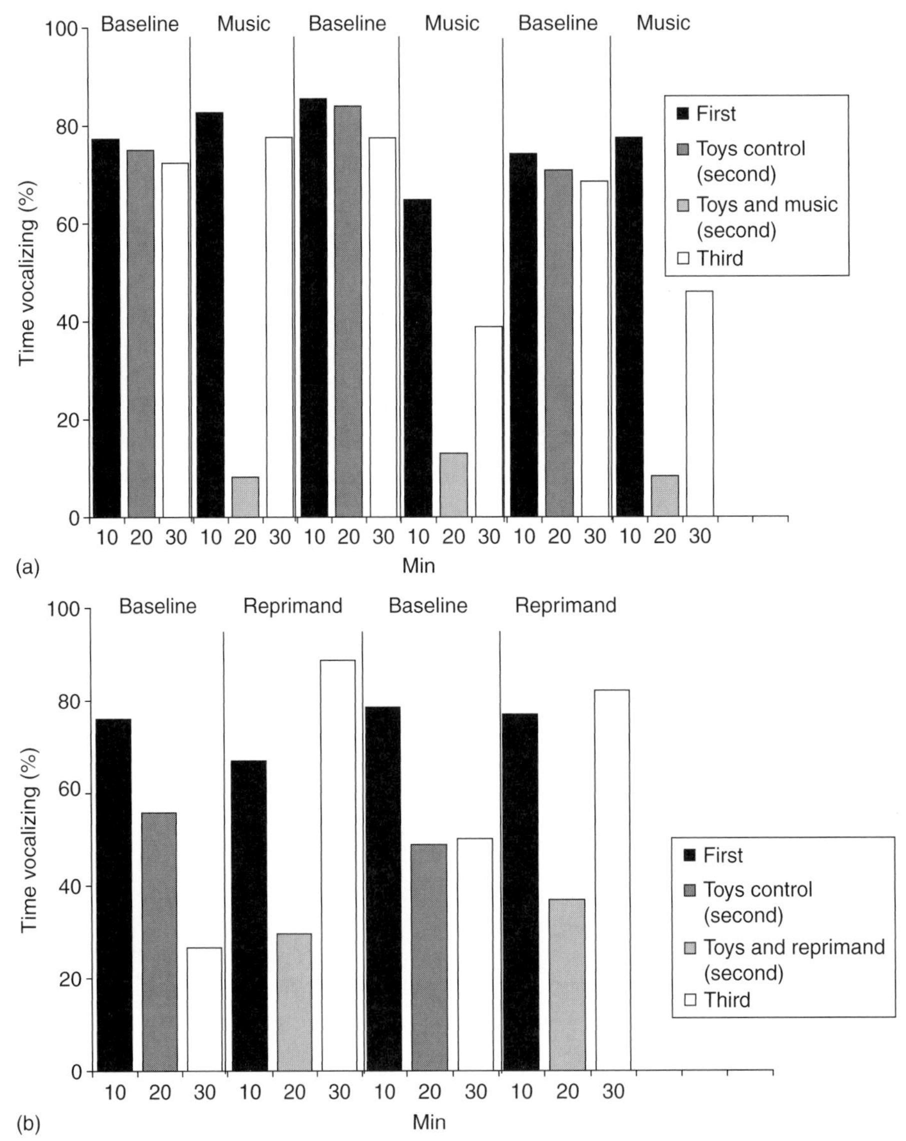

Figure 5 Percentage of time the individual engaged in vocalizations: (a) during baseline and music sequences and (b) during baseline and reprimand sequences. Reproduced from Rapp JT (2007) Further evaluation of methods for identifying marched stimulation. *Journal of Applied Behavior Analysis* 40: 73–88, with permission from the Society for the Experimental Analysis of Behavior, Inc.

always the lowest when music was available. In addition, the lower level of stereotypy in the third segment of the Music conditions (compared to the third segment of the baseline conditions) suggests that the effects of the music on stereotypy persisted for a short period of time after the music was withdrawn. Specifically, although music was only provided for 10 min, the effects endured for a short period of time after music was removed; it is possible that a more enduring suppressive effect may have been exerted with 30 min of access to music. As a whole, decreased vocalizing in the presence of music suggests that the music (auditory stimulation) competed with the stimulation produced by vocalizing (also auditory stimulation). When the auditory stimulation was provided independent of stereotypy, moreover, the behavior decreased.

Although many researchers and clinicians view antecedent interventions as more acceptable than consequent interventions, such approaches are potentially limited insofar as the reinforcing consequence of stereotypy may be unaltered by the intervention. As such, stereotypy remains a part of the individual's behavioral repertoire. Researchers continue to evaluate these and related procedures.

Consequent Interventions

Although an oversimplification, consequent interventions for stereotypy may be divided into two subcategories: punishment and differential reinforcement. Punishment procedures involve the delivery or removal of stimulation following the occurrence of stereotypy. The intended effect of procedures that involve punishment is to directly decrease the amount of time an individual engages in stereotypy. By contrast, differential reinforcement procedures involve the delivery of preferred stimuli following the nonoccurrence of stereotypy or the occurrence of behavior that is topographically incompatible with stereotypy. In this way, the decreases in stereotypy produced with this type of intervention may be considered indirect.

Punishment

A number of consequent interventions have been shown to at least temporarily decrease stereotypy. As noted above, when a behavior occurs, a stimulus is added, and that behavior decreases, the process is referred to as positive punishment. Response blocking and verbal reprimands are examples of such procedures. Response blocking involves physically preventing or disrupting each instance of stereotypy. For example, when a child begins to flap his hands, a trainer would push the child's hand to his side and repeat this process following each attempt to hand flap. Following numerous blocked attempts, stereotypy gradually decreases. Verbal reprimands involve the delivery of a stern or loud statement of disapproval (i.e., an auditory stimulus) following the initiation of stereotypy. If verbal reprimands function as an aversive event (note that such consequences are not aversive for some individuals), stereotypy decreases following repeated exposure to the reprimands.

The bottom panel of **Figure 5** depicts levels of an individual's vocal stereotypy when no social consequences are provided (baseline condition) and when reprimands are provided for engaging in stereotypy (reprimand condition). As was previously described, each condition was conducted for 30 min and divided into three segments. During the baseline condition, no consequences were provided during any of the three segments. During the reprimand condition, a verbal reprimand was provided following each instance of stereotypy during only the second 10-min segment. In this way, the level of stereotypy could be evaluated before, during, and after reprimands were applied. As a whole, the results from these conditions show that stereotypy decreased when reprimands were provided; however, stereotypy increased above pre-intervention levels when reprimands were removed. Similar patterns wherein stereotypy temporarily increased following the removal of punishment procedures have been reported in the behavioral literature. This outcome suggests that punishment, alone, may not be the most effective method for permanently decreasing or eliminating stereotypy. Nevertheless, some studies have produced long-term suppression of stereotypy using positive punishment procedures.

If a behavior occurs, a preferred (or potentially reinforcing) stimulus is removed, and the behavior ultimately decreases, this process is referred to as negative punishment. Time-out is a behavioral procedure that involves the removal of on-going sources of stimulation following instances of stereotypy. Procedurally, access to one or more of those items is removed for specified period of time (e.g., 2 min) following the exhibition of stereotypy. Although stimulation generated by stereotypy remains available during time-out procedures, engagement in stereotypy becomes paired with the removal of other preferred events. Thus, the individual may learn to refrain from stereotypy to avoid the loss of valued items. Among other conceptual interpretations, researchers speculate that punishment procedures alter stereotypy by: (1) directly interfering with the stimulation generated by stereotypy, (2) motivating the individual to engage in a behavior that is not followed by the undesirable event (e.g., delivery of a reprimand or the loss of a preferred item), or (3) decreasing the value of the stimulation generated by stereotypy.

Differential reinforcement

The two differential reinforcement procedures that are most often used to decrease stereotypy are differential reinforcement of other behavior (DRO) and differential reinforcement of alternative behavior (DRA). Both of these procedures are described in this section.

DRO involves the delivery of highly preferred events (identified via stimulus preference assessments) for the omission of a behavior during a period of time. For example, a DRO 30-s procedure involves the delivery of a preferred event after each 30-s period wherein stereotypy is not displayed. To some extent, it is assumed that the event is more valuable than stereotypy (at least momentarily) because the individual forgoes stimulation generated by stereotypy in order to access the event. Although DRO procedures have been shown to be quite effective when small intervals are utilized, increases in stereotypy often occur as the size of the interval is increased to periods of time that are useful to caregivers (e.g., DRO 5 min). In addition, this approach is somewhat limited because no specific behavior is targeted to physically replace or occupy the time previously allocated to stereotypy.

Some of the limitations of DRO can be addressed with DRA. As with DRO, DRA involves the delivery of preferred events in the absence of stereotypy. In addition, the individual must engage in a specific alternative response in order to access the preferred event. The choice of the target response varies with the goals of treatment, but usually the target response is an adaptive behavior. Researchers have shown that these alternative responses can take the form of making requests for a variety of items (e.g., attention from adults, food, toys) or engaging in appropriate academic or vocational tasks. Interestingly, some studies have shown that appropriate alternative behavior can be increased if the opportunity to engage in stereotypy is provided as a consequence (i.e., a reinforcer) for the target. Not unlike DRO, the effects of DRA on stereotypy are largely dependent on the relative value of the events and the frequency with which those events are provided for engaging in the alternative behavior.

As a whole, differential reinforcement procedures likely exert their effects by increasing the value of behaviors that physically compete with engagement in stereotypy and by decreasing the value of stereotypy by withholding preferred events when stereotypy is displayed. As with antecedent interventions, a potential limitation of differential reinforcement procedures is that the stimulation generated by stereotypy is not directly influenced. That is, the relation between the behavior and the stimulation generated by the stereotyped behavior remains intact.

Neurobiological Considerations

In addition to the large amount of data collected demonstrating a role for contingencies of behavior and motivational variables, a great deal of data has been collected detailing important aspects of physiology and biochemistry that are important to understanding stereotypy. The latter body of work has been gathered primarily in research employing nonhumans, which offer some unique perspective on the conditions that give rise to stereotypy. Nonhuman research can offer special insights because many extraneous variables, such as upbringing, housing, diet, etc., can be directly controlled and examined. It is important to note that research into the biology of stereotypy is not offered as an alternative conceptualization, but rather that biology and environment tell different sides of the same story. Although each emphasizes slightly different characters and themes, they both must be intertwined to yield the most comprehensive account of the events that give rise to stereotypy.

The Brain and Movement

The brain has been likened to the command center of the body, because it controls the many organ systems throughout the body, receives all sensory input taken in, and initiates movements. We also think of the brain as the seat of cognitive events, such as thinking and memory. Though this analogy has some merit, we prefer to focus on the brain's role as a coordinator, because it does so much more than simply take in input and generate output. Its very function is the interplay between the various happenings of the body and the environment. As complicated is the job of the brain, so is the brain complicated. The brain alone is made up of over 100 billion neurons (10^{11} neurons). If you were to try to count each of them, say at 1 per second, it would take over 3000 years to count them all. Each of these neurons, moreover, may be connected to up to 100 other neurons, so the number of interconnections quickly rises to dizzying values. Fortunately, some generalities exist among populations of cells so that we do not have to count all these connections separately to garner some understanding of the role different brain regions play in behavior.

The specific brain regions of importance here pertain to what is typically considered voluntary movement, as stereotypy may be seen broadly as a maladaptation of voluntary movement. The brain pathways that execute voluntary movements are known as the pyramidal motor system. Pairs of neurons work in sequence in the pyramidal system. One neuron sends signals from the motor areas of the brain's cortex down to the spinal cord where a second neuron is activated and passes the signal out to the target muscle. If you are taking notes on this article right now, the movements of your fingers, hand, arms, are produced by activation of the pyramidal motor system. The movements of one's hands, fingers, arms, etc., however, do not move the same way all the time because other systems in the brain continuously modify and adapt the motor signals.

One brain system called the extrapyrimidal motor system is a primary system involved in the modulation of voluntary behavior. In what follows, we will examine the major features of the pathways through the basal ganglia, followed by a brief review of neurotransmission and several neurotransmitters that appear to play a role in repetitive movements. Finally, we examine the interaction between environment and the nervous system, and the potential role such interactions have for the expression of stereotypies.

The Basal Ganglia

The basal ganglia are set of deep subcortical and midbrain nuclei. The main structures of the basal ganglia are the caudate nucleus and putamen (the neostriatum); along with the nucleus accumbens these structures are collectively called the striatum, the globus pallidus, which is further subdivided into internal and external segments, the subthalamic nucleus, and the substantial nigra (named for its dark pigmentation it literally means 'black substance'). The substantial nigra contains the cell bodies that produce much of the neurotransmitter dopamine. Dopamine is a neurotransmitter very important for movement; it is discussed in more detail below.

Figure 6 examines the basal ganglia and how it interconnects with other parts of the brain. The striatum is the input region to the basal ganglia. Almost all regions of the cerebral cortex send signals into the striatum. The striatum also receives dopaminergic input from the substantia nigra, and also sends its own inputs right back to modify that input. Signals from the cortex pass from the striatum to the globus pallidus and subthalamic nucleus. The internal segment of the globus pallidus is the output portion of the basal ganglia. Signals from the internal segment are relayed by the thalamus back to the cortex. Although the many structures and connections present a complicated picture, what is important at the moment is to see the general flow of signals through the system. The basal ganglia receive input from the cortex at the striatum and send responses out through the globus pallidus internal segment to the thalamus and back to the cortex. The connection shows an important feature of the basal ganglia, that very little of its output is passed to other parts of the brain. The vast majority of its output returns right back to the cortex via the thalamus. This fact brings us back to the point that the basal ganglia serves to modulate cortical input. Rather than directly initiating movement, the basal ganglia fine-tune movement, suppress inconsistent behavior, and sequence the pattern of behavior so that each movement arrives at the appropriate time. Two pathways work together to accomplish these tasks. One, called the direct pathway, signals the thalamic neurons to stimulate movement; the other, called the indirect pathway, signals the thalamus to suppress movement. The precise anatomical features of each pathway are beyond the scope of this article. Suffice it to say, the

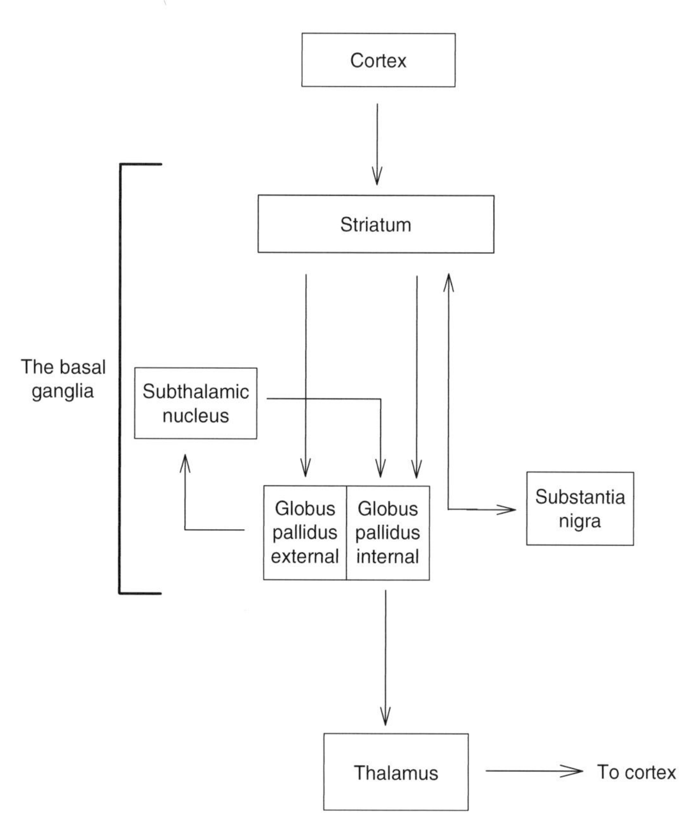

Figure 6 A schematic drawing of connections among the various nuclei of the basal ganglia. Note that all of the input from the brain's cortex enters the basal ganglia through the striatum and that the main output leaves from the internal segment of the globus pallidus. The output is fed back to the cortex via the thalamus.

names derive from the fact that the indirect pathway takes a very convoluted journey through several excitatory and inhibitory connections to accomplish its role, while the direct pathway takes a, well, more direct path.

Because mechanisms are in place to both excite and inhibit movement, the direct and indirect pathways can balance each other to ensure that voluntary movements are executed smoothly and in the proper order. Disruption in that balance can result in large changes in movements or even the potential for movements. As an illustrative example, Parkinson's disease is a neurodegenerative disorder primarily characterized by slow movements (bradykinesia) and an inability to initiate voluntary movements (akinesia). The difficulty in the initiation and performance of movement arises because the direct pathway has become largely inactive due to a depletion of brain dopamine. The reduction in dopamine results in a shift in the balance of movement control. Without its counterpart, the inhibitory indirect pathway is excessively active, so any and all movements are slowed or suppressed.

In summary, the balance between direct and indirect pathways is an important source of proper execution and sequencing of voluntary movement. Movement commands initiated in the cortical regions of the brain feed into the basal ganglia. Little output of the basal ganglia reaches the hindbrain or spinal cord; the vast majority of output goes right back to the cortex via the thalamus. Because one of the defining features of stereotypy appears to be an inability to turn off the behavior, or switch to a different response, the basal ganglia become an important centerpiece in understanding the neurophysiology underlying repetitive movement disorders. We continue probing into relation between the basal ganglia and stereotypy by examining some of the major neurotransmitters involved in movement signaling and neuroplasticity.

Neurotransmission Related to Stereotypy

A neuron is a highly specialized cell. Though several types exist, they all have one thing in common, they are designed to receive signals from other cells, like sensory cells or other neurons, and generate signals to other neurons.

Dopamine

Dopamine has been one of the most extensively studied neurotransmitters. Dopamine is produced in the cell bodies located in the substantial nigra and in a nearby region in the brain called the ventral tegmental area. The dopamine cells in the substantia nigra project onto the upper portion of the striatum and have been more generally implicated in stereotypy. Drugs that increase dopmaine's activity, such as cocaine and amphetamine, have been shown to induce prominent behavioral stereotypies at certain doses. Cocaine and amphetamine exert their effects by blocking the collection of dopamine from the synapse following its release. At low doses, both cocaine and amphetamine induce heightened locomotion and exploratory behaviors in rodents. As the dose is progressively increased, rodents display stereotyped sniffing and rearing responses, as well as grooming and sometimes scratching responses. The expression of these repetitive movements is accompanied by a loss of locomotion and other voluntary behavior. The entire syndrome may last many minutes to more than an hour depending on the dose of the drug. The relatively long time of expression, accompanied with a high degree of spatial confinement has led to the term focused stereotypy to be applied to this behavioral pattern.

The focused stereotypy displayed by rats has impressive periodicity. A representative graph of the stereotyped head-movements recorded by a force-plate actometer is shown in **Figure 7**. The data were obtained from a Sprague-Dawley rat administered 5.0 mg kg^{-1} *d*-amphetamine. The row of graphs indicated by set (a) show the frequency power spectrum of head movements on the left and a top-down view of the chamber on the right. In the tracing of position, the sides of the graph represent the walls of the experimental chamber, and the plot shows a continuous tracing of the rat's position throughout the recording sample as if you were

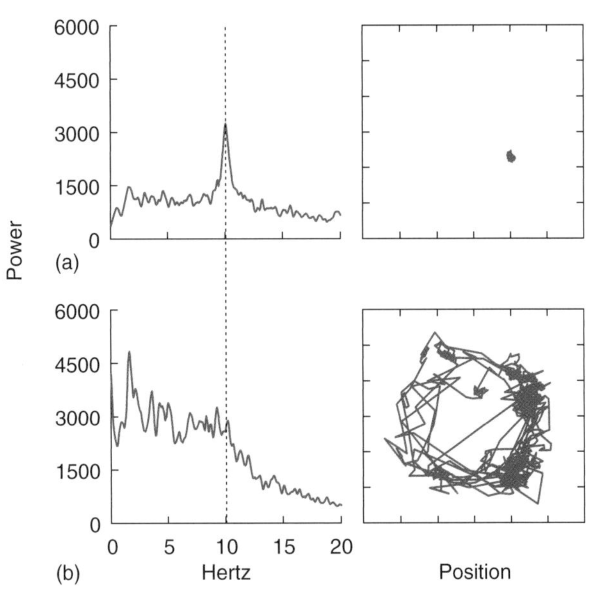

Figure 7 Amphetamine-induced stereotypies. (a) The left graph shows a spectral analysis of movement rhythms; the repetitive head movement stereotypy induced by amphetamine has a dominant rhythm near 10 cycles per second, or hertz. The right graph shows a 'top-down' graph of the rat's movement on the chamber floor during the stereotypy. Note that the rat is stationary while engaged in stereotypy. (b) The graphs are the same as those above, except raclopride was given after the amphetamine. The spectral characteristics of movement rhythms are in accord with that typically seen during locomotion. The graph of the movement pattern shows that indeed movement was restored after raclopride, showing amphetamine's effects were reversed.

standing over the chamber and looking down at the rat. The power spectrum indicates that movements are best characterized as a rhythm of 10 cycles per second (or hertz, abbreviated Hz), as indicated by the greater power in that frequency relative to all others. Also, note the recording of the rat's position across the 3-min period. The small point indicates that the animal was stationary during the entire sample period. The rat continued to exhibit patterns of behavior with these characteristics a total of about 50 min. Casual observations of rats during the expression of focused stereotypies suggest that they are generally unresponsive to all but the strongest of stimuli. The role of dopamine in the production of stereotypy is supported by the results of the administration of the dopamine-blocking agent raclopride ($0.2\ \mathrm{mg\,kg}^{-1}$), shown in the lower set of graphs labeled (b). Note the disappearance of a uniformly dominant frequency, which has been replaced by several lower frequencies, a pattern typically seen under locomotion. The tracing of the rat's position over the time block confirms that locomotion was restored following the administration of raclopride.

Human amphetamine users may also display similar repetitive behavior patterns. Physicians first noticed that amphetamine users would engage in repeated movements involving stacking or arranging items and seemed unable to break out of the routine. This behavior, often referred to as 'punding', appears to be related to dopaminergic action of amphetamine, as it may be effectively treated with dopamine-blocking drugs (e.g., haloperidol).

Animal models of drug-induced stereotypy have greatly furthered our knowledge of the involvement of dopamine-related systems in stereotypy, and several parallels exist between these models and clinical symptoms. Treatment drugs that block dopaminergic action have been moderately successful in decreasing some stereotypy, but they are not without problems. The most widely used drugs in the treatment of stereotypy have been the typical antipsychotics, such as haloperidol and raclopride, which block dopamine uptake at the synapse. Typical antipsychotics, however, may themselves induce unwanted motor side effects when given for prolonged periods. Side effects, called extrapyrimidal side effects, to indicate their relation to a change in basal ganglia function, can cause a host of tremors, restlessness, muscle rigidity, and involuntary movements. A common outcome of typical antipsychotic treatment is the development of tardive dsykinesia, a disorder characterized by uncontrollable orofacial tics and movements.

Serotonin

Serotonin (5HT) has been popularized as a neurotransmitter related to mood, depression, and even weight gain, but additionally the transmitter is thought to play a role in stereotypy. Serotonin has important neurotrophic effects that guide growing neuronal branches to their appropriate targets during development, and there has been much interest in the last couple of decades on the possible influence of serotonin systems on human stereotypy. For example, children with autism have higher circulating blood levels of serotonin than do children without autism. Interestingly, the high levels are not found in the brain, because serotonin does not cross the blood–brain barrier. Serotonin levels in the brain, on the other hand, are found to be lower in children with autism, though this decrease can diminish with age. Imbalances in the amount of serotonin may alter the normal development of growing neurons, and such changes have been implicated in altering neuronal development that may give rise to stereotypies. In addition to neurodevelopmental factors, serotonin modulates the release of dopamine in the basal ganglia, and also appears that serotonergic neurons may help in removing dopamine from the synapse. Thus, serotonin may affect movement by changing dopamine transmission.

The pharmacology and neurochemistry of the serotonergic system are extremely complex. There have been at least 15 different receptors identified throughout the nervous system. To date, basic research has not provided a definitive description of how serotonin plays a role in the expression of stereotypy. Though several experiments have found a role for serotonin in the production of stereotypy, many others have not. More recently, researchers have produced genetically altered mice that lack specific neurotransmitter receptors. This manipulation allows researchers to isolate independent contributions of different types of serotonin receptor. Possible interactions, however, are numerous and extensive research will be required before conclusive statements can be made.

Despite incomplete knowledge on serotonin's role in stereotypy, drugs that increase serotonin's activity have been used clinically to treat stereotypy. At present, several studies have evaluated the serotonergic agent clopmiprimine on the repetitive behavior of children and adults with autism. Generally, the data suggest that clopmiprimine can be an effective agent in the treatment of some symptoms of autism, including some forms of stereotypy (e.g., body rocking) that are often displayed by individual with the disorder. It is important to note that not all studies have demonstrated a clinical benefit of clopmiprimine, and some research suggests important age-related differences in the effectiveness of treatment, specifically that younger children may have poorer outcomes compared to older children. Additionally, some studies have reported little or no side effects, while other studies have reported marked increases in aggressiveness and irritability. In short, although current data are promising, more research is needed to evaluate the suitability of serotonergic compounds in the treatment of human stereotypy.

Glutamate

The excitatory amino acid glutamate is also thought to have a role in the production of stereotypies. This is not surprising, as it is found almost everywhere in the body. Glutamate has been shown to have excitatory effects on neurons everywhere it has been examined, and in fact the excitatory inputs from the cortex into the striatum are glutamatergic. Glutamate is an important neurotransmitter in the initiation and maintenance of neuroplasticity. It has now been well established that appropriate stimulation of certain neurons promote enduring changes in the sensitivity of those neurons to stimulation many hours, or even days later. Said loosely, the connection between two neurons becomes changed for a relatively long time. Sometimes these changes relate to increased responsiveness to later stimulation, generally termed long-term potentiation (LTP); some of these changes relate to diminished sensitivity to further stimulation, or long-term depression (LTD). Changes in responsiveness are induced and maintained in large part by changes in glutamatergic receptor populations on the cell's surface. Such prolonged strengthening or weakening of connections may determine the strength of certain behavior patterns, and it is this alteration in response strength that may lead some behavior patterns to be expressed as stereotypy.

Laboratory research has primarily focused on the role of glutamate in drug-induced stereotypies. Compounds that inhibit or block glutamatergic receptor activation have been shown to attenuate the expression of stereotypies by nonhumans that are typically induced by cocaine and amphetamine. Reduction in the stereotypies involves glutamatergic activity in the cortex, as well as interactions with the dopamine systems in the basal ganglia. It has been difficult to apply our knowledge of the role of glutamate to pharmacotherapies for stereotypy displayed by humans because excessive glutamate is extremely toxic and may kill neurons. Thus, while it is important to recognize the role glutamate plays in synaptic connections and its interactions with dopamine in determining basal ganglia function, one must be cautious in altering normal regulation of glutamate as a source of treatment.

Effects of Environmental Complexity in Stereotypy

It has been well established that children with special needs who are raised in austere institutional settings often display more extensive stereotypies than similar children reared in a more stimulating environment. Studies with nonhumans have also shown benefits of environmental enrichment. Animals raised in relatively barren environments may develop cage stereotypies. Upon visits to a zoo, most of us have seen the prototypical example of the lioness pacing back and forth along one wall of her cage, in a seemingly endless to-and-fro motion. Other animals display their own species-specific patterns, for example, rodents and birds repetitively groom, scratch, or pick themselves to the point of causing tissue damage. Animals that are housed in complex environments that promote species-appropriate behavior, such as exploration and foraging opportunities, and interaction with conspecifics are less likely to display spontaneous stereotypies in caged situations. Such considerations have led to the more open arenas and the inclusion of play toys more common in modern zoos.

The induction of stereotypies by barren environments may be related to changes in the neurotransmitter systems discussed above, as well as morphological changes in the brain. Mark Lewis at the University of Florida and colleagues have done some very interesting work along this line. Lewis has studied the spontaneous behavior displayed by a particular deer mouse with a high rate of spontaneous stereotypies. The stereotypy displayed by these mice is an interesting model for study because it is naturalistic, as opposed to stereotypies induced by drugs or lesions. In one experiment, Lewis and colleagues compared the stereotypy of mice reared in austere environments to those reared in a complex environment. Mice raised in the complex environment were less likely to display stereotypies. More interestingly, later examinations of the striatum in the mice revealed interesting changes in the medium spiny neurons of the striatum. The medium spiny neuron is a type of neuron found in the striatum, named for its branching dendrites, which are covered in spiny projections. It is the most common type of neuron in the striatum, accounting for about 95% of striatal neurons. The medium spiny neurons are related to voluntary movement, during which they become very excited. Lewis and colleagues found that mice raised in enriched environments had spiny neurons with much denser branching and thicker spines than did mice raised in relatively uncomplicated environments. Other changes in brain hormone and neurotransmitter levels and gene expression have also been identified in several laboratories.

The alteration in so many biological processes demonstrates how powerfully the environment may shape the nervous system. Returning to the idea that the brain works in concert with the happenings of the environment and with the happenings of the body, we may see how the environment may facilitate or hinder stereotypy by the kind of nervous system it fosters. Because a barren environment supports the execution and fine tuning of only a limited repertoire, only a limited range of behaviors become probable. Consider a rodent in a very simple environment, what behavior patterns are we most likely to see displayed? Sniffing, grooming, rearing, locomotion, and probably little else – the very behavior patterns that are likely to dominate as stereotypy. Couple those observations to the idea that repetitive practice has a self-strengthening effect, as repeated execution of a motor pattern makes it easier to execute over time (an effect due to the glutamate system discussed above) and one can see how the environment and nervous system interact in the expression of behavior. An austere environment promotes only limited engagement of the individual's repertoire across development, and so promotes the growth of a limited nervous system to handle the few responses executed over and over again. Those few behaviors come to be highly probable in the patterns observed in the individual. In a more complicated environment, growth and development of a nervous system that will support many varied response patterns is facilitated, and so the individual is prepared to meet environmental challenges with a more extensive repertoire.

Summary

In summary, a substantial amount of research on stereotypy has been generated in the past four decades by researchers from various disciplines. The volume of research that was conducted during this time has contributed to an increased understanding of and appreciation for this complex behavioral phenomenon. We provided an overview of definitions for and prevalence of stereotypy within typical and atypical development, behavioral and neurobiological conceptualizations of stereotypy, and behavioral and pharmacological interventions for stereotypy. In doing so, we attempted to highlight important variables both outside and within the individual that may contribute to the development and maintenance of stereotypy. It is our hope that the present review sets the occasion for further discussion and investigation about this most interesting and puzzling class of behavior.

See also: Autism Spectrum Disorders; Discipline and Compliance; Sensory Processing Disorder.

Suggested Readings

Lerman DC and Rapp JT (2006) Antecedent assessment and intervention for stereotypy. In: Luiselli JK (ed.) *Antecedent Intervention: Recent Developments in Community Focused Behavior Support.* Baltimore, MD: Paul H. Brooks Publishing.

Lewis MH, Gluck JP, Bodfish JW, Beauchamp AJ, and Mailman RB (1996) Neurological basis of stereotyped movement disorder. In: Sprague RL and Newell KM (eds.) *Stereotypy: Brain Behavior Relationships.* Washingtion, DC: American Psychological Association Press.

MacDonald R, Green G, Mansfield R, *et al.* (2007) Stereotypy in young children wiith autism and typically developing children. *Research in Developmental Disabilities* 28: 266–277.

Rapp JT (2004) Effects of prior access and environmental enrichment on stereotypy. *Behavioral Intervention* 19: 287–295.

Rapp JT (2007) Further evaluation of methods for identifying methods for identifying matched stimulation. *Journal of Applied Behavior Analysis* 40: 73–88.

Rapp JT and Vollmer TR (2005) Stereotypy I: A review of behavioral assessment and treatment. *Research in Developmental Disabilities* 26: 527–547.

Rapp JT and Vollmer TR (2005) Stereotypy II: A review of neurobiological interpretations and suggestions for an integration with behavioral methods. *Research in Developmental Disabilities* 26: 548–564.

Rapp JT, Vollmer TR, Dozier CL, St. Peter C, and Cotnoir N (2004) Analysis of response reallocation in individuals with multiple forms of stereotyped behavior. *Journal of Applied Behavior Analysis* 37: 481–501.

Stress and Coping

E M Cummings and C D Kouros, University of Notre Dame, Notre Dame, IN, USA

Glossary

Attachment theory – A psychological theory focusing on the emotional social bond between a primary caregiver and child, including the functioning of this emotional bond in children's coping with everyday stressors, including separation. Attachment patterns are assessed by examining how infants use their caregiver as a secure base from which to explore, as well as infants' pattern of responses to being separated from a primary caregiver in an unfamiliar setting.

Cognitive appraisal – The process of monitoring and evaluating a specific person–environment interaction with respect to the individuals' well-being and goals.

Coping – This is an often complex, multidimensional process by which infants regulate emotion, behavior, cognition, physiology, and/or the environment when faced with a stressful event.

Coping efficacy – This refers to a child's belief that his or her coping strategy will be successful. Coping efficacy affects children's decisions about their responses in the face of stress.

Emotion-focused coping – Coping responses aimed at regulating or minimizing the negative emotions elicited by stress.
Emotional security theory – Theoretical framework for understanding the effects of stressful family processes on children's adjustment. Notably, this theory posits that marital conflict is a stressor that affects infants by threatening their emotional security. Threats to the infant's emotional security motivate and organize their coping responses, for example, emotional and behavioral regulatory responses.
Problem-focused coping – Coping responses aimed at managing, changing or regulating the source of stress.
Stress – A wide range of adverse stimuli (physical or mental) that disrupt normal functioning of an individual and elicit a physiological and/or psychological response.
Temperament – Individual differences in emotional and behavioral reactivity that is evident from early on in life and consistent over time and across situations. Temperament has a biological basis with genetic origins. At the same time, temperament can be influenced and modified by early experiences.

Introduction

Stress is an inevitable and normal part of everyday life. How individuals cope with stress has strong implications for their current as well as future well-being and adjustment. While most people deal with stress with no adverse consequences, children exposed to chronic stress or who do not have effective coping responses may be at risk for mental and physical health problems. Stressful events elicit both physiological and psychological responses and the coping strategies children use in the face of stress lead to patterns of behavior that are predictive of developmental trajectories of adjustment and maladjustment. Thus, the stressors encountered by infants and the coping mechanisms used by infants may have lasting implications for coping with stress later in life, and ultimately, the way individuals develop.

A strength of infancy research on stress and coping is the emphasis on a biopsychosocial perspective of stress and coping. Thus, research has emphasized the impact of stress on multiple aspects of infant's physiological and psychological responding, as well as the importance of social context for the impact of stress on infants. That is, social context is seen as affecting children's exposure to stress, how they react to stress, and their ability to employ and access various coping strategies, including the availability of parents, caregivers, or others in a position to help the infant. Moreover, the role of individual differences and biological dispositions in stress and coping is emphasized through the systematic study of the construct of temperament.

Stress and coping research is perhaps unusual in that in the past 20 years or so a high level of consensus has been reached with regard to a particular definition and conceptual model for the nature of stress and coping. Richard Lazarus and Susan Folkman define stress as "a particular relationship between the person and environment that is appraised by the person as taxing or exceeding his or her resources or endangering his or her well-being." Coping is conceptualized as a dynamic process, that is, "constantly changing cognitive and behavioral efforts to manage specific external and/or internal demands that are appraised as taxing or exceeding the resources of the person." In other words, coping is what the infant does to manage the demands of a stressful situation. Additionally, coping is conceptualized as often a multidimensional process that extends over time and is highly sensitive to context (e.g., the availability of a caregiver). The way an infant copes with stress may vary widely depending on the context and coping responses may change over time in response to a specific context.

When coping is defined in this way, it follows that coping for infants may include emotional and social responses in observable behavior, or physiological responses of heart rate, blood pressure, and other such domains. Responding may also be extended in time, so that it becomes important for the coping researcher to observe or record infant responses over a pertinent time course. In addition, it follows that it is important to be concerned with the meaning and interpretation of coherent patterns of responding, that is, strategies or higher-order coping styles (e.g., infant attachment patterns), not just isolated response domains, which can give a limited if not distorted picture of response processes.

There are many different types of stressors that infants and children face during childhood, as well as a wide range of possible coping responses that change throughout development. This article presents a brief overview of historical perspectives on stress and coping, which includes physiological responses to stress, and current views on psychological processes for stress and coping models in infancy and early childhood. An in-depth discussion of stress and coping is provided for two significant themes in childhood research: attachment patterns and exposure to interparental conflict. In particular, attachment theory and the emotional security theory (EST) are presented as important frameworks for understanding how children's coping with stress can account for the associations between exposure to stress and children's adjustment. An example of an individual differences approach is provided in terms of the construct of temperament.

Historical Perspective on Stress and Coping

Early views of stress and coping focused primarily on a person's physiological response to stress. The study of physiological responses of stress and coping has a distinguished and long history. In the early 1930s, the biopsychologist Walter Cannon used the term stress to describe challenges and disturbances to homeostasis, that is, the ability for an individual to maintain internal equilibrium by making adjustments to physiological processes. In an influential article in 1936, Hans Selye used the term stress to refer to any demand made upon the body; however he focused specifically on the physiological reactions to such demands. Selye described three stages of a General Adaptation Syndrome to explain how stress affected physical health. The first stage is the Alarm Stage which is an immediate physiological response to stress that prepared the body to channel resources to immediate muscular needs. In the process, immune functioning, the digestive system, and other responses could be suppressed, leaving the individual more vulnerable to illness and other negative outcomes. In the second stage, Resistance, the individual acclimated to the stressful situation allowing the individual to adapt to stressful conditions. However, over time, the third stage, Exhaustion, may take place, in which due to prolonged suppression of the immune system, the body is no longer able to handle the stress and begins to break down. In the years since these early conceptualizations and definitions of stress, psychological responses to stress remain recognized as pertinent to understanding the nature of stress. Notably, stress refers to a wide range of adverse stimuli (physical or mental) that may disrupt the normal functioning of an individual and elicit significant physiological and/or psychological responses.

Conceptualizations and Definitions Regarding Physiological Responses to Stress

The responses of infants and young children to stress may be informative with regard to the impact of stress on multiple dimensions of physiological functioning. Notably, the body's physiological response to stress can be sophisticated and complex. The stress response may prepare the individual to act in order to escape, avoid, or deal with the stressor or prepare the body for potential injury. The physiological response of the individual may function to take energy away from parts of the body where it is not immediately needed (e.g., digestive system) and move this energy to, as well as create energy for, other parts of the body that need it to deal with stress (e.g., large muscles). Stressful events activate the sympathetic nervous system (SNS), which is a branch of the autonomic nervous system, and the hypothalamic–pituitary–adrenal axis (HPA axis). The parasympathetic nervous system (PNS), another branch of the autonomic nervous system, is also activated to assist the individual in resting and recovery.

In the early 1900s, Walter Cannon introduced the concept of 'fight or flight' response to describe the response of the SNS to threats to the individual in general. The SNS is partly responsible for regulating the body to maintain homeostasis. Specifically, activity of the SNS stimulates the adrenal medulla (the inner core of the adrenal glands), which are located above the kidneys, to secrete catecholamines, including epinephrine (adrenaline) and norepinephrine (noradrenaline). SNS activation diverts blood and energy away from processes such as digestion and the immune system to large muscles and processes necessary to immediately respond to the stress. As a result, heart rate and blood pressure increase, perspiration increases, and hearing and vision become more acute. Because of these responses, one may experience dry mouth, sweating, dilated pupils, and insomnia in response to stress.

A standard and noninvasive approach to measuring SNS reactivity is skin conductance, typically measured by attaching electrodes to the first and second fingers of the child's nondominant hand. Skin conductance refers to the electrodermal activity (electric impulses on the surface of the skin) resulting from activity of sweat glands that are innervated solely by the SNS. Thus, skin conductance is an unbiased marker of SNS activity. Another, newer approach for measuring SNS activity is to examine changes in pre-ejection period (PEP) in response to stress. PEP is a measure of cardiac contractibility; that is, it is a measure of the time interval between blood entering and exiting the heart. The shorter the time period, the more active the heart is and the more quickly blood is being pumped out to the body, reflecting greater physiological arousal.

Additionally, stress activates the HPA axis, which affects almost every organ and tissue of the body, as well as the brain. An illustration of this process is depicted in **Figure 1**. Specifically, the hypothalamus stimulates the anterior pituitary gland to secrete the adrenocorticotropic hormone (ACTH). ACTH travels through the blood to the adrenal cortex (outer layers of the adrenal gland) to stimulate the release of the hormone cortisol, which is released in the bloodstream. Among its effects, the release of cortisol increases blood pressure and blood sugar levels, and suppresses immune system functioning. A relatively easy and noninvasive measurement of cortisol is the use of salivary samples. Cortisol is also easily assayed in the blood and urine.

The newborn brain is biologically prepared to respond to certain types of stressors that threaten homeostasis, such as pain, bright lights, cold, heat, loud noises, and hunger. Newborns are alert to these types of physiological stressors and their autonomic nervous system responds.

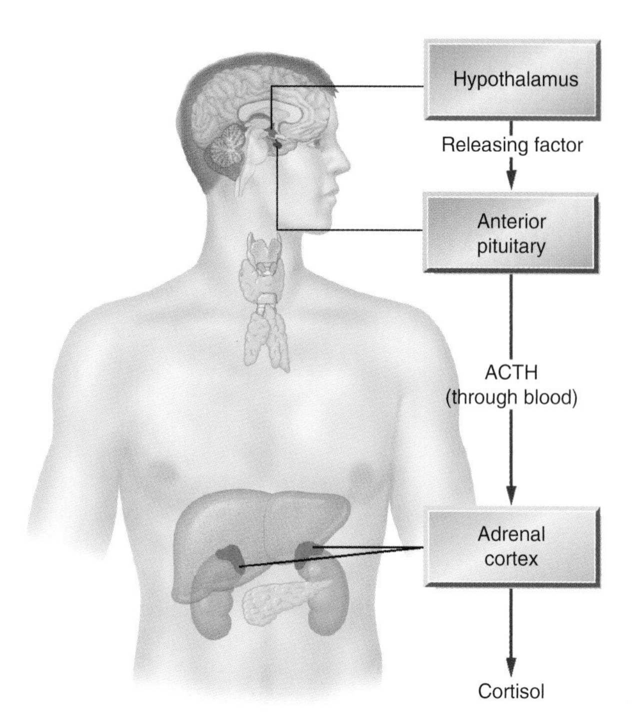

Figure 1 Illustration of the activation of the HPA axis in response to stress. From Biological Psychology 6th edition by Kalat. 1998. Reprinted with permission of Wadsworth, a division of Thomsan Learning. (ACTH), adrenocorticotropic harmone

For example, a commonly studied stressor in newborn infants is pain via heel stick procedures. A heel stick involves pricking the newborn's heel in order to draw blood, and is used as a screening test before babies leave the hospital after birth. Research has found that the heel stick procedure is stressful for infants, as evidenced by activation of the HPA axis, an increase in cortisol, and increased crying. By 3 months of age, as the HPA axis matures and develops, cortisol response to these physiological stressors are not as intense.

Psychological Processes of Stress and Coping in Infancy and Childhood

While physiological responses play a critical role in coping with various stressors and may describe stress and coping response for newborns, current perspectives and research highlight the increasing importance of psychological processes as infants get older. Specifically, cognitive appraisals further articulate stress and coping as a process that may be pertinent to understanding stress and coping in infancy and childhood, and also toward advancing the study of links between stress and coping processes in older children and their possible origins in infancy and toddlerhood. As individuals get older, cognitive appraisal is increasingly emphasized in the study of stress and coping. Individuals are continuously monitoring their environment in relation to their well-being and a hierarchy of goals. Two levels of appraisal are often differentiated: primary and secondary. Primary appraisals are evaluations of the personal significance of a person–environment encounter. If the individual evaluates that there is no harm to their well-being, the situation is appraised as irrelevant. However, if the person–environment interaction is appraised as harming, threatening, or challenging the well-being of the individual, the situation is appraised as stressful. Finally, if the outcome of a specific person–environment relationship is perceived as preserving or enhancing the individual's well-being, the situation is appraised as benign-positive. Primary appraisals are influenced by a person's beliefs about himself or herself and the world, as well as their beliefs about the resources available to him or her for coping, such as level of problem-solving skills and financial resources. Notably, individual differences in these beliefs may lead one person to appraise a situation as stressful, whereas another person may appraise the same situation as irrelevant.

Given that a situation or event is appraised as stressful, a secondary appraisal is made in which the individual evaluates his or her options for coping. Such appraisals include an assessment of what coping options are available, how likely a particular coping option will work, and whether the individual will be successful in applying that particular coping strategy.

For example, infants and toddlers from high-conflict homes are more likely to appraise conflict as threatening to their well-being (primary appraisal) and decide the most effective option for coping is to intervene in their parents' conflicts (secondary appraisal), either by distracting the parents from their conflicts or attempting to comfort parents. Together, primary and secondary appraisals influence the type and intensity of emotional responses to stress and influence an individual's coping response. Cognitive appraisals are seen as continuously occurring and are not necessarily a conscious process.

Another issue is how to categorize coping responses. In this regard, two types of coping responses are generally recognized, problem-focused coping and emotion-focused coping, which have influenced many contemporary models of stress and coping. Problem-focused coping is aimed at resolving the stressful event or situation and may include seeking information, generating solutions, and taking action to change the stressful person–environment interaction. For example, even infants as young as 1 year of age may attempt to intervene in their parents conflicts with behaviors such as comforting or distracting parents. Emotion-focused coping is directed at minimizing the negative emotions elicited by the stressful situation and may include expressing emotions, seeking support from others, selective attention, or avoiding the source of stress. For example, infants may cover their ears or leave the room when exposed to interparental conflicts. In some cases, emotion-focused coping can lead to a reappraisal of the situation as not stressful. Some response strategies may incorporate both problem-focused and emotion-focused coping, thus these two forms of coping are not mutually exclusive. Moreover, these categories are not exhaustive of the different ways in which an individual may cope with a stressful event.

Coping responses have also been categorized in terms of those aimed at primary control as opposed to responses aimed at secondary control. Primary control refers to responses toward gaining personal control over, or influencing, the stressful situation or regulating one's own emotional reaction. Secondary control, on the other hand, refers to responses aimed at adapting and fitting in with the stressful situation. This includes accepting the situation or reappraising the stressful conditions as nonstressful. Another common distinction among coping behaviors is engagement vs. disengagement. Engagement consists of responses aimed at the stressor or one's own negative emotions and thoughts (e.g., generating solutions), whereas disengagement reflects responses in which the individual withdraws or avoids the stressor or his or her own emotions and thoughts.

Cognitive appraisals emerge as a key element in psychological perspectives on stress and coping. However, there is considerable variability in the use and effectiveness of cognitive appraisals among infants compared to young children. Infant and child models of stress and coping are derived from adult models and as such, perspectives on infant stress and coping imply that cognitive appraisals are also a critical element in stress and coping responses among this age group. However, there is a lack of empirical research testing the role of cognitive appraisals in stress and coping processes with infants and young children. Instead, research is focused on specific child responses to specific stressors, with little attention given to the processes underlying stress and coping responses among infants and young children.

Thus, the study of coping in infancy and early childhood has lagged behind research with adults with regard to the construct of cognitive appraisal. However, there have been important efforts toward modifying the conceptualization of coping for the study of infants and children. For example, Nancy Eisenberg, Richard Fabes, and colleagues propose that coping is a component of self-regulation, or more specifically, emotion-regulation. They posit that children are constantly regulating their behavior and emotions. Thus, coping is seen as the process of children regulating their behavior and emotions when faced with stress, motivated by the presence or expectation of negative emotional arousal.

Eisenberg and colleagues outline three aims of coping among infants and children. First, coping may be concerned with children's regulation of their internal negative emotional experience and emotion-related physiological responses, including cognitive strategies such as cognitive restructuring of events (e.g., 'This stressful event isn't so bad'), redirecting one's attention, approaching or withdrawing from the stressful stimulus and seeking comfort from others. Second, coping may be concerned with regulation of the behaviors associated with the experienced emotion. Third, coping may take the form of efforts to regulate the emotion-eliciting context, including modifying the source of emotional arousal, such as active approach behavior, but can also include behaviors such as seeking support.

Bruce Compas and colleagues conceptualize coping as a component of children's broader self-regulation processes. They define coping as conscious, volitional efforts by children to regulate emotion, behavior, cognition, physiology, and the environment when faced with a stressful event. Coping strategies are a function of the biological, social, cognitive, and emotional development of the individual. Although Eisenberg and colleagues allow for unconscious efforts to be classified as coping mechanisms, Compas and colleagues define only conscious, volitional responses as coping. They note this distinction allows for more precise and useful definitions of coping, excluding certain regulatory processes during stress, such as innate reflexes and automatic responses.

Finally, another significant construct often included in assessing stress and coping in infants and young children is coping efficacy. Coping efficacy refers to a child's belief that his or her coping strategy will be successful. Coping efficacy affects children's decision about their responses in the face of stress. Coping efficacy may be influenced by previous experiences such that children may feel more competent and confident using responses that have been successful in the past. Infants and children with low coping efficacy may feel they have limited options in the face of stress and therefore may experience elevated stress responses.

Evidence for Cognitive Appraisals among Infants and Young Children

Studies on infant brain and cognitive development in other domains provide some evidence for the use of cognitive appraisals in infants and young children. While newborn stress responses are considered to be reflexes and automatic, by 8–12 weeks, these newborn responses become less frequent as the brainstem begins to develop. At this time, there is evidence of more advanced cognitive abilities, including increased attention. Among researchers, there is controversy regarding whether young infants possess complex cognitive structures. However, there is increasing evidence that by 7 months, infants have developed advanced cognitive functions, which correspond to the further development of the prefrontal cortex and other brain regions.

One of the most critical cognitive abilities at this age relevant to stress and coping is the retrieval of schemata for past events and developed working memory abilities. That is, newborns are biologically equipped to perceive and create representations of the world. With increased experiences, infants begin to develop expectations of the world, objects, and people. Thus, infants develop schema, or organized mental representations of knowledge and expectations, about the world, people, and events. By 7 months of age, infants can access these schema and hold them in their working memory (short-term memory that temporarily stores and holds information). The implication of this is that infants are able to appraise new situations in relation to their expectations, or schema. If this new information cannot be assimilated into these schema, infants may appraise the situation as stressful. For example, infants around this age who encounter unfamiliar situations or interactions that violate their expectations show fear responses and may show avoidance or crying responses. Individual differences in these fear responses result partly as a function of whether or not infants believe they can control the unfamiliar event. Thus, research on infant brain and cognitive development suggest that infants starting at around 7 months possess the cognitive capabilities to appraise events as stressful.

Infants' use of social referencing around 12 months also suggests that young infants are capable of cognitive appraisals. Social referencing refers to infants seeking information during a novel or ambiguous event by looking at the emotional reaction of another person (frequently a primary caregiver) to regulate their own behavior. Social referencing, and more generally eye gaze perception, is thought to serve as a means for infants to appraise (or reappraise) situations as stressful or not and guide infants regulation in the face of stress.

At the same time, it is quite difficult to assess stress and coping processes in infancy and therefore, this theme is often overlooked. While research in cognitive development suggests that infants possess the capabilities to cognitively appraise situations and events, whether these processes are at work in the context of stress and coping remains important questions for future research.

Common Themes in Stress and Coping Research in Infancy and Early Childhood

Although there is no consensus on the precise processes at work, various themes identify a stress and coping perspective on child development, including infancy and early childhood. First, coping is seen as a complex, multidimensional process, including a wide range of responses that can occur cognitively, emotionally, behaviorally, physiologically, socially, or in any combination of the above. Additionally, coping may be influenced by both characteristics of the infant (e.g., temperament) and the environment (e.g., the availability of a parent).

Second, coping is not a static response, but rather a dynamic, changing process. Coping is also context specific; an infant does not respond to all stress in the same way. An infant may use various different strategies or combinations of strategies during the course of a stressful event. Even given the same stressor, an infant may employ different coping strategies over time.

Third and relatedly, coping is a developmental process; coping responses change depending on one's age and the socioemotional and cognitive abilities of the individual. Accordingly, coping responses among infants may differ from the responses among 3-year-olds, even in the context of the same stressor. For example, infants typically seek proximity or contact from parents in unfamiliar laboratory contexts, whereas 3-year-olds are more likely to use distance interaction strategies, such as talking to the mother or keeping track of her whereabouts visually. Additionally, what constitutes a stressful event or situation may change with age or development. For example, an infant may be highly distressed by separation from the mother in day care whereas a 3-year-old may show little, if any, visible distress.

Fourth, the function of coping is to limit, control, minimize, or eliminate stress, including changing the stressful environment or changing one's own negative arousal or cognitions about the stressful event (e.g., cognitive restructuring, distracting yourself by refocusing your attention). A response that aims to eliminate stress or a stressful situation is still considered a coping response regardless of whether it was a successful strategy. That is, although coping efficacy is an important construct with regard to stress and coping among infants and young children, the effectiveness of a response does not factor into definitions of coping.

Stress and Coping in Infancy through Early Childhood

Coping with stress is an important developmental task in infancy that has implications for children's future well-being. Since the newborn infant possesses limited coping strategies, there is often reliance on the caregiver to help alleviate particular stressors. Caregiver–infant interactions serve to immediately soothe the infant and also foster the development of infants' positive representations of the world, which influence later coping responses. As children undergo rapid growth in cognitive, emotional, social, and physical developmental domains during the first year of life, the coping strategies of children become more differentiated and complex. As children get older they rely less on their caregiver for comfort and are able to engage in self-soothing coping responses and more complex cognitive problem-solving strategies.

Although longitudinal studies examining within person change in coping responses during development from

Table 1 Summary of observed infant coping responses to stress

Signals to elicit caregiver help	*Caregiver soothing responses*	*Infant initiated coping*
Body postures	Baby massage	Self-soothing
Crying	Holding	Non-nutritive sucking (thumb/pacifier)
Eye contact	Non-nutritive sucking (thumb/pacifier)	Clasping hands
Fussing	Rocking	Body rubbing
Facial expressions (e.g., grimacing)	Smiling	Use of security object (e.g., blanket, toy)
Gesturing	Sucrose	Distraction
	Vocalizations	Gaze aversion
		Closing eyes
		Turning head
		Playing with toy
		Looking/playing with hands
		Vocalizing distress
		Seeking proximity to caregiver/attachment behaviors
		Cognitive restructuring/reappraisal (e.g., changing thoughts or behavior given cues from social referencing)
		Anticipatory coping behaviors

infancy to later childhood are a gap, cross-sectional studies provide an overview of some common coping strategies utilized by infants and children in the face of stress. Considerable individual differences are evident in infants' reactivity to stress and their responding to caregiver or self-initiated coping behaviors. Some commonly observed coping responses among infants are presented in **Table 1**.

Types of Stressors in Infancy and Early Childhood

Although infants early in life cannot use language to let us know they are feeling stressed, physiological and behavioral responses indicate that infants do experience stress. Responses that indicate infants are stressed include increased cortisol levels and heart rate, crying and grimacing, and movements such as arching the back or turning the head. Older infants evidence distress by decreasing exploration and seeking proximity to a caregiver. Additionally, infants exposed to stress may show disruptions in their sleeping and eating patterns and may be more prone to becoming sick. However, a confound in research is that it is sometimes difficult to distinguish between stress and coping responses among infants. For example, crying is a sign that an infant is stressed; however, it can also be a coping response with the function of eliciting caregiver help. Moreover, some situations and interactions may be stressful for infants, even if they do not exhibit behavioral signs of distress.

There are many different events and interactions that are stressful for infants, as well as great individual variability in the types of situations that induce stress. Some of these stressors are physiological stressors, which can include events that cause discomfort or bodily pain. These include stressors such as being hungry or tired, having a wet diaper, cold or hot temperatures, physical exams, being weighed and handled, inoculation and heel stick procedures, changes in routines, and maternal separation. Also, loud noises, bright lights, or overstimulation may be stressful experiences for infants. These stressors are common among newborn and young infants. Other stressors are psychological stressors. These types of stressors include certain person–environment interactions or interpersonal interactions. Environmental stressors are changes in the infant's physical environment, including changes in a child's routine or being in an unfamiliar environment (e.g., doctor's office) or exposed to unfamiliar objects. Interpersonal stressors include interactions with others that induce stress. Among infants as young as 1–3 months, certain types of interactions that include inappropriate levels of stimulation, even with familiar adults can be distressing. For example, studies using a still-face paradigm, in which mothers are instructed to present a still face to their infants and not respond to them, suggest that infants are particularly distressed by these interactions. In contrast, overstimulation, such as intrusive play which can include getting very close to an infant's face or repeatedly presenting the infant with toys can also be distressing. Essentially, when the level of stimulation does not match the level of stimulation an infant is expecting or desires, the interaction can be distressing. Other types of interpersonal stressors that emerge around 7–8 months of age include interactions with unfamiliar people or separation from a primary caregiver. There is considerable individual variability in how infants respond to these interpersonal stressors. For example, infant responses when exposed to unfamiliar people may depend on the physical characteristics and behavior of the person, as well as if the environment is unfamiliar as well.

The types of events that are stressful for infants and children change over time. For example, exposure to strangers is not stressful to a 1-month-old baby; however, this same experience is quite stressful for children at around 7–8 months. For older infants, events that interfere with their goals and desires are distressing, such as having a favorite toy taken away.

Infant stress can be assessed both through physiological (e.g., cortisol) and behavioral (e.g., crying, facial expression) responses. However, behavioral and physiological indices of stress do not necessarily show similar results and each response may serve a different function. For example, an infant may cry during a physical exam (behavioral index of stress), but not show elevated cortisol levels (physiological index of stress). Therefore, there is no gold standard or best method for assessing the level of stress experienced by infants. Given these factors, using multiple indices of stress is optimal.

Caregivers Responses to Infant Stress

Newborn and young infants have limited coping response. Caregivers' responses to stress are one of the important ways that young infants cope with stress. Thus, infants, in the early part of life, heavily rely on their caregiver to help alleviate their stress. Moreover, the caregivers' responses to their infant's signals of stress are critical to their child's physiological and socioemotional development. For example, young infants show increased cortisol levels when exposed to mild stressors, such as routine physical exams. Over the first year of life, cortisol reactivity decreases such that mild stressors no longer activate cortisol release. However, there is a hypersensitive period early in life in which the caregiving environment can significantly impact the activation, and development, of the HPA system and the developing brain.

While the caregiver of an infant certainly can include fathers, the majority of research in this area involves the mother–child relationship. Mother–child, or caregiver–child, interactions during times of stress have long-lasting implications for infants' socioemotional development, which has been especially well-documented on studies of mother–infant attachment and behaviors associated with the attachment relationship. Specifically, sensitivity and responsiveness of the mother to her infant's needs is especially important in shaping the infants' attachment security, including internal working models of herself as worthy of support and love and the world as a positive environment.

Infant crying and fussing signals to and motivates caregivers to respond to the source of their baby's stress. Interestingly, maternal responsiveness to infant cries is associated with decreased crying over the first year of life. As infants become older, they are able to more actively seek the support of their caregiver through eye contact, gesturing, vocalizations, and seeking proximity to their caregiver. Caregivers' responsiveness and sensitivity to their infants' stress responses are critical for their socio-emotional development, and especially the development of a secure attachment, which can buffer children from the effects of stress.

Early in infancy, caregivers play an especially active and important role in paying attention to when their infant is stressed and helping their infant cope with this stress, including soothing. Substantial research has been concerned with the effectiveness of maternal soothing behaviors. The effectiveness of soothing behaviors applied by fathers remains a question for future research. One method with empirical support for soothing is the use of sucrose. Specifically, sucrose has been found to serve as an analgesic and reduce infant crying, especially among newborns. Caregivers may also soothe their infants with massage. Tiffany Field and colleagues have conducted extensive research on infant massage therapy. Infant massage consists of stroking motions for about 15 min in length. Non-nutritive sucking, through the use of a pacifier has also been shown to be effective in reducing infant crying. Maternal soothing behaviors can include both proximal and distal responses. Proximal behaviors include actions in which the mother has direct contact with the infant, such as rubbing the infant's back or the use of massage. Distal behaviors include responses such as vocalizations (e.g., 'It's okay, baby') and smiling.

By attending to their infants' signs of distress and soothing them, caregivers can help infants learn how to cope effectively and regulate themselves during times of stress. Thus, caregivers' responses to infant stress serve two functions: (1) to immediately soothe and calm the infant; and (2) to help the infant develop a repertoire of effective strategies to cope with future stress.

Coping Responses in Infancy

While there is heavy reliance on caregivers, the newborn infant possesses coping mechanisms to deal with stress. While these responses are limited at first, they become differentiated and complex as the infant develops. Physiological coping appears in newborn infants and is an unconscious and automatic process. That is, the newborn is capable of regulating physiological changes that occur as a result of stress in order to regain homeostasis within a short period of time. Reflexes, such as sucking and particular body movements, also characterize coping processes in newborn and young infants. However, as mentioned previously, the caregiving environment influences infants' physiological coping with stress.

Infants also engage in psychological coping strategies. The primary coping strategies frequently observed among newborns include emotion-focused and self-soothing strategies, such as head or gaze aversion, looking at hands or clasping hands, body rubbing, non-nutritive sucking (e.g., pacifier, thumb-sucking), and signals to elicit help from a caregiver (e.g., crying, fussing). Psychological coping strategies, however, become more prominent around 3 months of age. By 3 months, infants' coping strategies include responses in which they withdraw from the environment, such as averting their gaze or closing their eyes, or responses in which they interact with the environment, such as distracting themselves with an object. However, while infants have a number of coping strategies available to them, which one they actually choose depends on a number of factors, including their motor capabilities, temperament, level of distress, and caregiver signals. From 3 to about 9 months, the number of coping behaviors increases and the frequency with which infants use multiple coping responses also increases.

Infant coping skills become further developed as their motor abilities and skills become more sophisticated. For example, as infants begin to crawl, they can seek proximity to their caregiver and as infants' reach and grasp abilities develop, in addition to their visual development, they are able to use objects to help self-soothe. They can pick up objects, use them in new ways, and observe the textures and various features of a toy. Essentially, this is a form of self-distracting.

Coping Responses in Early Childhood

Compared to newborns and younger infants, the coping responses of older infants, in general, are more differentiated. Older infants use more self-soothing and problem-focused coping strategies as their motor, language, and cognitive skills develop in comparison to younger infants who rely primarily on the caregiver or tactics such as gaze aversion.

However, older infants still seek their caregiver in times of stress. As their awareness of different arousal states increases and they gain an understanding that their caregiver has an effect on their arousal, infants more actively seek support from their caregiver. They also begin to display communicative behaviors, such as seeking eye contact. Children are able to use language to vocalize their distress, as well as nonverbal behaviors, such as pointing and gesturing.

During early childhood, the use of crying decreases and the use of strategies requiring cognitive processing increase. By around 12 months of age, the emergence of problem-solving strategies is evident. For example, older infants can leave a stressful situation or physical act to remove a stressor (e.g., remove an obstacle to a favorite toy). Additionally, children have the ability to talk about their emotions. Older infants also engage in anticipatory coping responses. That is, given their experiences, they can prepare themselves for imminent stressors (e.g., doctor's visit). For example, children may develop a preference for a particular object, such as a security blanket, that they seek in times of stress to help them self-soothe.

Links between Stress and Coping and the Well-Being of Infants and Young Children

Adversity, stress, and exposure to risk do not lead directly to developmental disorders or health-related problems in infants. The development of disorder or health-related problems is assumed to reflect a series of micro-social processes that occur interactively over time, typically reflecting gradual adaptations by individuals to circumstances. Even a stressor that has relatively immediate health-related consequences does so by inducing complex patterns of change at a micro-social level; that is, specificity and multidimensional characterization of response processes remain important to the possibility of causal explanation. Thus, stress and coping processes, responses, and styles that occur in specific biopsychosocial contexts account for relations between risk factors on the one hand, and adjustment or health-related outcomes on the other.

The stress and coping perspective has proved to be useful for advancing a process-oriented study of infant development. That is, this perspective advances a notion of functioning and development in terms of complex processes of responses unfolding over time. Thus, this approach has fostered moving the discipline of infancy research beyond simply the identification of associations between predictors (e.g., stressor) and outcomes, and conceptualizations of infant functioning in terms of static notions of global outcomes or diagnostic classifications.

Rather than focusing on infant coping in terms of something the infant 'has', the stress and coping perspective fosters the study of an individual's dynamic, constantly changing adaptations to situations and contexts of family, day care, or other settings. This approach stresses how children adapt to an ever-changing and constantly flowing pattern of events. Change, for good or ill, occurs gradually and in terms of multiple and multidimensional responses to challenges, exigencies or demands of daily life. Although traumatic events may sometimes have disproportionate effects (e.g., loss of a parent, long-term separation from a parent), regardless of the rate of change, it is still the case that change is micro-social and, ultimately, involves highly specific patterns of intra- and extraorganismic interactions.

While stress is an inevitable part of life, effectively responding and coping with stress is important for successful development. Exposure to certain types of stress can be a risk factor for later psychopathology. Studies of these links support the importance and significance of stress and coping for understanding the course of infant and early child development. The coping responses used by infants and their caregiver have been linked with both concurrent and later child outcomes. With regard to physiological development, Megan Gunnar and colleagues have shown how stress can affect the neurobiology of infants. Whereas a majority of studies on the neurobiological effects of stress have been conducted with laboratory mammals (e.g., rats), studies with human infants have examined links between how infants and young children cope with family stress and later adjustment, including studies of temperament and attachment and later development. In the specific context of marital conflict, heightened negative emotional reactivity and arousal, withdrawal, direct intervention, and aggressive responding have been linked with later externalizing and internalizing problems. Externalizing problems refers to behaviors such as aggression, delinquency, and hyperactivity. Internalizing problems refer to behaviors such as anxiety, depression, somatic complaints, and withdrawal.

Notably, although certain coping responses may be linked with poor outcomes later in life, these responses may also be adaptive for children in the short term. That is, these responses can help infants and children immediately deal with the current stressor. However, over time, these coping responses may develop into a pattern of behavior that is inappropriate in other settings or situations, becoming maladaptive. For example, non-nutritive sucking is an effective coping strategy for infants, decreasing infant crying. As children become older, non-nutritive sucking, either thumb or pacifier, may be maladaptive in that children do not learn to vocalize their distress or learn active problem-solving strategies to cope. Additionally, in certain cultures thumb-sucking or the use of a pacifier may be socially unacceptable.

Some levels of stress may actually be beneficial for young children and in some contexts may enhance development. Exposure to stress allows children to develop a set of coping strategies and through experience children learn which strategies are effective. However, exposure to severe forms of stress, such as child neglect or physical aggression, or chronic levels of even mild stress pose a significant risk for children's developmental outcomes, especially when the child has not developed effective coping strategies.

A point meriting emphasis is that relations between risk factors, stress and coping processes, and psychological and physical health may change significantly during development. For example, the infants' use of parents as attachment figures or for exploration of the social or physical environment is different in important ways from the way adolescents use parents as attachment figures. However, there may be important continuities and similarities between infancy and later periods of development. For example, attachment security is clearly important for the adjustment and well-being of both infants and adolescents. However, age, *per se*, is not necessarily the best index of period of development. In other words, since aging itself is a process, periods of development may be better conceptualized in terms of processes of biopsychosocial functioning rather than chronological age.

Current Research on Stress and Coping among Infants and Young Children

There is limited research on theoretical perspectives of stress and coping in infants, and most research is stressor specific. Below current knowledge on two common areas in the stress and coping literature in which there is substantial conceptual development are reviewed, along with theoretical frameworks for understanding stress and coping processes and children's development and adjustment. First, infant attachment patterns as a working model for dealing with stress is reviewed. Next, children's exposure to marital conflict is discussed and the EST is presented as a theoretical framework for understanding children's coping with family stress.

Infant Coping and Attachment

The exact coping response a caregiver or infant uses is, of course, dependent on various factors, including the particular context or stressor. Therefore, an extensive review of infant coping responses is difficult without considering the specific stressor eliciting responses from infants. We have considered stress responses among infants, effective responses among caregivers for alleviating infant stress, and coping responses observed by infants and young children. Next, we discuss children's coping responses to maternal separation (or separation from a primary caregiver) and the role of attachment in infant stress and coping. Mother–infant attachment is not only an indication of the mother–children relationship, but attachment behaviors are activated during times of stress. Thus, understanding children's attachment provides a window from which to explore children's coping responses to stressful events and situations.

Historical overview of infant attachment research

The theoretical framework for attachment was developed by John Bowlby and Mary Ainsworth. Bowlby posited that infants had an evolutionary drive to attach to their caregivers and that attachment was necessary for infants' survival. Moreover, Bowlby posited that infants were active, competent, and self-motivated to form an attachment with their caregiver. His position, however, ran counter to the popular position among psychoanalysts who considered infant attachment important solely because caregivers provided food and nourishment.

Bowlby proposed that attachment was more than just a function of meeting infants' biological needs, such as feeding, and that the security and comfort provided by caregivers was critical to the development of an organism. Bowlby's position was consistent with Harry Harlow's seminal study with rhesus monkeys in 1958. Specifically, Harlow found that when given the choice between a wire surrogate mother (constructed mother-figure made of wire) with a feeding nipple and a cloth surrogate mother, infant rhesus monkeys preferred the cloth 'mother' and used this surrogate as a means of comfort when scared or stressed. This study underscored the idea that mothers could provide a source of comfort for their infants during times of stress.

Bowlby proposed four stages of attachment. In the first stage, when infants are between 0 and 3 months old, infants do not differentiate among individuals and do not seem to be attached to one particular person. Thus, their signals when stressed are not directed toward any particular person. Their main goal is to preserve homeostasis. When stressed, infants in this stage cope by signaling distress primarily by crying, thereby promoting proximity and contact with a caregiver. Additionally, sucking responses help soothe infants in this stage.

The second stage occurs approximately between 3 and 6 months. In this stage, infants prefer to be with a select group of people, primarily the caregiver. Infants in this stage utilize more self-comforting coping responses, such as non-nutritive sucking. Infants in this stage also begin to understand that their caregiver is a source of safety and comfort and signals of distress are directed to one or more discriminated caregivers. Thus, infants in this stage are seeking proximity and contact with a particular person(s).

By the third stage, which occurs between 6 and 12 months, infants have formed an attachment with a primary caregiver (e.g., mother) and perhaps a secondary caregiver (e.g., father). During this time, the use of transitional objects (e.g., toy, security blanket) is an effective means of coping with stress. Additionally, the child is able to use the caregiver as a secure base to explore the world. In times of stress, infants can use their locomotion skills to actively seek proximity and contact with their caregiver.

Bowlby also described a fourth stage characterized by goal-corrected behavior which occurred later in life (at about age 3 years), in which the child is able to understand the mental state of her caregiver and adjust her behavior. Bowlby's model of attachment was not constrained to infancy; rather, it takes a lifespan developmental perspective.

A key component of Bowlby's model of infant attachment is the development of an internal working model concerning the self and others in relation to the self. Bowlby posited that through her interactions with the world and her caregiver, the infant begins to develop expectations about the caregiver's availability and responsiveness, as well as her own deservingness for care. This internal working model is partly responsible for individual differences in attachment styles. Moreover, attachment reflects information regarding the infants' current state (stressed vs. nonstressed), the state of the environment, and the availability of the caregiver. Ainsworth's work on attachment provided empirical support for Bowlby's theory, and marked an important new direction for empirical study of infants' socioemotional development.

Attachment patterns and coping with stress

Ainsworth noted three distinct attachment styles: labeled secure, insecure-ambivalent, and insecure-avoidant. Attachment patterns are measured by observing children's responses to being separated from their caregiver (i.e., a stressor), in an assessment called the Strange Situation. Secure children feel comfortable exploring the unfamiliar room while their mother is present, effectively using the mother as a source of security in a stressful context. For example, these children might explore a new toy in the room, but they also turn around to interact with their mothers by showing them the toy. They are distressed by being separated from their mothers, but are quickly soothed and comforted during the reunion phase when their mothers return. Ambivalent children, however, are fearful of the unfamiliar situation and clingy with their mothers from the beginning. They are relatively more distressed (e.g., cry more) during the separation period and are not quickly comforted by their mother's return (e.g., continue to cry). Insecure-avoidant children appear independent and generally do not interact with their mothers, evidenced by little conversation with the parent, physical drifting and orienting the face and body away from the mother. They do not appear distressed when separated from their mothers and often do not react when reunited with their mothers, sometimes snubbing the mother. In 1990, Mary Main and Judith Soloman added a fourth category, labeled disorganized/disoriented. These infants were highly aroused and distressed while being separated from their caregiver and appear to have no coherent coping strategy for dealing with the stressful situation.

However, researchers have noted the difficulty in examining stress and coping responses of children when separated from a caregiver or any other stressful situation. For example, is it the case that insecure-avoidant children are not stressed by being separated from their mothers, or could it be the case that they are stressed but cope with the situation by distracting themselves or using avoidant coping strategies? Therefore, some have argued that differences in attachment behavior could indicate differences in appraisal of the situation (stressful vs. not stressful) or differences in children's abilities to cope effectively.

Ainsworth had also conducted home observations with families and noted associations between infants' attachment behavior and mothers' parenting behavior. Specifically, securely attached infants had mothers who were responsive to their children's needs; whereas insecurely attached infants had mothers who were unresponsive, intrusive, or inconsistent in their caregiving behavior. The link between caregiving patterns and infant attachment provided support for Bowlby's notions of the effects of these early experiences on infants developing internal working models of self and the world, including caregivers. That is, infants whose mothers are neglectful and ignore their child seemingly develop a representation of the world in which the caregiver is seen as unreliable. Nonetheless, even insecure attachments can be seen as adaptive in the short term. For these children, it is adaptive to be more independent. Similarly, for mothers who are inconsistent in their caregiving, it is adaptive for ambivalent children to cry a lot in order to gain their mothers' attention and have their needs met.

Attachment security, coping, and later development

Alan Sroufe and colleagues at the University of Minnesota provided further empirical support for the attachment categories observed by Ainsworth, based on longitudinal study. Empirical findings from his studies have shown that securely attached children in infancy are better problem-solvers at age 2 years. These children are less frustrated by challenging tasks and appropriately use their mother for help. Insecure children, however, are easily frustrated by difficult tasks and are not as good at problem-solving. Moreover, insecure attachment has been linked with poor academic achievement and ratings of unpopularity in school by both teachers and peers.

Grazyna Kochanska and colleagues have found that insecure attachment is related to displays of more negative, and less positive, emotions and the inability to delay gratification. Moreover, Gunnar and colleagues have noted that insecure attachment is related to increased production of cortisol during stressful events that can have potentially harmful consequences for children's neurological development. Increased cortisol is also related to inabilities to concentrate and lack of impulse control, which may affect coping responses. Thus, whereas an insecure attachment style is adaptive for infants in the short-term, the potential negative consequences of these attachment behaviors may make them maladaptive for socioemotional functioning and coping responses across the life span.

Coping with Exposure to Marital Conflict in Infancy and Early Childhood

Infants and young children are not only affected by events and situations that directly involve them, but can become stressed by seeing other family members that are stressed. Family processes and the relationship among other family members have been implicated as important factors shaping children's developmental trajectories. For example, interparental conflict is a risk factor for children's broader adjustment, linked with both internalizing and externalizing problems, as well as social, academic, and physiological functioning (e.g., sleep). Highlighting the significance of marital conflict as a stressor in early childhood, marital disagreements are inevitable and children are likely exposed to conflict on virtually an everyday basis. Moreover, exposure to marital conflict is stressful for children, and children's coping responses to conflict mediate over time the effect of conflict on children's development.

Although popular belief is that infants are too young to understand and be affected by marital interactions, empirical studies have shown that infants as young as 6 months can distinguish between interadult anger and other emotions, and respond differently depending on the emotional tone of the interaction. Infants and children exposed to marital conflict show signs of increased negative emotional arousal and facial expressions of distress, cry, and distressed body movements, such as freezing (remaining motionless for an extended period of time) or covering their ears. Some children may verbalize their discomfort or leave the interaction or distract themselves by playing with a toy and refocusing their attention. Children as young as 12 months may become involved in interparental conflicts as a mediator in order to try and resolve and stop their parents' dispute. Somatic responses when exposed to interparental conflict include increased heart rate and systolic blood pressure and elevated skin conductance compared to baseline levels.

However, as with other stressors, there are individual differences in children's appraisals of marital conflict as a stressful event and their responses to cope with exposure to conflict. There is also great variability in children's outcomes associated with marital conflict. Why are some children distressed by marital conflict while others appear unaffected? And why do some children respond to conflict by withdrawing (e.g., hiding in their rooms), while other children, for example, respond aggressively (e.g., misbehaving to distract their parents). With regard to these issues, EST, proposed by Patrick Davies and E. Mark Cummings, provides bases for understanding children's regulatory processes in response to marital conflict (see **Figure 2**). EST has also been recently extended to apply to other family processes in addition to marital conflict that may be stressful for children (e.g., parental depression, parental drinking problems).

Theoretical model of children's coping responses to family stress: Emotional Security Theory

The EST has roots in attachment theory and posits that children's responses to marital conflict serve the function of preserving or regaining a higher-order goal of emotional security within the family. Thus, children appraise marital conflict in terms of the implications the interaction has for their felt security and safety within the family system. For example, marital conflict that is negative in nature (i.e., negative emotional displays, destructive conflict tactics) is more likely to threaten a child's sense of security and thus more likely to be stressful for children compared to a marital disagreement that is positive in nature (i.e., calm discussion of each person's perspective, working together toward a resolution). Therefore, not all marital conflict is distressing for children; rather, destructive interparental conflict that affects the well-being and security of the child and family is stressful. This type of

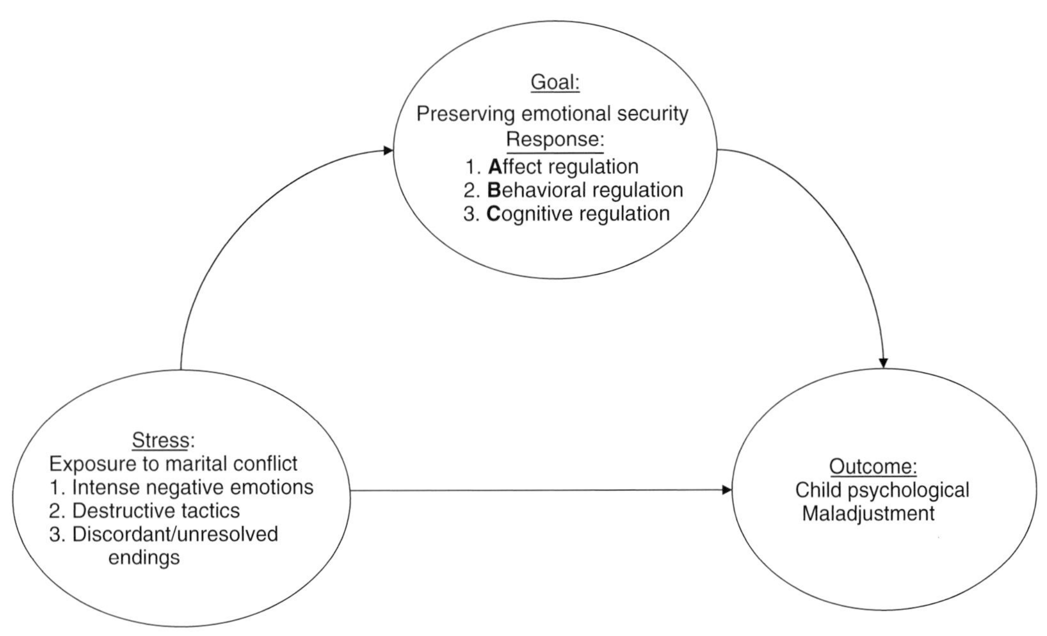

Figure 2 EST: theoretical model of the effects of marital conflict on infant and child outcomes.

interaction elicits the most pronounced activation of regulatory response systems.

EST is a developmental theory that assumes the child's emotional security can be enhanced or undermined by the quality of family relations over time. EST also emphasizes the transactional process between a child and the family system in predicting children's outcomes. That is, children's development is a dynamic interaction between the child and his or her environment that is continuously changing. Under this framework, marital conflict is not simply an environmental stressor that impacts children's development; rather, marital conflict has effects on children depending on children's prior exposure to marital conflict and the characteristics of any ongoing conflict, with children's coping processes among the processes accounting for the dynamic interaction between the child and family context. Thus, preserving emotional security is a critical goal for children, organizing their responses to marital conflict and other stressful family processes.

Children's coping responses have been implicated as a possible pathway by which marital conflict relates to children's broader adjustment. The global construct of emotional security can be measured in terms of specific regulatory processes. One regulatory process is children's emotional reactivity to interparental disagreements, which may include physiological reactions. When disagreements are perceived as threatening, children may react with fear, anger, or sadness. Characteristics of the disagreement and children's history of exposure to conflict both influence the form, intensity, and duration of these emotions.

Another regulatory process is children's behavioral reactions. Insecure children may attempt to intervene directly in the marital disagreement as a mediator, or become involved indirectly by trying to distract their parents from the argument at hand. Alternatively, children may withdraw from the interaction, removing themselves from the immediate environmental stressor in order to avoid exposure to destructive conflict. They may also become highly dysregulated in the context of emotional arousal and threats to emotional security such that no effective coping strategies are exhibited (e.g., freezing).

In sum, marital disagreements that threaten children's emotional security are stressful for children, motivating and organizing their specific coping responses in order to maintain or reinstate a sense of security. While some of these coping responses are effective and adaptive in the short-term, certain responses (e.g., misbehaving) may generalize into patterns of behavior that are inappropriate in other settings or situations (e.g., classroom), thereby potentially becoming a maladaptive coping strategy for the future and contributing to the development of adjustment problems later in life.

A useful analogy for thinking about regulatory processes in the service of emotional security is to think about emotional security as a bridge between the child and the world. When the marital relationship is functioning well, it serves as a secure base, a structurally sound bridge, supporting the child's exploration and relationship with others. When destructive conflict erodes the bridge, children become hesitant to move forward and lack confidence, or may move forward in a dysregulated way, unable to find appropriate footing within themselves or in interactions with others.

Individual Differences in Infant Stress and Coping: Temperament

Why are some infants more vulnerable to stress than other infants? And why do some infants cry during stress while other infants distract themselves with a toy? Child temperament has been implicated as one of the many factors (e.g., cognitive and motor skills) that may account for individual differences in infants' and children's responses to stress. Temperament has been defined as individual differences in emotional and behavioral reactivity that is evident from early on in life. Moreover, temperamental traits are consistent over time and across situations, and, therefore, stable over time. It is posited that temperament has a biological basis with genetic origins, however it is acknowledged that temperament can also be influenced and modified by early experiences.

One of the first studies dealing with infant temperament was the New York Longitudinal Study, which was conducted by Alexander Thomas and Stella Chess in 1956. During this study, they observed great individual differences in infant behavior and identified nine temperamental traits. These nine temperamental traits were clustered into three categories characterizing children: easy, difficult, and slow-to-warm up. Studies on infant and child temperament also frequently use the categories behaviorally inhibited and behaviorally uninhibited to characterize children.

Temperament, thus, affects what is stressful for infants and may facilitate or hinder responses to stress, including initial physiological responses to stress. For example, children high in attentional control may be better able to use coping skills involving distraction or shifting one's attention. Infants with high negative emotionality may have a tendency toward feeling anxious or threatened; therefore, they may be more likely to find novel situations stressful, be less receptive to soothing strategies, and find it more difficult to implement emotion-focused coping strategies compared to infants with high positive emotionality.

Studies on temperament and coping pioneered by Jerome Kagan and colleagues have found that behaviorally inhibited children are high in reactivity and therefore have a lower threshold for stress and a slower recovery time from stress, and exhibit elevated cortisol responses to stress. Inhibited temperament is related to the use of avoidance or withdrawal as coping mechanisms. Uninhibited children, in contrast, are low in reactivity and more likely to use approach-oriented coping strategies. Temperament is also related to attachment style such that inhibited children are more likely to be insecurely attached.

However, an important concept in temperament research is goodness of fit. That is, although research has demonstrated associations between temperament and specific developmental outcomes, ultimately it is the match between infant temperament and the caregiving environment that influences children's development. For example, whereas behaviorally inhibited children are more reactive to stressful events and interactions, having a responsive caregiver to help aid the infant in coping effectively and self-soothe can buffer children from any negative developmental outcomes.

Summary and Future Directions

Stress and coping research is challenging to conduct with infants and young children who cannot directly tell us how they feeling or what they are thinking. Understandably, currently models of stress and coping in infancy are based on adult models. These models elucidate the processes that may be at work during times of stress and the mechanisms underlying exposure to certain risk and stress and later development. However, future research is needed to enhance and better articulate these models for infants and young children. For example, more evidence for children's cognitive appraisals during stress would help strengthen current models of stress and coping, or provide direction for modifying models to more accurately capture the processes at work for young infants.

While the precise processes underlying infants' coping with stress need refining and further development, studies show that coping is a complex, multidimensional process that is constantly changing as infants develop more sophisticated motor, cognitive, emotional, and social skills. Newborn infants possess some abilities to deal with stress, such as reflexes and physiological regulatory abilities; however, the primary coping skills among young infants are signals for caregiver responses. Caregivers play a pivotal role in soothing their infants, as well as helping infants learn effective strategies to cope with stress. As the infants grow older, they are able take a more active role in coping with stress and their repertoire of responses grows and becomes more sophisticated. Additionally, with experience young children learn which strategies are effective. Stress is an inevitable part of life, yet most children do develop a repertoire of effective coping strategies and develop without any adverse consequences.

See also: Attachment; Crying; Endocrine System; Risk and Resilience; Self-Regulatory Processes; Separation and Stranger Anxiety; Temperament.

Suggested Readings

Compas BE, Connor-Smith JK, Saltzman H, Thomsen AH, and Wadsworth ME (2001) Coping with stress during childhood and adolescence: Problems, progress, and potential in theory and research. *Psychological Bulletin* 127(1): 87–127.

Cummings EM, Greene AL, and Karraker KH (eds.) (1991) *Life-Span Developmental Psychology: Perspectives on Stress and Coping.* Hillsdale, NJ: Lawrence Erlbaum Associates.
Davies PT and Cummings EM (1994) Marital conflict and child adjustment: An emotional security hypothesis. *Psychological Bulletin* 116(3): 387–411.
Field TM, McCabe PM, and Schneiderman N (eds.) (1992) *Stress and Coping in Infancy and Childhood.* Hillsdale, NJ: Lawrence Erlbaum Associates.
Gunnar MR (2006) Social regulation of stress in early child development. In: McCartney K (ed.) *Blackwell Handbook of Early Childhood Development*, pp. 106–125. Malden, MA: Blackwell Publishing.
Gross JJ (ed.) (2007) *Handbook of Emotion Regulation.* New York: Guilford Press.
Kalat JW (1998) *Biological Psychology,* 6th edn. Belmont, CA: Thompson Brooks/Cole Publishing Co.
Kopp CB (1989) Regulation of distress and negative emotions: A developmental view. *Developmental Psychology* 25(3): 343–354.
Lazarus RS and Folkman S (1984) *Stress, Appraisal, and Coping.* New York: Springer.
Lewis M and Worobey J (eds.) (1989) *Infant Stress and Coping.* San Francisco: Jossey-Bass.
Wolchik SA and Sandler IN (eds.) (1997) *Handbook of Children's Coping: Linking Theory and Intervention.* New York: Plenum.

Suckling

E Blass, University of Massachusetts, Amherst, MA, USA

Glossary

Calorimetry – Measuring heat transfer.
Catabolism – Metabolic breakdown of stored nutrients.
Inclusive fitness – Number of one's surviving offspring.
Obligatory renal clearance – Loss of fluids through the kidneys necessary to clear metabolic waste from the body.
Postprandial – After a meal.

Introduction

The nursing–suckling dynamic is the defining mammalian social behavior. It takes place in every mammalian habitat – in air, on earth and in its tunnels, and in the oceans. This conserved functional relationship reflects extraordinary morphological, hormonal, and behavioral evolutionary reorganizations that allow infants to withdraw milk sequestered from the dam's circulation from her nipple. Milk is withdrawn when nipple or teat is grasped and drawn deeply into the oropharynx under the extreme vacuum pressure exerted by the bucal musculature. Ultrasonic cinematography of suckling in human infants has revealed that milk withdrawal is achieved through the synchronized action of the infant tongue pushing up against the base, while soft palate contractions squeeze the breast from above. The pumping motion is accompanied by extreme suction that whisks the expressed milk caudally.

Morphological reorganization permitting this coordination surely started with the modification of jaw hinging in the early proto-mammals. The contrast between reptilian and mammalian jaw articulation can be appreciated from **Figure 1**, which presents in sagital plane the skull of a Tyrannosaurid and of a beaver. The reptilian articular-quadrate joint, shown in the lower-right corner of **Figure 1(a)** is thought to maximize jaw opening thereby allowing ingestion of enormous volumes in single bites (witness swallowing whole, medium-sized animals by pythons and other constrictors. Dentary-squamosal hinging of the mammalian lower jaw at the temporomandibular joint (**Figure 1(b)** right side of beaver photo, midway in vertical plane, 15% in from right) mechanically precludes the reptilian feeding pattern. However, it has permitted the evolution of the complex musculature that allows a vacuum seal to form on the milk source.

Another prominent orthodontal transition is from the reptilian full dentition at birth, with recurrent replacements, to delayed emergence with a single replacement in mammals. Although the selective advantages during the process of delayed emergence are not obvious, the endpoint has allowed for suckling to occur without the extraordinary pain that surely would result from placing highly vascularized and highly enervated mammary tissue under the extreme vacuum pressure of mature dentition.

Perhaps the most remarkable characteristic of the suckling system is that it is the ingestive pattern common to all mammals regardless of their post-weaning eating mode. This characteristic is manifest three times over. First, the topography of the suckling act differs completely from mature ingestion, which emerges fully formed. Second, approaches to the feeding source differ radically among mammals following weaning. They include pursuit and attack by carnivores, grazing, and rumination by herbivores, and the multiple forms of food approach and

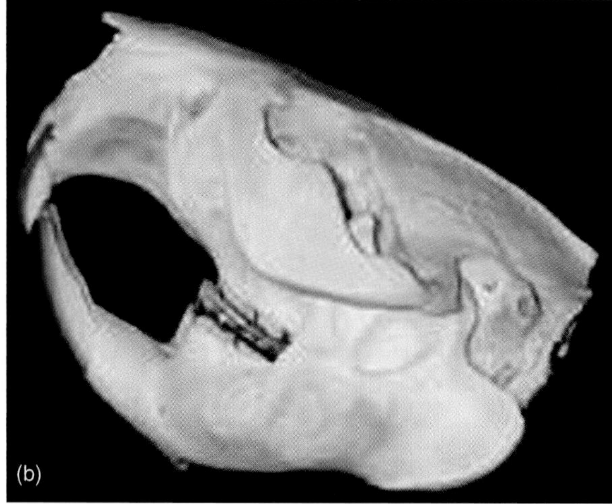

Figure 1 Skulls of a Tyrannosaurus and of a beaver that reveal the unique reptilian and mammalian articulations (see text). All extant reptilians have maintained the articular-quadrate joint arrangement.

ingestion by omnivores such as ourselves. In contrast, the suckling act shares fundamental qualities among all mammals, whether suckling takes place on land or in the water. Third, the gastrointestinal (GI) tracts of all mammals are essentially identical during the suckling period, making small allowances for the degree of fat content in the milk. At weaning, however, digestive systems have taken on the specialized characteristics that support the animal's independent feeding style.

Divining the selective advantages that were conferred during the evolution and the ultimate meshing of change between mother and offspring from the perspective of enhancing inclusive fitness is hazardous. Identifying individual steps and their corresponding selective advantages that evolved during phylogeny, culminating in the nursing–suckling adaptations, cannot be identified with any confidence, although some of the speculations are of interest. Nonetheless, core nursing–suckling systems are well conserved in mammals that inhabit remarkably different territories in which different specializations have arisen. These include differences in milk composition according to climatic demands, infant age, and available maternal diet. One of the more radical changes is in the simultaneous, independent milk fabrication, storage and delivery systems in kangaroos which deliver their second joey while they continue to nurse the elder.

However, all contemporary mammals share important organizational, morphological, and physiological features that have been integrated according to a number of base principles, that are worthy of study. Two of these principles are foundational for this article. First, nursing–suckling specializations are predicated on mechanisms of energy sequestration, transfer, and utilization. In this regard a host of effectors – physical, behavioral, and neural – accord with thermodynamic laws to reduce heat transfer from infant to surround, thereby conserving the energy donated by the mother and investing it in infant growth, especially of the central nervous system (CNS).

Second, through suckling, milk receipt, and other nest activities, infants discover a remarkable amount about food safety, kin identity, and, in principle, protection against inbreeding. Infants also learn who their mothers (parents) are and develop strong affiliative and affectional bonds with them. This intimacy allows infants to follow their parents into the world and learn about hazards and benefits without the risk inherent in trial and error. The rest of this article elaborates upon these two principles, provides experiential bases for their manifestation, and addresses underlying neural mechanisms.

Milk intake is not under physiological control until infants reach weaning age: the data substantiating this assertion are strong in rats but less extensive in humans. Drawing milk via suckling from an unlimited milk supply, either artificially or naturally, can result in a remarkable average increase of 17% body weight in pre-weaning rats during the course of a protracted suckling bout. This level of intake is not the hallmark of a system that operates under adult physiological controls. It is predicted, however, by the principle that suckling is controlled by the demands of growth and development and not by proximal changes caused by ingestion. In fact, suckling ceases because infants fall asleep. Indeed, infant rats continued to draw milk from lactating dams for as long as they were kept awake. Remarkably one rat took in 25% of its body weight in a single 2 h session. Reflux of previously ingested milk from the packed GI tract precluded further intake. An increase of this magnitude in humans can only be imagined. Some perspective is gained by considering that the sense of fullness experienced by Americans post-thanksgiving dinner is caused by only a 1.0–2.0% body weight increase. These and other data strongly suggest that the act of milk withdrawal in rats, through suckling, is not under the control of any physiological factor, that is known to curb adult intake, until 2 weeks of age, the start of the weaning period. Among these factors are gastric and GI distentions, GI peptides such as cholecystokinin that inhibit adult feeding, and acute and chronic dehydration.

The Mother as Rate-Limiting Milk Intake

Under normal circumstances the dam is the rate-limiting agent of milk intake. Her capacity to sequester milk cannot keep up with the demands of infant growth. Under such circumstances as infant rats fall asleep during a nursing bout before milk supply is exhausted, rat dams separate themselves from the infants, often leaving the nest. Human mothers, of course, put their infants down for a nap. When awakened during this immediate postprandial period, however, additional suckling and milk withdrawal will occur in both species.

Limiting milk availability is not necessarily a bad thing. Human bottle-fed infants tend to be heavier at weaning and more overweight from childhood onward than breastfed infants. Early weight biases have been well established in animal studies for decades. Manipulating rat litter size, through contraction to four or expansion to 18 pups/litter, yields different 'populations' by weaning. Body weights differed markedly as would be predicted. The differences were maintained during the growth trajectory; indeed, perturbations from the trajectory either through food restriction or food supplementation were corrected when *ad libitum* access to the basal diet was restored. Intake was adjusted and the weight trajectory re-attained. Thus early suckling experience determined weaning weight and set the parameters for later weight gain, trajectory, and defense. The mechanisms underlying these adjustments are not known. Understanding them is of particular current import given the contemporary incidence of obesity, especially in the US.

Mechanisms of Energy Conservation

Conserving the energy provided through milk is cardinal both for mother and infants. For the latter, it is transparent that a calorie lost comes at the expense of growth and development, especially of the CNS. For the mother, or both parents in species in which fathers contribute to food gathering and childrearing, the risks are not as readily quantifiable. The calculation of benefit–risk ratios must take into account the risk that mothers take to obtain food, the amount of work (energy) that they must expend to locate and seize food, and the metabolic costs of converting it into an energy form that can be utilized by the infant. Bear in mind that in order for her to maintain equilibrium, the mother eats for herself, for the energy that she is transferring to the infants and for the energy needed to convert her food to sustain infant growth. This takes on heroic proportions for smaller mammals in which litter mass can exceed that of the dam within days of parturition. Mothers of some species reduce risk by allowing the infants to 'eat off her'. The dams catabolize fat that had been stored during pregnancy so that at weaning mothers weigh less than at conception. Incidentally, obtaining water poses a more acute problem because although mothers can store food, either as a cache, or through weight gain, they can neither hoard water, nor store it systemically because of obligatory renal clearance, although some water is gained through fat catabolism.

In this light, one would predict multiple systems to minimize infant heat loss. Many of these effectors are behavioral. The simplest, of reducing infant surface:mass ratio, starts when the mother establishes contact with her young. This act markedly attenuates the rate of passive heat loss. Because rate of loss is from the entire unit, consider the following: for a 14 lb, 18 inch infant, the body mass index (BMI), that is, surface:mass ratio is $30.4\,\mathrm{kg\,m^{-2}}$; when picked up by his/her 125-lb mother, BMI is reduced to 22.4, 24.0, for a 135-lb woman and 25.7 for a 145-lb woman.

Without speculating as to why adults find infants cute and choose to pick them up and hold them or maintain other forms of contact, the reduction of heat loss passively through infant–adult contact and concomitant change in surface ratio is impressive. Of course, the thermoregulatory contribution of contact is reduced in contemporary societies through insulation of residence and clothing.

Considerable energy is also lost during crying and multiple defenses have evolved to minimize it. Crying cessation, by definition, reduces energy loss. The most effective means of arresting spontaneous crying in human infants is to mimic those facets of the mother that are involved in nursing/suckling exchanges. Thus, holding an infant is comforting, letting her suck on a pacifier also arrests crying, and when infants taste milliliter volumes of sweet or fat-flavored solutions, both crying and heart-rate are very much reduced. Crying cessation also yields considerable energetic savings. According to **Figure 2**, energy expenditure is reduced by 15% in both premature and full-term infants, as measured by direct calorimetry. Each vertical pair of data points demonstrates that stopping crying reduced caloric expenditure in each infant studied. Infants are presented in order of ascending body weight, that is, lowered surface:mass ratio, indicate reduced rate of heat loss in the larger infants, as seen in the descending slopes. Parallel slopes during crying and its cessation demonstrate that energy expended through crying was stable across infants and not linked to body weight, at least in the weight range studied by Rao *et al.*

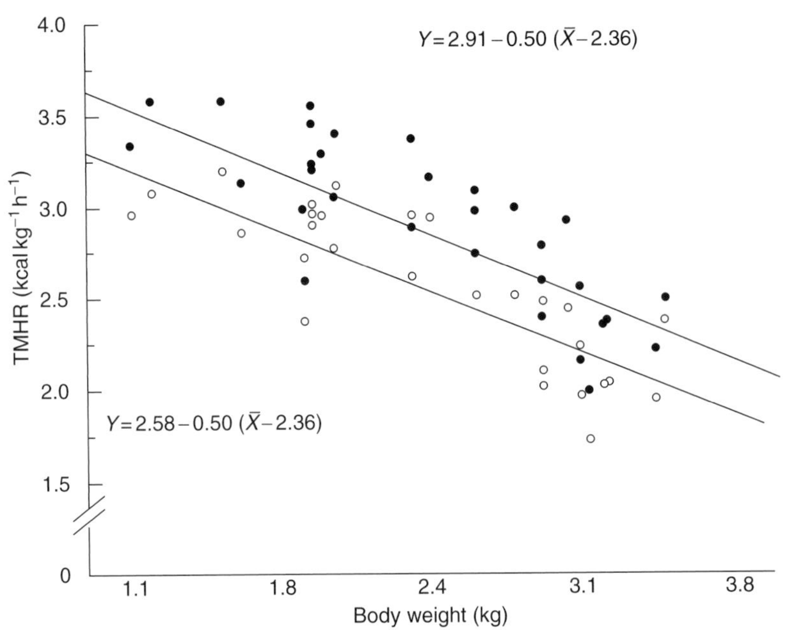

Figure 2 Rate of heat loss, measured via direct calorimetry, in premature and term infants, during crying, and its termination through sucrose administration. Each pair of points in vertical orientation represent heat loss from a single infant ($N=20$). Parallel slopes demonstrate a constancy of savings independent of body weight when crying ends. Note the declining slope of heat loss with increased body weight, that is, reduction of surface:mass ratio.

Because vulnerable newborns encounter painful stimulation during their initial hospital stay, including routine heel stick and, for many males, circumcision, we sought to identify natural means of pain alleviation. As reviewed by Blass and Barr, most compounds in the pharmacopia that relieve juvenile or adult pain are either ineffective in newborns (e.g., acetometaphin) or downright dangerous (morphine). Accordingly, solutions that reduce vocalizations and are nocifensive in rodents were evaluated in human newborns. The rat studies framed the hypotheses to be tested in human infants. Tasting sweet (sucrose, fructose, glucose) or fatty solutions considerably elevate escape from heat stress in infant rats. Parallel findings were obtained in human infants. Sweet solutions eliminated spontaneous crying and markedly reduced crying caused by heel lance that allowed blood collection for phenylketonuria (PKU) evaluation. The parallels between rat and human infants concerning pain relief abound. Thus, nonnutritive sucking (NNS) is analgesic for both, as is simple contact in the absence of suckling. Moreover, crying during and following circumcision is markedly reduced in infants who suck a sweetened pacifier before, during, and following the procedure. This may underlie the effectiveness of having infants suck gauze sweetened with wine during Jewish ritual circumcision. (A number of Mohels have told me that they further sweeten the already sweet ceremonial wine with sucrose, to help reduce crying.)

Parallel neurotransmitter mechanisms between rat and human are also in play further attesting to the remarkable 'point-to-point' conservation between these omnivores. The broad-spectrum opioid antagonists, naloxone and naltrexone, block sweet- and fat-induced analgesia in rats. Comfort provided by dam contact or NNS, however, is not blocked even by very high doses of naloxone. Although antagonists cannot be administered for experimental purposes in human infants, opioid mediation can be studied indirectly in infants born to women who had been in methadone treatment during pregnancy. Long-term methadone treatment functionally raises the threshold for opioid efficacy. As predicted, sucrose did not reduce crying in these infants; pacifier sucking did, however. Parallel antagonist effects on vocalization and pain in newborn rats provides indirect evidence for common, multiple, conserved pathways of distress and pain relief in these two omnivores that eat common diets in their niches of co-habitation.

Contemporary histochemical techniques help address fundamental issues concerning newborn pain. Activity in pain transmission pathways can be quantified through radioactive ligands that indicate activity of early genes triggered by noxious stimulation at different levels of the neuroaxis, Ren *et al.* demonstrated that sucrose taste blocked pain afferents before they entered the spinal cord. It works like this. Sucrose and other sweet solutions engage taste afferents that synapse in the brainstem with the descending inhibitory tract. The tract crosses the spinal cord to synapse in the dorsal horn, thereby blocking pain afferents at their spinal point of entry. Obviously such studies cannot be undertaken with current technology in human infants.

The following is suggestive for parallel mechanisms, however. First, every characteristic of pain inhibition and vocalization reduction in rats has also been obtained in humans in all details. This includes counterintuitive findings such as flat dose–response functions and additivity of afferents, contact, and taste. As indicated, provisional data support independent neurochemical pathways for taste and tactile calming and antinociception afferents. The following events have impressed upon us the potency of pain blockade exerted by human mothers on their newborns. After watching the first 4 min of video-recording of a study to determine the protection offered by nursing against the pain of heel lance, we asked our colleagues, Lisa Miller and Larry Gray when the heel lance was going to occur. “Oh, about 3 minutes ago”, they chortled.

We reviewed the tapes in detail. There was no sign that the infant had experienced anything untoward. Brow did not furrow; heart rate did not increase and the infant did not cry. This infant’s response to the heel lance was representative. Although it is certainly possible that blockade was central in nature, the total absence of any hint of painful experience is consistent with the idea that the pain sensation did not reach the brain and was stopped at the entry to the spinal cord. This will have to be resolved by imaging studies.

In short, a wealth of studies attest to elaborate, redundant, parallel, evolutionarily maintained features of mammalian mother–infant interactions that reduce energy expenditure and protect against stress. These redundant systems, by conserving infant energy for the business of growth and differentiation, presumably enhance infant fitness. Moreover, because the energy provided by the mother is not wasted through crying and activity, she has to eat less with a concomitant reduction in time away from the litter and all of its attendant risks. These speculations have not been put to empirical test.

Conditioning in the Nest

The past 25 years have witnessed sea changes in how newborn human and animal cognitive and learning capacities are conceptualized and in their potential for experiential enrichment. Many of these advances in understanding of newborn and infant cognitive capacities and structures are admirably covered in these volumes. In what follows we discuss conditioning that occurs during suckling exchanges in the nest and in other interactions between infants, mothers, and siblings. The discussion hinges on infants’ capacities to represent and be attracted to their mothers (fathers and siblings too) through her sensory characteristics and behaviors that either predict or are associated with two vital events that underpin neural growth and differentiation during the nursing period. One refers to energy gain and conservation, as discussed above. A second refers to the punctate episodes of excitation provided by mothers prior to nursing their infants. This excitation, so vital for normal central growth, provides a basis for sustaining behavior and inducing preference for the stimulating source. Central stimulation induces the neural reorganizations that underlie formation of maternal representations and their attractiveness to infants. Let us first address calming in rats and humans as a source of maternal attraction, and putative underlying mechanisms.

A series of studies by Shide and Blass in which either sucrose or corn oil was infused into infant rats mouths during and following exposure to an astringent orange scent, helps reveal the nature of the attraction. Ten-day-old infants were first exposed to orange odor and then either injected with isotonic saline (control) or naloxone. Then either sucrose or corn oil was infused orally and the infants were soon returned to their mothers. They were individually tested 2 days later by being placed on a screen fitted into a container covered with bedding, half of which was scented with orange, the other half contained plain bedding. In a replicate study, infants were conditioned in the same manner, but without receiving any injections prior to the oral infusions. They received either naloxone or control injections 2 days later just prior to testing.

Linking orange odor with either sucrose or corn oil infusions markedly altered infant rat preference behavior. Whereas rats that had been previously exposed to orange odor avoided it, those for which the odor predicted either sucrose or corn oil, preferred the odor relative to controls. Naloxone pretreatment reversed the preference, suggesting that conditioning hinged upon opioid release by the solutions, which presumably targeted reward elements in the brain.

The endogenous opioid system must be both functional and available for preference expression because naloxone injections prior to testing eliminated preference for the conditioning odor. Infant rats and humans are attracted to odors that had predicted or were linked with substances causing opioid release. The odor either releases endogenous opioids, or sensitizes (i.e., upregulates), opioid receptors. Such changes may underlie attractiveness of mothers to their infants. The mechanisms underlying attraction to mothers based on infant contact or suckling have not been identified, but they are not opioid mediated.

The balance between excitation leading to brain stimulation, on the one hand, and calming through contact, promoting energy conservation, and infant growth, also contributes to infant’s learning about their mothers and forming preferences for them. There are multiple pathways through which this is achieved. A prenatal pathway for learning about maternal voice was identified by DeCasper and his students who demonstrated that newborns differentially sucked a pacifier that allowed them to hear their mother's voice. The mechanism presumably reflects the repetitive exposure to the mother's voice *in utero*. Infants must also match the critical features *ex utero* absent the noisy uterine ambient provided by cardiovascular and intestinal rumblings and taking into account the shift from transduction through bone conduction to airborne transduction.

Maternal recognition in rats also reflects synchrony between prenatal fluid-borne olfactory stimulation of the vomeronasal organ and postnatal airborne stimulation of the primary olfactory mucosa. Rat newborns match the odor of amniotic fluid deposited by the mother on her nipples with that of amniotic fluid sampled as fetuses. The match appears to occur at the junction of the basolateral and basomedial amygdalar nuclei that carry afferents from vomeronasal and primary olfactory systems, respectively.

Preventing an agreement between the olfactory properties of the odors experienced pre- and postnatally, prevents initial suckling, even when newborns are held in contact with the nipple. This suggests that the matched olfactory stimulation 'permits' the tactile features of the nipple to elicit the rooting and grasping behaviors that culminate in nipple attachment.

The rat studies introduced excitation as an important element into the mix of factors that could sustain learning about certain maternal olfactory characteristics. Brain excitation through catecholamine release is vital for brain development, and this starts at birth. For rats, catecholamine release appears to be triggered by the vigorous maternal licking when she cleans each infant after birth. There is a multiplicity of paths toward this end. For sheep, release occurs when the mother bites and severs the umbilical cord. For giraffes, which are delivered while the mother is standing, catecholamines are released when the umbilical cord snaps during the expulsion of the infant at birth, because the umbilicus is shorter than the mother's legs and breaks before the infant hits the ground. Absent this surge newborns become comatose and die. Thus, mammalian mothers must induce two states in their infants that may seem contradictory. They must help conserve energy, as has been described above. They must also ensure that the brain is adequately stimulated through punctate events that cause bursts of catecholamine release.

In an effort to determine whether and how excitation and energy conservation could serve as a basis for learning about and being drawn to the mother's face, Carole Ann Camp and myself have studied the bases of human infant face preference within the contexts of calming and excitation provided by an experimenter. Infants were studied once only at 6, 9, or 12 weeks of age and were randomly assigned in advance to receive a particular treatment. Depending upon their state infants were studied while either calm or crying. They received one of eight treatments (2 state $\times$ 4 delivery) at each age studied: sweet (sucrose) pacifier during eye contact with the experimenter; sweet pacifier absent eye contact; sucrose with eye contact; sucrose without eye contact. Sucrose was delivered over 30 s each minute in 0.8 ml aliquots. The remaining three conditions at each age consisted of either receiving eye contact alone, sucrose or pacifier-sucrose alone, or neither eye contact, nor tastant.

Eye contact was studied because of Wolff's observation that starting at 4 weeks of age, infants established and maintained eye contact with their mothers for sustained periods of time. Zeiffman, Dulaney, and Blass further reported that sucrose calmed spontaneously crying 4-week-old infants only if it was delivered when the experimenter was in eye contact with the infant. Thus eye contact exerted a powerful motivational influence in very young infants.

At the end of the 4 min training period, the experimenter left the infant for 30 s to return with an identically clad confederate. They stood on either side of the infant, and engaged the infant by softly calling his name. They did not touch the infant. After 30 s the experimenters changed positions to prevent position bias. Testing lasted for a total of 3 min. Infant looking at one or the other experimenter was recorded, as were spontaneous behaviors, of which there was considerable variety. The behaviors were striking and, thus, reliably classified and scored from the tapes recorded during the session.

We thought that some general rules would underlie looking preference, but were proved wrong. For 6-week-olds, only infants who started the training session in a crying state preferred the experimenter who had provided the infant with a pacifier dipped in sucrose. This is of considerable interest because both sucrose and sweet pacifier had reduced crying. Remarkably, infants who had started the study in a calm state did not prefer experimenters who had provided them with a sweet pacifier to suck, or sweet sucrose to taste. These calm infants who had received sucrose by syringe or pacifier did not prefer their experimenter, even though they accepted all of the proffered sucrose.

Older infants presented different face-preference patterns depending upon infant state and mode of sucrose delivery. Space precludes description of these studies, their predictions, and the data and models that they generated. Suffice it to say that preference shifted to a calm state.

Thus, to the central theme of this communication, the suckling setting provides many opportunities for infants to learn about the characteristics of their mothers, and the Blass and Camp studies provide initial motivational bases for affective change as well as information on the facial features to which infants attend. Lumeng, Patil, and Blass then asked if this information could be extended to an experimental setting that most closely approximates the natural one in which mothers provide their infants with milk with and without eye contact. Accordingly, infants, 6–12 weeks of age, received their normal bottled milk feedings from either mother or stranger.

Each infant was studied six times, twice while being fed by the mother and four times by different nurses. Maternal feedings proceeded as usual, with the mother not receiving any instructions except to feed her infant in her usual manner. Nurse feedings were of four varieties:

1. Held-socially engaged. The infant was held during feeding. The nurse also initiated eye contact, and called the infants name.
2. Held-not socially engaged. The infant was held, as above, but was not socially engaged. The nurse looked at the infant's chest and fed in silence.
3. Not held-socially engaged. The infant was fed while sitting in an 'infant-seat' with social engagement as above.
4. Not held-not socially engaged. As described above.

Although the amount of formula ingested did not differ among conditions, intake patterns differed markedly. Intake that occurred when infants were 'not' socially engaged with the nurse was linearly related to the interval between meals ($y = 8.3x - 3.6$). The linear relationship with a near-0 intercept for nondeprived infants, formally describes an ingestion system that is responsive to physiological events, currently nonspecified (**Figure 3**).

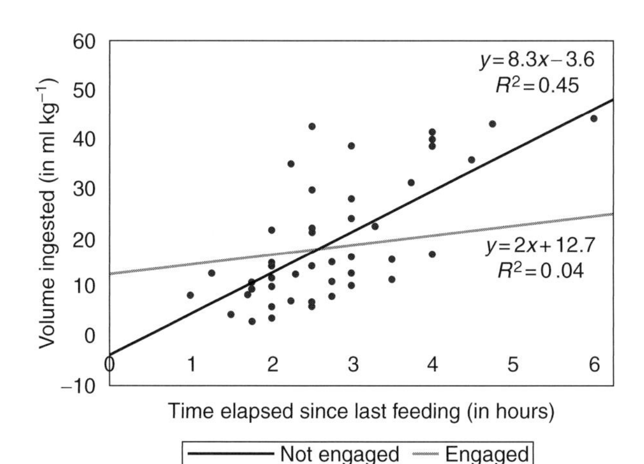

Figure 3 Regressions of milk intake (from bottle) in the same infants fed under two different conditions. In one, they received their milk from nurses who fed them while maintaining eye contact. In the other condition the same infants were fed by nurses who averred eye contact.

In contrast, intake that occurred by these same infants while socially engaged differed radically. The dose–response relationship was essentially flat ($y = 2.0x + 12.7$). Intake was clearly not governed by physiological events when an infant was socially engaged by the feeder. Lack of physiological control is further manifest by the intercept of 12.7, asserting that the nondeprived infant would ingest 12.7 ml kg^{-1}, provided that he/she was sucking while engaged by the feeder.

These findings complement the major thrust of this article. They suggest the existence of a suckling system that is under two separate control mechanisms, in the service of two distinct functions. One control is physiology of growth and differentiation and helps assure that appropriate volumes of milk (formula) are ingested to sustain these signature developmental processes. The other control is social and is in the service of learning about the feeder, biologically the mother. When fed by their mothers, intake was linearly related to the intermeal interval ($y = 5.0\ x + 6.9$). The infants only very occasionally looked at their mothers during the feedings. Presumably at about 4 weeks of age, the point that infants start to engage their mothers socially through eye contact, intake would not be related to privation length. This is a matter that will be decided by further research.

See also: Attachment; Birth Complications and Outcomes; Breastfeeding; Circumcision; Crying; Feeding Development and Disorders; Learning; Newborn Behavior; Obesity.

Suggested Readings

Blass EM and Barr RG (2000) Evolutionary biology and the practice of medicine: the case of management of infant pain experience. *Journal of Developmental and Behavioral Pediatrics* 21: 283–284.

Blass EM and Camp CA (2003) Biological bases of face preference in six-week-old infants. *Developmental Science* 6: 524–536.

Gray L, Miller LW, Phillip BL, and Blass EM (2002) Breastfeeding is analgesic in healthy newborns. *Pediatrics* 109: 590–593.

Lumeng J, Patil N, and Blass E (2007) Social influences on formula intake via suckling on 7- to 14-week old infants. *Developmental Psychobiology* 49: 351–361.

Rao M, Blass EM, Brignol MM, Marino L, and Glass L (1997) Reduced heat loss following sucrose ingestion in premature and normal human newborns. *Early Human Development* 48: 109–116.

Ren K, Blass EM, Zhou Q, and Dubner R (1997) Suckling and sucrose ingestion suppress persistent hyperalgesia and spinal Fos expression after forepaw inflammation in infant rats. *Proceedings of the National Academy of Sciences USA* 104: 1471–1475.

Shide DJ and Blass EM (1991) Opioid mediation of odor preferences induced by sugar and fat in 6-day-old rats. *Physiology and Behavior* 50: 961–966.

Zeifman D, Delaney S, and Blass EM (1996) Sweet taste, looking and calm in two- and four-week-old infants: The eyes have it. *Developmental Psychology* 32: 1090–1099.

Symbolic Thought

S M Carlson and P D Zelazo, Institute of Child Development, Minneapolis, MN, USA

Glossary

Cognitive flexibility – The capacity to consider and selectively attend to more than one aspect of a situation or problem.
Executive function – Conscious control over thought and action, including resistance to interference, set-shifting, and withholding a dominant response; reflection on the self is implicated, as are processes of working memory and inhibitory control.
Inner speech – Silent self-directed talk, preceded developmentally by private speech in which children talk aloud to themselves; utilized to facilitate problem solving.
Intentionality – The property of 'aboutness' or directedness that can be said to characterize the relation between a symbol and its referent (i.e., the stimulus represented by the symbol), as well as between conscious thoughts and their content.
Mediation (symbolic) – The knowing substitution of a symbol for a direct experience of a stimulus, which allows behavior to be controlled in light of the symbol rather than the stimulus itself.
Psychological distancing – Cognitive separation from the immediate perceptual/behavioral environment through the use of representation and reflection.
Reflection (self) – Awareness and conscious consideration of one's own sensations, perceptions, thoughts, and behavioral tendencies.
Zone of proximal development – Transitional period in cognitive development in which the child is close to achieving explicit understanding of a concept or success on a problem, but cannot do so without guidance or scaffolding from more knowledgeable others.

Introduction

Symbols are ubiquitous in children's lives. They include paintings on the wall, pictures and written words in books, traffic signs, numbers, scale models, maps, toy replicas, and communication signals in gesture and speech. How children come to understand and use symbols is a key question because symbolization allows children to engage in a wide variety of sophisticated intellectual activities (e.g., language, mathematics, art) that are unique to our species. Research suggests that the development of symbolic thought follows a gradual course that is closely tied to the development of self-reflection and that depends importantly on cultural practices and social interaction.

Definition and Overview

Symbolic thought is thought that involves symbols, or things that represent (or stand for) something else. To play their constitutive role in symbolic thought, however, symbols must be intended to be representational by the person using them. By definition, then, symbolic thought requires some degree of self-reflective understanding of the relation between the symbol (e.g., a drawing of a dog) and the referent (e.g., the dog drawn). A drawing may represent a dog, but only if someone understands it as such.

Discussions of symbolization and symbolic thought often make reference to two key (and related) constructs: mediation and intentionality. First, like all thought, symbolic thought mediates between stimuli and responses. In symbolic thought, however, a symbol (e.g., a word, picture, number, visual image, or even an idea) is knowingly substituted for a direct experience of a stimulus, which allows behavior to be controlled in light of the symbol rather than the stimulus itself. This type of mediation may be referred to as symbolic mediation.

Second, the term intentionality – in the philosophical sense – refers to the property of aboutness or directedness that can be said to characterize the relation between a symbol and its referent (i.e., the stimulus represented by the symbol): the symbol is about, or in some sense directed at, the referent. Again, this is a property of all conscious thought; symbolic thought is simply a special case. In the case of symbolic thought, however, an agent is aware of the intentional relation between the symbol and the referent: he or she knows that the symbol represents the referent. Many of the cognitive and behavioral consequences of symbolic thought may derive from this feature of reflection on the intentional relation and the concomitant psychological distancing from stimuli (i.e., from reality) that takes place.

Symbolic thought develops gradually during infancy and early childhood. We suggest that it progresses through a series of levels corresponding to increasing degrees of reflection on the nature of the symbol-referent relation. These levels, which correspond to the age-related increases

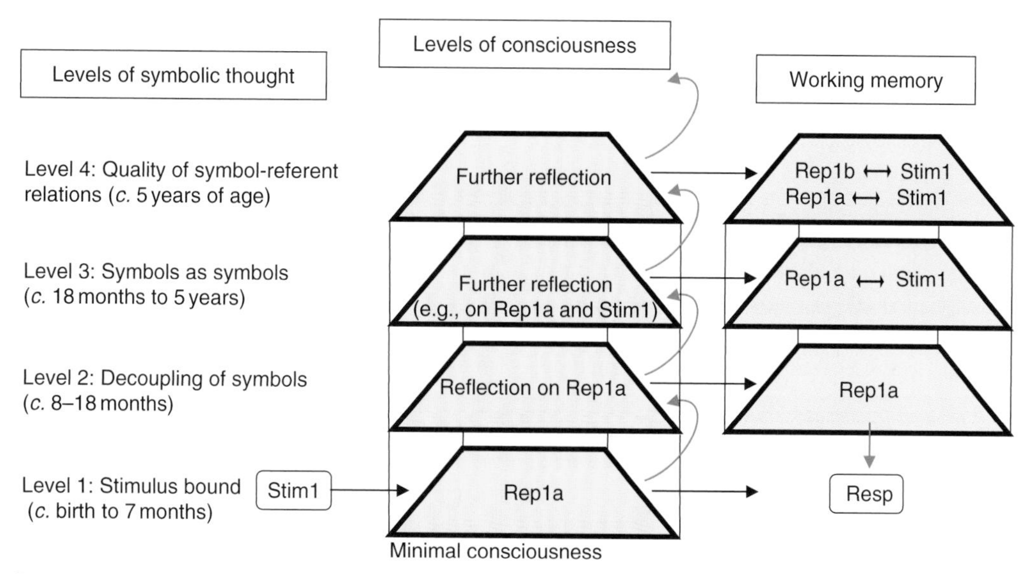

Figure 1 Consequences of reflection for symbolic thought. Development of the capacity to reflect on the contents of one's own consciousness, resulting in higher, more reflective levels of consciousness, allows for more aspects of symbols and symbol-referent relations to be considered and maintained in working memory. Reflection is interposed between perception of a stimulus (Stim1) and responding (Resp). The contents of minimal consciousness at one moment, together with new information about a stimulus, are fed back into minimal consciousness. Figure illustrates the different contents of working memory made possible by different degrees of reflection. Rep1a and Rep1b are alternate symbolic representations of the stimulus.

in reflection identified in Philip David Zelazo's Levels of Consciousness model, may be summarized briefly (see **Figure 1**).

1. At the first level, spanning from birth to approximately seven months of age, there is no evidence of symbolic thought. Conscious thinking is representational (i.e., it is intentional) and it mediates between stimuli and responses, so there is a sense in which it is symbolic, but in the absence of reflection on one's representations, behavior is tied directly to stimuli (i.e., behavior is 'stimulus bound').
2. During the latter half of the first year, infants acquire the ability to keep representations of stimuli (i.e., symbols) in mind even in the absence of the stimuli themselves (e.g., as when objects are hidden and infants search for them). At this point in development, however, infants still do not reflect on the relation between the symbol and the referent – instead they merely substitute the symbol for reality – so their thought is not properly called symbolic according to the definition provided earlier. Nonetheless, there is a decoupling of symbols from referents, and this is an important step in the development of symbolic thought.
3. During the second year of life, children begin to treat symbols 'as' symbols, as when they engage in pretend play. This developmental advance marks the beginning of genuine symbolic thought insofar as there is, for the first time, reflection on the fact that there is a relation between symbol and referent. Children's symbolic thought is still limited, however, and they generally fail to consider the nature or quality of the symbol-referent relation.
4. Finally, further increases in children's reflection during the preschool years allow children to consider the quality of the symbol-referent relation (e.g., detecting ambiguity in which referent is being symbolized), and eventually to consider multiple symbol-referent relations in contradistinction (e.g., allowing them to appreciate irony).

Development of Symbolic Thought

Thinking about symbolic thought in this way allows us to trace its development from simple consciousness (referred to as minimal consciousness) through the conspicuously self-reflective instances seen in some forms of art. The foundations of symbolization are inherent in infant perception. According to Jean Piaget, infants and toddlers interact with the world in terms of sensorimotor schemes and schemata. A scheme is a behavioral category, and a schema is an abstract representation of the distinctive characteristics of an event – it is a category in terms of which stimuli are interpreted. A father's finger, for example, might be experienced by a young infant as a suckable thing, and this description might trigger the stereotypical motor scheme of sucking. Sensorimotor schemata are modified through practice and accommodation (i.e., learning can occur), and they can be coordinated into higher order units. In contemporary parlance, schemata would be referred to as representations.

Level 1: Intentionality and Mediation Without Reflection

Several decades' worth of research on infant visual perception, attention, categorization, and memory indicates clearly that human infants process stimuli in terms of representations, and that these representations may be modified by experience. Rather than responding directly to stimuli, infants (and indeed, fetuses during the third trimester) seem to respond on the basis of representations, or interpretations, of these stimuli. The behavioral consequences of this representational mediation include habituation, pattern completion, and expectation, among many other phenomena. In all cases, infants go beyond the information that is given in any particular presentation of a stimulus.

Infants' perception of color serves as a good example. Despite continuous variation in the wavelength of light, infants reliably categorize this continuous spectrum in the same way as human adults. For example, they may show greater attentiveness when a shade of red changes to yellow than when a lighter shade of red merely replaces a darker shade of red, despite the fact that both differences correspond to comparable differences in the relevant dimension of the physical stimulus (i.e., in the wavelength of reflected light). Different instances of red are assimilated to a single category of color; they are represented as red.

Interestingly, infants' categories may be quite abstract, as demonstrated by research on cross-modal perception. For example, if infants suck on a nubby pacifier without being able to see it and then are shown that pacifier alongside a smooth one, they will usually look longer at the nubby pacifier. They will also look longer at other stimuli that share the feature of having a discontinuous surface, like the nubby pacifier, as opposed to a continuous surface, like the smooth pacifier. For example, they will look longer at an incomplete circle. One interpretation of this finding is that infants may categorize stimuli without regard to sensory modality and interpret the sucked-upon pacifier as a discontinuous thing. When shown another example of discontinuity, they may recognize this characteristic and be more or less interested in it depending on the results of their initial processing of discontinuity.

The representations underlying infant categorical behavior are symbolic insofar as they function in ways that allow them to stand for classes of stimuli, and these representations are likely to provide a foundation for subsequent developments in symbolic thought. However, these representations are probably not symbols that can be used in the absence of current stimulation. Young infants obviously display evidence of memory and learning, but this evidence seems to be tied to ongoing perceptual processing. For example, young infants show recognition memory, responding differentially to a familiar vs. a novel stimulus, but there is no clear evidence of recall memory in the absence of the remembered stimulus. In short, young infants might be said to be stimulus bound.

Level 2: Thinking about Representations in the Absence of Stimuli

In contrast, toward the end of the first year of life, most infants begin to exhibit behaviors suggesting that they are responding not to current stimulation but to information maintained in working memory or recalled from past experience. This advance becomes apparent when an infant watches an adult hide an object under a cloth and must wait a short period of time before being allowed to reach for it. Six-month-olds will not reach under the cloth for the hidden object, presumably because they forget that the object was placed there ('out of sight, out of mind') – although some understanding of the object's continued existence may be demonstrated using more sensitive (albeit more ambiguous) measures such as looking times. Twelve-month-olds, however, will reach for the object even after a 30-s delay period, presumably because they are able to maintain a representation of the hidden object and respond in light of this representation rather than in light of the current stimulation (i.e., no visible object). The representation of the object – a symbol that stands for the object – can now be decoupled from the object itself and considered in the absence of the object. These improvements enable infants to relate an event in their environment to similar events in the past. As a result, they begin to anticipate their mother's positive reactions when the two are in close face-to-face interaction, and they may behave as if inviting her to respond. Infants may also develop new fears, such as those of objects, people, or situations with which they are unfamiliar – that is, which they cannot relate to past experiences using recall memory.

Infants make robust advances in recognition memory during their first year, but it is not until the end of the first year that there is convincing evidence for recall memory. As noted, recall memory involves remembering an event or object that is not currently present – retrieving a representation of it. One way to demonstrate recall memory is via delayed imitation. Imitation may be defined as behavior that duplicates that of another person. One-year-olds become capable of imitating an act some time after they have actually observed it; for example, they may imitate a novel action they witnessed 1 day – or even 2 weeks – earlier, especially if placed in the same physical setting. These findings suggest that infants are able to hold in mind schematic representations – particularly of the actions of caregivers – for increasingly longer periods of time, and these representations stimulate re-enactment through imitation, even when the evocative stimulus is not present.

Level 3: Treating Symbols as Symbols

Keeping a symbolic representation in mind, however, is not the same as treating it as a symbol. Jean Piaget argued that deliberate symbolization typically emerges during the second half of the second year of life, and contemporary analyses are generally consistent with this account. Many authors agree that there are changes during the second year in children's reflective awareness, and these changes should allow them to consider the relation between a symbol and a referent. Pretend play is a good example. In the earliest forms of pretense, one treats something (a pretense object) as something else (a real object), such as treating a bowl as a hat. Not only is there a decoupling of a representation from what is represented, as in level 2 of symbolic thought, but there is also some degree of reflection on the relation between the symbol and the referent: the child knows he or she is treating the bowl as a hat.

Over the course of the second year, children become more likely to perform pretend actions (e.g., talking on the telephone) with pretense objects (e.g., a spoon) that bear little physical resemblance to the real objects. They also are increasingly less likely when pretending (or symbolizing, more generally) to respond on the basis of the actions suggested by the real objects. Thus, in this context, one sees increasing independence from the literal context, and an increasing reliance on imagination. Piaget observed his daughter Jacqueline at 15 months place her head on a pillow and close her eyes, thus simulating the gestures of sleep using the real props associated with sleeping. Only later in development did she substitute a symbol for the pillow – resting her head on her bear and a plush dog. As Lev Vygotsky put it: "It is remarkable that the child starts with an imaginary situation that initially is so very close to the real one. A reproduction of the real situation takes place." Eventually, however, children become capable of creating symbolic representations on the basis of more subtle suggestions, and we might say that their representations are less dependent on external context and more internally determined.

These developments continue into the third year, and may be seen in domains other than pretend play. By 3 years, for example, children are capable of simple metaphor (e.g., playing with two wooden balls of different size as if they symbolized a parent and child). At this age, children also become more likely to perform pretend actions without objects altogether (such as pretending to drink from an imaginary cup), and they may begin to create imaginary companions with detailed biographies. Children's drawings also become symbolic during the second and third years and begin to contain forms that look like (or at least are intended to represent) animals, people, and various objects. These developments all appear to be refinements of a basic ability to treat a symbol as a symbol, and to transcend the limitations of reality via imagination.

An important developmental milestone occurring in the third year is the growing realization that an object can be understood both as a thing itself and as a symbol for something else – that is, dual representation. For instance, a mature understanding of pictures requires the reconciliation of two fundamental requirements: identifying the representation with its referent, while, at the same time, recognizing the distinction between referent and representation. Evidence suggests that children's conceptual understanding of pictures (e.g., photographs and drawings) develops gradually. Even infants can recognize objects in pictures and discriminate depicted objects from actual objects, although they sometimes try to manipulate a picture as if it were the object itself, such as 'grasping' a pictured bottle. By 20 months of age, this confusion about pictures typically is overcome. At age 2 years, however, children still have difficulty using photographs or live video to guide their search for a hidden toy in a simple object-retrieval task (e.g., a photo of a toy hidden behind a sofa). In contrast, 2.5-year-olds readily use pictures for this purpose.

Two-year-old children's use of pictures to guide search for hidden objects may indicate some understanding of representational specificity – that the picture is not merely a picture of a toy behind a sofa, but rather is a picture of the particular toy hidden behind the sofa in the laboratory room. This understanding may emerge relatively early for photographs and video in part because these media are familiar and in part because they function primarily as symbols – children are rarely encouraged to consider pictures as objects in themselves (e.g., with particular formal properties such as size and texture). Rather, children habitually 'look through' pictures to what the pictures represent.

Two-year-olds' use of photographs and video to guide search is in contrast to their difficulty using three-dimensional (3D) scale models. In one experimental paradigm introduced by Judy DeLoache, children's understanding of the symbolic relation between a scale model and the larger space it represents is assessed using a procedure in which children are first familiarized with a life-size room and a miniaturized scale model of that room. Then the child watches as an attractive toy (e.g., a tiny Snoopy dog) is hidden within the scale model (e.g., behind the miniature sofa). Next, the child is invited to find an analogous toy that has been concealed in the corresponding place in the room itself (e.g., a large Snoopy dog hidden behind the full-sized sofa). Lastly, the child is returned to the model and asked to retrieve the miniature toy, as a check on children's memory for the hiding location. The results were dramatic. Across numerous studies and manipulations of the procedure, 2.5-year-olds failed to search correctly for the object in the analogous location (less than 20% did so), despite accurately remembering the original hiding event. By contrast, most 3-year-olds had no difficulty retrieving the object in either location (about 80% did so). One interpretation of these results is that the 3D model is a salient object (like a dollhouse), and this interferes with their appreciation of it as a symbol. As a result, they have difficulty looking through it to what it represents, and instead treat the model only as an object in itself.

This representational insight has also been investigated with respect to children's understanding of toys as symbols. In one set of studies by Michael Tomasello and colleagues, young children were asked to select objects that had been previously represented by either a gesture or a symbol. For example, when the target object was a hammer, the experimenter used her fist to make a hammering motion in the gesture condition, and showed children a miniature hammer from a dollhouse in the symbol condition. Children of 18 months correctly selected the real hammer on test trials only in the gesture condition, whereas 26-month-olds performed well in both conditions. The younger children apparently failed to see the toy replica as a symbol for the larger object, in addition to seeing it as a toy. Understanding pretense gestures might come earlier than understanding toys because, like photographs, gestures do not generally demand dual representation; as with words, the primary function of gestures is symbolic – to represent something else. Again, however, it should be noted that using measures of preferential looking, other researchers have shown that recognition of the relation between iconic toy symbols and their real-world referents begins to emerge earlier, around 14 months of age.

Limitations on children's developing understanding of symbol-referent relations can be seen not only in their failures to use symbols to make inferences about reality, but also in their confusion about the relevance of stimulus properties and symbol properties. For example, toddlers continue to make 'scale errors' with iconic symbols. That is, they sometimes treat a miniature or gigantic replica as if it had the functional properties of the thing it represents (e.g., trying to climb into the driver's seat of a doll-sized car). Even older children continue to struggle with non-iconic symbols. They appear to operate on the assumption that perceptual similarity of the symbol and referent matters. In reading, writing, and understanding maps, preschool children are more likely to select an item that looks like the referent than one that does not, such as a word written in red ink to stand for 'tomato'. They also reject symbols based on a lack of perceptual similarity, such as claiming that a red line on a map cannot represent a road because roads are not red.

The increasing capacity for reflection on symbols as symbols during the early preschool years allows for much more control of symbolic thought. As we have described, this is apparent in terms of both transferring information from external symbols to their real-world analogs, as well as overcoming errors of misappropriation of certain perceptually salient symbols to real-world functions. Nonetheless, difficulties in attending selectively and flexibly to different aspects of the symbol-referent relation persist at this level of symbolic thought. For example, research has explored 3- to 5-year-old children's ability to respond to pictures on the basis of their formal properties (i.e., the way in which something is represented) as well as on the basis of their content using a match-to-sample task in which children were shown a sample picture (e.g., a blurry bird) and test pictures that matched the sample according to content (e.g., a nonblurry bird), form (e.g., blurry gloves), or neither (e.g., a nonblurry violin). Whereas most 5-year-olds were successful at matching pictures according to both content and form, 3-year-olds often failed to match according to form. These findings provide support for the notion that younger children still 'see through' pictures, experiencing particular difficulty with the dual requirement of representing pictures with respect to both their semantic and formal properties. That is, 3-year-olds seem particularly captured by content, and have difficulty attending to form in the presence of conflicting content information.

Another study found that preschoolers are indeed capable of responding to formal features of pictures – in particular, to the artistic style of paintings. In this study, preschoolers (3–5 years of age) were presented with slides of paintings in which artistic style (i.e., artist) and subject matter were varied independently. Children of all ages were capable of making both style and subject matter matches. When shown abstract paintings, for example, children were able say that two paintings by the same artist were more similar than two paintings by different artists. However, children exhibited a strong reliance on subject matter over style when these cues conflicted (e.g., when asked whether a still life by Seraut was more similar to a portrait by Seraut or a still life by Brueghel, they selected the two still lifes).

Related phenomena have been observed in even older children. Six-year-olds have difficulty evaluating paralinguistic cues (i.e., how a speaker's voice sounds) in the presence of conflicting propositional content (i.e., what is said). For example, children erroneously reported that a speaker was happy when she uttered a positive proposition in a sad voice (e.g., "My mommy gave me a treat" in a sad voice). Subsequent experiments demonstrated that 6-year-olds could respond on the basis of paralinguistic information when it was not in conflict with propositional content. For example, they could judge whether a speaker was happy or sad when she spoke a foreign language. Moreover, when children heard conflicting sentences and were first told to judge on the basis of content, and then told to switch and judge on the basis of prosody, children who noticed the conflict and described it when asked, tended to switch successfully. This finding reveals the important link between the complexity of children's representation of the problem, made possible by increases in reflection on multiple aspects of the communicative symbols, and their ability to resist interference from a salient aspect of the problem.

More generally, these findings situate the development of conceptual understanding of representations in the context of general changes in cognitive development, including the well-established changes in executive function that occur from 3 to 6 years of age. Executive function refers to conscious self-control of thought, action, and emotion, including resistance to interference, set-shifting, and withholding a dominant response; reflection on the self is implicated, as are processes of working memory and inhibitory control. It is closely associated with the development of prefrontal cortex. The limitations seen in children's symbolic thought at level 3 may be in part attributable to a tendency in early childhood to focus attention on highly salient but misleading or interfering aspects of stimuli. With increasing reflective capacity and control, children are able to inhibit a dominant way of construing things (e.g., seeing only the subject matter in pictures) and entertain more abstract and flexible representations (e.g., appreciating stylistic similarities and differences).

Level 4: Reflection on the Quality of the Symbol-Referent Relation

The epitome of symbolic thought is language, which uses words or symbols to transcend concrete reality and allows intangibles to be manipulated (as in mathematical symbols). Although infants begin to link words with their referents in speech beginning around 12 months, research on children's understanding of language has revealed changes during the preschool period in children's evaluation of the quality of the symbol-referent relation. For example, even 5-year-olds tend to confuse what is meant with what is said when they hear ambiguous verbal messages. In one study, an experimenter and a child sat on opposite sides of an opaque screen, and each had his or her own set of cards, which varied along two dimensions (e.g., large/small and red/blue flowers). They then played a game in which they took turns choosing a card from their set and describing it in a way that allowed the other participant to choose the identical card from his or her set. On some turns, when the experimenter acted as the speaker, the utterances were intentionally ambiguous. For example, the child might be told: "Pick up the red flower," an expression that described both the big red flower and the small red flower. Subsequently, the child was asked to make a judgment about what was said. Children heard one of three types of utterance: a disambiguated version of the original utterance (e.g., "Did I say 'the big red flower'?"), a verbatim repetition of the original utterance (e.g., "Did I say 'the red flower'?"), or an incorrect version of the original utterance (e.g., "Did I say 'the blue flower'?"). Five-year-olds were quite good at rejecting the incorrect version (81% of the time) and at accepting the verbatim repetition (76% of the time). However, they incorrectly accepted the disambiguated version 60% of the time. Thus, children behaved as if the two utterances were indiscriminable, suggesting they did not recognize the referential ambiguity. Indeed, similar to younger children's understanding of visual representations, children appear to 'see through' linguistic expressions to the intended referent, failing to 'see' expressions in and of themselves.

Related phenomena in later childhood include the development of understanding of irony and sarcasm, as well as the nuances of artistic representation and aspects of scientific reasoning (e.g., relations between theory and data). These developments may also be made possible by age- and experience-related increases in children's reflection on their symbolic representations. Reflection allows children to consider complex sets of relations among symbols and various symbol-referent relations (e.g., ideal vs. actual models of reality), setting the stage for still more abstract and imaginative relations in adolescence.

Facilitation of Symbolic Thought

Now that we have described the developmental progression of symbolic thought in terms of increases in reflection, we next turn to the question of how it might be fostered by experience and enculturation. First, by using representations, one comes to understand more aspects of the representing relation. Lev Vygotsky viewed this as an instance of a more general developmental law: ". . . [C]onsciousness and control appear only at a late stage in the development of a function, after it has been used and practiced unconsciously and spontaneously." Recent work has also emphasized the transformative effect of using representations. For example, there appears to be a correlation between when children start using pictures to guide search for a hidden object and when they start producing pictures. Drawing may provide insight into the artist's intention to represent a particular referent – it may provide a first-person appreciation of this intention.

At the very least, using symbols provides an opportunity for the discovery of certain of their properties – including properties of symbols in general and the special properties of the particular types of symbols used. For example, training in the use of maps diminishes children's tendency to be overly literal in their interpretation of them (e.g., thinking that 'north' is always straight ahead). This work suggests that children can overcome symbol-referent errors with increasing experience. Similarly, research has shown that early pretense with parents and siblings jumpstarts children's own progression through the stages of pretending, perhaps because it provides both modeling and practice, and alerts children to the possibilities inherent in pretend play.

Second, as Lev Vygotsky emphasized, a key influence on the development of symbolic thought is the appropriation and internalization of the 'tools' of a particular culture. These tools are cultural practices, such as the use of speech, writing, numbers, and music. Vygotsky described a process whereby the formal structure inherent in these cultural practices is first acquired in overt behavior and then reflected in one's private thinking through a gradual process of interiorization. An essential piece of the reflection process we have described is the notion that symbolism is recursive: symbols feed and fuel symbolic thought, with the outcome being increasingly higher levels of conscious reflection on external and, eventually, internal symbols. But the foundation of this process is basic symbolization. Hence the symbols or 'tools' that a culture, school, or home provide for children will determine, in part, the kinds of reflective symbolic thought in which children engage – for example, symbolic thought involving numerals, words, and even whole mythologies. Cultural differences also will determine which symbol systems are most valued and imparted to children earlier in development. For example, Chinese children's rapid learning of counting in comparison with North American children might be mediated by both a difference in the structure of the numbering system (a base-10 system) and a high cultural value placed upon mathematical skills.

It is important to note, however, that the influence of practice and the provision of cultural tools on the development of symbolic thought will be constrained by age-related, domain-general limitations on the complexity of the conceptual relations children can formulate – and ultimately on the degree of self reflection in which they can engage. For example, no amount of training or practice appears to help 2-years-olds appreciate the relevance of the 3D scale model to the location of the large toy in Judy DeLoache's search task. This finding is consistent with Lev Vygotsky's zone of proximal development principle; children are most receptive to intervention at certain points in development that are under biological as well as contextual control.

The Role of Symbolic Thought in Problem Solving

We have discussed some of the possibilities for how symbolic thought is derived and fostered in development. Next we consider where it leads children; in other words, what does symbolic thought 'buy' them? In addition to providing the raw materials for the imaginative enjoyment of objects and simulation of real-world events in pretend play, symbolic thought plays an essential role in children's increasingly sophisticated problem solving ability.

Although symbolic thought figures prominently in play, it may also be initiated by recognition of a discrepancy or a problem to be solved; it may be elicited by a sense of novelty, surprise, complexity, incongruity, or ambiguity. Once initiated, however, how might symbolic thought contribute to success in problem solving? One possibility is emphasized by the psychological distancing hypothesis of Heinz Werner and Bernard Kaplan, and more recently developed by Irving Sigel. By way of the substitution of symbols for stimuli themselves, one's attention is moved away from the concrete and motivating (e.g., appetitive) properties of the stimuli and toward a more abstract characterization. The dimension in which this movement is hypothesized to occur is referred to as psychological distance.

Psychological distancing may facilitate problem solving in several ways. First, simply by decreasing the salience of certain aspects of a stimulus or problem, psychological distancing may help children to resist a temptation to respond impulsively – to select prepotent but inappropriate responses. Second, symbols may permit one to notice alternative aspects or implications of a problem that were not initially obvious. This, in turn, may allow a wider range of possible responses to be entertained and executed.

Research has indeed shown that symbols can provide degrees of distance from reality, which then might make it possible to reflect on the self and govern one's responses more effectively. For example, in Walter Mischel's delay of gratification task, children need to wait alone in the presence of food rewards if they want to receive the larger reward; otherwise, if they do not wait until the experimenter returns, they can take only the smaller reward. A symbolic strategy that was highly effective in extending preschoolers' delay times involved a cognitive transformation in which children were asked to pretend that the marshmallows in the experiment were 'white fluffy clouds'. Presumably this symbolic ideation decreased the salience of the food reward, thus enabling children to delay gratification.

A more direct demonstration of the role of symbols in psychological distancing comes from the Less is More task, developed by Stephanie Carlson. In the Less is More task, children are presented with two piles of candy, one large and one small, and must point to the small pile in order to obtain the large pile. Three-year-olds, compared to 4-year-olds, have difficulty inhibiting their tendency to point to the preferred, larger reward. In one study, 3-year-olds were trained on symbolic representations for the quantities of treats, in increasing degree of separation from reality, before being given the task (e.g., one-to-one correspondence with rocks vs. a mouse and elephant to stand for small and large amounts, respectively). Children in the symbol conditions performed better than children presented with real treats, and improved as a function of the degree of symbolic distancing from the real rewards.

Like symbol substitution, verbal labeling also seems to promote psychological distancing, and the facilitative effects of labeling have been examined on several tests of executive function in children. Alexander Luria assessed the effects of labeling on a Go-Nogo task. When 3-year-olds were asked to accompany their manual responses (i.e., pressing on Go trials) with self-directed commands such as 'Press', they were better able to regulate their responses. By contrast, when 3-year-olds were asked to accompany their nonresponses (i.e., withholding responding on Nogo trials) with self-directed commands such as 'Don't press', their performance deteriorated. Older children's performance improved when they labeled both Go and Nogo trials. One possibility is that younger children can regulate their behavior using the concrete, physical, expressive aspect of labels, but they have difficulty using the more abstract, semantic aspects when these aspects conflict with the expressive aspects or with children's prepotent tendencies. This pattern is similar to the examples described earlier (e.g., children's difficulty using the semantic meaning of a 3D scale model). Preschool children seem to have difficulty reflecting on and using multiple aspects of a symbol, and instead they rely only on the most salient aspects.

The fact that labels may help children to reflect on their symbolic representations was shown by Sophie Jacques and colleagues in work using the Flexible Item Selection Task. On each trial of the task, children are shown sets of three items designed so one pair matches on one dimension, and a different pair matches on a different dimension (e.g., a small yellow teapot, a large yellow teapot, and a large yellow shoe). Children are first asked to select one pair (i.e., selection 1), and then asked to select a different pair (i.e., selection 2). To respond correctly, children must represent the pivot item (i.e., the large yellow teapot) according to both dimensions. Four-year-olds generally perform well on selection 1 but poorly on selection 2, indicating inflexibility. However, asking 4-year-olds to label their basis for selection 1 (e.g., "Why do those two pictures go together?") improved their performance on selection 2. This was true whether children provided the label themselves or whether the experimenter generated it for them. These results suggest that labeling does not simply change the relative salience of stimuli and re-direct children's attention to the postswitch dimension, but instead may facilitate reflection on their initial construal of the stimuli, allowing them to recognize that, for example, they initially represented the large teapot as a teapot but now may represent it as a large thing.

Mature symbolic thought is marked by fluency, originality, and flexibility of one's approach to problems, in other words, thinking 'outside the box'. As these examples suggest, symbolic thought appears to assist problem solving at least in part by improving cognitive flexibility. Being able to consider more than one alternative to a situation is fostered by representing and reflecting upon the situation from more than one angle. Dual representation – thinking about a representation in two different ways at the same time – is a crucial requirement not only for understanding the semantic meaning of representations but also for problem solving more generally. Examples include appreciating that a single reality can be understood in different – sometimes conflicting – ways, as in the appearance-reality distinction, and by different people, as in the false belief task. Similarly, social role-play, common by age 4 or 5 years, fosters thinking about other points of view. When pretending to be someone else, children are simulating the other's beliefs, desires, and emotional responses to situations. Perhaps not surprisingly then, some researchers have reported that training children to pretend to be another person improves their ability to take that person's perspective.

This last observation highlights an important pathway in the development of cognitive flexibility. As with pretend play, the development of perspective taking is characterized by a decreasing reliance on external support and an increasing reliance on imagination. Consistent with a long tradition of work on social mediation and dialogic thinking, symbolization facilitates the imaginative appreciation of other people's perspectives, and then, with practice, the ability to adopt alternative perspectives becomes internalized – engaged in symbolically – resulting in cognitive flexibility.

Clearly, then, symbols not only play an instrumental role in the development of cognitive flexibility, but they also provide the medium in which much flexible cognition occurs. In particular, a great deal of conscious, directed thinking appears to occur in terms of potentially silent, self-directed speech – or symbolic rules. By formulating and using rules, children essentially talk their way through challenging problems. This notion is consistent with the Vygotskian view that 'private speech' has an adaptive function in the self-regulation of behavior. Private speech is overt speech that is not addressed to a listener, when one essentially is talking to oneself. According to Lev Vygotsky, it is a stage that serves to move children from social speech and overtly verbal thought toward the gradual internalization of dialogic interpersonal language (e.g., between the child and caregiver), leading ultimately to 'inner speech' (i.e., verbal thought that takes place with no outward signs). The central premise for a link between private speech and self-regulation is that 'talking through' the features of a problem enables children to 'think through' the problem more effectively, by regulating their representations, response selections, and monitoring of outcomes. Indeed, as we have described, several studies have demonstrated empirically that private speech during problem solving is positively related to task performance. By reflecting on the rules that they represent, children are able to embed these rules under higher order rules that control their application. For example, in the Less is More task described earlier, children are able to say to themselves, "Yes I want the larger pile of candy, but in this game, if want the larger pile, then I have to point to the smaller pile." The use of higher order rules allows children to respond flexibly across a wider range of situations (i.e., including counterintuitive situations like the one in the Less is More task).

Summary

The ability to create, utilize, and think with and through symbols is a remarkable ontogenetic achievement. We have defined symbolic thought as thought that knowingly involves symbols, or things that represent (or stand for) something else. Two key features of symbolic thought are symbolic mediation (the symbol is understood to be a buffer between direct experience of a stimulus and action upon the stimulus) and intentionality (the symbolizer is aware of the intentional relation between the symbol and what it stands for).

We proposed that the development of symbolic thought proceeds gradually through a series of hierarchical levels. The levels are characterized in terms of the degree of reflection on the symbol-referent relation and are hypothesized to correspond to concomitant increases in self-reflection that are manifested in children's executive control over thought and action more generally. First, infants exhibit mediated thought in various ways but there is no reflection on the symbol-referent relation. Second, toward the end of the first year, infants can substitute a representation for reality (such as holding in mind an absent stimulus) but there is still no clear reflection on the relation. Third, beginning in the second year, there are major and dramatic advances in children's ability to treat symbols as symbols, that is, to reflect on the duality of symbols as being both objective and representational. Examples included children's understanding of pictures, toy replicas, scale models, and maps. However, we pointed out several limitations in children's symbolic thought and confusions that are only gradually overcome at this level. Finally, in the later preschool and early elementary school years, increases in self-reflection enable children to reflect further on the nature of symbol-referent relations, to disambiguate them, and to consider multiple such relations from a higher order perspective, including the understanding of irony.

We next considered ways in which symbolic thought is facilitated. In accord with Lev Vygotsky's sociocultural view, we asserted that using symbols and, relatedly, having certain symbolic 'tools' available in a given culture, will direct the development of symbolic thought in a recursive fashion. Lastly, we provided examples of the ways in which symbolic thought aids children's problem solving ability by way of psychological distancing (e.g., noniconic images, verbal labeling), consideration of multiple alternative perspectives or solutions, and inner speech or rule use. In this way, the development of symbolic thought corresponds to well-established increases in executive function that occur in infancy and early childhood. Age-related increases in both symbolic thought and executive function are made possible by increases in self-reflection, but symbolic thought, executive function, and self-reflection also interact to influence performance in a wide range of situations.

There are several up-and-coming research directions on symbolic thought in early childhood. One is identifying the neural underpinnings of self-reflection in order to move descriptions of this process – evident in children's behavior – to another level of analysis, a level that might help to explain deficits in symbolic thought in certain populations of children (e.g., children with autism). Another new direction is to examine more closely how it is that 'experts' (parents, teachers, older siblings) transmit information about symbols and promote their use (thus influencing the development of symbolic thought both directly and indirectly), and how these practices vary within and across cultures. Finally, there are advances to be made in our understanding of the role of symbolic thought in problem solving, particularly with respect to the conditions in which symbols provide specific or generalized effects (e.g., positive transfer from symbolic to real contexts), and the mechanisms by which these effects occur (such as distancing and inner speech). Addressing these important questions about symbolic thought will contribute to our own reflections on what is perhaps the fundamental developmental achievement of human cognition.

See also: Artistic Development; Cognitive Development; Cognitive Developmental Theories; Imagination and Fantasy; Object Concept; Piaget's Cognitive-Developmental Theory; Play; Vygotsky's Sociocultural Theory.

Suggested Readings

Baldwin JM (1897) *Social and Ethical Interpretations in Mental Development: A Study in Social Psychology.* New York: Macmillan.
Bruner JS (1983) *In Search of Mind: Essays in Autobiography.* New York: Harper & Row.
Carlson SM, Davis A, and Leach JG (2005) Less is more: Executive function and symbolic representation in preschool children. *Psychological Science* 16: 609–616.
DeLoache JS (1995) Early understanding and use of symbols: The model model. *Current Directions in Psychological Science* 4: 109–113.
Lee K and Karmiloff-Smith A (1996) The development of external symbol systems: The child as a notator. In: Gelman R and Au T (eds.) *Perceptual and Cognitive Development: Handbook of Perception and Cognition,* 2nd edn. 185–211. San Diego, CA: Academic Press.
Luria AR (1961) *The Role of Speech in the Regulation of Normal and Abnormal Behavior.* In: Tizard J (ed.). New York: Liveright Publishing Corporation.

Mischel W, Shoda Y, and Rodriguez ML (1989) Delay of gratification in children. *Science* 244: 933–938.
Piaget J (1947/1966) *Psychology of Intelligence.* New Jersey: Littlefield, Adams, and Company.
Sigel I (1993) The centrality of a distancing model for the development of representational competence. In: Cocking RR and Renninger KA (eds.) *The Development and Meaning of Psychological Distance*, pp. 91–107. Hillsdale, NJ: Erlbaum.
Vygotsky LS (1962) *Thought and Language*. In: Hanfmann E and Vakar G (trans.). Cambridge, MA: MIT Press (original work published 1934).
Werner H and Kaplan B (1963) *Symbol Formation: An Organismic Developmental Approach to Language and the Expression of Thought.* New York: John Wiley.
Zelazo PD (2004) The development of conscious control in childhood. *Trends in Cognitive Sciences* 8: 12–17.

Taste and Smell

R L Doty and M Shah, University of Pennsylvania School of Medicine, Philadelphia, PA, USA

Glossary

Amniotic fluid – The water-like fluid, also known as 'bag of waters', that fills the amniotic sac surrounding the developing baby. This fluid supports and protects the baby, permits it to move around, prevents heat loss and provides a barrier to infection.

Amoebae – Plural for amoeba. A single-celled organism, many species of which live free in water. A few are pathogens; amoebic dysentery is caused by an amoeba that parasitises the gastrointestinal tract. Their overall shape and pattern of movement is similar in character to the way many animal cells behave, although the latter are usually much smaller. Such cells are often referred to as amoeboid.

Brainstem – The lower extension of the brain where it connects to the spinal cord. Neurological functions located in the brainstem include those necessary for survival (breathing, heart rate) and for arousal (being awake and alert).

Classical conditioning – The learning that results from the association of stimuli with reflex responses. For example, punitive authority figures experienced early on in life may reflexively elicit feelings of anxiety that become 'conditioned', creating patterns of emotional responses which carry on into adult life. Classical conditioning is used in clinical settings to help patients 'unlearn' anxieties such as phobias.

Electrolyte – Ionized salts in blood, tissue fluids, and cells, including salts of sodium, potassium, and chlorine.

Embryo – The stage of an organism's development directly following fertilization and zygote formation. The term embryo is often used to describe all developmental phases between the first cell cleavage and birth/hatching of a developing organism.

Habitat – An area in which a specific plant or animal naturally lives, grows, and reproduces; the area that provides a plant or animal with adequate food, water, shelter, and living space.

Hedonic – Of, relating to, or marked by, pleasure or displeasure.

Juxtapose – Two objects placed closed together or side-by-side for comparison or contrast. Often helpful in showing scale in an image.

Morning sickness – Nausea and vomiting experienced early in a pregnancy, affecting about half of all pregnant women.

Paramecia – Plural for paramecium. A free-living unicellular animal, a protozoan. The surface of paramecium is covered in cilia that beat in wave patterns to power swimming.

Prenatal – The time before birth, while a baby is developing during pregnancy. The period of time between the conception and birth of an infant.

Preterm – Preterm means simply 'before full-term'–before 40 weeks after the first date of the last menstrual period (LMP). Preterm labor is labor (regular contractions and cervical change) that begins before the end of the 37th week of pregnancy. A preterm baby is one who is born before 37 weeks, gestation.

Primorda – Organ or tissue in its earliest recognizable stage of development.

Receptor – A molecule within a cell or on a cell surface to which a substance (such as a hormone, chemical, or drug) selectively binds, causing a change in the activity of the cell.

Taste buds – Special sensory organs located primarily on the surface of the tongue and usually embedded within papillae. They contain chemoreceptors, providing the sense of taste or gustation.

Trigeminal nerve – The trigeminal nerve is the fifth (V) cranial nerve, and carries sensory information from most of the face and oral cavity, as well as motor supply to the muscles of mastication (the muscles enabling chewing), tensor tympani (in the ear), and other muscles in the floor of the mouth.

Introduction

The ability to sense chemicals was essential for the evolution of life on this planet. Some such chemicals were destructive and required avoidance, whereas others provided nourishment and sustenance. Even single-celled organisms, such as paramecia and amoebae, developed multiple chemical receptors that determined whether they should approach or avoid a given situation. In the case of the bacterium *Escherichia coli*, for example, the direction of rotation of the whip-like appendages that propel them through their environment is influenced by the chemicals they encounter. Chemicals important for sustenance produce a counterclockwise rotation, resulting in smooth and somewhat linear swimming movements. Noxious chemicals, in contrast, produce a clockwise rotation in such appendages, inducing tumbling and movement away from the stimulus source.

Like single-celled organisms, the sensing of chemicals was critical for the evolution of multicelled organisms, and most developed sophisticated chemosensory systems for that purpose. In both invertebrate and vertebrate species, the senses of taste and smell play a significant role in habitat selection and in determining what materials are eaten or rejected. As humans, these senses protect us from a range of environmental hazards, including leaking natural gas and toxic foodstuffs. Importantly, they determine our preferences for foods and nutrients – preferences upon which life depends and some of which begin before birth.

This article describes the structural and functional development of the senses of taste and smell in humans, with a major focus on the prenatal (intrauterine) and early postnatal (neonatal) periods. These senses work together with other senses within the oral and nasal cavities (e.g., touch, temperature) to produce the overall perception of flavor. The receptors for the olfactory system are located within a specialized epithelium in the upper recesses of the nose (**Figure 1**), whereas those for the taste system are located within taste buds usually found on bumps – called papillae – that protrude from the surface of the tongue (**Figure 2**).

Olfaction

The olfactory receptors are sequestered within the highest regions of the nasal passages (**Figure 1**). Large blood swollen structures within these passages, called turbinates, aid in warming, humidifying, and filtering the incoming air steam, as well as directing 10–15% of the inspired air toward the olfactory receptors. Relatively minor changes in the nasal architecture and airflow can result in substantial blockage of air to the olfactory epithelium, significantly altering the ability to smell.

The olfactory receptors are specialized proteins located at the surfaces of hair-like extensions, termed cilia, of the olfactory receptor cells. Odorous molecules bind with the receptors after being absorbed into the mucus, electrically activating the olfactory receptor cells. The receptor cells then signal information about the detected chemicals to central brain structures via long extensions (termed axons) that pass from the nasal cavity into the brain. The first of these central structures, the olfactory bulb, is a distinct outgrowth of the brain located at its base. Nerve cells then project from this layered structure to higher brain regions involved in odor identification, detection, discrimination, and memory.

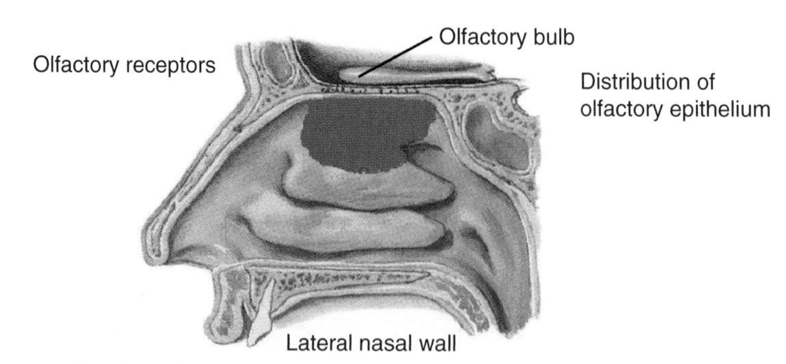

Figure 1 Olfactory Receptors. Reprinted from Felten DL and Joefowic R (2003) *Netter's Atlas of Human Neuroscience*. London: Elsevier, with permission from Elsevier.

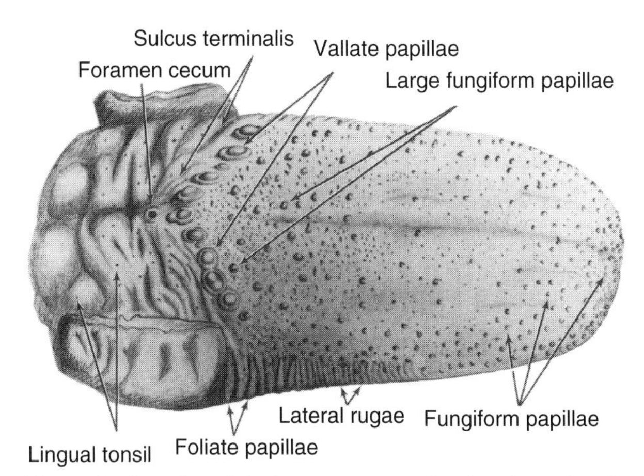

Figure 2 Drawing of the human tongue showing the regional location of the lingual papillae. Reprinted from Doty RL (2003) *Handbook of Olfaction and Gustation*. New York: Marcel Dekker.

Olfaction in the Fetus

Anatomical development

The olfactory system undergoes major development during the first third of pregnancy. The olfactory epithelium is well developed in the fetus, with the olfactory cilia appearing by 9 weeks of gestation, a time when the fetus only weighs around 2 g. The receptor cell axons appear at the base of the brain about 2 weeks prior to the appearance of the cilia. A dramatic increase in cilia numbers takes place during weeks 10 and 11, along with an increase in proteins important for neural transduction and propagation of information to higher brain regions. Mature looking ciliated receptors are seen as early as 11 weeks, when the fetus weighs around 7 g. The olfactory bulb begins to show adult-like layering by 19 weeks. It is reasonable to assume that the olfactory system is functional to some degree at the beginning of the third trimester of pregnancy, since a specialized protein known to be present in functioning receptor cells appears within the olfactory structures at this time.

The trigeminal nerve (CN V), the fifth of 12 nerves that originate from the brain (so-called cranial nerves), is also well formed in the uterus. This nerve mediates intranasal and intraoral irritative responses to volatile and nonvolatile chemicals, as well as skin sensations (e.g., coolness, fullness, sharpness, warmth). Skin regions around the mouth innervated by this nerve are the first regions in the embryo to respond to touch (*c.* 7.5 weeks).

The vomeronasal (VNO) or Jacobson's organ, an elongated blind pouch located near the base of the nasal septum – a structure that separates the nasal cavity into two cavities – is well developed by the second trimester of the human fetus, but regresses in the third trimester. In many vertebrates, the VNO is involved in a wide range of chemosensory-related behaviors, including mating, fighting, and feeding. For example, when a snake flicks its tongue in and out as it moves, it is sampling environmental chemicals and inserting them into the opening of the VNO. Whether the human VNO functions *in utero* is not known, but, contrary to some popular reports, this organ is not functional in the adult. While a remnant of this organ is connected to the human adult nasal cavity via a small opening, this remnant has very few receptor cells and lacks biochemical machinery essential for its function. Unlike species, with a functioning VNO, it has no neural connection to central brain structures.

Development of function

The receptors of the olfactory system develop during pregnancy in an environment rich with chemical stimuli. Multiple chemicals bathe the developing fetus, entering the surrounding watery amniotic fluid via excreted urine, respiratory, and gastrointestinal tract wastes, as well as from the mother's diet and other constitutional sources. The developing fetus inhales much more fluid than it swallows, implying that the receptors are likely stimulated by a wealth of odorous materials during the later stages of fetal life. Importantly, the range of stimuli to which the fetus is exposed increases with age. This reflects, in large part, the fact that the barrier that separates the maternal blood supply from that of the fetus becomes more permeable. Since diffusion rates for odorants in amniotic fluid are similar to those in olfactory mucus, it is possible that odor detection is actually facilitated in the intrauterine environment.

There is evidence that the human fetus can respond to odorants *in utero*. Premature infants appear to reliably detect and discriminate odorants by 29 weeks, and exhibit some odor preferences by 31 weeks. Interestingly, newborns can remember and make use of olfactory information acquired during amniotic life. For example, newborns turn their head preferentially toward the odor of their mother's amniotic fluid when given a choice between the smell of that fluid and that of amniotic fluid from an unfamiliar mother. Anise, when introduced into a pregnant mother's diet, results in offspring who is attracted to anise-spiked amniotic fluid, implying transfer of the odorant from the pregnant mothers circulation into the amniotic fluid. Maternal ingestion of alcohol during pregnancy is similarly associated with postnatal responses to alcohol odor, independent of whether the development of the brain is influenced by the presence of the alcohol (e.g., as in fetal alcohol syndrome). Alcohol exposure before birth influences odor preferences for alcohol many years later and may, in some cases, increase the likelihood of alcoholism.

In addition to evidence that positive associations to odors can be learned *in utero*, there is evidence that negative reactions to odors can also be conditioned. Studies demonstrating this phenomenon have been largely performed in rodents. In such studies, offspring of pregnant mothers who have been intentionally made sick following infusion of an odorant into the amniotic fluid show postnatal aversions to that specific odor.

In rats, infusion of minute amounts of milk into the oral region of the late-term fetus produces behavioral responses similar to those observed in the newborn pup; that is, mouthing, changes in arousal, and body extension. Such infusion also attenuates responsiveness to an unpleasant or noxious stimulus. Interestingly, other tastants, such as sucrose, lactose, corn oil, or human milk formulas, fail to induce these behavioral alterations, suggesting selectivity in such responses. Preterm human infants exhibit similar appetitive responses to milk odor.

Olfaction in the Newborn

In light of the ability of the embryo to detect odorants, it is not surprising that newborn infants perceive odors which seem to induce behavioral responses reflective of feelings of pleasure or distress. Such behaviors can occur as early as the first day after birth. Researchers in the late nineteenth and early twentieth centuries reported that various nonbiological odorants, including asafoetida, bone oil, oil of geranium, tincture of gentian, and orange extract, elicited specific movements and facial expressions in neonates. Modern studies have confirmed such observations using electrical monitors to assess body movements, and heart rate, as well as video analysis of facial expressions and head movements. In general, orienting and positive facial gestures are directed to smells perceived as pleasant by adults and avoidance responses to odors perceived as unpleasant by adults (**Figure 3**).

The sense of smell is involved in the earliest infant–mother bonding processes, and likely plays a role in the infant's emotional and subsequent social adjustments. Soon after birth, infants use olfactory cues to discriminate between individuals or members of different social categories, including the father. The infants' discriminative performance in regards to social odors and the incentive value they assign to them is determined by their earliest social experiences. Suckling young infants rapidly develop the ability to recognize their own mother's odors and respond preferentially to them, as shown in studies where they orient more toward breast pads from their own mothers than toward breast pads from unfamiliar

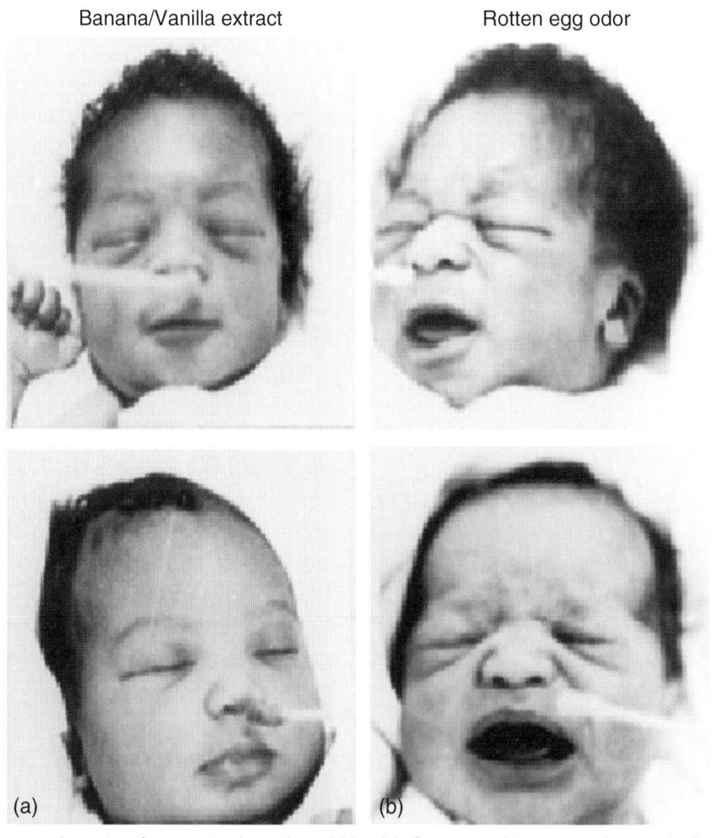

Figure 3 Facial responses to odorants of neonates less than 12 h old. Compared to a no-odor control condition, neonates display distinct responses to odors: (a) a 'smiling' expression accompanied by sucking movements (interpreted as acceptance, satisfaction, or liking) following presentation of banana/vanilla odor. (b) a 'dislike or rejection' response typified by a depression of the mouth angles or a pursing of the lips. Modified from Steiner JE (1977) Facial expressions of the neonate infant indicating the hedonics of food-related chemical stimuli. In: Weiffenbach JM (ed.) *Taste and Development: The Genetics of Sweet Preference*, pp. 173–188. Bethesda, MD: US Department of Health, Education and Welfare Publications.

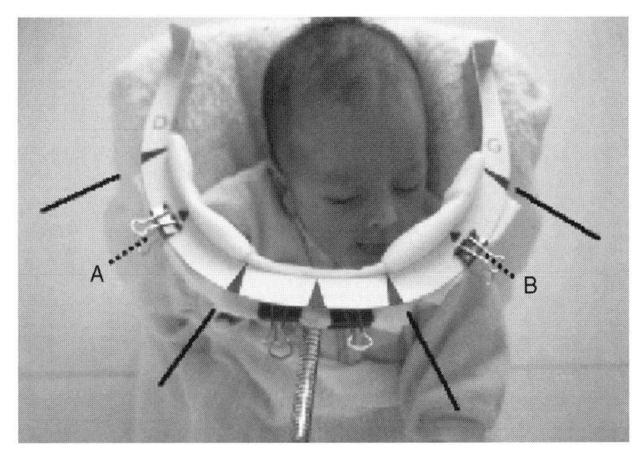

Figure 4 Testing apparatus for assessing olfactory responses of newborn infants. Two gauze pads (A and B) are fixed symmetrically on each side of the infant's midline, and the infant's head turning and other behaviors are recorded on film. Reprinted from Marlier L and Schaal B (2005) Human newborns prefer human milk: Conspecific milk odor is attractive without postnatal exposure. *Child Development* 76: 155–168.

mothers (**Figure 4**). This preference is learned within the first few days of mother–child interaction, and increases as a function of time as the mother breastfeeds the infant. The nipple region of the mother, including the surrounding areola, provides a rich assortment of maternal odors to the infant during lactation. Thus, in addition to secreting colostrum/milk from the lactiferous ducts (which is influenced by the mother's diet, genetic constitution, and metabolism), the nipple is densely supplied with a number of types of glands that secrete fat into the milk and produce characteristic odors.

Breastfed neonates of ~2 weeks of age also respond to other maternal odors. For example, they preferentially orient toward pads containing their mother's arm-pit odors relative to analogous odors from another lactating mother or a nonlactating unfamiliar mother. Bottle-fed infants fail to show this phenomenon, implying that the breastfed infants also learn to respond to the arm-pit odors. No preference is observed when arm-pit odors of the father are juxtaposed to those of an unfamiliar male, suggesting a need for their being learned when in close contact with the mother. Similar learned preferences for the perfume worn by the mother have also been reported.

Studies examining odor preferences of newborns for human vs. formula milk suggest that by 3–4 days of age, infants show a preference for the odor of human milk. Thus, infants orient more frequently and longer to pads containing the odor of human milk, as compared to formula milk, and exhibit more sucking-like behaviors toward the pads impregnated with the human milk. This preference is apparently independent of whether they are breastfed or formula-fed, although the inspection time for formula milk is greater for those that are formula fed.

Although it is known that newborn rodents can remember many odors for considerable periods of time, few studies have examined odor memory in human newborns. In one of the few studies on this topic, 2-day-old babies were exposed to cherry or ginger odor for approximately 22 h. The odorant was removed at the end of the exposure session, and infants had no further contact with that scent until tests were conducted 2 weeks later. At that time, they spent reliably more time oriented toward a pad treated with the exposure odor than to a pad treated with a novel scent, suggesting they remembered the familiar odorant over this time period.

It is of interest that blood levels of the so-called stress hormone norepinephrine are markedly elevated in the newborn for some period of time after birth. Given that this hormone facilitates olfactory learning in a range of species, the human neonate would appear to be primed for such learning soon after birth.

Olfaction in Children and Teenagers

Most children are familiar, at a relatively young age, with a broad range of odors. For example, by 6 years of age, American girls correctly identify over 75% of the 40 odors of the University of Pennsylvania Smell Identification Test (UPSIT), a standardized test of smell function. By 10 years of age they perform, for all practical purposes, at adult levels on this test. Boys, while not performing at the level of girls, still correctly identify approximately two-thirds of the odors by the age of 7 years, and achieve adult levels of performance before the teenage years (**Figure 5**).

A strong statistical association has been found between age and UPSIT scores obtained from several hundred children 4–12 years of age. To determine if the age-related changes in odor identification scores are mainly a reflection of knowledge of the visual sources of the odors, a subset of ~100 of these youngsters were also administered the picture identification test (PIT), a test that uses pictures of the sources of the odors employed in the UPSIT. Even 4–5-year-olds were found to be familiar with the odor objects and name concepts. Statistical analyses found that familiarity with the odorant source or its name was unlikely to be the basis for the observed age-related changes in odor identification ability. The poorer performance of children on odor naming and odor identification tasks relative to adults is a deficit that is erased by the late teens. This deficit likely reflects their not having experience with a number of odors represented on this test and their lack of learning of verbal descriptors of such odors. The latter likely explains why children also underperform on odor recall and recognition memory tests.

There is controversy as to whether children are more sensitive, in terms of their ability to detect low concentrations of odors, than adults. As early as 1899, one study reported that children were more sensitive than adults to

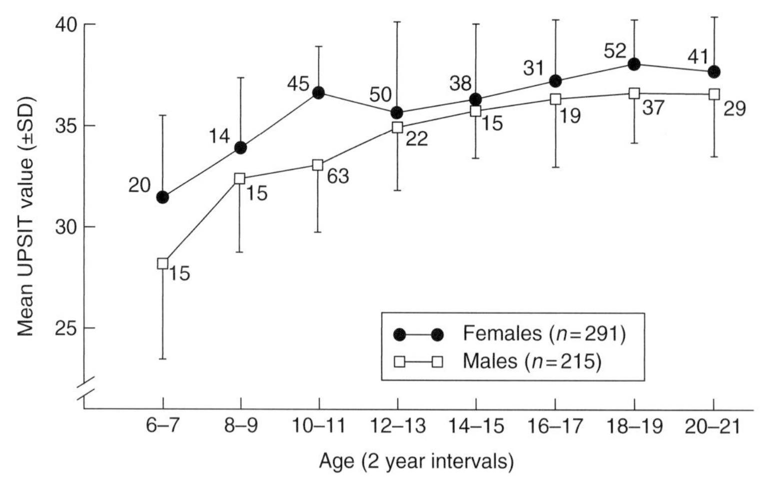

Figure 5 University of Pennsylvania Smell Identification Test (UPSIT) scores as a function of subject gender across the prepubertal, adolescent, and early adult years. Reprinted from Doty RL (1986) Gender and endocrine-related influences on human olfactory perception. In: Meiselman HL and Ravlin RS (eds.) *Clinical Measurement of Taste and Smell*, pp. 377–413. New York: Macmillian Publishing Company. SD, standard deviation.

camphor. Although no attempt has been made to specifically replicate this work, modern studies have found little evidence that youngsters are more sensitive than adults to most odors. In one study, for example, thresholds for the banana-like smelling agent, amyl acetate, were determined in 9–20-years-old subjects. The thresholds of the youngsters were similar to those of the young adults, although some prepubescent youngsters were unable to detect the musk odors of various chemicals (e.g., muskalactone) at the concentrations detected by adults, implying they may be less sensitive to these specific odorants. This is supported by another study in which 25 men, 25 women, 22 prepubescent boys, and 25 prepubescent girls rated the intensity of crystalline muskalactone odor as: either absent or very weak, weak, strong, or extremely strong. Significantly more of the boys, girls, and men rated the odor absent or very weak, as compared to the adult women, who typically rated the odor as strong or very strong. These and other studies suggest that subtle differences may exist between children and adults in terms of threshold sensitivity, but that such differences are present only for some odorants.

The weight of evidence suggests that the odor preferences of young children are, for the most part, similar to those of adults, although some differences may be present and the role of culture (e.g., advertising and peer-group pressure) on such preferences is not well understood. In one study, the preference rankings of 7–13-year-old children for 14 diverse odorants correlated highly with those obtained from 18–24-year-olds. Another study examined the preferences of 30 males aged 8–9, 14, and 16 years for 10 food-related odors: meat (roast beef gravy), fish, chocolate, onion, vegemite, peanut butter, spearmint, chicken, espresso coffee, and parmesan cheese. The only statistically significant differences were between 8–9-year-old subjects and the other groups for meat and chicken odors, and between the 14-year-old subjects and the other groups for peanut butter odor. The preference ratings for the odor of coffee changed from dislike to like as the age of the subjects increased. Puberty had no major effect on any of the preferences.

In summary, the olfactory system is functional prior to birth, and newborns exhibit the ability to smell a wide range of environmental stimuli. The degree to which *in utero* learning of the meaning of odors occurs is poorly understood, but there are instances when such learning has been shown to clearly influence postnatal odor preferences. In general, children exhibit adult-like capabilities for detecting and identifying odors, although they perform more poorly than adults on tests that require odor naming, identification, and memory. These deficits are erased by the late teens, likely reflecting experience with odors and the learning of verbal descriptors. Whether some such deficits reflect a less mature olfactory system than that seen in adults is debatable.

Taste

As noted in the introduction, the receptors for the sense of taste are largely found in taste buds, which are made up of dozens or even hundreds of cells organized into grapefruit-like structures with small openings that appear at the surface of the tongue. Most taste buds are found on the tongue's papillae. As shown in **Figure 2**, several types of papillae harbor taste buds, including ones shaped like little mushrooms (fungiform papillae), ones that appear as folds along the tongue's lateral margins (foliate papillae), and very large ones shaped like flattened hills located near the rare of the tongue (circumvallate or vallate papillae).

Arrowhead-shaped filiform papillae located across the tongue's surface contain no taste buds, but aid in the movement of materials within the oral cavity.

The receptor cells within the taste buds connect to nerve fibers that then send extensions into the brain. The first relays occur within a region of the brain-stem, from which other cells project to higher brain regions where tastes are recognized or identified.

Taste in the Fetus

Anatomical development

All mammalian fetuses exhibit spontaneous swallowing at some point in development. For example, the human fetus chews, swallows, and even regurgitates during the second half of gestation, and at term swallows 70–260 ml of fluid per day per kilogram of body weight. Such swallowing is critical for fetal amniotic fluid resorption, recirculating lung and urine fluid volumes, gastrointestinal development, and physical development, and is likely the sole means by which fetal resorption of the principal amniotic fluid electrolytes is made. The role of such swallowing on the taste system is not known, although tastants introduced into the amniotic fluid of animals variably increase the frequency of such swallowing.

The taste bud-containing papillae of the tongue are observed by the tenth week of gestation. The circumvallate papillae develop earlier than the fungiform papillae. Taste pores, the openings into taste buds which typically signify functional maturity of the buds, are observed in fetal fungiform papillae between 10 and 14 weeks of gestational age, although the early taste bud primorda makes synaptic contacts with nerve fibers as early as 8 weeks. Taste buds continue to differentiate after the opening of the taste pores, and the development of connections between receptors cells and the nerve cells to which they connect becomes apparent between 8 and 13 weeks.

Functional capacities

Most of what is known about taste function in the human fetus comes from studies of premature infants. Similar to the situation with olfaction, taste-induced behavioral responses have been observed in premature infants 6–9 months of gestational age. For example, a drop of pure lemon juice increases sucking vigor, reflexive salivation, and in some cases, retching in premature babies. Low concentrations of bitter tasting agents decrease their sucking responses. Sweet-tasting stimuli, such as sugar, can increase sucking frequency. Facial expressions seemingly reflecting pleasure or displeasure are seen in such infants.

Interestingly, premature babies transiently cease crying when given solutions of sucrose or glucose orally, but not water. In addition, palatable (e.g., sweet) taste stimuli appear to decrease the pain such infants experience during heel lance and other invasive procedures. Such responses are taste-bud mediated, since the same sweet solutions are ineffective in producing this effect when administered directly into the stomach. The calming effects are induced within seconds of sucrose delivery, well in advance of stomach clearance or absorption.

Individual differences in facial expressions have been noted in premature infants and appear to be most marked to 'salty' stimuli. For example, in one study 20 premature infants (1.2–2.9 kg) were orally presented with a low concentration of common table salt. More than half responded with a rejecting grimace, although four readily accepted this solution. In another study, a similar solution of table salt produced indifference in two-thirds of the premature infants, and rejection in the other third.

In summary, the taste buds are functional to some degree and capable of conveying at least some types of gustatory information to the central nervous system by the sixth gestational month. Such information is available to neural systems that organize salivation, sucking, facial expressions, and other observable behaviors at this early age.

Taste in the Newborn

Anatomical development

The newborn is endowed with a rich population of taste receptors which remains remarkably consistent in number through early adulthood. In the first year of life, each of the 9–12 circumvallate papillae contains ~250 taste buds. During this same time period, the foliate papillae contain ~1500 buds, whereas each fungiform papilla contains 0–12 taste buds. By the time of birth, ~2500 taste buds are dispersed over the other oral tissues, including the soft palate, the flap that covers the trachea during swallowing (epiglottis), the space behind the mouth that serves as a passage for food from the mouth to the throat (pharynx), and the upper end of the windpipe that contains the vocal cords (larynx).

Functional capacities

Few studies of taste thresholds have been performed in neonates. Early classical conditioning work suggests that that the sensitivity of 2–9-month-old infants is within the range of sensitivity of that of young adults. During the first neonatal year, sucrose and other sugars are preferentially ingested in larger amounts than bitter, sour, salty, or neutral tastants, such as water, and strong, bitter, and sour stimuli become avidly rejected. Heavier infants tend to consume greater absolute volumes of sweetened solutions than lighter ones. Sweet-tasting solutions reliably elicit hand–mouth contacts in the first few days of life, a behavior that declines in frequency over course of xthe next few weeks. Newborns distinguish between different concentrations of sweet stimuli, as measured quantitatively by assessing sucking rates, duration of sucking bursts, interburst intervals, and within-burst pace of sucking. Increasing sucrose concentrations across the 0.0612–0.5 M range leads to increases in the number of sucks regardless of birth weight.

Infants under 4 months of age are seemingly indifferent to the taste of salt, showing no preference for weak concentrations of sodium chloride solution over water. In contrast, those between the ages of 4 and 24 months exhibit heightened preference or acceptance of such solutions. However, children 2.5 to 5 years of age prefer water to saline solution in choice tests, suggesting developmental changes in the maturation of the salt sensing system, either at the receptor level or in more central gustatory structures. A similar phenomenon occurs for bitter-tasting urea. Although seemingly indifferent to the taste of urea during the first week of life, over the course of the next few months infants begin to exhibit facial expressions and body movements indicative of displeasure and rejection. Older infants exhibit a marked decrease in intake of this substance.

In general, behavioral responses to tastants, particularly unpleasant ones, are initially reflex-like in nature but become more voluntary over the course of the preverbal first year of life. The most notable example of this fact is the distinct facial responses of acceptance and rejection to tastants that occur in children with anencephaly (a defect in the brain development that results in small or missing hemispheres). Thus, spontaneous facial expressions to taste stimuli, which are fairly stable over the first postnatal month, gradually decrease, being replaced by more noticeable intentional behaviors such as refusal to open the mouth or pushing the spoon away with the hands.

It is important to emphasize that early experience with tastants can alter subsequent taste preferences. Thus, infants fed sweetened water any time during the first 6 months of life maintain the high sweet preference noted at birth for at least 1.5 years, while those not so fed diminish their sweet preference during this time. Fetal exposure to electrolyte imbalances and accompanying dehydration also alter postnatal ingestive responses. In one study, 16-week-old infants of mothers who had experienced morning sickness or had vomited during pregnancy exhibited stronger preferences to weak solutions of salt than infants of mothers who had no such experiences. They also ingested larger volumes of the stronger of such solutions. Moreover, the babies of the sick mothers were less likely to express aversive facial reactivity patterns, and more likely to exhibit hedonically positive responses, to the salt solutions. This altered salt preference likely continues into adulthood, since adults whose mothers experienced marked morning sickness exhibited, relative to ones whose mothers did not, (1) greater self-reported use of salt, (2) greater intake of salt in the laboratory, and (3) stronger preferences for salty snack food. These observations suggest that, overall, preterm infants can, in fact, taste salt but under normal conditions are indifferent to it.

As in the case of premature babies, cessation of ongoing crying, as well as mitigation of pain reactivity, can be produced by infusing as little as 0.1 ml of sucrose or aspartame into the oral cavities of newborns. Such effects are maintained for minutes after the cessation of the stimulus. Other tastants (e.g., milk flavor, weak solutions of quinine) can also produce this effect, but not to the same degree. Oral tactile stimulation, such as induced by a pacifier, can also contribute to this effect, although the effects are not long lasting and, unlike the situation for sucrose, are generally unaccompanied by decreases in heart rate. The ability of the sweet-perceptive system to regulate ongoing crying or pain is strongest right after birth, and appears to decrease somewhat over the first 6 weeks. Varying the type of sweet tastant, its concentration, volume, and means of presentation (e.g., flow or dipped pacifier) do not differentially affect the calming or pain-reducing effects of sweet tasting stimuli. This suggests to some the possibility of an 'on–off' rather than a graded relation between the sensory taste information carried to the brain and the central neural processes associated with the mitigation of the pain responses.

Taste in Children and Teenagers

Anatomical development

Children and teens have the same general number of taste buds as neonates, as described above. However, the size and distribution of the papillae and taste buds differs significantly, reaching an adult distribution by the late teenage years. In general, the anterior tongue attains adult size by 8–10 years of age, whereas the posterior tongue, which contains fewer fungiform papillae, continues to grow until 15–16 years of age. Thus, the anterior tongue of the adult retains the full compliment of papillae and taste buds present in earlier life.

Microscopic studies of selected regions of the anterior tongue have found that male children (8–9 years) have higher densities of both taste papillae and taste pores (openings into taste buds) than do male adults (18–30 years). The same average number of taste pores per papilla is present in both groups. The papillae of boys are smaller and more round than those of men, whose papillae take on the characteristic mushroom-like shape.

Functional capacities

Although it is generally believed children, relative to adults, have a heightened preference for sweet-tasting foods, and a lowered preference for bitter-tasting ones, it is not entirely clear whether children are more sensitive than adults to tastants. Some studies support a general tendency for greater sensitivity in 6–15-year-olds relative to 16–25-year-olds, although other studies have reported the opposite. In one study, 5–7-year-old children were tested for their sensitivity to a bitter substance (6-*n*-propylthiouracil or PROP). The ability to perceive PROP is a genetically determined trait. 'Tasters' were defined as those children who clearly tasted PROP, had low thresholds to this agent, and provided higher intensity ratings across the four PROP concentrations tested. Since there were proportionally fewer 'nontasters' than predicted by adult data, it was suggested that PROP thresholds rise with age and may partially account for the greater food finickiness observed in many children.

Taste sensitivity is dictated by a number of factors, and is generally correlated with the number of taste buds within the lingual region being evaluated. When small tongue regions are compared for their sensitivity between children and adults, children have been found to be more sensitive, presumably reflecting the greater density of receptors within the regions evaluated. However, whole-mouth testing rarely finds children more sensitive than adults. In a recent study, for example, whole-mouth detection thresholds for sucrose, sodium chloride, citric acid and caffeine were measured for 68 children 6–8 years of age and for 61 young adults. Thresholds were no different between girls and either the adult men or women. Boys were less sensitive, on average, than the adult women to all of these stimuli and less sensitive than the men to all but caffeine. They were also less sensitive than girls to sucrose and sodium chloride. Considerable individual variation and overlap between groups in the threshold test scores were present.

Preferences for salty foods established early in life are maintained throughout early childhood and early adolescence before stabilizing at adult levels. In one study of 3–6-year-old children, 7–10-year-old children, and 18–26-year-old young adults, children preferred soups containing, on average, 0.4 M salt, whereas adults preferred soups containing 0.2 M salt. Hispanic preschoolers expressed a higher salt preference than their non-Hispanic white counterparts. Other studies have also found that children, relative to adults, prefer higher concentrations of sucrose and lactose and that, on average, males prefer higher concentrations than females.

As with the case of newborns, experience plays an important role in determining food preferences of children and teenagers. In general, infants increase their acceptance of a novel food, even food that is initially aversive, after repeated dietary exposure to that food. For example, one study exposed 4–5-year-olds to either plain tofu or tofu made sweet or salty multiple times over the course of several weeks. When tested months later, the neonates preferred the tofu with which they had experience. The taste preference did not generalize to other foods of similar color and texture (e.g., ricotta) that were made similarly sweet or salty. Context and culture are also important for establishing preferences. For example, in a study of first- and second-generation Chinese adolescent immigrant boys to Canada, the second generation boys and those with more accultured patterns of language use gave higher flavor and prestige ratings to dessert, snack, and fast foods, and discriminated better among nutrient-rich and poor foods.

Summary

The ability to sense chemicals, which was essential for the evolution of life, is critical for the well being and functioning of humans, and largely determines food preferences, nutrient intake, and protection from such environmental hazards as leaking natural gas and spoiled food. Although newborns are responsive to a wide range of odorants and tastes, so are premature infants. Indeed, the senses of taste and smell appear operative in the later stages of fetal development, during which time preferences and aversions to some odorants and tastants develop. For example, maternal ingestion of alcohol during pregnancy influences the infant's later responses to alcohol odor, and may even potentiate the development of alcoholism. Even though newborns appear to be somewhat indifferent to the taste of salt, this is not the case with other taste stimuli, such as sugar, which can mitigate pain responses induced by tactile and other forms of aversive stimulation.

Taste sensitivity is dictated by a number of factors, including genetics, and is generally correlated with the number of taste buds within the lingual region being evaluated. When small tongue regions are compared for their sensitivity between children and adults, children have been found to be more sensitive, presumably reflecting the greater density of receptors within the regions evaluated. However, whole-mouth testing rarely finds children more sensitive than adults.

The influences of exposure of infants to tastants can have long lasting effects on taste preferences. In one study, infants fed sweetened water during various periods of the first 6 months of life maintained the high sweet preference noted at birth for at least a year and a half, while those not so fed diminished their sweet preference during this time period. In another study, 16-week-old infants of mothers who had suffered morning sickness or had vomited during pregnancy exhibited stronger preferences to weak solutions of salt, and ingested larger volumes of salt solutions, than infants of mothers who had no such experiences. The babies of the sick mothers were less likely to express aversive facial reactivity patterns, and more likely to exhibit positive responses to salt solutions. This altered salt preference seems to continue into adulthood, since adults whose mothers experienced marked morning sickness exhibited, relative to ones whose mothers did not, (1) greater self-reported use of salt, (2) greater intake of salt in the laboratory, and (3) stronger preferences for salty snack food. Other studies suggest that preferences for salty foods established early in life are maintained throughout early childhood and early adolescence before stabilizing at adult levels.

The senses of taste and smell play an important role in the early infant–mother bonding, and likely influence later emotional and social adjustments. Soon after birth, babies use olfactory cues to differentiate between individuals, and nursing newborns rapidly develop the ability to recognize their own mother's odors and respond preferentially to them. Youngsters rapidly learn to identify odors in their environment. By the age of 6 years, for example, American girls correctly identify over 75% of the odors on the UPSIT, a standardized test of smell function. By 10 years of age they perform, for all practical purposes, at adult levels on this test. Boys, while not performing at the level of girls, still correctly identify approximately two-thirds of the odors by the age of 7 yeasrs, and achieve adult levels of performance before the teenage years. Although there is little evidence that young persons are more sensitive to odors or tastes than older ones, they appear to be more reactive to the pleasant or unpleasant elements of chemicals.

As with the case of neonates, experience plays an important role in determining food preferences of children. In general, infants increase their acceptance of a novel food, even food that is initially aversive, after repeated dietary exposure to that food. Context and culture are also important for establishing food preferences. For example, in a study of first- and second-generation Chinese adolescent immigrant boys to Canada, the second generation boys and those with more accultured patterns of language use gave higher flavor and prestige ratings to dessert, snack, and fast foods, and discriminated better among nutrient-rich and poor foods.

See also: Breastfeeding; Feeding Development and Disorders; Fetal Alcohol Spectrum Disorders; Newborn Behavior; Prenatal Development; Perceptual Development; Suckling.

Suggested Readings

Chuah MI, Schwob JE, and Farbman AI (2003) Developmental anatomy of the olfactory system. In: Richard LD (ed.) *Handbook of Olfaction and Gustation,* 2nd edn., pp. 115–138. New York: Marcel Dekker.

De Graaf C and Zandstra EH (1999) Sweetness, intensity, and pleasantness in children, adolescents, and adults. *Physiology and Behavior* 67: 513–520.

Doty RL (1986) Gender and endocrine-related influences on human olfactory perception. In: Meiselman HL and Ravlin RS (eds.) *Clinical Measurement of Taste and Smell*, pp. 377–413. New York: Macmillian Publishing Company.

Doty RL (2003) *Hand book of Olfaction and Gestation*. New York: Marcel Dekker.

Doty RL, Bagla R, Morgenson M, and Mirza N (2001) NaCl thresholds: Relationship to anterior tongue locus, area of stimulation, and number of fungiform papillae. *Physiology and Behavior* 72: 373–378.

Felten DL and Joefowic R (2003) *Netter's Atlas of Human Neuroscience.* London: Elsevier.

Ganchrow JR and Mennella JA (2003) The ontogeny of human flavor perception. In: Richard LD (ed.) *Handbook of Olfaction and Gustation,* 2nd edn., pp. 823–846. New York: Marcel Dekker.

James CE, Laing DG, and Oram N (1997) A comparison of the ability of 8–9-year-old children and adults to detect taste stimuli. *Physiology and Behavior* 62: 193–197.

Lehrner JP, Glück J, and Laska M (1999) Odor identification, consistency of label use, odor threshold and their relationships to odor memory over the human lifespan. *Chemical Senses* 24: 337–346.

Marlier L and Schaal B (2005) Human newborns prefer human milk: Conspecific milk odor is attractive without postnatal exposure. *Child Development* 76: 155–168.

Mennella JA, Pepino MY, and Reed DR (2005) Genetic and environmental determinants of bitter perception and sweet preferences. *Pediatrics* 115: 216–222.

Mistretta CM and Hill DL (2003) Development of the taste system: Basic neurobiology. In: Richard LD (ed.) *Handbook of Olfaction and Gustation,* 2nd edn., pp. 759–782. New York: Marcel Dekker.

Ross MG and Nijland MJM (1998) Development of ingestive behavior. *American Journal of Physiology* (*Regulatory Integrative Comparative Physiology 43*) 274: R879–R893.

Steiner JE (1977) Facial expressions of the neonate infant indicating the hedonics of food-related chemical stimuli. In: Weiffenbach JM (ed.) *Taste and Development: The Genetics of Sweet Preference*, pp. 173–188. Bethesda, MD: United States Department of Health, Education and Welfare Publications.

Temple EC, Hutchinson I, Laing DG, and Jinks AL (2002) Taste development: Differential growth rates of tongue regions in humans. *Developmental Brain Research* 135: 65–70.

Television: Uses and Effects

J P Murray and A D Murray, Kansas State University, Manhattan, KS, USA

Glossary

Attention deficit hyperactivity disorder (ADHD) – A biologically based psychological disorder that is characterized by restlessness, impulsivity, inattention and distractedness.
Autism (or autism spectrum disorders) – A developmental disorder characterized by deficiencies in language and communication, social interaction skills, and the presence of repetitive behaviors and obsessive-compulsive disorder (OCD) interests.
Formal features – Production features of television and other screen media programs such as pace, film angles and cuts, sounds, voices (male, female, child), frequency of scene changes, temporal integration.
Mirror neurons – Areas of the brain that are responsive to – and 'mirror' – the observed physical actions of others; first discovered in the 1990s by Giacomo Rizzolatti when studying primate brains.
Moderate discrepancy hypothesis – The notion that young viewers will attend to visual portrayals that are moderately novel, moderately complex and somewhat surprising in the context of the viewer's experience (see traveling lens model).
Screen media/screen time – A general category of a range of media involving visual stimulation, including computer games, CD material, television, and video. Also, the amount of time spent with such media is described as 'screen time'.
Traveling lens model – A model for describing the factors that enhance or diminish children's attention to screen media; factors such as novelty, complexity, consistency, integration, and repetitive versus unpredictability.
Trigger hypothesis – The notion that viewing television, video, or DVDs extensively during infancy may trigger the onset of autism in vulnerable children.

Introduction

The history of research and policy discussions concerning media and early childhood is largely a history of research on television and children. Indeed, the concern about the impact of television on the cognitive development and social behavior of children began in the 1950s in the US and was initially focused on social behavior, particularly the impact of media violence. By the mid- to late-1960s, there was a developing concern about the role that media (i.e., television) could play in facilitating or retarding cognitive development. The landmark research in this latter area was the research designed to establish and evaluate 'Sesame Street', and other programs for preschool children. However, by the 1990s and the first decade of the twenty-first century, concerns about young children and media had broadened to include computers, video games, and other forms of electronic screen media or interactive toys.

As a result of research and public discussion of children and media, legislators and scientific and professional associations began to suggest the need to formulate public policy and parental recommendations. These were designed to monitor and curb some of the negative effects of media, while encouraging patterns of use that enhance the positive effects of media in the lives of young children.

The negative effects of screen media were associated with excessive amounts of time spent with media and the harmful effects of particular content such as violence or advertising. The concerns about excessive time spent on media focused on the fact that screen time might take time away from other important activities of childhood such as imaginative play or interaction with other children as well as time spent with parents, being read to and playing, or exploring their expanding social world. So too, the concerns about specific content such as violence, sexuality, and social role portrayals became important. In addition, advertising for unhealthy food products that may lead to disordered food preferences and eating patterns that encourage unhealthy lifestyles were a major concern. Finally, it has been suggested, by some psychologists and pediatricians, that extensive viewing leads to reduced attention span or increased hyperactivity and, in some recent speculative research by a team of economists, that early television viewing can facilitate the induction of Autism in young children.

In response to these concerns, various professional and scientific organizations, such as the American Psychological Association, the National Association for the Education of Young Children and the American Academy of Pediatrics – including one of its most important advocates for children's television, Berry Brazelton – have issued policy statements and recommendations about screen media effects such as violence, early childhood learning needs, and children's social development and obesity.

Early in the twenty-first century, the American Academy of Pediatrics issued an advisory to its members entitled, 'Children, Adolescents and Television Policy Statement', in which it recommended zero screen time for infants under the age of 2 years and only 1–2 h of quality educational media per day for those beyond 2 years of age. This is a fairly 'lean' diet for infants and young children and far below the levels that we know, from studies such as those conducted by the Kaiser Family Foundation, these youngsters consume in their typical daily lives.

Why would major professional organizations concerned with the health and well-being of young children adopt such stringent recommendations? How have scientists studied these issues over the past 50 years of research? What do we know about the patterns of use and the effects of television and other media on the development of young children? How can screen media (television, video games, internet information, interactive toys, and CD-rom or video educational material) be used to enhance the learning and lives of infants and young children?

Research Approaches and Concerns

The research history is best described in terms of the nature of the methodological approaches used: correlational, experimental (laboratory and field), and cross-lagged panel studies. Each of these methodologies will be discussed within an historical context, and the ways in which government and public concerns over the years have set the agenda for social science research.

Setting the Agenda

Concern about the influence of televised violence as an issue in the US began as early as the start of this new medium. The first Congressional hearings were held in the US in the early 1950s. At these early hearings, developmental psychologist Eleanor Maccoby and sociologist Paul Lazarsfeld presented testimony that relied upon some early studies of violence in films, such as the 1933 report, *Boys, Movies and City Streets,* to outline a necessary program of research on the issue of televised violence and its effects on children.

As the 1960s progressed, concern in the US about violence in the streets and the assassinations of President John F. Kennedy, Dr. Martin Luther King, Jr., and Robert Kennedy, stimulated continuing interest in media violence. In response, several major government commissions and scientific and professional review committees were established to summarize the research evidence and public policy issues regarding the role of television violence in salving or savaging young viewers.

Across five decades, six principal government and professional commissions and review panels – the 1969 National Commission on the Causes and Prevention of Violence; the 1972 Surgeon General's Scientific Advisory Committee on Television and Social Behavior; the 1982 National Institute of Mental Health Television and Behavior Project; the 1982 Group for the Advancement of Psychiatry, Child and Television Drama Review; the 1992 American Psychological Association Task Force on Television and Society; and the 2002 Surgeon General's report on Youth Violence – have been central to setting the agenda for research and public discussion.

In 1982, the National Institute of Mental Health (NIMH) published a 10 year follow up of the 1972 Surgeon General's study. The two-volume report, collectively titled, *Television and Behavior: Ten Years of Scientific Progress and Implications for the Eighties*, provided a reminder of the breadth and depth of knowledge that had accumulated on the issue of televised violence. In this regard, the NIMH staff and consultants concluded:

After 10 more years of research, the consensus among most of the research community is that violence on television does lead to aggressive behavior by children and teenagers who watch the programs. This conclusion is based on laboratory experiments and on field studies. Not all children become aggressive, of course, but the correlations between violence and aggression are positive. In magnitude, television violence is as strongly correlated with aggressive behavior as any other behavioral variable that has been measured.

In 1986, the American Psychological Association (APA) empanelled a Task Force on Television and Society to review the research and professional concerns about the impact of television on children and adults. The nine psychologists assigned to this committee undertook reviews of relevant research, conducted interviews with television industry and public policy professionals, and discussed concerns with representatives of government regulatory agencies and public interest organizations. The final report, entitled *Big World, Small Screen: The Role of Television in American Society,* published in 1992, included the following observation about television violence:

American television has been violent for many years. Over the past 20 years, the rate of violence on prime time evening television has remained at about five to six incidents per hour, whereas the rate on children's Saturday morning programs is typically 20–25 acts per hour. There is clear evidence that television violence can cause aggressive behavior and can cultivate values favoring the use of aggression to resolve conflicts.

Clearly, both the federal government and the medical establishment had identified media violence as a problem worthy of extensive inquiry. It is not surprising that the social science researchers took up the topic as well.

Early Correlational (Survey) Studies

The early studies of television's influence began almost simultaneously in England, the US, and Canada in the mid-1950s. They were designed to take advantage of the regulated introduction of the new medium in order to examine its impact in those early years.

In England, a group of researchers at the London School of Economics and Political Science, under the direction of Hilde Himmelweit, began the first study of children's television viewing patterns while television was still relatively new. (At the time, there were only three million television sets installed in the 15 million households in England.) Although proposed by the Audience Research Department of the British Broadcasting Corporation (BBC), the study was conducted by independent researchers. Begun in 1955, the study was published in a 1958 report, *Television and the Child: An Empirical Study of the Effect of Television on the Young*. The American and Canadian study was conducted by Wilbur Schramm and his colleagues at Stanford University. Begun in 1957, the study was published in a 1961 report, *Television in the Lives of Our Children*.

These studies, both correlational in that they compared television viewers and nonviewers in a real-world setting (as opposed to manipulating viewing in a laboratory), provided very important benchmarks for understanding the broad and general effects of television on children. With regard to aggression, these correlational studies did not support an association. Himmelweit and colleagues "did not find that the viewers were any more aggressive or maladjusted than the controls," and concluded that "television is unlikely to cause aggressive behaviour, although it could precipitate it in those few children who are emotionally disturbed. There was little support for the view that programmes of violence are beneficial; we found that they aroused aggression as often as they discharged it". The conclusions of Schramm, Lyle, and Parker have become something of a mantra, and go a long way toward also summarizing (or foreshadowing) the findings of 50 years of research:

> For 'some' children under 'some' conditions 'some' television is harmful. For 'other' children under the same conditions, or for the same children under 'other' conditions, it may be beneficial. For 'most' children under 'most' conditions, 'most' television is probably neither particularly harmful nor particularly beneficial.

Yet they also concluded that those Canadian and American children studied who had high exposure to television and low exposure to print media were more aggressive than those with the reverse pattern. Thus, the early correlational studies identified some areas of concern about television violence and set the stage for more focused investigations.

The demonstration of a relationship between viewing and aggressive behavior in daily life circumstances is a logical precursor to studies of the causal role that televised violence may play in promoting aggressive behavior. The correlational studies that followed the Himmelweit and Schramm reports found consistent patterns of significant correlations between the number of hours of television viewed (or the frequency of viewing violent programs) and various measures of aggressive attitudes or behavior.

Correlational Panel Studies

While correlational studies can show us that there is a relationship between viewing media violence and behavior and/or beliefs, they do not address the issue of cause and effect. Although authors might interpret correlational data to provide evidence of cause and effect, they cannot say for sure in which direction the relationship goes. For example, might naturally aggressive children/teens be more drawn to violent media? And yet, there are some special-case correlational studies in which 'intimations of causation' can be derived from the fact that these studies were conducted over several time periods. Three of these special surveys and 'panel' studies (so named because the same panel of respondents are studied at various points in time) have been highly influential – a 1978 retrospective survey of viewing and current behavior, funded by the private television network CBS; a 1982 panel study, funded by the private television network NBC; and another panel study, funded by the Surgeon General's Committee and NIMH from 1969 to 1986.

The 1978 CBS study was conducted by William Belson in England with 1565 youths who were a representative sample of 13–17-year-old males living in London. This retrospective survey looked at the history of viewing violent programs that had been broadcast over 12 years in England and related that to the behavior of the boys during the previous 6 months. The boys were interviewed concerning the extent of their exposure to a selection of violent television programs (broadcast during the period 1959 through 1971 and rated by members of the BBC viewing panel for level of violence) as well as each boy's level of violent behavior as determined by his report of how often he had been involved in any of 53 categories of violence over the previous 6 months. The degree of seriousness of the acts reported by the boys ranged from only slightly violent aggravation, such as taunting, to more serious and very violent behavior such as: "I tried to force a girl to have sexual intercourse with me"; "I bashed a boy's head against a wall"; "I burned a boy on the chest with a cigarette while my mates held him down"; and "I threatened to kill my father." Approximately 50% of the 1565 boys were not involved in any violent acts during the 6-month period. However, of those who were involved in violence, 188 (12%) were involved in 10 or more acts during the 6-month period. When Belson compared the behavior of boys who had higher exposure to televised violence to those who had lower exposure (and had been matched on a wide variety of possible contributing factors), he found that the high-violence viewers were more involved in serious interpersonal violence.

The NBC study (published in 1982), undertaken by Ronald Milavsky and his colleagues, was conducted over a 3-year period from May 1970 to December 1973 in two cities, Fort Worth and Minneapolis. Interviews were conducted with samples of second- to sixth-grade boys and girls and a special sample of teenage boys. In the elementary school sample, the information on television viewing and measures of aggression was collected in six time periods over the 3 years. The aggression measure consisted of peer ratings of aggressive behavior. In the teenage sample there were five waves of interviews over the 3 years and the aggression measures were self-report rather than peer-reported aggression. The results showed that there were small but clear causal effects of viewing violence in the samples of boys and that these effects grew in strength over the 3 years of the repeated measures during the study period.

Finally, one of the longest panel studies, 22 years, is the work of Leonard Eron and his colleagues. In the initial studies, conducted for the Surgeon General's investigation of televised violence, the researchers were able to document the long-term effects of violence viewing by studying children over a 10-year period from age 8 to 18. At these two time periods, the youngsters were interviewed about their program preferences and information was collected from peer ratings of aggressive behavior. The violence levels of their preferred televised programs and other media and measures of aggression across these two time periods suggested the possibility that early television violence viewing was one factor in producing later aggressive behavior. In particular, the findings for 211 boys followed in this longitudinal study demonstrated that televised violence at age 8 years was significantly related to aggression at age 8 years; and the 8-year old violent television preferences were significantly related to aggression at age 18; but televised violence preferences at age 18 years were not related to aggressive behavior at the earlier time period, age 8. When other possible variables, such as parenting practices and discipline style, were controlled it was still clear that early media violence could be part of the cause of later aggressive behavior. Furthermore, in a 1984 follow-up study, when these young men were now age 30, the authors found a significant correlation between televised violence levels at age 8 years and serious interpersonal criminal behavior (e.g., assault, murder, child abuse, spouse abuse, rape) at age 30 years.

Thus, it seems clear that a correlation between television violence and aggression can be established from diverse studies. And, some special cases of longitudinal correlational studies (described as cross-lagged/panel studies) can lead to intimations of causation. However, the issue of causation is best assessed in experimental designs that allow for random assignment of subjects to various treatment conditions or, in the case of field studies, take advantage of naturally occurring variations in television viewing experiences.

Early Experimental Studies

The earliest experimental studies on the effects of media violence on young people emerged in the 1960s, and have proved to be so influential (and even controversial) that they are still cited today. These initial experiments were conducted by Albert Bandura, at Stanford University, who studied preschool age children, and Leonard Berkowitz, at the University of Wisconsin, who worked with college-age youth. In both instances, the studies were experimental in design, which meant that subjects were randomly assigned to various viewing experiences, enabling the researchers to apply the results of this manipulated viewing to address the issue of causal relationships between viewing and behavior.

The early Bandura studies, such as 'Transmission of aggression through imitation of aggressive models or Imitation of film-mediated aggressive models', were set within a social learning paradigm and were designed to identify the processes governing the ways that children learn by observing and imitating the behavior of others. In this context, therefore, the studies used stimulus films (videotape was not generally available) back projected on a simulated television screen. Immediately following the viewing period, the behavior of the children was observed and recorded in a playroom setting. The children who have viewed the model beating a inflated clown (the Bobo doll, hence the generic reference to 'Bobo-Doll-Studies') were more likely to attack the similar toy in the playroom and imitated the voices and words used by the model in the film. Despite the structured nature of these studies, Bandura's research was central to the debate about the influence of media violence.

Moreover, the work of Berkowitz and his colleagues, such as 'Effects of film violence on inhibitions against subsequent aggression', studied the aggressive behavior of youth and young adults following the viewing of segments of violent films, such as a Kirk Douglas boxing film, 'The Champion'. The demonstration of increased willingness to use aggression against others following viewing, further fueled the debate about the influence of media violence.

While the studies of Bandura and Berkowitz set the stage, later experimental studies have employed both the structured, laboratory-based settings as well as more naturalistic settings in schools and communities. For example, one of the earlier studies in this genre, assessed the effects of viewing segments of a violent television program, 'The Untouchables', on the aggressive behavior of 5–9-year-old boys and girls. In this study, the children viewed either 'The Untouchables' or a neutral, but active, track race. Following viewing, the child was placed in a playroom setting in which he or she could help or hurt another child who was ostensibly playing a game in another room. The subject could help the other child by pressing a button that would make the game easier to play and allow the other child to win more points. Similarly, the child could hurt the other child by pressing a button that would make the game very difficult to play and hence lose points. The results indicated that youngsters who had viewed the violent program manifested a greater willingness to hurt the other child than youngsters who had watched the neutral program. Moreover, an elaboration of this study by Paul Ekman and colleagues included the recording of the facial expressions of these children while they were watching the television violence. In this instance, the children, whose facial expressions indicated interest or pleasure while watching televised violence, were more willing to hurt the other child than the youngsters whose facial expressions indicated disinterest or displeasure while watching televised violence. Thus, this set of studies identified some potential moderating variables in the violence-viewing/aggressive-behavior equation.

Other early experiments by researchers using physiological measures of arousal (e.g., GSR – known as galvanic skin response, a measure of sweating on the palms of the hand – and heart rate and respiration changes) while watching violent cartoons found that children were emotionally responsive even to cartoon violence. So too, other studies found that exposure to even one violent cartoon led to increased aggression in the structured playroom settings. Furthermore, studies by Ronald Drabman and his colleagues showed that children who view violent television programs became desensitized to violence and were more willing to tolerate aggressive behavior in others. Moreover, studies with emotionally disturbed children in the 1990s by Tom Grimes and his colleagues found that these youngsters may be more vulnerable to the influence of televised violence. For example, Grimes found that 8–12-year-olds who were diagnosed as having either attention-deficit-hyperactivity disorder, oppositional defiant disorder, or conduct disorder, manifested less emotional concern for victims and were more willing to accept violence as justified than a matched group of children who did not have these disorders – the beginnings of concerns about hyperactivity and attention deficit hyperactivity disorder (ADHD) which will be seen in more recent studies on autism and neurological deficits.

All of these experimental studies described above were conducted in fairly structured laboratory or playroom settings where the display of aggression or emotional arousal or desensitization were relatively contiguous to the viewing of televised violence. However, questions remain about what might happen in more naturalistic settings or field studies of violence viewing and aggressive behavior.

One early study that assessed these issues was the 1973 work of Aletha Huston Stein and Lynette Friedrich-Cofer in which they assessed the impact of viewing aggressive versus prosocial television programs on the behavior of preschoolers in their normal childcare settings. In this study, the preschoolers were assigned to view a diet of either Batman and Superman cartoons, or Mister Rogers' Neighborhood, or neutral programming that contained neither aggressive nor prosocial material (i.e., special travel stories for preschoolers). The 'diet' consisted of 12 30-min episodes that were viewed 30-min per day, 3 days per week, for 4 weeks. The researchers observed the children in the classroom and on the playground for 3 weeks prior to the start of the viewing period, to establish a baseline for the amount of aggression or prosocial behavior, and continued to observe the children during the 4 weeks of viewing and for an additional 2 weeks. The results were that children who were initially more aggressive and had viewed the diet of Batman and Superman cartoons were more active in the classroom and on the playground, played more roughly with toys, and got into more aggressive encounters. Conversely, youngsters from lower income families who had viewed the Mister Roger's diet increased their prosocial helping behavior. One suggestion from this early field study is that viewing aggressive program content can lead to changes in aggressive behavior, while the opposite is also true for prosocial programming. Moreover, these changes were demonstrated in a relatively short viewing period (12 30-min sessions) and in the context of other viewing that took place outside of the classroom setting.

Other field studies have used restricted populations such as boys in detention centers or secure residential settings. In one such study, published in 1971 and conducted for NBC, Seymour Feshbach and his colleague presented preadolescent and adolescent males in a security facility with a diet of aggressive or nonaggressive television programs over a 6-week period and measured their daily aggressive behavior. They found that the youngsters who watched the nonaggressive programs were more aggressive than the other group. However, this study was criticized on methodological grounds relating to the selection of subjects and the assignment of viewing conditions and a subsequent replication failed to duplicate the findings. Moreover, a later study conducted by Leonard Berkowitz and his colleagues, using aggressive or nonaggressive films presented to adolescent males living in minimum-security institutions, did demonstrate increases in both verbal and physical interpersonal aggression among the teens viewing the aggressive diet.

Another approach to field studies involved the assessment of the effects of naturally occurring differences in the television exposure available to children in communities with or without television or communities with differing television content. In the 1970s, John Murray and Susan Kippax were able to study the introduction of television in a rural community in Australia, in contrast to two similar communities that had differing experiences with television. In a second set of studies by Tannis Macbeth and her colleagues, the research team studied the introduction of television in a rural Canadian community, in contrast to two similar communities with differing television experience. In general, the results of both the Australian and Canadian studies converge in showing that the introduction of television had a major influence on restructuring the social lives of children in these rural communities. In this regard, both studies found that television displaced other media use and involvement in various social activities – a finding not dissimilar to the earlier studies of children in England by Himmelweit or the US and Canada by Schramm. However, with regard to the effects of televised violence, these newer field studies provide stronger evidence of negative influence, in differing but complementary ways. Murray and Kippax found changes in perceptions of the seriousness and prevalence of crime among children in the town exposed to higher levels of television violence, while Macbeth found increases in aggression among children following the introduction of television in the town.

Given the range of research approaches identified over the past 50 years, what can be said about the influences of media on very young viewers? What are the patterns of use and the effects on the youngest viewers?

Patterns of Use

Studies of American households consistently demonstrate that television, since its inception 50 years ago, has been a major feature of daily activities and, increasingly in recent years, computers, video games, and other electronic entertainment are woven into the fabric of family life.

A 2004 report by the Kaiser Family Foundation, noted that babies 6 months to 3 years of age spend an average of over 1 h per day watching television and about three-quarters of an hour using other screen media (computers, video games, and other video/CD material). Children between the ages of 4 and 6 show similar patterns, with other screen media increasing to about 1 h per day. In addition to these patterns of use, the recent expansion of the production of television programs, videos, and CDs for infants, such as 'Teletubbies or Baby Einstein' and related programming, have raised questions about the impact and appropriateness of such material for very young viewers. A result that was confirmed in a 2007 report by Ellen Wartella and colleagues.

Studies conducted in Australia by the Australian Broadcasting Authority, as well as studies in the Netherlands and the US, have documented the widespread use of screen media by infants and toddlers. The media environment, children living in industrialized nations experience, is both rich and varied, even accounting for the differences in social and economic conditions across various groups within those countries. For example, a study conducted in 2000 by the Annenberg Public Policy Center in the US, which was a national interview survey of 1235 parents of 2–17-year-olds and interviews with 416 youngsters ages 8–16 years, found that homes with children under the age of 17 years contained a wide range of media: 98% of the households had at least one television set, 97% had a VCR, 78% subscribed to basic cable television services – with 31% subscribing to premium cable (with its expanded programming for children, along with more adult programming), 70% owned a computer, 68% owned video games, and 52% of households had access to online services connecting to the Internet.

In a related study by the Kaiser Family Foundation in 2003, which was a survey of 1065 parents of children birth to 6 years, it was found that children under 6 years were spending approximately 2 h per day with screen media (including television, computer use and video games – with 48% using a computer and 30% playing video games). And, among the 4–6-year-olds who used the computer and video games, they did so for an average of 1 h per day. In the Australian study of 157 families in Sydney – which was a longitudinal tracking of children at ages 4 months, 12 months, and 30 months – they found that infants were exposed to 44 min of television per day at age 4 months, 62 min per day at 12 months, and 84 min per day at 30 months. So too, a study using a nationally representative sample of the parents of American children, ages birth to 12 years, found that children aged 2 and younger watched an average of 10 h and 45 min of television each week, while the same report, in a longitudinal study of 240 children from low-income families, found that total television viewing increased from 19.2 to 20.8 h per week between the ages of 3–5 years.

Thus, it seems clear that screen media, particularly television, occupy a significant portion of the daily activities of infants, toddlers, and young children. The next question is how do children come to understand and process the images that they are viewing and does this viewing and media interaction have any positive and negative effects on these youngsters?

Viewing Processes

We know that children begin viewing television and video material in infancy, and are exposed to significant amounts of this electronic storytelling throughout their earliest years. Therefore, the process of viewing has received some research attention in recent years. For example, in the Netherlands researchers investigated the attention patterns of 50, 6- to 58-month-olds while they viewed segments of Sesame Street, Teletubbies, the Lion King, and news clips, in their own homes. The authors hypothesized that attention to the screen material should be maximized when the content was congruent – but slightly discrepant – with the infant's developmental needs and interests, related to familiarity with the topic and content. This approach posited the 'moderate-discrepancy' view, which states that children pay most attention to television content that is only moderately discrepant from their existing knowledge and capabilities. In this study, 'salient' content features (such as loud noise, bright or fast visual changes in the display) attracted the attention of the youngest viewers. The authors report that these features also attracted the attention of the older viewers but, in addition to the salient content, the older children were also attracted to the nonsalient content features such as moderate action by the characters, letters and numbers, and meaningful dialogue. The authors noted that this shift from salient to nonsalient content started between 1.5 and 2.5 years. This is a particularly interesting finding because it tracks closely the long-known theoretical formulations of Jean Piaget concerning the use of symbols in the transition from sensorimotor to preoperational stages of cognitive development. Related to this finding, recent research on mirror neurons (areas of the brain that respond to the observed behavior or emotions of others by showing identical patterns of brain activation as that occurring in the other person – hence mirroring the other person's experience) and the development of language, by Michael Arbib and Giacomo Rizzolati, suggest that the ability to imitate the physical actions of others – controlled by the mirror neurons – may be the neurological basis of the development of language, a notion first raised in the mid-twentieth century by both Jean Piaget and Lev Vygotsky in their descriptions of language as 'internalized actions'. On a broader scale, we are beginning to see that these internalized actions, drawn from observations of others in the child's environment, may control both thought and behavior in the infant and young child.

In other studies, a program of research on attention and comprehension by John Wright and Aletha Huston has provided an outline of the sequence of shifts in attention and comprehension during the early years of viewing. In this program of research, the authors followed the viewing patterns of 240 children from low-income families in a large city in the Midwestern area of the US, for 3 years, in two cohorts, from ages 2 to 5 years and 4 to 7 years. The authors found shifts in the types of programs viewed by preschoolers and early school years – a shift from less cognitively demanding to more demanding program content (with cognitive demand measured by the redundancy of scenes and characters – easier – and the amount of temporal integration required to understand the scene and storyline – harder).

Building on the earlier work of Dan Anderson and colleagues, who demonstrated that children attended to content that was comprehensible even when it was not presented with salient features, Huston and her colleagues outlined a clear pattern of shifts in attention based on children's understanding of the production conventions associated with particular media content. In this instance, the authors proposed that children quickly learn the 'formal features' of programs that are 'child-friendly' and easily understood – the formal features of such programs include, for example, child and female voices as a prominent content feature. As a result of these studies, the authors developed the notion that young children 'sample' the television content to determine whether the program is child-oriented and potentially interesting and understandable. This stimulus sampling model suggested that initial brief attention to the screen will increase if the child recognizes that the material is 'appropriate' for their interests. This notion was elaborated into the concept of the Traveling Lens Model of attention and comprehension in children's viewing patterns, which is outlined in **Figure 1**.

Thus, the arousal of interest and attention will be highest if the stimulus material is perceived as falling between the poles of familiar versus novel; simple versus complex; redundant versus inconsistent; repetitive versus unpredictable; and expected versus surprising. Hence, children attend most to scenes that are moderately novel, of intermediate complexity, somewhat regular, somewhat ordered, and recognizable.

Effects of Viewing

So, what are the implications of this extensive use of screen media in infancy and early childhood, coupled with the changing patterns of attention and comprehension throughout the early years of viewing?

Most of the concern about this early viewing and screen time has focused on the lack of interactivity between the infant and toddler and his or her caregiver. As the American Academy of Pediatrics, noted, the most important activities and interactions in infancy are those social, face-to-face, interactions that establish the basis for interpersonal relationships. Television and video viewing tends to be more solitary, although there are newer videos, such as that developed by Sesame Workshop ('Sesame Beginnings: Beginning Together'; a DVD for 6 months and up) that encourages parental involvement in the viewing experience by explicitly designing 'co-viewing' tasks for caregiver and infant.

However, other concerns have been raised about the early viewing experience and the effects on later development. Marie Evans Schmidt and Dan Anderson, in the

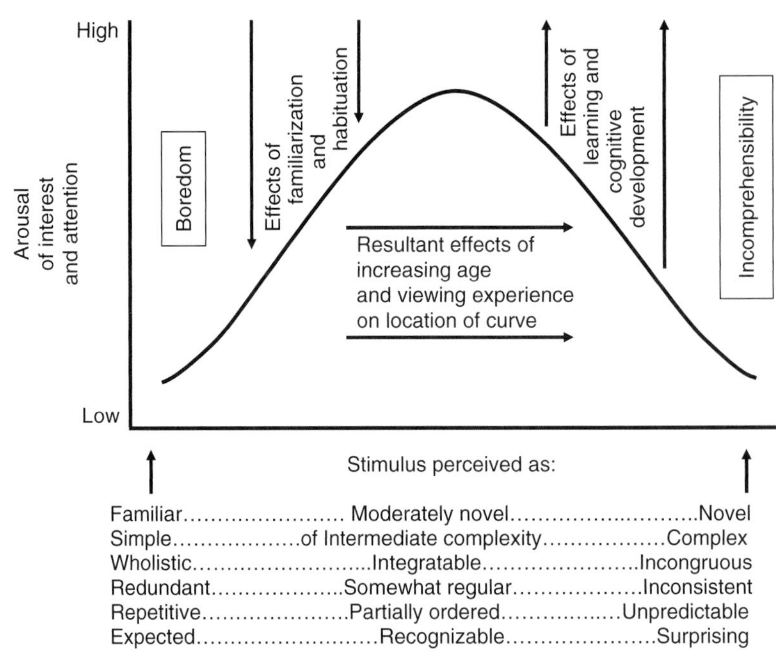

Figure 1 The traveling lens model of children's attention to television content. Source: Huston AC, Bickham DS, Lee JH, and Wright JC (2007) From attention to comprehension: How children watch and learn from television. In: Pecora N, Murray JP, and Wartella EA (eds.) *Children and Television: Fifty Years of Research*, p. 52. Mahwah, NJ: Lawrence Erlbaum Associates.

Pecora, Murray, and Wartella book (*Children and Television; Fifty Years of Research*), review the evidence for and against such viewing by noting the positive gains from viewing specific educational programming versus the tradeoffs concerning lost interpersonal interaction and the charges that such viewing leads to reduced attention span or intellectual and physical passivity. As the authors note: "To us it is clear that most of the effects of television on cognitive development and academic achievement stem from the particular content viewed. There is little question but that educational television programs teach, and that this teaching has beneficial short- and long-term consequences for schooling. These consequences are due not only to academic content and skills learned from the programs, but also from the social teaching of impulse and aggression control. Most of the negative effects of television stem from entertainment programs, particularly those with violent content. The negative effects include reading displacement in the early elementary years and modeling of aggression, restlessness and impulsivity."

With regard to the development of behaviors that are incompatible with smooth progress in social and intellectual development, it is the issue of the fostering of restlessness, impulsivity, and disrupted attentional processes that has sparked the most concern. For example, Dimitri Christakis and his colleagues, in a study of 1345 children, found that an extra hour of daily television viewing at ages 1 and 3 years led to a 10% higher probability that children would exhibit behaviors consistent with a diagnosis of ADHD by age 7 years. Also, a 2007 report by Carlin Miller and colleagues in the *Journal of Pediatric Psychology*, confirms the risk of attentional problems in preschool children who engaged in extensive television viewing. Moreover, in a 2007 report in the *Journal of Pediatrics*, Fredrick Zimmerman and his colleagues found that every hour of daily veiwing of 'baby videos' such as 'Baby Einstein' was associated with a 17% 'decrease' in scores on a standard language development assesement.

Following on this research, a team of economists led by Michael Waldman at Cornell University explored the possibility that extensive television viewing in infancy and early childhood might serve as a 'trigger' for the development of autism in young children. This is a highly controversial proposition, but the authors provide interesting statistical analyses showing correlations between autism rates at the county level in California, Oregon, Washington, and Pennsylvania and variables that should be correlated with early childhood television viewing. Using the US Bureau of Labor Statistics study of the 'American Time Use Survey' they first show that television viewing by children under age 3 years is positively related to the amount of precipitation in the environment. They then examine county level autism rates in California, Oregon, and Washington (which have varying levels of precipitation), and show that autism diagnosis rates are positively related to precipitation – as the television-as-trigger hypothesis would suggest. In a second test of the hypothesis, the authors compared cohorts of children in California and Pennsylvania who were born between 1972 and 1989 and found that the county-level autism rates were significantly related to the percentage of households who subscribed to cable television even after controlling for the trend increase in cable percentages during the time period (which was spreading rapidly through those areas during that 1972–89 time period). Thus, the authors conclude that the findings from their 'natural experiments' are sufficiently suggestive of the television-as-trigger hypothesis that more direct testing is warranted.

Naturally, there is much discussion about the speculative and complex trail of correlations outlined in the Waldman *et al.* study of autism and early television viewing. However, there is evidence discussed earlier by Schmidt and Anderson and Christakis and his colleagues, suggesting that both the content (violent, high-action programs) and the amount of time spent viewing television in early years can lead to increases in impulsivity and disorders of attention. Furthermore, the speculations about the relationship of viewing and hyperactivity, as a neurological problem of focus and attention that relates to autism, may be supported in the recent reports of longitudinal studies of the effects of extensive television viewing in the development of attention and learning difficulties during adolescence, in a 2007 report by Jeffrey Johnson and his colleagues. Also, brainmapping studies by John Murray and Mario Liotti and their colleagues, of older children (8–12 years), demonstrated that there are unique patterns of brain activations associated with viewing violence. Indeed, in looking at the brain scans of the youngsters while they were viewing video violence there was evidence that they were attempting to imitate the violent boxing actions through activation of the prefrontal cortex – premotor cortex in the right hemisphere (see **Figure 2**, area PF9/6) suggesting the role of mirror neurons in affecting the thought and behavior of young viewers.

And, descriptions of the behavioral manifestations of autism note that one of the striking characteristics of children at high-risk for autism (children who have older siblings who are autistic) is their failure of 'disengagement of visual attention' such as their inability to 'break attentional contact' with the television screen when viewing. Clearly more research is needed in this area, but this highlights some of the concerns about excessive amounts of 'screen time' and the potential influence on infants and young children.

So too, on a more positive note, Anderson and his colleagues, in a 2001 report in the *Monographs of the Society for Research in Child Development,* reported on their longitudinal study of the impact of educational programs such as 'Sesame Street'. Their findings show that 'Sesame Street' viewing at age 5 years not only prepared children for preschool and early school years but also predicted better High School grades in English, math, and science.

Thus, there are both positive and negative outcomes from early experience with screen media. However, the

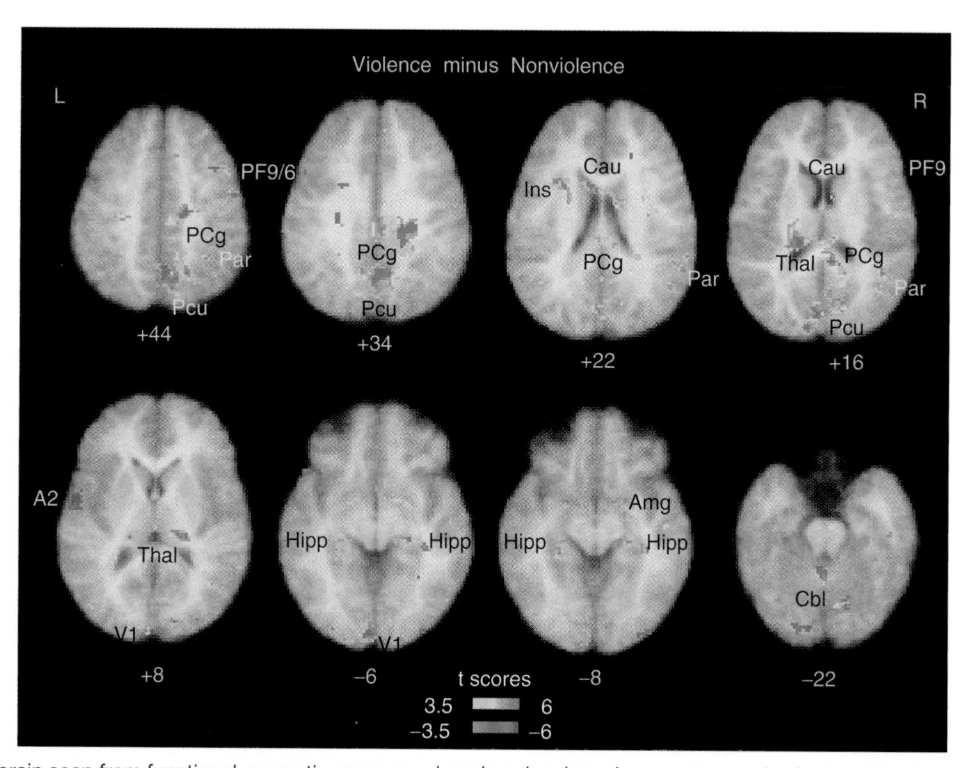

Figure 2 A brain scan from functional magnetic resonance imaging showing mirror neurons active in the prefrontal cortex – the right hemisphere premotor Area (PF-9/6; PF-9). Source: Murray JP, Liotti M, and Ingmundson PT, *et al.* (2006) Children's brain activations while viewing televised violence revealed by fMR1. *Media Psychology* 8(1): 25–37.

cautious response to questions about the effects of television and other screen media in infancy and early childhood is to limit the amount of exposure to these media and to very carefully monitor the content of the program material by emphasizing planned educational programming and maintaining parental interaction in the young child's viewing experience. As many psychologists and pediatricians have noted, it is the 'human interaction factor' and not technology, that most advances the intellectual and social development of infants and young children.

See also: ADHD: Genetic Influences; Anger and Aggression; Attention; Autism Spectrum Disorders; Cognitive Developmental Theories; Imagination and Fantasy.

Suggested Readings

Anderson DR, Huston AC, Schmitt K, Linebarger DL, and Wright JC (2001) Early childhood television viewing and adolescent behavior: The recontact study. *Monographs of the Society for Research in Child Development* 66 (Serial No. 264).

Arbib MA (2002) Towards a neuroscience of the person. In: Russell RJ, Murphy N, Meyering TC, and Arbib MA (eds.) *Neuroscience and the Person: Scientific Perspectives on Divine Action.* Citta del Vaticano: Libreria Editrice Vaticana.

Arbib MA and Rizzolatti G (1997) Neural expectations: A possible evolutionary path from manual skills to language. *Communication and Cognition* 29: 393–424.

Brazelton TB (1992) *Touchpoints: Your Child's Emotional and Behavioral Development.* New York: Perseus Publishing.

Christakis DA, Zimmermann FJ, DiGiuseppe DL, and McCarty CA (2004) Early television exposure and subsequent attentional problems in children. *Pediatrics* 113(4): 708–713.

Fisch SM and Truglio RT (2001) *"G" is for Growing: Thirty Years of Research on Children and Sesame Street.* Mahwah, NJ: Lawrence Erlbaum Associates.

Huston AC, Bickham DS, Lee JH, and Wright JC (2007) From attention to comprehension: How children watch and learn from television. In: Pecora N, Murray JP, and Wartella EA (eds.) *Children and Television: Fifty Years of Research,* p. 52. Mahwah, NJ: Lawrence Erlbaum Associates.

Johnson JG, Cohen P, Kasen S, and Brook JS (2007) Extensive television viewing and the development of attention and learning difficulties during adolescence. *Archives of Pediatric Adolescent Medicine* 161: 480–486.

Miller CJ, Marks DJ, Miller SR, *et al.* (2007) Brief report: Television viewing and risk for attention problems in preschool children. *Journal of Pediatric Psychology* 32(4): 448–452.

Murray JP (2007) *Children and Television: Using TV Sensibly – A Guide for Parents and Teachers.* San Antonio, TX: Mind Science Foundation. (available online at www.mindscience.org/murray_research.html).

Murray JP, Liotti M, Ingmundson PT, *et al.* (2006) Children's brain activations while viewing televised violence revealed by fMRI. *Media Psychology* 8(1): 25–37.

Pecora N, Murray JP, and Wartella EA (2007) *Children and Television: Fifty Years of Research.* Mahwah, NJ: Lawrence Erlbaum Associates.

Phillips H (2007) Mind-altering media. *New Scientist* 33–37.

Vandewater EA, Rideout VJ, Wartella EA, Huang X, Lee JH, and Shim M (2007) Digital childhood: Electronic media and technology use among infants, toddlers and preschoolers. *Pediatrics* 119(5): 1006–1015.

Waldman M, Nicholson S, and Adilov N (2006) *Does Television Cause Autism?* (Working Paper No. 12632). Cambridge, MA: National Bureau of Economic Research.

Zimmerman FJ, Christakis DA, and Meltzoff AN (2007) Associations between media viewing and language development in children under age 2 years. *Pediatrics* (in press).

Temperament

M K Rothbart, University of Oregon, Eugene, OR, USA
M A Gartstein, Washington State University, Pullman, WA, USA

Glossary

Constitutional – Factors related to the biological make-up of the individual.

Cortisol – A corticosteroid hormone produced by the adrenal cortex that is involved in responses to stress; it increases blood pressure, blood sugar levels, and suppresses the immune system.

Executive attention – Attentional control in situations that require conflict, overcoming habitual responses, action planning, error detection and compensation, and dealing with novel, difficult, or dangerous conditions. These capacities are seen to underlie temperamental effortful control.

Hemispheric asymmetry – The brain's left hemisphere has been associated with approach and positive affect, the right hemisphere with negative affect and avoidance processes.

Heritability – The proportion of variation in a population attributable to genetic variation among individuals, as opposed to environmental factors. Heritability analyses estimate the relative contributions of genetic and nongenetic factors to the total phenotypic variability in a trait.

Individual differences – Variability among individuals in the expression of specific characteristics such as temperament traits.

Psychopathology – The study of mental distress, problem behaviors, and major difficulties in adjustment indicative of mental illness or psychological impairment.
Surgency – A personality attribute associated with dominance, self-confidence, competitiveness, outgoing, extroverted, and decisive actions. Surgency involves patterns of behavior that are generally exhibited in reward-oriented situations and in the social context, also presumably rewarding to individuals with high levels of this characteristic.

Introduction

When you ask a friend about the origins of their adult personality, they will likely talk about what happened to them in childhood, with the parent playing a major role. The tendency to turn to parents as causal influences is consistent with the *tabula rasa* approach to infancy, viewing infants as molded by socializing agents into functional adults. More recent efforts to understand the origins of personality, however, have expanded to include 'child effects', those effects on development that can be attributed to the individual child. Temperament has emerged as a key mechanism in child effects, with characteristics observed early in life predicting later personality, behavioral and emotional patterns, adjustment, and the presence and severity of clinically significant symptoms.

The study of temperament has a long history, with only relatively recent attention to the development of these attributes. Individual differences in temperament were described in the fourfold typology of the Greco-Roman physician, Vindician, which persisted throughout the middle ages and the Renaissance. Early in the twentieth century, major schools in Europe contributed to temperament research. In the UK, studies of individual differences in temperament and personality were carried out using adults' self-reports, which yielded several factors, or broad dimensions, including introversion–extraversion, emotional stability–instability (later called by Eysenck, 'neuroticism'), and volition or will. Jeffrey Gray later revised this model, proposing individual differences in behavioral activation and inhibition, as well as tendencies to fight and flight.

Perhaps the single most influential investigation of children's temperament was conducted in the US. The New York Longitudinal Study (NYLS) conducted by Alexander Thomas, Stella Chess, and colleagues formed the basis for much of the recent research on temperament in children. Thomas and Chess identified nine dimensions of temperament: activity, approach/withdrawal, threshold, mood, intensity, rhythmicity, adaptability, distractibility, and attention span/persistence. They also described 'difficult temperament' as including low rhythmicity, high withdrawal, slow adaptation, high frequency of negative mood, and intense reactions. The 'easy temperament' category, on the other hand, was described as including regular eating, sleeping, elimination cycles, a positive approach response to new situations, along with frustration tolerance, whereas 'slow-to-warm-up children' were characterized as showing negative responses when exposed to new situations, but slowly accepting these with repeated exposure.

Alexander Thomas and Stella Chess also introduced the concept of goodness-of-fit, which is the degree of match between the child's characteristics and the parent's demands or expectations. They proposed that in order to understand how certain children demonstrate positive adjustment, while others show behavioral problems and symptoms of psychopathology, the 'goodness-of-fit' between child temperament, intellectual ability, and environmental factors (parenting in particular) need to be considered. The basic thesis is that a good match leads to more positive adjustment, whereas a poor fit between child temperament, other characteristics, parental demands, and expectations leads to problematic outcomes. These ideas paved the way for a variety of investigations addressing early appearing individual differences, some of which have led to significant revisions in the NYLS list of temperament dimensions.

Conceptual Definitions of Temperament

Mary Rothbart and Douglas Derryberry defined temperament as constitutionally based individual differences in emotional, motor and attentional reactivity, and self-regulation, demonstrating consistency across situations and relative stability over time. The term constitutional stresses the connection between temperament and biology. Over the long history of study, individual differences in temperament have been linked to the constitution of the organism as it was understood at the time. Reactivity refers to the latency, rise time, intensity, and duration of response to stimulation. Self-regulation refers to processes serving to modulate reactivity; these include behavioral approach, withdrawal, inhibition, and executive attention. This definition of temperament has been appealing to researchers because it can be applied to temperament observed in infancy, childhood, and adulthood, whereas other approaches have focused on applications to adults, or other developmental periods (e.g., the newborn period).

Other approaches to the study of temperament include the work of Jerome Kagan, who adapted temperamental characteristics of fear and surgency into temperamental categories, assigning children to inhibited and uninhibited extreme groups. Inhibited children can also be described as shy, cautious, fearful, and motorically tense. Uninhibited children tend to be social and outgoing (extraverted) in novel situations, and do not show as much motor restraint. Kagan and colleagues have reported a number of physiological differences between inhibited and uninhibited youngsters in the first 5 years of life. These include higher, more stable heart rates, and higher levels of cortisol for inhibited children, and they see the classification system as reflecting underlying biological differences. A number of unresolved issues, however, include the stability of classification, variability within the two groups, and specific patterns of physiological response.

Arnold Buss and Robert Plomin have applied two criteria, early appearance and heritability, as defining properties of temperamental traits. They identify emotionality, activity, and sociability as the three key dimensions of temperament, conceptualized as stable, with little change evidenced over time. They exclude traits that fail to persist into adulthood, such as rhythmicity (the degree of regularity in sleeping and eating patterns). While heritability plays a key role in their conceptualization of temperament, Buss and Plomin note that environmental forces can act upon the individual to promote change.

Hill Goldsmith and Joseph Campos propose that the basic emotions are the core of temperament, describing individual differences in temperament as the likelihood of experiencing and expressing the primary emotions, and in the frequency of emotional experience. Their emotions include anger, sadness, fear, joy, pleasure, disgust, interest, and surprise. Goldsmith and Campos note the importance of both the expressive and receptive aspects of individual differences in social interactions; that is, in children's ability to express emotions and to recognize, decode, and understand the emotional expressions of others.

Although a number of theorists have their own distinctive definitions, fundamental points of consensus regarding the nature of temperament have been identified. First, temperament refers to a set of traits. Studies of temperament, therefore, typically involve a variety of dimensions (i.e., fear, sadness, arousal level, activity level, etc.) rather than a single construct. Temperament constructs also consist of behavioral predispositions, rather than direct links to behavioral outcomes. Temperament does not provide a complete 'formula' for behavior; rather it provides a framework within which observed tendencies can be interpreted and behavior predicted. Temperament serves as a mechanism to explain how individuals contribute to their own social–emotional development in a given environmental context.

A third common emphasis is the belief that temperament is biologically based and relatively stable across time and situations. In the course of development, however, links between temperament and its manifestations become much more complex. Thus, infancy has been traditionally considered the developmental period during which temperament can be interpreted most directly. A fourth and final commonality is the assumption that temperament refers to a quality that varies among individuals, with different temperament predispositions leading children to experience the same events in a different way.

Dimensions of Temperament: Structural Definitions

Research addressing the structure of temperament has most frequently relied on caregiver reports (often using paper-and-pencil questionnaires) allowing study of relations among dimensions, as done in the NYLS. More recently, individual differences have been examined broadly in terms of general characteristics, and narrowly, identifying fine-grained attributes and taking advantage of the caregiver's extensive observations of the child. Studies have identified higher-order temperament constructs, such as negative emotionality, positive emotionality/extraversion, and effortful control/regulatory capacity, which in turn consist of sets of more fine-grained temperament attributes. Whereas negative emotionality typically consists of related dimensions of sadness, anger, irritability, and fear, positive emotionality/extraversion typically consists of approach, smiling and laughter, activity level, and sociability. Early in life, regulatory capacity reflects orienting and self-soothing; later in life, effortful control reflects the ability to inhibit a dominant response in order to perform a subdominant response, and includes perceptual sensitivity and attentional control.

In addition to the research outlined above, recent work with parent-report instruments has led to revisions of the list of temperament dimensions originally identified in the NYLS. Responses to questions or items on questionnaires allow an examination of the clustering of these items via factor analysis (a statistical technique used to determine the extent of clustering and the degree of homogeneity within and across the clusters of items). The use of this approach has not provided support for the original NYLS dimensions; instead, recent studies provide evidence for a smaller number of relatively independent temperament characteristics seen in early childhood. For instance, instead of supporting bipolar scales such as approach vs. withdrawal, withdrawal items, along with items from adaptability and other fear-related items, tend to cluster together in a fear or inhibition/withdrawal factor. Approach items, in contrast, tend to cluster with positive affect items from the mood scale to form a positive affect/approach factor. In the assessment of negative emotionality, fear tends to be differentiated from irritability or frustration. Other factors extracted more closely resemble the NYLS dimensions of activity level, persistence or duration of orienting, and rhythmicity, but rhythmicity tends to be a more minor factor containing few items. Threshold as a factor has been found in an extremely limited context in one instrument only, and 'intensity' does not emerge in the factor structure of the instruments, because of its lack of generalizability across different kinds of response. Dimensions of temperament in the revised list seem to correspond more to specific affective-motivational processes than to overall styles of behavior.

For instance, infant behaviors that reflect positive emotionality include smiling, laughing, and approaching novel stimuli. Positive emotionality is frequently used interchangeably with the term surgency or extraversion, which reflects behaviors described as outgoing, enthusiastic, alert, and active. Individuals higher in positive affect also have the tendency to be engaged with, rather than disengaged from, their environment. Extraversion/surgency in infancy is now thought of as a developmental precursor to the personality dimension of extraversion evaluated in older children and adults. In research on 3–12-month-old infants, a negative emotionality factor has also been found, consisting of irritability, fear, sadness, anger, frustration, and discomfort. Negative emotionality has been linked to the personality trait of neuroticism observed later in childhood and adulthood.

There has been occasional debate as to whether positive and negative emotionality reflect two different constructs or are opposite poles on one dimension of emotionality. Evidence suggests, however, that these constructs are related, but distinct. That is, positive and negative affectivity ratings are largely nonoverlapping, although low to moderate associations between negative and positive emotionality have also been reported. Activity level (i.e., the degree to which infants engage in physical movement) is another early emerging temperamental characteristic. Although it has been measured at various stages of development, there is some question as to whether it is a unique construct or if it appears as an aspect of positive or negative emotionality. For example, Escalona noted that newborns tend to engage in more motor activity when in a negative rather than in a positive state. However, later in infancy, higher levels of activity become associated more with positive emotionality, in the context of exploration, play, or approaching novel objects.

The regulation-oriented dimension of temperament emerges in early infancy and undergoes rapid development throughout childhood. In infancy, this factor has been labeled as orienting capacity/regulation and includes attributes associated with attentional duration of orienting, positive affect, and soothing. Interestingly, the infancy orienting/regulation factor includes the low-intensity pleasure scale, addressing the child's ability to enjoy calm pleasant activities (e.g., looking at pictures). This relation is consistent with the findings reported for effortful control in the preschool period. Despite this similarity, there are considerable differences in the characteristics related to self-regulation in infancy and later in childhood, and these reflect significant developmental shifts in related attentional processes. For example, inhibitory control, a central component of effortful control for toddlers and preschoolers, does not come 'online' in the first year of life (e.g., infants are not able to engage in a delay following instructions). So-called higher-order attentional skills contributing to inhibitory control scale have been linked to the development of the executive attention system, exerting its influence toward the end of the first year of life and continuing to develop throughout childhood. The immaturity of infant control of attention often necessitates external (i.e., caregiver) involvement in regulatory functions, and the child characteristics of soothability and cuddliness also contribute to the orienting/regulatory domain of temperament in infancy. As children develop, self-regulatory skills becoming more proficient at effortful control, adult interventions aimed at regulating behavioral and emotional reactions become less prominent, and the child is said to have developed self-control.

Effortful control is a regulatory aspect of temperament that is responsible for suppression of a dominant response in favor of performing a subdominant response. Effortful control serves to override a prepotent response as well as to initiate and/or maintain an alternative behavioral or emotional response. Effortful control is also involved in the ability to shift attention and to voluntarily alter one's focus from one location to another. Currently, it is believed that effortful control emerges in the late infancy/toddler period, coinciding with rapid development of executive attentional mechanisms in the brain. Executive attention, a brain network involving prefrontal cortex and anterior cingulate as well as basal ganglia, appears to be a process underlying effortful control. Effortful control includes focused attention, perceptual sensitivity, inhibitory control, and low intensity pleasure. Given the range of abilities in which effortful control plays an important role, it is not surprising that effortful control has been found to relate to the development of conscience and aggression. Effortful control is also a protective factor for the development of problems, promoting the child's obedience to parental rules.

Assessment of Temperament in Early Childhood:

How Do We Measure Temperament?

Temperament assessments in early childhood often rely on structured observations of temperament-related behavior or information collected from the caregiver. Observational measures of newborns and young infants include assessments of reactivity to multiple modes of stimulation, whereas observations of older infants, toddlers, and preschoolers also permit evaluation of attention-based regulatory capacity. Observations of young children are frequently carried out in the laboratory, following a structured set of procedures; however, such observations can also be conducted in the child's home or the hospital. Caregiver report methodology consists of asking parents, or other care providers, questions about the frequency of behaviors related to child temperament characteristics. A variety of questionnaires, based on caregivers' observations, have been developed for this purpose, providing researchers with tools for assessing temperament from birth into the preschool period and beyond.

At least three major goals have been pursued in the assessment of temperament in early childhood. One has been to measure individual differences in reactivity and self-regulation under controlled conditions, typically through observation in a laboratory setting. More recently, it has involved the development of laboratory marker tasks, tests that assess variability in children's behavior in the laboratory that has been associated in adult imaging studies with the activation of specific brain regions or networks. A second goal has been to identify the structure of temperament via parental responses to paper-and-pencil questionnaires addressing multiple child attributes. Information provided by caregivers is sometimes presented together with data from additional sources (e.g., home observations or other temperament measures) because caregiver report possesses both unique strengths and potential weaknesses, as do other methods (elaborated on in the next section).

The third goal has been to adapt temperament measures to clinical uses. Clinical adaptations have included the informal use of questionnaires or observations in clinical diagnosis and treatment, as well as a means to encourage parents to pay attention to their children's behavior patterns. Measures of temperament have also been used in studies of the development of behavior problems, and have been linked to adjustment in adulthood. Measures developed for the assessment of temperament in early childhood have not yet achieved the measurement qualities necessary for predicting future problems for specific individuals, but they have been helpful in our general understanding of the development of behavior problems.

Recent studies have begun to include physiological measures such as assessments of children's vagal tone, cortisol levels, and hemispheric asymmetry, yielding results of interest in relation to caregiver reports and observations of children's temperament-related behavior. The use of these methods along with other temperament assessment approaches (e.g., caregiver-report) may allow validation of each method, and provide valuable information regarding the processes involved in the development of temperamental individual differences. Consistent patterns of findings across different measurement modalities would also provide conclusive validation for each of the approaches involved. The use of physiological tools in concert with behavioral measures provides an added benefit of allowing researchers to identify mechanisms underlying individual differences in temperament.

Confidence in Measures of Temperament: Reliability and Validity

Researchers of temperament development in early childhood have traditionally been very concerned about possible sources of error in their measurement. These so-called sources of error include any contributors to the temperament rating other than the indications of child temperament themselves. For instance, researchers often worry that social desirability, or the tendency to answer questions in a manner consistent with perceived social expectations, will lead parents to inflate their ratings of child positive emotionality (e.g., smiling/laughter). Although this concern is typically voiced in relation to caregiver-report, potential effects of sources of error (e.g., effects of the laboratory environment on the child's behavior) extend to observational measures as well.

Error affects the reliability and validity of the assessments. Reliability refers to the consistency of a particular measure across time, raters, or items, whereas validity represents the extent to which the estimate accurately reflects the temperament attribute under investigation. Not surprisingly, low levels of reliability and validity lead to decreased confidence in the measures of temperament, and a problem for a meaningful interpretation of findings.

Each approach described above has a set of potential sources of error as well as distinctive strengths, and these are discussed in turn. Sources of error that can affect observation-based indices include those related to characteristics of the rater, effects of the measure on child behaviors, and interactions between rater characteristics and child behavior (e.g., subtle differences in the experimenters' reactions to infants in distress, with more soothing behavior directed toward these children relative to nondistressed participants).

In caregiver report, error may occur due to an inability of the caregiver to understand items and instructions, lack of knowledge of the child's behavior and its meaning, lack of knowledge of the behavior of other youngsters to whom the child is compared, and the accuracy of caregivers' memory of events involving the child. These concerns can be partially addressed by careful pretesting of items, asking only about recently occurring events, and inquiring about concrete child behaviors, rather than asking the parent to make abstract or comparative judgments. A second set of problems includes the extent to which caregivers' responses are driven by their own state or clinical disorder, or response sets such as social desirability. In our review of research relating maternal characteristics to their reports of infant temperament, the two sets of variables are related, but the degree of this association is low to moderate, and could be related, at least in part, to genetic inheritance.

In the laboratory, concerns about the observer also apply, but these are moderated by the possibility of carrying out detailed coding of videotapes, rather than doing all of the coding as the behavior occurs. In video analysis, multiple behaviors can be coded. Work may be done by multiple coders, and strict controls on reliability are possible. In all approaches, there are problems with detecting ambiguous reactions of the child. Concerns with sources of error in laboratory observations also include the effects of the novel laboratory environment and/or experimenters. For instance, the lack of familiarity in this environment may lead children to behave in a more fearful manner, especially as the development of the behavioral inhibition system accelerates toward the end of the first year of life. The latter may pose no problem in the assessment of fear/behavioral inhibition; however, these effects are likely to adversely impact the ratings of positive affectivity, serving to attenuate reactivity. Despite the ongoing efforts to improve our assessment tools, enhancing their reliability and validity and decreasing the influence of different sources of error, research with existing measures has already lead to an increased understanding of temperament development in early childhood.

Development of Temperament in Early Childhood (Birth–5 years)

Although Arnold Buss and Robert Plomin argued that temperament measures must show both early appearance and long-term stability, developmental changes in temperament-related processes have been found throughout childhood and beyond, and at no time are these changes as rapid as in the first year of life. Expressions of temperament differ greatly in the newborn, the 3-month-old, and the 12-month-old, and develop further into the toddler and preschool periods. In fact, it is not possible to measure all of the temperament attributes across all developmental periods in early childhood because the developmental emergence of particular primary emotions and attentional processes varies across early childhood. Moreover, because some emotions and attentional processes regulate other emotions and actions, the time of onset of these control dimensions has important implications for other temperamental characteristics.

Early Infancy (Birth–3 Months)

During early infancy, smiling and laughter are emerging as part of a positive affectivity dimension, and motor activity comes to be linked to infants' positive as well as negative affect displays. In addition, infants by 2 months are demonstrating anger/frustration when their actions no longer control an interesting outcome. Infants during this period also often show a high susceptibility to distress to overstimulation and colic. Cindy Stifter has found, however, that measures of colic during this period are not predictive of later measures of temperament. Colic is generally defined as uncontrollable, extended crying in an infant who is otherwise healthy and well-fed. That is, although every infant cries, babies who cry for more than 3 h a day, 3–4 days a week, are identified as having colic. In general, this condition appears at around 2–4 weeks of age and can last for 3 months, or longer in some cases. In addition, measures of distress proneness during this early period do not consistently predict to later measures of the negative emotions.

Infancy (4–12 Months)

Whereas earlier distress signals may not often be easily identified as being associated with specific emotional reactions, such differentiation is achieved during this developmental period. Fear and irritability, for example, are becoming increasingly differentiated during this period, with behavioral inhibition (fear) being increasingly associated with novel and/or unpredictable experiences. Susan Calkins and colleagues have noted that high motor activity and positive affect at 4 months is associated with bold behavior in later childhood. At 4–5 months, infants' motor capacities allow them to reach for and grasp objects, and rapid (short latency) grasp of objects is positively related to smiling and laughter, suggesting that a neurobehavioral system underlying approach, or reward-oriented tendencies, can be assessed during this period. Later, by 9–10 months, behavioral inhibition will come to exercise a good deal of control over approach. Infants at 4–6 months also tend to be quite tractable and interested in the stimuli presented in the laboratory. The period of 4–6 months may thus be especially appropriate for the study of early approach and attention.

Behavioral inhibition and other aspects of fear are developing late in the first year (between 9 and 12 months of age), and coming to modulate infants' approach responses. By this time, the novelty of the laboratory can suppress positive affect and approach for infants, to a greater degree for some infants than for others. It nevertheless continues to be important to consider approach tendencies separately from fear responses in the assessment of temperament. This can be done by observing approach of the infant at the earlier period of 4–6 months, and/or by assessing older infants' reactions under both novel and challenging, and familiar conditions.

Toddler/Preschool Period (1–5 Years of Age)

Temperamental characteristics are not all in place at the end of the first year. Positive emotionality becomes increasingly stable later in infancy, with most of surgency/extraversion's associated characteristics identifiable by toddlerhood. Although changes in negative emotionality during infancy have been reported, considerable stability is noted by the toddler period.

Development of the executive attention system during the toddler and preschool periods is particularly important for effortful control, planning, and the ability to inhibit or delay action and expression. The development of effortful control is closely linked with advances in a variety of attentional skills, which provide the basis for emerging self-regulation. Development of the executive attention system during the toddler and preschool periods is particularly significant, with important implications for effortful control, including increasing abilities to plan and inhibit or delay action and expression, providing children with opportunities for more flexible control of emotion and action. Researchers have developed 'marker tasks', known to activate a given brain region, and adapt these for use with children. Michael Posner, Mary Rothbart, and Gina Gerardi-Caulton, for example, have developed a promising spatial conflict task, in which the child must respond to a spatially conflicting stimulus by inhibiting the dominant response and executing a subdominant response. Children sit in front of two response keys, one located to the child's left and one to the right. Each key displays a picture, and on every trial a picture identical to one member of the pair appears on either the left or right side of the screen. The spatial conflict occurs when the picture appears on the side of the screen opposite of the correct (i.e., matching) response key, since the dominant response is to press the key that is compatible in terms of its location.

Remarkably, between 2 and 4 years of age, children progress from an almost complete inability to carry out this type of task to relatively good performance. Whereas 24-month-old children tended to perseverate on a single response, at 36 months, children performed with considerable accuracy. Similar to adults, the 36-month-olds responded more slowly and with reduced accuracy to incompatible trials. Youngsters who performed well were also described by their parents as more skilled at temperamental attentional shifting and focusing, less impulsive, and less prone to frustration reactions. Another important aspect of executive attention, the detection and correction of errors, can also be evaluated via the spatial conflict task, wherein longer reaction times (RTs) following incorrect trials interpreted as slowing down associated with error detection/correction. Such longer RTs were observed for 30- and 36-month-old children, whereas no evidence of slowing following an error was found at 24 months.

Although precursors of effortful control are not yet well understood, recent evidence suggests that development of this set of attributes is rooted in earlier temperament. For example, there is evidence that infant orienting/regulatory capacity is related to toddler effortful control, which in turn predicts effortful control in the preschool period. Thus, there appears to be an indirect stability of the underlying regulatory dimension of temperament. The relationship of surgency and effortful control, however, changes as a function of age, with infant surgency and positive emotionality predicting higher levels of effortful control in toddlers, but toddler and preschool surgency associated with lower effortful control.

Gender Differences in Early Temperament

Although a number of gender differences have been reported for older children and adults, few have been found for children younger than 1 year of age. Differences in infancy have been limited to activity level and fear/behavioral inhibition, with higher activity level and approach for boys, and girls exhibiting greater hesitation in approaching novel objects. Darren Campbell and Warren Eaton applied meta-analytic procedures that enabled them to summarize results across 46 studies of activity level in infancy, demonstrating small, but reliable gender differences. Gender differences in approach-withdrawal have also been reported for cross-cultural samples, with parents rating males higher in their levels of approach. Fearfulness differences between male and female infants have also been reported, with girls receiving higher scores. There is also evidence suggesting that girls exhibit higher levels of regulation-related skills in early childhood. Grazyna Kochanska, for example, demonstrated that girls exhibited higher levels of inhibitory control, an important component of effortful control, on laboratory tasks, and caregiver report.

From Temperament to Personality

Research addressing dimensions of temperament in early childhood also suggests possible links with studies of adult personality. For example, investigations of children's temperament frequently reveals broad factors that are consistent with the 'Big Three' and 'Big Five' factors reported in research with adults. There remain, however, important differences between concepts of temperament and personality. First, temperament traits emerge in infancy and early childhood, while personality characteristics are generally thought of as emerging later in development. Second, personality includes many more characteristics than does temperament, including self-concept, attitudes, expectations, and preferred coping strategies. Personality develops out of the early temperament traits in conjunction with the child's experiences.

Infants' and young children's temperament provides the building blocks of personality, but additional personality characteristics will develop with maturation and experience. For instance, individual differences in positive emotion at 6 months of age are related to differences in approach tendencies, sensation seeking, activity level, and lack of shyness later in childhood. Preschool children who exhibit strong approach tendencies often become adolescents who tend to be impulsive and ineffective in the social context. Children who show the highest levels of inhibition of approach in infancy tend to be more fearful and shy later in childhood, although not all those inhibited as infants continue to demonstrate inhibition. Temperament includes individual differences in emotional processing and the evaluation of experience, so that a particular stimulus provides different emotional experiences for children who vary in temperament. Thus, temperamental dispositions can serve as biasing factors on the development of attitudes, expectations, and the nature of social learning, further contributing to the development of personality.

Temperament contributes directly to social–emotional and personality development, and interacts with parenting, family, and other environmental variables, which in turn affect the development of children. Sandra Scarr and Kathleen McCartney have described 'niche picking', where individual differences in temperament contribute to children's selection of their own environments. This selection can be seen in children's adaptations to preschool. Nonshy children show effects of stress associated with their rapid approach to a new setting at the beginning of the year, but these reactions decrease over time. Shy children do not show stress initially, likely because they are avoiding potentially stressful interactions. However, over time the more shy children begin involvement, and then show effects of stress.

Interactions between temperament and attachment have important implications for social–emotional development. Attachment refers to the child's thoughts, feelings, and behaviors in relation to important others, most often the caregiver. Attachment security is generally assessed by observing the child's reactions during a 'strange situation' procedure, designed for children between 10 and 24 months of age, largely on the basis of work by Mary Ainsworth. The strange situation consists of several episodes that involve brief separations from the parent, and the entrance of an unfamiliar experimenter. The stress of the situation is gradually increased in order to intensify attachment behaviors (e.g., crying, approaching, and clinging). As stress increases, the child should also decrease his/her affiliation with the experimenter. Children who show distress during separation from their parents attempt to search for them, and readily approach them when reunited are classified as securely attached.

Attachment security assessed through the strange situation procedure is associated with the caregiver's sensitivity and responsiveness to the infant. Insecure or anxious attachment patterns are classified as resistant, avoidant, or disorganized. Infants classified as resistant are likely to show a great deal of distress when separated from caregivers. However, upon reunion, these children tend to actively resist contact with the parent (sometimes angrily). Avoidant infants, on the other hand, are less likely to be distressed during the separation, despite the fact that their heart rates are elevated, relative to other classification groups. A child classified as belonging to the avoidant attachment category appears to regard the stranger in much the same way as the parent. The disorganized classification has been added more recently, and can be applied in situations when infants present with atypical behaviors (e.g., disorientation), making classification into one of the more traditional categories difficult to achieve.

Child temperament appears to have two associations with attachment security. First, temperamental characteristics, such as fear or approach, influence the attachment classification. For example, a child low in fear is likely to appear to be less securely attached because she or he may not react to the presence of a stranger as a stressor. Thus, a child who is not fearful may not attempt to gain comfort from the mother upon reuniting with her. Second, temperament during the first year of life appears to influence the relationship with the primary caregiver, contributing to the caregiver's behavior and subsequent development of the child's attachment security.

Although not all studies have provided consistent support for these relationships, numerous significant associations between temperament and attachment measures have been found. Children higher in negative reactivity and distress to limitations have been described as exhibiting lower levels of attachment security. Irritable newborns were also found by Dymph van den Boom to be more likely to later exhibit insecure attachment than newborns who were not irritable. One interpretation of this finding is that infant irritability prevents mothers from acting in a sensitive/responsive manner, so that they may not use effective soothing techniques. A larger sample of irritable infants and their mothers took part in an intervention study where half the parents were trained in parenting skills, prompt soothing, and positive interaction when the infant was not in distress. This intervention resulted in greater maternal responsiveness, infant sociability, self-soothing, and higher levels of exploratory behavior. In addition, more of the infants were categorized as securely attached.

Another important interaction between child temperament and socialization involves mutual influences of temperamental characteristics and the quality of parenting on the children's adjustment. Children with temperamental attributes, including negative affectivity, appear to be more likely to experience ineffective parenting practices (e.g., harsh and inconsistent discipline). The quality of parenting may in turn be related to children's development of behavior problems. Children's temperament also affects the development of coercive family processes, interactions characterized by escalating aversive behaviors, in which children and parents engage in progressively more and more noxious actions directed toward each other. The child's refusal to follow the parents' requests and their tendencies toward frustration and aggression are also more likely to occur when the child has lower regulatory capacity. In turn, this contributes to ineffective discipline practices (e.g., harsh punishment, inconsistent enforcement of rules), which subsequently lead to child conduct difficulties.

Children with challenging temperamental characteristics may also be at risk for insufficient and/or ineffective guidance and instruction from the parent. Youngsters described as 'difficult' in fact received more cognitive assistance and disapproval from their mothers during a problem-solving task, and these mothers showed greater involvement in more challenging aspects of the task. These behaviors are not ideal for guiding children through a problem-solving task. According to Lev Vygotsky, optimal strategies involve providing the child with structure during problem solving (e.g., reminding the child of the rules, providing suggestions regarding possible approaches to the problem), but allowing the child to discover strategies independently, and take on greater responsibility in the activity as she or he gains more skill. This kind of guidance ultimately promotes further development of self-regulation, and may be limited or lacking for children with temperament profiles perceived as difficult by caregivers.

Certain dimensions of temperament may also interact with each other (i.e., modify each others' influence), working in tandem to contribute to children's adjustment. For instance, children classified as 'unsocial' and 'poor emotion regulators' in temperament ratings were described as more aimless and anxious during play, and exhibited higher levels of behavior problems including social withdrawal, anxiety/depression, and frequent complaints about aches and pains, by their mothers. Relations between fearful behavioral inhibition and approach tendencies have been described by Douglas Derryberry and Mary Rothbart. A relatively fearless child with strong approach tendencies may respond impulsively, and is likely to focus on rewarding, rather than punishing, aspects of the experience. Alternatively, children who are strong in approach, but also have strong fear tendencies are more likely to inhibit impulsive behaviors, and to appreciate rewards and punishments more equally in a given situation. Thus, fear motivation may play an adaptive role in regulating approach behaviors and may also lead to lower levels of aggression. Effortful control may also influence the way in which negative emotionality, approach, and aggression are related to each other. Children with effective effortful control can be expected to show little aggression, even when they are experiencing high levels of approach and negative emotionality. Thus, effective effortful control can be expected to prevent the expression of excessive levels of approach and negative emotionality associated with aggressive behavior.

Temperament Risk and Protective Factors: Symptoms of

Psychopathology and Competence in Early Childhood

Psychopathology in childhood (e.g., depression, conduct problems, and ADHD) is associated with significant costs to society and frequently precedes psychological difficulties in adulthood. Identification of risk and protective factors (contributors linked with either escalation of difficulties or those associated with resilience in the face of stressors), especially those present early in life, could help in intervention and prevention efforts, resulting in considerable reductions of costs to society. Although considerable attention was originally given to some risk factors, such as economic factors, parent psychopathology and parenting, only recently have contributions of child temperament started to receive more widespread attention. **Table 1** summarizes most of the recent investigations addressing temperament in early childhood, with a considerable number of studies linking child characteristics and environmental factors (e.g., parenting) to later positive and negative outcomes for youngsters.

In these studies, early negative emotionality has been linked with broad behavioral and emotional difficulties, often referred to externalizing (associated with 'acting-out', or undercontrolled behavior and emotions) and internalizing (or overcontrolled behavioral/emotional expressions) problems later in childhood. There is also evidence of specificity of risk, with temperamental anger/frustration associated with externalizing problems, and fear and sadness aspects of negative affectivity predicting internalizing difficulties. For example, results of the Bloomington longitudinal study (BLS), conducted by John Bates and colleagues, indicated that resistance to control (associated with frequent and intense anger and frustration) predicted externalizing problems later, especially when parents exhibited lower levels of control. More recently, Susan Crockenberg showed that higher levels of frustrations in infancy were associated with externalizing difficulties, whereas greater distress to novelty was associated with internalizing symptoms, for children experiencing long hours in nonparental care. Other factors appear to be important in shaping the impact of early negative emotionality on later childhood outcomes. For example, infant negative emotionality in the context of greater maternal sensitivity, and higher levels of infant soothability, were not associated with adverse effects on child social–emotional development. Research conducted by Susan Warren also pointed to the importance

Table 1 Research (1995–2006) addressing temperament and behavior problems in early childhood (0–5 years of age)

Authors	*Constructs assessed*	*Sample description (N; age range; characteristics)*	*Major findings*
Abrams S (2005)	Infant temperament, maternal temperament, parental stress level	65; 6–12 months	Infant temperament does not correspond to maternal temperament characteristics to a significant degree.
Austin M *et al.* (2005)	Maternal trait anxiety, life event stress and depression, infant temperament	970; third trimester of pregnancy – 6 months postpartum	Maternal trait anxiety is predictive of 'difficult' infant temperament, independent of concurrent depression, and key risk factors.
Bates JE and Pettit GS (1998)	Resistance to control restrictive parenting externalizing behavior	168; 6, 13, 24 months	Stronger links between temperamental resistance to control and externalizing behavior for parents low on control, in comparison to parents who were more restrictive.
Belsky J *et al.* (2001)	Attentional persistence, negative emotionality social competence, problem behavior, and school readiness	1038; 1–36 months	High negative emotionality associated with low social competence when attentional persistence was poor. High negative emotionality related to high levels of school readiness at high levels of attentional persistence.
Belsky J *et al.* (1998)	Negative emotionality, parenting during toddler years, externalizing behaviors, inhibition	125; 27–37 months; males	Negative mothering predicted higher externalizing scores, less negative fathering, and more positive fathering forecast more inhibition at age 3 years.
Blair C (2002)	Negative emotionality in infancy, early intervention	985; 12–36 months; low birth weight, preterm	With early intervention, infants with higher levels of negative emotionality at 12 months had a twofold decrease in the occurrence of behavior problems, and fourfold decrease in the occurrence of high-risk profiles at age 3 years.
Calkins S and Fox NA (2002)	Self-regulatory processes, personality, and behavioral adjustment	81; 4–14 months	Links between behavioral inhibition and frustration tolerance, and physiological, attentional, and emotional regulatory development.
Calkins S (2002)	Frustration distress, aggression/venting, defiance, and maternal interactive style	73; 18–24 months	Aggressive 'venting' behavior at 24 months predicted by interaction of early child aversive behavior and low maternal positive guidance.
Conway AM (2005)	Maternal sensitivity, infant negative emotionality, emotion regulation, attentional control	181; 7 and 33 months	Maternal sensitivity and infant negative affect at 7 months predicted later emotion regulation flexibility; maternal sensitivity and child negative affect at 33 months related to emotional resilience.
Coplan RJ *et al.* (2005)	Maternal state and trait anxiety, infant temperament	60; third trimester of pregnancy to 3 months postpartum	Maternal trait anxiety predicted infant distress to novelty and limitations, and difficulty soothing. Antenatal state anxiety predicted less infant positive affect and lower attention-span. Postnatal state anxiety related to infant activity level and distress to limitations.
Crockenberg SC and Leerkes EM (2005)	Quantity and type of nonparental care, infant temperament, internalizing and externalizing problems	64; 6–30 months	Long hours in nonparental care associated with externalizing problems for children easily frustrated as infants, and internalizing symptoms for children highly distressed in response to novelty as infants.
Crockenberg SC and Leerkes EM (2006)	Infant regulatory behaviors, infant reactivity to novelty, maternal behavior, and anxious infant behavior	64; 6–30 months	Infant regulatory behaviors moderated associations between reactivity to novelty and anxious behavior at 30 months. High reactivity to novelty, with withdrawal and poor attention control, predicted anxiety when mothers were less engaged or less sensitive.

Continued

Table 1 (Continued)

Authors	*Constructs assessed*	*Sample description (N; age range; characteristics)*	*Major findings*
De Rosnay M *et al.* (2006)	Maternal social anxiety, infant-stranger interactions	24; 12–24 months	Following a socially anxious mother–stranger interaction, infants significantly more fearful and avoidant with a stranger than following a normal mother–stranger interaction; high-fear infants were more avoidant in the socially anxious condition than low-fear infants.
Diener ML and Kim D (2004)	Child self-regulation, child temperament, maternal separation anxiety, social competence in preschool	110; 24–56 months	Child age, temperament, self-regulation, and maternal characteristics predicted social competence in preschool.
Dixon WE Jr. and Smith P (2000)	Attentional control, positive affectivity, language acquisition	Study 1: 40; 13, 20 months Study 2: 47; 7–21 months	Attentional control and positive affectivity predicted language production and comprehension.
Gerardi-Caulton G (2000)	Spatial conflict, self-regulation, negative affectivity	68; 24–36 months	Children responded slower and less accurately when location and identity were in conflict. Ability to resolve conflict was linked to individual differences in effortful control and negative emotionality.
Ghera MM *et al.* (2006)	Infant soothability, negative infant temperament, maternal sensitivity	56; 4–9 months	Infant negative emotionality and maternal sensitivity positively related at higher levels of infant soothability; negatively related when maternal ratings of infant soothability were low.
Gill K *et al.* (2003)	Aggression, empathy	474; 2 years	Aggressive children showed more behaviors indicative of empathy than nonaggressive children.
Gutteling BM *et al.* (2005)	Prenatal stress, toddler temperament, and problem behavior	103; prenatal–27 months; nulliparous women	Increased levels of maternal prenatal stress associated with difficult temperament and behavioral problems in toddlers.
Hagekull B *et al.* (1997)	Stability of early feeding problems, infant temperament, maternal sensitivity	115; 10 month–2 years	Less sensitive mothers with less manageable infants reported more feeding refusal behaviors.
Hane AA and Fox NA (2006)	Variations in maternal caregiving behavior (MCB)	185; 4–9 months	Infants with low-quality MCB showed more fearfulness, less positive joint attention, and greater right frontal electroencephalogram (EEG) asymmetry than infants with high-quality MCB.
Harden B *et al.* (2000)	Internalizing problems parental psychopathology child temperament	155; 4.1 years; children enrolled in Head Start	Externalizing behavior associated with child internalizing behavior, parental psychopathology, child temperament, family environment and exposure to community violence. Children with externalizing behavior had specific social problem-solving skill deficits.
Huizink, AC *et al.* (2002)	Maternal prenatal stress and infant temperament	170; 2) 3–8 months; nulliparous women	Increased maternal prenatal stress associated with temperamental variation of young infants.
Karp J *et al.* (2004)	Utility of the behavioral style observational system (BSOS) vs. material ratings	160; 12–72 months	Observational measures and maternal ratings alone not sufficient to assess children's temperament; evaluations of children's temperament should include both observational measures and maternal ratings.
Keenan K *et al.* (1998)	Difficult temperament (12–24 months), aggression (12–24 months), noncompliance (12–24 months), internalizing problems (36, 60 months), externalizing problems (36, 60 months)	104; 1–5 years; low income families	Evidence for continuity of emotional and behavioral problems; support for early differentiation between internalizing and externalizing problems accounting for early difficult temperament.

Continued

Table 1 (Continued)

Authors	*Constructs assessed*	*Sample description (N; age range; characteristics)*	*Major findings*
Kivijarvi M *et al.* (2005)	Maternal sensitivity behavior (MSB) and infant temperament	56; 3–12 months; Finnish dyads	Moderate temperament stability during first year; MSB related to infant temperament characteristics at 3, 6, and 12 months. Gender differences in temperament evident at 6 and 12 months.
Kochanska G and Knaack A (2003)	Effortful control	106; 22–45 months	Effortful control mediated the reported relations between maternal power assertion and impaired conscience development in children, even when child management difficulty was controlled.
Kochanska G *et al.* (1997)	Inhibitory control and conscience development	83; 2.5–5 years	Strong links found between inhibitory control and measures of children's conscience at early school age, with girls outperforming boys.
Kochanska G *et al.* (2000)	Effortful control	106; 22, 33 months	Greater effortful control at 22 months linked to more regulated anger; at 33 months linked to more regulated anger and joy and to stronger restraint.
Leerkes EM and Crockenberg SC (2003)	Maternal remembered childhood care, prenatal depression, sensitivity, and concordance between maternal reports of temperament and temperament observed in the laboratory (distress to novelty, distress to limitations).	90; 6 months; primiparous mothers	Higher concordance between maternal reports and behavior observation of Distress to Novelty when mothers reported having needs met as a child and low prenatal depressive symptoms. Distress to Limitations higher when mothers less sensitive during observational tasks.
Leve LD *et al.* (2001)	Maternal sensitivity, infant temperament, pleasure in parenting, marital happiness	99; mean age 5 months; adopted infants	Parents who rated infants as showing more distress to limitations reported less pleasure in routine parenting, mediated by marital happiness for fathers. Mothers reported less pleasure in parenting with infants perceived as more fearful.
Little C and Carter AS (2005)	Infant emotional reactivity, infant emotion regulation, maternal–infant emotional availability	45; 12 months; low income	Maternal hostility significantly associated with infant difficulty in regulating distress during an emotion challenge and in postchallenge conditions, over and above the impact of emotional reactivity.
Maxted AE *et al.* (2005)	Infant colic, maternal depression, infant, parent, and family difficulties	93; 2 months	More severe depressive symptoms in mothers related to fussy/difficult infant temperament, more parenting stress, lower parental self-esteem, and more family-functioning problems.
Maziade M *et al.* (1998)	Infant temperament, attitudes to discipline, stressful events, clinical status at an older age	358; 4.7 years	Extremely difficult temperament had no strong direct association with clinical outcomes at 4 years, temperament assessed at 4 years, family attitudes to discipline, and stressful events were related.
NICHD Early Child Care Research Network (2004)	Affect dysregulation within mother–child relationship, cognitive and socioemotional problems	1364; 1–54 months	Affective dysregulation associated with less maternal sensitivity and stimulation, maternal depressive symptoms, and lower income over first 36 months. Affect-dysregulation linked to cognitive, social and emotional problems at 54 months.
Park S *et al.* (1997)	Infant temperament, parenting, and child inhibition	125; 12–36 months; first born males	Supportive parenting and high negativity with low positivity in infancy predicted high inhibition.
Pauli-Pott U *et al.* (2004)	Caregiver depression/anxiety, caregiver social support, caregiver sensitivity, infant emotionality, infant withdrawal/fear	101; 4–12 months; first born infants	Caregiver characteristics predicted negative emotionality and withdrawal/fear, but not positive emotionality.

Continued

Table 1 (Continued)

Authors	*Constructs assessed*	*Sample description (N; age range; characteristics)*	*Major findings*
Pesonen A *et al.* (2005)	Gestational age, gestational weight, parental ratings of temperament	152; 6 months	Infants born small for gestational age were rated by both parents as significantly more fearful and negatively reactive compared to infants born appropriate for gestational age.
Raikkonen K *et al.* (2006)	Parental stress and perceived infant temperament	292 families/584 parents; 6 months	The more stress one parent reported, the more negatively tuned were the parents' reports of their own functioning, and their perceptions of the infant.
Rothbart MK *et al.* (2001)	Extraversion/surgency, negative affectivity, and effortful control	262; 3–7 years	Factor analyses reliably recovered a three-factor solution indicating three broad dimensions of temperament: extraversion/surgency, negative affectivity, and effortful control, which also appeared reliably in ratings of children in other cultures.
Rothbart MK *et al.* (2003)	Effortful control	192; 18–36 months	Performance on marker tasks designed to address attentional mechanisms underlying effortful control related to aspects of effortful control and negative affect at an older age.
Rubin KH *et al.* (2002)	Inhibited temperament parenting style, and stability of behavioral inhibition	Time 1: 108; time 2: 88; 25–51 months	Toddler inhibition predicted socially reticent behavior at preschool age; maternal behaviors (intrusive control and derision) moderated the relation between toddler peer inhibition and social reticence.
Rubin KH *et al.* (2003)	Conflict-aggression, emotion and behavior, dysregulation, parenting, externalizing problems	104; 2–4 years	Emotional and behavioral dysregulation at 2 independently predicted externalizing problems at 4 years; relation between conflict-aggression at 2 years and externalizing problems at 4 years strongest for toddlers with high levels of maternal negativity.
Rubin KH *et al.* (1995)	Emotional regulation and social interaction	96; 4 years	Emotional dysregulation associated with psychological maladaptation; the association was modified depending on the degree to which children engage in social interaction.
Shaw DS *et al.* (1997)	Negative emotionality, attachment, life experiences, child-rearing disagreements, parenting daily hassles, and internalizing problems	86; 12–60 months; low-income families	Negative emotionality, disorganized attachment, negative life events, and exposure to child-rearing disagreements and parenting hassles related to the development of preschool age internalizing problems.
Sokolowski M (2006)	Marriage, spousal personality, parental expectations for temperament, life stress, continuity of parental sensitivity	30; third trimester of pregnancy, 3.5 months, 12 months	Marital adjustment and parental personality moderated child temperament and parenting behaviors. Change and stability in mother–infant relationship related to multiple factors; change and stability in father–infant relationship mostly related to maternal personality.
Vaughan AE (2005)	Temperament (sociability, self-regulation), joint attention, social competence, externalizing and internalizing problems	65; 24–30 months	Response to Joint Attention (RJA), self-regulation, and social fearfulness negatively related to externalizing behavior at 30 months. RJA and self-regulation negatively predicted intemalizing behavior at 30 months. RJA and self-regulation positively predicted social competence at 30 months.
Wachs T and Kohnstamm G (2002)	Maternal rating of child shyness, temperament characteristics, social behavior	570 families; 3.5–4.5 years	Social maturity mediated the influence of temperament on children's adjustment to kindergarten.

Continued

Table 1 (Continued)

Authors	*Constructs assessed*	*Sample description (N; age range; characteristics)*	*Major findings*
Warren S and Simmens SJ	Difficult temperament, maternal sensitivity, symptoms of anxiety, and depression	1226; 1–36 months	Children with more difficult temperament were more likely to show decreased anxiety/depressive symptoms if their mothers had been more sensitive. Temperamentally difficult boys with more sensitive mothers were significantly more likely to show decreased symptoms of anxiety and depression, compared to girls.

of maternal sensitivity in the context of predicting internalizing type difficulties, wherein children identified as having more difficult temperament were significantly more likely to show decreased anxiety/depressive symptoms, if their mothers had been more sensitive. Interestingly, this effect was further qualified by gender, with boys showing a greater protective impact of maternal sensitivity on lowering the levels of anxiety and depression.

The link between positive emotion and psychopathology has only recently been investigated in childhood, and studies addressing positive emotionality in early childhood have not been widespread. Investigations with older children and adolescents have generally provided results consistent with findings in the adult literature, that is, low positive emotion is associated with increases in depressive symptoms. Although there is some debate as to whether activity level is an independent temperament construct or is part of the higher order constructs of negative or positive emotionality, research has demonstrated links between activity level and behavioral difficulties. Most frequently, higher levels of activity have been associated with externalizing difficulties (e.g., aggression, hyperactivity, inattention, conduct problems, and impulsivity). A number of studies have also examined the role of regulatory capacity/effortful control in the development of behavioral and emotional difficulties in early childhood. Effortful control has emerged as an important contributor to both internalizing and externalizing difficulties in childhood, with lower levels of effortful control contributing to increasing the level of risk for such problems and higher effortful control playing a protective role. Even earlier manifestations of self-regulation have been linked with preschool symptoms of psychopathology by Crockenberg. Infant regulatory behaviors were found to moderate the relationship between reactivity to novelty and later anxious behavior, with high reactivity to novelty with poor attention control predicting later anxiety, especially when the mothers were rated as less engaged or sensitive.

The majority of studies have examined temperament characteristics in an effort to explain the onset or maintenance of childhood psychopathology. However, some have addressed the role of temperament in the development of competence. Recently, Jay Belsky and colleagues showed that high levels of child negative emotionality predicted more advanced school readiness, but only when children also demonstrated high levels of attentional persistence. In another study conducted by Marissa Diener, child temperament, self-regulation in particular, along with maternal characteristics, predicted social competence in preschool; fewer prosocial behaviors were demonstrated by children at increased risk related to these factors. Wally Dixon and colleagues' investigation also demonstrated that attentional control and positive affectivity predicted language production and comprehension in early childhood.

Connections between temperament attributes and the development and maintenance of childhood psychopathology are still being investigated, and already intervention efforts are underway, taking advantage of the available information. Understanding early precursors of developmental psychopathology and behavior problems has enabled researchers to target youngsters demonstrating characteristics linked with risk for later difficulties (e.g., frequent/severe negative emotionality, irritability), preventing the manifestation and/or escalation of such problematic patterns of behavior. Similar to van den Boom is intervention for highly irritable infants, leading to increased attachment security. Clancy Blair recently demonstrated that with early intervention, infants with higher levels of negative emotionality at 12 months had a twofold decrease in the occurrence of behavior problems, and fourfold decrease in the occurrence of high-risk profiles at age 3 years, relative to children not participating in treatment. Preventative efforts have also been advocated, for example, providing all parents of newborn infants with information regarding early developmental milestones, in order to prevent child abuse and neglect.

Conclusions

The study of temperament in early childhood has a recent but exciting history, with interest in this area continuing to grow. There have also been a number of advances in our understanding of the basic temperament attributes and their development in the first 5 years of life. Some researchers have focused on theoretical definitions, providing guidance for others in formulating hypotheses regarding the structure of temperament, that is, relationships between different domains or characteristics. This work had a direct impact on the development of measurement tools available for the study of temperament in development, with parent-report questionnaires developed and revised on the basis of theoretical advances. Most recently, a widely used parent-report instrument examining infant temperament has been revised to include items that address early manifestations of regulatory capacity.

Another important area of study involves attempts to explain and predict the development of various temperament attributes. This research is especially important in early childhood, given the rapid developmental changes that occur during this period. Interestingly, a number of developmental changes in temperament attributes can be linked with changes in other areas of maturation. For instance, higher levels of activity and approach reported for older children may stem, at least in part, from increased capacities for locomotion. Increases in anger/frustration may also be related to frustrations of the goals of locomotion, as well as to emerging cognitive skills, including goal directed thinking and working memory, allowing goals to be kept in mind, and creating greater potential for frustration. Infants developing these capacities are more likely to show distress when unable to grasp desired objects, or when a caregiver removes a desired object.

The development of the brain's executive attention system supports the rapid increases in Effortful Control during the toddler and preschool years. Increases in attention are also due, in part, to advances in comprehension and language development. As children are better able to understand their environment, this increased appreciation of their surroundings helps them to sustain attention for longer periods of time. The emergence and development of language also contribute to further advances in impulse control, which in turn are related directly to increases in sustained attention.

The evaluation of how temperament and its development are related to other domains of social–emotional functioning and later psychopathology represents another important area of study. The study of early temperament, and its links to later adjustment or behavioral/emotional problems, is of particular importance given the potential for application of findings. A more precise understanding of early appearing temperament underpinnings of later difficulties may enable clinical psychologists to formulate more effective prevention and early intervention approaches, capitalizing on this information. If future research confirms the importance of infant regulatory capacity in shaping later attention-based regulation (e.g., effortful control), interventions aimed at facilitating the development of these early attentional skills that have already shown some progress could be implemented.

See also: Abuse, Neglect, and Maltreatment of Infants; Anger and Aggression; Attachment; Behavior Genetics; Birth Order; Crying; Down Syndrome; Discipline and Compliance; Emotion Regulation; Empathy and Prosocial Behavior; Endocrine System; Exploration and Curiosity; Family Influences; Fear and Wariness; Independence/Dependence; Genetics and Inheritance; Humor; Mental Health, Infant; Mental Health, Intervention and Prevention; Parenting Styles and their Effects; Postpartum Depression, Effects on Infant; Risk and Resilience; Separation and Stranger Anxiety; Shyness; Social and Emotional Development Theories; Safety and Childproofing; Self-Regulatory Processes; Siblings and Sibling Rivalry; Sleep; Socialization in Infancy and Childhood; Stress and Coping; Twins.

Suggested Readings

Gerardi-Caulton G (2000) Sensitivity to spatial conflict and the development of self-regulation in children 24–36 months of age. *Developmental Science* 4: 397–404.

Kagan J (1994) *Galen's Prophecy: Temperament in Human Nature.* New York: Basic Books.

Posner MI and Rothbart MK (1998) Attention, self-regulation, and consciousness. *Philosophical Transactions of the Royal Society of London* B(353): 1915–1927.

Rothbart MK and Bates JE (2006) Temperament. In: Damon W, Lerner R, and Eisenberg N (eds.) *Handbook of Child Psychology: Vol. 3. Social, Emotional, and Personality Development,* 6th edn., pp. 99–166. New York: Wiley.

Rothbart MK and Derryberry D (1981) Development of individual differences in temperament. In: Lamb ME and Brown AL (eds.) *Advances in Developmental Psychology,* vol. 1, pp. 37–86. Hillsdale, NJ: Erlbaum.

Rothbart MK and Posner MI (2007) *Educating the Human Brain.* Washington, DC: APA.

Stifter CA and Braungart J (1992) Infant colic: A transient condition with no apparent effects. *Journal of Applied Developmental Psychology* 13: 447–462.

Thomas A, Chess S, Birch HG, Hertzig ME, and Korn S (1963) *Behavioral Individuality in Early Childhood.* New York: New York University Press.

Van den Boom DC (1994) The influence of temperament and mothering on attachment and exploration: An experimental manipulation of sensitive responsiveness among lower-class mothers with irritable infants. Erratum. *Child Development* 65: 1457–1477.

Teratology

R Seifer, Brown University, Providence, RI, USA

Glossary

Behavioral teratology – The study of behavioral occurring in childhood (usually early in life) associated with anomalies feral of exposure to toxic substances.
Developmental embryology – The study of *in utero* development in terms of factors such as of timing, sequence, growth-promotion factors, growth-inhibition factors, and organ systems development.
Developmental psychopathology – A theoretical perspective that simultaneously considers understanding of normative development and understanding of maladaptive development; each is presumed to fundamentally inform the other.
Direct effects model – Explanations of development where single factors are presumed to have causal effect on a specific characteristic, independent of other causal factors.
Direction of effect – Attributions about causality when two or more things are associated.
Effect size – A metric that indicates the size of an association in statistical terms, which can be generalized across specific measurements, and often expressed as a proportion of the variability observed in the measurements.
Interactive effects model – Explanations of development where the effect of single factors on a specific characteristic depends on other causal factors.
Meta-analysis – A statistical approach to combining findings from multiple studies of the same association, designed to provide the best evidence-based estimate an effect size.
Sleeper effects – Behavioral effects not immediately apparent that can only be detected substantially later in development.
Teratology – The study of physical malformations occurring in childhood (usually early in life) associated with exposure to toxic substances.
Toxicology – The study of physiologic processing of substances to which an individual is exposed.
Transactional model – Explanations of development where multiple factors are presumed to have causal effect on a specific characteristic, resulting in transformations of the developmental process.
Translational research – Research that examines phenomena simultaneously at multiple levels of analysis, which might include genetic variation, neurotransmitter action, physiology, behavior, social processes, and health outcomes.

Introduction

Teratology is derived from the Greek noun *teras*, meaning monster, and historically has referred to the study of malformations early in life that result from exposure to chemicals such as mercury, lead, and other complex compounds. The original focus of this work was on gross physical malformations (and hence the borrowing of the Greek noun for monster), and more recently has referred to malformations that result from exposure to chemicals such as lead, mercury, or other compounds. In the period from the 1960s to 1980s, the concept was gradually extended to the domain of behavioral teratology, most clearly articulated by Riley and Voorhees. The key elements of this extension are twofold. First, the focus is on behavioral anomalies, rather than physical malformations. Second, and perhaps more far reaching, is an appreciation that many behavioral anomalies may be subtle in nature and not apparent at all stages of development. Closely aligned with the field of behavioral teratology is the field of toxicology. For the most part, behavioral teratology focuses on variations in behavior that are associated with some known or suspected exposure to a potential toxin in utero.

Like many areas of scientific inquiry, investigation in behavioral teratology was initially inspired by blatant examples of the phenomena. In teratology, severe physical malformation, and in the behavioral realm, frank mental retardation constituted these eye-catching events. By the second half of the twentieth century, several well-publicized events helped establish links between physical and behavioral events and exposure to toxins, and other areas of inquiry subsequently came into play. For example, knowledge from developmental embryology was brought to bear on how and when during embryogenesis the malformations might occur (so we now ask many questions regarding dose, duration, and timing of exposures). Furthermore, the behavioral teratology logic could also be turned on its ear. Instead of pursuing an epidemiologic type of inquiry (how to explain a cluster of congenital malformations), investigators also began inquiries focused on purported antecedents, rather than observed consequences. Thus, substances known or believed to be toxic (though not because of documented links with early malformations) came to be examined with regard to possible physical and behavioral effects. This occurred in the context of widespread public concern about pollutants (in the wake of mercury, polychlorinated biphenyl (PCB) contamination, and identification of lead in many parts of the environment), prescribed and over-the-counter drugs (following the thalidomide exposures), illicit drugs (in tune with increased societal use), and environmental agents such as pesticides (after the publication of books such as *Silent Spring*). The types of malformations and behaviors examined also became far more subtle in nature. Instead of the blatantly negative consequences that drove the field at its outset, investigators began to look for behavioral signs such as attention problems or poor school performance in place of more severe manifestations such as mental retardation.

A large majority of the published papers in behavioral teratology describe studies performed with nonhuman animals. This is quite understandable. Given that the focus is on toxic exposures that can lead to behavioral deficits, intentionally exposing humans to these substances would be unethical. Thus, the ability to investigate basic processes is typically available only in animal models (more about this in the next section). This context of basic research with animals has set the stage for the mostly nonexperimental human research in behavioral teratology that will be the focus of this article. These animal models typically provide excellent starting points for generating and testing hypotheses in humans.

From a broad theoretical perspective, existing models in behavioral teratology in humans parallel those found in the broader field of human development research. A simple tripartite differentiation of common approaches was articulated by Sameroff and colleagues. Direct effects models examine one-to-one correspondence between antecedents and consequences, with strong causal inferences drawn. In behavioral teratology, for example, a direct effects model would imply that sufficient exposure to a toxin would inevitably result in an identifiable change in a specific developing system. 'Interactive effects models' simultaneously consider multiple antecedents, often a combination of constitutional and contextual factors, in the prediction of developmental outcomes. These effects are linear in nature, easily captured by a typical analysis of variance (ANOVA) interaction model. To exemplify in the behavioral teratology realm, effects of a toxin might only occur when a particular characteristic is present in an individual (e.g., a particular genetic feature). Transactional models, like interactive effects models, consider multiple antecedent factors. Where they differ, however, is in positing developmental transformations in dynamic organism in complex systems – thus making simple predictions from single antecedents to distal outcomes very difficult. In a behavioral teratology example, a particular toxin combined with a particular genetic characteristic might serve to predispose a child to have difficulty with certain types of learning; however, the presence of the learning problems could change the environment, so to speak, so that the learning context is enriched enabling the child to overcome those obstacles, such that the predisposition no longer has developmental consequences. Existing studies in the behavioral teratology literature exemplify these generic models, and the framework will be used to integrate the current knowledge base.

Human and Animal Studies

Behavioral teratology is one area where the contrast between animal studies and work with humans is at its sharpest. In a sense, this contrast highlights the fundamental obstacle in studying teratology in human populations. Put simply, owing to ethical concerns, we cannot conduct the relevant experiments with humans that would allow for less ambiguous understanding of phenomena than we currently possess.

Human Studies

There are two research strategies that characterize virtually all work in human teratology. The first is natural experiments. Although not truly experiments (e.g., there is no random assignment of people to experimental conditions), researchers rely on identification of discrete populations where individuals were exposed *in utero* to a potential teratogen. A classic example of this strategy was examination of mercury exposure in populations living proximal to an industrial discharge site in Minamata, Japan. The second strategy is naturalistic observation studies. In these studies, populations are examined for naturally occurring levels of prenatal exposure to a particular potential teratogen, and follow-up studies are conducted of the children to identify postnatal effects – this design has been the staple of studies of prenatal tobacco exposure. Often, the study group is chosen because it is known to be proximal to the potential teratogen under study, and this represents a hybrid of the two research designs described above – studies of PCB exposure in communities near Lake Michigan exemplify this hybrid approach. In all of these human research designs, however, the defining characteristic is that the researchers do not have control over the exposure (amount, timing, duration) that is examined with respect to outcomes in young children.

Animal Studies

In contrast to human studies, with animal models we can ethically introduce the presumed toxins in order to study their effects on developing organisms. Differences in animal and human work, however, do not end with variation in how substances are introduced to individuals. Another critical feature of animal studies is the degree to which nonexperimental features of the individuals' circumstances are controlled. In animal work, the contexts of the individuals, ranging from housing, to activity levels, to environmental resources, to nutrition can be held relatively constant. In humans, however, researchers rarely have any degree of control over these factors. More troublesome yet is that some important factors in the studies of humans are systematically biased in those populations prone to various types of substance exposures.

Features of the populations of animals can also be systematically varied. Strains of animals may be employed because they have been bred to express specific physical and/or behavioral characteristics of interest as potential consequences of the exposure. For example, tumor-prone animals may be employed if an outcome under study is carcinogenic effects; propensity to prefer alcohol may be used if behaviors related to substance use are of interest as outcomes.

As technology has improved in recent years, questions regarding interaction of exposure to potential teratogens with genetic factors have become feasible, with different models being used. One of these models is 'knockout' designs, where specific gene sequences have been removed or inactivated in a strain of animals to examine how the absence of the genes interacts with exposure to affect behavior. Alternatively, animals with known gene polymorphisms (individual differences in specific gene sequences) can be examined to identify which variants might interact with a teratogen to yield a developmental effect.

In all of these animal models, dose, timing, and duration of exposure can be carefully controlled and systematically varied. In similar fashion, the timing, frequency, and method of subsequent behavioral and physical testing of offspring can be systematically varied and controlled as well. It is also feasible to replicate findings and to develop research programs that proceed through the testing of theoretical models in a rational and stepwise manner.

Implications of Animal Studies for Research with Humans

The experimental controls just described for animal studies are not available for humans (e.g., we cannot breed genetically altered strains). The question then becomes: how can animal models inform studies of humans? The answer is threefold. First, potential human teratogens and their mechanisms of action can be identified in animals to generate hypotheses for human studies. Second, possible thresholds regarding dose, timing, and duration of exposure can be identified in animals and extrapolated to humans to again generate testable hypotheses. Third, potential genetic interactions can be identified in animals that could again generate hypotheses for studies with humans.

These efforts at translational research represent cutting edge efforts in scientific inquiry, but enthusiasm must also be tempered by the realities of translating animal models to human experience. First, animals, while they have similarities to humans in many ways, also differ in important ways. These differences become more pronounced as we move further away from humans in terms of phylogenetic similarity (e.g., rodent brains have far less in common with human brains than do primate brains). Perhaps more important for the agenda of behavioral teratology, the behavior of nonhuman species does not match the complexity and organization of human behavior. For many behaviors of interest (e.g., math or reading), there is simply no equivalent or analogous animal behavior. The variety of social and contextual influence in humans is far more influential in behavioral outcomes than anything that could be modeled in an animal laboratory. It is thus essential that even well-established animal models of teratogenic effects be clearly replicated in humans before making scientific claims with any confidence. Finally sleeper effects may occur, which in humans can take very long periods to detect. A well-known physical example is diethylstilbestrol (DES; a synthetic estrogen) exposure in pregnancy, which did not reveal itself until reproductive problems occurred in offspring decades later. In the behavioral realm, certain types of cognitive processes do not emerge until middle childhood, which precludes their detection earlier in life.

Behavioral Teratology in Infancy and Early Childhood: Timing of Exposure, Timing of Outcome

The focus of this volume is on infancy and early childhood. In behavioral teratology, however, only part of the story has emerged by the time children enter elementary school (one traditional marker for the end of early childhood). As will become evident in subsequent sections, many of the concerns around potential toxins are in behavioral domains that do not emerge (at least in well- or fully developed form) until middle childhood. Some examples include executive function, school failure, and antisocial behavior.

In a related vein, the timing of exposure to potential toxins is an important factor when considering infancy and early childhood. The strict definition of teratology includes only prenatal exposures (and that will be the focus of this article). Of course, exposure to toxins at any point in development resulting in changes in behavior would be of concern. Early exposure, however, is generally of most concern because of the increased developmental vulnerability of maturing neurological systems.

Prenatal exposures are typically indirect. Exposures to the mother are mediated in various ways before the child is affected. Some examples are the speed at which mothers metabolize substances or the degree to which a substance (or its metabolites) crosses the placental barrier. As such, the nature and extent of exposure may be less certain than with certain types of postnatal exposures. Finally, the rapidity of development during the prenatal period makes the timing of exposure important when considering the expectable type of developmental consequences.

An important characteristic of exposure to most toxins is that they cross the boundary of pregnancy to infancy. Thus, in many research studies the teratogenic effects are occurring in the context of postnatal exposures. Unlike prenatal exposure, postnatal exposures are typically direct – they affect the child via direct experience with the teratogen, and perhaps are more potent as a result. One postnatal route of exposure that mimics some of the qualities of prenatal exposure (see below) is breastfeeding. Although the developing infant is exposed directly, this type of exposure is again mediated by maternal amount of exposure, metabolism, and expression in breast milk, all of which affects the actual experience of the child. This important research confound needs to be considered when attributing findings to the prenatal period.

Many Types of Substances in Many Types of Conditions Are Evaluated as Potential Teratogens

Potential teratogenic effects have been studied in many types of foods, pollutants, drugs, and naturally occurring elements and compounds. Although we have well agreed upon conceptualizations of these categories, the boundaries often become very blurry when examining the association of organismic exposure and developmental sequelae. Mercury, for example, occurs naturally in the environment, occasionally in areas where it runs off into lakes and streams. In addition, mercury has been an important mining resource and used in many industrial applications because of its unique properties of being a metallic element that is liquid at normal temperatures. Because mercury evaporates when exposed to air, it can travel widely from mining and industrial sites; it is also ubiquitous in aquatic environments in compound form as methylmercury, which makes its way into the human food chain via fish consumption. Finally, mercury has been used in dental amalgam fillings and vaccine stabilizers at various points in history. Thus, it is difficult to distinguish between the category of food, pollutant, drug, or naturally occurring substance when discussing mercury exposure.

Leaving the niceties of clean categorization aside, one can identify many different types of substances thought to be potential teratogens. Environmental pollutants have been a consistent focus in behavioral teratology. Examples include heavy metal exposure (including mercury and lead), PCBs, and dioxins. Pollutants can be found in air, in water, in foods, and in consumer products (ranging from stone-age ceramics to electronics-age microchips). Exposures may occur proximal to pollution sites (as in waste or runoff from manufacturing processes) or very distal from those sites (as in mercury distributed atmospherically throughout the world and absorbed by fish, thereby becoming part of the food supply).

Non-natural substances used for one purpose may have unintended results. This is most apparent in the domain of pharmaceuticals. Perhaps the most notorious example of a teratogenic drug is thalidomide. Prescribed as a sleep aid and antiemetic for pregnant women, the drug ultimately proved to have strong association with limb deformities among children exposed prenatally. One result of the thalidomide experience is that the US Food and Drug Administration (FDA), and other regulatory bodies around the world, now require explicit testing and labeling of pharmaceuticals regarding their teratogenic risk during pregnancy. Most testing is done in laboratory animals, often at doses far exceeding the human-equivalent dose, and it is very difficult to extrapolate such findings to human teratology potential. It is the case, in fact, that few drugs are actually tested in humans during pregnancy, but are simply labeled with generic warnings that risks are unknown; phase III clinical trials almost exclusively prohibit pregnant women and women not using effective contraception from participation. As a result, most newer drugs used by pregnant women for purposes unrelated to pregnancy and childbirth are prescribed without benefit of clear evidence as to safety to the developing fetus, and most knowledge is gained from *ad hoc* postmarketing studies among women and offspring who have chosen to use the drug in question.

Drugs given directly to children may also have unintended effects. Compared with adults, children are relatively in better health and thus have fewer prescribed medications. One class of medications used far more often in children than adults is vaccines. Most immunization strategies focus on children in the first years of life, with attempts to have universal coverage. Although strictly speaking not teratogenic because of their postnatal administration (but still useful for appreciating how to interpret teratogenic effects), the vaccines have become a focus of interest being potentially harmful, particularly in relation to the documented rise in rates of autism spectrum disorders. Most attention has focused on the mercury-based stabilizers commonly used until recent years, while some attention has focused on less-specific components of vaccines.

Use of pharmaceuticals for recreational purposes during pregnancy, either licit drugs used for nontherapeutic purposes or street drugs, may have similar teratogenic potential. Interest has focused on opiates, synthetic opiates, cocaine, marijuana, and methamphetamine among other recreational drugs. These substances are of particular interest because of their psychoactive effects, which in turn lead to suspicion that they may pose particular hazard to the developing central nervous systems. In this vein, two legal substances are important to note: tobacco and alcohol. Both are marketed and used specifically for their physiologic and psychoactive effects, and both have been the focus of intense scrutiny regarding their teratogenic sequelae.

Problematic Developmental Phenomena

Our environments, food supplies, and pharmaceuticals contain many natural and synthetic substances. Only a very small number of them have received any attention as potential teratogens. On a daily basis, people eat, drink, swim, breathe, and otherwise have contact with many facets of their environments. It is typically the case that when unexpected clusters of adverse developmental events or illnesses occur, that a search for proximal causes leads to suspicion of teratogens of some sort. In a minority of cases, very probable cause–effect relationships can be established. These typically occur when exposures are high, when groups exposed are relatively isolated or otherwise clearly distinguishable, and when well-defined syndromes are associated with the exposure.

More frequently, the situation is far more ambiguous. Interest in a teratogen may result from hypotheses derived from the well-identified high-exposure relations described above, which are generalized to lower levels of exposure. Examples include examination of low levels of lead or mercury, capitalizing on well-established associations noted in high-level exposures. Another route to identifying potential teratogens is from clusters of children exhibiting non-normative developmental pathways. Such clusters may be geographically proximal or temporally proximal – the interest in vaccines in regard to autism spectrum disorders is a good example of inquiry motivated by temporal clustering of cases. In general, these types of associations have been far more difficult to demonstrate in unambiguous fashion. Furthermore, because of the ambiguity inherent in the inquiry, advocacy positions (intellectual beliefs, parents advocating for their children, etc.) often enter into the progress of the science and the interpretation of data.

Normative Phenomena with Specific Problematic Instances

Behavioral teratology examines inherently developmental phenomena. Outcomes of interest are typically in the standard domains of interest to developmental scientists. Timing of exposures *in utero* is of prime interest. Many of the mechanisms proposed target interruptions of complex developmental pathways in attempting to explain the sequelae of interest. It is still the case that behavioral teratology is often not well integrated with other developmental theories.

Of particular note is that the developmental psychopathology approach, which has proven useful in many other domains of atypical development, has only been applied to some portions of the research on behavioral teratology, as noted by Wakschlag and colleagues. In this developmental psychopathology vein, which emphasizes the continuum of normative to pathological development, nutrition may be viewed as a normative phenomenon that under some circumstances is relevant to teratology. Healthy diet is believed to be characterized by a wide variety of foods with high nutritional content. But fish (a good source of high-quality protein) may enter into the behavioral teratology equation when it contains super-threshold levels of environmental contaminants. In similar fashion, breast milk may also contain substances because of mother's diet or substance use/exposure.

Exposure to potential teratogens must always be considered in the larger developmental context. We know that broad variations in social context have profound effects on normative developmental patterns. Often, poverty and minority racial/ethnic status are associated with lower levels of achievement measures on standard metrics and poor developmental outcomes in general. Furthermore, when contextual adversities co-occur, the association with poor developmental outcomes is especially strong. In some circumstances, what may be relatively small effects of substance exposures are dwarfed when compared to those of contextual influences (such that they are difficult to detect or difficult to appropriately interpret). In other circumstances, the confounding of substance exposures with contextual characteristics may mislead investigators as to the source of variation in children's outcomes. Dilworth-Bart and Moore's recent commentary highlights the fact that exposures are not equitably distributed in the population, but are more likely to occur in those from economically distressed and racial/ethnic minority groups.

While emphasizing the importance of context, it is also important to note that the same developmental context will not affect all children in the same way. The notion of individual-by-environment interaction, which has been well articulated by Wachs, is particularly applicable in the realm of behavioral teratology. The complex of substance exposure, other contextual characteristics, and individuals' constitutional characteristics will together help explain variation in children's developmental outcomes. The example of asthma in children succinctly illustrates this point. Some children are constitutionally prone to bronchoconstriction and airway inflammation, in part by virtue of family history and perhaps maternal exposure to air pollutants during pregnancy. Symptoms of asthma, however, are not simply a function of a child's propensity to these physiologic processes. Rather, the presence of triggers that are somewhat specific to individual children (e.g., allergens, mites, rodent droppings, cockroach) will exacerbate symptoms. Furthermore, such triggers are more likely to occur in housing conditions found more frequently among families living in poverty; medical control of symptoms is also less likely when poverty restricts access to healthcare. Finally, chronic activation of these biological responses, from the combined effects of environmental conditions and lack of optimal healthcare, can result in long-lasting increase in propensity of the physiologic responses that underlie asthma symptoms. This combination of prenatal exposure, constitutional propensities, environmental exposures, and promotive contexts should always be considered when attempting to understand the effects of potential behavioral teratogens. Many will recognize this scenario as a classic example of (cumulative) risk and resilience interpretations of human development.

In addition to the broad theoretical conditions on interpreting the behavioral teratology literature, there are specific research concerns as well. Perhaps the most important is the issue of effect size. The interpretation of exposures at very high levels is typically relatively easy – effects on children follow regular patterns that are easily identified and occur in a large proportion of those exposed; this is the usual route by which we become interested in particular teratogens. Most current work, however, is concerned with lower-level exposures where the effects on children are far less pronounced. Typically, children are affected in different ways (many are apparently not affected at all), and the overall sizes of the effects are small. This set of circumstances makes interpretation very difficult. From a pure research perspective, small effects will be statistically significant only in large samples, and it is often the case that some degree of data mining has occurred before the effects are detected (owing to the expense of compiling this difficult-to-obtain data). It is thus important to consider the functional implications of statistical differences that may have small effect size.

We now turn to summarizing results in several specific domains of behavioral teratology. The first sections concern environmental pollutants, followed by sections on substances used by pregnant women. This is not a comprehensive review of all potential behavioral teratogens relevant to infants and young children, but rather a sampling of some of the most notable domains of work.

Environmental Teratogens

Lead Exposure

Lead, which is ubiquitous in the environment, is the teratogen that receives the most attention from a public health perspective. Although much of the attention with regard to lead is on postnatal exposure of children, there are prenatal exposures as well. Exposures can occur in paint, soil, and ceramics; it is a common pollutant in air as well, with gasoline being one historical source (although banned in recent years). Lead exposure at high levels has demonstrable effects on child development. Physical health can be affected in areas as diverse as growth, fertility, hearing, and renal function (even leading to death at very high exposure levels); effects extend to the behavioral realm as well, including intelligence, attention, memory, and self-regulation. To combat these known effects, testing for lead levels is widespread, and therapeutic interventions to reduce levels in the body and in the environment are common when high levels are detected.

The effects of low levels of lead (typically examined between 10 and 20 $\mu g\ dl^{-1}$) are less clear. It has been widely presumed that low levels of lead would have similar, albeit smaller, effects on young children – assumptions reflected in public health policies. Data supporting this assumption are far from conclusive. A large number of published studies identify effects on a wide variety of behavioral outcomes. Many other studies, however, have found little or no effects on the same behavioral parameters. In the case of intelligence quotient (IQ), for example, some argue that small effect sizes (3 IQ points or less) are both of limited practical significance and conceptually suspect in the context of numerous methodological difficulties noted in the extant literature; such limitations include poor inclusion of confounding variables, lack of attention to parental IQ, little control for multiple statistical comparisons, examination of extreme groups, and poor quality control in data collection. This set of arguments (which indeed can be applied to all areas of behavioral teratology) has been refuted, noting that the corpus of studies on lead exposure is commensurate in quality with those in the human development literature in general.

Meta-analysis, often useful in resolving uncertainty in the face of conflicting findings, has generated as much debate as the corpus of original empirical studies. Indeed, Kaufman's commentary in 2001 presents aggregate evidence in the domain of IQ, arriving at a relatively noncontroversial estimate of effect size of about 2–3 IQ points for the increase from 10 to 20 $\mu g\ dl^{-1}$. What becomes controversial, however, is the nonquantitative portion of meta-analytic procedures. High-quality meta-analyses examine not only the specific estimates of associations or group differences, but also examine variance associated with various study characteristics, including quality. It is at this point that disagreements often occur (as is true for the literature on low lead levels) as the criteria are inherently more subjective.

Polychlorinated biphenyl Exposure

PCBs are a class of compounds derived from commonly occurring hydrocarbons combined with chlorine. PCBs are very stable compounds ranging from viscous to solid, and have desirable insulating, nonflammability, and lubricating properties. Used widely in a variety of industrial applications, their use has been curtailed dramatically since environmental concerns became apparent in the 1970s. Their stability has resulted in large accumulations in various industrial sites, and PCBs have found their way into the food chain as well, mostly in adipose tissue in fish. Physical health effects have been noted, including some cancer risk, skin conditions, and liver function changes, and animal studies suggest immune system changes as well.

Early reports of health effects in workers exposed to large concentrations of PCBs in Asia, as well as effects on children born to exposed women, fueled many subsequent cohort studies focusing on prenatal exposure. Interpretation of the original Asian exposures has been difficult to interpret regarding PCBs, owing to the presence of other PCB derivatives known to be far more toxic than the PCBs themselves. Findings from early studies were contradictory, but subsequent work has converged on the presence of small (and perhaps nonspecific) subtle effects on physical and cognitive functioning. Effects include lower birth weight, smaller head circumference, poorer long-term memory, less response inhibition, longer reaction time, and changes in P300 duration (a physiological brain response to a sensory stimulus). These findings are not uncomplicated, however. Breastfeeding, for example, appears to be protective rather than additive in terms of PCB effects, perhaps because breastfeeding mothers provide more optimal contextual supports.

Mercury Exposure

As noted above, mercury enters the environment in natural ways and as part of industrial processes; it is found in the food supply and in pharmaceuticals. High-level exposures were observed in notorious industrial pollution sites in Japan. As noted in McCurry's historical description of the Minamata mercury exposure, symptoms were first noted in cats and birds, and quickly thereafter in humans. Severe neurological problems (paralysis, convulsions, speech problems, etc.), often resulting in death, were widespread. The widespread publicity of these events (one of my own early childhood memories is seeing the compelling pictures of affected residents in *Life* magazine) resulted in substantial attention to the issue of mercury pollution, environmental controls, and subsequent interest in low-level and prenatal exposures. For example, studies of adult dental workers have identified associations among mercury levels, gene mutations affecting pro-survival proteins (brain derived neurotrophic factor), and performance deficits on simple cognitive-motor tasks.

Many studies identify associations between prenatal mercury exposure and childhood deficits in cognitive and motor performance. Associations with IQ, language, and achievement tests have been observed in a New Zealand cohort of 6–7-year-old children; analyses identify levels of about $10\,\mathrm{mg\,kg^{-1}}$ as being potential thresholds at which deficits are noted. Another cohort from the Faroe Islands exhibited associations of prenatal mercury exposure and simple motor and cognitive tasks at 14 years of age. Associations with postnatal exposure were not identified. Some investigators strike a somewhat different tone, noting that most assessments of cognitive and motor function at 9 years of age did not reveal associations with prenatal mercury exposure.

In a combined quantitative analysis of these cohorts, it is estimated that the dose–response relationships is about 0.7 IQ points $\mu\mathrm{g\,g^{-1}}$ of mercury detectable in hair samples. Given that the median value is $0.2\,\mu\mathrm{g\,g^{-1}}$ and the 90th percentile is $1.4\,\mu\mathrm{g\,g^{-1}}$, the ultimate meaning of these associations is uncertain. In commenting on the Myers *et al.* findings, Lyketsos in 2003 asserts that there is no contraindication for prenatal fish consumption in most parts of the world, although in a few isolated areas where shark and whale are consumed (with higher mercury concentrations) the recommendation might be different.

Stepping outside the strict realm of behavioral teratology for the moment, perhaps the most contentious issue regarding mercury exposure concerns thiomersal use in vaccines. Many have hypothesized that the mercury exposure is related to subsequent autism and other neurodevelopmental problems. Most epidemiologic studies do not support this view. One potential reason for the lack of effect may be that the ethyl-mercury in the vaccine preservative is less toxic than the methylmercury typically found in more naturally occurring mercury. This set of studies has not, however, diminished the debate, as a brief visit to the world-wide-web reveals. Western countries have mostly eliminated thiomersal from vaccines, but less-developed countries have not in part because of expense and in part because of the need for effective preservative. Thus, discussion of the effects has become framed in terms of short- to medium-term costs and benefits of vaccine use in prevention of disease, use of public heath funds, and risks of thiomersal-containing vaccines.

Licit and Illicit Substances

Tobacco Exposure

Tobacco is a legal substance used primarily for recreational purposes. There is a large literature on the association of tobacco use during pregnancy and subsequent pregnancy and child outcomes. The vast majority of tobacco use is via cigarette smoking, particularly for women. In addition to direct use by pregnant women, there is also passive contact with environmental tobacco smoke (both to pregnant women and to young infants after birth) as a potential additional source of exposure. Still, the bulk of the literature on tobacco exposure concerns maternal smoking during pregnancy.

Approximately 20% of American women smoke during pregnancy. Rates are highest among unmarried, unemployed women from lower socioeconomic status

(SES) backgrounds, likely affecting about 800 000 births per year. Although we know little about the effects on young infants, it is important to note that women who smoke during pregnancy continue to do so after pregnancy, thereby exposing children to the hazardous effects of prenatal smoking as well as to those associated with environmental tobacco smoke.

Extrapolations from existing data indicate that smoking during pregnancy is responsible for up to 4800 infant deaths as well as 26 000 infants needing neonatal intensive care annually. Smoking causes important changes in fetal neurological development and also results in increased rates of spontaneous abortion, placenta previa, placental abruption, and perhaps sudden infant death syndrome (SIDS). Furthermore, a dose–response relationship between smoking and birth weight exists, with infants born to smokers being typically 150–250 g lighter in comparison to infants of nonsmokers.

In addition to the well-documented associations of prenatal tobacco use and pregnancy outcomes, behavioral functioning of infants may be affected in the realm of poor cognitive function (especially executive processes), unregulated behavior, attention difficulties, and difficult temperament. In the first days of life, infants present as difficult and unregulated. Sucking behavior, perhaps the most basic organized function of neonates, is weaker and less efficient. Crying of tobacco-exposed infants is also affected, with high pitch and excessive crying, which is indicative of a less well-organized system. There is also indication of early difficulty on Brazelton's Neonatal Behavior Assessment Scale indexes of tremulousness, irritability, and habituation.

As children grow older, their behavior becomes more organized. With respect to regulatory behaviors, there are several indications that the early neurobehavioral differences persist into later childhood. Furthermore, these characteristics have been implicated in pathways to delinquency and substance abuse. General temperamental difficulty is increased in nicotine-exposed children, in particular activity level. From a more clinical perspective, tobacco-exposed children exhibit more symptoms of, and are diagnosed more frequently with, attention deficit hyperactivity disorder. Regulation differences are also manifest at the physiologic level, where nicotine-exposed children exhibit lower autonomic arousal.

Cognitive functioning is also related to prenatal nicotine exposure. General effects are present in lower scores on standardized tests beginning in infancy and extending to the school years. Also, nicotine-exposed children have more difficulty with complex cognitive executive functions. Specific learning and reading problems are also evident as children enter school, and the related cognitive manifestations of attentional problems are also noted in tobacco-exposed children. As with behavioral regulation, these cognitive and attentional processes have been implicated in the development of antisocial behavior (see below).

Another notable association with prenatal tobacco exposure is conduct disorder and antisocial behavior. Beginning early in childhood, prenatally exposed children have more conduct problems. Later in adolescence and young adulthood, these conduct problems may manifest as delinquent and criminal behavior. There is, however, some concern that these associations may be more related to postnatal characteristics of families where pregnant women smoke, rather than prenatal smoking. Associations of prenatal exposure and conduct problems are particularly intriguing in the context of associations with behavior regulation, temperament, attention, and executive function. All of these characteristics have been implicated in the development of antisocial behavior in adolescents and young adults. Low physiological reactivity has also been associated with conduct problems, although there is less evidence for the association with prenatal nicotine exposure. Taken together, these findings highlight that identifying early in life the roots of behavioral dysregulation, poor attention and cognitive functioning, and difficult temperament would provide some developmental insights into the long-term effects of prenatal nicotine exposure.

Alcohol Exposure

Like tobacco, alcohol is a legal substance used primarily for recreational purposes. Although alcohol is present in some medications and foods, almost all exposure relevant to behavioral teratology is via voluntary recreational use. Alcoholic beverages are significant in almost all cultures; they have been available since ancient times when beer and wine were widely produced and were integral to economic development. Patterns of use vary widely both among cultures and individually within cultures. The association of alcohol use with adverse pregnancy/child development outcomes has been widely acknowledged over the past 30 years.

Virtually all interest with regard to alcohol exposure and young children's development concerns prenatal alcohol exposure; there is little reason to suspect that direct exposure occurs in the postnatal period. Heavy use during pregnancy is associated with fetal alcohol syndrome (FAS), which was initially identified by Jones and Smith in 1973. FAS is characterized by facial deformities, microcephaly, muscular/skeletal abnormalities, memory problems, and perhaps other cognitive deficits. Drinking thresholds for occurrence of FAS are unclear, but it is likely substantial – on the order of an average (or multiple instances of) five or more standard drinks per day for extended periods during pregnancy. Furthermore, timing of exposure may be important, with much attention on first trimester effects.

The consequence of lower levels of exposure is far less clear. Public health guidelines in the US recommend no drinking at all during pregnancy, for example, as recommended in 2004 by the National Center for Birth Defects and Developmental Disabilities. But research findings are far less clear regarding negative effects of drinking at low levels during pregnancy. Many studies have identified associations with small effect size when examining cognitive functioning in children whose mothers drank during pregnancy. These studies, however, often have conflicting findings. In many cases, specific tests are associated in some studies but not in others, or associations are found for some subgroups but not for others. When examining young children, one meta-analysis identified associations at one age (12 months) but not at two other ages. Such patterns of findings bring into question the degree to which effects of low levels of prenatal alcohol use are indeed associated with specific or nonspecific developmental problems, independent of other confounding factors.

Some have gone further and questioned whether the cultural context in which the science of alcohol effects developed has influenced interpretation of findings. Most notable among these critiques is the work of Abel and Armstrong during the past decade. Abel notes that for FAS, incidence rates among heavy drinkers are far higher in the US than in Western Europe, despite the fact that many of the European countries have higher drinking rates than the US. He likens this phenomenon to the well-known 'French paradox' where high alcohol and fat consumption are not associated with high rates of heart disease. Explanations for the 'American paradox' for FAS incidence may range from patterns of alcohol consumption to reporting biases to SES and race differences. In a more pointed analysis, Armstrong and Abel note that the response to (and public recommendations regarding) the use of alcohol during pregnancy is far different in the US than in other countries. Whereas the US Surgeon General recommends no alcohol consumption during pregnancy, European countries such as the UK recommend that drinking at low levels (less than seven standard drinks per week) during pregnancy is not dangerous to the developing fetus, while noting potential harm at higher levels (embodied in the 1996 statement by the Royal College of Obstetricians and Gynecologists). Armstrong and Abel contend that the US response is a moral panic (i.e., an exaggerated response to a perceived social problem) that is embedded in a moral, political, and media context peculiar to this country.

Illicit Drugs

Tobacco and alcohol are the two legal psychoactive substances most often used for recreational purposes. There are, of course, many illicit psychoactive substances, many of which are used by pregnant women. Those that have received the most attention with respect to behavioral effects in young children are cocaine, marijuana, opiates, and (more recently) methamphetamine. As with tobacco and alcohol, almost all studies have focused on prenatal exposure; cocaine and methamphetamine both have the potential for passive postnatal exposure because smoking is one common route of administration, and for methamphetamine, there is also potential for passive exposure because it is often manufactured in home-based laboratories.

Much of what is known about prenatal marijuana exposure emanates from the work of two large cohort studies conducted by Fried and colleagues and Goldschmidt and colleagues. Marijuana (especially the active ingredient Δ-9-tetrahydrocannabinol (THC)) likely acts on cerebral blood flow, cerebral glucose metabolism, and binds to cannabis-specific receptor sites (which may be over-represented in frontal cortex). Behavioral effects have been reported in infancy and early childhood (e.g., increased tremulousness), but have not been very consistent across time and study, and most comparisons have revealed no effects. Later in childhood, however, evidence converges to some extent on effects in the realm of executive function. Although a loosely defined term, executive function typically is used to convey higher-order volitional cognitive processes (e.g., sustained attention, inhibition, working memory). Beginning around age 4 years, a pattern of findings implicates a series of executive function measures, including memory, attention, visual–spatial skills, impulsivity, and problem solving. Even so, the effect sizes of the marijuana associations are small, and the pattern of findings inconsistent. These samples have been followed through early adolescence.

Cohort studies of prenatal cocaine exposure began 10–15 years later than those focused on marijuana exposure. Whereas the marijuana cohort studies were conducted largely motivated by scientific interest, the cocaine cohort studies were accompanied by a far greater degree of public concern about the fate of so-called 'crack babies'. Cocaine has a multitude of physiologic effects, most notably blocking synaptic reuptake of catecholamines (norepinephrine, dopamine) and serotonin by specific, presynaptic plasma membrane transporters. Cocaine also blocks the reuptake of catecholamines in adrenal cells, all leading to elevated circulating catecholamine levels. Sympathetic nervous system responses including hypertension, tachycardia, vasoconstriction, agitation, euphoria, and excitation are likely downstream effects, which in turn suggest many behavioral processes that may be modified.

Early in life, prenatal cocaine exposure appears to affect arousal, excitability, acoustic cry characteristics, and the auditory brainstem response. These are specifically manifest in greater excitability, many state transitions, more state transitions associated with stimulation, more rapid arousal from sleep, and increased physiological lability. More organized attention- and information-processing system deficits have been reported in cocaine-exposed infants, as have differences in mother–child dyadic interaction and attachment security. Prenatal cocaine exposure has also been shown to influence the hypothalamic–pituitary–adrenal (HPA) axis. Salivary cortisol in nonchallenging situations, as well as in the context of noninvasive and invasive challenges is low.

As cocaine-exposed children grow older, there is evidence that they may have cognitive and/or executive function deficits as well as other behavioral and physical problems. Cognition and attention functions are poorer at 4 years of age. Event-related potentials in high-density EEG assessments are longer in duration (indicating less efficient processing) in response to word stimuli in 8-year-olds. Dysmorphic physical features have been noted in some samples of prenatally exposed children. Aggression at age 5 years has also been related to prenatal cocaine exposure. Overall, the effect sizes in most studies are small, and interpretation of the degree of effect must always keep this point in mind.

Fewer follow-up studies exist for examination of opiates and methamphetamine. Neonatal abstinence syndrome has been clinically recognized for some time in response to 'withdrawal' of opiates in newborns of mothers who were chronic users. Most of what we know about later development, however, comes from follow-up of children whose mothers used methadone during pregnancy. A related issue historically was the effect of opiate medications used during labor, which is less relevant given current labor and delivery practice. Methamphetamine, on the other hand, has only recently been a focus of those interested in the effects of prenatal exposure.

With regard to opiate exposure, effects on behavior are observed in newborns and in the first years of life. As noted above, neonatal abstinence syndrome, affecting autonomic, gastrointestinal, and respiratory functions, is widely observed, although dose–response relationships are difficult to establish. Difficulties in the social–emotional realm may be present (e.g., disorganized attachment), but it may be the case that this is only true for those families with multiple contextual adversities. There is little evidence of generalized cognitive or motor deficits in opiate-exposed children. Methamphetamine exposure currently has a very small empirical knowledge base, as the first studies have been reported only in the past few years. There does, however, appear to be some indication of fetal growth restriction.

Some general issues in the substance-exposure literature are worth noting here. Most available work is focused on identifying effects of specific substances, in line with specific main-effects-type developmental models. This is the case despite the well-known phenomenon that pregnant women who use one of the licit or illicit substances reviewed here tend to use more than one. Thus, in the absence of the ability to conduct more rigidly controlled experiments, analyses of effects of single substances are almost always in the context of many other potential teratogens to which the developing fetus is exposed. Furthermore, as noted by Lester and Hans in separate commentaries in the past decade, there are also clear associations of broad contextual factors (poverty, racial/ethnic minority status) as well as more subtle lifestyle and parenting characteristics of the families in which the children are reared. Finally, it is also likely that the subtle exposure effects on children will themselves alter the developmental trajectories of the emergent parent–child relationship system.

Concluding Remarks

Several consistent themes emerge from a very diverse literature on teratogenic effects of prenatal (or early in life) exposure to a variety of substances:

- Exposures at high levels are associated with substantial developmental consequences for children, in some cases with distinct physical/behavioral syndromes.
- Exposures at low levels are far less clear cut – effects may not be present; when present, the effect sizes are small; the pattern of effects is inconsistent (across studies, or at different ages in longitudinal follow-ups of the same cohort); the functional significance of the effects may be small or nonexistent.
- Much of the focus has been on cognitive and motor performance, with less emphasis on social–emotional development.
- Investigation of multiple exposures is rare; when multiple exposures are identified, analysis tends to focus on untangling effects of individual substances.
- Exposures occur in larger social context that affects the developmental outcomes of interest – some studies address these issues well, but many do not.
- Complex developmental analyses are virtually nonexistent in this literature.

Given these general characteristics of the human behavioral teratology literature, we should remain cognizant that each set of scientific studies reviewed exist in a highly charged social and political context. On a general level, there are strong advocacy groups on both sides of the environmental pollutant debate, each of which would like to minimize or maximize the adverse developmental effects found in exposed children. The balance of economic development vs. small (and sometimes controversial) developmental effects is viewed differently on each side of this debate. In similar fashion, the literature on licit and illicit substance use (particularly in the US) exists in the framework of a declared war on drugs. Again, those concerned with eliminating drugs from the culture would have very different perspectives on research findings than those with a more *laissez faire* attitude. In other instances, the advocacy is very direct, with the issue of thiomersal exposure and neurodevelopmental problems being perhaps the best example. When science is conducted in these conditions, the end user of the science must be constantly vigilant for potential biases associated with promoting one's political or social views, need for funding, publication patterns, and degree of data mining to find results that satisfy either the publications biases or one's own scientific/social/political views.

To be more useful in the future, the field would benefit from several new or re-emphasized directions. These include examination of exposure in larger family and social context, application of more complex developmental models, examination of multiple exposures (particularly across boundaries where lines of investigation currently do not overlap), better reporting of nonsignificant findings (especially when samples are large enough to have low type II error), good meta-analyses to aggregate findings across studies, and interpretation of findings in the context of quality of life and cost-effectiveness models.

See also: Birth Defects; Endocrine System; Fetal Alcohol Spectrum Disorders; Lead Poisoning; Prenatal Care; Prenatal Development; Screening, Prenatal.

Suggested Readings

Abel EL (1998) Fetal alcohol syndrome: The 'American paradox'. *Alcohol and & Alcoholism* 33: 195–201.
Armstrong EM and Abel EL (2000) Fetal alcohol syndrome: The origins of moral panic. *Alcohol and Alcoholism* 35: 276–282.
Brown RT (2001) Behavioral teratology/toxicology: How do we know what we know? *Archives of Clinical Neuropsychology* 16: 389–402.
Dilworth-Bart JE and Moore CF (2006) Mercy mercy me: Social injustice and prevention of environmental pollutant exposures among ethnic minority and poor children. *Child Development* 77: 247–265.
Fraser S, Muckle G, and Despres C (2006) The relationship between lead exposure, motor function, and behavior in Inuit preschool children. *Neurotoxicology and Teratology* 28: 18–27.
Fried PA and Smith AM (2001) A literature review of the consequences of prenatal marihuana exposure: An emerging theme of a deficiency in aspects of executive function. *Neurotoxicology and Teratology* 23: 1–11.
Hans SL (2002) Studies of prenatal exposure to drugs focusing on parental care of children. *Neurotoxicology and Teratology* 24: 329–337.
Kaufman AS (2001) How dangerous are low (not moderate or high) doses of lead for children's intellectual development? *Archives of Clinical Neuropsychology* 16: 403–431.
Lester B, Lagasse L, and Seifer R (1998) Prenatal cocaine exposure: The meaning of subtle effects. *Science* 282: 633–634.
McCurry J (2006) Japan remembers Minamata. *Lancet* 367: 99–100.
Olds D (1997) Tobacco exposure and impaired development: A review of the evidence. *Mental Retardation and Developmental Disabilities Research Reviews* 3: 257–269.
Riley EP and Vorhees CV (1986) *Handbook of Behavioral Teratology.* New York: Plenum.
Sameroff AJ, Lewis M, and Miller SM (eds.) (2000) *Handbook of Developmental Psychopathology,* 2nd edn. New York: Plenum.
Testa M, Quigley BM, and Eiden RD (2003) The effects of prenatal alcohol exposure on infant mental development: A meta-analytical review. *Alcohol and Alcoholism* 38: 295–304.
Wachs TD (2000) *Necessary but not Sufficient: The Respective Roles of Single and Multiple Influences on Individual Development.* Washington, DC: American Psychological Association.
Wakschlag LS and Hans SL (2002) Maternal smoking during pregnancy and conduct problems in high-risk youth: A developmental framework. *Development and Psychopathology* 14: 351–369.

Theory of Mind

J W Astington and L A Dack, University of Toronto, Toronto, ON, Canada

Glossary

False-belief task – An experimental task that assesses young children's ability to attribute beliefs to others. Children are given different information about a situation – for example, an object is moved from one place to another, witnessed by child but not other, or a familiar container has some unexpected content seen by child but not other. Children are asked what the other will do, or think, or say. About 4 years of age they respond correctly by attributing to the other a belief that is different from their own, and false from their point of view.

Intentional causation – The idea that intentions are fulfilled only if a person's intention causes the action that brings about the outcome, despite the fact that one's desires may be fulfilled, however, the outcome is achieved.

Interpretive diversity – The understanding that two people may make different interpretations of the same external stimulus and that both interpretations may be legitimate.

Metarepresentational understanding – The ability to represent one's own and another person's different relationships to the same situation. Children who pass false-belief tasks demonstrate such metarepresentation, as they understand that another person will act on the basis of his or her mental representation, even when this is a misrepresentation of the actual situation in the world as represented by the child.

Modularity theory – The theoretical explanation of theory-of-mind development that proposes that theory of mind depends on maturation of a particular brain structure – an innate cognitive theory-of-mind module. While experience might be required as a trigger, the module will not be modified in differential ways by different experiences.
Simulation theory – The theoretical explanation of theory-of-mind development that proposes that mental-state concepts are derived from children's own direct experience of such states. The theory says that children can understand other people's behavior through a process like pretence. They can imagine having the beliefs and desires that the other person has, and imagine what they themselves would do if they possessed those imagined beliefs and desires.
Theory of mind – People's understanding of themselves and others as psychological beings, whose beliefs, desires, intentions, and emotions differ. Theory of mind underlies the ability to understand human behavior, as people explain their own actions, as well as attempt to interpret and predict other people's actions, by considering mental states.
Theory–theory – The theoretical explanation of theory-of-mind development that proposes that children's theory of mind develops via a process of theory construction and change, analogous to construction and change in scientific theorizing. With this view, children construct a theory about the mind, whereby their concepts of mental states are abstract and unobservable theoretical postulates used to explain and predict observable human behavior.

Introduction

Theory-of-mind research investigates children's understanding of people as mental beings, who have beliefs, desires, emotions, and intentions, and whose actions and interactions can be interpreted and explained by taking account of these mental states. Children's understanding of mental life was first investigated by Jean Piaget early in the last century and it has been of interest to psychologists ever since, for example, in studies of perspective taking and metacognition. However, recent years have seen an explosion of research in the area and given it a new name: theory of mind.

What is a Theory of Mind?

Developmental psychologists often refer to children's theories of different domains – for example, physics or biology – by which they mean that children have an integrated set of concepts underlying their understanding of how things work in a particular domain. The characteristics of theories in general and theory of mind in particular are shown in **Table 1**.

Table 1 Characteristics of theories and theory of mind

Theories	*Theory of mind*
Make ontological distinctions and define a domain	Distinguishes between mental and real and defines mental world
Coherent set of inter-related concepts	Concepts of mental states: belief, desire, intention, emotion, etc.
Underlie explanations and predictions within the domain	Explains, predicts, and interprets human behavior
Change in light of counter-evidence to predictions	Changes and develops throughout childhood, especially early childhood

Theory of Mind

Children's theory of mind underlies their ability to understand human behavior. It is called a theory of mind rather than a theory of behavior because much of people's behavior depends on what goes on in their minds. We explain our own actions by referring to our beliefs, desires, and other mental states, and we attempt to interpret and predict other people's actions by considering their mental states. Such mentalistic explanations, interpretations, and predictions of human behavior are fundamental to social interaction. Theory of mind is therefore an important part of social understanding or social cognition.

The term theory of mind might seem to portray children as little psychologists or philosophers but this is not what is intended – children do not hold the theory explicitly as a psychologist or philosopher would. They cannot articulate their theory of mind, but rather we have to infer it from what they say and do in naturalistic and experimental situations. Both are required because the natural setting shows the child's abilities as an interacting participant within the social world, whereas the experimental setting allows for more control, in order to reveal the precise level of the child's own understanding.

However, the fact that theory of mind is inferred from behavior leads to the vexing question of whether the child 'has' a theory of mind in a first-person sense or whether it is merely a third-person ascription. That is, is theory of mind a psychologically real structure underlying the child's behavior or is it merely a way of describing the child's behavior – as if it were guided by a theory of mind? It may be that only verbal self-ascription can provide unequivocal evidence for theory of mind in a first-person sense but this is not possible for preverbal children or nonhuman primates.

It is worth noting that the term first entered the developmental literature after it had been applied to nonhuman primates in a landmark article by David Premack and Guy Woodruff entitled, 'Does the chimpanzee have a theory of mind?' These researchers reported that they had shown a chimpanzee videotapes, in which a man was faced with a problem (e.g., trying to get bananas that were hung out of his reach) and the animal then had to choose between two photographs, one of which depicted the solution to the problem (e.g., the man standing on a box). The animal chose the correct photograph significantly more often than the other one. The researchers claimed that this demonstrated that chimpanzees have a theory of mind, which they defined as a system of inferences about mental states that can be used to make predictions about behavior (e.g., the man 'wants' bananas and so he will stand on a box to get them).

The focus of Premack and Woodruff's study was on the animal's recognition of the man's desire or intention. However, other researchers' commentaries on the article made it clear that the critical inference revealing theory of mind is the attribution of belief – in particular, in a case where observer and observed have different beliefs about a situation. Only in this case can one be certain that the observer is actually attributing a mental state to the observed and not merely responding as he himself (or she herself) would do in the same situation.

Understanding False Belief

The commentaries on Premack and Woodruff's article led two Austrian psychologists, Heinz Wimmer and Josef Perner, to develop the 'false-belief task', which assesses whether children have a theory of mind in the Premack and Woodruff sense. That is, it shows whether a child can make inferences about mental states, in order to predict behavior. In the task, children are told a story that the experimenter acts out with toy figures and props. A character in the story has a false belief about a situation and the child has to predict what that character will do (see **Table 2**).

At the end of the story children are asked a question about the character's subsequent action, which in this example is: 'Where will Maxi look for the chocolate?'

Table 2 Example of a 'false-belief' story

Mother returns from a shopping trip with some chocolate. Her little boy, Maxi, puts the chocolate away in the cupboard. Then he goes outside to play. Mother takes the chocolate from the cupboard and uses some to make a cake. Then she puts the remaining chocolate away in a drawer, not in the cupboard, and goes upstairs. Maxi then comes back inside, hungry and wanting some chocolate.

They are also asked where he put it and where it is now. Numerous studies have shown that children of about 4 years of age and older say that Maxi will look where he put it, in the cupboard. However, younger children say that he will look in the drawer where the chocolate now is, even though they remember where he put it at the beginning of the story.

The catch is that children have to recognize that the story character's belief about the location of the chocolate is different from their own. That is to say, this is one of those cases where the observer (the child) and the observed (Maxi, the boy in the story) have different beliefs about a situation. Children can respond correctly only by attributing to the boy a belief that is different from their own, and false from their point of view. They further have to recognize that the boy's belief is what guides his actions, even though it is false.

This simple demonstration reveals a most important aspect of theory of mind. Children who can correctly predict that the boy would look for the chocolate in the cupboard understand that people act not on the basis of the way things actually are in the world but on the basis of the way they 'think' that they are. That is, successful performance on the false-belief task demonstrates an understanding of the idea that people's relationship to the world is mediated by their mental representation of it. Children who pass the false-belief task understand that the world is represented in mind and that people act on the basis of their mental representation even when this is a misrepresentation of the actual situation in the world. To be precise, they are capable of 'metarepresentation' – that is, they not only represent a situation but they can also represent their own and another person's different relationships to this situation. Expressing it this way draws on a philosophical work on the representational theory of mental states, which has informed research on children's theory of mind and which is briefly described in the following section.

Mental Representation

Mental states such as beliefs and desires are representations that mediate our activity in the world. They are also referred to as 'intentional' states, not with the everyday meaning of 'deliberate' or 'on purpose' but with a technical meaning from the philosophical literature: 'aboutness'. Intentional states are always 'about' something. One does not just have a belief, for example, but rather one has a belief about something – this is the content, or propositional content, of the intentional state. Such states are often described as attitudes to propositions. That is, a person has a certain attitude toward the propositional content – such as holding it to be true or wanting it to happen – and this attitude denotes what type of mental state it is, as shown in **Table 3**.

A person can hold different attitudes to the same propositional content, resulting in different mental states. For example, the boy can 'believe' the chocolate is in the cupboard, 'hope' the chocolate is in the cupboard, 'want' the chocolate to be in the cupboard, and so on.

Beliefs and Desires: Truth and Fulfillment

There is obviously a difference between believing something to be true and wanting something to be the case, even when the propositional content of the belief and the desire are the same. This difference is due to a difference in the nature of the representational relation. There are two basic types of relation, characterized by truth/falsity or by fulfillment/unfulfillment, as shown in **Table 4**.

Belief-type states are true or false, whereas desire-type states are fulfilled or unfulfilled. If the propositional content of a belief corresponds to the way things actually are in the world, then the belief is true. If it does not correspond, then it is false. If it is false, it can be made true by changing the belief – by making the mind fit the world. This is described as a mind-to-world 'direction of fit'.

Desires (and also intentions) are different from beliefs because they are neither true nor false. They are fulfilled or unfulfilled. If the propositional content of a desire does not correspond to the way things actually are in the world, then the desire is unfulfilled. However, it cannot be fulfilled by changing the desire. In order to fulfill the desire, things in the world have to change to fit the representation that is held in mind. That is, desires and intentions have a world-to-mind direction of fit.

Predicting and Explaining Behavior

As mentioned, theory of mind is used to explain and predict human behavior. The basic premise is that actions are produced by desire and belief in combination (**Figure 1**).

Table 3 Examples of intentional states

Attitude (type of mental state)	*Propositional content (what it is about)*
Believe	Chocolate is in cupboard
Want	Eat some chocolate
Intend	Open the cupboard

Table 4 Two basic types of intentional state

Beliefs	*Desires and intentions*
True or false	Fulfilled or unfulfilled
Caused by events in the world	Bring about changes in the world
Changed to fit the world: 'mind-to-world' direction of fit	World has to change to fit them: 'world-to-mind' direction of fit

That is, people act to fulfill their desires in light of their beliefs. This is why false beliefs lead to misguided actions. If a person's belief and desire are known, one can predict how the person will act (as in the false-belief task). Alternatively, if the desire is known, a misguided action can be explained by attributing a false belief to the person.

In fact, intentions are mediators between desires and actions. If someone desires something they may form an intention to obtain it, which causes them to act in a way that will lead to fulfillment of the desire (**Figure 2**).

That is, a desired outcome can be achieved through the action of a person whose intention causes the action. Actually, desires may be fulfilled however the outcome is achieved (the dotted line in **Figure 2**) but, importantly, intentions are fulfilled only if the person's intention causes the action that brings about the outcome. This is known as intentional causation.

Development of Theory of Mind

The ability to explain and predict human behavior using concepts of false belief and intentional causation typically develops toward the end of the preschool years. However, children's first awareness of mental life begins much earlier. There is, indeed, no single moment when children acquire a theory of mind. On the contrary, their understanding changes and develops from infancy on into the school years, so that perhaps it would be better to refer to children's theories (rather than theory) of mind. **Table 5**

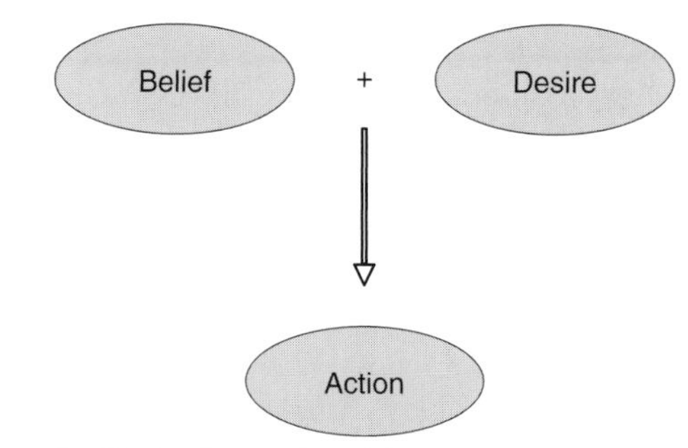

Figure 1 The basic premise of theory of mind.

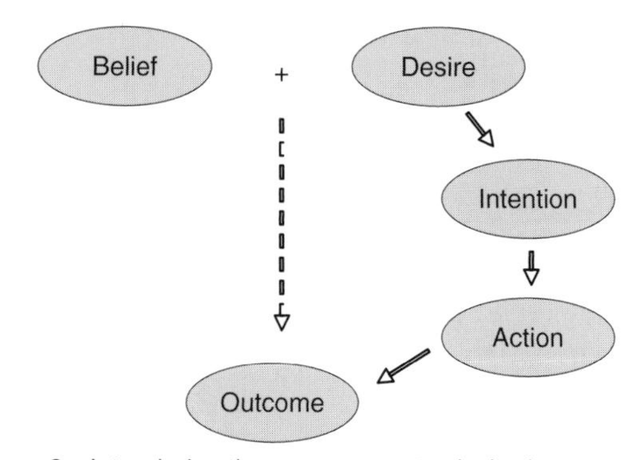

Figure 2 Intended actions are means to desired outcomes.

Table 5 Development of theory of mind

Period	*Age range*	*Major development*
Infancy	Birth–18 months	Social perception
Toddler and early preschool	18-month-olds to 3-year-olds	Mental-state awareness
Preschool	4- and 5-year-olds	Metarepresentation
School age	6 years onwards	Recursion and Interpretation

highlights the major development occuring at each of the stages which are described in the following sections.

Social Perception in Infancy

When Premack and Woodruff asked, "Does the chimpanzee have a theory of mind?" they took it for granted that human beings do. Their definition of theory of mind – a system of inferences about mental states that can be used to make predictions about behavior – was taken up by developmental psychologists and the question became: "When does the child acquire a theory of mind?" Inge Bretherton and colleagues gave one of the first answers, arguing that infants' ability to engage in intentional communication implies that they have a theory of mind, at least an implicit and rudimentary one. However, most theory-of-mind research during the 1980s focused on preschool children's success on the false-belief task as providing evidence for theory of mind. It is only more recently that there has been much investigation of developments during the infancy period that may underlie theory of mind. This is now a burgeoning area of research.

It is obvious that even young infants 'have' beliefs, desires, and intentions (e.g., they become upset when their desires are frustrated or show surprise when their expectations are unrealized) but this is different from having 'awareness' of belief, desire, and intention, and attributing such states to others. It is the latter that is theory of mind, and it is debatable whether theory of mind in this sense is developed during infancy. However, infants do have some important precursors to theory of mind.

From birth, infants are interested in other people and prefer social over nonsocial stimuli. They attend to human faces and voices more than to nonhuman sights and sounds and they can soon discriminate the mother's face and voice from those of others. Infants can also imitate human facial movements from very early in life. Even newborns can imitate – for example, by protruding their tongue in response to an adult's tongue protrusion. Infants only see the other's face and only feel their own response yet, in some way, they can connect the visible bodily actions of the other with their own internal state, thus demonstrating that they can match their own actions to those of another individual. This ability – referred to as 'cross-modal matching' – shows that infants can make a connection between self and other, at least at some primitive level, which is important because the similarity between self and other is at the heart of theory of mind.

Infants soon begin to participate in social interactions with those around them. Around 2 months of age they start to interact by smiling and vocalizing (e.g., cooing and, later, babbling). At first these interactions are dyadic, in that only two participants – infant and adult – are involved. However, around 9 months of age triadic interactions appear, in which both participants are focused on the same object. For example, the infant and adult may engage in turn-taking with a toy, continuously switching their focus between each other and the toy. Such 'joint attention', which is the ability to coordinate attention with others by following gaze or pointing gestures, is a major feature of infant social behavior. It is more than just looking at the same thing but involves mutual awareness (at some level) that both are engaged with the same object. Between 9 and 12 months of age, infants develop the ability to follow an adult's eye gaze or an adult's point even to objects not in their line of sight. Also, if the adult points or gazes and there is no evident object of attention, the infant will look to the adult, as if checking back. Likewise, when infants point, they will look toward the adult as well as toward the object to monitor the other's attention.

At this stage infants also begin to engage in social referencing, in which they look to an adult (often their mother) when they are unsure how to react in an ambiguous situation and then respond in accord with her positive or negative emotional expression. Social referencing is triadic, in that infants are able to respond to their mother's reaction to an object.

Dishabituation experiments, in which infants look longer at a novel stimulus than one seen earlier, are used to demonstrate their sensitivity to mental states. Findings show that infants can distinguish between agents (that have goals) and inanimate objects (that do not). They are more sensitive to the goals of an action than to the physical movements involved. They understand actions as goal-directed and linked to perceptions/emotions. They are also more sensitive to interruptions in action that occur before a goal is achieved than to interruptions occurring as the goal is achieved. They also respond differentially based on knowledge states of the agent.

In sum, infants have many abilities relevant to social understanding (see **Table 6**).

These early developing behaviors may be referred to as social perception, social intuition, person perception, intersubjectivity, or even 'early' or 'implicit' theory of mind – but, the latter is controversial. Although there is general agreement on the behavioral findings, there is

Table 6 Theory of mind in infancy

Social perception in infancy, from birth to 8 months of age
Characteristic behaviors and abilities • Imitation • Dyadic smiling and vocalizing • Joint attention: Follow other's pointing and gaze Direct other's attention with point and gaze Social referencing • Discriminate animates from inanimates • Discriminate goals from movements • Sensitive to agents knowledge state

much disagreement over their interpretation. The debate centers on whether the appropriate level of analysis is behavioral or mental. That is, some researchers maintain that infants are merely able to detect statistical regularities in behavior, whereas others claim that infants understand the subjective nature of psychological experience – that is, they are aware of other people as intentional agents, whose behavior is governed by goals and perceptions. Yet other researchers argue that this is a false dichotomy and that interpersonal perception only later splits into separable bodily and mental aspects. Although this debate is not yet resolved, it is clear that infants display behaviors that are relevant to theory of mind. Certainly, social perception is not supplanted by later-developing aspects of theory of mind but rather it continues to exist and underpins the complexities of social understanding right on into adulthood.

Mental-State Awareness in Toddlers and Young Preschoolers

Important changes come at about 18 months of age, when children clearly begin to show awareness of the subjective nature of psychological experience. This depends on their ability to think about more than what is directly perceived. Although infants think about things in the world, they do not think of alternative possible worlds. Around the middle of the second year, children can think and talk about absent and hypothetical situations. This is seen in Piagetian sensorimotor stage 6 behaviors, such as, finding invisibly displaced objects, and solving problems by insight. It is also revealed as language develops – toddlers can talk about past and future events and things out of sight or only imagined. For example, a child building a tower out of blocks may say 'uh-oh' as the tower collapses. This use of 'uh-oh' indicates the discrepancy between what the child imagined would happen and what actually happened. What is important is that the child is able to think of the hypothetical and compare it with the reality.

The ability to imagine a possible alternative reality is also seen – perhaps best seen – in young children's pretend play, which begins to develop at about 18 months of age. Through pretend play (e.g., pretending that a banana is a telephone), toddlers show that they can distinguish between the object – the banana – and thoughts about the object – the banana as a telephone.

The ability to distinguish between objects and thoughts about them can also be demonstrated in experimental tasks. For example, 3-year-olds can tell the difference between a boy who is thinking about a cookie, and a boy who has got a cookie. That is, they know which boy can see, touch, share, or eat the cookie. They know that people's thoughts are private, they cannot be seen or touched, and sometimes, as mental images, for example, they can be made to come and go at will.

Toddlers' awareness of the subjective nature of psychological experience is also seen in their recognition of people's intentions and desires. For example, 18-month-olds can use the direction of a speaker's gaze to infer the referent of a novel word. When adults are labeling objects, they understand that the word the adult is using refers to the object the adult is currently looking at, not the one they themselves happen to be looking at. That is, children of this age clearly attribute communicative intentions to the other person. They can also recognize intention in an adult's behavior. For example, if 18-month-old infants watch an individual attempt to perform a task but fail (e.g., attempt to push a button with a stick, but miss the button) and are then given the opportunity to handle the objects themselves, they will demonstrate the intended task, rather than imitate the way in which the other person failed (i.e., the infant will push the button with the stick). That is, they are aware of what someone wants to achieve.

Also at this age, children can recognize that there may be a difference between what they want and what another person wants. For example, if an experimenter shows pleasure toward one food and disgust toward the other, 18-month-old infants understand that they should give her the one toward which she showed pleasure, even if they themselves prefer the other food. Three-year-olds are able to reason more explicitly about desires and emotions. For example, if they are told what a story character wants, they are able to predict what the character will do to fulfill this desire. Further, they can predict the character's emotion based on whether or not the desire is fulfilled. That is, they understand that people will feel happy when they get what they want and will feel sad when they do not.

During this period children also begin to show some understanding of how people get to know things. For example, 2-year-olds know that in showing something, they have to orient it toward the person. Two-year-olds also take account of people's knowledge states when asking others for assistance, in that they will give more information to someone who is ignorant about the situation. Three-year-olds understand that if an object is

Table 7 Theory of mind in toddler and early preschool period

Mental-state awarness, 18-month-olds to 3-year-olds
Characteristic behaviors and abilities • Distinguish between mental and real • Pretend play • Aware of intentions, desires, and emotions • Desire-based reasoning • Aware of perception and knowledge acquisition • Use mental-state terms

hidden inside a box, only those who have looked inside the box will know what is inside.

A developing awareness of mental states is seen in children's language too. Around 2 years of age, children start to talk about what people 'want' and 'like' and 'feel'. They produce explicit contrasts – distinguishing between what they want and what another person wants, or between what they wanted and what they got or what happened. Toddlers also talk about emotions, using terms like 'happy, sad, mad', and so on. When they are 3 years of age they also talk about what people 'think' and 'know'.

In sum, it is clear that 3-year-olds are aware of the subjective nature of psychological experience (see **Table 7**). They know that there is a difference between thoughts in the mind and things in the world; they are aware of people's wants, feelings, perceptions, and knowledge; and they use mental-state terms in their talk.

There is more to theory of mind, however, than being aware of mental states and reasoning about action based on desire. As mentioned earlier, mental states are representations that mediate our activity in the world. The two basic types of mental state – desires and beliefs – differ in the nature of the representational relation. Desire-type states are characterized by fulfillment/unfulfillment, whereas belief-type states are characterized by truth/falsity. Three-year-olds understand that people act to fulfill their desires and they are able to use information about a person's desire to explain or predict actions or emotions. However, 3-year-olds do not understand truth and falsity; therefore, they cannot take into account that people act to fulfill their desires in light of their beliefs even when they are mistaken (recall 3-year-olds' failure on the false-belief task described in an earlier section).

Metarepresentational Ability in Older Preschoolers

Understanding truth and falsity and taking false beliefs into account in predicting action depend on the development of metarepresentational understanding. This is the understanding that people's beliefs, desires, and intentions are mental representations that mediate their actions in the world and their interactions with others in the world. Children with this understanding think of beliefs, desires, and intentions as representations that are produced by the mind as a result of certain experiences and that effect actions in the world in certain specific ways. They have the ability to represent their own and another person's different relationships to the same situation – as clearly demonstrated in successful performance on the false-belief task.

Children's understanding of false belief is undoubtedly the most striking and most studied aspect of their theory of mind. As described earlier, this research began in the early 1980s with the task devised by Heinz Wimmer and Josef Perner, in which a story is acted out for children. A character in the story is off the scene when an object that he has left in one location is moved to a different place. The character therefore has a false belief about the object's location. When he returns to the scene, children are asked where he will look for the object or where he thinks it is. By 4 or 5 years of age, children recognize that the character's representation of the situation is different from their own and they can predict the character's action based on his false belief.

One criticism of this 'change-of-location' false-belief task is that children have to follow a complicated story narrative and have to attribute beliefs to dolls. Researchers attempted to make false belief easier for 3-year-olds, by letting children actually experience a false belief themselves, and then asking them about another person's belief in the same situation. For example, they showed children a familiar candy box, all closed up, and then let them find out that it contained pencils, not candy. Then they put the pencils back and asked what another person, who had not seen inside the box, would think was inside it. Most 3-year-olds claimed that the other person would think there were pencils in the box but by 4 or 5 years of age children realized that the other person would think as they themselves had done, that it had candy inside. That is, they could represent and distinguish between their own and another's different relationships to the same situation.

The traditional Piagetian explanation of 3-year-olds' failure on this 'unexpected-contents' false-belief task is that such young children are egocentric and thus cannot understand that other people may have beliefs different from their own. However, 3-year-olds' lack of understanding is more profound. In this experiment, children were also asked what they themselves had thought was in the box before it was opened. Three-year-olds found it as difficult to remember their own previous false belief as to predict the other person's false belief. They could not metarepresent, that is, they could not represent themselves as representing both the past and the present situations and see that what was true for them in the past was false for them in the present.

Children's performance on these types of false-belief task is an extremely robust, much-replicated finding.

In fact, a recent meta-analysis determined that there were no age differences in children's ability to attribute false beliefs to others or to themselves in the past. In addition, children's success did not differ based on the experimental procedures used, for example, the change-in-location-story task or the unexpected-contents-box task. These meta-analytic findings support the argument that there is a genuine conceptual change – that is, the development of metarepresentational understanding – underlying performance on different types of false-belief task.

The development of metarepresentational understanding is associated with the development of a number of other behaviors and abilities. False-belief task performance correlates with children's recognition of the relative certainty implied by use of the term 'know' over 'think' or 'guess'. In addition, since deception is the intentional creation of false beliefs, once children understand false belief, they are able to understand deception and to act deceptively or to tell lies. Some researchers claim that there is evidence for deception and lying earlier, before children understand false belief, but this is controversial. It may be that younger children act intentionally in ways that affect others' beliefs even though that may not be their motive in so acting – rather, they may just want to affect what the other person will do.

Metarepresentational ability also underlies children's understanding of the distinction between appearance and reality. For example, children are shown a piece of painted sponge that looks just like a rock, and then they squeeze it and discover that it is really a sponge. Once they know it is a sponge, 3-year-olds say that it looks like a sponge, but by 4 or 5 years of age children understand that its appearance is misleading – it looks like a rock but it is really a sponge.

At this age children also come to understand aspects of knowledge acquisition. They realize that information comes from different sources, that is, beliefs are derived from perception (e.g., feeling or seeing) or from communication (e.g., being told). They can remember the source of their own information and they remember, if they have just learned something new, that they did not know it previously. By 4 or 5 years of age, children also understand that different sensory modalities yield different kinds of information, for example, seeing gives information about color, whereas touching gives information about texture.

The development of metarepresentational ability also allows for a new understanding of desire and intention. Recall that intentions are mediators between desires and actions – although a desire may be fulfilled however the outcome is achieved, intentions are fulfilled only if the person's intention causes the action that brings about the outcome (intentional causation). As discussed earlier, toddlers have some understanding of desire and intention but they may think of both as mental states that motivate actions and outcomes, without distinguishing between the two types of state. Metarepresentational ability allows them to differentiate between desire and intention and to recognize cases of fortuitous success – in which the desire is satisfied even though the intention is unfulfilled. This ability also allows children to understand cases where two people's desires are in conflict, that is, situations where the satisfaction of one person's desire necessarily means that the other person's desire is not satisfied.

Table 8 Theory of mind in older preschool period

Metarepresentational ability, 4- and 5-year-olds
Characteristic behaviors and abilities • Understand false belief in self and others • Understand deception • Distinguish appearance and reality • Understand aspects of knowledge acquisition • Distinguish between desire and intention • Understand intentional causation • Understand belief-based emotions

Emotional understanding continues to develop in 4- and 5-year-olds. In particular, toward the end of this period, children can make belief-based emotion attributions, for which they have to assess whether characters believe their desires will be fulfilled, not simply whether the desires will be fulfilled. Children also come to understand the distinction between appearance and reality in the emotional realm. For instance, they recognize that people might feign happiness even when they are sad, for example, because their desires are unfulfilled.

In sum, the development of metarepresentational ability in the later preschool period underlies a range of new behaviors and abilities that become apparent during this period (see **Table 8**).

Once metarepresentation is clearly established, children reach a new level of understanding of social interactions – including surprises, secrets, tricks, and lies. Of course, there are further developments in social cognition after the preschool years, which can be construed as further development in theory of mind, although research on social cognition during the school-age years has been less specifically focused on theory of mind.

Recursive and Interpretive Abilities in School-age Children

One of the main developments in theory of mind at the beginning of the school years is an understanding of mental-state recursion, that is, the embedding of one mental state in another (e.g., 'Mother thinks that Maxi thinks that the chocolate is in the cupboard'). Children become aware that people have beliefs, not just about the world, but about the content of others' minds (e.g., about others' beliefs) and, like people's beliefs about the world, these too may be different or wrong. Such beliefs about beliefs are referred to as second-order beliefs. Tasks designed to assess children's second-order false-belief understanding show that it develops by about 7 years of age. Somewhat earlier, children acquire the ability to understand second-order representations involving desires and intentions, such as understanding that someone wants to make another person believe something. Somewhat later, children acquire the ability to deal with third-order representations involving beliefs, desires, intentions, and emotions (e.g., 'Mother wants Maxi to think that she intended to hide the chocolate' or 'Mother thinks that Maxi wants her to know that he could not find the chocolate').

Such recursive ability underlies the more mature understanding and use of complex language, particularly indirect speech acts, such as irony and metaphor, that develop during the school-age years. In indirect speech there is a distinction between what a person means and what their words appear to mean; that is, what is actually said is not really what is meant. In verbal irony, for example, someone says something that is false but does not intend the listener to believe it to be true, but rather to recognize the falsity and interpret the statement as funny or sarcastic. Likewise, metaphors are not intended as statements to be literally interpreted but are used to create poetic images. Children's understanding of irony and metaphor begins to develop during the early school years, although it takes some years to reach maturity.

The ability to comprehend recursive mental states also underlies an increasing sensitivity to the interpersonal dynamics of social situations. For example, during the early school years children come to understand 'white lies' where something untrue is said to protect a person's feelings. They also recognize when someone has produced a 'faux pas' and unintentionally revealed secret information or created hurt feelings. As well, they can invent or select persuasive strategies, which require the manipulation of a person's mental states in order to get them to believe or do something. Children's use of language during the school-age years also reflects their more sophisticated understanding of the mind, as children begin to comprehend and produce more complex mental-state terms, such as 'interpret', 'infer', 'doubt', and many more.

Other developments in the early school years involve increasing understanding of knowledge acquisition and of the mind as an active interpreter of information. For example, around 7 years of age children recognize interpretive diversity, that is, they understand that even given the same external stimulus, two people may make legitimate but different interpretations of it, which requires more than understanding the possibility of true vs. false beliefs. Also by age 7 years, children come to understand the role of inference in knowledge acquisition and to recognize ambiguity and referential opacity. Children of this age also have a simple understanding of evidence for belief and can distinguish between the cause of a phenomenon and a person's reason for believing it. This allows them to engage in scientific reasoning by evaluating evidence.

Understanding the mind as an interpreter of information is related to understanding the dynamic nature of mental activity. Until the early school years, children are unaware of the stream of consciousness that fills the waking mind and they are not able to introspect about their own thinking. Preschool children can report the content of their mental states – but without recognizing that it is produced by the mind's activity. Participation in formal school activities may facilitate children's introspective abilities. Indeed, the investigation of a number of metacognitive abilities that are demonstrated in school tasks, such as metamemory and comprehension monitoring, began during the 1970s, before the explosion of research into children's theory of mind. Undeniably, although such metacognitive abilities, as well as the social cognitive abilities described earlier in this section, can be interpreted in the framework of children's theory of mind, it is fair to say that much of the research predates the theory-of-mind field and even now is conducted somewhat independently of it (**Table 9**).

Table 9 Theory of mind in school-age children

Recursive and interpretive abilities, 6 years and older
Characteristic behaviors and abilities
• Understand second- and higher-order mental states
• Recognize interpretive diversity
• Understand indirect speech, for example, irony and metaphor
• Aware of white lies, faux pas, and persuasion
• Use and comprehend complex mental-state terms
• Understand inference, ambiguity, referential opacity
• Aware of stream of consciousness, introspect

Differences in Development

The preceding section provides an overview of typical development of theory of mind from infancy through the early school years. Although approximate age norms are given, there are marked individual differences in typical development. In addition, there are variations in development in atypical populations. Furthermore, the overview is derived from research conducted primarily with samples of middle-class, Western children – however, theory-of-mind development may not be universally the same across cultures. Therefore we need to consider individual differences in typical development, diverse atypical developments, and cultural differences in theory of mind.

Individual Differences

The main focus of research so far has been on examining factors, both within the child and in the child's environment, that are associated with the development of false-belief understanding, which some children achieve soon after they are 3 years of age and others not until age 5 years. A number of factors, such as executive functioning, language ability, and social competence, are correlated with the understanding of false belief – both contemporaneously and across time in longitudinal studies. The causal or consequential nature of such earlier or later correlates is a matter of some debate, requiring careful consideration.

Executive functioning. Executive functions are self-regulatory cognitive processes, such as inhibition, planning, resistance to interference, and control of attention and motor responses. During the years from 3 to 5, children's performance on executive function tasks is correlated with their performance on false-belief tasks. This may be because executive function tasks require suppression of a habitual response in favor of a new response and, likewise, in standard false-belief tasks children must resist making the more salient (incorrect) response. This suggests that there are executive functioning demands embedded within false-belief tasks. However, most researchers believe that the relation between theory of mind and executive function extends beyond the fact that false-belief tasks require inhibition. Some argue that executive functioning is actually required for children to develop a theory of mind, in that children must be able to control their own representations of the world before understanding others' representations. Others argue that the relation is in the opposite direction, in that children must understand mental states before they are able to control their own actions. Yet a third group propose that the relation between theory of mind and executive function is due to the acquisition of the general ability to reason about complex problems relating to selective attention. In turn, this ability improves performance on both false-belief and executive function tasks.

Fantasy and pretense. Pretend play is a context in which children can simulate feelings and desires they do not currently hold and imagine states of the world that do not currently exist. Researchers argue that pretend play encourages theory-of-mind development and this is supported by data showing that preschoolers who score higher on theory-of-mind tasks engage in more fantasy and pretense. There is also evidence that acting out roles in pretend play precedes and supports false-belief understanding, whereas explicit assignment of roles and plans for joint action in pretend play follow and result from false-belief understanding.

Language ability. It is well established that there is a strong relation between language ability and theory-of-mind development that is independent of age. In 9- to 15-month olds, joint attention behaviors are correlated with language production and comprehension and may be instrumental in language development at this stage. Subsequently, many studies have shown relations between false-belief understanding and various language skills, including general language, receptive vocabulary, semantics, and syntax. Moreover, it is likely that there is a causal relation involved such that children's linguistic development supports their theory-of-mind development at this later stage. Longitudinal studies show that changes in children's false-belief understanding are predicted by their language competence but the reciprocal relation (i.e., prediction of language development by false-belief test scores) is much weaker. It is not likely that the verbal requirements of false-belief tasks can alone explain these findings since the correlations are found for a wide range of theory-of-mind measures, some less verbal than others.

The role of language in the development of theory of mind is complex, reflecting the multifaceted nature of language, which includes pragmatics, semantics, and syntax. Pragmatic ability allows children to participate in communicative exchanges, where they hear mental terms used in complex syntactic structures. From this experience they acquire awareness of different points of view, concepts of mental states, and mastery of the syntax for representing false beliefs. Both the social environment that provides this input and the child's own cognitive resources that make use of it are needed for the child's theory of mind to develop.

Family environment. A number of studies show that the kind of conversational experiences that children have is related to theory-of-mind development. In particular, children whose mothers use more mental terms in their conversations acquire false-belief understanding at an earlier age than children whose mothers use fewer such terms, even when the children's own language ability is taken into account. However, it is certainly possible that it is not the use of mental-state terms in particular that is important for children's understanding of the mind, but rather, that use of mental-state terms is an easily countable measure that is likely to be found in mothers who also tend to introduce varying points of view into conversations with their children. In addition, both parenting style and disciplinary strategy are associated with children's false-belief understanding. As might be expected, children whose parents explain and discuss, rather than only punish unacceptable behavior, score more highly on false-belief tasks.

Children from larger families develop false-belief understanding sooner. Perhaps this is because they have more experience of tricks, jokes, and teasing among their siblings, or perhaps because they are more exposed to talk about thoughts and wants as parents try to settle disputes among the children. Other studies have shown a similar effect for children who interact with more adults and who interact with older children including both siblings and peers. The relation between family size and performance on theory-of-mind tasks is stronger in the case of children with poorer language skills. This means that children with poor linguistic competence can acquire an understanding of false belief through social interaction with siblings in their home.

Evidence from the attachment literature also demonstrates the importance of the family environment and parenting style to theory-of-mind development. Children who are classified as having secure maternal attachments in infancy develop false-belief understanding at an earlier age than children with less secure attachments. Some researchers argue that mothers' 'mind-mindedness', that is, their propensity to treat their infants as individuals with minds, is an important factor in determining attachment security, as well as underlying their children's developing awareness of other minds.

Social competence. One might expect that children's developing theory of mind would be related to their social competence – that is, children's awareness of others' mental states should have consequences for their relationships with others and for their social behavior in general. And indeed, research shows that individual differences in false-belief understanding are associated with actual differences in behavior in the social world. These behaviors are: communication abilities, as seen in more connected and more informative conversation; imaginative abilities, as seen in more frequent and more sophisticated pretend play; ability to resolve conflicts and to maintain harmony and intimacy in friendships; teacher ratings of global social competence; happiness in school; and peer-rated empathy and popularity. Importantly, in most if not all cases, the relations with false-belief understanding are independent of age and language ability. Conversely, preschoolers who are rejected by their peers and who do not have stable friendships tend to perform more poorly on theory-of-mind tasks. However, the directionality of this finding is not known. It is possible that these children's low scores on theory-of-mind tasks are due to their limited opportunities to engage in pretend play and the use of shared mental states with other children. On the other hand, it is possible that these children's lack of social understanding weakens their ability to develop friendships and gain acceptance from peers. Either way, children with a better understanding of false belief tend to be more successful in their social relationships.

However, theory-of-mind understanding is also related to children's antisocial behavior. For example, children who are bullies have sophisticated theory-of-mind abilities and the skill of manipulating other people's beliefs. As well, children who show a highly developed understanding of mental states tend to be better at lying. These paradoxical findings of the effects of theory of mind on social behavior have led some researchers to suggest that the concept of theory of mind be separated into 'nice theory of mind' (prosocial behavior requiring theory of mind) and 'nasty theory of mind' (antisocial behavior requiring theory of mind). In fact, research has suggested that these truly are distinct cognitive abilities. Yet the consequences of theory-of-mind development are perhaps most striking in their absence, suggested by studies of atypically developing populations.

Atypical Development

Autism. Children with autism show impairments in communication and social interaction. Because of these deficits, there has been intensive investigation of theory-of-mind development in autism. Although autism is not usually diagnosed until after 2 years of age, children at risk for autism do not show the typical joint attention behaviors of late infancy and do not engage in pretend play. Later in the preschool years, they do show some understanding of others' desires, although their ability lags behind that of typically developing children. Most striking, though, is their difficulty in understanding other people's beliefs, as shown in their performance on the false-belief task. Only about 20% of children with autism succeed on standard false-belief tasks. This finding has been replicated numerous times in many different studies. Children with autism also tend to fail theory-of-mind tasks that require deception and have difficulty understanding belief-based emotions.

As in typical development, autistic children's false-belief understanding is predicted by their language ability, perhaps to an even greater degree than for typically developing children. Notably, children with autism require far higher verbal mental age to pass false-belief tasks than typically developing children do. Some researchers suggest that high levels of language ability allow these children to pass false-belief tasks by working around their lack of intuitive social understanding. However, even with high levels of language ability, few individuals with autism develop the ability to understand second-order false beliefs and they have particular difficulty with nonliteral language use, such as sarcasm, irony, white lies, and metaphor.

One thing that is clear is that the difficulty that children with autism have in passing theory-of-mind tasks is not due to a lack of intelligence. Evidence for this comes from the fact that children with Down syndrome tend to be successful on false-belief tasks, despite the fact that their intelligence scores are, on average, significantly lower than those of individuals with autism.

Sensory impairments. Theory-of-mind development in children who are deaf differs depending on their family environment. Deaf children with hearing parents are delayed in their false-belief understanding, whereas deaf children with deaf parents are not. This is because, even though both groups of children engage in social interaction, the children with hearing parents are delayed in their acquisition of sign language, which again shows the important role of language in theory-of-mind development. Deaf children whose language development is delayed fail false-belief tasks even though the tasks are adapted to their mode of communication and they completely understand the basic story facts in the task. Furthermore, they find nonverbal theory-of-mind tasks just as difficult and their performance on such tasks is predicted by their level of language development.

Children who are blind cannot see facial expressions and gestures and tend to have delayed language development. These children too show delays in theory-of-mind development, particularly in understanding false belief. There are also studies indicating deviations from typical theory-of-mind development in children with cerebral palsy, Williams syndrome, and fragile X syndrome.

Behavior problems. A few studies have examined theory-of-mind development in children with behavior problems but the findings are somewhat inconsistent, with some studies suggesting a mix of enhanced and impaired performance on theory-of-mind tasks in 'hard to manage' preschoolers and others describing no deficit in theory-of-mind competence in school-age children with attention deficit hyperactivity disorder (ADHD).

Cultural Differences

Theory-of-mind development has been investigated primarily in middle-class children in North America, Europe, and Australasia. Most researchers assume that it is a universal development, or at least that there is a universal core to theory of mind that is acquired in the early years. In support of this idea, research shows that Chinese and Japanese children's theory-of-mind development is quite similar to that of Western children, with slight variations in timing and perhaps more emphasis on social roles in the explanation of behavior. However, these children are also generally from middle-class, literate cultures. There are a few studies of children in unschooled, nonliterate populations, such as Baka and Mofu of Cameroon, Tolai and Tainae of New Guinea, Quechua of Peru, and Mopan Maya children in Central America. The findings from these studies are somewhat contradictory – some indicating development comparable to that in Western children, and others indicating delays or differences in development.

However, cross-cultural research, in which tasks like false-belief tasks are adapted for local use, may not be the best way to investigate cultural diversity in theory of mind. Western theory of mind, which explains and predicts behavior by imputing mental states to self and others, underlies the design of such tasks. Yet other cultures may have quite different conceptions of mind, or the concept of mind may not exist in every culture. That is to say, there could be ways of interpreting social behavior that do not necessarily rely on theory of mind. It is possible that theory of mind is not universal and not all cultures explain and predict behavior as people do in Western society. This issue could be effectively addressed by collaborations among developmental psychologists and anthropologists.

Furthermore, evidence provided by ethologists and comparative psychologists is also relevant here. If nonhuman primates were shown to possess theory of mind, then it would be more likely that theory of mind is universal in the human species – at least its basic core, even if there is cultural diversity in its further development. As mentioned, research on children's theory of mind was initiated by reports of theory of mind in the chimpanzee. In more recent years, however, the issue has been highly controversial. Although most researchers agree that chimpanzees do not understand false belief, there is disagreement over whether they do understand simpler psychological processes, such as seeing, or whether they are simply able to detect statistical regularities in behavior without any awareness of mental states or ability to reason about mental states.

Importantly, these debates – concerning the universality of theory of mind in humans, and whether theory of mind is a unique cognitive specialization in humans – inform ongoing debate on how to explain theory-of-mind development.

Explanations of Theory-of-Mind Development

Theory of mind is defined as an integrated set of mental-state concepts underlying the interpretation of human social activity that develops gradually from infancy onwards. Various competing theories have been put forward to explain how this development comes about. The characteristics of theory of mind described in the first section of this article are associated with one particular explanation, one that gives a literal interpretation to the term 'theory of mind'. The proposal is that children's theory of mind develops via a process of theory construction and change, analogous to construction and change in scientific theorizing. That is, the theory says that children construct a theory about the mind, which has led to this view being referred to as the 'theory–theory' (see **Table 10**). On this view, children's concepts of mental states are abstract and unobservable theoretical postulates used to explain and predict observable human behavior.

Table 10 Theoretical explanations of theory-of-mind development

Theories	*Characteristics*
Theory–theory	Children construct theory of mind through a process of theorizing
Simulation theory	Children simulate others' experience based on their own
Modularity (nativist) theory	Theory of mind depends on maturation of an innate cognitive theory-of-mind module
Social-constructivist theories	Theory of mind is collaboratively constructed in linguistically mediated social interaction
Domain-general theories	Theory-of-mind development depends on domain-general developments, for example, in executive functions

The concepts are coherent and interdependent, and the theory can interpret a wide range of evidence using a few concepts and laws. The theory is not static but is reorganized over time when faced with counter-evidence to its predictions.

A somewhat similar explanation is provided by 'simulation theory' (see **Table 10**). However, on this view, mental-state concepts are derived from children's own direct experience of such states and are not postulated in some process of abstract theorizing. The theory says that children are intuitively aware of their own mental states and can understand other people's behavior by a process of simulation, using their abilities for pretence that develop early in the preschool years. Children can imagine having the beliefs and desires that the other person has, and imagine what they themselves would do if they possessed those imagined beliefs and desires.

Another explanation is provided by 'modularity theory'. On this view, theory-of-mind development depends on maturation of a particular brain structure – an innate cognitive theory-of-mind module. Like theory – theory, modularity theory regards children's concepts of mental states as abstract theoretical entities, organized into causal laws that can be used to interpret a wide range of evidence. However, the theory is not acquired through any process of 'theorizing', but rather the theory-of-mind module is innate and matures. The module constrains development in a precise way – the theory is not subject to revision based on experience. Although experience might be required as a trigger, the module will not be modified in differential ways by different experiences, which predicts that the acquisition of a theory of mind will be a universal human achievement.

These three views – that posit theory construction, simulation, or an innate module – all focus on theory of mind as an individual cognitive achievement in which children construct or employ a conceptual structure – the theory of mind. An alternative view gives social factors a much greater role in theory-of-mind development. 'Social constructivist theories' assert that theory of mind is embodied in the folk ways and speech practices of a culture and theory of mind develops as children participate in interaction and dialogue with more knowledgeable members of the culture. Importantly, social constructivist views are not passive enculturation explanations that allow the child no active role. Rather they recognize the contribution both of the child and of the social environment, arguing that children's understanding of mind is collaboratively constructed in linguistically mediated social interaction.

Against the aforementioned four views, other researchers argue that children do not develop a domain-specific theory about the mind. Rather, theory-of-mind development is a reflection of domain-general changes in cognitive processes, such as executive function, working memory, or reasoning abilities (**Table 10**).

Evidence for and against each of the proposed theories is hotly debated and there is no overall consensus clearly supporting one theory over all the others. The same empirical evidence is used to support different theories and, furthermore, evidence that some researchers use to refute a particular theory is dismissed by others as not relevant. Indeed, some researchers maintain that the differences between some of the theories (e.g., theory-theory and simulation theory) are philosophical differences that cannot be refuted by empirical evidence.

Many researchers argue that the striking absence of theory-of-mind abilities in children with autism occurs because of impairment in the theory-of-mind module, which is taken as evidence in support of modularity theory. However, cultural variation in theory of mind speaks against modularity theory and in favor of social constructivist theories. Researchers generally agree that domain-general resources are needed for successful performance on theory-of-mind tasks but the origin of domain-specific mental-state concepts still requires explanation.

In recent years, substantial attention has been paid to the role that the brain plays in theory-of-mind reasoning, with an attempt to isolate brain regions that are specific to this ability. However, most of this research has focused on adult participants, making it difficult to draw conclusions about how theory of mind develops. The limited research conducted with young children has attempted to examine the relationship between functional brain development and theory-of-mind development. Findings suggest that the neural systems associated with children's ability to reason about mental states (i.e., theory-of-mind reasoning) are independent of those associated with other kinds of reasoning (e.g., reasoning about reality). There is also evidence to suggest that it is the frontal lobes in particular that are required for theory-of-mind reasoning, and that this may be lateralized to the left hemisphere of the brain. Given the recent rise in interest in cognitive neuroscience research, significant future work in this area is to be expected and this may inform the debate over theoretical explanations of theory-of-mind development.

See also: Attention; Autism Spectrum Disorders; Cognitive Development; Cognitive Developmental Theories; Empathy and Prosocial Behavior; Fragile X Syndrome; Friends and Peers; Grammar; Imitation and Modeling; Milestones: Cognitive; Pragmatic Development; Social Interaction; Symbolic Thought.

Suggested Readings

Astington JW (1993) *The Child's Discovery of the Mind.* Cambridge, MA: Harvard University Press.

Astington JW and Baird JA (eds.) (2005) *Why Language Matters for Theory of Mind.* New York: Oxford University Press.

Baron-Cohen S (1995) *Mindblindness: An Essay on Autism and Theory of Mind.* Cambridge, MA: Bradford Books/MIT Press.

Carpendale J and Lewis C (2006) *How Children Develop Social Understanding.* Oxford: Blackwell.

Carruthers P and Smith PK (eds.) (1996) *Theories of Theories of Mind.* Cambridge, UK: Cambridge University Press.

Malle BF and Hodges SD (eds.) (2005) *Other Minds: How Humans Bridge the Divide between Self and Others.* New York: Guilford Press.

Moore C (2006) *The Development of Commonsense Psychology.* Mahwah, NJ: Erlbaum.

Perner J (1991) *Understanding the Representational Mind.* Cambridge, MA: Bradford/MIT Press.

Tomasello M (1999) *The Cultural Origins of Human Cognition.* Cambridge, MA: Harvard University Press.

Wellman HM (1990) *The Child's Theory of Mind.* Cambridge, MA: Bradford/MIT Press.

Toilet Training

B Taubman and N J Blum, University of Pennsylvania School of Medicine, Philadelphia, PA, USA

Glossary

Detrusor – The muscle in the wall of the bladder.

Encopresis – Repeated passage of feces in inappropriate places, usually the clothing, in a child over 4 years of age. Primary encopresis refers to this phenomenon in a child who was never toilet trained for passing stools.

Enuresis – Repeated voiding of urine into the bed or clothing in a child over 5 years of age.

Stool toileting refusal – Refusal to defecate on the toilet that persists for at least 1 month after the child is regularly urinating on the toilet or potty.

Valsalva maneuver – Increasing intra-abdominal pressure by contacting the abdominal muscles and diaphragm during forced expiration against a closed glottis and thus facilitating defecation.

Introduction

Although almost all children are eventually toilet trained, there is substantial variability in the age at which different children achieve this milestone, the ease in which it is attained, and the types of difficulties children or families have along the way. There are few developmental milestones that are associated with as much anticipation by parents and for which they feel as much pressure when it is not occurring at the time parents or other family members expect it to. Increasing this pressure are preschool policies that require children to be toilet trained to attend certain classes. Further complicating the toilet training process is the fact that there are a variety of different and sometimes conflicting recommendations made by professionals about the best approach to toilet training

Approaches to toilet training may vary substantially between cultural groups and even within a culture over fairly short periods of time. For example, in the US in the 1920s and 1930s, it was often recommended that toilet training begins in the first year of life using rigid schedules and anal stimulation procedures that just 20–30 years later were viewed as inappropriate. Since the 1950s, a child-oriented approach to toilet training that emphasizes training when the child demonstrates he or she is ready has been widely recommended and accepted. However, researchers have demonstrated that behavioral approaches to training can be effective for some children. In addition, there is currently a small group of professionals that are again recommending toilet training in the first year of life, although the more invasive components of the procedures used in the 1920s are not advocated.

Understanding some of the controversies and conflicts involves considering what one means when one describes a child as toilet trained which we will consider first. We then review the physiology that allows for toilet training and discuss what is known about when children toilet train. The principles of a child-oriented approach to toilet training are reviewed. Behavioral approaches to toilet training and research on the outcomes of this approach are discussed. Early toilet training will be briefly mentioned. Finally, approaches to selected toilet training problems will be reviewed.

What Is the Definition of Toilet Trained?

This question may be more complex than it first appears. There would be widespread agreement that the child who self-initiates urinating and defecating in the toilet, wears underwear during the day without having accidents, and is dry at night is toilet trained. However, most parents and professionals consider children toilet trained who do not meet these stringent criteria. Many children who wet the bed are considered toilet trained. Most preschool-age children who are toilet trained will have at least occasional daytime accidents, but the frequency of accidents that is acceptable for a child to still be considered toilet trained is not agreed upon.

The role of parent or adult support and differences in environmental demands are typically not considered. Is the child who goes to the bathroom on a regular schedule dictated by his or her parents and thus is able to wear underwear with few accidents, toilet trained? Some might not consider a child this dependent on adults to be toilet trained or might describe the child as 'schedule trained'. However, most parents provide some support like reminding the child to go to the bathroom before long trips or at other times when a toilet will not be rapidly accessible and yet consider the child to be toilet trained. The level of parental support felt to be acceptable is a critical difference between advocates of early toilet training and those who advocate for a child-oriented approach to training. Similarly, the requirements for a child to remain accident-free are much less if the child spends most of his or her time in locations where toilets are easily accessible. In contrast, a child who frequently goes on long car trips or is out with parents in public places will have to be able to defer urinating or defecating for longer periods of time in order not to have accidents.

The factors described likely affect at what age and how easily children are toilet trained and yet they are rarely discussed when parents, professionals, or even researchers define children as toilet trained or discuss the goal of toilet training children. Failure of professionals to define what they mean by toilet training certainly accounts for at least some of the conflicting advice that is often given on this subject.

Physiology

Bladder Control

Urine produced in the kidneys flows through the ureters to the bladder where it is stored before it is eliminated from the body through the urethra. Where the urethra leaves the bladder it is surrounded by a muscular sphincter known as the external urinary sphincter. When this sphincter muscle is contracted it closes off the urethra thus blocking flow of urine from the bladder. The bladder can be thought of as a muscular sack. When the bladder muscle (also referred to as the detrusor) contracts, the bladder gets smaller expelling urine out the urethra. During the typical bladder-filling cycle of an older child or adult, the detrusor is relaxed and the external urinary sphincter is contracted. This allows the bladder to fill with low pressure inside the bladder. When it is socially appropriate to urinate, there is a coordinated contraction of the detrusor and relaxation of the external urinary sphincter allowing complete emptying of the bladder. Most older children and adults urinate 3–8 times per day.

Urination in infancy differs from the mature pattern described earlier. Although there is significant individual variability, on average infants urinate hourly. Detrusor contractions occur reflexively instead of under control of the brain; thus, infants have very limited ability to anticipate when they are going to urinate. In addition, contraction of the detrusor and relaxation of the external urinary sphincter are not always well coordinated. Thus, the bladder may not fully empty with each episode of voiding. As the infant develops, the brain gains the ability to inhibit the reflexive bladder contractions allowing the capacity of the bladder to increase. As the bladder capacity increases, the child will be able to go for progressively longer periods of time between urinating. Thus, being able to maintain a dry diaper for at least a couple hours between voids is one commonly assessed sign of toilet training readiness. During toilet training the child will need to learn to volitionally control the external urinary sphincter and initiate detrusor contractions at socially appropriate times.

Bowel Control

The distal portions of the colon are referred to as the sigmoid colon followed by the rectum, which leads to the anus. Muscles in the colon wall move stool through the colon and muscular sphincters that surround the colon provide a barrier to leakage of stool from the rectum. The internal anal sphincter is under reflex control and is maintained in a contracted state that provides a barrier to leakage that is in place without the individual having to think about it. Thus, even infants who are not toilet trained do not continually leak stool, but have intermittent bowel movements.

Stool is stored in the sigmoid colon. During this time the body reabsorbs water in the stool. Thus, if stool spends a long time in the sigmoid colon, it is likely to become harder which can lead to constipation. When the sigmoid colon becomes full, contractions of the muscles in the wall of the sigmoid colon push stool into the rectum. These contractions are most likely to occur upon awakening in the morning or after a meal (gastrocolic reflex) explaining why people are particularly likely to defecate at these times. When stool is pushed into the rectum, the rectum is stretched and it is this stretching which is sensed by the body as an urge to defecate. This stretching also reflexively causes relaxation of the internal anal sphincter. The external anal sphincter, which is under volitional control, becomes the final barrier to defecation. If it is not appropriate to defecate, contraction of this sphincter and some related muscles ejects stool from the rectum back into the sigmoid and the urge to defecate will subside until contractions of muscles in the wall of the sigmoid again push stool into the rectum. When it is appropriate to defecate, relaxation of the external anal sphincter in combination with sitting or squatting, which straightens the anal canal, and pushing with the diaphragm and abdominal muscles (referred to as a Valsalva maneuver) facilitates defecation.

Epidemiology

Investigations of the epidemiology of toilet training are very limited. Variations in the definition of toilet trained (discussed earlier) or lack of a definition are problematic in many studies. In addition, all the studies have used relatively small subgroups of a population as opposed to a nationally representative sample of children. Despite these limitations there is widespread consensus that in the US children are toilet training later that they did 50 years ago. For example, in the 1950s, Dr. Berry Brazelton followed over 1000 children from a single suburban pediatric private practice that advised parents to use a child-oriented approach to training. He found the average age for completion of daytime toilet training was 28.5 months and over 97% were toilet trained by 36 months of age. In contrast, a study by the authors from a similar suburban pediatric practice that also advised use of child-oriented approach to training in the late 1990s found a mean age of toilet training of 36.8 months and 16% did not complete training until after 42 months of age. Some data suggest that parents waiting until children are at an older age to initiate toilet training and an increasing incidence of constipation may explain some of the trend toward later completion of toilet training. Other factors such as improving diaper technology that has made diapers more convenient for parents and more comfortable for children have also been hypothesized to play a role, but have not been systematically investigated. On average girls tend to train at slightly younger ages than boys.

Whether the trend toward completing toilet training at older ages is occurring in all children in the US is somewhat less clear. Both of these studies mentioned investigated well-educated, predominately white, populations. There is some evidence that children in nonwhite families and children living in single-parent families tend to toilet train earlier than children in white two-parent families. In addition, studies from Europe and Asia suggest that children toilet train at somewhat younger ages than in the US. There is, however, even on these continents, some evidence of a trend toward training at older ages.

Child-Oriented Approach to Toilet training

In 1962 Dr. Berry Brazelton published his seminal paper on toilet training titled 'A child-oriented approach to toilet training'. In it he describes an approach very different from the one used in the US prior to the 1950s when most people were introducing toilet training during the first year of life as described earlier.

Early toilet training fell out of favor for two reasons. Child psychoanalysis was becoming popular and in this field the toilet training process was felt to have lifelong effects on the personality of the child. Psychoanalytic theorists saw the early introduction of toilet training as the primary cause for problems such as constipation, fecal soiling, (encopresis) and daytime or night-time wetting (enuresis). The second impetus for change was the influence of developmental specialists like Dr. Arnold Gesell. He and others argued that toilet training should be viewed as a developmental milestone that the child will obtain when the central nervous system is mature enough. Thus, early attempts at toilet training were seen as inconsistent with the child's developmental readiness.

The child-oriented approach to toilet training recommends that it should not begin until the child has reached a certain level of physical and emotional readiness. Commonly recommended signs of toilet training readiness are listed in **Table 1**. Children will not demonstrate most of these readiness skills prior to 18 months, but there is substantial variability in when different children will demonstrate these skills. In addition, children do not demonstrate all these skills at the same time. For example, half of the children will demonstrate an interest in the potty by about 25 months of age, whereas they will not be dry for 2 h during the day until approximately 27 months of age and will not pull their pants up and down

Table 1 Signs of toilet training readiness

Signs of toilet training readiness
Understands and follows verbal instructions
Imitates parents or other important adults
Demonstrates desire to please parents
Demonstrates independence by saying 'No'
Tells parent before urinating or defecating
Expresses interest in toilet training (e.g., follows parent into bathroom)
Child can stay dry during the day for 2 h or longer
Sits and walks independently
Can pull pants up and down

independently until after 30 months of age on average. The skills or combination of skills listed in **Table 1** that best predict readiness have not been determined. Similarly, the age at which most children are ready for toilet training has not been determined, although one study of a child-oriented approach to toilet training found no advantage to starting active training (defined as asking the child to use the potty three or more times a day) prior to 27 months of age.

There are four stages to the child-oriented approach to toilet training as described by Brazelton. The first stage is putting the child, fully clothed, on the potty for a few minutes. Sitting on the potty should be made as pleasant as possible by giving treats and or having the parents read to the child. After a week or so the child is gradually encouraged to sit on the potty with the diaper off. In the third stage the child is taken to the potty after soiling the diaper. The contents of the soiled diaper are placed in the potty and it is explained to the child that this is the purpose of the potty. If the child seems willing the parents can try to catch the child starting to void or defecate and put him/her on the potty. During the fourth stage the diaper is removed for short periods of time and the child is encouraged to use the potty independently. Once this occurs for both urine and feces, the child is on the way to being fully trained. It is important to stress that should the child exhibit significant resistance at any stage, the parents must return to the previous stage or stop the training process altogether for 1 or 2 months. It is often not appreciated that when using this approach it takes, on average, 5–10 months from the time of beginning active toilet training until the child completes daytime training.

The child-oriented approach to toilet training is the one most commonly used in the US today. It is endorsed by the American Academy of Pediatrics, taught to pediatric residents and recommended by the majority of pediatricians. It was hoped that this approach to toilet training would eliminate the problems of stool-withholding, stool toileting refusal, enuresis (wetting), and primary encopresis (soiling). Unfortunately, these problems persist despite the widespread acceptance of this approach to training. Methods for addressing some of these problems are discussed later in this article.

Intensive Behavioral Approaches to Toilet training

Intensive behavioral approaches to toilet training were largely developed in the 1960s and 1970s to toilet-train individuals with severe cognitive disabilities. The success of these approaches for individuals with disabilities led Drs. Nathan Azrin and Richard Foxx to study this approach in typically developing children. Their study of 34 children between 20 and 36 months of age, published in 1973, remains one of the largest studies of intensive toilet training published till the early years of 2000s.

For this study all children were screened for toilet training readiness by assessing their ability and willingness to follow 10 parental instructions. Children under 20 months and an occasional child over 20 months did not follow these instructions and was not included in the study. Training was conducted by a trained trainer (not the parent) and only the trainer and child were present in order to minimize distractions. Increased fluids were given to increase the frequency of urination. When this approach is used, toilet training is broken down into multiple steps (see **Table 2** for an example), and instructions and reinforcers are provided for each of these steps (not just for urinating on the toilet). In addition, children are prompted to check their underwear every 5 min to see if it was dry and were offered reinforcers for dry underwear. It is important to note that children can and should be earning reinforcers very frequently and thus reinforcers needed to be changed over the course of the training to maintain the child's interest. If a child fails to follow an instruction he or she is manually guided to complete the task. When children wet themselves they are briefly verbally reprimanded, placed in time-out for 5 min, required to change into dry pants, and then required to practice going to the toilet, pulling down pants, and sitting on the toilet 10 times.

All 34 children in the study were toilet trained within 30 min to 14 h and all but one maintained their toilet training at 4 months' follow-up. On average, children 26–36 months of age took 2 h and 15 min to train and children 20–26 months took 5 h to train. The rapid success of an intensive behavioral approach to toilet training contrasts dramatically with the slower child-oriented approach described earlier.

Subsequent studies have shown that an intensive behavioral approach to training can be implemented successfully by parents when they are taught the procedures, although the length of time it takes parents to train their children is slightly longer than in the Foxx and Azrin study described. However, despite this evidence for very

Table 2 Example of steps that a child would be trained to perform using an intensive behavioral approach to training

Approaching the potty chair or toilet seat
Grasping the pants
Pulling down the pants
Sitting on the potty chair or toilet seat
Urinating or defecating while sitting on the potty chair or toilet seat
Wiping oneself
Pulling up the pants
Flushing the toilet
Washing hands

rapid effectiveness, this method of toilet training is not nearly as widely accepted as the child-oriented approach. This may relate, at least in part, to the fact that the behavioral methods elicit tantrums in some children. Indeed, the most common reason that parents report for failure of an intensive behavioral approach to training is negative emotional reactions in response to the manual guidance, time out, or toilet training practice components of the procedure. Furthermore, most of the studies that have demonstrated success with these approaches have included at least a few hours of training parents on how to implement the procedures. However, for most parents this type of professional training is not easily available.

In summary, intensive behavioral approaches to toilet training are likely to be the most effective means of toilet training individuals with severe cognitive disabilities. They can be rapidly effective in typically developing children over 20 months of age. However, parents are much more likely to be able to effectively implement the procedure if they have professional guidance. Without this guidance a significant portion of children will resist the training and have tantrums that limit the acceptability and effectiveness of these approaches.

Early Toilet Training

Early toilet training is being advocated again by some professionals. These professionals note that early training is practiced in many countries and that a child-oriented approach has not prevented the toilet training problems that were ascribed to early training in the past. The expense of diapers, environmental consequences of diaper use, and the risk of both diaper dermatitis (diaper rash) and infection from changing diapers in daycare settings are often mentioned as reasons to advocate for early toilet training.

The early toilet training that is most frequently recommended today is not the rigid scheduling and coercive methods that were recommended in the 1920s to 1940s. Early toilet training today emphasizes teaching parents or other adults to recognize the infant's signals that he or she is about to urinate or defecate. These signals may be subtle such as grimaces, facial flushing, increased or decreased body movements, or other behaviors. When these signals are noted, the infant must be rapidly taken to the potty so they can urinate or defecate. If the infant urinates or defecates within a few minutes, they are rewarded with hugs, songs, or a favorite object. It is clear that using these methods, children as young as 12 months of age can be trained to signal the need to use the potty and briefly withhold urination or defecation for long enough to urinate and defecate in the toilet or potty on most occasions. When accidents do occur they should be viewed as a failure of the adult to recognize the child's signals and not as the child's failure. Despite past concerns about early toilet training, there is no evidence that this approach to early training results in problems. However, one needs to clearly distinguish this type of training from self-initiated toileting, which is an entirely different goal. If parents do not understand the careful observation and rapid access to the potty that this approach requires, they may become frustrated and upset, or even angry with the infant. If early toilet training leads to these emotions it may interfere with healthy parent–infant interactions. Finally, those utilizing an early toilet training approach should expect a possible increase in accidents as they move from parent-initiated toileting to child-initiated toileting when the child is of toddler or preschool age.

Toilet training Problems

Stool Toileting Refusal

A common problem parents may face when toilet training their child is stool toileting refusal. This is the term used when a child always urinates in the potty but refuses to have bowel movements there. This behavior occurs in up to one out of five children during the toilet training process. The child is usually put in underpants by the parents. When in underpants the child can respond in several ways. Some may defecate in the underpants. More often they will ask to be put in a diaper or wait to be put in one at night to defecate. Parents often consider these children as toilet trained or 'almost trained' since they do not soil their underpants.

Parents are often not concerned that their child is refusing to have bowel movements in the potty and the majority of children with stool toileting refusal will eventually train without the intervention of a professional such as a pediatrician, family physician, or psychologist. However, children with stool toileting refusal may develop several problems and as many as 25% of them will require intervention. For some children, stool toileting refusal progresses to stool-withholding. They go from refusing to have a bowel movement in the toilet to trying not to have a bowel movement in the diaper as well.

Stool-withholding in turn causes painful rectal contraction. The parents often misinterpret this situation. They think the child is in pain because he/she is trying to have a bowel movement and cannot rather than trying not to have one. If the child succeeds in not defecating for several days when he/she finally goes, the bowel movement will be large, hard, and painful. This gives the child even more incentive not to defecate and a vicious cycle begins (see **Figure 1**). One step toward interrupting the cycle of stool-withholding, painful defecation, and more stool-withholding is to remove the initial motivation for stool-withholding and ambivalence to toilet training. Returning the child to diapers and stopping the toilet training process takes away one reason the child is stool-withholding. Next, one must ensure that no matter how long the child withholds having a bowel movement, when defecation finally occurs it is painless. Giving the child a stool softener will be necessary to assure a painless bowel movement. Over time the child will no longer associate defecation with pain and the stool-withholding will stop. In the authors' experience when children older than 3.5 years of age are placed back in diapers they usually toilet train within weeks to a couple of months.

When a child older than 4 years of age engages in stool toileting refusal it may not be acceptable to the parents to return the child to diapers. In this situation a behavioral protocol that offers the child small reinforcers for small steps toward having a bowel movement on the toilet can be successful (see **Table 3**). For this approach to be successful, it is critical that the child is having soft painless bowel movements. In addition, it is very important that the initial steps be small enough so that the child experiences success in doing what the parents are asking. Offering the child a reward for having bowel movements on the toilet is usually unsuccessful because it is too large a step from having bowel movements in the diaper.

Children with stool toileting refusal train later than children who never experience stool toileting refusal. For example, Taubman, in his 1997 study, found that 66% of children without stool toileting refusal were toilet trained at 36 months of age as compared to only 29% of children who had experienced stool toileting refusal. This is the second reason a professional may be consulted. Having a child still not toilet trained after 42 months of age can be quite stressful on the family; Taubman found that 20% of children with stool toileting refusal fall into this category. Trying to train such children can cause conflicts between the parents and behavior problems in the child. If parents have consistent difficulty getting a child to follow their directions or if toilet training is resulting in disruptive behaviors in the child or high level of parental anxiety, consultation with a psychologist may be needed.

The cause of stool toileting refusal has not been determined. One hypothesis is that it is just one manifestation of difficult parent–child interactions around limit setting. There is a study that did find that parents found setting limits for their child difficult and felt the child had more control over them than they did over the child. Yet

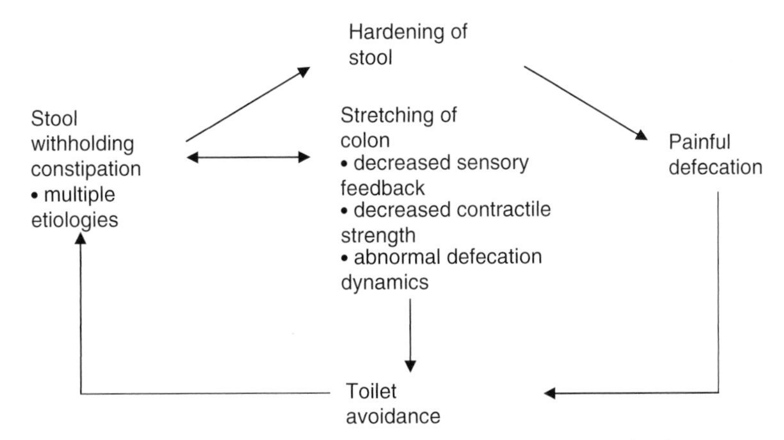

Figure 1 Relationship between stool-withholding, painful defecation, and stool toileting refusal.

Table 3 Example of a behavioral procedure for the treatment of stool toileting refusal

Offer the child a small reward for each of the following steps. When the child achieves one step on three consecutive days move to the next step:

1. Having bowel movements (with the diaper on) in the bathroom instead of in another location
2. Have bowel movement (with diaper on) while sitting on the toilet with the top down
3. Have bowel movement (with diaper on) while sitting on the toilet with the top up
4. Create magic diapers that are decorated by the child and have the back cut out of them so the stool falls in the toilet when the child defecates. Allow the child to wear magic diapers to defecate for a few days

another study, which videotaped parents asking their child to put toys away he or she had just played with, found no difference between the children with stool toileting refusal and those without. This study also found no evidence of more behavior problems between the two groups of children. When one looks for a difference in temperament as a cause of stool toileting refusal, there is some evidence that children with this problem may have a more difficult temperament than those that do not, but the differences between the two groups are not large.

Constipation is known to contribute to the development of stool toileting refusal. Blum and colleagues in 2004 reported 71% of children with stool toileting refusal had at least one hard bowel movement during the toilet training process and 44% had a painful bowel movement. In 93% of the children, the hard bowel movement occurred before the onset of stool toileting refusal and in 74% of the children the painful bowel movements also occurred before the onset of stool toileting refusal. This suggests that most children who develop stool toileting refusal have a physiologic or dietary predisposition to develop constipation that is present before the toileting refusal behavior begins.

At the present time no specific toilet training intervention has been shown to prevent stool toileting refusal. However, given the frequent negative consequences of late toilet training and stool-withholding, some professionals advise parents not to put their child in underpants until he or she is both urinating and defecating in the potty at least half of the time.

Constipation

Constipation, the passing of hard bowel movements, is common in children from 18 months to 4 years of age. This is the age when toilet training takes place. The most common cause is dietary. Excessive intake of milk and absence of fiber in the diet are associated with constipation. Constipation often causes painful bowl movements, which in turn may lead to stool toileting refusal or stool-withholding as shown in **Figure 1**. Even when constipation is not connected with stool toileting refusal, it is associated with completion of toilet training at an older age.

Therefore to make the toilet training process go as smoothly as possible constipation should be treated aggressively as soon as it occurs. Treatment should include dietary changes. Milk intake should be decreased and fiber increased. Stool softeners also can be useful in treating the problem.

Primary Encopresis

Primary encopresis is an uncommon but serious consequence when the triad of constipation, stool-withholding, and stool toileting refusal is not effectively treated. The term refers to a child who is older than 4 years of age, but frequently soils his or her underpants. Most commonly, primary encopresis is the result of the child developing a large rectal stool impaction, which he or she is unable to pass, and around which watery stools leak onto the underpants. Normally when feces enter the rectum, the sudden stretching that occurs sends out a message to the brain that the rectum is full and the need to defecate is felt. If defecation is delayed the impulse will fade until more feces enter the rectum causing more stretching. Then the impulse to defecate will return and be even stronger. However, if constipation and stool-withholding persist they can slowly stretch the rectum so that it is becomes very enlarged and the sudden stretching cannot occur. The child becomes unaware that there is a large hard fecal mass sitting in his/her rectum. This disrupts normal sphincter functioning described in the section of bowel physiology, and the anus becomes dilated from the pressure of the impaction. In this situation the child cannot feel or control the stool leaking onto his or her underpants.

Primary encopresis due to a stool impaction requires medical intervention to resolve. It cannot be treated by behavior modification or counseling alone. The older the child is at the time of intervention, the more resistant the problem is to treatment. In one study of 12 children who presented at a mean age of 7.3 years only one patient was no longer soiling after 1 year of medical treatment. The age of the children at the time they presented to the physician was 7.3 ± 2.7 years.

Treatment consists of first removing the fecal impaction with enemas or large doses of orally administered laxatives. The child is then put on a laxative or stool softener so that he or she has a daily bowel movement. The child must sit on the toilet and attempt to defecate twice a day after meals as in most cases they will not get the urge to defecate because the rectum can remained stretched for months after the stool impaction is relieved. This prevents re-impaction and allows the rectum to return to a more normal size. The parents are encouraged to put the child on a high-fiber diet.

One major cause of treatment failure is the family's inability to get the child to follow through with the treatment plan, whether it is taking enemas or oral medication. The child also may have emotional problems as a result of having encopresis for so many years. In these cases it is often helpful to have the child and family work with a therapist familiar with encopresis.

Daytime Wetting

The age at which daytime wetting should be considered problematic is the source of some controversy. However, if a typically developing child older than 4 years of age is

Table 4 Causes of daytime wetting

Urinary tract infection
Chemical urethritis
Constipation
Vaginal reflux of urine
Dysfunctional voiding syndromes
Toilet avoidance or deferral
Anatomic abnormalities
Diabetes insipidus or mellitus
Chronic renal disease
Sexual abuse

having frequent daytime wetting, or if a child who has been consistently dry during the day for a few months begins to wet his or her pants, it should prompt further evaluation. Conditions that can cause daytime wetting are listed in **Table 4**. If the urethra gets inflamed due to an infection or exposure to a chemical (e.g., soap, bubble bath) children will urinate frequently and may develop daytime wetting. Constipation has also been associated with daytime wetting and is often missed by parents or physicians who may pay closer attention to the urinary symptoms than the bowel symptoms when a child is wetting. Vaginal reflux of urine may occur if girls urinate with their legs closed together. Some urine refluxes into the vagina and leaks out when the child stands up. The characteristic of wetting immediately after standing up from the toilet differentiates this form of daytime wetting from the others. If the child does not have one of these conditions, then toileting avoidance/deferral or a dysfunctional voiding syndrome is the most likely cause of the daytime wetting. The other problems listed in **Table 4** are much less common and will not be discussed in this article.

The child's symptoms can often help distinguish toileting deferral from dysfunctional voiding. Children who wet ignore the signals from the bladder that it is getting full until it is too late. They do not urinate more frequently than is typical and wetting tends to occur when the children are engaged in an activity that they do not want to stop. In contrast, children with the most common type of dysfunctional voiding, urge syndrome, tend to urinate frequently. In children with urge syndrome the bladder behaves more like an infant's (described earlier) than a mature one in that the brain does not successfully inhibit some bladder muscle contractions. Thus, these contractions occur without warning and the child has a sudden and sometimes painful urge to void. In response to the bladder muscle contractions these children often cross their legs, or squat on their heels in an attempt to mechanically block the urethra and prevent the flow of urine. Both, children with toileting deferral and children with urge syndrome, tend to benefit from scheduled toileting. In addition, if the child with the urge syndrome is using the Valsalva maneuver on voiding, he or she should be taught to just take a deep breath and sigh as voiding is taking place. If the symptoms should persist a pediatric urologist who can assess the severity of the voiding dysfunction and the need for additional interventions should be consulted.

Summary

Almost all children are eventually toilet trained. The child-oriented approach to toilet training is the most commonly recommended approach by pediatricians and professional organizations. Using this approach most children will train by 3.5 years of age, but some children, particularly those that develop stool toileting refusal, may not train until 3.5–4 years of age or later. Intensive behavioral approaches can rapidly and effectively train some children, but may cause tantrums or parent–child conflict in others. When a child is not toilet trained by 4 years of age or a previously trained child begins having accidents, a variety of medical conditions may be contributing to the problem. In this situation, the child should be evaluated by a medical professional.

See also: Bedwetting; Physical Growth.

Suggested Readings

Azrin NH and Foxx RM (1974) *Toilet Training in Less than a Day.* New York, NY: Pocket Books.

Blum NJ (2006) Elimination disorders. In: Greydanus DE, Patel DR, and Pratt HD (eds.) *Behavioral Pediatrics*, pp. 206–235. New York, NY: Universe, Inc.

Blum NJ, Taubman B, and Nemeth N (2003) Relationship between age at initiation of toilet training and duration of toilet training: A prospective study. *Pediatrics* 111: 810–814.

Blum NJ, Taubman B, and Nementh N (2004) During toilet training constipation occurs prior to stool toileting refusal. *Pediatrics* 113: e520–e522.

Brazelton TB (1962) A child-oriented approach to toilet training. *Pediatrics* 29: 121–128.

Casale AJ (2000) Daytime wetting: Getting to the bottom of the issue. *Contemporary Pediatrics* 17: 107–116.

de Vries MW and de Vries MR (1977) Cultural relativity of toilet training readiness: A perspective from East Africa. *Pediatrics* 60: 170–177.

Felt B, Wise CG, Olson A, Kochhar P, Marcus S, and Coran A (1999) Guideline for the management of pediatric idiopathic constipation and soiling. *Archives of Pediatrics and Adolescent Medicine* 153: 380–385.

Foxx RM and Azrin NH (1973) Dry pants: A rapid method of toilet training children. *Behaviour Research and Therapy* 11: 435–442.

Luxem M and Christophersen E (1994) Behavioral toilet training in early childhood: Research, practice, and implications. *Journal of Developmental and Behavioral Pediatrics* 15: 370–378.

Luxem MC, Christopersen ER, Purvis PC, and Baer DM (1997) Behavioral-medical treatment of pediatric toileting refusal. *Journal of Developmental and Behavioral Pediatrics* 18: 34–41.

Schmitt BD (2004) Toilet training: Getting it right the first time. *Contemporary Pediatrics* 21: 105–116.

Schonwald A, Sherritt L, Stadtler A, and Bridgemohan C (2004) Factors associated with difficult toilet training. *Pediatrics* 113: 1753–1757.

Schum TR, McAuliffe TL, Simms MD, Walter JA, Lewis M, and Pupp R (2001) Factors associated with toilet training in the 1990s. *Ambulatory Pediatrics* 1: 79–86.
Stadler AC, Gorski PA, and Brazelton TB (1999) Toilet training methods, clinical interventions, recommendations. *Pediatrics* 103: 1359–1361.
Taubman BT (1997) Toilet training and toileting refusal for stool only: A prospective study. *Pediatrics* 99: 54–58.
Taubman B and Buzby M (1997) Overflow encopresis and stool toileting refusal during toilet training: A prospective study on the effect of therapeutic efficacy. *The Journal of Pediatrics* 131: 768–771.

Touch and Pain

T Field, University of Miami School of Medicine, Miami, FL, USA
M Hernandez-Reif, University of Alabama AL, USA

Glossary

Epidermis – Outermost layer of skin.
Meissner corpuscles – Skin receptors located between the epidermis and dermis on hairless parts of the body that respond to the lightest forms of stimulation.
Merkel's disks – Skin receptors located just beneath the skin that respond to constant pressure.
Pacinian corpuscles – Skin receptors located near joints and deep tissue that respond to pressure, vibration, and high-frequency sounds.
Ruffini endings – Skin receptors located deep below the skin that register pressure and temperature.

Introduction

The field of touch and pain in infancy have only recently been explored. Touch is the earliest developing sense and even as early as the newborn period, the sense of touch is well developed, and the newborn experiences pain. In this piece research is reviewed on early touch perception including temperature, texture, and weight perception by infants. Studies are also reviewed on infants' behavioral and physiological responses to pain and effective interventions for pain including stimulation of other senses through aromas and sucrose and activity such as nonnutritive sucking.

Touch and Pain in the Infant

Touch is typically defined as stimulation of the skin by thermal, mechanical, chemical, and electrical stimuli. These stimuli cause changes in the skin that give us the sensations of pressure, warmth, and vibration. Understanding the physical components of the skin and how stimulation signals are conveyed from the skin to the brain is important for understanding the various functions that touch serves.

The skin is the oldest, the largest, and the most sensitive of our organs. The whole body is covered and protected by our skin. Touch has been called 'the mother of the senses' perhaps because it was the first to develop in evolution. In the *Oxford English Dictionary*, touch is defined as "the most general of the bodily senses, diffused through all parts of skin, but (in man) specially developed in the tips of the fingers and the lips." The fingers and lips have a disproportionately large number of neurons that travel to and from the brain. The fingers and the lips are the means by which the infant does most of its early learning.

Touch is the earliest sensory system to develop in all species. When a human embryo is less than 1 in long and less than 2 months old, the skin is already highly developed. When the palm is touched at 2 months' gestation, the fingers grasp the palm. The fingers and thumb will close at 3 months when the palm is touched. The skin and the nervous system arise from the same embryonic cell layer, the ectoderm. The central nervous system (CNS) develops as the internal portion of the general surface of the embryonic body. The rest of the surface covering (after the differentiation of the brain and spinal cord) becomes the skin, hair, nails, and teeth. Thus, the skin may be regarded as an exposed portion of the nervous system or an external nervous system. Touch can have strong effects on our physiology. When the skin is touched, that stimulation is quickly transmitted to the brain, which in turn regulates our physiology.

Different types of touch lead to different responses. Light pressure touch, for example, can lead to physiological arousal, and moderate pressure touch can be calming.

The skin comprises about 18% of our body. A section of skin the size of a quarter features 50 nerve endings. As a sense organ, the skin is critical for perceiving and processing the meaning of different touch stimuli. The outermost layer of skin (called the epidermis) can be thick or thin, hairy or smooth, loose or tight, and flat or furrowed. The ridges and valleys in the fingertips are critical for the perception of texture. The many receptors in the skin are named after their discoverers (Meissner corpuscles, Ruffini cylinders, Merkel disks, and Pacinian corpuscles). These structures are responsible for conveying the neural signals from thermal, mechanical, chemical, and electrical stimuli. Meissner corpuscles are located between the epidermis and the dermis on the hairless parts of the body, including the fingertips, the palms, the soles of the feet, and the tongue. They respond to the lightest forms of stimulation. The Pacinian corpuscles are located near the joints and deep tissues. They respond to pressure, vibrations, and high-frequency sounds. Merkel's disks are located just beneath the skin and respond to constant pressure. Ruffini endings, which are located deep below the skin, can also register pressure and temperature. The hairiest parts of the body are generally the most sensitive to pressure, because many sense receptors are found at the base of each hair. The skin is also thinnest where there is hair.

The Nerve Fibers and the Cortex

The term touch includes the senses of pressure, pain, temperature, and muscle movements. Any stimulus that touches the skin is transmitted to the spinal cord on nerve fibers that are sometimes no longer than a meter. The nerve fibers that carry pain stimulation are small. Mechanical information such as pressure is carried by larger fibers up the spinal cord to the brain. Motor nerves then move from the brain to the body where they control muscles and glands.

The stimulation traveling to the brain ultimately crosses the sensory cortex to the opposite side of the brain where it is processed. To determine where the stimulation of the body gets processed in the brain, scientists have placed electrodes on the surface of a patient's cortex and have noted where in the brain the skin stimulation is received. A diagram of where that stimulation is received from different parts of the brain is called the homunculus. The homunculus illustrates how much space is needed on the cortex depending on how dense the nerves are in that body part. For example, areas with many more nerve endings such as the fingertips and the lips require more space on the cortex than the back which has far fewer nerve endings. The nerve cells in the cortex are also sensitive to specific types of stimulation, so that some cells may be sensitive only to stroking the surface of a body part in a single direction or at a specific frequency. Different types of stimulation may alter the size of the cells in the cortex as well as the number of cells responding to different types of stimulation.

Sensory Thresholds

Researchers use brush bristles and air puffs to produce sensations of pressure and vibration to determine an individual's thresholds to the intensity, frequency, and temperature of the tactile stimulus. One popular measure is how far apart two touch points must be for a person to perceive them as separate. One or two hairs are touched to the skin, and the individual is asked to indicate the number of points felt. The thresholds are lower in parts that have more nerve endings, for example, in the fingertips and the lips. These areas are not only the most sensitive areas for perceiving texture, temperature, and other tactile stimulation, but also for sensing pain. A dolorimeter (a rod that exerts pressure) is pushed against the skin to determine pain thresholds. The wide differences in individuals' sensory thresholds probably explain to some degree the individual differences noted in pain tolerance. But little is understood about these relationships.

Touch Perception in the Fetus

The sense of touch is the first to develop *in utero*, and the most developed at birth. Thus, the newborn has already experienced tactile stimulation *in utero*. Fetal research has shown that as early as 3 months' gestation, the fetus will turn its head toward a tactile stimulus, and the fetus responds to electrical stimuli and puffs of air that are even difficult for adults to discriminate. These very sophisticated perceptual skills occur as early as 3 months' gestation.

Touch Perception in the Neonate

Very little research has been conducted in the area of touch perception, also called haptic perception. Research suggests that touch discrimination by mouth and hands occurs as early as the newborn period. Different texture nipples (nubby vs. smooth) can be discriminated by the newborn's mouth and by their hands. In a study that showed this discrimination, the newborns explored the different texture nipples by their mouths and by their hands. After some experience with one nipple, they stopped sucking but when a new texture nipple was presented, they started to suck again as if noticing that the new nipple was a different texture.

Texture perception has also been shown in 3-day-old infants with a smooth or granular object. After holding the object, babies were given either a familiar or a new textured object. Two measures were recorded including (1) holding time as a measure of interest and discrimination of objects, and (2) hand pressure on the object to explore the newborns' ability to adjust their manipulation to new-texture objects. Both measures showed perception of the texture of objects by newborns.

Weight perception has also been shown by newborns. To demonstrate weight perception, which would not be expected by newborns since they have no experience carrying objects, a light-weight (2 g) or a heavier-weight (8 g) object (vials of cotton or pellets, respectively) were placed in the right hand of full-term newborns. After the infants no longer showed interest in one weight, they were tested with the opposite weight object. Infants of depressed mothers were also tested because they are thought to learn more slowly than infants of nondepressed mothers. The infants of depressed mothers did not respond to the novel weight, and only 15% of those infants showed hand movements that might have facilitated their perception of the object's weight (e.g., hand-to-mouth or hand-to-face, turning/moving of the wrist or hand). In contrast, 78% of the infants of nondepressed mothers showed hand activity that would lead to weight perception, and as a group, they held the novel weight longer, suggesting that they had perceived the weight change.

Given that newborns perceive weight, it was surprising to find that the same French team that studied weight perception in newborns also studied weight perception in much older (1-year-old) infants. The authors not only documented weight perception by 1-year-old infants, but also the ability to adjust their hand manipulation of the weights. Two dependent measures were recorded: (1) holding times in order to assess their interest in the weight as well as reaction to novel weights; and (2) manual pressure exerted on the object to investigate the infants' ability to adjust their manipulation to the object's weight. The results suggested that infants perceive weight differences and can adjust their manipulation to different weight objects.

Newborns can also visually recognize the shape of an object that they have previously manipulated with their right hand but without seeing their right hand. That is, newborns can extract shape information in a tactual format and transform it into a visual format before they have had the opportunity to learn from the combination of visual and tactual experience. However, the same authors later showed that this ability was only characteristic of the right hand and did not occur when the left hand was involved.

At a later age this still appears for both hands. Girls needed more time to learn with their left hand than with their right hand, than the boys did which was surprising. That possibly occurred because the girls had already developed handedness (hand preference), as girls in general mature more rapidly than boys. Discrimination was found though, for both hands and for both sexes. Infants were better at retaining information on an object's shape with their left hand vs. their right hand; this was true for both sexes. We do not know if the opposite is true for infants who later become left-handed.

Temperature Perception

The related sense of temperature has not been studied with the newborn until recently although it is a very important sense clearly to keep from getting burned or frozen. To demonstrate temperature perception by mouth, newborns have been given cold and warm nipples. The newborns did not show a preference for cold or warm nipples, but those newborns who received the cold nipple before the warm nipple, sucked more on the cold nipple, perhaps to warm the cold nipple.

To show temperature perception by hand, newborns were given tubes containing cold or warm water to hold onto with their hands. The infants learned the difference between the warm and cold tubes, as indicated by a decrease in holding, after experience with one tube and an increase in holding when the other tube was given to them. The newborns of depressed mothers, once again, showed slower learning, possibly because they did not actively explore the tubes with their hands.

Pain Perception

Another touch sense is the sense of pain. Painful stimuli lead to a stress response as early as the newborn period. Pre-term infants experience up to 60 invasive procedures before being discharged from the neonatal intensive care unit. The heelstick has been the most common painful procedure. Animal and human research have demonstrated that repetitive pain has adverse effects on the neurodevelopment of the neonate. Although there are still some neonates who do not receive analgesia during invasive procedures because they are not thought to experience pain, neonates clearly show physiological and behavioral responses during heelsticks and other invasive procedures.

Behavioral Responses to Pain

Pre-term infants typically show behavioral distress during invasive procedures. Although facial expressions and crying are the most widely studied responses to pain, body movements have also been reported as distress behaviors in pre-term infants experiencing heelsticks. Extension of the arms and legs (80%) and finger splays (70%) are examples of behavioral responses to heelsticks. Pre-term infants who experienced invasive procedures more frequently and were lower gestational age showed more motor stress behaviors after the heelstick. The flexion reflex or withdrawal of the limb from the stimulus has also been reported as a response to invasive procedures. Photogrammetry has been used to document the flexion reflex during routine heelsticks. Infants have been noted to withdraw both legs and cry immediately after the first heelstick which is not unlike adults' responses to pain.

Typical facial expressions following an invasive procedure are a brow bulge, eye squeeze, lip purse, stretched mouth (horizontal or vertical), and chin quiver. Male and female infants show some different responses to pain. For example, female infants have been noted to cry louder than males, and their cries are higher-pitched than those of males. However, males and females do not seem to differ on their facial expressions in response to pain.

Some say that infants who have experienced the most frequent invasive procedures since birth show fewer facial reactions to heelsticks. Others, however, found no relation between the number of invasive procedures experienced by pre-term infants and their behavior during heelsticks. Experienced infants appear to anticipate the painful stimulus, but no change in reactivity has been noted over days for most pre-term infants.

Infant crying would be the most obvious pain response to invasive procedures. However, some pre-term infants do not seem to cry, perhaps because of their weakness. Thus, clinicians pay attention to pre-term infants' facial expressions to detect painful responses.

Facial grimacing and fussing have been noted more often in older infants while younger infants display fewer of these responses, and spend more time sleeping. Going into deep sleep following pain, for example, after a circumcision, is called the conservation withdrawal response. Stronger behavioral responses were accompanied by stronger heart rate responses to the heelstick.

Physiological Responses to Pain

Pain has also been measured by physiological measures such as heart rate. Disorganized physiological responses have also been noted for neonates during and following invasive procedures including changes in heart rate, respiration, and blood pressure. Pre-term and full-term neonates experiencing heelsticks and circumcision have shown increased heart rate and blood pressure both during and after invasive procedures.

Heart rate elevations as high as 18% above baseline have been reported for pre-term infants during heelsticks. The physiological disorganization in response to repetitive heelsticks may redirect energy and oxygen, may disturb sleep cycles, and may increase morbidity and mortality.

Greater experience with painful procedures has led to a reduced stress hormone response (measured by reduced cortisol) to subsequent invasive procedures. In a study by the same group, however, infants who have received numerous invasive procedures at birth have elevated stress hormone (cortisol) levels later in infancy. Cortisol (stress hormone) levels are a good measure of the response to invasive procedures because they can be measured in saliva, and saliva samples are easy to collect. Saliva can be collected by a new filter paper method that simply involves touching the infant's tongue with the filter paper for 30 s.

Pain in pre-term infants has also led to increased cortisol (stress hormone) and a decrease in immune cells. Recent animal research indicates that toxic chemicals are released during repetitive painful events in the neonatal rat, which may have deleterious effects on the developing CNS. In turn, these negative effects on the CNS may affect pain thresholds and long-term behaviors. Thus, decreasing or preventing the disorganized responses to invasive procedures is important for infant well-being and normal development.

Pain Interventions

Pain can be decreased by touching. For example, newborns can suck on nipples to reduce pain during heelstick, or massaging the infant can reduce pain. One of the theories for the effectiveness of touch in alleviating pain is that touch receptors (neurons) are longer and more myelinated (more insulated) and they therefore can transmit a signal to the brain faster than pain receptors can. Pain receptors are shorter and less insulated. The first received touch message then 'closes the gate' (a biochemical/electrical phenomenon), so that the pain message that is the slowest to reach the brain is not received. This is called the 'gate theory'. The adult analog is rubbing a bumped 'crazy bone'.

Pain can also be alleviated by stimulating other senses, for example, smell and taste. Aromatherapy is an effective intervention for reducing pain including milk and lavender aromas. Following heelsticks newborns who received milk and lavender aromas had a lower stress hormone (cortisol) response. A familiar aroma during invasive procedures can also reduce pain, suggested by less crying and grimacing during the procedure. In contrast, infants who experience an unfamiliar aroma or have no aroma during the heelstick show increased grimacing and crying.

Sucrose, presented on a pacifier or via an eye dropper on the tongue also reduces pain, as judged by reduced crying in newborns following a heelstick. Sucrose has been compared to other substances such as water, and has been noted to be the most effective pain-reducer.

Infants who receive water during a heelstick also show increased relative right frontal electroencephalogram (EEG), which is a pattern that typically accompanies negative emotions. In contrast, the EEG of infants who receive sucrose does not appear to change. And, infants who receive sucrose show decreased heart rate after the heelstick, whereas heart rate remains elevated in infants who receive water.

Sucrose has also helped premature infants experience less pain during eye examinations. Eye examinations can be painful for the neonate. The use of topical anesthetic for the eye examinations is routine in some neonatal intensive care units, but does not completely decrease pain. Sucrose on the tongue combined with topical anesthetic can decrease pain during eye examinations. Newborns have received either topical anesthetic plus sucrose, or topical anesthetic plus water (placebo) prior to the eye examination. Sucrose was the most effective solution for alleviating pain. When pacifiers and sucrose were combined, the combination was the most effective in decreasing pain and crying.

Positive effects also occur following sucrose combined with holding the infant next to the adult's chest. In one study, crying, facial activity, heart rate, and vagal tone were measured before and after heelsticks for infants who received water or sucrose with holding vs. without holding. Crying was reduced by sucrose and holding, and when the interventions were combined, there were additive effects. The greatest reduction in heart rate occurred during the sucrose plus holding condition. Sucrose is thought to release endorphins that are responsible for the reduced pain. Animal studies suggest that sucrose may involve opioids, and sucking on a pacifier may release serotonin, which also blocks pain.

The mother's heartbeat has also been effective in reducing pain, as measured by a decrease in cortisol. When the mother's heartbeat was compared to a Japanese drum, cortisol decreased only during the mother's heartbeat, not during the drum. Thus, sounds, aromas, sucking and holding, and touch can alleviate pain as measured by cortisol, heart rate, and behavioral responses.

These interventions are critical because repeated pain stimuli have long-term effects. In one study, for example, a greater number of invasive procedures since birth were associated with dampened facial and heart rate reactions to a finger prick, and changes in the brain and spinal cord occurred with repeated painful experiences. More frequent pain experiences have also been related to lower cortisol responses to pain and to lower facial reactivity to pain.

Future Directions

Research on touch as one of the critical senses has been slow to develop, most particularly for infants' touch perception. Although the infants' early learning depends on their exploration by mouth and then by hand, very little is known about how the tactile world is perceived by mouth, and by hand. Skin-to-skin contact is also noted to be critical to early bonding, but, again, very little is known about how the infant perceives skin-to-skin contact. Perception of other touch modalities such as temperature and weight also need further research. Pain perception by infants and interventions for pain have received considerable attention, but only recently, because many people thought that the infant did not experience pain or had no memory for pain. Even though infants are now known to experience pain, painful procedures are still conducted on young infants without interventions. Future research is needed on different types and different combinations of interventions to prevent the cumulative effects of pain. Additional research is also needed on underlying mechanisms for touch perception and pain alleviation so that interventions can be adopted into clinical practice.

Acknowledgments

This research was supported by funding from Johnson and Johnson Pediatric Institute and Biotone.

See also: Attachment; Circumcision; Depression; Habituation and Novelty; Newborn Behavior; Perceptual Development; Prenatal Development; Taste and Smell.

Suggested Readings

Field T (2003) *Touch.* Cambridge: A Bradford Book.
Montagu A (1986) *Touching.* New York: Harper and Row.

Twins

L F DiLalla, P Y Mullineaux, and K K Elam, Southern Illinois University School of Medicine, Carbondale, IL, USA

Glossary

Conjoined twins – When an egg divides, leading to monozygotic twinning, but the division occurs late in development and therefore is incomplete, the two resulting embryos may not completely separate, leading to partial fusion, or conjoined twins. Twins may be joined physically at different places and to different extents, and we are not certain what causes this.

Gene–environment (GE) correlation – Genes and environment can be correlated three different ways. Passive GE correlation happens when both genes and environment come from the parents and thus are correlated. Reactive GE correlation happens when people in the environment react to something genetically influenced in the child, making the child's genes and subsequent environment correlated. Active GE correlation occurs when a child chooses an environment partly because of his or her genetic make-up.

Heritability – The extent to which genetic make-up influences behavior is called heritability. Genetic influences on behavior are indirect via proteins that are coded for by genes and that have effects on the brain. Heritability is a statistic that is specific to the population for which it is calculated. The comparison between monozygotic (MZ) and dizygotic (DZ) twins can be used to calculate the heritability of a particular behavior.

Twin research – Twins are a wonderful natural experiment because MZ and DZ twins can be compared to provide information about the extent to which genes influence behavior. MZ twins share 100% of their genes, whereas DZ twins share approximately 50% of their genes. Therefore, if MZ twins are more similar to each other on a particular behavior than DZ twins are to each other, then genetic influences can be assumed to be important for influencing that behavior.

Twins – Twins are children who are conceived at the same time from the same mother. There are two types of twins: MZ, when one egg is fertilized by one sperm and then the zygote splits in two, forming two genetic copies, and DZ, when two separate eggs are fertilized by two separate sperm, resulting in two siblings who share approximately 50% of their genetic material.

Introduction

Twins occur when two fetuses share the same uterus during a pregnancy. Overall, twins occur in approximately 1 in 32 births in the US. When this happens, resources must be shared during development in the uterus. This causes most twins to be born prematurely and with a lower birth weight than normal infants. Single births have a gestation period of approximately 40 weeks, whereas twin births normally range from 34 to 36 weeks. Twins are usually born in quick succession and are often kept for observation due to low birth weight and increased possibility of complications found in multiple births.

Two basic types of twinning can occur (monozygotic (MZ) and dizygotic (DZ)) depending on the number of eggs (zygotes) that are fertilized during pregnancy. MZ twins, sometimes known as identical twins, are the result of a single egg that is fertilized during conception that then splits into separate embryos. MZ twins, therefore, are 100% genetically the same because they result from a single fertilized egg. This causes them to look very similar and to be the same sex. (There are rare exceptions to this, however, as noted below.) After they split, these separate embryos develop into two fetuses that share the uterus during pregnancy. MZ twins may share the same amnion (the inner fetal membrane that contains the amniotic fluid) and placenta (the organ joining the mother and fetus that allows transfer of oxygen and nutrients to the fetus and waste from the fetus), or just share the same placenta. MZ twins occur in about 1 in 250 of all births.

Dizygotic twins, sometimes called fraternal twins, develop when two eggs are released at about the same time and both become fertilized. These eggs then develop into two separate fetuses. Because DZ twins are a result of two different eggs, they are as genetically similar as siblings and they share on average 50% of their genes. Opposite sex twins can occur in fraternal pairs because different sperm fertilize the two eggs, and sex is determined by whether the sperm carries an X or a Y chromosome. Thus, DZ twins do not necessarily look alike and may have differing features as well as similar ones. Dizygotic twins occur in about 1 in 36 of all births.

Since the 1990s, multiple births, especially dizygotic, have become more common as a result of infertility treatments, although multiple births may also occur naturally. In addition, certain maternal factors such as higher maternal age and race may contribute to multiple births.

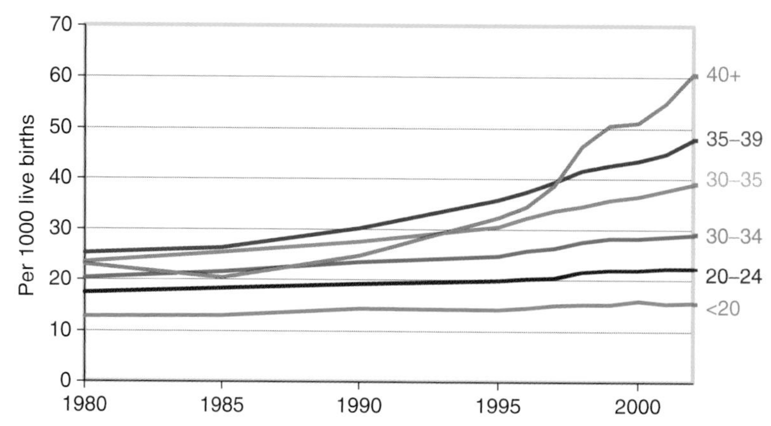

Figure 1 Twin birth rates by age of mother: US, 1980–2002. Source: National Vital Statistics System, NCHS, CDC.

The risk of having multiples doubles in women over the age of 35, partly because these women are more likely to use fertility drugs to conceive (see **Figure 1**). Also, women who are African American have a greater likelihood of having multiples.

Multiple births of three or more children can be comprised of any combination of MZ and DZ pairs. For instance, a single fertilized egg can split (resulting in twins), and then one of those can split again (resulting in genetically identical triplets). Similarly, three different eggs can be released simultaneously and can be fertilized by three different sperm, resulting in dizygotic triplets. Combinations of each of these can also occur, resulting in a combination of MZ and DZ multiples. DZ multiples are more common and often result from infertility treatments, such as implanting multiple eggs in the uterus or giving a woman fertility drugs that increase the likelihood of her releasing multiple eggs simultaneously. The overall rate for triplets is 1 in 535 of all births, and the frequency for having more than three children at once is even smaller at approximately 1 in 8700 of all births.

More unusual types of twinning can occur as well. Conjoined twins are the result of a fertilized zygote that fails to split completely. This causes the bodies of the twins to be fused together during development in the uterus. Conjoined twinning occurs on an average of 1 in 50 000 births, with only about 1 in 200 000 live births. Conjoined twins have a low survival rate, between 5% and 25%. Conjoined twins are most often males prenatally, but more females survive to birth, with the most common type of conjoining occurring at the front chest wall.

Other unusual outcomes of twinning can result in twins of opposite races or identical twins of opposite sex. Twins of opposite races occur only in DZ twins but can happen in two different ways. Two eggs can be released during ovulation and can be fertilized by two different fathers. Also, in an extremely rare situation, if both parents are of mixed race and if two eggs are released and fertilized by the same father, it is possible that the mother's and father's genes will contribute in such a way that one twin inherits only one skin color while the other twin inherits the other. Identical twins of opposite sex are also very rare and result from chromosomal birth defects that determine sex.

Other rare kinds of twinning are vanishing twins, thought to occur when multiple eggs are fertilized but one dies *in utero* and is reabsorbed by the mother. This usually occurs very early in pregnancy. Another case can occur when one twin fails to develop in the uterus, which can be detrimental to the other developing fetus. This is known as a parasitic twin and is similar to a conjoined twin. When this happens, the undeveloped twin is absorbed into the body of the developing fetus. The remains of this twin may appear as remnants such as teeth or bones in the healthy body of the surviving twin.

Twin Behaviors

Although there have been few systematic studies of twins as a special population, we do have some information about typical twin development and behavior. Twins are born into a unique and special situation by virtue of having a same-age sibling right from the early prenatal period. This can lead to both positive and negative consequences. For one thing, twins immediately have a same-age peer throughout development, and this typically yields a very close friend who is always there in their own home. However, twins must also share resources, beginning in the uterus and extending throughout childhood because they share parental attention and both emotional and financial resources of their parents. These consequences of being a twin can lead to behavioral outcomes that may be different from those for singleton, nontwin children. Some of the areas in which this has been examined include prosocial behaviors, psychological closeness, shyness, school behaviors, and language development.

Prosocial Behaviors

There do not appear to be differences in early social behaviors in same-sex vs. opposite-sex DZ twins during the preschool years. This is somewhat surprising if we assume that twins who have a co-twin who is more different from them (opposite-sex twin pairs) would have more experience with differences in playmates and therefore would be more socially prepared to interact well with other children. However, thus far it appears to be the case that DZ twins do not differ in their social competence based on whether they have a same-sex or an opposite-sex co-twin. They do appear to show poorer social competence than singletons, though. In general, preschool twins show less social independence and fewer friendships with other children than do singletons.

As twins get older, this trend begins to shift. At age 5 years, there is no difference between MZ and DZ twins in terms of their prosocial behaviors with nonfamiliar, same-age peers, but both types of twins show fewer prosocial behaviors than do singletons. However, in adolescence this difference in prosocial behaviors seems to disappear, although twins in this older age group begin to show more aggressive behaviors than do singletons.

Studies of the prosocial behaviors of twins are in the early stages, but they point to a possible risk for twins to exhibit less prosocial behavior than singletons. Twins at ages 3–5 years have been shown to have fewer friends and to exhibit fewer prosocial behaviors when they interact with other children. It has been hypothesized by researchers such as Nancy Segal that these behaviors may result from twins becoming used to playing with a same-age sibling who shares both genes and environment with them, and therefore they are less interested in playing with other children or are less able to communicate well with them on a social level. This behavior may put twins at risk for later social interaction difficulty, and therefore research on the causes of this lack of prosocial behavior must continue.

Psychological Closeness

MZ twins appear to share a special bond that sets them apart from other types of relationships. This does not appear to be a result of parental training, because even twins whose parents try to treat them differently are likely to behave similarly and to develop this bond. This bond can be so strong that it persists even when something happens to set the twins apart, including such severe events as partial paralysis or even death. MZ twins typically define their co-twin as their 'best friend'. This does not mean that these twins never fight. In fact, they frequently do, and they are as likely as DZ twins to describe their rate of fighting as 'sometimes' on a scale from never to sometimes to always. The important point is that these fights do not detract from their love for each other or from their feelings of closeness. It is not unusual for MZ twins to bicker constantly but then to stand up for each other if anyone else should try to harm either one of them.

Dizygotic twins also share a special bond, but it does not seem to be of the same quality as the bond that MZ twins share. DZ twins tend to be less close to each other than are MZ twins. They probably are more comparable to nontwin siblings in terms of psychological closeness. Nonetheless, many do have special bonds with their co-twins. There has not been a reported difference in closeness between same-sex and opposite-sex twins, but this may be because it has not been explored in research. DZ twins appear to share the same sort of feelings toward each other as other nontwin siblings share, although their feelings of closeness may be slightly increased simply by virtue of their growing up at the same time together in the same family environment.

Differences in cooperative behavior have been demonstrated by Nancy Segal and colleagues for school-age twins, with MZ twins being more cooperative with each other than were DZ twins. However, this difference did not extend to their cooperation with other children. This suggests that the bond they feel with each other is special and is not simply training for how to behave in general with other children. MZ twins may be more cooperative because they are so much more similar to each other and therefore it is easier for them to work together toward a common goal. They understand each other's styles and they conceptualize the work in more similar ways than do DZ twins.

Comparable studies of twin closeness have not been conducted with infants or preschoolers. It would be very interesting to know at what age twins begin to sense this special bond and to become aware of the presence of another person who is so similar to them and who shares the environment with them. Infants begin to show social referencing and separation anxiety toward the end of their first year of life, demonstrating an awareness of the differences in the people around them. It is likely that it is about the same time that twins, especially MZ twins, might begin to form the special bond between them that becomes the basis for their closeness as they grow.

Although few investigations of twin closeness during infancy have been conducted, twin attachment behavior (a close emotional bond between the twins) has been examined. In 1994, Nathan Gottfried and colleagues demonstrated that the presence of the co-twin served as a source of security during the absence of the mother which is a highly stressful event for this age group (18–34 months). Even though the twins exhibited lower levels of distress when their co-twin was present during the mother's absence, the twins did not actively soothe or comfort each other. This suggests that early co-twin attachment provides some degree of comfort and acts as a buffer in stressful situations experienced during infancy.

Shyness

It is possible that MZ twins are shyer than either DZ twins or nontwins because they are used to interacting with another child, their co-twin, who is genetically the same as them and therefore is probably physically and behaviorally like them. Because they spend so much time with these genetically identical co-twins, they may not learn how to interact with other, different children as well. Therefore, they may feel more uncomfortable with others and show shy behaviors. If this is true, then it also would be expected that DZ twins would be less shy than MZ twins, but they might be shyer than nontwins because they are used to interacting with another child (their co-twin) who is quite similar to them, often more so than other children. However, it is also possible that twins may be less shy than nontwins for the opposite reason. They are used to interacting with another child their same age, and therefore they may feel more comfortable interacting with other children.

Research exploring these two possibilities has been sparse. However, some researchers have studied shyness in twins in order to better understand genetic influences on this behavior (see the section on 'Internalizing behavior') rather than to compare twins to nontwins. One study by Lisabeth DiLalla and colleagues in 1994 noted that 2-year-old MZ twins appear to score higher on measures of shyness than do DZ twins. Another study by Lisabeth DiLalla and Rebecca Caraway in 2004 on 5-year-old children has demonstrated that both MZ and DZ twins behave more shyly than do nontwins when they interact with unfamiliar peers. Thus, twins appear to be shyer than nontwins, perhaps because they are so used to playing with a genetically similar playmate (their co-twin) and therefore are shyer about playing with someone they do not know as well. However, parent ratings actually have shown exactly the opposite trend, with twins being rated as less shy than nontwins. This might be a result of parents seeing their two twins playing together so frequently that when they rate the twins, they imagine them as being fairly outgoing. If this is the reason for the different results, then parent rating biases are playing an important role and it is necessary to consider this carefully whenever parent ratings are utilized. Parent ratings are frequently used when infants and young children are studied, so it is important to be careful about the results that are obtained.

Although there is little scientific evidence concerning how shy twins are, they do appear to be more inhibited when they are interacting with unknown children their same age. This is not consistent with parent reports, but it is enough to suggest that this might be an area that requires further exploration. In addition, parents of twins often are concerned when one twin appears to be much shyer than the other twin. This is an area that has not been addressed in twin research and it also bears further examination.

School Behaviors

One issue that twins but not singleton children experience is whether to place the twins in the same or in different classrooms during the school years. In general, this decision is made by the specific school system that the twins attend and often this decision is made without consulting the opinion of the twins' parents. Legislation has been proposed by a few states such as Minnesota that would require twins to be kept in the same classroom at the parents' request. There are two competing reasons why twins should be kept together or separated in the classroom. Proponents of placing twins in separate classrooms claim that the close social relationship of twins may impede their development by not allowing the growth of their individuality and independence. Conversely, proponents of keeping twins in the same classroom claim that separating twins may be more stressful and lead to distress and emotional difficulties for these twins because it is the first time the twins may have spent a significant amount of time apart. Although educators, the school systems, and parents may have differing opinions about whether or not it is best to separate twins at school, there has been little research conducted to address this debate.

Researchers have focused primarily on the impact of class separation on internalizing behaviors (fear, shyness, withdrawal, depression), externalizing behaviors (aggression, disruptiveness, impulsivity), and academic achievement. Lucy Tully and colleagues examined the impact of placing twins in separate classrooms and found that twins who were placed in different classrooms when they began school exhibited more internalizing problems than those twins who were placed in the same classroom for the first year of school. These internalizing problems persisted over time for MZ twins. This indicates that placing twins in separate classrooms may be more distressing for MZ twins than for DZ twins.

The impact of class separation on externalizing behaviors differs from that of internalizing problem behaviors. There is evidence that twins who are separated do not exhibit more externalizing problems than those twins who were not separated. In 2007, Lisabeth DiLalla and Paula Mullineaux investigated the impact of separating twins on problem behaviors reported by multiple informants. For MZ twins identified with conduct problems (behaviors characterized as noncompliant, aggressive, and rule-breaking) before beginning school, separating these twins actually increases the incidence of conduct and peer problems as rated by teachers and parents. This indicates, at least for conduct and peer problems, that MZ twins may have fewer behavioral problems when placed in the same classroom.

With regard to academic achievement, there appear to be benefits for keeping MZ twins in the same classroom but there are some advantages to separating DZ twins after the first year of school. In 2003, Lacy Tully and colleagues found that MZ and DZ twins who are placed in separate classrooms are likely to have poorer reading abilities than twins who are placed in the same classroom. Later separation in school may be beneficial for DZ twins. When DZ twins are separated after the first year of school, they tend to be rated by teachers as working harder than DZ twins who are placed in the same classroom. Later separation in school may be beneficial for DZ twins. When DZ twins are separated after the first year of school, they tend to be rated by teachers as working harder than DZ twins who are placed in the same classroom. The long-term affects of early separation on academic achievement was examined in 2005 by van Leeuwen and colleagues. No significant differences in academic performance on mathematic and language exams were observed between the groups of twins who always had been separated in school and those twins who had never been separated in school. Interestingly, those twins who had experienced both separation and nonseparation performed the best on the mathematic and language exams.

Overall, research has indicated that separating twins in school may not be beneficial for twins with regard to problem behaviors and academic achievement. In addition, there is some indication that the impact of school separation may differ for MZ and DZ twins. Currently, the research that has been conducted on the effects of classroom separation has focused on the early school years. It is possible that keeping twins in the same classrooms is only beneficial during the early schooling experience. Additional research on the impact of separation during later elementary school and beyond must be conducted to determine if the advantages of keeping twins in the same classrooms persist.

Twin Language

Twins experience a unique childhood because they coexist with a companion (their co-twin) with whom they learn and grow. The twins are at a similar developmental level by virtue of being the same age. The language development of twins is often not the same as singleton children but may lag behind by about 3 months. This has been attributed in part to low birth weight, which is common among twins. Another possible explanation is that twin children have co-twins who are so developmentally and socially intimate that a separate form of communication may arise, possibly interfering with normal language development. This unique form of communication has been termed twin language, criptophasia, autonomous language, and secret language. In the past, the lack of a concrete definition of twin language has made identifying nontraditional language development in twins difficult. 'Private language' and 'shared understanding' are two well-defined terms used in twin language studies. Private language is defined as comprehensible communication solely used between twins. This type of communication has often been called secret language as it is not used to communicate with others. Shared understanding is verbal communication not comprehensible to persons outside the twin pair but comprised of language not used exclusively within the twin pair. Around 40% of twins develop some personal way of communicating with each other. This occurs most frequently with identical twins, which may reflect a closer social relationship between those twins. While the most obvious cases of twin language are verbal adaptations of normal language, many twins also develop nonverbal methods of communicating as well.

The verbal communication that takes place between twins is most often an adaptation of language learned from parents and others in the twins' lives. This type of speech is not a new language altogether as speech often adheres to the sentence structure and grammar of 'normal' language. Twin language has been proposed as a form of immature speech during the process of normal language development. These examples of twin language are seen to emerge during periods when normal language development would take place, around 2 years of age and older. Twins usually grow out of using unique speech. Often, placement of twins in different classrooms or introducing playmates who are capable of normal language enhances normal development. These steps foster language development as twins' lack of interaction with others is thought to increase the likelihood of using twin language.

Social factors have been linked to the development of twin languages. The lack of outside interaction has been shown to contribute to using twin language. Twins who participate in nonverbal play, do not attend preschool, and do not have any older siblings appear to be most likely to use a unique twin language. Nonverbal play is thought to decrease the need for verbalization. Attending preschool and being in the presence of older siblings may act to introduce social forces that require a twin to participate in ordinary language exchanges, thus fostering normal development. A risk factor that may contribute to special twin language development is that twins receive less verbal communication and more nonverbal communication from their mothers than do singletons. Mothers of twins have also been shown to exhibit less affection and more controlling behaviors than do mothers of singletons. This may be a product of a more stressful environment from raising two same-aged children compared to one child. The combination of social isolation and less parental communication may result in the development of a special twin language.

Twin language is a remarkable phenomenon. The fact that a variation of normal language develops between children who are so young, and that it is often incomprehensible to those outside of the twin pair, contributes to the fascinating nature of twin language. Even though this language is often foreign, even to parents of the twins, the language component of this communication indicates a step toward normal language development. The often isolated nature of the social world of twins contributes to the intimate communication that may form between twins. This interesting step in the development of language reflects the unique social and developmental world that twins experience.

Why and How We Use Twins to Study Behavior

Unlike behavioral studies conducted with other species, studies of human behavior are limited to naturally occurring genetic and environmental variation. Fortunately, nature has provided a naturally occurring experimental situation through twinning that can be used to identify the impact of genes and environment on human behavior.

Comparing MZ and DZ Twins

By comparing MZ and DZ twins, we are able to test the relative influence of genes and the environment on human behavior. It is this comparison between MZ and DZ twins that allows us to begin to disentangle the impact of genetic and environmental influences on human behavior. This can be done because MZ twins share 100% of their genes and DZ twins share, on average, 50% of their genes. If genetic influences are important for a particular behavior, then MZ twins will be more similar to each other than are DZ twins for that behavior. If environmental influences are important, then MZ and DZ twins will be fairly similar for that behavior. This is because shared environmental influences impact MZ and DZ twins equally.

There are two basic types of twin studies: twins reared together and twins reared apart. Twins reared together are twins who are not separated and who are raised in the same home. Sometimes twins are separated at birth or shortly thereafter and are adopted into different families and raised in different environments. Twins reared apart still share the same percentage of genes (100% for MZ twins and on average 50% for DZ twins) as twins reared together, but MZ and DZ twins share none of their environment when they are raised apart. Thus, any similarities between twins reared apart would be due to genetic influences, whereas similarities between twins reared together may be due to genes or environmental factors and can only be determined by comparing the two twin types.

Heritability

Heritability (h^2) refers to the amount of phenotypic variation among individuals that is due to genetic influences. This statistic can be roughly estimated by subtracting the DZ twin correlation for a trait from the MZ twin correlation for that trait and doubling the difference. Thus, we can determine whether genes are impacting a behavior and how much they impact that behavior. For example, if the MZ correlation for intelligence quotient (IQ) is 0.86 and the DZ correlation for IQ is 0.60, then roughly 52% (twice the difference between 0.86 and 0.60) of the difference observed among individuals for IQ is attributed to genetic influences. This also tells us that the other ~–50% of the differences in IQ scores are due to environmental influences.

Environment

There are two types of environmental influences: shared environment (c^2) and nonshared environment (e^2). Shared environment, also called common environment, includes the aspects of the environment that are shared among twins. By definition, both MZ twins and DZ twins share 100% of their shared environment. This includes environments such as their home environments, neighborhood environments, and school environments. Shared environmental factors are those factors shared by individuals that make them more similar. Conversely, nonshared environment, also called unique environment, refers to aspects of the environment that only one member of the MZ or DZ twin pair experiences and makes the twins less similar to each other. Examples of nonshared environment include one twin experiencing an illness that the other twin does not, having different teachers at school, participating in different activities, and socializing with different friends. Just as with heritability, we can estimate how much impact shared environment (c^2) and nonshared environment (e^2) have on behavior. Shared environmental influences are estimated by subtracting h^2 from the MZ twin correlation. Nonshared environment is estimated by subtracting the MZ twin correlation from 1.0. Any error variance is represented in the nonshared environment estimate. Using the MZ and DZ twins from the above example, where the MZ correlation was 0.86 and the DZ correlation was 0.60, shared environment would explain 34% of the variance in IQ scores and nonshared environment (and any error) would explain 14% of the variance in IQ scores. Heritability (h^2), shared environment (c^2), and nonshared environment (e^2) always equal 1.0, which represents 100% of the genetic and environmental influences impacting a behavior.

Genetic Influences on Environmental Influences

Certain measures traditionally have been believed to represent children's environments (e.g., how often mothers name objects when interacting with infants). However, we now know that there are genetic influences on these measures of the environment. This suggests that parents are responding to differences in children's genetically influenced characteristics and therefore are creating differences in the child's environment that are related to the child's genetic propensities. These are called gene–environment correlations.

The Equal Environments Assumption

One of the most important criticisms of the twin method is that MZ twins may experience a more similar environment than DZ twins. Critics suggest that MZ twins may be treated more similarly because of being labeled as MZ twins and because it is easier to identify MZ twins based on physical appearance than DZ twins. This may cause people to create a more similar environment for them because of the label or their similar appearance. This criticism challenges the 'equal environments assumption' (EEA), which is based on the belief that the environment that MZ twins experience is not significantly more similar than the environment that DZ twins experience. If this assumption is violated because MZ twins experience a more similar environment than that of DZ twins, then the estimate of genetic influence would be overestimated. Several studies have specifically investigated the EEA, and in general the assumption appears to be supported for most behaviors. Likewise, the effects of mislabeling twin pairs (e.g, labeling MZ twins as DZ twins) have shown that zygosity (MZ or DZ) is a better predictor of how similar twin behavior is than parents' perceptions of zygosity.

Gene–Environment Correlation and Interaction

Twin research allows us to consider the extent to which environment and genes affect behaviors. This method was essential for advancing our understanding of behavior, from the belief during most of the twentieth century that all behavior can be attributable to environmental influences to our more recent understanding that our genetic make-up also plays an important part in influencing our behaviors.

However, the picture is much more complicated than we originally thought. The interplay between genotype and environment is difficult to disentangle conceptually and even more difficult to measure. For instance, infants who live in chaotic homes often are more temperamentally difficult. We must ask 'why' these infants are this way. It is possible that their environment is so noisy and unstructured that they respond by behaving in a difficult manner (they may cry more, they may be hard to soothe). However, it is also possible that difficult infants make their parents so tired and anxious that the home environment provided by the parents becomes more chaotic. Finally, it is possible that these infants and their parents share genes that make them difficult in infancy and more chaotic and unstructured in adulthood.

At the basis of this question is the issue of genotype–environment (GE) correlation. These correlations probably occur with most of the behaviors that we study, but they are extremely difficult to measure. There are three types of GE correlations (see **Table 1**). The first is 'passive' GE correlation. This occurs when a child gets both genes and environment from the parent. Infants of course inherit their genotype from their parents, and also they are raised in the home environment that is shaped by their parents. Thus, their genes and their environment are correlated with each other. The second type of GE correlation is called 'reactive' or 'evocative'. This occurs when children behave a certain way that is partly genetically influenced, and then this behavior evokes certain responses from the people around them, thus influencing their environment. Again, in this case the genes and the environment are now correlated with each other. The third type of GE correlation, which does not occur until children are older, is called 'active'. With this, children (or adults) choose a particular environment based in part on personal attributes that are genetically influenced. Once again, genes and environment are correlated with each other when this happens.

One other way in which genes and environment work together is through gene–environment interaction. This happens when people with certain genotypes respond differently to a specific environment than do people with other genotypes. For example, an infant who is temperamentally reactive (partly as a result of genetic

Table 1 Three types of gene–environment correlation

Type of correlation	*Definition*	*Typical ages*	*Example*
Passive	Genes and environment come from the same source (the biological parent)	Birth through adolescence, but most important early in life	Child inherits athletic ability from parent, and parent constantly plays ball with child (thus, genes and environment are correlated)
Active or evocative	Child evokes certain environments from others based in part on his or her genetic make-up	Throughout life	Child is genetically athletically inclined, therefore parents and coaches encourage athletic activities for the child
Active	Child actively seeks environments that match with his or her genetically influenced preferences	Childhood and throughout adulthood	Child is genetically athletically inclined, therefore he or she chooses to attend a college with a strong athletic department

make-up) may be overwhelmed by a chaotic home environment and may cry and fuss quite a lot, whereas an infant who is temperamentally easy may find this same environment to be stimulating or at least may not be bothered by it. Thus, it is not only genes or only environment that cause certain behaviors, but it is also the complex way in which these two influences work together that lead to certain behavioral outcomes.

It is critical to understand genetic effects because if we ignore them then we incorrectly interpret findings of environmental effects as either stronger or weaker than they really are. This has important implications for policies and intervention programs. If we assume that the environment is responsible for making children either aggressive or smart or sociable, but in fact their genetic make-up is also important for these behaviors, then the intervention programs that are designed will be inadequate. Thus, a greater understanding of the ways in which genes and environment work together to lead to behavioral outcomes in children will add important information that we can use when designing programs to help children maximize their potential in all areas.

Twin Study Results on Normal Development

The study of twins allows us to learn more about genetic and environmental influences on various behaviors, including temperament, cognition, and social behaviors. This section details information we have learned about these behaviors in general from studying twins and reviews evidence from twin studies about genetic effects that we believe are generalizable to all children.

Temperament

Experiments with twins have yielded valuable information useful for understanding aspects of personality and development in nontwins as well. One of these areas is temperament, which is a stable, early developing tendency to experience and express emotion in a particular way. For example, children may be perceived as fussy, easygoing, or shy depending on how they respond to everyday situations in life. Temperament is attributed to both biological and environmental factors. Individual biological differences in emotional expression have been based on reactivity and self-regulation. Self-regulation is the active control of emotional expression. Examination of self-regulation measures such as attention, approach, avoidance, and behavioral inhibition (inhibition to new stimuli, or extreme shyness) have indicated that biological influences on temperament are dependent on the child's level of maturation. Physiological measures such as heart rate, cortisol levels, and brain activity have been used to study how reactive children are to new stimuli. In periods of competition, decreased positive emotional expressions are seen in conjunction with increased cortisol levels and increased heart rate. Inhibition in children has also been related to an increase in heart rate during novel situations, suggesting a physiological bias for behavioral inhibition.

Genetic effects on temperament have been studied extensively from infancy to adulthood using twins. Recent research on infants and toddlers has found that many temperamental traits are moderately influenced by genes. In general, negatively valenced traits such as aggression have shown evidence of being largely genetically influenced. Positively valenced traits such as happiness show moderate genetic influence with more environmental effects. Inhibition has shown moderate genetic influence and small effects of the environment, although extreme inhibition has shown very strong genetic effects.

Environmental factors that children experience have also been shown to affect the development of temperament. The main sources of environmental influence on temperament appear to be parent–child relationships. One important aspect of the mother–child relationship is synchrony, which is a state of shared focus, with communal exchanges between interacting partners. Synchronous mother–child pairs rated high on positive emotion and engagement yielded children who were rated as more socially competent. Mother–child pairs rated high on negative emotion and low engagement predicted children who were more aggressive and less socially competent. Mother–child synchrony is beneficial for the child by providing the child a guide for later patterns of social and emotional response. More recently, the emotional impact of such parental relationships has been researched. One twin study found that fearful and pleasurable aspects of temperament in 3–12-month-old children were associated with low or high amounts of parental sensitivity, respectively, as seen in parent–child interactions.

Twins have been invaluable in the study of temperament. They have helped researchers explore the biological, genetic, and environmental effects on temperament. It is through the use of twins that we are able to uncover how these processes unfold in normal human development.

Cognition

Twins also have been instrumental in elucidating the impact of genetic and environmental influences on cognitive ability across the lifespan. By comparing MZ and DZ twins' similarities on measures of cognitive ability over the course of development, we are able to determine whether the impacts of genetic and environmental factors are stable from one age to the next. Genetic influences have been indicated for measures of general cognitive ability with genetic and environmental influences each accounting for, on average, 50% of the observed variance for measures of cognitive ability. Although both genetic and environmental influences impact cognitive ability, the balance between genetic and environmental influences changes over the lifespan. Heritability estimates of cognitive ability appear to increase with age, from less than 20% in infancy, to 40% in early childhood, to 50–60% in early adulthood, and finally increasing to 80% in late adulthood. This indicates that genetic factors become increasingly important for cognitive ability and the impact of environmental influences decreases over the lifespan.

Cognitive ability is considered to be fairly stable over the lifespan. This does not mean that cognitive ability does not change over the course of development or that the cognitive ability of a 6-month-old is the same as that of a 6-year-old. What stability in cognitive ability reflects is the relative constancy of individual differences or the extent that children's rank order in comparison to peers is constant. In general, infants' performance on cognitive measures of novelty preference, memory, and learning spatiotemporal rules is related to their performance on cognitive measures during childhood, although infant measures of sensory and motor skills which reference the infant's developmental level are not highly related to their later performance on cognitive measures during childhood.

Twin studies have also been utilized when examining cognitive growth over time and the changing impact of genetic and environmental influences. Infants' scores on standard measures of cognitive ability are comparable for MZ and DZ twins from 3 to 12 months, which does not suggest genetic influences on these behaviors at these ages. This is also true of some measures of specific cognitive abilities in infants, such as visual anticipation of patterns. However, some other measures of specific cognitive abilities, such as recognition of novel faces, appear to show slightly greater genetic influences. During early childhood, MZ twins begin to perform significantly more similarly than DZ twins on measures of cognitive ability, suggesting new genetic influences. Additionally, Ronald Wilson in 1983 found evidence indicating that the pattern of change in cognitive abilities over time is more similar for MZ twins than for DZ twins, indicating that the spurts and lags experienced during early cognitive growth are being influenced by genes.

The use of twins in studying the development of cognition has led to a better understanding of the impact of genetic and environmental influences on cognitive development.

Externalizing Behaviors

Externalizing behaviors refer to acting out behaviors, such as being aggressive or engaging in delinquent activities (including things such as stealing or vandalizing). Children who engage in these behaviors typically may have more difficulty making friends or fitting in well with society. Children who engage in many of these behaviors often drop out of school or are neglected or rejected by their peers. By understanding the development of problem behaviors, perhaps we can help these children have better and more productive lives in society. Twin research has been valuable in shedding light on some of the causes of externalizing behaviors in children.

Although most research on the genetic effects on externalizing behaviors in children has been conducted on school-aged twins, there is some recent work examining the heritability of externalizing problems in preschoolers and some work specifically on 2- and 3-year-olds. Research on older children, aged 5 and up, mostly suggests that there is a heritable effect on externalizing behaviors, meaning that part of the reason why children either do or do not exhibit externalizing behaviors has to do with their genetic make-up. However, genes only account for about half of the influence on these behaviors. The rest seems to be a result of nonshared environmental influences which are influences that make children less similar to each other. This is counter-intuitive because many have believed that the ways in which parents raise and discipline their children are responsible for behaviors such as aggression. However, the research based on twins does not support this, or, if discipline is an important influence, the twin research suggests that it must vary across children within the same family.

One possible problem with much of the early research on twins and externalizing was that most researchers relied on parent ratings of children's behaviors. It is possible that parent ratings are biased and that parents may rate MZ twins more similarly because they look more alike. Therefore, it is also important to have other types of ratings on children before we can state confidently that externalizing behaviors are genetically influenced. Fortunately, a few recent studies on 5-year-old twins using teacher reports and observational ratings from testers have been conducted. The results of these studies support the earlier work based on parent report, that aggressive behaviors in 5-year-olds do have genetic influence.

The question still remains whether these behaviors are genetically influenced even earlier, especially during the first few years of life. Very few twin studies have examined infants' externalizing behaviors, but these appear to support a genetic influence on these behaviors even at such young ages. One study examining parental ratings of aggression during the second half of the first year of life showed a strong influence of genetic factors on externalizing behaviors. In addition, at ages 2 and 3 years there also appears to be a large influence of genotype on aggressive and acting-out behaviors. Studies from Canada and Denmark have shown this, suggesting that these results are not specific to certain cultures. However, these findings rely on parent ratings. In the future, it will be important to show the same effects using other, unbiased methods of rating children's aggression as well.

Empathy and Prosocial Behaviors

Prosocial behaviors, which include helping, sharing, and caring for others, have been studied much less than problem behaviors, and therefore we know less about them in terms of what causes them. Initial twin studies examing prosocial behaviors indicate a slightly different pattern from externalizing or acting-out behaviors. Although there appear to be genetic influences on prosocial behaviors, there are also notable environmental effects. Because these behaviors are so important for humans, it makes sense that they should be taught and reinforced in the family environment. There is some evidence that the shared family environment is indeed an important influence on prosocial behaviors in young children, which supports this view.

Prosocial behaviors and empathy are difficult to measure in infancy and parent reports are often used. Parent reports are based on behaviors such as showing concern when another is hurt and offering to help another person. However, as with externalizing problems, parent reports may be subject to rater bias, with parents rating MZ twins more similarly than DZ twins. Thus, it is always important to utilize other sources, such as behavioral ratings of twins by trained coders.

In the MacArthur Longitudinal Twin Study, researchers Carolyn Zahn-Waxler, Joann Robinson, and colleagues have attempted to examine empathy in infants from 1 to 3 years of age by observing infant twins' responses to their mothers' demonstrations of pain, such as pretending to hurt her foot. They also observed twins' responses to hearing another child cry. Whether or not these behaviors are equivalent to more mature versions of empathy is uncertain. However, the researchers did find that MZ twins responded more similarly to each other than did DZ twins, suggesting a genetic influence on these behaviors. These results were not corroborated by parent reports of empathetic behaviors of the infants, which failed to show evidence of genetic influence on empathy.

Thus, there is still much to learn about the causes of empathy and prosocial behaviors using twins. There is evidence that genotype has an impact on these behaviors. However, until further research is conducted, using multiple methods of assessment, we cannot be certain about these findings. As with externalizing problem behaviors, it is most likely that the reason that genotype is a significant influence on prosocial behaviors is via the link with temperament. It is probable that genotype influences temperament, which in turn manifests a direct influence on both problem and prosocial behaviors in children.

Internalizing Behavior

From birth, infants interact differently with the world around them. Some infants respond and interact with others freely. Other infants will warm up to others only after a period of time. There are also those infants who never warm up to others and are withdrawn and timid in social situations. Shyness and inhibition are precursors of a child's developing personality during childhood.

Being shy or inhibited can last into the early childhood years. A general trend has been found for children to become less inhibited as they age, displaying better inhibitory control. Studies on twins have shown that behavioral inhibition can be attributed to both genetic and environmental factors. The genetic component of inhibition and shyness also contributes to its stability over time. In twin studies, behavioral measures of shyness for children have shown a moderate correlation with later inhibition in different situations. Also, inhibited behavior between MZ twins has been observed to be more similar than that of DZ twins. This suggests that shyness is a cross-situational attribute that has consistency across age. Changes in inhibition are thought to be mediated by normal child development and environmental factors.

The discontinuity of inhibition is also proposed to have a genetic influence as normal child development is in part genetically driven. The concordance of change in the behaviors of MZ twins, including shyness, is more similar than that of DZ twins. The similarity in the pattern of change between MZ twins suggests that this change is genetically driven by developmental processes. Other environmental factors such as parenting and traumatic episodes have also been observed to contribute to child inhibition.

In contrast to normal inhibition, extreme inhibition has shown a very high estimate of genetic influence. This suggests that it is a separate construct from normal shyness, possibly related to other disorders such as social phobia or obsessive–compulsive disorder. The twin literature has shown that such extreme inhibition is also a more stable trait over time. Children identified as very inhibited early in life are more likely also to be very inhibited later in life. The presence of genetic effects on extreme inhibition is quite clear. Work with twins has led researchers to study promising causes of this behavior. The serotonin transporter promoter region polymorphism gene (a gene that regulates serotonin expression) is one possible cause of inhibited behavior. This gene has both a long and a short form. The long form of this gene has been associated with shyness in children. Other genes have been proposed to relate to inhibition and anxiety-related behaviors, but less support is present. These behaviors might have a number of genes that influence behavior rather than one key gene. As findings from molecular genetic studies become clearer, so will the role that genes have on behavior.

Twin studies have also shown that physiological measures of temperament relate to inhibition. Measures of heart rate, cortisol levels, and brain activity have shown that extremely inhibited children have a physiological propensity to be behaviorally inhibited. Physiological reactions related to shyness might produce the actual feelings that account for inhibition behavior and feelings. Behavioral inhibition is thought to be linked to physiological reactions through stress-sensitive systems that govern reaction to environmental stimuli in inhibited children. Specifically, inhibited children have been shown to have higher heart rates as well as less variable heart rates in general. The role of the sympathetic and parasympathetic nervous systems have been proposed as factors in inhibition as well.

Through the use of twins, researchers have been able to study the genetic, environmental, and physiological bases of many forms of behavior. As research continues, knowledge of genetic and environmental contributions to psychological behaviors can be pinpointed. With the use of molecular genetic research, the field of twin research will move closer to understanding the impact specific genes may have on various behaviors.

Summary

Twins have always intrigued us, and they continue to fascinate psychology researchers today. Twins are interesting both in their own right as human beings growing up together, and also as a natural experiment for researchers interested in understanding genetic and environmental influences on development. Because there are two types of twins – MZ, who share 100% of their genes, and DZ, who share on average 50% of their genes – these two types can be compared to obtain estimates of the genetic and environmental influences on behaviors. There is speculation about individual characteristics of twins, such as why they seem to be more shy, more psychologically close to each other, and more likely to form special languages, but we are only beginning to examine these aspects of twins in infancy. There is still much to learn about the secrets of being a twin.

See also: Anger and Aggression; Behavior Genetics; Endocrine System; Fear and Wariness; Genetics and Inheritance; Language Development: Overview; Nature vs. Nurture; Social Interaction; Temperament.

Suggested Readings

DiLalla LF (ed.) (2004) *Behavior Genetic Principles: Perspectives in Development, Personality, and Psychopathology.* Washington: APA Press.

Segal N (1999) *Entwined Lives: Twins and What They Tell Us about Human Behavior.* New York: Dutton Books.

Segal N (2005) *Indivisible by Two: Lives of Extraordinary Twins.* Boston, MA: Harvard University Press.

Thorpe K and Danby S (2006) Special section on the social worlds of children who are twins. *Twin Research and Human Genetics* 9(1): 90–174.

V

Vision Disorders and Visual Impairment

J Atkinson, University College London, London, UK
O Braddick, University of Oxford, Oxford, UK

Glossary

ABCDEFV – Atkinson Battery of Child Development for Examining Functional Vision.
Accommodation – Adjustment of the lens of the eye to bring objects at different distances into sharp focus on the retina.
Acuity – A measure of the ability to detect fine detail.
Ambylopia – A loss of visual acuity that cannot be explained by the optical effects of refractive error or by pathology of the eye. Amblyopia is believed to result from functional changes in neural connections, primarily in the visual cortex, that results from degraded visual input.
Anisometropia – A difference of refraction between the two eyes.
Aphakia – Absence of the lens of the eye.
Astigmatism – A difference in refraction of the eye between different meridians, usually caused by the cornea having different degrees of curvature in different directions.
Binocular – Using the two eyes together.
Binocular disparity – Difference between position of images of an object as viewed by the two eyes.
Cataract – An opacity in the lens of the eye.
Contrast sensitivity – The ability to detect the difference between light and dark parts of the image.
Cornea – The curved transparent surface at the front of the eye, through which light passes into the pupil.
Crowding – The effect that acuity for recognizing a letter is reduced if it is surrounded by other letters.
Cycloplegia – The relaxation of the muscles that control accommodation of the lens.
Dorsal stream – A series of cortical areas, transmitting visual information from V1 to the parietal lobe of the brain, that extracts information and provides a sense of spatial relationships and the basis for visually guided actions.
Electroretinogram (ERG) – An electrical signal recorded from the surface of the cornea, that originates in the retina and can help to diagnose disease conditions of the photoreceptors and other retinal elements.
Extrastriate cortex – The collection of visually responsive areas of cortex that surround *area V1* and receive input from it directly or indirectly. It includes areas V2, V3, V3a, V4, V5, and lateral occipital (LO).
Fixation – The act of moving the eye, or maintaining its direction, so that the object of interest is focused on the fovea. Sometimes called 'fixing' in newborns.
Form coherence – A measure of the global visual processing that integrates information about static shape and pattern in the ventral cortical stream.
Fovea – The region in the center of the retina where the cone photoreceptors are most densely packed, and which therefore provides the highest acuity.
Frontal eye fields (FEF) – A region of the frontal cortex, that is involved in eye movements control.
Fusiform face area (FFA) – A region of the brain presumed to be a specialized center for processing the visual information used to detect and recognize faces.
Glaucoma – A disorder where the pressure of fluids within the eye is abnormally high.
Habituation/recovery – A method of investigating the ability of young infants to distinguish different visual patterns. If one pattern is presented repeatedly, the time spent by the infant looking at it declines (habituation). If the looking time increases when a new pattern is presented (recovery), this is evidence that

the infants can distinguish the two patterns and so respond to the novelty of the new pattern.

Hyperopia or hypermetropia – Far-sightedness.

Hypoxic-ischemic encephalopathy (HIE) – Widespread brain damage caused by a general deprivation of oxygen (hypoxia).

Lateral geniculate nucleus (LGN) – A nucleus in the thalamus where the fibers of the optic nerve terminate.

Lateral occipital (LO) – An area on the lateral and ventral aspects of the human occipital cortex, which responds strongly to intact images of objects and scenes as opposed to scrambled versions of the same images.

Mirror neuron – A neuron which responds either when an animal is executing a certain action, or when it sees that action being performed by another.

Monocular – Relating to one eye only (contrast with binocular).

Motion coherence – A measure of visual processing that detects elements moving in a consistent direction, although the remaining elements are moving in random directions.

Myopia – Near-sightedness.

Nystagmus – Repetitive oscillatory movements of the eyes.

Optokinetic nystagmus (OKN) – Nystagmus induced by motion of all, or a large part of, the field of view. The eyes repetitively follow the movement of the field and then flick rapidly back in the opposite direction.

Orthoptic – The clinical practice of exercises designed to improve eye movements, develop accurate and reliable control of vergence and encourage the establishment and maintenance of binocular function.

Parahippocampal place area (PPA) – A region of the brain, active when viewing scenes such as the interior and exterior of buildings, especially for familiar locations.

Photoreceptors – Cells within the retina that convert light energy into electrical signals that can be processed by other nerve cells in the retina and brain. Rod photoreceptors are sensitive to dim light but do not provide good acuity or color vision. Cone receptors, provide high acuity and can signal the difference between colors.

Photorefraction – A method of estimating the refractive state of the eye, by recording photographically the pattern of light returning through the pupil of the eye from a flash.

Posterior parietal cortex (PPC) – A complex of brain areas that receive information from extrastriate visual areas and form part of the dorsal stream.

Preferential looking – A method of testing infant vision by measuring the infant's preference for looking at a patterned screen compared with a blank one.

Refraction – The process of measuring the distance at which an eye is focused when relaxed.

Retina – The neural network, with supporting tissues and blood vessels, that covers the inside of the back of the eyeball.

Spatial frequency – A measure of the scale of detail present in a pattern.

Stereopsis or stereoscopic vision – The ability to perceive the relative distance and three-dimensional modeling of objects in the scene. It depends on nerve cells in visual cortex receiving and processing signals from the two eyes together, and can be impaired or abolished when strabismus prevents this from occurring.

Strabismus – A condition where the axes of the two eyes are misaligned and so look in different directions.

Striate cortex – An alternative name for area V1, named from the 'Stripe of Gennari' where the fibers of the optic radiation terminate.

Superior colliculus – A structure in the midbrain, also known as the optic tectum, which receives input from the retina by a branch of the optic nerve. It sends output to oculomotor nuclei for the control of eye movements, and so is believed to be responsible for orienting behavior, including in newborn infants whose cortex is immature.

Visual evoked potentials or visual event-related potentials (VEP/VERP) – Electrical signals recorded noninvasively from the surface of the head, that arise from visual processing events in the underlying brain structures.

Ventral stream – A series of cortical areas, transmitting visual information from V1 to the temporal lobe of the brain, which extracts information that enables the visual recognition of faces, objects, and scenes.

Vergence – An eye movement which alters the relative direction of the two eyes.

Vernier Acuity – The ability to make fine visual comparisons of position, for example, whether two vertical lines are aligned or misaligned.

V1 – (striate cortex) The primary receiving area in the ocipital lobe of the brain for visual information.

V2, V3, V3a, V4, V5 – Extrastriate visual areas of the brain.

Visual cortex – The region in the occipital lobe of the brain that carries out the early stages of processing of the visual image.

Introduction

To understand visual development and its disorders, it is necessary to understand in outline the structure and function of the visual system. This is a technical subject with a specialized vocabulary.

An optical image of the visual world is formed in the eyes and is encoded into neural signals in the retina. These signals are transformed, first by the neural network of the retina, and then by transmission through a series of interconnected brain areas. Complex brain processing is required to use incoming visual information for recognizing objects, people, and events; for location in the environment; and for guiding visuomotor actions. Developmental disorders of vision can arise from problems at all levels of this process. Furthermore, the development of the later, brain-based stages depends on the signals that are received from the eye, so disorders of the eyes can lead to more pervasive problems of visual perception and cognition.

A sharp optical image depends on the cornea (front surface of the eye) and lens focusing light rays on the retina, and on the media within the eye being clear and transparent. The retinal photoreceptor cells (rods and cones) signal the light intensity falling upon them, and a neural network in the retina lead to the optic nerve fibers that carry information to the brain. These fibers are routed so that signals from the each eye are transmitted to each side of the brain via a relay in the thalamus (the lateral geniculate nucleus LGN).

The signals arrive in the striate cortex (or area V1) in the occipital lobe of the brain, where the neurons are specialized to extract various kinds of information, notably the orientation of lines and edges, directions of motion, and to bring together information from the two eyes for depth perception based on binocular disparity (stereopsis – the 3-dimensional 3D vision*)*. V1 is surrounded by a series of extrastriate visual areas, such as V2, V3, V4, and V5, which have distinct specializations of function; for example, area V5 (also known as MT) combines the directional information coming from V1 to detect more global patterns of motion over larger spatial areas. Pathways through these extrastriate visual areas send information to the temporal and parietal lobes of the brain. The ventral stream, involving the temporal lobe, is specialized for recognizing shapes and objects, including human faces, while the dorsal stream, involving the parietal lobe, encodes the spatial and motion information needed for visually guided actions. This whole complex of neural circuitry is called the cortical visual system. Some specialized areas for processing information about faces (fusiform face area), objects (lateral-occipital – LO), places or scenes (parahippocampal place area – PPA) have been identified in adults from Functional magnetic rescrarce imaging (FMRI) brain imaging studies. Other pools of cortical neurons are involved in specific visuomotor actions (e.g., mirror neurons in the frontal lobes) together with specific networks for discriminating emotional states from visual expressions and gestures.

The brain based processing of visual information can be called perception, cognition, spatial cognition, sensorimotor cognition, or spatial attention. In development these all involve overlapping neural circuitry. Notably, the deployment of selective attention determines how we act on visual information coming in. Visual information is integrated with other senses and with planning and on-line control of action, and gives us our ability to orient ourselves in space and to manipulate spatial information.

A minority of fibers in the optic nerve do not connect to the cerebral cortex, but to midbrain structures, in particular the superior colliculus. This pathway primarily serves to control eye movements, in particular saccades, the abrupt jerk eye movements which shift gaze from one object to another. Midbrain nuclei also control the smooth eye movements enable us to follow moving objects, and the reflex optokinetic nystagmus (OKN) that stabilizes vision when the whole field of view moves. In adults, all these eye movement functions interact strongly with the more complex analysis taking place in the cortex, via connections that run both ways between subcortical visual centers and visual cortical areas, in particular involving the frontal eye fields (FEF) and posterior parietal complex (PPC).

Techniques Used to Measure Normal and Abnormal Vision

One of the most basic measures of visual development is that of visual acuity. One measure, detection acuity, is the thinnest line or dot that can be distinguished from a uniform background. If the line to be detected has sharp high-contrast edges it may still be detected with blurred vision. An edge can be blurred either because of optical blurring in the formation of the optical image within the eye itself and/or due to processes that degrade the retinal image within the neural system. Single dots or white balls are often used in standard pediatric clinical tests of acuity (such as the STYCAR balls test) and give an approximate measure of the child's real-life visual limitations of vision under these particular viewing conditions. For measuring resolution acuity a bar or grating pattern is commonly used in the method of preferential looking. At some level of blur the grating becomes indistinguishable from a uniform gray. Grating acuity is often expressed in terms of spatial frequency.

A second basic measure is contrast sensitivity, where the bars of a grating are varied in contrast against the background as well as in width. For measurements of acuity and contrast sensitivity for children between

2 and 6 years of age various behavioral matching or searching tasks have been devised such as the Cambridge crowding cards. This test, for children aged between 4 and 7 years, conducted at a 3 m (10 ft) viewing distance (rather than 6 m (20 ft) – the standard viewing distance for letter charts for adults), gives a line equivalence of a Snellen letter chart for preschool children. Another effective standardized test for preschool children is the Lea Symbols test. These preschool tests can be used with older children with physical and mental disabilities, such as children with minimal responses with cerebral palsy. Besides these behavioral methods, acuity and contrast sensitivity have been estimated using electrophysiological techniques, visual-evoked potential (VEP) or visual event related potentials (VERP), including the sweep VEP method.

For measuring cortical responses in infants and children, marker tasks have been devised to identify responses in particular neural pathways specific for certain visual attributes (such as orientation or shape, motion, color, binocular disparity), combining results from electrophysiological and behavioral methods such as forced-choice preferential looking (FPL) and habituation. This has provided a neurobiological account of early eye–brain development, underpinning normal development of spatial vision. This model gives the sequence of developmental visual milestones, together with the broad neural processes corresponding to them, against which abnormalities can be identified.

For assessing functional vision in both normal and clinical populations, a portable battery has been standardized for testing from birth to 6 years, the ABCDEFV. This includes standard procedures for core vision tests (such as measures of acuity and control of eye movements) and additional tests for higher-level functions in the visuocognitive domain (shape matching, spatial tasks such as block construction copying). From such a standardized battery an approximate age equivalence can be given for children who are lagging behind their peers and areas of concern can be identified for further testing. Some findings using this battery are described briefly later.

Model of Normal Visual Development

Studies of human infants show that the newborn, starting with very limited visual behavior, develops over the first months of life many of the complex visual processes of pattern and depth perception. Neurophysiological and anatomical evidence, and clinical observations, show that this is achieved by a programmed sequence of maturation interacting closely with activation by the environment

Visual development goes through a number of stages, presented diagrammatically in **Figure 1**.

At birth, the infant can make saccadic eye movements and imprecise, slow head movements to orient toward high-contrast targets, a function mediated by a subcortical system involving the superior colliculus, with functioning of the visual cortex being, at best, rudimentary. This newborn 'where?' orienting system only operates well when there is no competition between targets for the newborn's attention. It is likely to operate across sensory modalities as a nonspecific alerting system, shown by the ability to orient the head and eyes to a lateral auditory stimulus in the first few hours after birth.

Over the first 6 months of life a set of specific neural networks (sometimes called channels or modules) become functional for processing different visual attributes in the cortex. Onset after birth of cortical visual processes for orientation selectivity is around 3–6 weeks of post-term age; directional motion selectivity around 2–3 months of post-term age of; and binocular interaction for stereopsis is functional around 4 months of post-term age. The infant can use perspective information for depth perception from 6 months onwards. Pools of neurons, sensitive to these different visual attributes, form the first stage of the two main cortical streams of processing, the dorsal and ventral streams. It has been suggested that because sensitivity to orientation and color develops a little earlier than channels for motion and binocular disparity that the ventral stream starts to function at these lower levels slightly earlier than the dorsal stream.

At the next stage of processing in dorsal and ventral streams, in extrastriate cortex, global cortical processing takes place. The development of global motion processing – a function of extrastriate dorsal stream processing – can be compared with global processing of form in the ventral stream, where analogous thresholds can be measured in young children. In infants, form coherence discrimination is apparent from 4 to 6 months of age from preferential looking and VEP/VERP studies. Global organization based on pattern orientation is found to be less effective in determining infant behavior than global organization based on motion coherence (sensitivity to the latter is apparent from around 9 weeks of age onwards). At this stage of dorsal and ventral stream processing, the dorsal stream areas appear to be processing stimuli for global motion coherence earlier than those in the ventral stream for global static form coherence.

Sensitivity in these channels is followed by development of integrative processes across channels within a single stream so that the infant can build up internal representations of objects, including discrimination of individuals in face recognition. However, faces are a special case, for which there may be an earlier, possibly subcortical, mechanism operating from birth, which biases visual attention to configurations that are face-like in the newborn. This may be replaced by a cortical system operating from a few months after birth for discrimination of faces using more detailed information from features. At present there is a discrepancy between the behavioral and

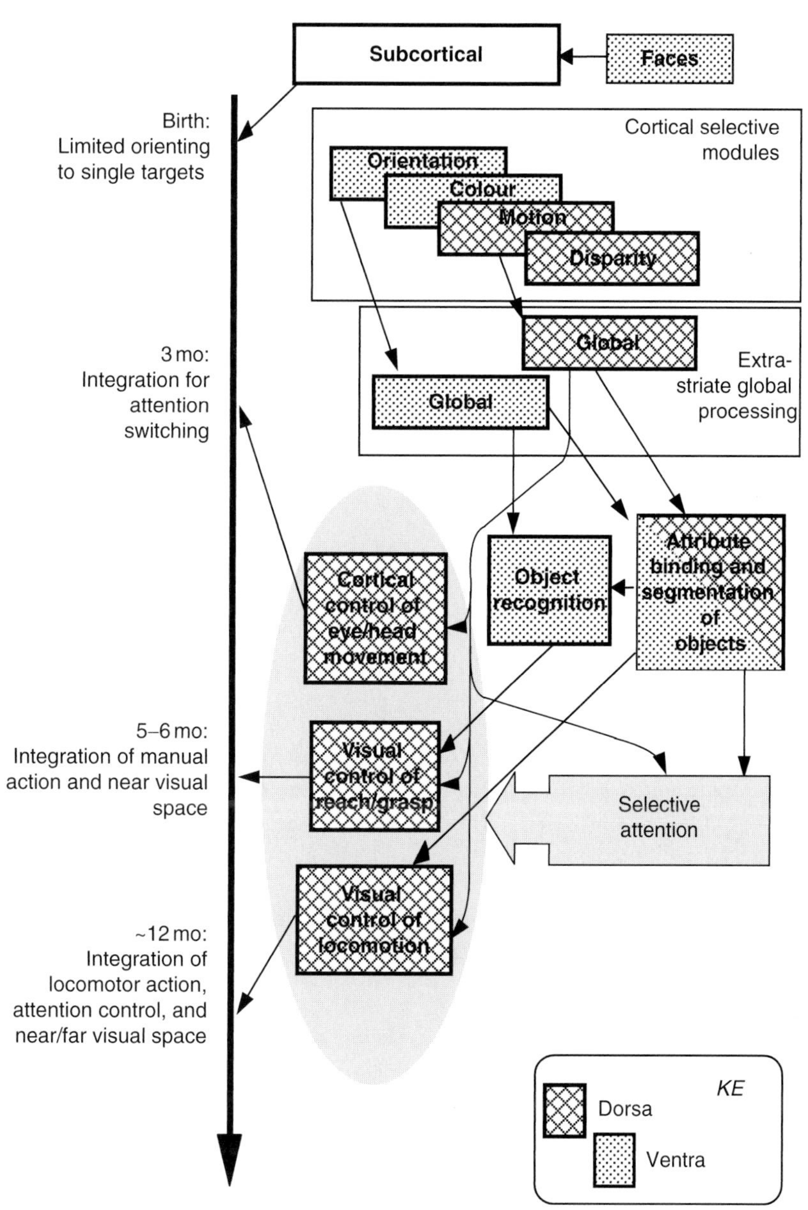

Figure 1 Schematic neurobiological model of visual development over the first year of life.

VERP data; behavioral studies indicate that infants can discriminate faces from 3 months onwards but evidence from VERP studies suggests that the maturation of the FFA, is later, toward the end of the first year.

These cortical channels for visual attributes are linked into the first functional cortical networks for selective attention. Orienting or switching attention to a peripheral novel stimulus or target, when the infant is already fixating a centrally presented stimulus, requires modulation and disengagement of the subcortical orienting system by cortical processes. In normally developing infants, the cortical system for active switches of attention between competing targets starts to function around 3–4 months of age. Evidence for the role of the cortex comes from studies of infants who have undergone hemispherectomy, surgical removal of one complete hemisphere to relieve intractable epilepsy. Postoperatively these infants can shift gaze toward a target appearing in the peripheral field contralateral to the removed hemisphere when a initial central fixation target disappears, but fail to disengage to fixate the peripheral target when the central target remains visible, although they can do so toward a target in the intact visual field. This 'sticky fixation' when two targets are competing has also been observed in infants with focal lesions in parietal areas and infants with diffuse hypoxic ischemic encephalopathy (HIE). It resembles the problems seen in adult patients as part of the visual neglect syndrome.

Attribute binding and figure-ground segregation: Throughout development there must be interactions and integration between information in the dorsal and ventral streams. For objects to be represented, information about color, shape, and texture must be integrated with motion information at a relatively early stage, so that objects can be segregated from each other in space and separated from their background. This basic 'figure-ground' segmentation has been shown to start functioning at around 3 months of age. These processes provide object representations that must be integrated with dorsal-stream spatial information to allow the infant to act and respond, first with selective eye and head orienting action systems, then later with the emergence of action systems associated with reaching and grasping, and later still with exploratory action systems involving locomotion. These action systems require maturation and integration in both visual attentional systems and visuomotor systems and are integral parts of the dorsal stream.

Alongside emergence of these qualitative functional changes, there are steady quantitative improvements in vision in terms of visual acuity, the range of velocities for motion perception, the control of pursuit eye movements (smooth pursuit), and the range of retinal disparity for stereo vision. In tracking eye movements there is a gradual change over the first 6 months of life from slow inaccurate saccadic tracking to smooth pursuit. Anticipatory eye movements are observed from around 2 months post-term age for reappearance of an object which has disappeared from view while the infant was tracking it. There is massive improvement in visual acuity in the first 6 months of life. Using FPL, the estimated acuity for an infant at birth and over the first few weeks of life is equivalent to around 20/600 in Snellen terms. By 3 months of age acuity is 20/200, at 6 months 20/100, and at 12 months about 20/50. VEP measures give comparable results, although some studies claim higher values at the youngest ages. Although an acuity of 20/600 would be legal blindness in an adult, newborn acuity and contrast sensitivity in near space is certainly good enough for everyday recognition tasks of people and large objects (such as the mother's face or a baby bottle) and for discriminating between different adult facial expressions. The rapid improvement in acuity over the first few months of life means that older infants' behavioral limitations are unlikely to be due to lack of acuity and are more likely to be due to the visuo-cognitive or visuomotor demands of the task. After 1 year of age there is a slow rise to adult levels by 6–7 years, with adult levels of grating acuity from FPL estimates earlier at around 3 years of age. Certainly single letter matching acuity values for 3-year-olds can often be the equivalent of 20/30 Snellen letters, and by 4–5 years acuity is equivalent to adult 20/30 from crowded letter matching tests (e.g., Cambridge crowding cards), provided the child is sufficiently motivated.

Several changes in the visual system underlie the very rapid improvements in acuity and 'contrast sensitivity' in infancy.

1. While the optical media are clear at birth, and infants' refractions (on average moderately hyperopic or far sighted) should not impose a limit, infants at 0–1 month of age generally accommodate (adjust the lens focus) at a near distance (e.g., 50 cm). They are capable of some adjustment of focus, but this becomes accurate over a much wider range of distances over the first 6 months. The range of refractive errors in infants and their development is discussed later.
2. At birth, the cone photoreceptors of the fovea are small and sparsely spaced. Although this imposes a serious limit on acuity and contrast sensitivity, overall visual development probably depends more critically on neural changes, especially in the cortex.
3. Progressive myelination of the visual pathway over the first years of life.
4. The number of synaptic connections throughout the visual system increases rapidly, particularly in the first 9 months, with later pruning.

Other aspects of the child's visual capabilities change a great deal between 2 and 7 years of age. The more complex aspects of perceptual or cognitive processes are underpinned by maturation of the massive interconnectivity between different cortical areas and networks. Standardized pediatric assessment batteries (e.g., Griffiths and Bailey), and the ABCDEFV battery contain tests that measure some of these visual components, such as shape matching tests.

Ventral and dorsal stream development in childhood have been measured from comparisons of form and motion coherence thresholds (using stimuli which have been matched to give equal thresholds in adults). Motion coherence thresholds have been found to mature later than form coherence, with children reaching adult levels for form coherence at around 8 years of age and for motion coherence around 10 years of age. A consistent deficit (or delay) in motion coherence processing has been found in certain developmental disorders (discussed below). Specific areas associated with form and motion coherence tasks have been identified in fMRI studies of normal adults. Distinct circuits are activated in global processing of form and motion, although each circuit involves parts of occipital, parietal and temporal lobes.

A caveat is necessary: It is over-simple to show visual development in infancy and childhood as a linear sequence; there are likely to be important feedback loops, by which the consequences of a new development can affect the way that earlier established processes work. Furthermore, a description of the sequence is only the start. There is still much debate as to why there are timing differences in functional onset and plasticity in one system as opposed to another.

Division of Childhood Visual Disorders

A major division is normally made between childhood visual disorders related to the functioning in the eye itself and disorders related to eye–brain neural connections and functioning in the visual brain. This tends to be emphasized by the division between two branches of clinicians who study childhood visual disorders – those trained in ophthalmology, optometry, orthopics and related professions (health/education professions related to the visually impaired and their treatment), and those trained in neurology (pediatricians, pediatric neurologists, health/education related professionals in neurological disorders). There are also those trained in neuropsychology and developmental cognitive neuroscience, who tend to emphasize brain rather than eye abnormalities. In infancy and childhood the distinction between visual disorders arising from eye or brain function are sometimes hard to make, as the two interact strongly in development and different aspects may be manifest at different stages.

A second categorization of visual disorders is made in terms of severity, ranging from severe, but usually rare, abnormalities including varying degrees of 'blindness', to milder deficits, particularly common in the developed world, such as strabismus and amblyopia, dyslexia related to vision and visual attentional disorders (attention deficit hyperactive disorders ADHD).

Epidemiology of Childhood Visual Deficits

Childhood is defined by UNICEF as an individual under 16 years, and blindness as a refractively corrected visual acuity of 3/60 (20/400) or below in the better eye or a central visual field of less than 10 degrees around the point of central fixation. This definition raises problems of appropriateness and reliability when applied to infants, children, and individuals with difficulties of communication and/or additional physical and mental disabilities. In such case blindness is often difficult to separate from unawareness and lack of responses, for example, abnormal eye and head movements. In young infants, the diagnosis of congenital blindness may also be confused with what has been termed delayed visual maturation.

From registration (which is likely to be an underestimate because many children with multiple impairments are not registered as blind), the prevalence of blindness in Europe is around 0.1–0.3 per 1000 and in developing countries three to four times greater, giving at least 1.5 million children worldwide. Although these children may be registered as blind, this does not necessarily mean that they have no useful vision. Many will have good enough vision for some crude navigation, provided that light levels are adequate. Additionally, from Scandinavian registers there are around 0.08 per 1000 registered visually impaired children (with acuity less than 6/18 = 20/60) per year. A difficulty with registers of visual impairment and blindness in children is that these cannot be static measures made for all time. Because of cascading processes of visual development throughout infancy and childhood, a measured visual loss which would not constitute a serious handicap in infancy can be a source of disability in late childhood and adulthood. For example, a moderate near acuity loss would not prevent a 9-month-old infant playing and manipulating most toys appropriate for age, but might prevent reading text in school. At present there are very few measures of quality of life appropriate for the entire age range from birth to adulthood, and although adult scales can be used with some modification for older children, there are very few measures for infants and especially for children with multiple disabilities, which may include severe cerebral visual impairment. The interactions between visual loss and other physical limitations in causing disability are still poorly characterized or standardized.

In industrialized countries genetic conditions (15–50% of blindness), and conditions occurring as a result of perinatal events, are the major causes of child blindness. In Eastern Mediterranean regions, two-thirds of blindness has been attributed to genetic causes, 50% of which is autosomal-recessive disease. Genetically related parents are known to increase the risk of recessive diseases and multifactorial disorders.

Intrauterine causes of blindness include rubella, toxoplasmosis, cytomegalovirus, drugs, alcohol, or maternal metabolic disturbance (e.g., diabetes). Perinatal causes of blindness (between 25 weeks, gestation to 28 days after term birth) are retinopathy of prematurity, the results of sexually transmitted diseases, (e.g., HIV infection, and gonorrhea), and lesions of the optic nerve and higher visual pathways in the brain. In developed countries many of these are related to birth asphyxia, with approximately 50% of those with brain lesions having additional problems such as cerebral palsy. In many cases such perinatal brain damage is associated with extreme prematurity.

Acquired diseases (measles, vitamin A deficiency) are unusual causes of blindness in children in industrialized countries, but are very important in poorer developing countries. Studies in Africa suggest that 1–3% of children develop ulcerations of the cornea following measles.

The most common of the rarer childhood visual disorders is congenital cataract, with prevalence around 2.5 per 10 000, around 40% being in one eye only. A significant proportion of blinding eye diseases does not have a determined cause (from Nordic studies, 32% of blind children, with a higher proportion in developing countries).

Less severe childhood visual loss, but the most common in developed countries, is congenital or early onset strabismus and related refractive error and amblyopia.

Childhood Visual Disorders Related to Functioning in the Eye

Retinal dystrophies. A small but significant source of visual defects in childhood is the degeneration of the photoreceptors of the retina, generally as a result of an inherited photoreceptor degeneration (IPD). These are not common diseases (6–9 per 100 000 births) but are a major fraction of childhood blindness. As many as 25 000 different genes may be expressed in the retina, and an unusually high number (30–50%) are specific to the retina. Many different genes have been identified as associated with IPDs, both in human pedigrees and in mouse models, but they are believed to act by affecting a relatively small number of molecular pathways.

Among the most severe, and a relatively large proportion, of these disorders is Leber's amaurosis, which affects both rods and cones. Although it is progressive, children are already seriously affected at birth, with nystagmus and very low acuity, and can be diagnosed by the lack of the electrical response from the retina (electroretinogram, ERG).

Some receptor disorders affect only one type of receptor. Congenital achromatopsia is a complete loss of cone function, with no color vision, very poor acuity, nystagmu, and often photophobia (aversion to bright light). Conversely, congenital stationary night blindness is a failure of rod vision from birth: children have normal acuity and color vision at high light levels, but poor vision at low levels.

Retinitis pigmentosa is a wide, and genetically diverse class of IPDs, generally progressive and affecting rods and cones, although the rod system is usually affected earlier and more severely. As a result, night-blindness is the usual symptom in childhood, with the loss is most evident in peripheral vision.

Recent advances in gene therapy and stem-cell transplantation provide an optimistic future for eradicating or lessening the impact on quality of life from these visually devastating diseases.

Retinopathy of prematurity (ROP) is a result of excessive oxygen delivered to aid survival of the premature neonate in intensive care, which adversely affects the immature vascular system of the premature retina. It emerged as a cause of blindness in the late 1940s. A lowering of the incidence of ROP in the 1970s was related to better monitoring of oxygen, but with later improved neonatal care and survival of infants under 32 weeks, gestation, there has been another increase in developed countries and in countries (e.g., in Latin America) where an increase in Cesarean delivery has led to more premature births.

In the initial phase of ROP, the growth of the retinal blood vessels is delayed after premature birth; excess oxygen in this phase causes a growth factor molecule called vascular endothelial growth factor (VEGF) to be released, which in a second phase stimulates the proliferation of vessels that distort and damage the retina. Treatments that counteract VEGF are currently being developed, but current therapy is to stop retinal damage by laser treatment or cryotherapy (local freezing). These treatments reduce the incidence of blindness by approximately 25%, although the visual outcomes are often poor. It must be recognized, however, that very premature infants requiring oxygen in intensive care are also those most likely to suffer perinatal brain damage, with visual consequences that are discussed below.

Cataract is an opacity in the lens of the eye that, if large and dense, allows only diffuse light to reach the retina. The child is deprived of pattern vision until the defective lens is removed surgically and the eye is fitted with a compensatory optical correction, either an intraocular lens implant or a contact lens. The optimal age for surgery remains controversial, although the best results seem to be achieved if surgery is very early, in the first few months of life. Early correction is desirable because the complete deprivation of pattern vision, in either one or both eyes, has strong effects on the development of visual brain mechanisms at a stage when the developing connections among visual neurons are extremely plastic. The consequences of this plasticity are amblyopia, a form of vision loss discussed in later.

Optic Nerve Problems

Optic nerve hypoplasia or atrophy is a developmental defect of the optic nerve fibers of one or both eyes (bilateral). If bilateral and severe, it leads to complete blindness. Neurological defects such as quadriplegia and hemiplegia are often associated. It can be related to maternal diabetes and to fetal alcohol syndrome. Optic atrophy is rarely isolated and is often associated with rubella virus, brain malformations, or hypoxic-ischemic encephalopathy (HIE) (brain damage caused by lack of oxygen).

Glaucoma is an increase of pressure within the eye which ultimately damages the optic nerve. It is rare in infants (1 in 10 000), with very heterogeneous causes and prognosis. It is usually treated with surgery, but the majority of children remain myopic when the pressure has successfully been reduced.

Refractive errors. Vision may be degraded if the eye does not optically bring images to a sharp focus on the retina. Such refractive errors may be myopic (short- or near-sighted; the eye cannot focus distant objects), hyperopic (long- or far-sighted; excessive effort is required to focus on close objects), or astigmatic (lines at different angles cannot be sharply focused together). As well as the immediate reduction in image quality, these conditions may have longer-term effects on development that are discussed in the section on Amblyopia and Plasticity.

In a well-focused (emmetropic) eye, the curvature of the cornea and lens bring light to a focus at the distance of the retina, so refractive error is a consequence of the shape and size of the eyeball as it matures. However, these structural aspects cannot be considered independently of visual processing. In general, as the eye grows there is a trend toward emmetropia, and there is much evidence, both from experimental animal models and from clinical conditions, that this change is actively controlled. Image blur or visual deprivation can affect the course of refractive change, and so does habitual accommodation. Furthermore, childhood refractive error is correlated with aspects of cognitive and visuomotor development.

Myopia is rare in the first year of life in Caucasian populations, but commonly has an onset between early school age and adolescence, and tends to increase progressively. There are undoubtedly familial genetic factors, but these appear to interact with environmental conditions. The latter are suggested by the increase in childhood myopia, especially in Far Eastern populations. The progression of myopia is correlated with near work (e.g., reading, extended viewing of computer screens), but there are also large individual variations in this effect. There are suggestions that reading in low light levels has a particularly strong effect; this has been related to the light-dependent release of dopamine that is known to affect eye growth in animal models.

Hyperopia. The average infant eye has a modest level of hyperopia. This is revealed when the child's accommodation is relaxed with cycloplegic drops. About 5% of infants (in Caucasian populations that have been studied) have significant hyperopic refractive errors (over +3.5D at age 9 months), with many of these showing marked degrees of astigmatism. This has a number of consequences. Some hyperopic infants put in very little accommodative effort and therefore have permanently blurred visual input. Hyperopia is also associated with early onset strabismus (cross-eyed squint). It is suggested that this is a result of the link between accommodation and convergence; the hyperopic child has to make a great accommodative effort to achieve a sharp image and this induces an abnormal degree of convergence of the eyes, overcoming the control processes which keep the two eyes' images in register. However, the detailed dynamics though which hyperopia leads to disruption of the sensory–motor binocular loop is still only poorly understood. Spectacles that reduce the need for accommodation (focusing in) are frequently an effective treatment for strabismus. It has also been shown, in randomized, controlled trials that prescribing a spectacle correction for infant with significant hyperopia reduced the risk of them developing strabismus and poor acuity, without adverse effects on their emmetropization.

In addition, the association with strabismus and amblyopia, significant infant hyperopia is associated with subtle small delays in development of visual attention and in visuocognitive, visuomotor, and spatial abilities (but not language abilities), first identifiable in the second year of life and persisting into the early school years. The deficit may be particularly associated with frontoparietal systems for spatial cognition and attention. Its basis is not yet known; it is as likely to have a common neurodevelopmental origin with hyperopia, as to be a consequence of any effects of hyperopia on the visual input. It offers the possibility of early identification a group of children at risk of preschool visuocognitive problems, in particular attention deficits, which may be a significant factor for educational achievement. Anisometropia is a difference in refraction between the eyes. Such differences, particularly if one eye is markedly hyperopic, are associated with the development of strabismus and, even if the eyes remain straight, can lead to amblyopia (see below).

Childhood Disorders Related to the Control of Eye Movements

The muscular systems that move the eyes are a key aspect of functional vision since they are necessary to maintain the stability of the image on the retina, to direct the high-acuity fovea to the object of interest, and to maintain coordination of the two eyes. Disorders of these systems generally reflect disorders of central neural control systems. However, since they are manifest in external examination of the eyes, they sit between the domains of ophthalmological and neurological professionals.

A number of conditions can cause oculomotor disorders in childhood.

Disorders of the cranial nerves linked to the eye muscles can lead to paralysis of one or more of these muscles (ophthalmoplegia). Congenital ophthalmoplegia is relatively common, especially Duane syndrome or retraction syndrome, in which poor development of the sixth cranial nerve which limits the ability of the eye to turn in (abduction) and causes the eyes to narrow when an outward (adduction) movement is attempted.

Congenital ptosis (drooping eyelid) is a relatively common condition. The resulting obstruction of vision may be a cause of deprivation amblyopia (see below).

Gaze palsies may arise from lesions at many different, higher brain levels and unlike peripheral palsies affect the movements of both eyes together are due to involvement of the supranuclear pathways that control the orientation of the head and eyes. They are often associated with hemiplegia as a result of cortical damage.

Ocular motor apraxia is a condition where the child's attempts to change fixation lead to very abnormal head and eye movements. The head may turn without any change of eye position, or with eye movements in the opposite direction to the head. The origin is often unknown, but it has been reported from brain scans that 30% of the cases showed delayed myelination, agenesis of the corpus callosum and cerebellar abnormalities.

Nystagmus is involuntary, rhythmical, oscillatory eye movements. It should be distinguished from the roving eye movements of totally blind children. Congenital nystagmus (which may be delayed for several months after birth) is often associated with low visual acuity, and is believed often to be a consequence of various retinal (especially macular) disorders degrade the sensory information controlling fixation. One common link is with albinism. Albinos have wide ranging disruption of the visual system, besides the problems caused by lack of pigmentation in the eye. In particular VEP and MRI studies confirm what has been found in animal models, that the uncrossed optic nerve fibers are reduced, causing the brain mapping of the two eyes' fields to be highly anomalous representation.

Strabismus. In strabismus (often called squint in the UK) the movements of the two eyes are not properly co-ordinated, so that they look in different directions rather than fixating at the same time on a single point. Paralytic strabismus comes under the oculomotor palsies described above. In the much more common disorders of concomitant strabismus, the eyes move together but with one eye either deviating inwards (convergent strabismus or esotropia, cross eyes) or outwards (divergent strabismus or exotropia). The amount of deviation may vary with vertical gaze; for instance in a V-pattern esotropia increases as the child looks down. Such patterns are attributed to a relative imbalance in the inferior and superior oblique muscles of the eyes – a motor explanation of strabismus. In contrast, maintaining binocular fixation requires cortical binocularity – the integration of information from the two eyes in the visual cortex. Weakness or absence of this mechanism may lead to strabismus, for example, in albino children where the misrouting of optic nerve fibers described above means that fibers from the two eyes do not reach the same cerebral hemisphere. However, in many cases of strabismus, stereo vision develops before the onset of strabismus, so a deficit of sensory binocularity does not appear to be the primary cause. Rather, the sensory–motor interaction is two-way; misalignment of the eyes means that signals from corresponding points of the two images do not come together in the cortex, so that the correlated signals needed to maintain connections from the two eyes to the same cortical cell are absent, and these binocular connections break down. The readiness with which this developmental feedback loop can be broken may explain why binocularity is vulnerable in infancy, and strabismus very frequent, in all kinds of neurodevelopmental disorders (Down syndrome, prematurity, perinatal brain insult, etc.).

The role of accommodation in disrupting normal convergence of the eyes, in children with hyperopic refractive errors, has been discussed above. However, convergent squint can occur without hyperopia. The strength of the link between accommodation and convergence varies greatly between individuals and it may be that in some cases even normal levels of accommodation are enough to break the maintenance of binocular fixation. As indicated above, some cases of strabismus can be controlled by refractive correction. However, frequently, surgical adjustment of the eye muscles is required. To restore secure alignment of the eyes, these treatments have to be accompanied by orthoptic exercises to encourage the active control of vergence. In addition, following surgery, the associated amblyopia (see below) will also require treatment.

Amblyopia. Amblyopia is a reduction of visual acuity, usually in one eye, that cannot be improved with refractive correction and for which there is not a detected organic cause in the eye. It is a very common condition affecting 2–4% of the population in developed countries. It is believed to be a developmental disorder of neural connectivity in the visual cortex; an eye whose image is degraded in some way has diminished input to cortical processing, as a result of plasticity of synaptic mechanisms in competition with the other eye.

There are three major causes of amblyopia. In deprivation amblyopia, one eye has pattern vision reduced or abolished, for example, by a dense cataract or a ptosis. Poor acuity remains even after the obstruction of vision is removed. Animal models of this condition, in which cortical responses are measured following occlusion of one eye, have led to the explanation of amblyopia in terms of activity-dependent competitive interactions between cortical synapses. Such experiments have also established the existence of a critical period following birth, in which these connections are much more readily modified than later in life. This concept leads to the importance, which has been clinically supported, of correcting the amblyogenic condition at the earliest practical age.

Anisometropic amblyopia results from one eye having a defocused image due to a difference in refraction from the other eye. It can be regarded as a partial form of deprivation amblyopia, where the relative deprivation is for fine detail rather than all pattern vision. In clinical practice care is needed not to confuse genuine amblyopia with uncorrected refractive error.

Strabismic amblyopia is a reduction of acuity in the deviating eye in strabismus. It is usually seen when one eye is predominantly used for fixation, most typically in convergent strabismus. The nature of the deprivation is less well understood than in deprivation or anisometropic amblyopia, and the cortical mechanism may be different. However, in many cases both strabismus and anisometropia are present, and the contributions of the two cannot be easily separated.

Although amblyopia is usually assessed in terms of visual acuity, the actual visual deficit is more complex. First, there is a reduction of contrast sensitivity for low- and medium-spatial frequencies. Second, there is often a severe effect on visual information about the position of image features, reflected in a greatly increased crowding effect (interference between acuity targets), a loss of vernier acuity, and sometimes reports that images appear scrambled. Statistical factor analysis shows that these different effects are to some degree independent. Amblyopes who also have a loss of binocularity – typically strabismic amblyopes – have a disproportionate crowding effect and vernier acuity loss relative to their contrast sensitivity loss. These results suggest that multiple mechanisms are at work.

The usual treatment for amblyopia is partial or continuous patching of the 'good' eye, once the refractive error, strabismus, or source of deprivation has been corrected. However, this needs careful monitoring: (1) To avoid the risk that an artificial deprivation amblyopia is induced in the patched eye and (2) because following strabismus surgery cortical binocularity is fragile, and to establish and maintain it requires correlated binocular input, that is, both eyes open. The optimal compromise between these therapeutic aims depends on (1) practical considerations of compliance with patching treatment in children; (2) the benefits of treatment and how long they last when patching is stopped; and (3) the relative disability and reduction in quality of life resulting from loss of binocularity or loss of acuity and contrast sensitivity. There are few systematic data on these, and the balance will of course depend on age and the presence of any accompanying developmental conditions. However, from data from treatment trials, it appears that 2 h per day of patching can achieve significant improvements of acuity.

The importance of treating amblyopia rests in part on the long-term risk of losing vision in the 'good' eye, leading to severe visual disability. This lifetime risk has been estimated at 1.2%. The risk of injuring the good eye of an amblyope is three times that in a nonamblyopic individual.

Analysis of visual abilities in children who were treated for congenital cataract suggests that there are important aspects of plasticity in central visual processing that are not captured by measures of binocularity and acuity. Children with a few months of visual deprivation before a cataract removal in the first year, when tested at age 6–14 years, show persisting impairment in face recognition, and in tasks requiring integration of local elements in global form and motion perception. These deficits are much greater than would be expected from any remaining acuity loss. They occur even though at the age vision was restored, these aspects of high-level visual processing were quite immature. These data indicate that early visual experience is required to set up the infrastructure for later development involving both the dorsal ('where') and ventral ('what') streams.

Vision Screening

Screening refers to testing people who are asymptomatic in order to classify their likelihood of having a particular disease. It aims to identify as many as possible of those affected by the target condition as possible, while minimizing the number who are incorrectly suspected of having the disease. The criteria for worthwhile screening are that: (1) a large part of the at-risk population can be screened, (2) the condition screened for has a high prevalence, (3) it is significantly disabling, and (4) it has an effective treatment which is acceptable.

It is common to screen newborns in the neonatal ward by examination with an ophthalmoscope, to detect structural disorders in the eye and serious conditions (e.g., cataract, ROP, and retinal tumours). General surveillance methods in primary healthcare can often detect abnormalities with sufficient signs and symptoms, for example, strabismus and nystagmus. Given the importance of early correction of conditions leading to amblyopia, there have been a number of programs at later ages aiming to detect the conditions, in particular the refractive errors, which lead to amblyopia, but it is difficult to meet the screening criteria stated above. In screening children for poor acuity (the method in many preschool programs), it is often hard to achieve high attendance, and by the time acuity can be measured rapidly and reliably, it is relatively late for successful amblyopia treatment.

The Cambridge Infant Screening programs used photorefraction or videorefraction to detect potentially amblyogenic levels of hyperopia and anisometropia (as well as congenital strabismus) at 8–9 months of age, and achieved high rates of attendance (75–80% of the total targeted population). Photo- and videorefractive techniques offer the possibility of rapid, safe, reliable, inexpensive screening that is acceptable to parents and infants and children of all ages. As initial results with these measures have shown relatively successful visual outcomes, extensions of such programs across different populations (including clinical populations with multiple disorders) should lead to the prevention, reduction in number, and early effective treatment of the common visual problems of strabismus, refractive error, and amblyopia in the future. However, such programs depend on then successfully and accurately prescribing spectacle corrections, and regular frequent follow-up and counseling, which may be hard to achieve for infants and very young children in regular practice.

Childhood Disorders Related to Functioning in the Brain

Cerebral visual impairment (CVI). CVI usually refers to a severe deficit of visual behavior as a result of brain damage, usually perinatal, typically identified in infancy by poor fixation and following, and by the absence of reaching for objects in children with the motor capability to do so. It is the most common cause of permanent visual impairment in children in developed countries. Strabismus is common; nystagmus less so. There may be abnormal responses to light (either gazing at lights or photophobia). Eye examination may show anomaly of the optic nerves, but this is not severe enough to be the cause of the visual impairment exhibited.

The term cortical blindness has sometimes been used. However, cerebral visual impairment is preferred, since the damage is not necessarily cortical but may involve various parts of the central visual pathways, including white matter, and may not be anatomically well localized, e.g., when associated with epilepsy or metabolic disorders. Common causes include HIE in the term-born infant; periventricular leukomalacia (PVL) in the preterm infant; accidental or nonaccidental traumatic brain injury; neonatal hypoglycemia; infections (e.g., viral meningitis); and hydrocephalus shunt failure.

CVI is unlikely to be an isolated impairment; the underlying neurological damage will commonly lead to cerebral palsy, developmental delay, and/or other sensory impairments. It is important to discover the child's visual capabilities but these should be considered as part of an overall pattern of capability and disability for the individual child.

The term delayed visual maturation can be a source of confusion. Visual inattention in the first months of life is the presenting symptom of CVI, a condition which may show some long-term improvement but generally leaves an enduring deficit. There is, however, a distinct group of children who present with isolated visual inattentiveness in the first months and without known neurological damage. In such cases, it is common to see recovery with normal visual attentiveness by 6 months or soon after. This pattern suggests a delay in the onset of development of cortical visual mechanisms, but the reasons for such a delay are not understood.

Cerebral visual impairment should not be considered an all-or-none phenomenon. The brain basis of visual processing is complex, and perinatal brain injury can lead to a range of deficits from profound loss to more subtle impairments of specific function.

One pervasive deficit found across many clinical populations with suspected cerebral damage is an inability to change focus (accommodate) on targets at different distances, in the absence of a marked myopic or hyperopic refractive error. It seems likely that networks involving accommodative mechanisms in conjunction with cortical systems have never developed normally in infancy. Whether this is due to damage to accommodative systems *per se* or whether it is due to more central damage to cortical attentional systems, cannot be determined from these measurements alone.

Specific Cerebral Impairments of Spatial Vision: Deficits Related to Ventral Stream Function

Visual agnosia refers to a multitude of different disorders, in which recognition of objects and people is impaired. Some patients cannot recognize faces but can still recognize other objects, while others retain only face recognition. Some see only one object at a time; others can see multiple objects but recognize only one at a time. Some do not consciously perceive the orientation of an object but nevertheless reach for it with a well-oriented grasp; others do not consciously recognize a face as familiar but nevertheless respond to it. All of these conditions, known to occur in adults, have also been described for individual pediatric cases. In general lesions to occipital–temporal lobe areas have been suggested as underpinning these disorders. However, with new knowledge concerning the ventral and dorsal streams, some agnosias can be related to specific areas in these networks (see below). In a number of cases an association between agnosia and certain characteristics of autism spectrum disorder have been noted. This association (comorbidity) may relate to underlying, more pervasive attentional deficits.

Developmental prosopagnosia (DP) is an impairment in identifying faces which is present from early in life, accompanied by apparently intact visual function. DP, as strictly defined, refers to the impairment in the absence of any known lesion or neurological condition (such as autism spectrum disorder). Cases of DP are relatively rare in the literature and findings have been contradictory and inconsistent, with variability across individuals on various face processing tasks. Configural processing of faces can been divided into (1) first order – detecting that the configuration is a face because of the basic arrangements of features; (2) holistic processing – integrating features into a whole and thus rendering individual features less accessible; and (3) encoding the spacing among features. Cases of DP appear to vary in the level of deficit in these different aspects of configural processing.

Deficits Related to Dorsal Stream(s) Function

One particular clinical group, where all individuals show a common phenotype of massive visual spatial deficits across many different areas and types of task combined with relatively good (but not normal development of speech and language) is that of Williams syndrome (WS), a rare genetic disorder characterized by a deletion of around 30 genes on one arm of chromosome 7. WS infants and children generally reach all visuomotor milestones later than typically developing children, they are often delayed in learning to walk and in the development of fine motor skills, and show marked deficits on all standardized test of visuomotor and visuocognitive function. Problems that persist into later life include block construction copying and all related spatial tasks and games, uncertainty when negotiating stairs or uneven surfaces, and difficulty with the use of everyday tools and implements. This neuropsychological profile is consistent with the possibility that ventral stream processes at all levels is relatively unimpaired (but not necessarily normal) but dorsal stream function for visual control of all actions and the planning of these actions is abnormal. In tasks involving motor planning, WS individuals show great difficulties. The post-box (mailbox) task is based on a test which showed a striking dissociation in the Goodale *et al.* study of a ventral-stream impaired adult patient, who could accurately post a card (letter) through an oriented slot in the mailbox (dorsal control of action) but failed on perceptual matching of the slot orientation (ventral processing for perception and recognition). Children with WS showed the opposite deficit, with much greater inaccuracy in posting the card than in matching its orientation to that of the slot, compared with normally developing children. WS children are also poorer than normal children in matching the size of objects, in matching hand opening aperture in reaching and grasping objects of different sizes, and in 'end-state planning' when grasping an object so that it can be easily manipulated with the hand ending the action in a comfortable position. End-state planning is likely to involve the integration of ventral stream information in recognizing the object and dorsal stream information, with prefrontal areas involved in inhibiting inappropriate actions and coordinating the elements of action sequences. WS individuals also show many problems with executive function tests related to frontal lobe processing, and problems of spatial memory for location which is likely to involve additional frontal, hippocampal, and parahippocampal processing.

Studies comparing dorsal stream versus ventral stream development using motion versus form coherence thresholds (see above) have also found relative deficits in global motion processing in many individuals (even high-functioning adults) with WS. This apparent dorsal stream deficit has also been found in a subset of dyslexics, autistic children, children with hemiplegia and fragile X syndrome. This widespread pattern has been called dorsal stream vulnerability. It is important to make such a claim only when direct comparisons of dorsal and ventral stream function have been made using comparable tasks with the same children. The basic cause of this difference in plasticity between dorsal stream and ventral stream modules for global coherence is not yet well understood. It may have its origin in very low-level timing mechanisms in subcortical or early cortical areas, it may depend on a misbalance between the number of functional magnocellular and parvocellular cells and their integration, or it may reflect faulty integration of information from processing in many different occipital, parietal and frontal areas across both dorsal and ventral streams. Support for this relative deficit in dorsal stream networks in WS comes from recent studies using structural and fMRI. It seems that the transmission of spatial information to frontal systems within the dorsal stream is specifically disrupted in WS.

Children born very prematurely, who show a range of cognitive problems, have especially marked deficits in the visuospatial and visuomotor domains. On visual location memory tasks there are subgroups with differential patterns of impairment. For example, impairments to spatial updating for changes of viewpoint, produced when a child sees a toy hidden in one location and then walks to a point with a different viewpoint, may be related to poor detection of coherent motion, related to visual processing of optic flow, while performance on the perspective problem (changes of viewpoint produced by movement of the stimulus array) has been found to be correlated with frontal tests of inhibition and response selection, suggesting that frontal control processes are also involved in this task. Adults with WS showed only marginal ability to use local landmarks to solve the perspective problem, solved by typical children at 5 years. Young WS children tended to use an egocentric frame of reference in these tests. Success on all these spatial tasks must involve integration between visual processing in occipital, parahippocampal, parietal, and prefrontal areas and a failure at one stage of development may be different in its underpinnings from a failure at a different stage of development.

In cases of early focal cortical injury in the right hemisphere there are deficits in organizing spatial elements coherently into whole forms, while left hemisphere injury is associated with poor encoding of detail in complex forms. WS individuals have great difficulty copying the overall shape of relatively simple block constructed forms which is similar to deficits in children with right focal lesions. However, the deficit may be more marked and persistent in the case of WS. This suggests that in some developmental anomalies there may be a failure or difference in the level of hemisphere specialization and consequent visual processing.

Deficits in spatial attention in childhood: In conditions where two targets are competing for attention, infants with early focal lesions, HIE, and a subset of infants born very prematurely with white matter changes identified on structural MRI, have problems disengaging attention from the fixated target to a newly appearing target in the periphery (this is similar to the disengagement problem to one side of space for children who have undergone hemispherectomy). Early damage involving parietal and frontal areas is likely to underpin these deficits, although the exact location of the damage may vary considerably across individuals. These deficits of attention, identified early in the first few months of life with this fixation-shift paradigm, have been shown to correlate with later deficits on many visuocognitive and attentional tasks.

In school-age children there are many studies of spatial attention and spatial deficits related to visual attention. Three different components of attention have been identified from adult studies and patient populations, each with rather different neural underpinnings. The first component is linked to selective visual attention in visual search tasks. The second component is sustained attention which can be measured in vigilance tasks, and the third component involves inhibiting a prepotent response to switch task and make a new association, an aspect of executive control. Many studies have documented age-related improvements in these various components of attention, with some indication that developmental trajectories differ for different attention components. A small number of tasks have been developed to examine executive function in visuomotor tasks in preschool children demonstrating improvement between the age of 3 and 6 years. These tasks involve inhibition of a prepotent visuomotor response, an example being the test of counterpointing. The child first has to point as rapidly as possible to a visual target which appears to either the left or right of a fixation spot and reaction time is measured. The rule is then changed and the child is asked to point as rapidly as possible to the opposite side to where the target appears. This inhibitory control is achieved on average by 4 years of age in typically developing children, but is considerably delayed in children with WS and in a large subgroup of children born very prematurely who have suffered early brain damage. These tasks are likely to have some frontal lobe neural circuitry in common with that required for overcoming the 'A not B error' in Piagetian tasks of object permanence, where infants under 1 year of age fail to search for a toy if it is hidden in front of them in a new spatial location from where it has previously been hidden on a number of occasions. This perseverative failure persists in older infants and children with generalized brain damage (HIE), WS individuals, and in some autistic children.

Conclusions

The current level of understanding in both diagnosis and treatment for pediatric visual problems varies considerably both in identification of anatomical differences and differences of processing and function. Progress in terms of underlying genetics is rapid, but this alone is only one side of the starting point for understanding the much more difficult problem: how does the expression and interaction of genes become altered by subtle but pervasive environmental factors, from conception to adult maturity? In some cases we may serendipitously find the cure before we understand the underlying processes. Progress will only be made in improving quality of life for children with visual problems if we pool our knowledge and understanding across areas in interdisciplinary research and clinical practice.

Acknowledgments

The authors would like to thank the Medical Research Council for research funding and University College London, the University of Cambridge, and the University of Oxford for their support.

See also: Brain Development; Cognitive Neuroscience; Developmental Disabilities: Cognitive; Habituation and Novelty; Illnesses: Autoimmune Rheumatological Diseases; Intermodal Perception; Neurological Development; Perception and Action; Perceptual Development; Screening, Newborn and Maternal Well-being; Visual Perception.

Suggested Readings

Aicardi J (ed.) (1998) Disorders of the ocular motor and visual systems, In: *Disorders of the Nervous System in Childhood,* ch. 18. London: MacKeith Press.

Atkinson J (2007) *The Developing Visual Brain.* Oxford: Oxford University Press.

Atkinson J and Nardini M (2007) Visual spatial development. In: Reed J and Rogers JW (eds.) *Child Neuropsychology.* Oxford: Blackwell.

Braddick O, Atkinson J, and Wattam-Bell J (2003) Normal and anomalous development of visual motion processing: Motion coherence and 'dorsal stream vulnerability'. *Neuropsychologia* 41(13): 1769–1784.

Daw NW (1995) *Visual Development.* New York: Plenum Press.

Maurer D, Lewis TL, and Mondloch CJ (2005) Missing sights: Consequences for visual cognitive development. *Trends in Cognitive Science* 9: 144–151.

McKee SP, Levi DM, and Movshon JA (2003) The pattern of visual deficits in amblyopia. *Journal of Vision* 3: 380–405.

Moore AT (2000) *Paediatric Ophthalmology (Fundamentals in Clinical Ophthalmology).* London: BMJ Books.

Simons K (ed.) *Early Visual Development: Normal and Abnormal.* New York: Oxford University Press.

Stiles J (2001) Spatial cognitive development. In: Nelson CA and Luciana M (eds.) *Handbook of Developmental Cognitive Neuroscience* Ch. 27. Cambridge, MA: MIT Press.

Visual Perception

R N Aslin and A L Lathrop, University of Rochester, Rochester, NY, USA

Glossary

Acuity – The smallest pattern element that is just resolvable by the visual system.

Binocular disparity – Subtle differences in the size and shape of the two retinal images that enable stereopsis.

Brightness – The perception of intensity based on the physical luminance in a visual display.

Constancy – The ability to perceive invariance along some dimension despite fluctuations in other dimensions.

Contrast sensitivity – The smallest difference in luminance between adjacent pattern elements that is just resolvable by the visual system.

Optic flow – Complex patterns of retinal image motion defined across multiple elements in the visual display.

Retina – The receptor surface at the back of the eyeball that captures light and converts it into neural signals.

Sensitive period – An age range during which a given ability is susceptible to the effects of deprivation (or enrichment).

Spatial frequency – The number of alternations of a set of stripes that fits within a given visual angle (e.g., 10 cycles per degree).

Stereopsis, – The appreciation of depth based solely on binocular disparity.

Temporal frequency – The rate at which a stimulus varies in some dimension (e.g., luminance) per unit time (also called flicker frequency).

Introduction

The visual system provides exquisite information about the properties of the external world, but infants are initially insensitive to much of this visual information. Despite these insensitivities, infants have access to fundamental aspects of visual stimulation, including contours and their orientation, color, motion, and depth. During the first postnatal year, infants show remarkable improvements in all of these domains through a combination of maturational mechanisms and exposure to specific properties of the visual environment. When that visual environment is degraded, infants show slower rates of development and, in some cases, permanent deficits that cannot be overcome by subsequent experience. These basic visual sensitivities provide the foundation for higher level perceptual abilities such as object recognition, face perception, and the control of locomotion.

Visual Perception

One of the most remarkable human abilities, which is shared by other mammalian species, is our sensitivity to light and the conversion of photons striking the two retinas into highly diverse perceptual experiences, including color, shape, motion, and depth. Those of us who have no need for optical corrections, in the form of spectacles or contact lenses, or no deficiencies in the mechanisms that support color vision or depth perception, take it for granted that our visual system captures the true character of the external world. But for adults who have optical, color, or depth deficiencies the visual world is often confusing, and tasks that most others can perform effortlessly are either difficult or impossible.

The normal human infant enters the visual world rather suddenly and without the benefit of prior knowledge from other senses. This makes the task of the infant much more difficult than an adult who has already acquired considerable familiarity with the visual world and is suddenly presented with some distortion, such as looking through a magnifying lens or a red-tinted filter. How does the normal human infant make sense of the myriad of visual cues that provide information about the characteristics of the external world? Addressing this question has occupied philosophers for centuries and developmental psychologists (and vision scientists) for about 50 years. Based on relatively recent empirical evidence, the answer clearly involves two types of mechanisms:

1. Neural circuits, many shared with other mammals, that are tuned to the typical types of visual inputs present in the external world; these circuits are either present at birth (when light is first available) or are acquired by a maturational process that is relatively unaffected by visual inputs (or learning).
2. Neural circuits that are highly susceptible to the quantitative characteristics of visual inputs to which the young infant is exposed during the early postnatal period; in some cases these circuits acquire new

information, and in other cases these circuits lose sensitivities because the input is missing some key component.

There is no question that neural development prior to birth establishes rudimentary visual circuitry that enables some limited perceptual capacities in the newborn, and that further neural developments as well as interactions with the visual environment lead to substantial improvements in these capacities after birth. This article traces these improvements in visual capacities over the first 2 postnatal years, discusses the role that early visual input plays in these improvements, and concludes with some speculations on how the developing brain makes sense of the initially confusing array of visual inputs that confronts the newborn.

Resolving Fine Detail

Acuity. Perhaps the most basic question one could ask about infant vision is how well they can see small objects. This ability to resolve fine detail, called visual acuity, is what is assessed by an ophthalmologist or optometrist using an eye chart. Because infants cannot verbally report the smallest letter-size on an eye chart, some nonverbal technique must be used to estimate their visual acuity. Prior to 1960, most anecdotal and published accounts of the visual capacities of human newborns concluded that they were blind or, at best, severely visually impaired. These assessments, however, were based largely on insensitive methods, such as moving a single, small spot of light to elicit from the newborn a change in eye alignment (an ocular following or tracking response).

Three methodological breakthroughs in the late 1950s and early 1960s revealed that the visual capacities of young infants, although considerably less mature than in adults, were nevertheless quite sophisticated. These techniques were preferential looking, visual evoked potentials (VEPs), and optokinetic nystagmus (OKN). Robert Fantz developed the preferential looking technique based on a method originally used to test visual acuity in chickens. Newly hatched chicks have a natural tendency to peck at objects on the ground. Fantz noted that they pecked more to regions of the ground on which small kernels of feed were located than on adjacent regions devoid of feed. By systematically varying the size of the kernels of feed, Fantz could estimate the chick's threshold for sensitivity to the smallest resolvable visual element. This is a two-alternative simultaneous preference task since the stimulus (feed) is present on only one of the two locations on the ground in front of the chick.

Fantz adapted this two-alternative preference task for use with human infants by substituting a looking response for the pecking response. Infants are presented with two side-by-side stimulus locations, only one of which contains a set of black- and -white stripes. Even newborns have a natural tendency to fixate (look at) the side of the display containing the stripes over the side of the display devoid of stripes. An observer viewing the infant's eyes, and estimating the direction of gaze through a peephole in the stimulus display, judges which of the two stimulus locations is fixated more often or for a longer duration. To guard against bias, the observer is 'blind' (i.e., unaware of the location) of the stripes. By systematically varying the width of the stripes, the smallest stripe-width that is just barely resolvable (significantly greater than chance, or 50%) can be determined across a series of trials (with the side of the stripes randomly varied). In the late 1970s, Davida Teller established rigorous standards for using infant looking preferences to assess stimulus 'detection' (a choice between a stimulus and no-stimulus). Teller coined the term forced-choice preferential looking (FPL) to describe this technique.

The second technique – VEPs – employ surface electrodes attached to the scalp that record small changes in synchronized electrical activity from various brain regions. Spontaneous neural activity (electroencephalogram, or EEG) is much larger in amplitude than the neural responses elicited by the onset of a visual stimulus. However, because the average EEG is a flat line, the average evoked response can be revealed despite its smaller amplitude. The amplitude and the latency of several peaks and troughs in the VEP vary with the size and intensity of a visual stimulus. As with preferential looking, VEPs can be used to assess the smallest stripe-width that is just detectable.

The third technique – OKN – was originally developed for assessing visual acuity in flies. The fly was glued to a thin, vertical pole that was attached to a device that could measure the rotational force on the pole as the fly beat its wings to change direction from straight ahead. A set of black and white stripes was moved either leftward or rightward to induce the fly to change direction. If the stripes were made narrower and narrower, it was possible to determine the smallest stripe-width that the fly could just resolve. Newborns show poor evidence of steady and consistent fixations of a small visual target, and their ability to track (follow) a small moving target is very poor. They will, however, follow a set of moving stripes, provided that the stripes are visible. Since the eyes can only rotate about 40° from straight ahead, a pattern of smooth following and rapid return eye movements are generated, as in attempting to fixate a line of telephone poles from a moving vehicle. This pattern of slow and fast eye movements is OKN. By varying the width of the stripes, the characteristic OKN pattern will be obtained until the stripe width is too narrow. OKN can be measured by direct observation or by using one of two eye-tracking methods: electrooculography (EOG) or corneal-reflection videography.

The EOG technique involves the placement of two small electrodes on the surface of the infant's face next to each eye. Because the back (retina) of the eye is more metabolically active than the front (cornea) of the eye, any horizontal rotation of the eye induces an electrical current in the two electrodes. This change in current is proportional to eye rotation and can be used to detect the presence of OKN. The corneal reflection technique relies on the fact that any small light will create a bright reflection on the cornea. If the infant is looking directly at this light, then the reflection (to a first approximation) will be in the center of the pupil. As the eye rotates to look at positions away from the light, the reflection of the light on the cornea changes its relative position with respect to the pupil. Thus, detailed measures of the relationship between the corneal reflection and the pupil center can provide a fine-grained estimate of where an infant is looking. By using an infrared-sensitive video camera and a filtered light that is invisible to the infant (but visible to the camera), modern corneal reflection systems are both unobtrusive and accurate.

FPL, VEP, and OKN have been used to assess visual acuity in young infants. In each case, black- and- white stripes (or checks) are systematically varied in size to determine the smallest size that elicits a reliable response. Although there are some differences in estimates of visual acuity using these three methods (see **Figure 1**), two facts are quite clear. First, visual acuity in newborns is approximately five octaves (an octave is a factor of 2) worse than in normal adults. Using the Snellen notation, where 20/20 refers to normal visual acuity (average performance at a viewing distance of 20 ft), newborn visual acuity is approximately 20/640. This means that a newborn can see at 20 ft what a normal adult can see at 640 ft. Second, there is a rapid improvement in visual acuity between birth and 6 months of age, with average acuity rising to 20/40 within this postnatal period.

Contrast sensitivity. Most objects are not composed of features at the limit of resolution, but rather contain features sufficiently large to be well above the acuity threshold. For these features, size is less important than contrast. Contrast refers to the difference in luminance between adjacent object features. For example, a pair of black-and-white stripes has very high contrast because the luminance difference is large. As luminance is added to the black stripe and subtracted from the white stripe, the stripes become different shades of gray and have lower contrast. In the limit, when the stripes are equal shades of gray, contrast is zero and the stripes are no longer visible. Thus, for any feature above the acuity threshold, visibility is determined by sensitivity to contrast.

Figure 2 illustrates a typical contrast sensitivity function (CSF) obtained from an adult, as well as CSFs obtained from young infants. Notice that the adult CSF peaks at features with medium size and falls off for both smaller and larger sizes. The point on the far right of the CSF, where size is smallest and contrast sensitivity is least (i.e., stimulus contrast is maximal), is the estimate of visual acuity. The lower heights of the infant CSFs indicate that they are much less sensitive to contrast than adults at all feature sizes, and of course at maximal stimulus contrast visual acuity is much poorer. Importantly, even at medium feature sizes where both infants and adults can resolve a stimulus at high contrast, infants require much more contrast for minimal detection of that stimulus. Thus, there are many features of objects that have low contrast and, therefore, are invisible to the infant's visual system. One implication of this limited contrast sensitivity is that young infants cannot detect subtle variations in contrast used to recognize objects (e.g., the highlights that characterize facial features).

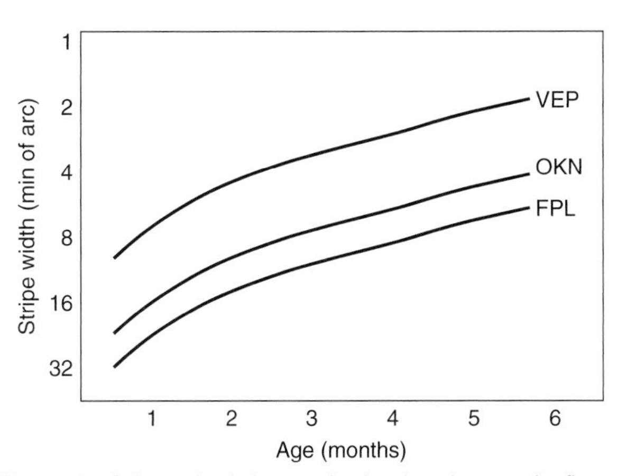

Figure 1 Schematized changes in visual acuity over the first 6 postnatal months using three measurement techniques: forced-choice preferential looking (FPL), visual evoked potentials (VEP), and optokinetic nystagmus (OKN).

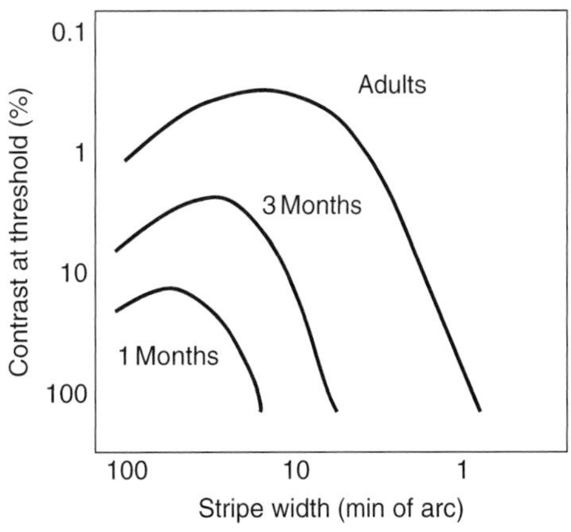

Figure 2 Schematized contrast sensitivity functions for 1-month-old and 3-month-old infants and for normal adults. The *x*-axis represents the width of each alternating black-and-white stripe in a display and the *y*-axis represents sensitivity to contrast (the difference in luminance between the black and white stripes that is just barely detectable).

Limiting factors. The two most obvious limitations on acuity and contrast sensitivity in early infancy are optical quality and neural immaturity. Adults with an optical error requiring spectacles or contact lenses show deficits in both acuity and contrast sensitivity when they fail to wear their correction. Although a small proportion of infants have optical errors (myopia: nearsightedness; hyperopia: farsightedness; astigmatism: errors that vary by stimulus orientation), the fivefold deficit in newborn acuity cannot be accounted for by optical errors. In fact, recent measurements show that the newborn's optics are well within the errors typical of the adult eye.

Another potential contributor to optical quality is accommodation (change in shape) of the lens in the eye, which optimizes the focus of the retinal image for different viewing distances. Although newborns show poor accommodative control, this deficit is the product of poor visual acuity; that is, the immature visual system is unable to detect subtle changes in stimulus blur that trigger an accommodative response. Thus, even when all optical errors are eliminated, young infants still show deficits in acuity and contrast sensitivity compared to adults.

These results suggest that the fundamental limitation on acuity and contrast sensitivity is neural, not optical. Classic data from the 1930s on the developmental anatomy of the visual cortex in human infants documented substantial elaborations of neural structures during the first two postnatal years. However, more recent data on the developmental anatomy of the retina suggest that much of the fivefold improvement in acuity can be accounted for by the increasing density of photoreceptors in the center (fovea) of the retinas and the increasing efficiency of photoreceptors in capturing light.

Both maturational and experiential factors influence the development of acuity. Evidence for the role of maturation comes from studies of premature infants using FPL. The time course of the developmental improvement in acuity is more closely linked to the infant's age postconception than to age postbirth, suggesting that normal visual experience after birth plays a relatively minor role in this developmental process. Evidence for the role of experience comes from studies of premature infants using VEP. The latencies of the primary peaks and troughs of the VEP waveform show a more rapid improvement in preterm infants than in full-term infants. Thus, there may be some advantage, at least initially, in being exposed to visual input prior to reaching full-term, although there is no evidence that this early benefit results in superior acuity or contrast sensitivity in later life.

In contrast to the effects of 'extra' visual experience among preterm infants, which are quite subtle, the absence of normal visual experience after birth leads to substantial deficits in acuity. Visual deprivation in the form of cataracts (opacities in the eye that prevent a clear retinal image) slows down the time-course and eventual level of acuity unless the cataract is removed very early in infancy. Cataracts usually involve a cloudiness of the lens, are easily detected in most cases shortly after birth, and can be alleviated by surgically removing the lens (or lenses if the cataracts are in both eyes). However, because surgery in young infants is difficult, it typically is not performed until the infant is 6–12 months of age. Once the lens is removed, the eye has a very large residual optical error and the absence of the lens prevents the retina from receiving focused images at different viewing distances. Thus, infants are fitted with a contact lens whose focal distance is fixed at a near viewing distance (where infants attend most often). This is not optimal, of course, because objects in the distance are never in focus, and because the eyeball grows substantially between birth and 2 years of age, the size and shape of the contact lens must be upgraded regularly.

Behavioral measures of visual acuity in infants who had a cataract removed show a very rapid improvement when the contact lens is placed in the deprived eye. In fact, the majority of the improvement seems to occur in the first few 'hours' after the contact lens is inserted. Interestingly, the acuity reaches almost normal levels during the postsurgery period in infants who had the cataract removed prior to 12 months of age. But as acuity continues to improve in normal children beyond 3 years of age, children who had a cataract removed and received contact lens correction begin to fall behind these improving age norms. One potential explanation for this delayed deficit is the imbalance in acuity between the two eyes: infants who had cataracts in both eyes show less severe deficits in acuity and pattern vision than infants who had a cataract in only one eye. This additional level of deficit in children with unilateral cataract could be due to the difficulty of forcing the child to use their 'bad' eye. The strong preference to use the 'good' eye in such cases leads ophthalmologists to prescribe a patching regimen in which the 'good' eye is covered for several hours each day to force the 'bad' eye to be used for all visual tasks.

Color

The retina contains four types of photoreceptors: the rods that are most sensitive to low light levels, and three classes of cones that are sensitive to different (overlapping) portions of the chromatic spectrum of moderate to high light levels. Chromatic discrimination requires at least two classes of photoreceptors (cones) that are sensitive to slightly different wavelengths of light. This is because signals from a single class of photoreceptors only provide information about the intensity of the light. Color is derived by the 'difference' in signals from two or three classes of photoreceptors. FPL, VEP, and OKN methods have been used to assess chromatic discriminations in very young infants to determine at what age the three classes of photoreceptors, and their associated percepts of color, are functional.

This question of chromatic discrimination is a subtle one and requires exquisite control over the visual displays because any chromatic stimulus has at least two properties: color (wavelength) and brightness (intensity). Consider an infant who has only a single class of photoreceptors and is presented with a checkerboard made up of red and green checks. If the brightness of the red and green checks is not perfectly matched (by varying the physical property of luminance), then the infant may see the checkerboard as a set of shades of gray and not as red/green. To overcome this so-called brightness confound, Davida Teller and her colleagues used the FPL technique to present a single bar of one color on a background of another color (see **Figure 3**). The bar appeared on the right or left side of the display from trial to trial, and the task was to determine whether the infant looked reliably at the side of the display on which the bar was presented. To eliminate the brightness confound, the luminance of the bar was varied over a wide range with respect to the fixed luminance of the background. By using small steps in luminance, it was assured that one of these displays contained a brightness match between the bar and the background. The logic of this task is that, if the infant had only one class of photoreceptors (and therefore perceived the bar and background as shades of gray), then when the luminance was perfectly matched the bar would be invisible. In contrast, if the infant had at least two classes of photoreceptors, then no matter what the luminance match of the bar and background, the bar would still be visible. This technique showed conclusively that 2-month-olds could discriminate red from green, thereby demonstrating that two classes of photoreceptors were functional at this age.

(a)

(b)

Figure 3 The appearance of an FPL display used to measure color discrimination when the infant (a) has color vision or (b) is colorblind. In both cases, the small bar differs in luminance from the background.

Subsequent studies addressed more subtle questions and showed that chromatic discrimination is not adult-like until at least 4 months of age. Whereas even newborns can discriminate red from white light (the latter contains all wavelengths), the class of photoreceptors sensitive to blue light are not functional until 4 months of age, at which point infants, like adults, are characterized as trichromats (having three functional classes of cones). Prior to 4 months, infants have much more difficulty discriminating small differences in color, and these deficiencies are largely the result of the immaturity of the photoreceptors (see previous section on retinal anatomy), which renders their signals noisy. Because color perception requires a computation of the difference in outputs from pools of two or three classes of photoreceptors, these noisy signals reduce chromatic discriminability.

Color constancy, the ability of infants to perceive the correct color despite variations in lighting (e.g., ignoring the reddish tint at sunset), emerges between 2 and 5 months of age. Infants were habituated to a colored surface that was illuminated with one of two light sources (e.g., slightly bluish) and then tested with a novel colored surface under that same lighting conditions or the same colored surface under novel lighting conditions (e.g., slightly reddish). Infants younger than 4 months of age treated both test displays as novel, whereas older infants treated the same colored surface with different illuminations as the same, thereby showing evidence of color constancy. Similar research has recently been conducted on lightness constancy: the ability to perceive the same black-white object as having a stable brightness (shade of gray) despite changes in the intensity of the light source that illuminates it. Again, evidence of lightness constancy was not present until 4 months of age.

Motion

Moving stimuli are more effective at capturing infants' attention than stationary stimuli. This natural bias to attend to moving stimuli has been used in preferential looking studies to estimate motion thresholds: the minimum stimulus speed required to discriminate a moving from an otherwise identical stationary stimulus. Motion thresholds improve dramatically in early infancy despite nearly adult-like temporal sensitivity at birth (e.g., ability to detect a flickering light), suggesting that these improvements in motion sensitivity rely critically on improvements in spatial resolution. It is clear, however, that by 6 weeks of age infants detect a moving set of stripes based on their speed and not their local flicker. This conclusion was demonstrated by pairing a moving set of stripes with an identical but stationary set of stripes in an FPL experiment. On half of the trials the stripes were doubled in width. Thus, if both narrow and thick stripes moved at the same speed, they would create different flicker rates. Results showed that speed and not flicker rate best predicted infants' thresholds for preferring the moving stripes over the stationary stripes.

Discrimination of different directions of motion is the definitive test of a motion mechanism because the responses of single neurons in many parts of the brain have a preferred direction of stimulus motion. The FPL technique has been used with two different arrays of randomly arranged dots that move in coherent directions on the two sides of the display. On one side, all the dots move in a single direction, and on the other side some of the dots move leftward and others move rightward (see **Figure 4(a)**). If infants can discriminate these different directions of motion, then they should prefer the side of the display that contains a motion-contrast over the side that contains a uniform direction of dot-motion. However, FPL studies have failed to demonstrate infants' discrimination of opposite directions of stimulus motion until 2 months of age.

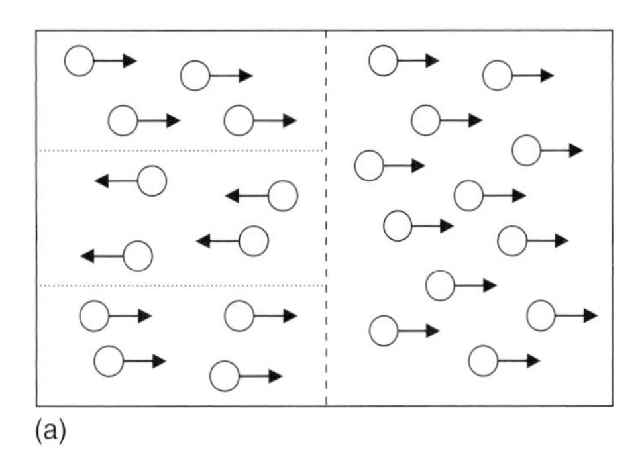

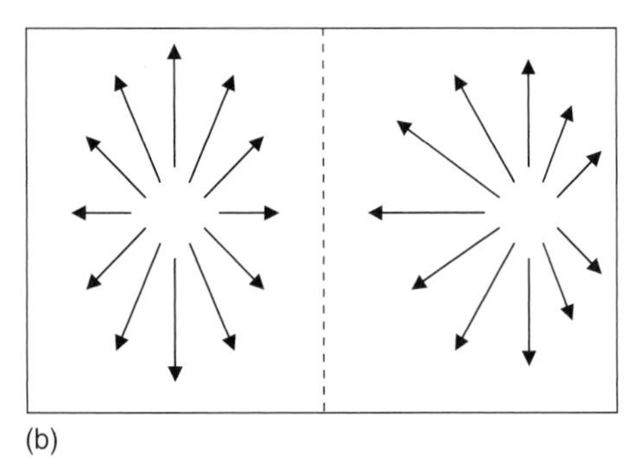

Figure 4 Two types of random-dot displays for measuring (a) direction-discrimination, and (b) optic flow. (a) Reproduced from Wattam-Bell J (1992) The development of maximum displacement limits for discrimination of motion direction in infancy. *Vision Research* 32(4): 621–630, with permission from Elsevier. (b) Reproduced from Gilmore RO and Rettke HR (2003) Four-month-olds' discrimination of optic flow patterns depicting different directions of observer motion. *Infancy* 4(2): 177–200, with permission from Taylor and Francis.

Notice that this use of the FPL technique is different from a 'detection' task (as in visual acuity) because now both sides of the display contain highly visible elements. When the FPL technique is used to assess stimulus 'discrimination', evidence of a significant preference allows for the conclusion that infants can discriminate the difference between the two stimuli. However, the absence of a significant preference is ambiguous because the two stimuli may be discriminable but fail to elicit a clear preference in looking behavior.

In an attempt to remedy this problem of equal stimulus preference, the habituation technique was developed to induce preferences that were not spontaneously present. Fantz noted in his early studies of preferential looking that when the same two stimuli were presented side-by-side, fixation durations declined across repeated trials. This decrement in looking duration is called habituation and indicates that the infant has processed and retained some information about the stimulus across time. Subsequent elaborations on the use of habituation as a measure of visual discrimination have resulted in an 'industry standard' that consists of two phases: habituation and test. During habituation, a single visual stimulus is presented and an observer records how long the infant sustains fixation (interrupted by no more than 2 s of distraction) to that stimulus on a given trial. Identical trials are repeated, tallying fixation duration until there is a preset decrement (typically 50%) from the initial level of looking on the first several trials. When this criterion of habituation has been met, the infant enters a test phase in which the same habituation stimulus and a novel stimulus are presented on alternating trials. Continued low levels of looking to the habituation stimulus and significant increases (recovery) of looking to the novel stimulus are taken as evidence of discriminating the habituation (familiar) from the novel stimulus.

The habituation technique has been used to assess direction discrimination of sets of random-dot displays. Infants viewed a coherent direction of dot-motion that was changed (e.g., from right to left) after the habituation criterion was met. As in the FPL paradigm, infants failed to discriminate a change to the opposite direction of motion until 8–9 weeks of age. This relatively late onset of motion discrimination is surprising because even newborns show directionally appropriate eye movements to stripe-motion during OKN. In addition, if infants view a large field of coherently moving dots in a FPL design, observers are quite accurate at judging in which the direction the dots are moving based on the infant's eye movements, even if full-blown OKN is not present. Moreover, this task shows no apparent changes in performance across the first

6 months of life. Thus, it has been concluded that cortical mechanisms of motion processing are not functional until the third postnatal month, whereas brainstem mechanisms of motion processing involved in eye-movement control are functional at birth.

Additional support for this dual-pathway theory of motion processing comes from studies of OKN in infants who have not yet attained functional binocular vision (under 3 months of age; see section on Depth and Binocular Rivalry). Binocular vision is clearly mediated by the cortex (not by brainstem mechanisms) and young infants show an asymmetry in the direction of OKN when one eye is patched (temporalward stripe motion is ineffective in eliciting monocular OKN in newborns). This asymmetry disappears by 3 months of age, presumably because cortical mechanisms override the brainstem mechanisms that initially control OKN. In addition, this nasal-temporal OKN asymmetry in young infants is mirrored in the VEP when assessed under monocular viewing conditions. That is, the minimum contrast required to elicit a VEP to a set of stripes moving nasally is less than the minimum contrast to a set of stripes moving temporally.

Motion stimuli in the natural environment do not consist entirely of uniform directions, but often involve complex patterns of motion directions. For example, when an observer moves through space in a forward direction, pattern elements projected on the retina move in a radial configuration, with the direction of heading creating a point in the retinal array that is stationary (see **Figure 4(b)**). This pattern of motion is called optic flow and is extremely useful for spatial orientation during locomotion. However, to use this optic flow information for guiding locomotion, infants must be able to discriminate different aspects of radial motion, such as the direction of heading. Recent FPL and habituation studies confirm that even 4-month-olds are very poor at discriminating changes in heading from optic flow displays. Thus, it has been proposed that until infants begin self-produced locomotion as they begin to crawl, they are relatively inattentive to these useful visual cues.

Orientation and Vernier Acuity

Another fundamental property of neurons in the visual cortex is orientation sensitivity, and this property is present in rudimentary form in newborn cats and monkeys. Human newborns are also sensitive to orientation, but only for gross differences. Studies have shown that when newborns are habituated to a set of horizontal or vertical stripes, they show increases in fixation to a change to the other orientation. Similar results have been obtained with a shift from one diagonal (45° tilt) to another diagonal (135° tilt). The VEP technique provides converging evidence for orientation discrimination. In this design a set of stripes of a particular orientation is flashed at a high rate (e.g., every 0.5 s) and at intermittent intervals (e.g., every 5–8 flashes) the orientation of the stripes is altered. By examining the electrical potentials that are elicited at these shifts in stripe orientation, one can determine if the shift was discriminated, and results indicated that they were at very early ages.

Although the foregoing results show that a rudimentary orientation mechanism is present at birth, a VEP masking technique has provided a more fine-grained measure of orientation sensitivity. Two sets of stripes with slightly different orientations were superimposed, and these sets of stripes were flickered at different rates. In adults, orientations that are similar reduce the amplitude of the VEP signal, whereas highly discrepant orientations (e.g., horizontal and vertical) have no effect on the VEP signal. Surprisingly, infants under 5 months of age showed no evidence of this orientation masking effect even for highly similar orientations, suggesting that the rudimentary orientation discrimination present in newborns improves substantially over the next several months.

An even more precise measure of orientation discrimination is assessed by so-called vernier or displacement acuity displays in which observers must discriminate the spatial offset of two line segments. In adults, vernier acuity is far superior to grating acuity; for example, adults can detect a stripe-width in a grating of 1 min of arc (1/60 of a deg), but they can detect the offset of two abutting line segments of only 10 s of arc (1/360 of a degree). Because the smallest receptive field in the center of the retina subtends only 20–30 s of arc, the term hyperacuity has been coined to describe the exquisite resolution on vernier tasks. In infants prior to 4 months of age, vernier acuity is poorer than grating acuity, but it improves at a more rapid rate and surpasses grating acuity. This developmental difference in the relation between vernier and grating acuity has been documented using both preferential looking and VEPs. One potential cue for solving a vernier acuity task is the slight orientation difference between the two line segments. Thus, the protracted development of orientation sensitivity may account for the developental crossover in the relation between vernier and grating acuity. The period of improvement in vernier acuity extends well into middle childhood.

There are several potential reasons why vernier acuity and orientation discrimination may be poor in infancy. One reason is the poor resolution of the photoreceptor mosaic which limits spatial resolution in general (as in grating acuity). Another is the elaboration of cortical mechanisms sensitive to fine spatial offsets and to contour orientation. A third reason is intrinsic noise in neural mechanisms used to make these two types of discrimination. Studies using FPL and VEP have been conducted with infants to assess the magnitude of this intrinsic noise. The logic of these studies is that adding physical noise to the stimulus display should have no negative consequences for infant performance as long as the added noise is less than the internal (intrinsic) noise. However, once the external noise exceeds the internal noise, performance should degrade with increasing external noise. This technique showed that infants do indeed have higher levels of intrinsic noise than adults, and the decreasing estimate of intrinsic noise predicted the developmental improvements in vernier acuity.

Depth and Binocular Rivalry

The relative distance (depth) of objects can be appreciated using three different sources of information: motion, retinal disparity, and pictorial cues (this last cue is discussed in the chapter by Arterberry). A rapidly approaching (looming) stimulus elicits a blink response in 1-month-olds, but only if the projected motion (an expansion pattern) is symmetrical, corresponding to a path that would collide with the infant's face. This finding is interesting in light of the rather poor sensitivity of infants to patterns of optic flow that do not correspond to a looming stimulus.

Another cue to depth is motion parallax, which is created whenever an object moves with respect to an observer (or an observer moves with respect to an object). The speed with which the image of the object moves across the retina is proportional to viewing distance (more rapid image speed for near than for far objects). Studies have shown that 3-month-olds are quite sensitive to small differences in object distance defined solely by motion parallax. Interestingly, these motion-defined cues entail much slower speeds than estimated from studies of motion thresholds using nondepth stimuli, suggesting that motion and depth cues are intricately related in the developing visual system. Importantly, sensitivity to depth from motion (in looming and motion parallax displays) is present in very early infancy and does not require the use of both eyes.

Although motion-defined depth is finely tuned in adults, purely binocular information has much greater resolution than motion information. Binocular disparity refers to the subtle differences in the images projected to the two retinas from an object at near (less than 5 m) viewing distances (see **Figure 5**). Stereopsis refers to the appreciation of depth based solely on binocular disparity. FPL and VEP studies using stereograms have demonstrated that sensitivity to binocular disparity does not emerge until 3–4 months after birth. This delayed onset, as in the case of direction discrimination for motion stimuli, does not appear to be a problem of spatial resolution or attention. Rather, it appears that the cortical mechanism that supports stereopsis is not functional until several months after birth. Moreover, the smallest binocular disparity that is just discriminable by infants, called stereoacuity, improves very

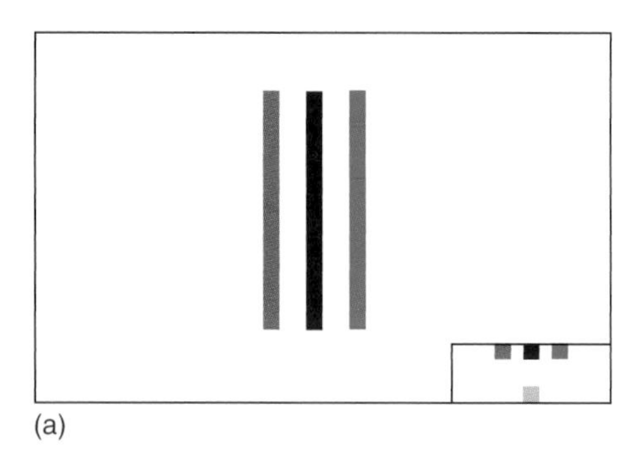

(a)

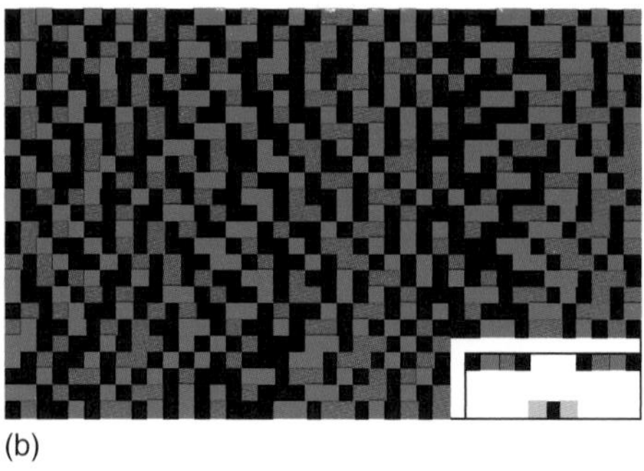

(b)

Figure 5 Two types of displays used to measure sensitivity to retinal disparity as the infant's eyes are covered by one red and one green filter: (a) line stereogram, and (b) random-element stereogram. The small box in the lower-right corner of each display represents a top-down view of how the elements in the display are perceived in depth to a normal adult.

rapidly between 3 and 5 months of age, progressing from no sensitivity to nearly adult values (less than 1 min of arc) in this age range.

During this same age range, infants become sensitive to binocular rivalry: the perceptual conflict induced by presenting grossly different images to the two retinas (e.g., horizontal stripes in one eye and vertical stripes in the other). Binocular rivalry occurs when the discrepant retinal images cannot be fused into a single percept. Prior to 3 months of age, infants appear to have a much greater tolerance for fusing discrepant images than adults, perhaps because of their poor acuity and contrast sensitivity. However, recent evidence calls into question this conclusion, and suggests that binocular rivalry may be present prior to the onset of stereopsis. One hypothesis that may accommodate both of these findings is that young infants spontaneously alternate fixation between the two eyes, thereby failing to experience binocular rivalry until the two eyes are precisely aligned on a single object of attention.

In adults, failure to align both foveas onto a stimulus typically leads to binocular rivalry and prevents stereopsis. Some individuals, including some infants, have an ocular misalignment (strabismus) that eliminates fusion and stereopsis. If uncorrected in infancy, this misalignment can result in a permanent loss of the capacity for stereopsis, even if the eyes are surgically realigned in childhood. Thus, there is a sensitive period during which a normally developing neural mechanism for stereopsis, present by 4 months of age, can be permanently disabled by subsequent abnormal binocular experience (strabismus). As discussed earlier (in the Motion section), infants younger than 3 months of age show an asymmetry in their monocular OKN (a nasal-temporal bias) that disappears once stereopsis emerges. Infants with strabismus who have not yet had their eye alignment corrected surgically, continue to show this OKN asymmetry. This suggests, again, that there is a tight linkage between motion and depth mechanisms during development.

Synethesia: Separate Pathways?

An unusual clinical syndrome that afflicts a very small percentage of the adult population is synethesia: the mixing of percepts between the sensory modalities. For example, some synesthetes perceive each letter of the alphabet as having a specific color, despite the fact that on the printed page all the letters are black. Other synesthetes experience specific tastes or smells when certain sounds are presented. Although one theory of synesthesia suggests that these cross-domain experiences were created by past associations, that seems unlikely in many cases because there was no consistent linkage between the specific domains in early childhood. An alternative hypothesis is that synesthesia is the normal state of the infant brain, which is then replaced by domain-specific pathways as 'extra' connections are gradually pruned away by early experience. Research with animals has shown that developmental pathways are much more interconnected in infants than in adults, and perhaps in some individuals these early pathways, although based on false correlations between modalities, are nevertheless retained.

Developmental Mechanisms: Nature and Nurture

The development of mature visual perception during early infancy is influenced by both maturational and experiential mechanisms. Maturational factors include neural developments, such as the migration of photoreceptors (increasing the packing density of cones in the fovea). Another is the increasing selectivity of receptive fields in the visual cortex. One result of such maturational factors is a reduction in the intrinsic neural noise that limits stimulus detection and discrimination. Experiential factors include periods of susceptibility to altered visual input. Although the range of visual inputs sufficient to enable 'normal' visual development is quite broad, visual deprivation (e.g., cataracts or strabismus) during a sensitive period can lead to permanent deficits in visual development.

Much has been discovered about the basic sensitivities of the visual system in young infants over the past 40 years. However, there is still much to be learned about how these basic abilities are converted into higher-level percepts and integrated with motor systems. The classic view that we begin life by perceiving elementary sensations (the proximal information impinging on the retina) and only later, by a protracted process of learning, construct internal representations of the external world (the distal information that we experience), has largely been shown to be incorrect. Newborns are already tuned to the distal properties of the environment (e.g., they blink to looming displays, perceive oriented contours, and discriminate colors). However, young infants have much to learn from their visual world, and their abilities increase substantially during the first postnatal year. These improvements in basic visual sensitivities set the stage for the higher-level perception of objects and events that is acquired by sophisticated learning mechanisms.

See also: Attention; Artistic Development; Brain Development; Habituation and Novelty; Nature vs. Nurture; Perception and Action; Perceptual Development; Vision Disorders and Visual Impairment.

Suggested Readings

Atkinson J (2000) *The Developing Visual Brain.* New York: Oxford University Press.
Daw NW (1995) *Visual Development.* New York: Plenum Press.
Gilmore RO and Rettke HR (2003) Four-month-olds' discrimination of optic flow patterns depicting different directions of observer motion. *Infancy* 4(2): 177–200.
Kellman PJ and Arterberry ME (1998) *The Cradle of Knowledge: Development of Perception in Infancy.* Cambridge, MA: MIT Press.
Kellman PJ and Arterberry ME (2006) Infant visual perception. In: Damon W, Kuhn D, and Siegler RS (eds.) *Handbook of Child Psychology: Cognition, Perception, and Language,* vol. 2, pp. 109–160. New York: Wiley.
Simons K (1993) *Early Visual Development: Normal and Abnormal.* New York: Oxford University Press.
Skoczenski AM (2001) Limitations on visual sensitivity during infancy: Contrast sensitivity, vernier acuity and orientation processing. In: Rovee-Collier C, Lipsitt LP, and Hayne H (eds.) *Progress in Infancy Research,* vol. 2. Mahwah, NJ: Ablex.
Wattam-Bell J (1992) The development of maximum displacement limits for discrimination of motion direction in infancy. *Vision Research* 32(4): 621–630.

Relevant Websites

http://www.pbs.org – PBS.
http://tinyeyes.com – Tiny Eyes.

Vygotsky's Sociocultural Theory

M Gauvain, University of California at Riverside, Riverside, CA, USA

Glossary

Cognitive socialization – The process by which parents and others ensure that a child's way of understanding and operating on the world conforms to those deemed appropriate to and valued by his or her culture.

Community of learners – An approach to classroom learning in which adults and children work together in shared activities, peers learn from each other, and the teacher serves as a guide.

Cultural-historical – Change associated with the cultural history of a community of people.

Egocentric speech – A form of self-directed dialogue by which the child instructs herself in solving problems and formulating plans; as the child matures, this speech becomes internalized as inner speech.

Elementary psychological (or mental) functioning – Psychological functions with which the child is endowed by nature, including attention, perception, and involuntary memory, that emerge spontaneously during children's interaction with the world.

Genetic method – An approach to human mental processes that uses developmental analysis; it is based on Vygotsky's view that these processes can only be understood by examining how they change over the course of growth.

Guided participation – Learning that occurs as children participate in activities of their community and are guided in their participation by the actions of more experienced partners in the setting.

Higher psychological (or mental) functioning – Psychological functions, such as voluntary attention, complex memory processes, and problem solving, that entail the coordination of several cognitive processes and the use of mediators.

Interpersonal (interpsychological) – Psychological experience that occurs across individuals.

Mediational means – Psychological tools or signs, such as language, counting, mnemonic devices, algebraic symbols, and writing that facilitate and direct thinking processes.

Microgenetic – Change associated with learning that occurs over the period of a specific learning experience or episode.

Phylogenetic – Change associated with the evolutionary history of a species.

Private speech – Internalized egocentric speech that guides intellectual functioning.

Ontogenetic – Change associated with learning that occurs over the lifetime of an individual.

Reciprocal instruction – A tutoring approach based on the ideas of the zore of proximal development ZPD and scaffolding.

Scaffolding – An instructional process in which the more knowledgeable partner adjusts the amount and type of effort he or she offers to the child to fit with the child's learning needs over the course of the interaction.

Signs – Language and other conventional forms of representing thought provided by culture that support thinking and regulate interactions between the individual and the world.

Social construction – An approach to cognitive development in which knowledge is seen as acquired and developed through social processes.

Tools – Objects or artifacts provided by culture, such as literacy and technology, that support thinking and regulate interactions between the individual and the world.

Zone of proximal development (ZPD) – The region of sensitivity for learning characterized by the difference between the developmental level of which a child is capable when working alone and the level she is capable of reaching with the aid of a more skilled partner.

Introduction

This article describes the sociocultural theory introduced by the Russian psychologist Lev S. Vygotsky (1896–1934), which emphasizes the contributions of the social and cultural world to cognitive development. Following a brief description of Vygotsky's life and the context in which he developed his ideas, the essay describes the distinction made by Vygotsky between elementary and higher mental functions that is important for understanding his approach. It then discusses three critical aspects of the approach: the role of mediational means in higher psychological functioning, the contributions of social and cultural experience in providing and supporting the development and use of these mediational means, and the primacy of the developmental or, in Vygotsky's terminology, genetic method. This article concludes with discussion of the contemporary influence of these ideas on the study and practice of developmental psychology.

Vygotsky's Sociocultural Theory

Vygotsky was a leader in the formation of a theoretical approach that emphasizes the contributions of the social and cultural world to intellectual development. This approach, which is called the sociocultural or cultural–historical approach to the study of the mind, has had substantial impact on theory and research in cognitive development in Russia since the 1920s. The influence of this perspective extended beyond Russia in the early 1960s when the first English translations of Vygotsky's writings appeared in the book *Thought and Language*. The sociocultural approach draws attention to the role played by cultural tools and signs in mediating thinking and intelligent action. It emphasizes how the social world is instrumental in the development and use of these mediational means, and therefore, is a constituent element of human intellectual functioning.

Three critical aspects of Vygotsky's sociocultural approach are the role of mediational means in higher psychological functioning, the contributions of social and cultural experience in providing and supporting the development and use of these mediational means, and the primacy of the developmental or, in Vygotsky's terminology, genetic method. This article discusses the theoretical features of this approach, including the distinction Vygotsky made between elementary and higher mental functions that is important for understanding his approach. A brief description of Vygotsky's life and the context in which he developed his ideas provides a useful backdrop for understanding this theory and the research derived from it.

A Brief Biography of L. S. Vygotsky

Lev Semenovich Vygotsky was born in 1896 in Orsha, a town in the western region of the Russian Empire, to a middle-class Jewish family. He was an excellent student in his youth and received many awards. From an early age, Vygotsky's intellectual interests were expansive. They included history, culture, social science, literature, philosophy, poetry, medicine, theater, and art. Discrimination toward the Jewish community was commonplace in Russia at this time and included quotas at universities for Jewish students. However, due to his excellent high school performance and some good fortune, Vygotsky was allowed to attend Moscow University, where he graduated in 1917 with a degree in law. While attending the university, Vygotsky also studied psychology and literature at Shanyavskii University in Moscow. His postgraduate study was at the Psychological Institute in Moscow, where he received his doctoral degree in 1925; his dissertation was entitled *The Psychology of Art*.

In the early 1920s, Vygotsky's health began a slow but steady decline from tuberculosis, the disease that eventually killed him in 1934 at the age of 37 years. At the time of his death, he was the head of psychology at the Institute of Experimental Medicine in Moscow and one of the most prominent Russian psychologists with a large and loyal following of students and colleagues. Shortly after his death, Vygotsky's influence on Soviet psychology, as it was then called, was stalled when the Stalinist regime took hold; Vygotsky's ideas fell into political disfavor and in 1936, his writings were banned in the USSR. Two of Vygotsky's closest colleagues in the development of his ideas, A. R. Luria and A. N. Leont'ev, became prominent psychologists themselves and they helped to sustain and advance Vygotsky's ideas following his death. Stalin died in 1953, and in 1956 Vygotsky's writings were once again published in Russia and by the early 1960s they were available to scholars outside Russia. Despite his short life, Vygotsky was a prolific scholar, he wrote close to 180 articles, essays, and papers, most of which have been translated.

One of the most significant features of Vygotsky's personal history for understanding his ideas was the social and political climate in Russia during his time. Vygotsky grew up and studied in Russia during a period of tumultuous social change. In his youth, Russia was an empire that was ruled by a monarch, Czar Nicholas. It included a massive expanse of land and people from many different cultural groups. When Vygotsky was young, the social divisions within the society were clearly marked and these divisions had enormous effects on the lives of the Russian people. In 1917, the year Vygotsky graduated from Moscow University, the Russian Revolution began and the entire society was in turmoil. This revolution was devoted to Marxist ideas and the influence of these ideas on Russian society and intellectual activity following the revolution was enormous.

Vygotsky, like many other Russian scholars during this period, strived to integrate Marxist ideas into his work. As Vygotsky launched his career as a psychologist, civil war and famine ravaged the country and the entire social structure of the nation changed dramatically. Many practical social problems plagued this new nation, the USSR, including widespread illiteracy, vast cultural differences among the people of the huge country, and few services for people in need, including children with learning difficulties due to mental retardation or other forms of disabilities. Consistent with Marxist ideology, Vygotsky felt that an important role for psychology in this new nation was to devise solutions for these types of social problems. However, to accomplish this goal Vygotsky needed to create a new form of psychology, one that stretched beyond a focus on individual performance and recognized and incorporated the breadth of human experience that was represented in these pressing social problems.

Vygotsky's Approach to Psychological Development

The sociocultural approach to cognitive development that is based on Vygotsky's ideas proposes that mental development is best understood as a product of social and cultural experience. Social interaction, in particular, is seen as a critical force in intellectual development. It is through the assistance provided by others in the social environment that people gradually learn to function intellectually as individuals.

In contrast to the emphasis on individual functioning that dominated other trends in psychology of his time, Vygotsky stressed the critical relationship between individual psychological development and the sociocultural environment in which human psychology develops and is expressed. He defined the sociocultural environment in very broad terms, including social interaction between individuals, the values and practices of the culture that appear in the routines, rituals, and customs in which people engage, and the tools and signs, most importantly language, that people use to support and extend thinking. However, Vygotsky did not view individual psychology or human cognition as a direct consequence of social experience, that is, socially determined. He proposed that human development, including cognitive development, is socially constructed. That is, in the course of social interaction, the cultural context of development, as instantiated in social behavior and cultural artifacts, and the biological aspects of the human system, including genetic, maturational, and neurological characteristics, create new understandings and capabilities. In other words, individual psychological functioning is an emergent property of the sociocultural experiences of the human organism. This means that psychological development is a dynamic and constructive process, the outcome of which cannot be known beforehand or by examining the individual and the social context separately from one another. Rather, development is generated by the processes that transpire over the course of human social experience in cultural context.

Vygotsky was particularly interested in social interactions involving more and less experienced members of a culture. As these partners collaborate in solving a problem, the more experienced partner assists the less experienced partner, the learner, in ways that support the learner's engagement in actions that extend beyond the learner's current individual capabilities. In an effective learning situation, this engagement occurs in what Vygotsky called the learner's zone of proximal or potential development, the region of sensitivity for learning. The more experienced partner supports the learner's activity through the use of signs and tools of the culture. As the learner gains competence at the activity, the more experienced partner gradually withdraws support and, in time, the learner comes to function on his or her own in a more advanced intellectual way. Thus, the interpersonal becomes the intrapersonal. For Vygotsky, what people do and learn in the course of collaborative cognitive activity is the foundation of cognitive development and, accordingly, social activity serves as the primary unit of psychological analysis in this approach.

Like other students of developmental psychology, Vygotsky was interested in the products or outcomes of development. However, his main focus was on the processes that underlie and motivate development. He considered development as a process of qualitative change, specifically one in which change occurs in the mediational means that an individual uses to understand and act upon the world. Vygotsky was especially interested in changes that occur when elementary mental functions, such as basic perception and involuntary memory, are transformed into higher mental functions, such as reasoning and voluntary memory. For Vygotsky, higher mental functions, which he considered the hallmark of human intelligence, are the result of the transformation of basic cognitive abilities into mental processes that are capable of devising and carrying out conscious goal-directed actions. Social and cultural phenomena are instrumental to this development. For instance, the elementary form of memory, which is similar to perception and largely composed of images and impressions of events, is an unintentional and direct mapping of features of the environment. As children develop, they learn to use psychological signs and tools, like language and literacy, to elaborate and extend this basic memory function into a more deliberate and explicit form. Children do not need to devise the psychological signs and tools that support higher mental functions; they already exist in the culture. However, children do need to learn about these signs and tools and how to use them effectively to support or mediate cognitive processes and carry out goal-directed actions, like intentional or voluntary memory. Children learn this information through the assistance of people in their culture who are experienced in the psychological signs and tools that support thinking. Some of this learning is informal, emerging from the everyday experiences and interactions children have, and some of this learning occurs in more formal societal settings, such as school. Both formal and informal arrangements of learning involve signs and tools that reflect the broader cultural context.

Vygotsky was interested in a range of mediational means, both symbolic and material, including language, mathematics, mnemonic devices, artistic symbols, and literacy. For Vygotsky, when people learn how to use and eventually adopt signs and tools that support thinking, the fundamental nature of thinking changes. Furthermore, mediators do not only support and extend an individual's intellectual functioning, they also connect the individual's thinking and action with the social and cultural context that devised and provides these mediational means.

With the assistance of more experienced partners, children develop their cognitive abilities in ways that are useful for solving the types of problems that are deemed important in the cultural setting in which they live. More experienced members of a culture, primarily family members, teachers, and older children, convey many important things about the mind and how to use it, including the types of problems that are important to solve, ways of approaching these problems, and how to use the material and symbolic tools in the culture to solve these problems. Language assumes great importance in this theory; it operates as the primary medational means by which social partners communicate information to each other and that individuals use to guide their own goal-directed actions.

Thus, according to Vygotsky, cultural tools and signs not only support the development and use of higher mental functions, they transform elementary mental functions and, in doing so, enable thought and action that would not be possible without the use of these tools. The adoption of these tools of thinking and the social methods through which they are learned also has the broader cultural consequence of aligning the child's thought and action in ways that are consistent with those that are practiced and valued by their culture. This developmental course provides a method of ensuring that new members of a culture develop the skills needed to become competent mature members of the community. In other words, children develop the skills that are suited to the types of problems, ways of thinking, and incorporate the valued tools and practices of their culture.

Elementary and Higher Mental Functions

Vygotsky distinguished two general forms of mental functioning: those that are biologically based and innate, which he called elementary mental functions, and those which he called higher mental functions that emerge from social and cultural experience. Basic psychological functions are shared with other primates whereas higher mental processes are unique to humans and cognitively complex, that is, they draw on and integrate many intellectual abilities.

Although they build on the elementary forms, higher mental functions are qualitatively different in that they are mediated by the social and cultural world through sign systems (e.g., language and mathematics), cultural tools (e.g., literacy and technology), and more experienced cultural members who convey to children ways of using these powerful mental abilities. Thus, higher mental processes are not simply more complex versions of elementary functions that can be accounted for solely by biological laws. Higher mental processes are qualitatively different in that in addition to biological laws, they also rely on historical laws or principles that are instantiated in cultural values and practices and mediated by signs, tools, and cultural participants. A discussion of memory processes illustrates the difference between these two types of mental functions. The elementary form of memory is constructed of images and impressions of events. This type of memory is very close to perception in that it is unintentional and the environment directly influences its content. The higher form of memory involves the use of signs to mediate memory functions intentionally and then uses memory to carry out a complex and conscious goal-directed action; for instance, an individual may write something down to remember it for later use or to communicate this information to others. In this example, literacy is used as a tool to elaborate on or extend the natural functioning of memory and it enables the actor to carry out an activity that would not be possible without the mediational means. Although this mediated example includes literacy, and therefore would apply to cultures in which literacy is present, there are many examples of mediated memory from nonliterate cultures. For example, the Quipu, which was devised and used by the ancient Incas in the land that is now Peru, was an elaborate set of knotted cords used to record important information about the community such as census figures, tax schedules, and the output of gold mines.

Four significant changes in intellectual functioning occur when elementary mental functions are transformed into higher mental functions. First, there is a shift in the control or regulation of behavior from other-regulation to self-regulation. Natural or basic mental functions are responsive to conditions in the environment, for example, involuntary memory in the form of eidetic images. In contrast, voluntary memory entails active effort by the individual to remember some information in the world. To encode and remember this information, the individual employs skills that support memory, such as selective attention and memory strategies like rehearsal and organization. Second, voluntary memory is conscious. The individual knows that a mental process, in this case memory, is being used. A third important feature of the distinction between elementary and higher mental functions is that the latter has social origins. Although elementary mental functions are natural, biological forms, higher mental functions are socially constituted. Finally, signs and tools of thinking mediate higher mental functions, a concept which scholars, such as J. V. Wertsch, who study Vygotsky's ideas consider to be the most important and unique contribution of this approach to intellectual development.

Cognitive Mediation through Signs and Tools

The use of signs and tools to mediate human mental functioning was, for Vygotsky, the single distinguishing feature of human intelligence. Whereas other primates, and human beings when they use basic mental functions, react to and use external features of the world to guide action, human beings are also capable of creating signs, such as language and number systems, and tools, such as navigational systems and computer technology, that affect how people think and interact with the world. In other words, human beings create and live in an organized social unit, called culture, which devises signs and tools for supporting and extending human thinking and action. For Vygotsky, this capability transforms the nature of human intelligence; it frees it from its biological base and creates what is referred to as a cultural mind. Moreover, cultural signs and tools are passed across generations from more to less experienced members of the group. Children cannot devise these tools nor can they learn about them on their own. Rather, they learn about them and how to use them from people who are more experienced in their use. In short, higher mental functions have sociocultural origins. Culture, both through its members and via the artifacts in which it is represented, provides mediational means that enable the development of higher-level cognitive skills. In this way, culture and social experience transform basic mental functions into higher-level cognitive functions.

Signs and tools are not static. They change over time in how they mediate an individual's actions as new capabilities, interests, and demands emerge. They also change across generations as culture changes and confronts new types of problems and concerns. Thus, the incorporation of signs and tools into mental functioning that transforms basic cognitive abilities into higher and more complex forms reflects temporal or historical experiences of the child and the culture. Vygotsky emphasized that this is a psychological and not a sociological process. The social world and its changes are manifested psychologically. Cultural signs and tools exist, that is, they are meaningful, by operations that occur inside individuals. In development, these signs and tools are initially experienced interpsychologically. With time and experience they become intrapsychological as individuals learn to use them to accomplish goal-directed action. It is significant that these signs and tools are not arbitrary, but stem from an organized and historical system, culture, and thereby contain psychological connections to other societal members and to cultural ancestors. When new societal conditions and problems emerge, ways of adapting must be crafted and these adaptations build upon prior forms. This process implies that full understanding of any current psychological form requires sensitivity to the individual, social, and cultural– historical forms that helped shape them.

What is important in Vygotsky's conception is that signs and tools are not merely external forces or stimuli to which children learn to respond. Signs and tools carry meaning and it is the meaning itself that is learned and adopted by children. For example, language is one of the primary sign systems that children learn. For language to contribute to cognitive development more broadly, children must learn more than just how words can be associated with particular objects or actions. Rather, they learn the meaning of words, which contains the essence of the word, such as the object of reference, along with its significance and place in the child's social world, for example, how important this object is, how it relates to other objects, and so forth. Participation in this meaning system allows the child to engage with others in meaningful, goal-directed ways as well as interpret and act upon the world in ways that make sense to other people and in their developmental context.

Contributions of the culture to cognitive development are evident in the mediational role of signs and tools in guiding and supporting thinking and intelligent action. This mediational role is conveyed to children largely through social interactions with other people, especially more experienced cultural members. Cultures also provide institutions and more formal social settings, such as rituals, that facilitate cognitive development. Formal institutions, such as school, significantly alter the ways in which people in a community think by emphasizing and providing access to particular and highly valued mediational forms. School is designed to promote and support the development of particular approaches to solving problems, including the use of certain signs and tools that aid problem solving. Less formal social institutions and social settings also influence cognitive development. For example, in cultures in which verbal explanation is highly valued, cultural practices related to this value such as oral narratives and story telling assume much importance and are part of children's everyday experience and cognitive development in that community.

Consistent with Vygotsky's formulations, as cultural signs and tools become an intricate part of intellectual activity, it can be difficult if not impossible to discern where the tool ends and the mental activity begins. The anthropologist G. Bateson offered an example that helps explain this point. When a blind man uses a walking stick, the man uses vibrations from the stick when it hits the ground to guide his steps. Where does the man's thinking about or perception of the ground begin? At the tip of the stick where it touches the ground, where the hand and stick meet, or when the vibrations travel through the nervous system and reach the man's brain? As this example shows, when a tool is intimately tied up with a mental activity, it is part of the mental activity and all attempts to describe the activity by dissecting it into its component parts are doomed to fail. Note especially that the tool in this example, the walking stick, has no content or cognitive meaning separately from the blind man's activity. This is an important point. Oftentimes signs and tools that have been devised to support thinking are viewed as embodying the cognitive activity. However, from Vygotsky's point of view, this is not true. And following up on this view, it is not surprising that Vygotsky believed that the most important knowledge humans possess is the knowledge of different ways or means for organizing and using mental processes in specific circumstances – the very type of knowledge that is embedded in communally held practices and transmitted across generations by people who engage in and value these practices.

Vygotsky's view of the cultural contributions to human intelligence suggests that any attempt to assess children's cognitive development must consider the cultural context as a critical force. If the culturally specific nature of children's learning is ignored, he claimed that one runs the risk of seriously underestimating children's development. Indeed, many cross-cultural studies have documented that children learn highly sophisticated and complex cognitive skills that are important in their culture. More experienced cultural members play significant roles in this process of cognitive socialization because they function as the most immediate representatives in children's lives of the mediational means to support thinking. Researchers have studied several social processes that promote children's learning of culturally valued skills, such as observational learning, the social regulation of attention in infancy, deliberate efforts to transfer knowledge from more to less experienced partners, social coordination during joint cognitive activity, and cognitive socialization through conversation and joint narratives. Taken together, this research suggests that social opportunities for children's learning appear in many forms and that culture determines the frequency and manner with which these processes occur.

Vygotsky's theory leads us to an appreciation of different cultures and their values, and connects cultural values and practices directly to cognitive development. Language plays a central role in Vygotsky's sociocultural approach. The acquisition and use of language is a primary component of children's developing intellectual abilities in a social context because language provides children with access to the ideas and understandings of other people. It also enables children to convey their own ideas and thoughts to others. Moreover, with development, language, which is a cultural product, comes to mediate individual mental functioning. In other words, as children learn to use language, it gradually becomes incorporated into their thought processes and, as a result, it both facilitates and constrains thinking.

For Vygotsky, thought and speech are independent in early development. However, around the second year of life they join together when children begin to use words to label objects. Within 1 year, speech assumes two forms: social, or communicative, speech and egocentric speech (also called 'private speech'). For Vygotsky, egocentric speech is a form of self-directed dialog by which the child instructs herself in solving problems or formulating plans. Thus, egocentric speech becomes a tool for intellectual growth and allows the child to become a more effective and skilled learner. By age 7 or 8 years, this form of speech becomes internalized in the thought process and becomes inner speech, that is, a form of speech that becomes internalized as thought. Thus, language serves as an aid for regulating cognition as well as a tool for communicating.

What is important to stress about Vygotsky's idea of mediation is the role it plays in development. Although Vygotsky did not outline or seek to define stages of development, he did see development as a process of qualitative rather than quantitative change. The types of qualitative changes he outlined were the result of changes in the forms of mediation that are used. Mediational means, both through signs or tools, function to inhibit direct and impulsive responses and facilitate the use of more consciously regulated and deliberate (or thoughtful) ways of operating on the world. For Vygotsky, these mediational means free human beings from a solely biologically based course of development and create a new, culturally based process of psychological development. For instance, before infants learn to use language, they have knowledge and carry out intelligent actions. But these processes are unmediated by language and, therefore, are absent of certain types of mental functioning that language supports. Encoding an object in a form that draws on linguistic conventions, such as grouping the object with other objects or with actions in ways that have meaning in the culture, transform how the child processes and remembers the object. This transformation serves many ends. It links the child's experience with the experiences of other people, it enables the child to communicate with others about the object, and it exists in the child's memory in a way that is amenable to reflection and reevaluation, albeit within a framework afforded by the cultural-linguistic system through which it was encoded and retained.

The idea that development is evident in the mediational means that are used to organize and support thinking was pivotal to Vygotsky's developmental method.

It directed his attention to the social experiences in which children learn these mediational means. It also allowed him to conceptualize development at multiple levels, including ontogenetic, phylogenetic, cultural–historical, and microgenetic.

The Role of the Social Experience in Psychological Development

Because of his interest in the social origins of intellectual functioning, Vygotsky was less concerned with children's individual intellectual capabilities at any particular point in time than he was with the child's potential for intellectual growth through social experience. To assess this potential and to understand how intellectual development occurs, Vygotsky proposed the notion of the 'zone of proximal development' (ZPD), which he defined as the difference between a child's "actual developmental level as determined by independent problem solving" and the child's "potential development as determined through problem solving under adult guidance or in collaboration with more capable peers." The child's ZPD is not static. Although the zone or region of sensitivity to learning is defined initially by the child's existing knowledge or competence in an area of intellectual growth, with proper support for learning the child's level of competence in this area changes, and the child's ZPD changes accordingly.

The concept of the ZPD is twofold. First, it represents an alternative approach to the assessment of intelligence – examining children's intellectual potential under optimal conditions, that is, conditions that are tailored to the child's specific learning needs and that build on the child's present capabilities. These ideas were especially relevant to Vygotsky's research in educational psychology and his concern with designing programs that could support the unique learning needs of children with disabilities or with mental retardation. Second, the ZPD represents a way of understanding how children's intellectual development occurs through social interaction with more skilled partners. As such, it builds bridges between the mind of the individual child and the minds of others.

According to Vygotsky, working within a child's ZPD – that is, with the assistance of an adult or more experienced peer – allows the child to participate in the environment in more complex and competent ways. In other words, in social interaction targeted toward the child's ZPD, a child has the opportunity to engage in more advanced cognitive activities than the child could undertake alone. This is because more experienced partners are able to break down an activity into component parts to make it more understandable and accessible to the learner. More experienced partners also help the learner by modeling new strategies for solving the problem and by encouraging and supporting the learner's involvement in the more complex components. In this process, the learner is introduced to and has opportunity to use signs and tools devised by the culture that support thinking. Finally, the more experienced partner may take on or assume some of the more difficult task components so that the learner can concentrate on other aspects. For example, an adult may keep track of what has been done so far in the problem or in relation to the goal so that the child can concentrate on the next immediate step.

Even though children learn from various types of social arrangements, Vygotsky's perspective on the social contributions to cognitive development more closely matches the types of interactions children have with adults than with peers. Because adults are more experienced than peers with many of the skills involved in informal instructional situations, such as turn taking and creating an overall plan for the activity, adult assistance is often superior to that given by peers. Of great importance is the child's active involvement in the interaction and the solution, which adults often verbalize and which fosters the child's understanding.

Vygotsky's theory has had considerable impact in the fields of psychology and education. For example, 'scaffolding', a form of instruction inspired by Vygotsky's ideas, is the process by which the more experienced partner or teacher adjusts the amount and type of support provided so that it fits with changes in the needs of the learner over the course of the interaction. By careful monitoring of the child's progress, the teacher adjusts the task to make it manageable for the child and provides assistance when needed. In scaffolding, which has been demonstrated in a variety of tasks, the teacher gradually reduces the amount of support he or she provides as the child becomes more skilled, so that eventually the child can execute the task in a skilled fashion independent of the partner's help. Other applications of Vygotsky's ideas to educational practice appear in the method of 'reciprocal instruction', introduced by A. Palinscar and A. Brown. This approach enhances children's reading comprehension by having the learner work in close and supportive collaboration with more experienced partners who help children develop skills critical to comprehension, such as explication and elaboration. A. Brown and her colleagues also introduced another related classroom application called the 'community of learners model'. In this approach, adults and children work together in shared activities, peers learn from each other, and the teacher serves as an expert guide who facilitates the processes by which the children learn. The teacher uses the technique of scaffolding to support children's learning and the students, who vary in knowledge and ability, actively help each other learn through their interchanges.

A way of describing children's informal learning experiences outside of school situations called 'guided participation' was introduced by B. Rogoff; it too is derived from Vygotsky's ideas. Guided participation highlights the fact that adults regularly support learning in the context of everyday activities by directing children's attention to and involvement in these activities. Sometimes these activities are child focused, such as in play or an organized game, but oftentimes they are adult activities in which the primary purpose is not to instruct children but to carry out the activity itself. In these situations, adults support children's involvement in specific but meaningful ways. For example, as a mother tries to make a cake her child may ask if he can help. The mother may agree and then structure the task in a way that gives the child some real responsibility in the activity. Over time, if the child remains interested in and continues to be involved in the activity, the child's and mother's participation will both change as the child's competence increases. Furthermore, as the child's roles and responsibilities change, the child's understanding of the activity also changes. As in Vygotsky's approach, the child is not merely a passive learner who follows the instructions or prompts of the more experienced partner. Rather, the child is a full and active participant who co-constructs with the partner, new ways of understanding and learning an activity.

For Vygotsky, the most significant aspect of social interaction for mental development is the fact that social experiences convey to children the mediational means for adapting basic cognitive abilities to higher cognitive functions. According to M. Cole, this view recasts the traditional dichotomy of nature versus nurture by proposing that it is human nature to nurture and that it is through nurturing that the individual mind grows. Vygotsky's view of the social processes that support cognitive development is broad in conception. Although he proposed specific processes of social interaction that are instrumental to intellectual development, he also emphasized other historical processes that are integrated with mental functioning and its development in his genetic method.

Vygotsky's Developmental or Genetic Method

For Vygotsky, the developmental method is the central method of psychological study. Vygotsky's interest in the processes of development led him to focus on dynamics of change, both within an individual, as captured in the idea of the ZPD, and in a culture, represented in its history and instantiated in the signs and tools that are used to organize and guide intelligent action. In contemporary psychology, the concept of development is primarily used to refer to child or adolescent development or in some cases to development in adulthood. Although the sociocultural approach has important views on and implications for understanding and studying development from this vantage, it is seen as only one of the ways in which development can be integrated in a meaningful way in psychological analysis. As M. Cole and S. Scribner pointed out, Vygotsky's abiding concern with the origins and development of human consciousness and behavior across generations and through process of human evolution reflects his broad conception of development. This stance is consistent with his view that psychological functioning can only be understood if it is observed in the process of change. For Vygotsky, the outcome of any psychological process is not predetermined, it emerges from the complex social–biological dynamics inherent to the situation in which learning occurs. For instance, the same conditions of learning will lead to very different outcomes for a child with a learning disability compared to a child without a learning disability.

Vygotsky emphasized that human psychological growth is a product of the social and cultural history of an individual. He was interested in four different ways in which history contributes to the development of higher mental functions: general cultural history, ontological history, the history of higher psychological functions, and the history of a particular learning experience. 'General cultural history' includes aspects of human social life that represent collective means of acting and thinking, such as material resources or tools that support thinking and socially organized activities and institutions in which intelligent actions occur. These aspects of social life, which are passed across generations, regulate human thinking and behaving. 'Ontological history' is a person's individual or life history. It includes the integration of biological processes that regulate the development of basic mental functions, such as perception and practical tool-based intelligence, and sociocultural processes that regulate the development of higher mental functions, such as voluntary memory and language acquisition. The 'history of higher mental functions' examines how specific mental functions, such as remembering, classifying, and conceptualizing, have changed over human history as they have adapted to the circumstances and environments in which people live. The 'history of a particular learning experience' includes change at the microanalytic level and is captured in the processes described in relation to the ZPD.

The genetic method requires analysis that stretches beyond the conventional boundaries of psychology. Its formulation was undoubtedly aided by the expansive scope of Vygotsky's own intellectual interests and background. Vygotsky recognized that examining any psychological phenomena at all these historical levels is a huge effort. However, he was concerned that ignorance or confusion about these various levels and their roles in human psychological experience could lead to a misinterpretation of psychological phenomena. Vygotsky's rejection of any form of reductionism stems from the complexity of this view of development. He did not believe that any single factor or set of explanatory principles could explain all of mental functioning and its development. He was critical of reductionist views of his time, such as Behaviorism, as well as theories that were broader in scope but nonetheless posited single explanatory forces for psychological functioning, such as Gestalt psychology with its emphasis on structural forms. Vygotsky emphasized the multiple forces underlying psychological phenomena and he argued that these forces were only apparent when they were 'in motion', that is, in the process of change or development.

Summary and Conclusions

Vygotsky's approach emphasizes the culturally organized and socially mediated nature of human cognitive processes. This perspective offers a view of cognitive development within the contexts in which this development actually occurs and, as such, it overcomes some of the limitations to theories that focus solely on the individual or on the environment. Vygotsky's theory has helped to make developmental psychologists more aware of the importance of the immediate social contexts of learning and cognition. In particular, through the notion of the ZPD and the related concepts of scaffolding and guided participation, this approach has pointed to new ways of assessing children's cognitive potential and of teaching reading, mathematics, and writing. Moreover, Vygotsky's approach has increased appreciation of the importance of culture in cognitive development. Vygotsky's theory also provides a way of conceptualizing the role played by sign systems and tools of thinking in cognitive development. This theory addresses how tools such as literacy and numerical systems, which are products of culture, get passed on across generations and become incorporated into the ways children learn to think and solve problems as they grow.

Limitations of this approach largely pertain to its lack of specification of processes of ontogenesis in cognitive development. Although the approach emphasizes change over time in a specific learning experience, or microgenesis, and the role of long-term historical influences on intellectual development as embodied in cultural practices, signs, and tools, Vygotsky was not specific in terms of age-related changes. Furthermore, like many other cognitive theories, this approach does not describe how changes in social and emotional capabilities contribute to changes in children's cognitive capabilities. Nor is it clear how cultural contexts that are available to children at different points of development support and promote cognitive change.

Over the last two decades educational programs that draw on Vygotskian and socicocultural views have increased. In these programs more knowledgeable people, especially teachers, play critical roles in arranging and supporting children's learning using techniques like scaffolding, collaboration, and the provision of tools that support learning and thinking. In the main, these approaches have been successful in demonstration programs. Although Vygotsky's own ideas were informed by practical social problems, especially those pertaining to education, adapting sociocultural ideas to classroom practice beyond demonstration programs remains a challenge. In part this is because there are few systematic descriptions of cognitive development in specific academic domains that incorporate in a central way the social basis of the development and expression of these abilities and skills. There is also limited understanding of how social experience before children enter school supports the development of cognitive abilities that are important in the classroom. It is also unclear how to calibrate or scale up the social learning processes based on sociocultural ideas that have been identified in controlled laboratory research to the demands and complexity of the classroom environment. Finally, the adaptation of these ideas to classrooms with diverse populations of students presents a unique set of difficulties. The sociocultural approach does suggest that language skills are central to cognitive development. These skills serve as the medium of information exchange and as a way of organizing and representing knowledge in the head. Ensuring that children have the language skills to access the social learning experiences of the classroom is vital, especially for language minority students who are at high risk of academic failure.

Vygotsky left developmental psychology a unique and valuable legacy of ideas. His approach to the development of the mind steers the field of psychology toward an entirely different set of questions than can be found in other contemporary theories of cognitive development. The depth and breadth of Vygotsky's thinking have led psychologists, such as J. Shotter, to characterize Vygotsky as a 'complete psychologist' in that he tried to conceptualize human development along every dimension of psychological functioning. Although Vygotsky worked almost a century ago, he concentrated on issues that are important to developmental psychology today, such as the complex and dynamic nature of cognitive development, the inherent links between internal and external forces in development, and qualitative changes in mental functioning as children grow. His unique emphasis on mediational means as central to intellectual development provides a cornerstone for contemporary research in a wide range of areas including language development, social cognition, problem solving, educational psychology, child socialization, and cultural psychology.

See also: Cognitive Development; Cognitive Developmental Theories; Reasoning in Early Development; Symbolic Thought.

Suggested Readings

Cole M (1996) *Cultural Psychology: A Once and Future Discipline.* Cambridge, MA: Harvard University Press.
Kozulin A (1990) *Vygotsky's Psychology: A Biography of Ideas.* Cambridge, MA: Harvard University Press.
Luria AR (1978) *The Making of Mind: A Personal Account of Soviet Psychology.* Cambridge, MA: Harvard University Press.
Moll LC (1990) *Vygotsky and Education: Instructional Implications and Applications of Sociohistorical Psychology.* New York: Cambridge University Press.
Rogoff B (2003) *The Cultural Nature of Human Development.* New York: Oxford University Press.
Van der Veer R and Valsiner J (1991) *Understanding Vygotsky: A Quest for Synthesis.* Oxford, UK: Basil Blackwell.
Vygotsky LS (1978) *Mind in Society: The Development of Higher Psychological Processes.* Cambridge, MA: Harvard University Press.
Vygotsky LS (1987) Vygotsky's sociocultural theory. In: Rieber RW and Carton AS (eds.) *The Collected Works of L. S. Vygotsky, Vol. 1: Problems of General Psychology.* New York: Plenum.
Wertsch JV (1985) *Vygotsky and the Social Formation of Mind.* Cambridge, MA: Harvard University Press.

Relevant Website

http://www.marxists.org – Lev Vygotsky Archive; Lev Vygotsky – Thinking and Speaking.

SUBJECT INDEX

This index is in letter-by -letter order, whereby hyphens and spaces within index headings are ignored in the alphabetization, and it is arranged in set-out style with a maximum of three levels of heading. Location references refer to the volume number and page number (separated by a colon). Major discussion of a subject is indicated by a bold page range.

A

B

C

D

E

F

G

H

I

J

K

L

M

O

P

Q

R

S

T

W

X

Y

Z